TEXTBOOK OF ORGANIC CHEMISTRY

CARL R. NOLLER

Professor of Chemistry, Stanford University

W. B. SAUNDERS COMPANY

PHILADELPHIA AND LONDON

PREFACE

Since 1860 the integrating theory behind the enormous mass of data that has been accumulated concerning organic compounds has been the theory of gross structure, that is the theory correlating the reactions and physical properties of organic molecules with the kinds of atoms present and with the order in which the atoms are bonded to each other in the molecule. This theory has been exceptionally fruitful and has led to the determination of the constitution of very complicated molecules and to the synthesis in the laboratory of hundreds of thousands of new compounds, many of which have important practical uses. It is these aspects of organic chemistry that are emphasized in this text.

Nevertheless the development of the theory of the electronic structure of atoms and molecules by mathematicians, physicists, and physical chemists has provided a more detailed picture of the nature of the forces holding atoms together, with the result that now it often is possible to give a reasonably consistent interpretation of the behavior of organic molecules. Consequently organic chemists are concerning themselves more and more with how organic reactions take place, that is with the mechanism of the reactions. The introduction of this material into basic organic textbooks, however, has been very slow. The essential facts regarding the mechanism of the addition of hydrogen cyanide to aldehydes, for example, were reported by Lapworth in 1903, and the manner in which many other organic reactions take place is known now with reasonable certainty. Yet most texts still pay little attention to current views on mechanism.

It is appropriate that current ideas concerning the mechanism of organic reactions and the forces which determine the chemical and physical properties of organic compounds be incorporated in an elementary textbook. Too often the student's criticism that the elementary course in organic chemistry merely is memory work is justified. Although "memory is necessary for all the operations of reason," it also is true that theories which correlate facts are an aid to memory. Moreover it is desirable that students majoring in chemistry and allied sciences become acquainted with the current ideas and language of chemistry. Therefore in this text considerable emphasis is placed on the explanation of physical properties and on the mechanism of organic reactions. Where such material is given, an effort has been made to keep the discussion as simple as possible even at the risk of being quantitatively inaccurate, for "except ye utter by the tongue words easy to be understood, how shall it be known what is spoken?"

In the earlier chapters the student is introduced to the subject matter gradually. No compound is used in the methods of preparation or in the reactions unless its structure has been discussed previously. For example when alkanes and alkenes first are considered, no methods of synthesis are given. Instead discussion of these procedures is delayed until the student is familiar with the methods of preparation and with the reactions of alcohols and alkyl halides. Reactions which are pedagogically bad, such as the halogenation of saturated hydrocarbons, are not presented until the student is able to see them in their proper perspective. Brief descriptions of experiments are given to make the reactions seem more real to the student who has not progressed very far in laboratory work. In equations illustrating the factual part of the text, the full formula for the usual reagent is given: for example NaOH or $Ca(OH)_2$ and not OH^-; HCl or H_2SO_4 and not H^+ or H_3O^+; $Na_2Cr_2O_7$ or $KMnO_4$ and not $Cr_2O_7^=$ or MnO_4^-. In this way the practical aspects of the subject are kept separate from the theoretical aspects, and the student who thinks in terms of the materials with which he works rather than in terms of more abstract ideas is not handicapped.

The uses of organic compounds are of great importance. It is a source of pride to most organic chemists that the results of their investigations have led to practical applications and that the organic chemical industry is important to the economic life and well-being of the individual and his nation. Moreover most of the students majoring in chemistry are preparing themselves for industrial positions. Hence the practical applications and economic aspects of organic chemistry frequently are discussed in some detail.

For some years textbooks have been published which present aliphatic and aromatic compounds simultaneously. There is some advantage in discussing as a single unit all compounds having like functional groups. However this treatment requires consideration of the effect of the rest of the molecule on the properties of the functional group and overloads the new student of organic chemistry with more detail than he can assimilate readily. It is the author's opinion that it is better first to cover all of the monofunctional aliphatic compounds, next to consider both monofunctional and polyfunctional aromatic compounds, and finally to return to polyfunctional aliphatic compounds. In the last portion aromatic compounds may be included wherever desired since the student is familiar with their behavior. This progression also permits the requirements of different students to be met by the same course. Those students who do not need a full year course can stop at the end of a term and still have a good introduction to organic chemistry.

This book is intended for those who desire a text containing an amount of material that can be covered in ninety to one hundred lectures. Nevertheless it is fairly comprehensive, and instructors may wish to be selective in making assignments. For this reason the material has been arranged and cross-indexed in such a way that sections or whole chapters may be omitted, or the sequence of chapters may be altered considerably without impairing the readability of the text. Since it is considered desirable to keep factual matter separate from theory, only the physical properties, methods of nomenclature, chemical reactions, and uses of organic compounds are printed in the standard-sized type. Portions which deal with mechanism or which are considered to be of a supplementary nature are printed in smaller type. For those who wish a text containing more material, including discussions of the molecular orbital treatment of covalent bonding and resonance, the author's "Chemistry of Organic Compounds" is recommended.

Several time-honored reactions have been omitted because they were considered not sufficiently general in their application, or not important enough to be included. The author hopes that he has been able also to correct a few misconceptions that have been handed down over the years, although he is certain that he himself has committed many to print of which he is not aware. Furthermore it is likely that in his efforts to generalize or to explain reactions, he has made statements contrary to fact. Readers are urged to bring these errors to his attention and to submit other suggestions or comments for improving the text.

Many persons have contributed directly or indirectly to the preparation of this text, and the author gratefully acknowledges their assistance. He is indebted especially to Richard H. Eastman and Charles D. Hurd, who have read the entire manuscript; to Arthur L. Fox, Bernard S. Greensfelder, George W. Hearne, J. Murray Luck, Harry S. Mosher, W. A. Peterson, and William E. Vaughn, who have read one or more chapters; to Mildred J. Hall, who typed the manuscript; to Anadel Smith Brown, who prepared the illustrations; and to Edna Rasmussen Noller, his wife, who has helped in the preparation of the manuscript and in the reading of proof.

CARL R. NOLLER

Stanford University

CONTENTS

PREFACE.   iii

1. INTRODUCTION.   1

2. ALKANES.   21

3. ALKENES.   36

4. NATURAL GAS, PETROLEUM, AND DERIVED PRODUCTS.   45

5. ALCOHOLS. ESTERS OF INORGANIC ACIDS.   58

6. ALKYL HALIDES. GRIGNARD REAGENTS.   81

7. MECHANISM OF ORGANIC REACTIONS.   90

8. SYNTHESIS OF ALKANES AND ALKENES. ALKYNES (ACETYLENES). . .   106

9. ETHERS.   114

10. CARBOXYLIC ACIDS AND THEIR DERIVATIVES.   120

11. WAXES, FATS, AND OILS.   150

12. ALDEHYDES AND KETONES.   161

13. ALIPHATIC NITROGEN COMPOUNDS.   183

14. ALIPHATIC SULFUR COMPOUNDS.   208

15. PROTEINS, AMINO ACIDS, AND PEPTIDES.   224

16. DERIVATIVES OF CARBONIC ACID AND THIOCARBONIC ACID.   237

17. STEREOISOMERISM.   254

18. CARBOHYDRATES.   277

19. AROMATIC COMPOUNDS. BENZENE AND ITS HOMOLOGS. COAL PRODUCTS.   310

20. HALOGEN DERIVATIVES OF AROMATIC HYDROCARBONS............ 326

21. AROMATIC NITRO COMPOUNDS. MECHANISM OF AROMATIC SUBSTITUTION.. 331

22. AROMATIC SULFONIC ACIDS AND THEIR DERIVATIVES............. 352

23. AROMATIC AMINES... 360

24. DIAZONIUM SALTS... 375

25. PHENOLS, AMINOPHENOLS, AND QUINONES...................... 380

26. AROMATIC ALCOHOLS, ARALKYLAMINES, ALDEHYDES AND KETONES. STEREOCHEMISTRY OF THE OXIMES......................... 398

27. AROMATIC CARBOXYLIC ACIDS AND DERIVATIVES................ 411

28. ARYLALKANES. FREE GROUPS. ARYLALKENES. BIPHENYL AND ITS DERIVATIVES.. 422

29. CONDENSED NUCLEAR HYDROCARBONS AND THEIR DERIVATIVES... 428

30. HETEROCYCLIC COMPOUNDS. ALKALOIDS....................... 444

31. COLOR. DYES AND DYEING.. 472

32. DIENES, RUBBER, AND SYNTHETIC RUBBERS................... 494

33. CHLORINATED AND FLUORINATED ALIPHATIC HYDROCARBONS...... 505

34. UNSATURATED ALCOHOLS, POLYHYDRIC ALCOHOLS, AND THEIR DERIVATIVES. AMINO ALCOHOLS AND POLYAMINES................ 516

35. HALOGENATED, HYDROXY, AMINO, AND UNSATURATED ACIDS...... 530

36. POLYCARBOXYLIC ACIDS.. 539

37. KETO ACIDS... 549

38. ALICYCLIC COMPOUNDS. TERPENES AND STEROIDS................ 557

39. ORGANIC PEROXIDES. AUTOXIDATION AND ANTIOXIDANTS........ 572

40. ORGANOMETALLIC COMPOUNDS. SILICON COMPOUNDS............. 584

Contents

Appendix A—Pronunciation.................................. 599

Appendix B—Greek Alphabet............................... 605

Index... 607

Periodic Table of the Elements...................*Inside Back Cover*

Chapter 1

INTRODUCTION

Most students beginning the study of organic chemistry already have some idea of the material with which it deals, because courses in general chemistry usually include a brief introduction to the subject. Not everyone, however, may be aware of the extent to which organic chemistry touches on everyday life. Man's chief requirements are food, fuel, and clothing. Food consists mainly of organic compounds, namely the fats, proteins, and carbohydrates. The digestion and assimilation of food takes place by organic chemical reactions, and the proper functioning of the animal organism requires other organic compounds such as the vitamins and hormones. Fuel is chiefly coal, wood, natural gas, and petroleum. Clothing is made from cotton, wool, silk, and synthetic fibers. Organic chemistry is concerned with all of these substances.

The study of the chemical behavior of these products of biological origin has enabled the organic chemist to convert them by chemical reactions into a host of other accessory substances. Soaps, perfumes, flavors, dyestuffs, protective coatings for wood and metal, plastics, photographic films and developers, explosives, synthetic rubber, artificial leather, synthetic fibers, and many medicinals, disinfectants, and insecticides add to man's comfort and pleasure. Hence it readily can be understood that the investigation of the chemistry of organic compounds has not merely extended chemical knowledge. It has influenced profoundly the health of man, his daily life, and the development of civilization. The study of organic chemistry may be considered to be a part of cultural training, as well as necessary background for certain scientific professions.

Beginnings of Organic Chemistry

Organic chemistry, as a separate branch of science, dates from the early part of the nineteenth century. Many compounds now referred to as organic must have existed on earth before life began, but only in very recent times has much progress been made in their study. The investigation of organic compounds lagged considerably behind that of inorganic compounds, because the naturally occurring organic compounds were more complex, their reactions were more difficult to understand, and they usually occurred as mixtures that were more difficult to separate than the mixtures of inorganic compounds.

Specific properties of a few organic compounds were known to the ancients. Noah was familiar with the effect of fermented grape juice on the human system. Acetic acid in the form of sour wine was well known; one of the proverbs of Solomon refers to the action of vinegar on chalk. Acetic acid was, in fact, the only acid known to the ancients. Indigo and alizarin have been identified as dyestuffs used on Egyptian mummy cloth, and royal purple was extracted from a Mediterranean mollusk by the Phoenicians.

The process of distillation first was described in detail by the Alexandrians in the beginning of the fifth century A.D., and was developed and used by their successors, the Arabians, during the eighth century to concentrate acetic acid and alcohol. However it remained for Lowitz [1] to prepare acetic acid sufficiently pure to obtain it in crystalline form in 1789, and to obtain alcohol free of water in 1796. Cane sugar had been obtained in crystalline form in northeastern India about 300 A.D., but it did not become known until about 640 to the Arabians, who introduced the growing of cane into Egypt and southern Europe. Tartar from wine was known at an early date, and the older alchemists experimented with it. Benzoic acid and succinic acid were prepared in the sixteenth century, and methyl alcohol, grape sugar, and milk sugar were isolated during the seventeenth century. Persistent **attempts to isolate pure organic compounds** came only with the rise of chemistry during the latter half of the eighteenth century. Scheele [2] was the first to isolate uric, oxalic, tartaric, lactic, citric, and malic acids, acetaldehyde, and glycerol. As late as the beginning of the nineteenth century, however, the view was held that acetic acid was the only vegetable acid, and that all others consisted of some combined form of acetic acid.

Along with the work on isolation, some **chemical transformations** were brought about. The reaction of ethyl alcohol with sulfuric acid was recorded as early as the thirteenth century, but apparently the first person to have a definite knowledge of ether was Valerius Cordus, a German physician, who died in 1544. His procedure for its preparation was not published until 1552. Later this work was forgotten, and only a mixture of ether and alcohol was used in medicine. It was not until 1730 that the properties of a relatively pure ether, insoluble in water, again were described, and not until 1800 that the absence of sulfur was proved, thus showing that the sulfuric acid was not incorporated into the ether molecule. Acetone was prepared by the thermal decomposition of lead acetate, and ethyl chloride was prepared from ethyl alcohol and hydrochloric acid during the seventeenth century. Ethyl acetate, formate, oxalate, and benzoate were prepared during the latter half of the eighteenth century. Scheele obtained oxalic acid by the oxidation of cane sugar, and mucic acid by the oxidation of milk sugar.

Much less was known about **compounds present in animal organisms.** At the end of the eighteenth century, the only accomplishments of importance were the isolation of urea from urine in 1773, and of uric acid from urinary calculi in 1776. It generally was assumed that there was a fundamental difference between animal and vegetable matter since distillation of the former always yielded ammonia.

Of greatest importance for the advance of organic chemistry was the **de-**

---

[1] Johann Tobias Lowitz (1757–1804), German-born Court Apothecary at St. Petersburg, who made several outstanding contributions to basic laboratory technique. He discovered the absorptive property of activated charcoal and used it in the purification of organic compounds. He also discovered the phenomenon of supersaturation, used ice and various salts to make freezing mixtures, and was the first to use calcium chloride to remove water from organic liquids.

[2] Carl Wilhelm Scheele (1742–1786), Swedish apothecary. Besides being the first to isolate and prepare many organic compounds, he was the first to prepare molybdic, tungstic, and arsenic acids, to show that graphite is a form of carbon, to characterize manganese and barium, and to note the insolubility of barium sulfate. He also discovered oxygen (independently and prior to Priestley) and chlorine.

velopment of methods for qualitative and quantitative analysis.
Lavoisier,[3] who was one of the earliest investigators to analyze organic compounds, showed that they contain carbon and hydrogen and usually oxygen.
He showed also that products derived from animal sources frequently contained nitrogen. Berzelius,[4] Liebig,[5] and Dumas [6] made further improvements in organic analysis particularly from the quantitative standpoint.

Originally no distinction was made between the chemistry of mineral compounds and the chemistry of those of biological origin, but the differences became so apparent, after a representative group of compounds had been isolated from natural sources, that a division soon was made. Bergman [7] in 1780 was the first to differentiate between organic compounds and nonorganic compounds, and Berzelius first used the term organic chemistry in 1808 and published the first independent treatment of organic chemistry in his textbook of 1827.

The slowness in the advance of organic chemistry before the nineteenth century has been ascribed to the belief that compounds occurring in living organisms or elaborated by them could not be synthesized from the elements without the intervention of a *vital force*. The rapid advance during the nineteenth century has been attributed to the renunciation of this theory after Woehler [8] reported in 1828 the synthesis of urea from ammonium cyanate. Actually this event had little effect in combating the vitalistic theory. Woehler himself had previously synthesized oxalic acid from cyanogen in 1824, but the raw materials for this synthesis as well as for that of urea came from natural products. It was not until the synthesis of trichloroacetic acid by Kolbe [9] in 1845 that it was proved that an organic compound could be made in the laboratory from the elements.

During this period, arguments for and against the vitalistic theory continued but did not deter chemists from trying to synthesize organic compounds. Their work, however, was leading them into chaos because of the con-

---

[3] Antoine Lavoisier (1743–1794), French scientist and public servant, who was condemned to death by a judge of the Revolutionary Tribunal with the remark, "The Republic has no need for savants."

[4] Joens Jacob Berzelius (1779–1848), Swedish chemist, known chiefly for his accurate work on the combining weights of the elements and for his support of the dualistic theory, which held that elements were either electrically positive or negative in character and that only elements oppositely charged were capable of combining with each other.

[5] Justus Liebig (1803–1873), German professor of chemistry, who first introduced laboratory work into general instruction in chemistry. He perfected the combustion method of organic analysis, established the theory of radicals, laid the foundations of agricultural chemistry, and was the forceful editor who built up the prestige of the *Annalen der Chemie und Pharmacie*.

[6] Jean Baptiste André Dumas (1800–1884), French chemist, teacher, and public servant. He was noted for the accuracy of his experimental work and for his clear thinking. His name is associated chiefly with his analytical methods and with the phenomenon of substitution in organic compounds.

[7] Torbern Olof Bergman (1735–1784), professor of mathematics and later of chemistry at the University of Upsala, Sweden.

[8] Friedrich Woehler (1800–1882), professor at the University of Goettingen and friend of Berzelius and Liebig. Besides his work in organic chemistry, he discovered aluminum when he was only 27 years old and did important work on boron, aluminum, and titanium.

[9] Adolph Wilhelm Hermann Kolbe (1818–1884), student of Woehler and professor of chemistry at the University of Leipzig. He is noted principally for his teaching and writings. Along with Frankland and Kekulé, he early recognized the tetravalency of carbon.

fusion that existed concerning **atomic and molecular weights.** Although
Avogadro's law provided the basis for atomic and molecular weight determinations in 1811, order did not begin to appear until Cannizzaro [10] clearly showed
in 1858 how the application of the hypothesis would resolve many of the difficulties. At about the same time, the **theories of valence and structure** ex-
pounded by Kekulé [11] and others paved the way for the extremely rapid ad-
vances of the next fifty years.

During the first half of the nineteenth century, it gradually was realized
that *the essential difference between inorganic and organic compounds is that
the latter always contain carbon.* Gmelin [12] was the first to state this fact in 1848.
At the present time, the number of carbon compounds synthesized in the laboratory far exceeds the number isolated from organic products, and the phrase
chemistry of the compounds of carbon would be more accurate than organic
chemistry. The latter term, however, is less cumbersome and is used almost
universally. The study of the chemical reactions taking place in living organisms is now termed *biochemistry.*

Differences Between Inorganic and Organic Compounds

Actually there are more cogent reasons for considering the chemistry of
carbon compounds as a separate branch of chemistry than their derivation
from organic sources or the presence of carbon. First the physical properties
of nonsalts, which include most organic compounds, differ sharply from the
physical properties of salts, the most numerous class of inorganic compounds
(Table 1). Then the reactions of most inorganic salts in solution are almost

TABLE 1
USUAL PHYSICAL PROPERTIES OF SALTS AND NONSALTS

SALTS	NONSALTS
High melting point (above 700°)	Low melting point (under 300°)
Nonvolatile	Distill readily
Insoluble in nonaqueous liquids	Soluble in nonaqueous liquids
Soluble in water	Insoluble in water
Conduct electric current in molten state and in solution	Solutions and melts are noncon- ducting

---

[10] Stanislao Cannizzaro (1826–1910), Sicilian revolutionist and politician, professor of
chemistry at the Universities of Genoa, Palermo, and Rome. His *Summary of a Course of
Chemical Philosophy*, which he wrote for his students, was published in 1858. An international
congress of the most eminent chemists was called by Wurtz and Kekulé and presided over
by Dumas at Karlsruhe in 1860 to try to bring order out of the confusion of atomic weights
and chemical notation. At the close of the congress, which had accomplished nothing,
Cannizzaro distributed his pamphlet among those present.

[11] Friedrich August Kekulé (1829–1896), professor at the Universities of Ghent and Bonn.
He extended the type theory and laid the foundations of structural theory in organic chemistry. It seems significant that before becoming interested in chemistry, he was a student of
architecture.

[12] Leopold Gmelin (1788–1853), professor of medicine and chemistry at the University
of Heidelberg, originator of *Gmelin's Handbuch der Chemie*, now in its eighth edition, and
member of a family noted for the large number and long line of prominent chemists it contained, beginning with Johann Georg Gmelin, born in 1674.

instantaneous whereas those of organic compounds usually are slow. Also the number of known compounds that contain carbon is about ten times the number that do not contain carbon. Finally the concept of structure or the way in which the atoms are linked together is essential for an understanding of organic chemistry.

Bond Types. The explanation for these differences can be found in the different types of bond formation [13] in the two groups of compounds, and a brief review of the qualitative aspects of the electron theory of bond formation may be of value. Since organic chemistry is concerned chiefly with the elements in the first three periods of the periodic table, the discussion is limited to these elements. According to the electronic theory, atoms consist of positive nuclei surrounded by a number of negative electrons equal to the positive charge on the nucleus (the *atomic number*). These electrons group themselves in a first shell with a maximum of two electrons (*K* shell), a second shell with a maximum of eight electrons (*L* shell), and a third shell with a maximum of eighteen electrons (*M* shell).

It is known that *atoms with filled electron shells*, such as helium and neon, *are extremely inert.* Only when the outside shell of an atom is incompletely filled, can it combine with one or more other atoms to form a relatively stable compound; that is, the filling of electron shells is accompanied by the liberation of energy and gives a more stable structure. Filling of shells can take place only by acquiring electrons from other atoms. The tendency of atoms to fill incomplete shells, which is referred to as their *electronegativity* or better as their *attraction for electrons* or *electron-affinity* (cf. p. 98), increases from left to right in a given period and decreases from the top to the bottom in a given column. The cause of the first effect is the increasing charge on the nucleus with approximately constant distance of the valence electrons from the nucleus. The second effect can be ascribed to the fact that, although the charge on the nucleus is increased and electrons for a given shell are held more strongly, the outer valence electrons in each successive period are much farther away from the nucleus than the valence electrons of the preceding period, and hence the former are held less strongly than the latter. Therefore *the ease of filling electron shells by acquiring electrons from other atoms increases from left to right or from the bottom to the top of the periodic table.*

In the extreme case of two elements at opposite sides of the periodic table such as sodium and chlorine, the attraction of the chlorine atom for electrons is much greater than that of the sodium atom; that is the energy liberated when the last orbital of chlorine is filled is much greater than the energy required to remove an electron from the sodium atom. The result is that *the sodium atom transfers its electron to the chlorine atom* to give a chloride ion with a negative charge and a sodium ion with a positive charge (Fig. 1). In a mixture of sodium and chloride ions, the positive ion would exhibit a strong attraction for negative ions and the negative ion for positive ions. The attraction obeys Coulomb's law, varying inversely with the square of the distance; hence as the ions approach each other closely the attractive forces become very large. In solid sodium chloride, the size of the ions permits them to group themselves

---

[13] The differences in physical properties do not depend so much on bond type as on the atomic arrangement and the distribution of the bonds. However there is some correlation between bond type and type of atomic arrangement.

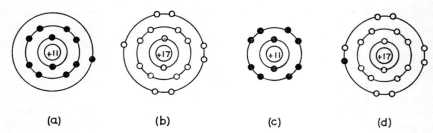

Fig. 1. Electronic representation of (*a*) the sodium atom, (*b*) the chlorine atom,
(*c*) the sodium ion, and (*d*) the chloride ion.

so that each sodium ion is surrounded by six chloride ions and each chloride ion by six sodium ions to give solid sodium chloride. This type of bond is known as an **electrovalence,** or as an **ionic bond.**

When there is less difference between the attractions of two atoms for electrons, insufficient energy is liberated when an electron is transferred from one atom to the other to make the new arrangement more stable than the old one. In the extreme case of two like atoms, such as two chlorine atoms, any energy gained by one atom acquiring an electron from the other would be offset by the energy necessary to remove the electron from the other atom. Yet it is known from experiment that chlorine is a diatomic molecule. Therefore there must be a second way in which bonds can be formed. Apparently *a considerable amount of energy is liberated when the unpaired electrons of two chlorine atoms occupy the shells of both chlorine atoms.* This process has been called a *sharing of electrons* and is illustrated diagrammatically in Fig. 2. In the alternative simplified formula, the symbol for the element represents the

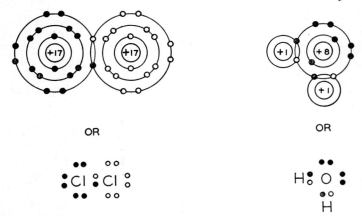

Fig. 2. Electronic representation of the   Fig. 3. Electronic representation of
chlorine molecule.   the water molecule.

nucleus with the inner full shells of electrons, and only the electrons in the outermost shell are indicated. Since each atom has gained as much as it has lost, there is no change in charge on the atoms, and the molecule as a whole is electrically neutral. This type of bond is known as a **covalence,** or as a

covalent or **electron-pair bond,** and occurs for the most part between atoms containing four or more electrons in the valence shell.

Just as a chlorine molecule consists of two chlorine atoms sharing one pair of electrons, the water molecule consists of two hydrogen atoms, each pairing one electron with one of the two unpaired electrons of an oxygen atom (Fig. 3). Since the K shell is filled when it contains two electrons, the hydrogen atoms have stable electronic arrangements, as does the oxygen atom with eight electrons in its L shell. Similarly in the ammonia molecule, three hydrogen atoms are joined by covalent bonds to a nitrogen atom, and in carbon tetrachloride, four chlorine atoms are joined to a carbon atom.

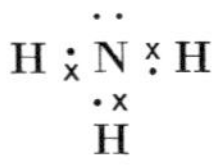

$$\overset{..}{\underset{\cdot \text{x}}{\text{H}\; \underset{\text{x}}{;}\, \text{N}\; \overset{\text{x}}{;}\, \text{H}}}$$
$$\text{H}$$

Ammonia, NH_3

$$\overset{\text{Cl}}{\underset{\cdot\text{x}}{\text{Cl}\; \underset{\text{x}}{;}\, \text{C}\; \overset{\text{x}}{;}\, \text{Cl}}}$$
$$\text{Cl}$$

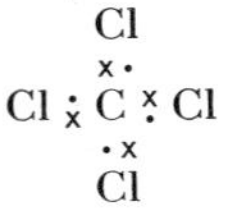

Carbon tetrachloride, CCl_4

In the above formulas, and occasionally throughout the text, different marks are used to differentiate between the sources of the electrons forming the bonds. For example in the ammonia molecule, the dots represent the valence electrons which belonged originally to the nitrogen atom and crosses those which belonged to the hydrogen atoms. Since electrons are all alike and constantly are interchanging (*electronic interaction*), there is no distinction between them once the bond is formed, and the above representation is justified only in that it simplifies the procedure in keeping track of electrons when writing formulas representing electronic structures.

The difference in properties between the typical salt, sodium chloride, and the typical nonsalt, carbon tetrachloride, now can be explained. In solid sodium chloride there are no individual NaCl molecules. The crystal is composed of positive sodium ions each surrounded by six negatively charged chloride ions, and negative chloride ions each surrounded by six positively charged sodium ions. Strong electrostatic forces hold the ions together, and high temperatures are required to cause melting or volatilization. In carbon tetrachloride, however, the CCl_4 molecule is a distinct entity which is electrically neutral. The bonds between the carbon and the chlorine atoms are strong, but only relatively weak attractive forces exist between the individual molecules. Since only a small amount of energy is required to separate the molecules, carbon tetrachloride is a liquid at room temperature and is vaporized easily.

Solubility. The difference in bond type also explains the difference in solubility behavior. Water is a polar compound (p. 63); that is when water molecules are placed in an electric field, they tend to be oriented with the hydrogen atoms toward the negative pole and the oxygen atom toward the positive pole. Because of this orientation the molecule appears to have a positive and a negative end and is called a *dipole*. The dipole is believed to arise from the difference in the attraction of hydrogen and oxygen for electrons. Even though the electrons are farther away from the nucleus in oxygen than in hydrogen, the nuclear charge of $+8$ on the oxygen atom is sufficiently greater than the $+1$ charge on hydrogen to cause the bonding electrons to be closer to the oxygen atom than to the hydrogen atom. Since the two bonds are not linear but at an angle of 105 degrees to each other, there will be a resultant dipole for the molecule as a whole. When sodium chloride is placed in contact with water, there is an *attraction between the positive sodium ion and the negative ends of water molecules,* thus forming the hydrated sodium ion. Similarly *the negative chloride ion attracts the positive ends of the water molecules* (Fig. 4). Actually each water molecule is associated with other water

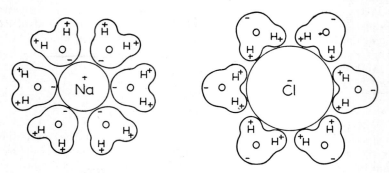

Fig. 4. Hydrated sodium and chloride ions.

molecules (p. 60), and a considerable quantity of water is affixed to each ion.

Water has a *high dielectric constant,* and when the water molecules come between the sodium ions and the chloride ions, they decrease the electrostatic attractions between the ions with the result that the ions are separated, and the salt dissolves in the water. This solution conducts the electric current because the ions are free to move, being insulated from each other by the water molecules. Salts are insoluble in most organic liquids because the latter either are not polar or do not possess a sufficiently high dielectric constant.

Carbon tetrachloride is insoluble in water because there is no charge on the molecule and no tendency for the carbon atom and the chlorine atoms to separate as ions. Hence there is no strong attraction for water molecules. Moreover water molecules have a relatively strong attraction for each other (see *association,* pp. 60, 64) which prevents simple mixing or intermingling of the water and carbon tetrachloride molecules. On the other hand the carbon tetrachloride molecules have no difficulty in mixing with the molecules of other organic compounds, such as the molecules in gasoline, that likewise have little affinity for each other.

Number of Organic Compounds. The large number of organic compounds also can be explained by the electronic structure of the carbon atom, which places it in the center of the first period. With four valence electrons, it is capable of uniting with the maximum number of monovalent atoms or groups,[14] and *it is able to form four strong covalent bonds not only with other kinds of atoms but also with other carbon atoms indefinitely.* Polyethylene, and many other high molecular weight plastics, have a thousand or more carbon atoms

---

[14] This statement applies to atoms with a coordination number of four, that is those having a maximum covalence of four. Atoms in the third and higher periods can combine with larger numbers of groups. They do not, however, bond with themselves to the extent that carbon does.

linked to each other chain-wise. Moreover the bonds formed by the carbon atom are directed to the corners of a tetrahedron (p. 23), and *three-dimensional molecules and molecules having atoms joined in polygons are possible.* Carbon is unique because the other elements having four valence electrons, such as silicon, germanium, and tin, have a decreasing attraction for their valence electrons because of the increasing distance from the nucleus, and hence they are less likely to form covalent bonds; that is they become more like a metal. Moreover, because of their larger size, the space relationships may be such that many types of compounds known for carbon are unknown for the other elements.

It may be stated, then, that organic chemistry is based on *two fundamental principles:* (*1*) **carbon has a valence of four;** that is it is able to combine covalently with four univalent atoms or groups of atoms; (*2*) **carbon can unite with itself indefinitely.** These principles were discussed independently and almost simultaneously by Kekulé and by Couper [15] in 1858, and formed the basis for the development of structural organic chemistry. They were enunciated long before chemists had any conception of the electronic nature of valence and were developed purely from observations of the composition and chemical behavior of organic compounds.

Isolation and Purification of Organic Compounds

Distillation. Before any study can be made of an unknown compound, it first must be isolated in a pure state. A number of processes are available for this purpose. Because of the small attractive forces between most individual organic molecules, many organic compounds can be converted into the gaseous state, without decomposition, by heating to a temperature at which the vapor pressure becomes equal to the external pressure. This temperature is known as the **boiling point** of the liquid. The vapors may be forced into a cooling device where they condense to the original liquid. This process is known as **distillation.** A simple distillation apparatus is shown in Fig. 5. The sub-

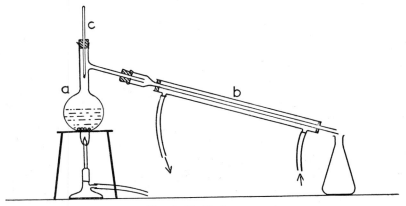

Fig. 5. Simple distillation apparatus.

[15] Archibald Scott Couper (1831–1892), brilliant young Scotch chemist whose career was cut short by illness in 1859. He was the first to publish formulas for organic compounds comparable to present-day structural formulas.

stance to be distilled is placed in a distilling flask a and connected to a water-cooled condenser b. A thermometer c is placed in the neck of the flask to record the temperature at which the vapors distill.

Because the attraction between the molecules of one compound differs from that between the molecules of another, different organic compounds usually distill at different temperatures. Hence distillation can be used not only to separate volatile organic compounds from nonvolatile materials but also mixtures of organic compounds having different boiling points. To separate substances whose boiling points are not far apart, it may be necessary to use fractional distillation or an efficient fractionating column.

In **fractional distillation,** the mixture is distilled into a number of fractions. These fractions will differ in composition from the original material, the lower-boiling fractions containing a higher percentage of the lower-boiling substance. By a systematic redistillation of the fractions a further separation takes place, and the process is repeated until the desired degree of separation has been achieved. A **fractionating column** is a device for bringing about a more efficient separation than can be obtained in an ordinary distilling flask. It consists of a tall column through which the vapors rise and a certain amount of liquid, known as *reflux,* descends. As the hot vapors from the still come into contact with the cooler descending liquid, a heat interchange takes place. The vapors are cooled slightly and some of the higher-boiling constituents condense. The heat of condensation given up to the reflux vaporizes a small amount of its lower-boiling constituents. Hence there is a gradual enrichment of the lower-boiling constituent in the vapors as they rise in the column, and an enrichment of the higher-boiling constituent in the reflux as it descends.

The operation of a fractionating column depends on intimate contact of the distilling vapors and the reflux, and many types of columns have been devised to achieve this. There are two main classes of columns, the **packed columns** and the **plate columns,** sections of which are illustrated in Fig. 6.

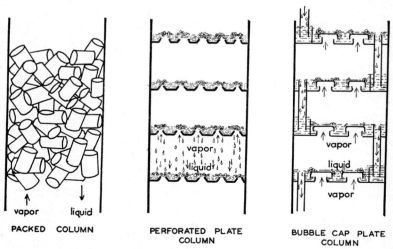

PACKED COLUMN   PERFORATED PLATE   BUBBLE CAP PLATE
                            COLUMN   COLUMN

Fig. 6. Sections through three types of fractionating columns.

Theoretically it is not possible to separate two liquids completely by distillation because, no matter how large the difference in their boiling points, the higher-boiling constituent always will exert its vapor pressure at the boiling point of the other constituent and some molecules of the higher-boiling constituent will distill.

This phenomenon can be demonstrated very readily. If a mixture of equal quantities of the colorless liquid ethyl alcohol, having a boiling point of 78°, and of the orange solid, azobenzene, boiling at 297°, are distilled from an ordinary distilling flask, the distillate of alcohol will be colored yellow by azobenzene molecules that have come over with the alcohol molecules, in spite of the fact that the difference in boiling point is over 200°. For all practical purposes, however, it is possible to separate by means of efficient fractionation, liquids boiling as little as 3° apart.

Distillation under reduced pressure, which frequently is called **vacuum distillation,** is used for high-boiling compounds to avoid the decomposition that might take place at the high temperatures necessary to produce distillation at atmospheric pressure. Since substances distill as soon as their vapor pressures exceed the pressure at the surface of the liquid, reducing the pressure enables the substance to distill at a lower temperature. **Steam distillation,** consisting of passing steam through the substance or distilling in the presence of water, accomplishes the same purpose since distillation takes place when the sum of the vapor pressures of the compound and of water exceeds the pressure in the distillation apparatus. This condition will occur at a lower temperature than for either component alone.

Crystallization. This procedure is useful for the purification of organic solids, just as it is an important method for salts. The solubilities of organic compounds usually have a high temperature coefficient. Hence the usual method of crystallization consists in making a saturated solution at the boiling point of the solvent and then cooling to room temperature or below. The pure compound crystallizes, and the more soluble or less abundant impurities remain in solution. A large variety of solvents is available, and the one most suitable for the material being purified can be chosen.

Extraction. Extraction with solvents also is an important method for isolating and purifying organic compounds. Solid mixtures are extracted with volatile solvents that will extract the desired constituents and leave the undesired constituents behind. Organic compounds can be separated from aqueous solutions by shaking with a water-immiscible solvent which will dissolve more of the desired material than will water. The organic compound passes into the organic solvent, from which the compound can be recovered by evaporating or distilling the solvent. Organic or inorganic salts can be separated from nonsalts by shaking the mixture with water and an organic solvent, the salt dissolving in the water and the nonsalt in the organic solvent.

Criteria of Purity. Pure substances distill at a constant temperature; hence *constancy of boiling point* is a good criterion of purity. Pure solid compounds usually *melt over a very narrow range of temperature* which is characteristic of the compound. Since these melting points are relatively low, they may be determined easily and form a second criterion of purity. Other useful criteria are *density, refractive index,* and *solubilities in various solvents.*

Analysis of Organic Compounds for the Elements

Qualitative Analysis. After a compound has been isolated in a pure state, any investigation of it must begin with the identification of the elements present. Qualitative tests for the elements depend almost exclusively on reactions of ions. Since the elements in organic compounds usually are not present in ions, other types of tests must be devised, or the organic compounds must be converted into ionizable salts. Both methods of attack are used. **Carbon** and **hydrogen** may be detected readily by heating the unknown in a test tube with dry copper oxide powder and passing the evolved gases into a solution of barium hydroxide. The hydrogen is burned to water which collects in droplets on the cooler portion of the test tube and may be observed visually. The carbon is burned to carbon dioxide, which reacts with the barium hydroxide solution to give a precipitate of barium carbonate.

Several methods are available for converting other elements into detectable ions, but the procedure most commonly used is heating the compound with molten sodium. This process is known as *sodium fusion.* **Sulfur** is converted to sodium sulfide, **halogen** to sodium halide, and **nitrogen,** in the presence of carbon, to sodium cyanide.

$$\text{Organic compound containing} \atop \text{C, H, N, S, X}^{16} \xrightarrow{\text{Na fusion}} {\text{NaCN} \atop \text{Na}_2\text{S} \atop \text{NaX}}$$

An aqueous solution of the ions is obtained by decomposing with water. The *cyanide ion* may be converted to insoluble Prussian blue by heating a portion of the aqueous solution with ferrous and ferric sulfate in alkaline solution. Addition of hydrochloric acid dissolves the iron hydroxides and leaves the blue precipitate.

$$18\ \text{NaCN} + 3\ \text{FeSO}_4 + 2\ \text{Fe}_2(\text{SO}_4)_3 \longrightarrow \text{Fe}_4[\text{Fe}(\text{CN})_6]_3 + 9\ \text{Na}_2\text{SO}_4$$

Sulfide ion is detected readily by acidifying the solution with acetic acid, heating to drive off hydrogen sulfide, and allowing the vapors to come in contact with a solution of lead acetate on filter paper. A dark, lustrous spot of lead sulfide will form if sulfide ion is present.

$$\text{Na}_2\text{S} + 2\ \text{HC}_2\text{H}_3\text{O}_2 \longrightarrow \text{H}_2\text{S} + 2\ \text{NaC}_2\text{H}_3\text{O}_2$$

$$\text{Pb}(\text{C}_2\text{H}_3\text{O}_2)_2 + \text{H}_2\text{S} \longrightarrow \text{PbS} + 2\ \text{HC}_2\text{H}_3\text{O}_2$$

To test for *halide ion,* the solution is boiled with nitric acid to remove cyanide ion and sulfide ion, and then aqueous silver nitrate is added. If halogen is present, a white, pale yellow, or deep yellow precipitate will be formed depending on whether chlorine, bromine, or iodine is present.

$$\text{NaX} + \text{AgNO}_3 \longrightarrow \text{AgX} + \text{NaNO}_3$$

Quantitative Analysis. The determination of the *kind* of elements present in a new compound under investigation is followed by the determina-

---

[16] The symbol X is used to indicate chlorine, bromine, or iodine.

tion of the *relative amounts* of the elements. **Carbon** and **hydrogen** are estimated by a procedure perfected by Liebig, which is based on the same principle used for qualitative detection, namely combustion to carbon dioxide and water. The apparatus and the functions of the various parts are given in Fig. 7.

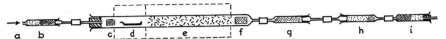

Fig. 7. Apparatus for the determination of carbon and hydrogen: *a*, source of air or oxygen; *b*, tube packed with solid absorbent containing sodium hydroxide for removing carbon dioxide, and a second solid absorbent such as anhydrous magnesium perchlorate or activated alumina for removing water; *c*, copper oxide gauze to oxidize vapor diffusing backwards; *d*, porcelain or platinum boat containing weighed sample and heated by sectional combustion furnace (dotted lines); *e*, packing of copper oxide wire heated to 600°–800°; *f*, reduced copper gauze to reduce oxides of nitrogen to nitrogen; *g*, weighed tube containing water absorbent; *h*, weighed tube containing carbon dioxide absorbent backed by water absorbent; *i*, safety tube packed with water absorbent and carbon dioxide absorbent to prevent diffusion of atmospheric moisture and carbon dioxide into *h*.

The combustion is carried out in a glass tube packed with copper oxide, which is maintained at 600°–800° by means of an electrically- or gas-heated furnace to insure complete oxidation of the organic matter. The tube first is swept out with purified air to remove moisture and carbon dioxide, and then the weighed sample is burned completely to carbon dioxide and water. The gases from the combustion tube are passed through an absorption train, which consists of a tube containing a water absorbent, a tube containing a carbon dioxide absorbent, and a safety tube containing an additional quantity of the carbon dioxide and water absorbents. After the initial decomposition, a slow stream of purified air or oxygen is passed through the tube to complete the combustion. At the end of the combustion the apparatus is swept out with purified air to drive all the carbon dioxide and water into the absorption tubes. The increases in weight of the first and second absorption tubes *g* and *h* of Fig. 7 give the weights of water and carbon dioxide respectively. From these data and the weight of the original substance, the per cent of hydrogen and of carbon can be calculated.

The *Dumas method* is the most important for the determination of **nitrogen,** since it can be used for any type of nitrogen compound. The apparatus is illustrated in Fig. 8. The weighed sample mixed with powdered copper oxide is placed in a tube which can be swept out with pure carbon dioxide. When the section containing the sample and copper oxide is heated, the sample is burned to carbon dioxide, water, and nitrogen, and the gases passed over more hot copper oxide to insure complete combustion. Any oxides of nitrogen that form are reduced to nitrogen by passing the gases over a reduced copper oxide spiral. At the end of the combustion, the tube is swept out again with carbon dioxide. The gases are passed into a nitrometer tube filled with 50 per cent potassium hydroxide solution,[17] which absorbs the carbon dioxide and leaves

---

[17] Potassium hydroxide is used instead of sodium hydroxide because potassium carbonate is soluble in concentrated potassium hydroxide solution, whereas sodium carbonate is insoluble in concentrated sodium hydroxide solutions and would precipitate.

the nitrogen. The volume is measured and the temperature and barometric pressure noted. The vapor pressure of the potassium hydroxide solution is obtained from a table and subtracted from the barometric pressure. From these data the weight of nitrogen and the per cent in the sample can be calculated.

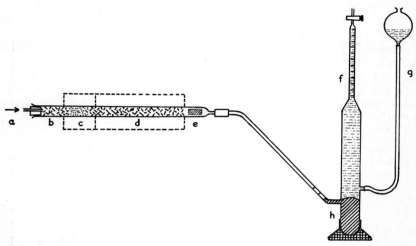

Fig. 8. Apparatus for the determination of nitrogen (Dumas): *a*, source of pure carbon dioxide; *b*, copper oxide wire; *c*, weighed sample mixed with copper oxide powder and heated by sectional combustion furnace (dotted lines); *d*, copper oxide wire heated to 600°–800°; *e*, reduced copper gauze to reduce oxides of nitrogen to nitrogen; *f*, nitrometer containing 50 per cent aqueous potassium hydroxide solution; *g*, leveling bulb and potassium hydroxide reservoir; *h*, mercury valve.

The *Kjeldahl method* is more limited, since certain types of nitrogen compounds give low results because of the evolution of nitrogen during the digestion or because of the difficulty of decomposing them completely. The procedure consists in heating a weighed sample with concentrated sulfuric acid and an oxidizing catalyst such as mercuric oxide, or copper sulfate and selenium. The nitrogen in the sample is converted to ammonium sulfate. At the end of the digestion, sodium hydroxide is added to liberate ammonia, which is distilled into a measured volume of standard acid. Back titration with standard alkali, using methyl red as an indicator, gives the amount of ammonia formed. The procedure lends itself to routine analyses of large numbers of samples and is very useful for those types of compounds for which it gives accurate results.

The only special feature in the quantitative determination of **other elements** is the necessity of converting them into ionized compounds. In the determination of **sulfur, halogen,** or **phosphorus,** for example, the compound may be fused in a Parr bomb with sodium peroxide, which burns the carbon and hydrogen to carbon dioxide and water, and converts halogen, sulfur, and phosphorus into the alkali halide, sulfate, and phosphate. Alternatively the compound may be oxidized with nitric acid in a sealed tube at elevated temperature (*Carius method*). When the conversion to the inorganic salts has been effected, the usual quantitative methods, gravimetric or volumetric, may be employed. No method for the direct estimation of **oxygen** is in general use. As a result this element is determined as the difference between 100 per cent and the sum of the per cents of the other elements.

The *quantity of material* needed for an analysis depends on the experience of the operator, on the apparatus, and on the sensitivity of the balance available. **Macroanalyses** use from 0.1 to 0.2 g. of substance, **semimicroanalyses** use from 0.01 to 0.02 g., and **microanalyses** use from 0.003 to 0.005 g. In each case a balance must be used that is accurate to four significant figures.

Empirical Formulas. From the analyses the relative proportion by weight of the various elements present may be calculated, but for convenience the results are expressed as an *empirical formula* which shows the relative number of different atoms in the molecule. To calculate the empirical formula, the per cent of each element is divided by its atomic weight. The result usually is in the form of fractions, and it is customary to convert these fractions into ratios of whole numbers.

The following example illustrates the general method for determining an empirical formula from analyses.

A sample weighing 0.1824 g. gave on combustion 0.2681 g. of carbon dioxide and 0.1090 g. of water.

$$\text{Weight of carbon in sample} = 0.2681 \times \frac{12}{44} = 0.07312 \text{ g.}$$

$$\text{Weight of hydrogen in sample} = 0.1090 \times \frac{2}{18} = 0.01211 \text{ g.}$$

$$\text{Per cent carbon in sample} = \frac{0.07312}{0.1824} \times 100 = 40.09$$

$$\text{Per cent hydrogen in sample} = \frac{0.01211}{0.1824} \times 100 = 6.64$$

$$\text{Per cent oxygen in sample} = 100 - (40.09 + 6.64) = 53.27$$

Element	Per cent by weight		Atomic weight		Atomic ratio				Atomic ratio in integers
C	40.09	÷	12	=	3.36	÷	3.33	=	1
H	6.64	÷	1	=	6.64	÷	3.33	=	2
O	53.27	÷	16	=	3.33	÷	3.33	=	1

The empirical formula therefore is CH_2O.

Molecular Formulas. Usually a determination of the empirical formula identifies an inorganic compound. For most organic compounds, however, the empirical formula is less definitive. One reason for this difference is that several organic compounds can have the same empirical formula but differ in molecular weight. Thus formaldehyde, acetic acid, lactic acid, and glucose all have the empirical formula CH_2O, but their molecular formulas, that is formulas indicating not only the ratio but also the number of atoms in the molecule, are respectively CH_2O, $C_2H_4O_2$, $C_3H_6O_3$, and $C_6H_{12}O_6$. The importance of determining molecular weights was brought to the attention of chemists by Cannizzaro in 1860, although the basis for their determination had been provided by Avogadro in 1811 (p. 4).

Several methods for determining molecular weights are available. The

Dumas method, which still is one of the most accurate, is suitable only for gases and low-boiling liquids. A glass bulb of known volume is weighed when it is completely evacuated, and when it is filled with gas. From the weight of the known volume of gas at the observed temperature and pressure, the weight of 22.4 liters at 0° and 760 mm. can be calculated.

In the *Victor Meyer* [18] *method*, which is suitable for easily volatilized sub-

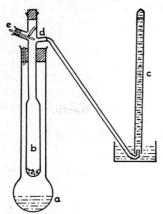

Fig. 9. Victor Meyer apparatus for the determination of molecular weights.

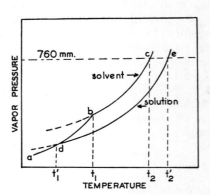

Fig. 10. Variation of the vapor pressure of solvent and solution with temperature.

stances, a known weight of the compound is vaporized in a closed system and the volume of air displaced is measured. The apparatus is illustrated in Fig. 9. A liquid boiling higher than the sample is placed in the jacket *a* and boiled uniformly until bubbles no longer are emitted from the outlet of the inner chamber *b*, indicating that temperature equilibrium has been reached. The eudiometer tube *c* is placed over the outlet, the sample *d* introduced through a device *e* into the chamber *b*, and heating continued until equilibrium again is reached. The volume of air collected is that which the substance would occupy if it were a gas at the same temperature and pressure at which the volume of the displaced air was measured.

Two methods which are more generally applicable than those given above are known as the *cryoscopic* or *freezing point method*, and the *ebullioscopic* or *boiling point method*. They depend on the effect of a nonvolatile solute on the vapor pressure of the solvent. This effect may be illustrated by the curves in Fig. 10. Curve *bc* represents the vapor pressure of the pure solvent in the liquid phase and curve *ab* that of the solid phase. The vapor pressure of a solid is lower than that of the liquid at the same temperature because of the heat of fusion of the solid. Since the vapor pressure is lowered by dissolved molecules of a substance having negligible vapor pressure, the vapor pressure of the solution may be represented by the curve *de*. The freezing point *b* of the pure liquid will be lowered to *d* for the solution, the difference being Δt_1. The boiling

[18] Victor Meyer (1848–1897), professor of chemistry at the University of Heidelberg. He is remembered not only for the apparatus which bears his name but also for his work on steric hindrance (p. 412), aliphatic nitro compounds (p. 201), oximes (p. 171), and thiophene (p. 444).

point c for the pure liquid will be increased to e for the solution, the difference being Δt_2. Since the lowering of the vapor pressure depends on the number of molecules dissolved, one gram molecular weight of any nondissociating substance dissolved in 1000 grams of solvent will lower the melting point $K_{f.p.}$ degrees, called the *molal lowering of the freezing point*, or raise the boiling point $K_{b.p.}$ degrees, the *molal elevation of the boiling point*. If W grams of a substance of molecular weight M is dissolved in G grams of solvent,

$$\Delta t = K \frac{W}{M} \times \frac{1000}{G}$$

$$\text{or } M = \frac{KW}{\Delta t} \times \frac{1000}{G}$$

The experimentally determined values of K for a few of the common solvents are given in Table 2.

TABLE 2

CRYOSCOPIC AND EBULLIOSCOPIC CONSTANTS

SOLVENT	$K_{f.p.}$	$K_{b.p.}$ (760 mm.)
Water	1.86	0.51
Acetic acid	3.86	3.07
Benzene	5.12	2.53
Exaltone	21.3	
Camphor	39.7	

In determining the molecular weights of unknown compounds, the boiling point or freezing point is determined in a special apparatus (Figs. 11 and 12),

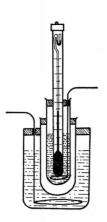

Fig. 11. Freezing point apparatus.

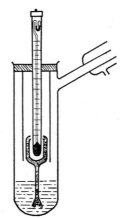

Fig. 12. Boiling point apparatus.

first on the pure solvent and then on a solution of known concentration. Knowing K, W, G, and Δt, the molecular weight M can be calculated. Because the changes in the boiling point or melting point usually are small, a special differential thermometer which measures small differences in temperature, such as the *Beckmann thermometer*, or the *Menzies-Wright thermometer*, is used, and relatively large amounts of material are needed. The molecular lowering of the freezing point of camphor, however, is large, and since it is a solid, the melting point lowering may be determined in a capillary tube using an ordinary thermometer (Fig. 13). This procedure is known as the *Rast camphor method* for determining molecular weights.

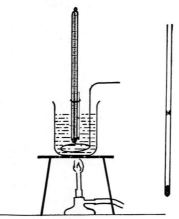

Fig. 13. Capillary tube melting point apparatus with enlarged view of sealed capillary melting point tube.

The relative error of molecular weight determinations rarely is less than ±5 per cent, and the result of a combustion analysis usually is considered acceptable if the absolute error is less than ±0.5 per cent.[19] Hence it is difficult to determine by analyses alone the exact molecular formulas of saturated hydrocarbons (compounds containing carbon and the maximum amount of hydrogen) having molecular weights greater than about 150. If other elements are present, the differences in the per cent composition of compounds differing by one carbon atom are considerably greater; thus if a compound contains carbon and hydrogen and one oxygen atom per molecule, empirical formulas can be determined for compounds having molecular weights up to about 400. Analyses for the elements usually are more accurate than ordinary molecular weight determinations, and the latter are used merely to determine whether the molecular formula is a multiple of the empirical formula.

Classification of Organic Compounds

The number of known organic compounds was estimated in 1948 to have been around 1,000,000. The reasons for this large number have been given,

---

[19] Accuracy is expressed in terms of absolute error or relative error. The error of a measurement is the deviation from what is thought to be the true value. The *absolute error* is the difference between the numerical value observed and the true value and is expressed in the units used to express the numerical value. The *relative error* usually is expressed as the per cent deviation and is the absolute error divided by the true value and multiplied by 100. For example if a compound has a molecular weight of 200 g. and the observed value is 210 g., the absolute error is 10 g. and the relative error is 5 per cent. If a compound contains 5.5 per cent hydrogen and the value found is 5.3 per cent, the absolute error is 0.2 per cent and the relative error is 3.6 per cent.

namely that a carbon atom is able to combine with four other atoms or groups of atoms, and that carbon atoms are able to combine with each other indefinitely to produce stable compounds. Apparently the possible number of compounds of carbon is infinite. Because of this large number of compounds, it might seem that the study of organic chemistry would be hopeless, but fortunately it is possible to divide these compounds into a comparatively small number of groups or *families of compounds.* Most members of each family may be prepared by similar methods, and most members exhibit similar chemical behavior. Moreover the individual members of each family differ from each other more or less regularly in their physical properties. The families, on the other hand, usually differ from each other markedly in their chemical properties and are prepared by different types of chemical reactions. Accordingly it is possible to concentrate on the methods of preparation and reactions of the families of compounds, and it is not necessary to discuss each member of a family. Special methods of preparation and special reactions of individual compounds then can be considered as additions or exceptions to the generalizations.

The numerous families may be grouped according to similarities in structure. The three main classifications are (*1*) acyclic compounds, which contain no ring structures of the atoms, (*2*) carbocyclic compounds, which contain rings made up solely of carbon atoms, and (*3*) heterocyclic compounds, which contain rings made up of more than one kind of atom. The acyclic compounds more commonly are called aliphatic compounds from the Greek word *aleiphatos* meaning *fat*, because the fats have this type of structure.

REVIEW QUESTIONS

1. Define the term *organic chemistry.*
2. What date usually is considered as the time when the modern science of organic chemistry began and why? When did it begin to be placed on a rational basis?
3. Give one significant contribution of each of the following men to the early development of organic chemistry: Scheele, Lavoisier, Liebig, Cannizzaro, Victor Meyer, Berzelius, Dumas, Woehler.
4. Discuss and give examples of the two common modes of bond formation between atoms.
5. List the important differences in the physical and chemical properties of most salts and most nonsalts, give the primary reason for these differences, and tell how it explains them.
6. How does the number and complexity of the compounds of carbon compare with the number and complexity of the compounds of other elements? Why is carbon unique in this respect?
7. Discuss the solubility of sodium chloride in water, carbon tetrachloride, and gasoline, and the mutual solubility relationships of the last three substances. Give an explanation of the facts.
8. List the more important processes used to purify organic compounds.
9. What is the usual procedure for the purification of organic solids by crystallization?
10. What physical properties are most commonly used as criteria of purity for organic compounds? Why are these criteria of little importance for inorganic salts?
11. Give a sketch of the apparatus and a brief description of the usual method for determining the per cent of carbon and hydrogen in an organic compound.
12. Give a brief description of the Dumas method for determining nitrogen in an organic compound.
13. Describe the Kjeldahl method for determining nitrogen in organic compounds. What are its limitations?
14. Why is it necessary to determine the molecular weights of organic compounds? What is the difference between an empirical formula and a molecular formula?

15. Give the formula relating molecular weight to the lowering of the freezing point of a solvent, together with the meaning of the symbols. How can the elevation of the boiling point be used to determine molecular weights?

16. Given a new organic compound mixed with other substances, outline briefly the experimental steps necessary for determining the molecular formula of the compound.

NUMERICAL PROBLEMS *

17. Calculate the per cent composition of (a) C_2H_6, (b) CH_4O, (c) C_2H_3BrO, (d) C_2H_5NO.

18. What are the differences in the per cent of carbon and of hydrogen for the compounds $C_{15}H_{32}$ and $C_{16}H_{34}$; $C_{15}H_{32}O$ and $C_{16}H_{34}O$; $C_{30}H_{62}O$, $C_{31}H_{64}O$, and $C_{30}H_{60}O$?

19. Calculate the volume of nitrogen that would be obtained at S.T.P.† when 0.059 g. of a compound having the formula C_3H_9N is burned in a Dumas apparatus.

20. A compound was found to contain carbon, hydrogen, sulfur, and possibly oxygen. Quantitative analysis showed 47.35 per cent carbon, 10.50 per cent hydrogen, and 42.06 per cent sulfur. Calculate the empirical formula of the compound.

21. A compound was found to contain carbon, hydrogen, and possibly oxygen. Quantitative analysis showed 54.54 per cent carbon and 9.09 per cent hydrogen. The molecular weight by the elevation of the boiling point method was about 130. Calculate the molecular formula of the compound. What is the exact molecular weight of the compound?

22. When 0.620 g. of a substance was dissolved in 15 g. of water, the freezing point was lowered 0.302°. What is the approximate molecular weight of the compound?

23. In a molecular weight determination by the Victor Meyer method, 0.168 g. of a compound displaced 49.8 cc. of air measured over water at 20° and 757 mm. (vapor pressure of water at 20° = 17 mm. of mercury). Calculate the approximate molecular weight of the compound.

24. A compound contains 22 per cent bromine. What is the minimum molecular weight of the compound?

25. A compound was found to contain carbon, hydrogen, and possibly oxygen. A sample weighing 0.1085 g. on combustion gave 0.3411 g. of carbon dioxide and 0.1394 g. of water. Calculate the per cent composition and the empirical formula. When 0.169 g. of the compound was vaporized in a Victor Meyer apparatus, the volume of displaced air corrected to S.T.P. was 45.2 cc. What was the molecular formula of the compound?

26. A compound containing carbon, hydrogen, bromine, and possibly oxygen, gave on combustion 0.2000 g. of carbon dioxide and 0.0955 g. of water from 0.1868 g. of sample. Fusion of 0.1550 g. with sodium peroxide, acidification with nitric acid, and precipitation with silver nitrate gave 0.2369 g. of silver bromide. Calculate the empirical formula of the compound.

27. Combustion of 0.2350 g. of a substance gave 0.3692 g. of carbon dioxide and 0.0756 g. of water. Combustion of 0.1792 g. in a Dumas apparatus gave 41 cc. of nitrogen measured over water at 735 mm. and 25° (vapor pressure of 50 per cent potassium hydroxide at 25° = 9 mm. of mercury). When 1.310 g. was dissolved in 25 g. of benzene, the freezing point of the benzene was lowered 1.17°. Calculate the molecular formula of the compound.

---

* When numerical problems are assigned as written homework, give and label clearly the steps in the calculations.

† Standard temperature and pressure, that is 0° and 760 mm. of mercury.

Chapter 2

ALKANES

Several families of organic compounds exist which contain only hydrogen and carbon in the molecule and are known as hydrocarbons. The simplest family of this group is known as the *alkanes*. For reasons which will become apparent, they are known also as *saturated hydrocarbons* or *paraffin hydro-carbons*, or the *methane series* of hydrocarbons. All other families of the acyclic or aliphatic series can be considered as derived from the alkanes, and hence a knowledge of their properties and constitution is the best preparation for further study.

The simplest member of this family of hydrocarbons contains only one carbon atom and is called *methane*.[1] It is a gas that liquefies at $-161°$ and has the composition and molecular weight corresponding to the molecular formula CH_4. The next member boils at $-89°$, has the molecular formula C_2H_6, and is called *ethane*. The third member, *propane*, C_3H_8, boils at $-42°$. It is apparent already that this family is a series of compounds having the general formula C_nH_{2n+2}, in which one member differs from each adjacent member by one carbon atom and two hydrogen atoms, that is by CH_2. Such a series is known as a *homologous series* and the members of the series are known as *homologs*.

Structural Formulas

The electronic structure of the carbon atom explains the composition of these compounds and the existence of a homologous series. The carbon atom has four electrons which it can pair with four electrons of other atoms. Since only compounds of carbon and hydrogen are being considered, the simplest compound would be that in which a single carbon atom had paired its four electrons with the electrons of four hydrogen atoms to give the molecule

H

H $\overset{x\,\cdot}{\underset{\cdot\,x}{\text{C}}}$ H, or CH_4. If two carbon atoms are in the molecule, they must be

H

united to each other by a mutual sharing of electrons, $\cdot\ \overset{\cdot}{\underset{\cdot}{\text{C}}}\ \overset{\circ}{\underset{\circ}{\text{C}}}\ \circ$, since the

hydrogen atom with only one valence electron cannot combine with more than one carbon atom. Six electrons remain to be paired by combination with six

H H

hydrogen atoms to give the molecule H $\overset{x\,\cdot}{\underset{\cdot\,x}{\text{C}}}\ \overset{x\circ}{\underset{\circ x}{\text{C}}}$ H, or C_2H_6. This process

H H

---

[1] For the pronunciation of chemical words see Appendix *A*. Pronunciation of chemical words, like that of other words, varies with individuals and with different parts of the country.

amounts to introducing a CH_2 group between one of the hydrogen atoms and the carbon atom in the methane molecule, or replacing a hydrogen atom by a CH_3 group. If three atoms of carbon are in the molecule the formula would be

$$\begin{array}{ccc} H & H & H \\ \cdot\cdot & \cdot\cdot & \cdot\cdot \\ H : C : C : C : H, & \text{or} & C_3H_8. \\ \cdot\cdot & \cdot\cdot & \cdot\cdot \\ H & H & H \end{array}$$

In the last electronic formula no distinction has been made between the electrons supplied by different atoms. This representation is less artificial than the previous ones, since all electrons are identical. The important points to observe when writing electronic formulas are that the total number of valence electrons is correct, that all are paired, and that the valence shells of the atoms are filled (two electrons for hydrogen and eight electrons for all elements in the next two periods).

The operation of building hydrocarbons by applying the rules for valence can be carried on indefinitely. Hence compounds should exist with the molecular formulas C_4H_{10}, C_6H_{14}, or in fact any compound with the general formula C_nH_{2n+2}, that is n CH_2 groups plus two hydrogen atoms to satisfy the remaining two unshared electrons. For alkanes having four or more carbon atoms, however, the situation becomes somewhat more complicated because two compounds are known having the same molecular formula C_4H_{10}. One boils at $0.6°$, and the other boils at $-10°$. Two or more compounds having the same molecular formula but differing in at least one chemical or physical property are known as **isomers** (Gr. *isos* equal and *meros* part, that is having equal or like parts), and the phenomenon is known as **isomerism.** It can be explained readily on the basis of electronic formulas. As soon as more than three carbon atoms are present, they can be arranged in more than one way. Four carbon atoms, for example, can be joined consecutively to each other,

$\cdot C : C : C : C \cdot$, or one carbon atom can be united to the central atom of a

chain of three atoms, $\cdot C : C : C \cdot$. Pairing the remaining unpaired electrons

$\cdot C \cdot$

with those of hydrogen atoms gives the formulas

$$\begin{array}{cccc} H & H & H & H \\ \cdot\cdot & \cdot\cdot & \cdot\cdot & \cdot\cdot \\ H : C : C : C : C : H \\ \cdot\cdot & \cdot\cdot & \cdot\cdot & \cdot\cdot \\ H & H & H & H \end{array} \qquad \text{and} \qquad \begin{array}{ccc} H & H & H \\ \cdot\cdot & & \cdot\cdot \\ H : C : & C & : C : H \\ \cdot\cdot & & \cdot\cdot \\ H & C : H & H \\ & \cdot\cdot & \\ & H & \end{array}$$

Ordinarily the electron pair bond is represented by a dash, and the above formulas may be written

$$
\begin{array}{c}
\text{H} \quad \text{H} \quad \text{H} \quad \text{H} \\
| \quad | \quad | \quad | \\
\text{H}-\text{C}-\text{C}-\text{C}-\text{C}-\text{H} \\
| \quad | \quad | \quad | \\
\text{H} \quad \text{H} \quad \text{H} \quad \text{H}
\end{array}
\quad \text{and} \quad
\begin{array}{c}
\text{H} \quad\quad \text{H} \quad\quad \text{H} \\
| \quad\quad | \quad\quad | \\
\text{H}-\text{C}-\quad-\text{C}-\quad-\text{C}-\text{H} \\
| \quad\quad | \quad\quad | \\
\text{H} \;\text{H}-\text{C}-\text{H}\; \text{H} \\
| \\
\text{H}
\end{array}
$$

N Butane   *é Butene*

Since the atoms are arranged differently in the two molecules, they should have different chemical and physical properties. The above two compounds are known as *butanes*. The compound with the carbon atoms linked consecutively in a chain is known as *normal butane*, and its isomer is called *isobutane*. Hydrocarbons having the carbon atoms linked in a continuous chain are called *normal* or *straight chain* hydrocarbons. If *side chains* or *branches* are present, as in isobutane, they are known as *branched chain* hydrocarbons. Formulas which show not only the number of atoms in the molecule but also the way in which they are united to each other are known as *structural* or *graphic formulas*.

If the formulas are written in a plane with the carbon bonds directed to the corners of a square, more than one propane should be possible also; that is

$$
\begin{array}{c}
\text{H} \\
| \\
\text{H}_3\text{C}-\text{C}-\text{H} \\
| \\
\text{CH}_3
\end{array}
\text{ might be expected as well as }
\begin{array}{c}
\text{H} \\
| \\
\text{H}_3\text{C}-\text{C}-\text{CH}_3. \\
| \\
\text{H}
\end{array}
\text{ Similarly a con-}
$$

siderably larger number of butanes should exist. Additional isomers, however, are not known, and the existence of optical isomers, which can be explained only by different arrangements in three dimensions (p. 263), led to the postulation that the bonds of a carbon atom are directed to the corners of a regular tetrahedron, as shown by the formula for methane (Fig. 14a). Stuart or

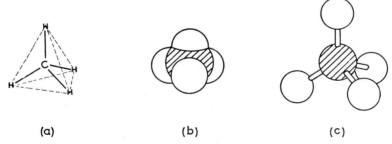

(a)   (b)   (c)

Fig. 14. Space representations of methane: (a) tetrahedral;
(b) Stuart model; (c) ball and stick model.

Hirschfelder models (Fig. 14b) give the correct interatomic distances and the distances of closest approach of different molecules as determined by X-ray diffraction studies. It is difficult, however, to see the mode of linkage of atoms in complicated molecules with this type of model, and the ball and stick type (Fig. 14c) more commonly is used. On paper or on the lecture board the plane formulas, which show only the order in which the atoms are linked to each other, are most convenient.

With a tetrahedral arrangement of the carbon valences, all of the hydrogen atoms in the ethane molecule are alike; that is each bears exactly the same space relationship to all the other atoms in the molecule (Fig. 15a). Hence

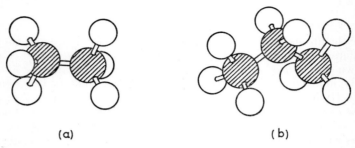

(a)   (b)

Fig. 15. Space representations of (a) ethane and (b) propane.

replacement of any hydrogen atom by another atom or group of atoms will give only one new compound, and the two plane formulas for propane become identical in the space formulas (Fig. 15b).

For compounds of more than three carbon atoms the tetrahedral distribution of the valences might be thought capable of giving isomeric compounds even for normal hydrocarbons. A five-carbon chain might be expected to exist in numerous configurations. In the examples illustrated in Fig. 16, only the

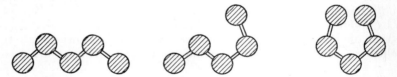

Fig. 16. Possible arrangements of carbon atoms in a five-carbon chain.

carbon skeleton is indicated. Actually no isomers corresponding to these different arrangements have been detected. It is believed that all of the above arrangements and an infinite number of others exist in gases and liquids, but that because of essentially free rotation about a single bond, the various forms readily interconvert at room temperature. The molecules do have preferred positions in which they exist most of the time. Gaseous ethane, for example, is believed to prefer the staggered position (Fig. 15a). It has been calculated that the barrier to free rotation about the carbon-carbon bond in the ethane molecule is around 3 kcal. per mole, whereas an energy barrier of approximately 20 kcal. per mole is required for stability of isomers at room temperature.[2] X-ray diffraction has shown that in the solid state long-chain paraffin hydrocarbons have the extended zigzag structure.

With these facts available, it is possible to predict the number of isomeric

---

[2] The ease with which a reaction takes place usually is expressed in terms of the *activation energy*, which is the energy that must be acquired by molecules before they can attain the half-reacted state from which they can pass to a new arrangement of the atoms (p. 91). This activation energy frequently is spoken of as the *energy barrier* to a reaction or as the *energy hump* over which the reactants must pass.

alkanes having five carbon atoms. Three arrangements of the carbon atoms, called *carbon skeletons*, are possible,

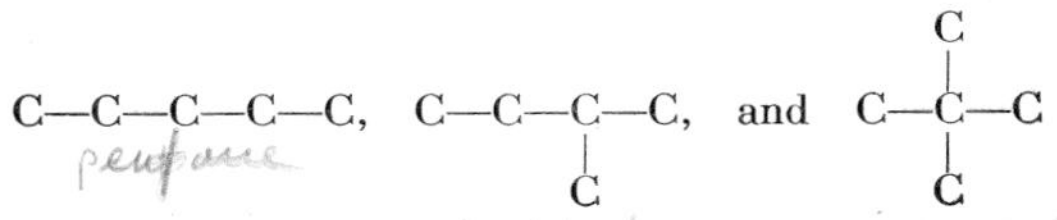

$$C-C-C-C-C, \quad C-C-C-C, \quad \text{and} \quad C-\overset{\overset{C}{|}}{\underset{\underset{C}{|}}{C}}-C$$

They give rise to the three hydrocarbons

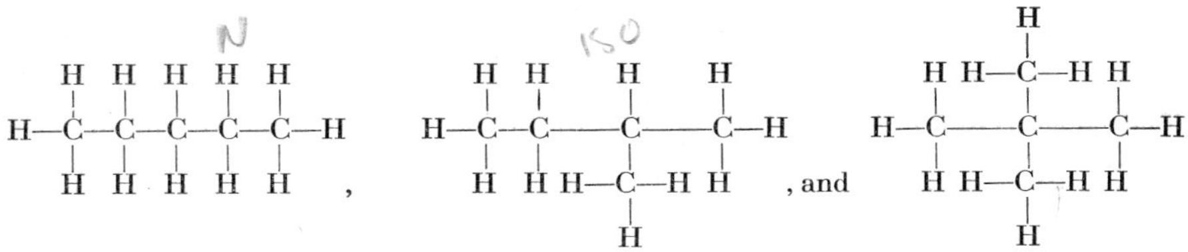

Actually three and only three compounds having the molecular formula C_5H_{12} are known. The compound to which the first structure has been assigned boils at 36.5° and is called *normal pentane*, that having the second structure boils at 27.9° and is called *isopentane*, and that having the third structure boils at 9.5° and is called *neopentane* (Gr. *neos* new). The above formulas are known as *extended structural formulas*. In order to conserve space and time in writing, they usually are replaced by *condensed structural formulas*, for example $CH_3(CH_2)_3CH_3$, $CH_3CH_2CH(CH_3)_2$ or $C_2H_5CH(CH_3)_2$, and $C(CH_3)_4$.

Nomenclature

Obviously each organic compound must have a name. The development of nomenclature in organic chemistry always has followed the same pattern. When only a few compounds of a particular type are known and before their structures have been determined, they are given names usually indicative of their source. These names are called *trivial* or *common* names. As more compounds of a series become known, an attempt is made to develop a more systematic nomenclature which shows the relation of the new compounds to the older ones. Finally an attempt is made to develop a truly rational system. In the meantime, however, the older names have become established, and it is difficult to replace them by new ones, with the result that the simpler compounds usually have two or three names. Since all of these names are in more or less general use and appear in the literature, it is necessary that the student become familiar with them and be able to use them interchangeably.

Common Names. In all systems names of the members of the alkane series end in *ane*. The names of hydrocarbons having four carbon atoms or less may be called common names since they are derived from the common names of the alcohols having the same number of carbon atoms. Above C_4 the names become a little more systematic by using the Greek (or Latin) [3] prefix to indicate the number of carbon atoms in the molecule.

---

[3] Most of the names are of Greek derivation, but the Latin combining form *nona* is used almost universally instead of the Greek *ennea*. Similarly *undecane* is used more frequently

C_5	pentanes		C_{16}–C_{19}	etc.
C_6	hexanes		C_{20}	eicosanes
C_7	heptanes		C_{21}	heneicosanes
C_8	octanes		C_{22}	docosanes
C_9	nonanes		C_{23}	tricosanes
C_{10}	decanes		C_{24}–C_{29}	etc.
C_{11}	undecanes		C_{30}	triacontanes
C_{12}	dodecanes		C_{31}	hentriacontanes
C_{13}	tridecanes		C_{32}–C_{39}	etc.
C_{14}	tetradecanes		C_{40}	tetracontanes
C_{15}	pentadecanes			etc.

These names do not indicate the structures of the many isomers existing in each case. When a second butane was found it was called *isobutane*, and the third pentane became *neopentane*, but new prefixes if coined indefinitely would become difficult to remember. The term *iso* still is retained for all compounds having a single carbon atom branch at the end of a straight chain. Thus isohexane is $(CH_3)_2CH(CH_2)_2CH_3$ and isononane is $(CH_3)_2CH(CH_2)_5CH_3$. The term *neo* is used in this series only for neopentane and neohexane.

As Derivatives of Methane. The necessity for devising a system that could be used for a larger number of isomers led to naming compounds as derivatives of a simple compound. Thus any alkane can be considered as derived from methane by replacing the hydrogen atoms by other groups of atoms. In isobutane three hydrogens of methane have been replaced by three CH_3 groups, in isopentane by two CH_3 groups and one C_2H_5 group, whereas in neopentane four hydrogens have been replaced by four CH_3 groups. If these groups are given names, the compounds can be named as derivatives of methane. The groups themselves are hydrocarbons less one hydrogen atom, and they are named by dropping the *ane* of the alkane having the same number of carbon atoms and adding *yl*. CH_3 is *methyl* and C_2H_5 is *ethyl*. Isobutane then becomes trimethylmethane, isopentane becomes dimethylethylmethane, and neopentane is tetramethylmethane. The prefix always is attached directly to the name to give one word.

It is customary to make use also of groups containing three and four carbon atoms in order to name more complicated compounds. Since there are *two kinds of hydrogen* [4] in propane, there are two propyl groups, $CH_3CH_2CH_2$— and CH_3CHCH_3. In order to indicate more clearly the carbon atom which

lacks a hydrogen atom, it is customary to attach a long dash. In a molecule the group must be bonded to some other atom or group of atoms at this

---

than *hendecane*. Purists object to these inconsistencies as they do to the use of terms such as *mono-*, *di-*, *tri-*, and *tetravalent*, where prefixes of Greek origin are used with a word of Latin origin. Once a word becomes a part of a language, however, it is impractical, even if it were desirable, to try to bring about changes in terminology merely to be consistent.

[4] This expression arises from the fact that the properties of an atom in a molecule depend not only on the atom itself but also on the atom or atoms to which it is bonded. It is possible to distinguish not only a hydrogen atom bonded to carbon from one bonded to oxygen or nitrogen, but also a hydrogen atom bonded to a carbon atom that in turn is joined to one carbon atom and two other hydrogen atoms, from a hydrogen atom bonded to a carbon atom joined to two carbon atoms and one other hydrogen atom.

point.[5] To distinguish between the two propyl groups by name, they are called *normal propyl* or *n-propyl*, and *isopropyl* or *i-propyl*, respectively. Two groups each can be derived from *n*-butane and isobutane. *n*-Butane gives rise to the *n-butyl* group, $CH_3(CH_2)_2CH_2$—, and a group $CH_3CH_2CHCH_3$ which is called

secondary butyl (*s-butyl*) because the carbon atom which lacks a hydrogen atom is united to two other carbon atoms. Such a carbon atom is known as a

TABLE 3
Alkyl Groups Containing up to Four Carbon Atoms

STRUCTURE OF GROUP	COMMON NAME	GENEVA (I.U.C.) NAME *
CH_3—	methyl	methyl
CH_3CH_2— or C_2H_5—	ethyl	ethyl
$CH_3CH_2CH_2$—	*n*-propyl	propyl
CH_3CHCH_3, $\begin{smallmatrix}CH_3\\ \diagdown\\ CH-\\ \diagup\\ CH_3\end{smallmatrix}$, or $(CH_3)_2CH$—	*i*-propyl	(methylethyl)
$CH_3CH_2CH_2CH_2$—	*n*-butyl	butyl
$CH_3CH_2CHCH_3$, CH_3CH_2CH-, $\begin{smallmatrix}|\\ CH_3\end{smallmatrix}$ or C_2H_5CH-, $\begin{smallmatrix}|\\ CH_3\end{smallmatrix}$	*s*-butyl	(1-methylpropyl)
CH_3CHCH_2— or $\begin{smallmatrix}|\\ CH_3\end{smallmatrix}$ $(CH_3)_2CHCH_2$—	*i*-butyl	(2-methylpropyl)
$\begin{smallmatrix}CH_3\\ |\\ CH_3C-\\ |\\ CH_3\end{smallmatrix}$ or $(CH_3)_3C$—	*t*-butyl	(dimethylethyl)

* At the I.U.C. meeting in Amsterdam in September 1949, the Commission on Nomenclature accepted all isoalkyl names and also *s*-butyl, *t*-butyl, and *t*-pentyl as alternates for the systematic names for these groups.

---

[5] In the past it has been customary to refer to these groups as *radicals*. The term *radical*, however, has taken on the connotation of a *free* group such as a *free radical*, which has an unpaired electron. Hence it is considered better to refer to the portions of a stable molecule as *groups*.

secondary carbon atom. Isobutane gives rise to the *isobutyl* (*i-butyl*) group, $(CH_3)_2CHCH_2$—, and to the group $(CH_3)_3C$—. The latter is known as *tertiary butyl* (*t-butyl*) because the carbon atom lacking a hydrogen atom is a *tertiary carbon atom;* that is it is united to three other carbon atoms. Since these eight groups form the basis for the systematic naming of a large number of compounds, their names and their structures must be memorized. Once this has been done the nomenclature of most organic compounds will be remarkably simple. For convenience these groups, which are known as *alkyl* groups, and their names are collected in Table 3.

Geneva or I.U.C. System. The system which names compounds as derivatives of methane has the disadvantage that the eight groups given in Table 4 still are not sufficient for naming the more complicated compounds. This disadvantage is overcome to a considerable extent in the system adopted by the International Congress held at Geneva, Switzerland, in 1892, which has come to be known as the *Geneva system.* This system, as extended by the meeting of the International Union of Chemistry at Liège in 1930 and at Amsterdam in 1949, attempts to cover all the more important phases of the nomenclature of organic chemistry.[6] A summary of the rules for alkanes follows.[7]

(*1*) The ending for alkanes is *ane.*

(*2*) The common names for the normal (straight chain) hydrocarbons are used.

(*3*) Branched chain hydrocarbons are regarded as derivatives of the normal hydrocarbons, the longest normal chain in the molecule being considered as the parent hydrocarbon. If there are two or more chains of equal length, that chain is selected which has the most branches, that is the one which is the most highly substituted.

(*4*) The branches or side chains are named and directly attached as prefixes to the parent name. Their position is indicated by a number. If two groups are on the same carbon atom the number is repeated. The numbers precede the groups and are separated from the groups by hyphens. Where more than one number is used, they are separated from each other by commas.

(*5*) The carbon atoms of the normal chain are numbered from the end which gives the substituents the smaller numbers. The order of naming the groups may be alphabetical but usually is in the order of increasing complexity.

(*6*) Alkyl groups are named by selecting the longest chain containing the point of attachment, which is called the number one carbon atom of the group. Side chains then are named and their position indicated by a number (see Table 3 for Geneva nomenclature of side chains).

These rules and the other methods of nomenclature are illustrated in Table 4 by the names for the five isomeric hexanes and for a still more complicated compound. The advantages of naming compounds as derivatives of

---

[6] The revised system has come to be called the *I.U.C. system* by some, but most chemists, in common talk, still call the modified system the *Geneva system.*

[7] The rules laid down by the International Union of Chemistry are not without ambiguity, and a certain amount of flexibility has been allowed. What may be the best system for indexing may not be the most suitable for general use. The rules given are considered to be those most widely followed by chemists in the United States.

parent hydrocarbons are that it is easy not only to assign a name to every compound but to write the formula from the name. Thus the structure for 2,2,5-trimethyl-3-ethylhexane is written by joining six carbon atoms in a row, numbering them from 1 to 6, attaching three methyl groups and an ethyl group at

TABLE 4

NOMENCLATURE OF ALKANES

STRUCTURE	COMMON NAME	AS A DERIVATIVE OF METHANE	GENEVA SYSTEM
$CH_3(CH_2)_4CH_3$	normal hexane	not used	hexane
$CH_3CH(CH_2)_2CH_3$ $\mid$ CH_3	isohexane	dimethyl-*n*-propylmethane	2-methylpentane
$CH_3CH_2CHCH_2CH_3$ $\mid$ CH_3	none	methyldiethylmethane	3-methylpentane
$CH_3CH—CHCH_3$ $\mid \quad \mid$ $CH_3 \ CH_3$	(diisopropyl *)	dimethyl-*i*-propylmethane	2,3-dimethylbutane
CH_3 $\mid$ $CH_3—C—CH_2CH_3$ $\mid$ CH_3	neohexane	trimethylethylmethane	2,2-dimethylbutane
$\overset{9}{CH_3}(CH_2)_3\overset{5}{CH}(CH_2)_3CH_3$ $\overset{\mid 4}{\underset{}{}}$ $CH_3—CH$ $\overset{\mid 3 \quad 2 \ 1}{\underset{}{}}$ $CH_2—CHCH_3$ $\mid$ CH_3	none	not possible using the first eight groups	2,4-dimethyl-5-butylnonane

* Occasionally a hydrocarbon is given a common name which indicates that it may be divided into two like groups.

the proper positions, and satisfying the remaining valences of the carbon atoms with hydrogen atoms.

A useful check on the correctness of a one-word name is that the sum of the carbon atoms in the various groups and in the parent hydrocarbon must equal the total number of carbon atoms in the molecule. In the last example of Table 4 each methyl group has one carbon atom, the butyl group has four, and the parent name nine, making a total of fifteen carbon atoms. This number checks with the number of carbon atoms in the formula. It should be noted also in this example that there are two different nine-carbon chains, but that by choosing the most highly substituted chain the necessity for naming a complicated six-carbon group is avoided. If it had been necessary to name this group, it would have been called the (1,3-dimethylbutyl) group. The parentheses are necessary to prevent confusion concerning the portion of the molecule to which the numbers refer. The compound

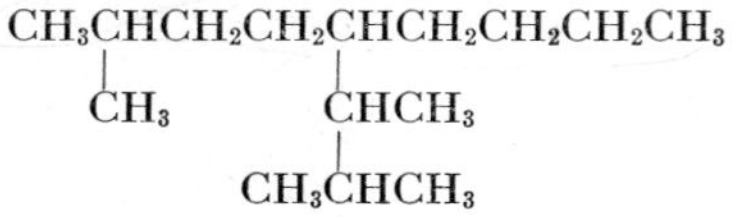

$$CH_3CHCH_2CH_2CHCH_2CH_2CH_2CH_3$$
$$\quad\;| \qquad\qquad\quad |$$
$$\quad CH_3 \qquad\qquad CHCH_3$$
$$\qquad\qquad\qquad\qquad |$$
$$\qquad\qquad\quad CH_3CHCH_3$$

for example, would be called 2-methyl-5-(1,2-dimethylpropyl)-nonane. Now that the I.U.C. permits the use of a larger number of common names for alkyl groups (see note to Table 3) this compound could be named 2-methyl-5-(1-methylisobutyl)-nonane. The first five compounds in Table 4 are all hexanes because they have six carbon atoms, regardless of the fact that they are named as derivatives of methane, butane, and pentane. The last compound of the list is a pentadecane even though it is named as a derivative of nonane.

In the naming of compounds as derivatives of another compound, it is conventional to consider the name as one word rather than to write the names of groups and parent compound as separate words or to use an unnecessary number of hyphens. It is preferable to limit the use of hyphens to the attachment of position numbers and symbols.

As the number of carbon atoms increases, the number of structural isomers possible soon reaches astronomical proportions as shown by the following figures which were arrived at by rather complicated mathematical formulas.

C_7 —9	C_{15}—4347
C_8 —18	C_{20}—366,319
C_9 —35	C_{30}—4,111,846,763
C_{10}—75	C_{40}—6.25 $\times$ 10^{13}

By 1947 all of the predicted alkanes through the nonanes, and over half of the decanes were known. Only a few isomers of each of the higher groups of compounds are known, not because they cannot be made, but because there has not been a sufficiently good reason for organic chemists to attempt to synthesize them or because those who are interested in them have not yet had time to do so. There is no question in the minds of organic chemists concerning the possibility of making any desired compound in this series, although they would admit that some of them would be rather difficult to prepare. The largest alkane of known structure and molecular weight synthesized so far has the molecular formula $C_{94}H_{190}$.

Physical Properties

The physical properties of organic compounds depend in general on the number and kind of atoms in the molecule and on the way in which the atoms are linked together. At 25° the normal hydrocarbons are gases from C_1 to C_4, liquids from C_5 to C_{17}, and solids for C_{18} and above.

Boiling Points. The boiling points increase with increasing molecular weight and when plotted against the number of carbon atoms fall on a smooth curve as shown in Fig. 17. The rise in boiling point is due to the increased attraction between molecules as the number of atoms increases. This attraction

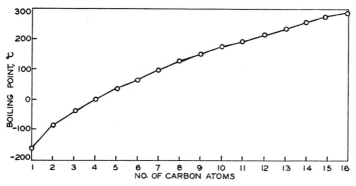

Fig. 17. Boiling points of normal alkanes.

is known as the *van der Waals force* [8] and comes into play when molecules are close to each other.

Branching of the chain always results in a lowering of the boiling point, the van der Waals force being smaller for a more compact molecule than for a longer molecule (p. 62). Thus *n*-pentane boils at 36.3°, isopentane at 27.9°, and neopentane at 9.5°.

Melting Points. The melting points of normal alkanes do not fall on a smooth curve but show alternation (Fig. 18). With the exception of methane

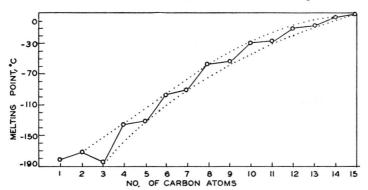

Fig. 18. Melting points of normal alkanes.

they fall on two curves, an upper one for the hydrocarbons having an even number of carbon atoms and a lower one for those with an odd number of carbon atoms. X-ray investigations of solid hydrocarbons have shown that

---

[8] So-called because it is the cause of the *a* term in the van der Waals equation, $\left(P + \dfrac{a}{V^2}\right)(V - b) = RT$ for one mole of gas. The law for a perfect gas, $PV = RT$, holds only if the molecules of a gas have no attraction for each other and occupy no volume. By introducing a constant *a* to take care of the attraction between molecules and a constant *b* to offset the volume occupied by the molecules, the equation fits more closely the experimental data. Constants *a* and *b* are characteristic for each compound. The source of the van der Waals force is discussed on page 62.

the chains of the saturated hydrocarbons are extended, the carbon atoms taking a zigzag arrangement. With compounds having an even number of carbon atoms the end carbon atoms are on opposite sides of the molecule, whereas for those having an odd number they are on the same side (Fig. 19). Apparently

Fig. 19. Extended chains having an even and an odd number of carbon atoms.

the molecules having an odd number of carbon atoms do not fit together so well as those having an even number, and the van der Waals force is not so effective.

Unlike the variation in boiling points, there is no regularity in the change in melting point with branching, since the melting point depends on how well the molecule fits into the crystal lattice to enable the molecules to get close enough for the van der Waals force to act. Thus n-pentane melts at $-129.7°$, isopentane at $-160°$, and neopentane at $-20°$. In general, however, the more symmetrical and compact the molecule, the higher its melting point. Hexamethylethane, $(CH_3)_3CC(CH_3)_3$, is interesting in that it melts at $100.7°$ and boils at $106.3°$.

Other Properties. The density of the normal alkanes gradually increases from 0.626 g. per cc. at $20°$ for pentane to 0.769 for pentadecane. This behavior is to be expected if the attraction between the molecules increases as indicated by the rise in boiling points. Similarly the density decreases with branching of the chain. The alkanes are almost completely *insoluble in water*, because they have little attraction for water molecules whereas water molecules have considerable attraction for each other (pp. 61, 64). They are miscible with many other organic compounds because the attractions between like molecules and unlike molecules are of the same order of magnitude.[9]

Sources of the Alkanes

The commercial sources of the saturated hydrocarbons are *natural gas* and *petroleum*. Paraffin hydrocarbons also are present in the *products of the destructive distillation of coal*. **Methane** is formed by the action of anaerobic organisms on cellulose and other organic matter. For example it is a product of the decomposition of vegetable matter under water in marshes, whence the common name *marsh gas*. Large amounts are formed during the treatment of sewage by the activated sludge process. It also is present in coal mines and, because it is one of the causes of explosions, it is known as *fire damp*. **n-Heptane** is present in the volatile oil of the fruit of *Pittosporum resiniferum*, and in the turpentine of the digger pine (*Pinus sabiniana*) and the Jeffrey pine (*Pinus jeffreyi*) of the Sierras. It readily can be obtained pure in quantity from the last source. The normal hydrocarbons having an odd number of

---

[9] The outstanding investigator of the relation of physical properties to chemical constitution was Herman Kopp (1817–1892), professor of chemistry at Heidelberg. He is well known also for his History of Chemistry, a four-volume work, the first volume of which was published in 1843, when Kopp was twenty-six years old, and the last in 1847. It still is the outstanding work in its field for the period concerned.

carbon atoms from C_{25} to C_{37} occur in many plant and insect waxes. For example the waxes from leaves of members of the cabbage family (*Brassica*) contain the C_{29} and C_{31} normal hydrocarbons, and spinach wax contains the C_{33}, C_{35}, and C_{37} hydrocarbons.

Individual alkanes of known structure usually are obtained by synthesis, that is by making them from certain other compounds. These methods of synthesis are given in Chapter 8.

Chemical Properties

1. ***Inertness to Most Reagents.*** The alkanes are not affected by aqueous solutions of acids, alkalies, oxidizing agents, or most other reagents at room temperature and frequently resist reaction under more drastic conditions. This inertness gave rise to the name paraffin (L. *parum* little *affinis* akin) for a saturated hydrocarbon.

2. ***Oxidation at High Temperature.*** Hydrocarbons in the presence of oxygen or strong oxidizing agents at high temperatures burn to carbon dioxide and water.

$$CH_4 + 2 O_2 \longrightarrow CO_2 + 2 H_2O$$

$$C_2H_6 + 3\tfrac{1}{2} O_2 \longrightarrow 2 CO_2 + 3 H_2O$$

$$C_3H_8 + 5 O_2 \longrightarrow 3 CO_2 + 4 H_2O$$

$$C_nH_{2n+2} + \frac{3n+1}{2} O_2 \longrightarrow n CO_2 + (n+1) H_2O$$

The oxidation or combustion of hydrocarbons to carbon dioxide and water takes place with the evolution of heat. The amount of energy liberated per mole of compound is known as the *heat of combustion* of the compound. The fact that the combustion of hydrocarbons is exothermic is the basis for their use as fuels. The inflammability depends on the volatility of the hydrocarbon. Mixtures of air and hydrocarbon vapors in the proper proportions explode on ignition, which gives rise to their use in the internal combustion engine. In a deficient oxygen supply carbon monoxide, or elementary carbon in the form of carbon black, may be produced.

3. ***Decomposition at High Temperature.*** At sufficiently high temperatures hydrocarbons decompose in the absence of oxygen, a phenomenon known as **cracking** or **pyrolysis** (Gr. *pyr* fire and *lysis* loosing). Methane yields carbon and hydrogen.

$$CH_4 \longrightarrow C + 2 H_2$$

For the reaction to proceed rapidly temperatures above 1200° are required. In the decomposition of ethane at 600° a new hydrocarbon is formed by the loss of one molecule of hydrogen from a molecule of ethane.

$$C_2H_6 \longrightarrow C_2H_4 + H_2$$

The new compound, ethylene, belongs to another homologous series, C_nH_{2n}, known as the alkenes, olefins, or unsaturated hydrocarbons (Chapter 3).

Propane at 600° decomposes to give four products which arise from the following reactions.

$$CH_3CH_2CH_3 \longrightarrow C_3H_6 + H_2$$
Propylene

$$CH_3CH_2CH_3 \longrightarrow C_2H_4 + CH_4$$
Ethylene   Methane

Actually ethylene and methane are the principal products (p. 92). Higher alkanes on cracking give hydrogen and complex mixtures of alkanes and alkenes having varying numbers of carbon atoms. This cracking process is of great importance to the petroleum industry (p. 49), since it provides a means of making smaller, more volatile hydrocarbon molecules from the larger, less volatile molecules that predominate in most natural petroleum.

    4. *Isomerization*. Although alkanes show a marked resistance to structural change, a phenomenon which is characteristic of carbon bonds and which van't Hoff (p. 262) termed "the inertia of the carbon system," they undergo certain reactions readily in the presence of suitable catalysts. Thus when either *n*-butane or *i*-butane is placed in contact with a catalyst of aluminum chloride and hydrogen chloride, an equilibrium mixture of 20 per cent *n*-butane and 80 per cent *i*-butane is formed at 27°.

AlCl₃, HCl

$$CH_3CH_2CH_2CH_3 \rightleftharpoons CH_3CHCH_3$$
$$\overset{\qquad\qquad\qquad\qquad}{\underset{CH_3}{|}}$$

The conversion of one isomer into another is known as **isomerization.** The isomerization of hydrocarbons plays an important part in the production of modern gasolines (p. 52).

    The alkanes also undergo other reactions such as alkylation (p. 51), controlled oxidation (p. 56), halogenation (p. 84), and nitration (p. 202).

REVIEW QUESTIONS

1. What is meant by the term *isomers?* How is the existence of isomers explained?
2. How does a structural formula differ from a molecular formula and why are structural formulas necessary for organic compounds? What are the fundamental assumptions on which structural theory is based?
3. What is meant by the term *homologous series?* Compare the physical and chemical properties of the members of a homologous series. Compare the chemical properties of the members of one homologous series with those of another series.
4. Give condensed structural formulas and names for all alkyl groups containing four carbon atoms and less.
5. Give condensed structural formulas for the nine isomeric heptanes. Name each as a derivative of methane and by the Geneva (I.U.C.) system. Give common names where possible.
6. What is meant by the terms *primary, secondary, tertiary,* and *quaternary* as applied to carbon atoms?
7. Name the compound having the formula:

$$C(CH_3)_3$$
$$|$$
$$(CH_3)_2CHCHCHCH_3$$
$$|$$
$$CHC_2H_5$$
$$|$$
$$CH_3$$

How many primary carbon atoms are in the compound? Secondary? Tertiary? Quaternary?

8. Write condensed structural formulas for the following compounds: dimethylethyl-*s*-butylmethane; *n*-decane; isononane; neohexane; hexamethylethane; 2,2,3-trimethylpentane; 5-(1-methylpropyl)-nonane.

9. What is wrong with the name 2-ethylpentane? Methyl-2-butane? Methylethyl-*t*-butylmethane?

10. Summarize the chemical properties of paraffin hydrocarbons, illustrating where possible by equations.

11. What is the relation of boiling point to molecular weight in a homologous series? What is the effect of branching on the boiling point? Is there any correlation between structure or molecular weight and melting point?

Chapter 3

ALKENES

Like the alkanes, the second family or homologous series of organic compounds also are hydrocarbons. They are known as the *ethylenes* from the name of the first member of the series, or *olefins* from *olefiant gas*, an old name for ethylene (p. 38). The members of this second series have the general formula C_nH_{2n}; that is each member has two less hydrogen atoms than the corresponding alkane. Since they do not contain the maximum number of hydrogen atoms, they frequently are called *unsaturated* hydrocarbons in contrast to the alkanes which are called *saturated* hydrocarbons. The generic name *alkene* has been recommended by the I.U.C. and is coming into general use.

Structure

The simplest member of this homologous series, ethylene, has two carbon atoms and the molecular formula C_2H_4, or two hydrogen atoms less than ethane. Three electronic formulas suggest themselves. Either one carbon atom has two unshared electrons (I), each has one unshared electron (II), or the carbon atoms are joined by two pairs of electrons (III).

$$
\begin{array}{ccc}
\text{H} \quad \text{H} & \text{H} \quad \text{H} & \text{H} \qquad \text{H} \\
\text{·x} \quad \text{xo} & \text{·x} \quad \text{xo} & \text{·x} \qquad \text{·x} \\
\text{H}\overset{x}{\underset{x·}{\text{C}}}\overset{o}{\underset{o}{\text{C}}}\text{o} & \text{H}\overset{x}{\underset{·}{\text{C}}}\overset{o}{\underset{o}{\text{C}}}\text{xH} & \text{C}\overset{·}{\underset{x}{:}}\text{C} \\
\text{H} & \text{H} & \text{H} \qquad \text{H} \\
\text{I} & \text{II} & \text{III}
\end{array}
$$

If I or II were capable of existence, $H\overset{·x}{\underset{}{C}}\cdot$ or $H\overset{·x}{\underset{x·}{C}}\cdot$ (with H) should be stable also,
but these groups have been detected only as highly reactive, short-lived *free radicals* (p. 91). Formula I is ruled out also on chemical grounds, since its reactions would involve only one carbon atom, whereas all known reactions of the olefins involve both carbon atoms. Formula III satisfies all requirements. Atoms sharing two pairs of electrons are said to be joined by a **double bond.**

Formulas for the homologs of ethylene can be constructed in the same way as formulas for the homologs of methane, that is by inserting CH_2 groups between hydrogen and carbon atoms or by replacing hydrogen atoms by alkyl groups. For example the next member of the series, propylene, C_3H_6, would have the formula $CH_3CH{=}CH_2$. Since the propylene molecule has three kinds of hydrogen atoms, there would be three isomeric butylenes, all of which are known.

$$CH_3CH_2CH{=}CH_2 \qquad CH_3CH{=}CHCH_3 \qquad \underset{\underset{CH_3}{|}}{CH_3C{=}CH_2}$$

The same formulas would have been obtained if the double bond had been put in all possible positions in normal butane and in isobutane.

Nomenclature

Common Names. The common names are derived by replacing the *ane* of the common name for the saturated hydrocarbon by *ylene*, but *n*-(normal) is omitted for straight chain compounds. Greek letters sometimes are used to distinguish between isomers (Table 5).

TABLE 5
Nomenclature of Alkenes

FORMULA	COMMON NAME	AS DERIVATIVE OF ETHYLENE	BY GENEVA SYSTEM
CH_2=CH_2	ethylene	none	ethene
CH_3CH=CH_2	propylene	methylethylene	propene
CH_3CH_2CH=CH_2	α-butylene	ethylethylene	1-butene
CH_3CH=$CHCH_3$	β-butylene	*sym*-dimethylethylene	2-butene

CH_3C=CH_2
  |
  CH_3
	isobutylene *	*unsym*-dimethylethylene	methylpropene

C_2H_5CH=$CHCH_3$	β-amylene †	*sym*-methylethylethylene	2-pentene

$\overset{6}{C}H_3\overset{5}{C}H_2\overset{4}{C}HCH_3$
  |
  $CH_3\overset{3}{C}$=$\overset{2}{C}H\overset{1}{C}H_3$
	none	*sym*-dimethyl-*s*-butylethylene	3,4-dimethyl-2-hexene

* The name isobutene, which frequently is used, is undesirable because it mixes two systems.

† Olefins having five carbon atoms are known as *amylenes* instead of *pentylenes* (see *fusel oil*, p. 67).

As Derivatives of Ethylene. The alkyl groups replacing the hydrogen atoms of ethylene are named and the word *ethylene* added. Since ethylene has two hydrogens on each of two carbon atoms, the replacement of two hydrogens by two groups would give rise to two isomers depending on whether the new groups were on different carbon atoms or both on the same carbon atom. In order to distinguish between these two isomers the one with the two groups on different carbon atoms is called *symmetrical* (prefix *sym*-); that is the groups are placed symmetrically with respect to the double bond. The isomer with both groups on the same carbon atom is called *unsymmetrical* (prefix *unsym*-). These designations apply only to the distribution of the two groups which give rise to the isomerism and have nothing to do with the symmetry of the molecule as a whole. In the last two examples given in Table 5, the molecules as a whole are unsymmetrical, but the methyl and ethyl groups in the one case, and the two methyl groups in the other, are placed symmetrically with respect to the double bond. Hence they are called *sym*-methylethylethylene and *sym*-dimethyl-*s*-butylethylene.

Geneva or *I.U.C.* System. The Geneva rules for naming alkenes resemble the rules for naming alkanes (p. 25): (*1*) the ending *ane* of the corresponding saturated hydrocarbon is replaced by the ending *ene;* (*2*) the parent compound is considered to be the longest chain containing the double bond; (*3*) the chains are numbered from the end nearest the double bond, and the position of the double bond is indicated by the number of the lower-numbered carbon atom to which it is attached; (*4*) side chains are named and their position indicated by a number.

Sources of the Alkenes

The chief commercial source of the alkenes is the gas from the *cracking* of petroleum hydrocarbons (p. 34). Methods of synthesis for individual olefins, for example from alcohols or compounds containing halogen, are given in Chapter 8.

Physical Properties

The general physical properties of the alkenes are much the same as those of the corresponding saturated hydrocarbons. The solubility of the lower alkenes in water, though slight, is considerably greater than that of the alkanes.

General Chemical Properties

In contrast to the saturated hydrocarbons, the unsaturated hydrocarbons are very reactive. Many reagents will add to the two carbon atoms joined by the double bond. In this process the reagent itself is decomposed, one part combining with one carbon atom and the other part with the other carbon atom. Such reactions are known as **addition reactions.** It appears that the bonding properties of one pair of electrons in the double bond are not fully satisfied, and that in the presence of a suitable reagent one pair reacts with the reagent to give a new bond system that is more stable. The double bond is destroyed and the reagent is said to have added to the double bond. The reactions may be divided into two groups, depending on whether the addenda are identical or nonidentical.

IDENTICAL ADDENDA

1. **Halogen.** The most characteristic reaction of the double bond is the rapid addition, in the liquid phase or in solution, of chlorine or bromine to those alkenes in which each of the doubly bound carbon atoms is united to at least one hydrogen atom.

$$CH_2{=}CH_2 + Cl_2 \longrightarrow ClCH_2CH_2Cl$$
Ethylene chloride [1]
(1,2-dichloroethane)

$$CH_3CH{=}CH_2 + Br_2 \longrightarrow CH_3CHBrCH_2Br$$
Propylene bromide
(1,2-dibromopropane)

---

[1] It is this reaction that gave rise to the old name for ethylene, namely *olefiant gas* (meaning *oil-making gas*), because the reaction of gaseous ethylene with gaseous chlorine gave liquid ethylene chloride.

The reaction in general may be expressed by the equation

$$RCH=CHR + X_2 \longrightarrow RCHXCHXR$$

where R is any alkyl group or a hydrogen atom, and X is any halogen atom. In practice the reaction is limited to chlorine and bromine, since fluorine reacts too violently to be controllable, and iodine does not give stable 1,2-diiodo derivatives except with a few simple olefins. If both hydrogen atoms on the same carbon atom of ethylene are replaced by alkyl groups as in isobutylene, addition of chlorine does not take place as readily as another reaction, *substitution*, in which a hydrogen atom is replaced by a chlorine atom (p. 509). Bromine, however, adds regularly, forming isobutylene bromide.

Since these halogen derivatives are colorless liquids, decolorization of a solution of bromine in water, or better in a mutual solvent such as carbon tetrachloride or acetic acid, may be used as a *test for unsaturation*, provided that no other functional group is present which reacts with bromine. To determine the amount of a known olefin in a mixture with other substances, the mixture can be titrated with a standardized solution of bromine. A similar titration of a pure unknown olefin would give the equivalent weight of the compound, that is the weight associated with one double bond. The number of double bonds would be equal to the molecular weight divided by the equivalent weight.

2. **Hydrogen.** In the presence of a suitable catalyst such as finely divided platinum, palladium, or nickel, hydrogen will add to a double bond with the evolution of about 30 kcal. of energy per mole.

$$CH_2=CH_2 + H_2 \xrightarrow{\text{Pt, Pd, or Ni}} CH_3CH_3$$

$$R_2C=CR_2 + H_2 \xrightarrow{\text{Pt, Pd, or Ni}} R_2CHCHR_2$$

If the olefin is a gas, a mixture with hydrogen may be passed over the catalyst. Liquid olefins, or solid olefins dissolved in an inert solvent, may be shaken with hydrogen in the presence of a suspension of the finely divided catalyst. The reaction can be used for analytical as well as for preparative purposes, since from the volume of hydrogen absorbed the amount of an unsaturated compound of known structure in a mixture with saturated compounds, or the number of double bonds in an unknown compound whose molecular weight has been determined, can be calculated.

3. **Ozone.** If a stream of ozonized air or ozonized oxygen is passed through a liquid olefin or a nonaqueous solution of an unsaturated compound, the ozone is removed rapidly and quantitatively with the formation of an ozonide.

$$CH_3CH_2CH=CHCH_3 + O_3 \longrightarrow CH_3CH_2CH \underset{O-O}{\overset{O}{\diamond}} CHCH_3$$

2-Pentene ozonide

$$R_2C=CR_2 + O_3 \longrightarrow R_2CH \underset{O-O}{\overset{O}{\diamond}} CHR_2$$

The evidence concerning the structure of ozonides indicates that both bonds of the double bond are broken with the formation of a five-membered ring containing three oxygen atoms (p. 576). The olefin is said to be *ozonized*, and the process is known as *ozonation* or *ozonization*. The former term seems preferable, since it is analogous to the term *oxidation*.

The ozonides would not be of importance were it not for the fact that they react readily with water with the formation of aldehydes or ketones (Chapter 12).

$$CH_3CH_2CH \underset{O-O}{\overset{O}{\diagup\diagdown}} CHCH_3 + H_2O \longrightarrow CH_3CH_2CHO + OCHCH_3 + H_2O_2$$

Propionalde- Acetalde-
hyde   hyde

$$RCH \underset{O-O}{\overset{O}{\diagup\diagdown}} CR_2 + H_2O \longrightarrow RCHO + OCR_2 + H_2O_2$$

An   A
aldehyde ketone

Ozonation of an unsaturated compound followed by decomposition with water therefore becomes a useful method for synthesizing aldehydes and ketones. Moreover since the aldehydes and ketones can be isolated and analyzed, the reaction can be used to locate the position of double bonds in unknown compounds. For example the formation of a three-carbon aldehyde and a two-carbon aldehyde from an olefin proves that it is 2-pentene. If it had been 1-pentene, a four-carbon aldehyde and a one-carbon aldehyde would have been formed.

The process of ozonation followed by hydrolysis is known as *ozonolysis*. The hydrolysis is somewhat more complicated than is indicated above, a mixture of organic peroxides and aldehydes or ketones being formed rather than hydrogen peroxide. Usually the decomposition is carried out in the presence of a reducing agent, such as zinc dust and acetic acid or hydrogen and platinum, to destroy the peroxides and prevent the oxidation of the aldehydes to organic acids (p. 172).

4. **Aqueous Permanganate.** Reaction with dilute aqueous permanganate solutions gives rise to the addition of two hydroxyl (OH) groups to the doubly-bound carbon atoms. Little is known about the mechanism of this reaction, but for the purpose of writing the equation it may be assumed that the permanganate supplies an oxygen atom which with a water molecule gives two hydroxyl groups, and that the latter add to the double bond.

$$R_2C{=}CR_2 + [O](KMnO_4) + H_2O \longrightarrow R_2COHCOHR_2$$

The symbol [O] does not indicate atomic oxygen, but some reagent capable of supplying oxygen in an oxidation reaction. Here the reagent is given in parentheses. This device avoids the necessity for writing balanced equations, but does not excuse the student from being able to write a balanced equation when required to do so. Since in neutral or alkaline solution three atoms of oxygen are available for oxidation from each two molecules of potassium permanganate, the balanced equation for the reaction is

$$3 R_2C{=}CR_2 + 2 KMnO_4 + 4 H_2O \longrightarrow 3 R_2COHCOHR_2 + 2 MnO_2 + 2 KOH$$

Methods for balancing oxidation-reduction reactions of organic compounds are considered on page 122.

Evidence of reaction with permanganate is the change in color from the purple of the permanganate ion to the brown of the precipitate of manganese dioxide. In the absence of sufficient reducing agent the permanganate ion may be reduced only as far as the green manganate ion, $MnO_4^=$. The change from purple to green should not be considered a positive test, however, since this change can take place in a strongly alkaline solution in the absence of reducing agent. The reaction with permanganate usually is referred to as *Baeyer's test for a double bond*. It should be pointed out, however, that like the reaction with bromine and with hydrogen, *this test is **not specific** for a double bond*. Reaction with permanganate indicates a double bond only in the absence of other easily oxidized groups.

Nonidentical Addenda

Numerous reagents add unlike groups to a double bond. For example sulfuric acid adds H and OSO_3H, halogen acids add H and X, and hypohalous acids add X and OH. If the molecule is symmetrical, that is if identical groups are on both of the doubly-bound carbon atoms, only one compound can be obtained on addition even if the addenda are not alike. However *if the olefin molecule is unsymmetrical, two isomers should be possible.* Actually *one isomer is formed in predominant amount, namely that in which the acid sulfate group of sulfuric acid, the halogen of the halogen acid, or the hydroxyl group of the hypohalous acid adds to the carbon atom having the smaller number of hydrogen atoms.* This generalization is known as the **Markovnikov rule.**[2]

1. Sulfuric Acid. Olefins add sulfuric acid to give *alkyl hydrogen sulfates.*

$$CH_3CH_2CH{=}CH_2 + HOSO_3H \longrightarrow CH_3CH_2CHCH_3$$

1-Butene OSO_3H

s-Butyl hydrogen sulfate

$$RCH{=}CR_2 + HOSO_3H \longrightarrow RCH_2CR_2$$
$$OSO_3H$$

In accordance with the Markovnikov rule 1-butene gives the same product as 2-butene.

$$CH_3CH{=}CHCH_3 + HOSO_3H \longrightarrow CH_3CH_2CHCH_3$$
$$OSO_3H$$

The ease of addition of sulfuric acid depends on the number of alkyl substituents at the double bond. For example ethylene reacts slowly at room

---

[2] Vladimir Vasil'evich Markovnikov (1838–1904), director of the Chemical Institute of the University of Moscow. Although his ideas concerning the effect of structure on the course of chemical reactions were published in Russian in 1869, they went unnoticed in Europe until 1899, because he refused to publish them in a foreign language. After 1881 he did important work on the chemistry of petroleum hydrocarbons.

temperature with concentrated sulfuric acid, requiring a catalyst such as silver sulfate for rapid addition; propylene reacts with 85 per cent sulfuric acid in the absence of a catalyst; isobutylene reacts with 65 per cent sulfuric acid at room temperature. Use is made of these differences in reactivity to analyze and to separate mixtures of olefins.

If the air in a 100 cc. cylindrical separatory funnel containing 10 cc. of 20 per cent fuming sulfuric acid is swept out with ethylene and the funnel stoppered and shaken, a vacuum will be created due to the reaction of the ethylene with the sulfuric acid to give the nonvolatile ethyl hydrogen sulfate, together with its sulfonation product, ethionic acid, $HO_3SCH_2CH_2OSO_2OH$. The presence of the vacuum can be demonstrated by dipping the end of the funnel beneath the surface of about 150 cc. of concentrated sulfuric acid and opening the stopcock. The sulfuric acid rushes into the separatory funnel and nearly fills it.

2. **Halogen Acids.** Olefins add halogen acids to give *alkyl halides.*

$$CH_3CH=CH_2 + HBr \longrightarrow CH_3CHCH_3$$
$$| \atop Br$$
i-Propyl bromide
(2-bromopropane)

$$RCH=CR_2 + HX \longrightarrow RCH_2CR_2$$
$$| \atop X$$

Halogen acids, like sulfuric acid, add more readily the greater the amount of alkyl substitution at the double bond. For example the order of ease of addition of hydrogen chloride is isobutylene > propylene > ethylene. The ease of addition varies also with the halogen acid, the order from concentrated aqueous solutions being hydrogen iodide > hydrogen bromide > hydrogen chloride > hydrogen fluoride.

The behavior of hydrogen bromide is anomalous if peroxides are present. Under these conditions the mode of addition for the most part is contrary to the Markovnikov rule. For example when propylene reacts with hydrogen bromide in the presence of peroxides, *n*-propyl bromide is formed instead of *i*-propyl bromide.

$$CH_3CH=CH_2 + HBr \xrightarrow{\text{(Peroxides)}} CH_3CH_2CH_2Br$$

A theoretical explanation of this behavior is given on page 103.

3. **Hypohalous Acids.** Olefins add hypohalous acids readily from aqueous solutions to give *halohydrins.*

$$CH_3CH=CH_2 + HOCl \longrightarrow CH_3CHCH_2$$
$$| \quad | \atop OH \ Cl$$
Propylene
chlorohydrin

$$RCH=CR_2 + HOX \longrightarrow RCHCR_2$$
$$| \quad | \atop X \ \ OH$$

The hypohalous acid solution is prepared by adding halogen to a cold 10 per cent solution of sodium hydroxide, and then adding a sufficient quantity of dilute mineral acid to liberate the hypohalous acid from its sodium salt. The olefin is shaken with the aqueous solution until all of the hypohalous acid has reacted.

4. **Polymerization.** A *polymer* is a high molecular weight compound whose structure can be considered as being made up of many smaller parts of like structure (Gr. *polys* many and *meros* part). The process by which polymers are formed is called *polymerization.* Under the influence of various catalysts olefins undergo a self addition known as *addition polymerization*, with the formation of compounds having two, three, four, or a thousand times the molecular weight of the original compound. For example when ethylene is heated above 100° and under pressures above 15,000 p.s.i. in the presence of 0.01 per cent of oxygen, it is converted into a high molecular weight saturated hydrocarbon.

$$n \, CH_2{=}CH_2 \longrightarrow (-CH_2CH_2-)_n$$

The product consists of long chains with n being from 100 to 1000, and is a valuable plastic known as *polyethylene.* It is a paraffin and is waxy to the touch, but it is tough and flexible and melts around 118°.

If isobutylene is passed into cold 60 per cent sulfuric acid and the mixture heated to 100°, a mixture of dimers and trimers (about 4 : 1), together with smaller amounts of higher polymers, is formed. The mixture of dimers is known as *diisobutylene* and consists of four parts of 2,4,4-trimethyl-1-pentene and one part of 2,4,4-trimethyl-2-pentene.

$$2 \, (CH_3)_2C{=}CH_2 \underset{H_2SO_4}{\rightleftarrows} (CH_3)_3CCH{=}C(CH_3)_2 \text{ and } (CH_3)_3CCH_2C(CH_3){=}CH_2$$
$$\text{20 per cent} \qquad\qquad\qquad \text{80 per cent}$$

The trimers and higher polymers are formed by reaction of the dimers with more isobutylene. If boron trifluoride is used as a catalyst at −100°, high molecular weight polyisobutylenes having from 400 to 8000 C_4H_8 units and varying from sticky viscous resins to elastic rubber-like solids are obtained, which are sold under the trade name *Vistanex.*

$$n \, (CH_3)_2C{=}CH_2 \underset{-100°}{\overset{BF_3}{\rightleftarrows}} [-C(CH_3)_2CH_2-]_n$$

The polymerization of 2-pentene can be observed readily. If a drop of concentrated sulfuric acid is added to about 2 cc. of 2-pentene, heat is evolved and the liquid boils. If water is added a dark oil separates which does not evaporate on boiling the mixture. Evidently the low-boiling pentene has been converted into a high-boiling polymer. The product is not pentyl hydrogen sulfate, since this compound is soluble in water.

All of the reactions of the alkenes that have been considered are dependent on the presence of the double bond. The rest of the molecule is inert like the paraffin hydrocarbons. A *reactive group such as the double bond is called a functional group.* Most of the homologous series have their characteristic functional groups. The methods of introducing this group are the methods of preparation for members of the series, and the effects of other agents on this group are the general reactions of the series. The number of functional groups is small in comparison to the number of organic compounds. By emphasizing the functional groups of each homologous series, the facts of organic chemistry are systematized and made easier to remember.

REVIEW QUESTIONS

1. Give the evidence for the commonly accepted structure of ethylene.
2. Write condensed structural formulas for the isomeric pentenes and name as derivatives of ethylene and by the Geneva (I.U.C.) system.
3. Write structural formulas for 2,4,4-trimethyl-2-pentene; *sym-n*-propyl-*t*-butylethylene; isobutylene; *unsym*-dimethylethylene; α-butylene.
4. Name the following compounds as derivatives of ethylene and by the Geneva (I.U.C.) system:

(a) $CH_3C(CH_3)_2CH{=}CHCH_3$; (b) $CH_3CH(CH_3)CH_2CCH_2CH_2CH_3$
$$\underset{\displaystyle C(CH_3)_2}{\overset{\displaystyle \|}{}}$$

5. Tell what is wrong with the following names and give correct ones: 2-ethyl-2-hexene; 2-methyl-4-hexene; isobutene.
6. State the Markovnikov rule and give an equation illustrating its application.

7. Give equations for the following reactions and give a suitable name to the organic compound formed in each case: (*a*) ethylene and bromine; (*b*) 1-butene and strong sulfuric acid; (*c*) *s*-butylethylene and hypochlorous acid; (*d*) 3-methyl-2-pentene and aqueous permanganate; (*e*) 1-butene and ozone followed by reaction with water; (*f*) propylene and hydrogen bromide in the presence of peroxides; (*g*) propylene and hydrogen chloride in the presence of peroxides.
8. Give reactions illustrating the preparation of the following compounds from the proper alkene: dimethylisopropylmethane; *t*-butyl chloride; *s*-butyl hydrogen sulfate; 1,2-dichloropropane.
9. A straight chain heptene on ozonation and decomposition of the ozonide gives a five-carbon aldehyde and a two-carbon aldehyde. What is the structure of the heptene?
10. What steps would be necessary to show that a compound, of unknown identity, is 3-hexene?

NUMERICAL PROBLEMS

11. It is found that 9.8 g. of a pure olefin having one double bond reacts with 16 g. of bromine. What is the molecular formula of the compound?
12. When 0.35 g. of a pure hydrocarbon having one or more double bonds was shaken with hydrogen in the presence of platinum catalyst, 112 cc. of hydrogen (S.T.P.) was absorbed. The molecular weight of the compound was found to be 77 ± 8 by the Victor Meyer method. How many double bonds were in the compound and what was its molecular formula?
13. When 5 g. of a mixture of pentenes and pentanes was hydrogenated, one liter of hydrogen (S.T.P.) was absorbed. Calculate the per cent of pentenes in the mixture.

Chapter 4

NATURAL GAS, PETROLEUM, AND DERIVED PRODUCTS

Natural gas and petroleum are important natural resources. Their chief use is as fuel for generating mechanical and electrical energy and for space heating. The world production of petroleum in 1948 was 450 million metric tons or 3.5 billion barrels of 42 gallons. Although the United States possessed only 30 per cent of the known world reserves, and because of the much more thorough exploration in the United States certainly much less of the actual reserves, it produced over 2 billion barrels or 60 per cent of the world consumption. In other words the petroleum resources of the United States were being depleted much more rapidly than those of foreign countries. Venezuela was responsible for 15 per cent of the world's production, the U.S.S.R. and Iran 6 per cent each, Saudi Arabia 4 per cent, and Mexico and the East Indies 2 per cent each. The remainder was widely distributed throughout the world. The reason for the high consumption in the United States is chiefly the large number of motor vehicles. Registration in the United States in 1946 was about 34.5 million compared with about 1.5 million for the rest of the Americas, 6.5 million for Europe, 1 million for Australia, and 0.5 million each for Asia and Africa.

Origin

Natural gas and petroleum were formed by the decomposition of vast quantities of organic material, undoubtedly of marine origin, buried in sediment. The view that petroleum is of biological origin, rather than that it was formed from inorganic carbides, or from carbon monoxide or carbon dioxide and hydrogen, is supported by the presence of organic nitrogen and sulfur compounds, optically active compounds (p. 259), and complex organic compounds known as porphyrins, which are produced only by plants and animals. The exact processes which converted fats, carbohydrates, and proteins into hydrocarbons, the principal components of petroleum, are not known. It is believed, however, that they took place for the most part at ordinary temperatures, because porphyrins would have been decomposed if elevated temperatures had been involved. Oil at depths of 10,000 to 15,000 feet has, of course, been subjected to temperatures of at least 150° to 200°. Hence heat has played a part in determining the composition of oils found or formed at these or lower depths.

Both natural gas and petroleum accumulate in porous formations capped by dome shaped impervious layers of rock or in other stratigraphic traps. When a well is bored through the impervious cap, hydrostatic pressure forces the gas or oil to the surface. After the pressure has been entirely released and oil no longer flows from the well, the oil is pumped out mechanically.

NATURAL GAS

Natural gas varies greatly in composition. A typical gas under high pressure would contain about 78 per cent methane, 13 per cent ethane, 6 per cent propane, and 3 per cent higher hydrocarbons. However one Pennsylvania well delivers natural gas containing 98.8 per cent methane, whereas gas from a well in Kentucky contains only 23 per cent methane. Natural gas, after the removal of propane and butanes by liquefaction, is used chiefly as fuel. Natural gas pipe lines serve practically every section of the United States and extend from Texas to New York and to California.

Large quantities of natural gas are converted by incomplete combustion into a finely divided form of carbon known as lamp black, carbon black, or gas black.

$$CH_4 + O_2 \text{ (air)} \longrightarrow C + H_2O$$

The carbon is deposited on a metal surface from which it is scraped continuously into conveyors. Carbon black and hydrogen are produced by the thermal decomposition of methane.

$$CH_4 \xrightarrow{1200°} C + 2 H_2$$

A tower of fire brick is heated to above 1200° by burning natural gas and air, and then the air supply is shut off and natural gas alone passed through. The carbon black remains in suspension in the exit gases, from which it is removed after cooling by passing through fabric bags. Around 450 million pounds is produced annually in the United States, of which 300 million pounds is used in the compounding of rubber, 50 million is used as pigment, and 100 million pounds is exported. From 6 to 10 pounds of black is obtained from 1000 cubic feet of gas.

Hydrogen and carbon monoxide may be prepared from methane or other hydrocarbons and steam.

$$CH_4 + H_2O \xrightarrow[450°]{Ni} CO + 3 H_2$$

The carbon monoxide may be converted to carbon dioxide and more hydrogen by the *water-gas catalytic process*.

$$CO + H_2O \xrightarrow[450°-500°]{Fe_2O_3 + \text{promoters}} CO_2 + H_2$$

The carbon dioxide is removed by scrubbing with water under pressure or with alkaline reagents such as solutions of sodium carbonate or ethanolamine (p. 526). Processes for the conversion of natural gas into acetylene (p. 112), halogenated hydrocarbons (p. 505), alcohols (Chapter 5), aldehydes and ketones (Chapter 12), and acids (Chapter 10) have been developed.

PETROLEUM

Petroleum is the liquid mixture of organic compounds obtained at certain points from the upper strata of the earth. Its composition varies widely depending on the area from which it is obtained. The chief components of this very complex mixture are hydrocarbons, which may be paraffinic, alicyclic (p. 557), or aromatic hydrocarbons (p. 310) in varying proportions. The separation of the individual components is very difficult, but by the end of 1946 the U. S. Bureau of Standards had isolated and identified from the gas, gasoline, and kerosene fractions of a midcontinent petroleum, 72 pure hydrocarbons of which 29 were paraffinic, 17 alicyclic, 22 aromatic, and 4 aromatic-alicyclic. In addition to carbon and hydrogen, petroleum contains 1 to 6 per cent of sulfur, nitrogen, and oxygen. The per cent of sulfur, nitrogen, and oxygen compounds, however, is much higher. Thus if a fraction has a sulfur content of 1 per cent, and the sulfur compound has a molecular weight of 300 and one atom of sulfur to the molecule, the sulfur compound would constitute approximately 10 per cent of the fraction by weight.

Refining

Petroleum is *refined*, that is separated into useful products, near the oil field, or it is shipped by pipe line or tanker to refineries located near centers of high population or readily available transportation. Refining consists essentially of dividing the petroleum into fractions of different boiling ranges by distillation, and of special treatments of the fractions to remove undesirable components. Originally the distillations were batch operations using horizontal cylindrical direct-fired stills. The fractions were cut according to density, the lighter fractions having the lower boiling point. When all of the volatile components had been removed, the still was cooled, and men entered through a manhole and dug the coke out with a pick and shovel. This type of still has been displaced by the tubular furnace with fractionating column illustrated in Fig. 20. Oil is pumped continuously through heated pipes and

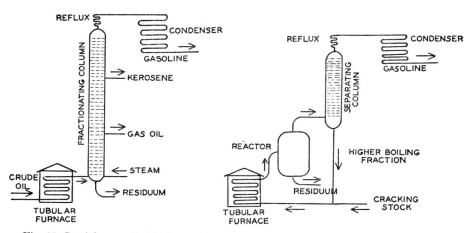

Fig. 20. Straight-run distillation unit.   Fig. 21. Dubbs cracking unit.

flashed into a fractionating column from which the various fractions can be withdrawn. The main fractions are gas, gasoline, kerosene, gas oil, and high-boiling residue. The residue can be distilled under reduced pressure for the recovery of lubricating oils and wax, or it can be cracked to gasoline (p. 49), or used directly as fuel. Here again the relative amounts of the different fractions vary widely with the source of the crude oil. Thus one yellow crude from California yields 2 per cent gas, 80 per cent gasoline, 10 per cent kerosene, and 8 per cent gas oil; a green crude from Texas yields 1 per cent gas, 39 per cent gasoline, 11 per cent kerosene, 22 per cent gas oil, and 27 per cent residuum; a black crude from California yields 1 per cent gas, 28 per cent gasoline, 8 per cent kerosene, 18 per cent gas oil, and 45 per cent residuum.

Gas. The gas fractions are obtained during the first distillation of petroleum and also result from cracking operations (p. 49). They consist chiefly of hydrocarbons having from one to five carbon atoms which are both saturated and unsaturated. They are separated into their various components by chemical methods and by efficient fractionating columns. The methane and ethane usually are burned as fuel. The olefins may be removed by conversion into alcohols (pp. 68, 70), or by polymerization or alkylation reactions (p. 51). The normal butenes are particularly valuable for the manufacture of high-octane gasoline and synthetic rubber (p. 501). The propane and butanes may be liquefied and distributed in high-pressure tanks and cylinders. A total of 2.2 billion gallons of liquefied petroleum gas was used in the United States in 1947. Large amounts of the butanes and most of the pentanes are blended into gasoline.

Gasoline. With the rapid increase in the use of motor vehicles since 1910, gasoline has become the most important product derived from petroleum. The composition of gasoline varies widely, but motor gasoline may be defined as a complex mixture of hydrocarbons boiling between 0° and 200°. Aviation gasoline boils between 30° and 150°. Initially the gasoline fraction obtained from the first distillation of petroleum, referred to as *straight-run gasoline*, was more than enough to supply the demands for motor fuel, but the increase in the number of automobiles soon made this source insufficient and recourse was had to the thermal decomposition of higher hydrocarbons into lower molecular weight molecules. The manufacture of gas from oil was discussed in England as early as 1792, and in 1865 Young distilled shale oil under pressure to raise the boiling point of the oil and cause partial pyrolysis (thermal decomposition) during distillation. Large-scale commercial cracking was developed in the United States in 1912 by Burton who carried out distillations under pressure in horizontal stills as a batch operation. Numerous continuous processes have been developed since then.

Qualities other than the proper volatility are important in gasoline, especially the *octane number*. Everyone is familiar with *knocking* in a gasoline automobile engine, the *ping* that develops when pulling up a long grade or attempting to accelerate a car too rapidly. In the operation of an engine the down stroke of the piston draws air through the carburetor where the air becomes laden with vapor and fine droplets of gasoline. This air-fuel mixture is next compressed by the piston to a small volume, the ratio of the initial and final volumes being known as the *compression-ratio* of the engine. When the piston reaches the top of the stroke, the ignition system produces a spark at the spark-plug, which ignites the air-fuel mixture. As the gases ignite and expand, the piston is forced down providing power to the crankshaft. During proper combustion the wave-front travels from the point of ignition through the fuel mixture at a rate of 25 to 250 feet per second. In *knocking*, the wave-front is normal during the first three-fourths of the combustion but then suddenly begins to travel at 1000 feet per second. This sudden increase in rate is accompanied by an increased rate of pressure increase which sets off shock waves of the same frequency as the sound of knocking. Knocking decreases power and increases wear on the engine. Engine efficiency increases with the compression ratio of the engine but so does knocking. Nevertheless the compression ratio of gasoline engines, which was around 4 to 1 in 1920, was 6-7.5 to 1 in 1942. This increase has been possible because of the development of anti-knock fuels. It has been found that the knocking characteristic of a fuel depends on the structures of the hydrocarbon molecules and that knocking can be increased or decreased by the addition of relatively small amounts of other chemicals.

As a means of measuring the knocking properties of a fuel, two pure hydrocarbons were selected as standards. One is *n*-heptane, which was worse in its tendency to cause knocking than any ordinary gasoline, and the other is 2,2,4-trimethylpentane [1] which was better than any gasoline known at the time. Blends of these two pure hydrocarbons could be made to match the knocking characteristics of any known fuel. The knocking property of the fuel then could be described by its **octane number,** the per cent of 2,2,4-trimethylpentane in the synthetic blend that matched the gasoline in knocking properties. Investigation of a large number of pure hydrocarbons has shown that in general the octane number increases with increase in branching, and that olefins and a class of compounds known as aromatic hydrocarbons (p. 316) are better than saturated hydrocarbons. The trend in gasoline production has been to develop methods for producing gasoline with higher and higher octane numbers. It is possible to design gasoline engines using special fuels, for example trimethylbutane (triptane), that will operate at compression ratios between 12 and 16 to 1 and have an efficiency equal to that of a Diesel engine (p. 53).

Thermal Cracking. Thermal decomposition of hydrocarbons results not only in smaller molecules of higher volatility but also in the production of olefins and aromatic hydrocarbons. Hence the cracking process results not only in a higher yield of gasoline but also in a product with higher octane number. The products formed depend on their relative thermodynamic stability and on the relative rates of the reactions taking place, both factors being dependent on temperature and pressure. Between 400° and 500° gaseous and liquid hydrocarbons of lower boiling range are formed. Above 500° gas production becomes more important. The commercial production of oil-gas (gas from oil) normally is carried out at about 700°. Around 900° the maximum yield of aromatic hydrocarbons (p. 310) is obtained, and above 1000°, methane. hydrogen, and carbon are the chief products.

The **basic cracking equipment** consists of a *heating coil* and a *reactor*. All the various possible reactions require time for the reaction to take place. Preheated oil is pumped through the coil and heated to the cracking temperature of 450°–500° so rapidly (contact time one-half to three minutes) that undesirable phases of decomposition, especially coke formation, do not have time

---

[1] Unfortunately designated *isooctane* by petroleum technologists. The prefix *iso* should be reserved for compounds having two methyl groups at the end of a straight chain (p. 26).

to take place in the coil. On passing into the reactor, which is simply an insulated cylindrical tank, the rate of flow is decreased sufficiently to give time for the completion of the reaction. The operation thus far takes place at pressures of 175–250 p.s.i., to increase the amount of material in the liquid phase. On leaving the reactor the oil is flashed into a fractionating column, where it is separated into the desired products. Figure 21, page 47, shows diagrammatically the *Dubbs process* which may be operated to yield only gas, gasoline, and residual fuel oil or coke from any type of stock. If clean recycle stocks are used which deposit practically no coke, it is possible to dispense with the reactor. A higher cracking temperature is used (500°–600°) and the cracking is permitted to take place in soaking tubes, an extension of the tubular furnace. Whereas the octane number of a straight-run gasoline will be 50–55, that of a thermally cracked gasoline will be 70–72.

Catalytic Cracking. Since the products formed during the cracking operation depend not only on their relative stability but on the relative rates at which the different reactions take place, the aim has been to find catalysts which will accelerate the rates of reactions leading to desirable products over those leading to undesirable products. As a result **catalytic cracking** has become of prime importance. By these processes gasolines with octane numbers of 77 to 81 are obtained. The catalysts used are natural clays or synthetic alumina-silica mixtures, and the operation is carried out at 450°–500° and relatively low pressures of 10–50 p.s.i. In all catalytic processes the catalyst becomes deactivated by the deposition of coke, which must be burned off periodically to regenerate the catalyst. The *Thermofor* and the *Fluid Catalyst* processes are continuous. In the Thermofor process the catalyst in the form of beads is carried through the reaction, purging, and regenerating zones by me-

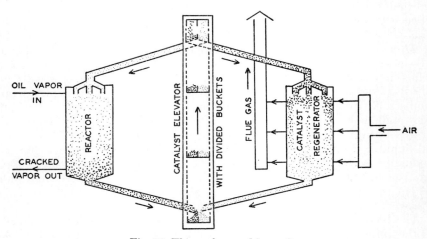

Fig. 22. Thermofor cracking unit.

chanical conveyors and gravity (Fig. 22). The Fluid Catalyst process is similar except that the catalyst is in the form of a fine powder which behaves as a fluid and is transported through the various zones by the gas streams. The catalyst is removed centrifugally from the cracked gases or from the flue gases by means of cyclone separators.

Since in the cracking processes the octane number is increased because of the formation of olefins and aromatic hydrocarbons, the octane number of straight-run gasoline can be increased by putting it through one of the cracking operations. This treatment is known as **reforming.**

Polymerization. The availability of large quantities of gases from the cracking operations has made it desirable to convert them into more useful products. One such procedure for the utilization of olefins is **polymerization** to liquid fuels. The polymerization of isobutylene to diisobutylenes has been discussed on page 43. If mixtures of ethylene, propylene, and the butylenes are used, an interpolymerization, called copolymerization, takes place. The polymerization may be carried out thermally at 500°–600° and 1000–5000 p.s.i., or catalytically, using as catalysts phosphoric acid on pumice at 200°–300° and 150–200 p.s.i. or 60–65 per cent sulfuric acid at 25°–100° and atmospheric pressure. The products have octane numbers of 80 to 85 and, as the equation for the dimerization of isobutylene shows (p. 43), still contain a double bond. Because of the unsaturation, the polymers on exposure to air are slowly oxidized and further polymerized to undesirable high molecular weight compounds known as *gums*. The rate of oxidation and polymerization can be greatly decreased by the addition of small amounts of substances known as *antioxidants* (p. 582). When used for this purpose they are called *gum inhibitors*. Gum formation can be completely eliminated by hydrogenating to a mixture of saturated hydrocarbons. Hydrogenation of the diisobutylenes with hydrogen and a nickel catalyst (p. 39) gives 2,2,4-trimethylpentane, the standard 100 octane fuel. These saturated, high-octane alkanes are blended with aromatic hydrocarbons for aviation gasolines (p. 319).

Alkylation. More recently it has been found possible to cause branched chain paraffins to add to the double bond of olefins, a process known as **alkylation.** At atmospheric pressure this process is thermodynamically possible only at relatively low temperatures, and a catalyst is necessary to make the reaction take place at a practical rate. However at high pressures the process is practical at higher temperatures. Hence both thermal and catalytic processes have been developed. As an example of thermal alkylation, ethylene and isobutane react at 500° and 3000–5000 p.s.i., to give neohexane of octane number 96.

$$CH_3CH(CH_3)CH_3 + CH_2{=}CH_2 \longrightarrow CH_3C(CH_3)(CH_3)CH_2CH_3$$

Actually pure neohexane is not obtained because of other concurrent reactions. Using 90 to 100 per cent sulfuric acid or anhydrous hydrogen fluoride as a catalyst at temperatures below 20°, isobutane reacts with the mixed butylenes to give a mixture of octanes having an octane number of 92 to 94. The advantages of the alkylation processes over polymerization are that the branched chain saturated hydrocarbons are used as well as the olefins and that the product is saturated, thus avoiding the necessity for hydrogenation or the use of gum inhibitors.

Isomerization. Of the lower-boiling saturated hydrocarbons the least useful are methane, ethane, propane, and *n*-butane, because they do not enter into alkylation reactions, and *n*-pentane and *n*-hexane because of their low octane numbers. Although *n*-butane and isobutane are stable indefinitely in the absence of catalysts, Fig. 23 indicates that at room temperature they

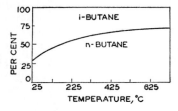

Fig. 23. Variation of the equilibrium composition of the butanes with temperature.

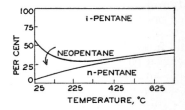

Fig. 24. Variation of the equilibrium composition of the pentanes with temperature.

should exist in equilibrium in the ratio of 1:4. Commercially catalysts consisting of a liquid complex of anhydrous aluminum chloride, dry hydrogen chloride, and hydrocarbon, or a solid catalyst of aluminum chloride on alumina is used to cause this equilibrium to be established rapidly at room temperature. The isobutane produced is used in the alkylation reactions. According to Fig. 24 the equilibrium mixture of the pentanes should contain large amounts of neopentane. No neopentane ever has been obtained, although either *n*-pentane or isopentane readily isomerizes to the equilibrium composition of the two isomers calculated from their relative thermodynamic stabilities. Isopentane and the branched hexanes formed by isomerization of *n*-pentane and *n*-hexane are valuable blending stocks for gasoline.

Dehydrogenation and Aromatization. Another use that can be made of ethane, propane, and the butanes is conversion into the more valuable olefins by thermal cracking, partial oxidation, or by dehydrogenation using chromic oxide on alumina as the catalyst. Figure 25 illustrates the equilibrium

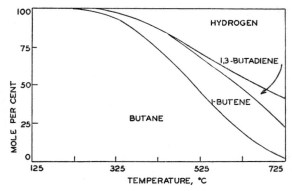

Fig. 25. Variation of equilibrium composition of butane, 1-butene, 1,3-butadiene, and hydrogen with temperature.

concentrations of *n*-butane, 1-butene, 1,3-butadiene, and hydrogen at one atmosphere from 100°–800°. Butenes may be used in the polymerization and alkylation processes, and butadiene is the basis for the large volume production of synthetic rubber (p. 502).

Paraffinic or alicyclic hydrocarbons may be converted into aromatic hydrocarbons by processes known as **aromatization.** Although these processes are discussed under aromatic compounds (pp. 317, 318), it should be mentioned that aromatic hydrocarbons such as benzene, toluene, and cumene are used in military aviation gasolines.

Knock Inhibitors. Numerous substances when added to gasoline increase its octane number. Iodine and aniline were recognized first as knock-reducing agents, but the metal alkyls are the most effective. Tetraethyllead, $Pb(C_2H_5)_4$ (p. 589), is by far the best and is the only compound now used commercially. One of the disadvantages of tetraethyllead when used alone is that the product of combustion is lead oxide which is reduced to lead and causes pitting. If ethylene bromide is added with the tetraethyllead, lead bromide is formed which is more resistant to reduction. The commercial *Ethyl Fluid*, which is added to gasoline, consists of approximately 65 per cent tetraethyllead, 25 per cent ethylene bromide, and 10 per cent ethylene chloride. It is of interest that the increased use of bromine in Ethyl Fluid and other tetraethyllead mixtures led to the development of processes for the extraction of bromine from sea water. The extent of improvement in octane number on addition of tetraethyllead varies with the hydrocarbon, and the increase in octane number per unit of addition of tetraethyllead is known as the **lead susceptibility.** The paraffin hydrocarbons have a better lead susceptibility than olefins or more highly unsaturated compounds. Hence although a straight-run gasoline may have a low octane number, it may be more desirable than certain types of cracked gasoline because of the small amount of tetraethyllead necessary to bring the octane number to a desired value.

Kerosene. Previous to 1910, kerosene was the most important product derived from petroleum because of its use in lamps for lighting purposes. Considerable quantities still are used for domestic heating with small heaters. The kerosene fraction distills at 175°–275°, and all of the olefins and most of the aromatics must be removed to enable it to burn from a wick with a white flame and leave no residue. Refining is accomplished by washing with concentrated sulfuric acid or with liquid sulfur dioxide (*Edeleanu process*). Although aromatics burn with a smoky flame, it is not necessary to remove them completely, since it has been found that the burning qualities of the kerosene actually are improved when up to 20 per cent is present. The demand for the kerosene fraction is increasing again, since it is being used as the fuel for gas turbines and jet engines.

Gas Oil, Fuel Oil, and Diesel Oil. Hydrocarbons distilling above kerosene and below lubricating oils (250°–400°) may be used in a variety of ways. They may be cracked to gasoline or more drastically to oil gas, they may be burned as such for the generation of heat, or they may be used in internal combustion engines of the *Diesel* type. These engines differ from the gasoline engine in that the combustible mixture of air and fuel is not ignited by a spark but by the high temperature generated during the compression of the air. Air is drawn into the cylinder on the downward stroke of the piston and highly compressed on the upward stroke. At the moment of maximum compression, oil is sprayed into the hot air by injectors. In order that the temperature will be high enough for ignition to take place, the compression ratio must be at least 12 to 1 and usually is 14–17 to 1. At the compression ratio of 16 to 1 the theoretical thermodynamic efficiency is about 50 per cent, compared with an efficiency of 40 per cent for a gasoline engine having a compression ratio of 6 to 1. The fuel must have a low spontaneous ignition temperature and be clean to avoid clogging of the jets. For the purposes of Diesel fuel, straight chain paraffin hydrocarbons are superior to branched chain hydrocarbons and aromatics. Cetane (*n*-hexadecane), which ignites rapidly, is rated as 100 and α-methylnaphthalene (p. 432), which ignites slowly, is rated as zero. The **cetane number** of a fuel is the per cent of cetane in a cetane-α-methyl-naphthalene mixture which has the same ignition qualities as the fuel. In addition to somewhat better efficiency than the gasoline engine, the Diesel engine has the advantage of being able to use less expensive fuel. A more recent development is the *gas turbine* in which, presumably, any type of combustible liquid or powdered fuel may be used.

Lubricating Oils. Friction is due to rough surfaces and molecular attraction. Before a journal starts to rotate in a bearing lubricated by some liquid, the journal and the bearing are in close contact, and the friction is at a maximum. As the journal picks up speed, the friction decreases rapidly until the journal is floating in a layer of lubricant. During this period of decreasing friction the journal is said to be in a region of *unstable lubrication*. As the speed of the journal continues to increase, the coefficient of friction again rises slowly because of increasing molecular friction in the lubricant. This period is called the region of *stable lubrication*. In the region of stable lubrication when the journal is floating in a complete layer of lubricant, any liquid of the proper viscosity should be satisfactory. On starting or stopping, however, the system is in the region of unstable lubrication where the behavior of the lubricant depends on the composition of the lubricant and the nature of the surfaces.

The resinous and asphaltic constituents of oil are not lubricants. Moreover the higher polycyclic and aromatic hydrocarbons are undesirable. At low temperatures, paraffin waxes would crystallize out in the oil line. Hence refining of lubricating oils aims at removal of the resinous, asphaltic, higher polycyclic, and wax constituents. The crude higher-boiling oil fractions or still residues are distilled at reduced pressure to obtain fractions of different viscosities and then extracted with suitable solvents such as liquid sulfur dioxide, furfural (p. 451), β-chloroethyl ether (Chlorex, p. 119), phenol (p. 380), or mixtures of liquid propane and cresylic acid (p. 380) (Duosol process), which remove the undesirable nonparaffinic constituents. Dewaxing is brought about by solution in a mixture of methyl ethyl ketone (p. 181) and toluene (p. 317), chilling, filtering the wax, and removing the solvent. Small amounts of additives such as esters of acids of phosphorus (p. 78) and sulfur compounds usually are added to improve the lubricating properties of the oil and to produce the present-day "extreme pressure" lubricants. Polyisobutylene (p. 43) may be added to improve the viscosity index, that is the change in viscosity with change in temperature.

Miscellaneous Products. Numerous fractions of petroleum are used as solvents. **Petroleum ether** is a fraction consisting chiefly of pentanes and hexanes boiling at 30°–60°. Fractions boiling at 60°–90° and 90°–110° usually are referred to as **ligroin**. **Solvent naphthas** and **paint thinners** boil at 140°–200°. Even though the boiling point range may be the same, the composition of these products may vary widely depending on the source of the petroleum and the refining process. For example a straight-run fraction from a Pennsylvania oil may contain 80 per cent paraffin hydrocarbons and only a trace of aromatic hydrocarbons, whereas a fraction of the same boiling range from a cracked California oil may contain as little as 15 per cent paraffins and as high as 40 per cent aromatic hydrocarbons. The naphthas are used as fat solvents, dry cleaning agents, and paint and synthetic enamel thinners. Gasoline never should be substituted for naphtha or mixed with it for any of these purposes, because gasoline contains low-boiling components whose vapors are ignited readily by a flame or spark. Moreover practically all commercial gasoline contains the highly toxic tetraethyllead. **White mineral oils** or **paraffin oils** are polycyclic high-boiling fractions that have been decolorized by activated Fuller's earth (a diatomaceous clay) or bauxite (crude aluminum oxide). **Paraffin wax** is a refined grade of the solid hydrocarbon fraction. The *ordinary paraffin wax* crystallizes from the wax distillate. It is removed by filtration and is purified by crystallization from methyl ethyl ketone (p. 181). The better grades melt at 52°–57° and consist for the most part of normal alkanes having from 26 to 30 carbon atoms. The *microcrystalline waxes* are obtained by crystallization of the still residues and consist of molecules having 41 to 50 carbon atoms. Because of the high molecular weight of the molecules, these waxes melt as high as 88°–90° and hence are more valuable for many purposes. Some are hard and brittle, and others are fairly tough and flexible. **Petrolatum (petroleum jelly** or **Vaseline**) is a semisolid fraction used chiefly for pharmaceutical purposes. **Greases** are made by dissolving metallic soaps (p. 159) in hot lubricating oils. On cooling, the solution sets to a semisolid mass. **Pitch** and **asphalt** are residual products used as protective coatings and as binding agents for fibers and crushed rock. If these residues are distilled to dryness, **petroleum coke** is obtained which can be calcined to a practically pure carbon valuable for the manufacture of carbon electrodes.

Destructive Hydrogenation and Synthetic Fuels

In the cracking process, the formation of olefins, coke, and cyclic compounds takes place because of a lack of hydrogen and can be prevented if an excess of hydrogen is supplied in the presence or absence of a catalyst. A low cracking temperature is used at pressures around 3000 p.s.i. During the process, which is known as **destructive hydrogenation,** nitrogen, sulfur, and oxygen are removed completely as their hydrides, and the gasolines and kerosenes obtained are saturated and do not require further refining. Moreover each barrel of oil yields over a barrel of liquid products.[2] Some experimental plants have been built, but the process is not used to any extent because of the high cost of operation.

A similar process has been used, however, for the conversion of coal and

---

[2] The increase in volume is not due to the amount of hydrogen absorbed but to the fact that the hydrocarbons of lower molecular weight have a lower density than the original hydrocarbons. Ordinary cracking also would result in increased volume were it not for the gases and coke produced.

other solid fuels to liquid fuel in countries which do not have petroleum resources. Germany was the pioneer in this development, but other countries have built experimental plants as a safeguard against the day when petroleum supplies have become exhausted.[3] The *Bergius process* is carried out in two stages. In the liquid phase treatment, powdered coal is mixed with heavy oil residues and a small amount of catalyst, presumably iron oxide, and converted to heavy and middle oils at 450° and hydrogen pressures of 10,000 p.s.i. In the second stage, the middle oils are vaporized and passed with hydrogen over a fixed catalyst. The products are separated by distillation.

More recently, processes based on the *Fischer-Tropsch synthesis* of liquid fuels have been investigated extensively. Coal or other carbonaceous material is converted into carbon monoxide and hydrogen by the water gas reaction.

$$C + H_2O \longrightarrow CO + H_2$$

The mixture of carbon monoxide and hydrogen is enriched with hydrogen from the water-gas catalytic process (p. 46) and passed over a cobalt-thoria catalyst on a suitable support at 200°–250° and atmospheric pressure. The reaction appears to involve the initial formation of cobalt carbide. Reduction of the carbide by molecular hydrogen gives methylene groups, which polymerize to straight chain paraffins and olefins.

$$2\,Co + CO + H_2 \longrightarrow Co_2C + H_2O$$

$$Co_2C + H_2 \longrightarrow 2\,Co + [CH_2]$$

$$x\,[CH_2] \longrightarrow (CH_2)_x$$

The gasoline fraction must be reformed to improve the octane number. In Germany the paraffin waxes were oxidized to fatty acids for use in soap manufacture and for the synthesis of fats (p. 151). An obvious advantage over the Bergius process is that equipment capable of withstanding high pressure and temperature is not necessary. Nevertheless most of the German synthetic fuels were made by the Bergius process.

Controlled Air Oxidation of Saturated Hydrocarbons

Although the development of the Fischer-Tropsch process for the utilization of natural gas has not been so rapid as once predicted, the controlled air oxidation of saturated hydrocarbons has been expanding rapidly. Several commercial plants are in operation for the production of methyl, ethyl, and *n*-propyl alcohols (Chapter 5), formaldehyde, acetaldehyde, and acetone (Chapter 12), and acetic and propionic acids (Chapter 10) from the propane-butane fraction of natural gas. The controlled air oxidation of paraffin wax yields fatty acids, which may be used for the production of soaps and synthetic fats (Chapter 11). Intensive efforts are being made to utilize methane for the

---

[3] The proven reserves of petroleum in the United States at the end of 1948 were 27 billion barrels. Production during the same year was 2 billion barrels. At this rate known reserves will be exhausted by 1961. Newer geophysical methods for locating oil pools will increase reserves somewhat but cannot do so indefinitely. Before the exhaustion of reserves, other sources of liquid fuel such as coal and oil shale must be developed if the United States wishes to remain independent of foreign sources.

synthesis of acetylene, a basic chemical for the synthesis of many organic compounds (p. 112).

REVIEW QUESTIONS

1. Discuss the source and composition of petroleum. What are the current theories concerning its origin and the conditions under which it was produced?
2. What is meant by the following terms: liquefied petroleum gas; petroleum ether; ligroin; straight-run gasoline; cracked gasoline; naphtha; kerosene; gas oil; Diesel fuel; lubricating oil; white mineral oil; petroleum jelly?
3. Give a brief discussion of knocking, octane number, anti-knock gasoline, Ethyl Fluid, cetane number.
4. Discuss briefly the Burton, Dubbs, Thermofor, and Fluid Catalyst processes for cracking petroleum, giving the advantages and disadvantages of each.
5. Describe the following processes as used by the petroleum industry: polymerization; alkylation; isomerization; reforming; dehydrogenation.
6. Give a brief description of the Fischer-Tropsch process and the Bergius process for the production of hydrocarbon oil from lignite or coal.

Chapter 5

ALCOHOLS. ESTERS OF INORGANIC ACIDS

ALCOHOLS

The simplest alcohols contain oxygen and have the general empirical formula $C_nH_{2n+2}O$. The first member, methyl alcohol, has the molecular formula CH_4O. Since oxygen has six valence electrons, it requires two more to complete its valence shell. It does this by pairing two of its electrons with two electrons from one or two other atoms or groups, thus forming two covalent bonds. In the alcohol molecule, CH_4O, the oxygen atom must be joined to both carbon and hydrogen, since if it shared both of the electrons with carbon, carbon would have only two valence electrons left to share with hydrogen and the formula would be CH_2O. If both electrons of oxygen were shared with hydrogen, a water molecule would result. Hence only one structural formula is possible, namely

$$H-\overset{\displaystyle H}{\underset{\displaystyle H}{C}}-O-H$$

or CH_3OH. This formula is in accord with the general methods of preparation and the reactions of methyl alcohol.

The number of possible structures for the other members of this homologous series can be predicted in much the same way as was done for the olefins, namely from a consideration of the possible positions which the functional group, in this case the *hydroxyl group* (OH), can occupy in the carbon skeletons of the alkanes. This procedure, for example, leads to one C_2 alcohol, two C_3 alcohols, four C_4 alcohols, and eight C_5 alcohols.

Nomenclature

The word *alcohol* has been applied to the active principle of intoxicating beverages since the sixteenth century. The usually accepted derivation is from *al-kuhl*, the Arabic word for finely powdered antimony sulfide used to darken eyelids. The Arabian alchemists, however, who were familiar with spirit of wine for centuries, never applied the word to this substance. Other possibilities are that the word *alcohol* is derived from a Chaldean word meaning *to burn*, or that it is a corruption of *spiritus alcalisatus*, an early designation for alcohol purified by drying over potassium carbonate. The term now is used as a family name.

Three systems of nomenclature are in general use. In the first the alkyl group attached to the hydroxyl group is named and the separate word alcohol is added. In the second system the higher alcohols are considered as derivatives of the first member of the series, which is called *carbinol*. The third method is the Geneva or I.U.C. system in which (*1*) the longest carbon chain containing the hydroxyl group determines the surname, (*2*) the ending *e* of the corresponding saturated hydrocarbon is replaced by *ol*, (*3*) the position of the hydroxyl group is indicated by the smallest possible number, and (4) the side chains are named and their position indicated by a number. The following examples illustrate these various systems.

CH_3OH	methyl alcohol carbinol methanol
C_2H_5OH	ethyl alcohol [1] methylcarbinol [1] ethanol
$CH_3CH_2CH_2OH$	normal propyl alcohol (*n*-propyl alcohol) ethylcarbinol 1-propanol
CH_3CHCH_3 $\overset{\textstyle |}{OH}$	isopropyl alcohol (*i*-propyl alcohol) dimethylcarbinol 2-propanol
$CH_3CH_2CH_2CH_2OH$	normal butyl alcohol (*n*-butyl alcohol) *n*-propylcarbinol 1-butanol
$CH_3CH_2CHCH_3$ $\overset{\textstyle |}{OH}$	secondary butyl alcohol (*s*-butyl alcohol) methylethylcarbinol 2-butanol
CH_3CHCH_2OH $\overset{\textstyle |}{CH_3}$	isobutyl alcohol (*i*-butyl alcohol) *i*-propylcarbinol 2-methyl-1-propanol
$\overset{\textstyle CH_3}{\overset{\textstyle |}{CH_3-\underset{\underset{\textstyle CH_3}{\textstyle |}}{C}-OH}}$	tertiary butyl alcohol (*t*-butyl alcohol) trimethylcarbinol 2-methyl-2-propanol

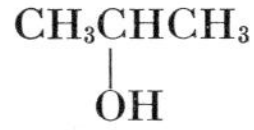

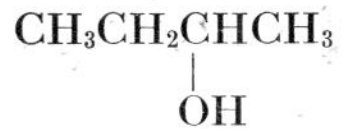

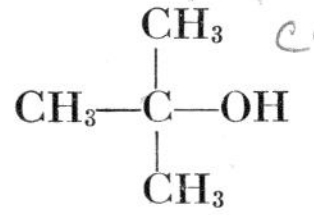

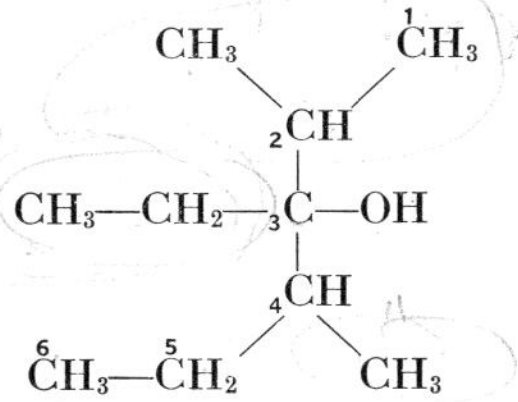

$$\begin{array}{c} CH_3 \qquad\qquad \overset{1}{C}H_3 \\ \diagdown\,\underset{2}{CH}\,\diagup \\ CH_3-CH_2-\underset{3}{C}-OH \\ \diagup\,\underset{4}{CH}\,\diagdown \\ \overset{6}{C}H_3-\overset{5}{C}H_2 \qquad CH_3 \end{array}$$

ethyl-*i*-propyl-*s*-butylcarbinol
2,4-dimethyl-3-ethyl-3-hexanol

Alcohols in general are divided into three classes. Those in which the hydroxyl group is united to a primary carbon atom, that is one united to one other carbon atom, are called *primary* alcohols. Those in which the hydroxyl group is united to a secondary carbon atom, that is one united to two other carbon atoms, are called *secondary* alcohols. Those in which the hydroxyl group is united to a tertiary carbon atom, that is one united to three other

---

[1] Whether a chemical name for an organic compound is written as one word or more than one depends on whether the compound is being named as a derivative of a chemical entity. Thus *carbinol* is a definite compound, CH_3OH, and names for compounds considered to be derivatives of it are written as one word, for example *methylcarbinol*. On the other hand *alcohol* is not the name of any compound but is the name of a class of compounds. Hence *ethyl alcohol* is written as two words.

carbon atoms, are called *tertiary* alcohols. In the above list ethyl, *n*-propyl, *n*-butyl, and *i*-butyl alcohols are primary alcohols, *i*-propyl and *s*-butyl alcohols are secondary alcohols, and *t*-butyl alcohol and ethyl-*i*-propyl-*s*-butylcarbinol are tertiary alcohols. Ordinarily methyl alcohol is classed as a primary alcohol although really it is in a class by itself.

Physical Properties

Methyl alcohol, the first member of the series, is a liquid boiling at 65° in contrast to methane which boils at −161°. Even ethane, which has almost the same molecular weight as methyl alcohol, boils at −88°. The alcohols in general boil at a considerably higher temperature than the saturated hydrocarbons of the same molecular weight. The boiling point is high for the same reason that the boiling point of water is abnormally high, namely association through *proton bonds*. The proton bond forms between a hydrogen atom combined with the strongly electron-attracting elements fluorine, oxygen, and nitrogen, and a second electron-attracting element having an unshared pair of electrons (p. 64). This type of attraction has been called *hydrogen bonding*, but since the attraction is between the positive nucleus of the hydrogen atom, that is the proton, and the electron shell of the second atom, *proton bonding* is a more descriptive term. Use of this term also avoids confusion with the normal covalent hydrogen bond.

Water may be represented as a mixture of associated molecules of various molecular weights (p. 64). Similarly methyl alcohol and other alcohols may be represented as a mixture of associated molecules.

```
    H    H           H                        CH₃
    |    |           |                         |
H—O : H—O : H—O : H—O :          CH₃—O : H—O :
    ..       ..      |                 |       ..
                     H                 H       H     CH₃
                                                     |
                                        CH₃—O : H—O :
                                             ..       ..


              ..                                        ..
            H—O :                                     CH₃—O :
    H         |               H      H      |        H      CH₃
    |        ..       ..       |      |     ..        |       |
H—O : H—O :    : O—H : O—H  CH₃—O : H—O :     : O—H : O—H
    ..   |        |     |        ..      |        |      ..
    H     H        H     H                CH₃      CH₃
```

Liquid water   Liquid methyl alcohol

Since alcohols are considerably less acidic than water (pp. 127, 191), that is the proton is held more strongly, they have less tendency to form proton bonds than water, and the degree of association is less. Hence methyl alcohol boils considerably lower than water even though it has a higher molecular weight.

The rise in boiling point of the straight chain primary alcohols with increasing molecular weight is about 18° for each additional CH_2 group, as shown by Fig. 26. For a given molecular weight, branching of the carbon chain lowers the boiling point just as it does in hydrocarbons. The boiling points of *n*-, *i*-, and *t*-butyl alcohols are respectively 117°, 107°, and 83°. The boiling

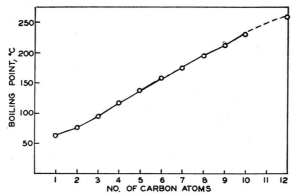

Fig. 26. Boiling points of normal alcohols.

point of *s*-butyl alcohol is 100° indicating that the hydroxyl group acts like a branch as might be expected.

Dodecyl alcohol is the first straight chain alcohol which is solid at room temperature, although the more nearly spherical branched alcohols with fewer carbon atoms, for example *t*-butyl alcohol, also may be solids at room temperature. There is no evidence for alternation in melting point (Fig. 27) as is ex-

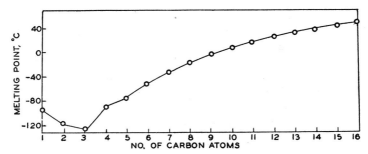

Fig. 27. Melting points of normal alcohols.

hibited by saturated hydrocarbons (Fig. 18, p. 31).

The alcohols containing three carbon atoms or less and *t*-butyl alcohol are miscible with water at 20°, but *n*-butyl alcohol is soluble to the extent of only about 8 per cent, and primary alcohols with more than five carbon atoms are less than 1 per cent soluble in water.

Solubility has been mentioned previously on page 7 and page 32. Solution is nothing more than the intermingling of molecules. Two liquids will not mix if the attractive forces of like molecules for each other are much greater than the attractive forces between unlike molecules. Moreover the more closely molecules are related in composition and structure, the more similar will be the attractive and repulsive forces between them. These statements explain the very approximate rule that *like dissolves like.* It is desirable, however, to have a somewhat clearer picture of the factors producing solubility and insolubility. From the differences in boiling points, it was concluded that the attraction between water molecules is considerably greater than between alcohol molecules, and it might be predicted that water and methyl alcohol would not mix. However alcohol molecules can form proton bonds with water molecules and vice versa with the result that the differences in attractive forces are decreased and intermingling takes place.

$$
\begin{array}{cccc}
\overset{\textstyle H}{\underset{}{|}}\;\;\overset{\textstyle H}{\underset{}{|}} & \overset{\textstyle H}{\underset{}{|}}\;\;\overset{\textstyle H}{\underset{}{|}} & \overset{\textstyle H}{\underset{}{|}}\;\;\overset{\textstyle H}{\underset{}{|}} & \overset{\textstyle H}{\underset{}{|}}\;\;\overset{\textstyle R}{\underset{}{|}} \\
R{-}\overset{..}{\underset{..}{O}}{:}H{-}\overset{..}{\underset{..}{O}}{:} & H{-}\overset{..}{\underset{..}{O}}{:}H{-}\overset{..}{\underset{..}{O}}{:} & R{-}\overset{..}{\underset{}{O}}{:}H{-}\overset{..}{\underset{}{O}}{:} & H{-}\overset{..}{\underset{}{O}}{:}H{-}\overset{..}{\underset{}{O}}{:}
\end{array}
$$

As the length of the hydrocarbon chain increases, the van der Waals forces between alcohol molecules increase until a point is reached at which the association with water molecules is no longer sufficient to prevent alcohol molecules from being attracted more strongly to each other than to water complexes, and two phases result. The separation is not complete, however. Some alcohol-water complexes remain in the water layer, and some remain in the alcohol layer. Thus 100 g. of *n*-butyl alcohol dissolves 37 g. of water, and 100 g. of water dissolves 7.3 g. of *n*-butyl alcohol at 15°. The fact that *t*-butyl alcohol is miscible with water agrees with the fact that it boils lower than *n*-butyl alcohol, since the higher solubility and lower boiling point are both dependent on the lower van der Waals forces between *t*-butyl alcohol molecules.

Attractive Forces Between Molecules

The boiling point of a compound at a given pressure may be taken as a rough measure of the attractive forces between molecules, since the boiling point is merely the temperature at which the thermal agitation of the molecules is sufficient to overcome the attractive forces between them. All attractive forces are electrical and vary continuously with the structure of the molecule. It is desirable, however, to distinguish between the following types which differ in the magnitude of the electrical attraction.

van der Waals Attraction. These forces arise because of the *polarizability* of the molecule. Although the negative charges of the electrons in a neutral molecule are balanced by the positive charges on the nuclei, the electrons are in motion, and the center of density of the negative charges of the electrons does not continuously coincide with the center of density of the positive charges of the nuclei. This condition gives rise to a transient slight separation of charge in the molecule, or an *electrical dipole*, which is called the *polarization* of the molecule. As a result of this dipole, molecules which approach each other closely enough and with the proper orientation tend to adhere, the ends of unlike charge attracting each other. Once the attractive force comes into play, the polarization of the molecule is increased. Therefore even simple molecules such as helium and hydrogen have some tendency to adhere. The ease of polarizability and hence the strength of the van der Waals forces increases as the number of electrons increases and hence as the number and complexity of the atoms in the molecule increases. For normal alkanes the forces amount to about 1.0 kcal. per carbon atom and account for the regular increase in boiling point with increasing molecular weight within a homologous series. It is not possible to distill without decomposition hydrocarbons having more than around 80 carbon atoms, no matter how perfect the vacuum, because the energy of about 80 kcal. per mole required to separate the molecules is approximately the same as that necessary to break a carbon-carbon bond (p. 92). The van der Waals forces vary inversely as the seventh power of the distance between the molecules and hence are operative only when molecules approach each other very closely. Branching of a molecule would tend to decrease the magnitude of the transient dipole and might prevent the optimum proximity of the molecules to each other, thus accounting for the lower boiling points of branched compounds.

Permanent Dipole Association. In the discussion of the formation of the covalent bond (p. 6), it was assumed that the pair of electrons is shared equally between the nuclei that they bind, that is that the probability distribution about each nucleus is the same. That they are not shared equally at all times, even in molecules made up of two like atoms, is indicated by the van der Waals forces between such molecules. If the molecule is made up of unlike atoms, another factor enters, namely the difference in nuclear charge of the two atoms. In a simple covalent molecule such as hydrogen chloride, the hydrogen nucleus has a charge of $+1$, and the chlorine nucleus has a charge of $+17$. Because of the larger charge, the chlorine nucleus will attract the electrons more strongly than will the nucleus of the hydrogen atom; hence the most probable position of the electron pair in the bond is not equidistant between the two nuclei but closer to the chlorine nucleus, giving rise to a difference in charge between the two atoms. In other words the hydrogen chloride molecule is an *electrical dipole*. This dipole is a permanent one in contrast to the dipoles resulting from the transient polarizability of the molecule.

The difference in charge between two unlike atoms is only a fraction of the 4.80×10^{-10} electrostatic units which would exist if there were a complete transfer of one electron (Table 6). It is by no means imaginary, however, and can be measured by physical means. Whenever such an unequal distribution of charge arises, an electrical moment, known as the *dipole moment*, exists. This moment is equal to the product of the difference in charge by the distance between the charges. These dipoles have a tendency to line up in an electric field, and hence a gas with a permanent dipole moment will change the capacity of a condenser. By measuring the dielectric constant of the compound at different temperatures, the dipole moment, μ, can be calculated. For hydrogen chloride it is 1.03×10^{-18} e.s.u. or 1.03 Debye units. Hydrogen, as would be predicted, has zero moment. Methane likewise has zero moment even though there is a difference in charge between each hydrogen atom and the carbon atom. The electrical moment of the molecule is the vector sum of the moments of the various bonds in the molecule, and since the carbon-hydrogen bonds are tetrahedrally distributed, the resultant moment of any three links is equal and opposite in direction to the moment of the fourth link, and the moment of the whole molecule is zero. Moreover since all alkyl groups have the same dipole moment, all saturated hydrocarbons have zero moment, and the dipole moments of the members of an homologous series are approximately constant.

These permanent dipoles add to those caused by transient polarizability and increase the attraction between molecules. For low molecular weight compounds, the attractive force due to dipole association is of the same order of magnitude as that due to van der Waals forces, but as the molecular weight increases the latter become much more important. Dipole-dipole forces are inversely proportional to the fourth power of the distance. Hence *dipole-dipole attraction* is effective only when molecules are rather close to each other, although the range over which they are effective is greater than that for van der Waals forces. In addition to dipole-dipole attraction, *ion-dipole attraction* such as that between sodium or chlorine ions and water molecules (p. 8) also can exist. These forces are inversely proportional to the cube of the distance.

Molecules which have a permanent dipole are known as *polar* molecules. It is only in this sense that the term polar should be used. Substances such as sodium chloride which have ionic bonds should be called ionic or electrovalent compounds. Liquids such as water should be called polar only if one is referring to their properties arising from the dipole in the molecule, and not when referring to their abnormal properties such as association, which is caused by proton bonding, or to their power to dissolve salts with the formation of electrically conducting solutions, which is dependent on ion-dipole interaction and a high dielectric constant. Although a high dielectric constant is related to a high dipole moment, other factors also are involved. Thus water, which is the best ionizing solvent, has a dipole moment of 1.84 and a dielectric constant of 81, whereas ethyl bromide, which does not dissolve salts, has the same dipole moment, but a dielectric constant of only 9. Although liquid hydrogen cyanide has a higher dipole moment (2.1) and dielectric constant (95) than water, it is a poorer ionizing solvent.

Proton Bonding. The hydrogen atom is unique in that it has but a single electron surrounding the nucleus. When it is bonded with other elements, the hydrogen nucleus is less protected by a cover of electrons than the nuclei of other elements, and it can approach the electron shells of other molecules more closely. If it can approach closely enough to the valence electrons of a nucleus of another molecule, the proton may be attracted by the electrons of the second nucleus. The strongest attractive force between two molecules would be expected (a) when the hydrogen atom is partially deprived of its share of electrons by being united to an element having a much greater attraction for electrons than the hydrogen nucleus, and (b) when the electron shell of an element in a second molecule is most concentrated and most exposed. The relative attraction for electrons can be approximated from the dipole moment of the link between hydrogen and the other element, and the distance between them. For example the moment for hydrogen chloride is 1.03×10^{-18} e.s.u., and the distance between the nuclei is 1.27 Å. Since the moment is the product of the difference in charge of the two nuclei and the distance between them, the difference in charge is $1.03 \times 10^{-18}/1.27 \times 10^{-8} = 0.81 \times 10^{-10}$ e.s.u. The values for the more common bonds of hydrogen with other elements are given in Table 6. If a difference in charge of one electron existed, it would amount to 4.80×10^{-10} e.s.u.

TABLE 6
Bond Moments and Differences in Charge Between Nuclei

LINK	MOMENT E.S.U. $\times 10^8$	DISTANCE BETWEEN NUCLEI Å	DIFFERENCE IN CHARGE BETWEEN NUCLEI E.S.U. $\times 10^{10}$
H—C	0.2	1.14	0.18
H—N	1.5	1.08	1.4
H—O	1.6	1.07	1.5
H—F	1.75	0.92	1.9
H—S	0.8	1.43	0.6
H—Cl	1.03	1.27	0.81
H—Br	0.78	1.41	0.55
H—I	0.38	1.61	0.24

The difference in charge between hydrogen and carbon is so small that in the H—C bond hydrogen has very nearly its share of electrons. For the H—N and H—O bonds the difference in charge is considerable and for the H—F bond it is even greater. Hydrogen united to nitrogen, oxygen, or fluorine forms strong proton bonds, the strength increasing continuously from left to right across the periodic table.

The second factor involved, namely the concentration of the negative charge in a second molecule and the degree of exposure of this charge, likewise increases from left to right across the periodic table. The concentration of charge decreases from top to bottom. Hence the strongest bonding of this type is that between molecules such as those of hydrogen fluoride, water, and ammonia. Hydrogen fluoride is associated even in the vapor state. In the hydrides of chlorine, sulfur, and phosphorus, not only is the difference in charge between hydrogen and the other atoms smaller, but the negative charge on the other atoms is too diffuse to be effective.

In proton bonding between water molecules, a single proton cannot attract more than one other water molecule. Because of the small size of the proton the two water molecules approach each other so closely that a third water molecule cannot approach the proton closely enough to be attracted appreciably. However a proton of a third water molecule can be attracted to one of the oxygen atoms, and this process can be repeated until the attractive forces balance the disruptive forces due to thermal agitation. Hence water is a mixture of complexes made up of varying numbers of water molecules. It has been estimated that the average degree of association is approximately three. This type of attraction is so distinctive that it is called *proton bonding*, or *hydrogen bonding* (p. 60). The phenomenon is known also as *association* and compounds exhibiting proton bonding are said to be associated.

It is convenient to represent this type of attraction as being between a hydrogen atom of one molecule and an unshared pair of electrons of another molecule. Actually the attraction is not concerned with an unshared pair. However it is only when an atom has an unshared pair, that is when it is united to less than four other groups, that the negative charge is sufficiently exposed for the hydrogen to get close enough to it for an attractive force to operate.

Alcohols of Commercial Importance

Methyl Alcohol. The word *methyl*, first used by Dumas and Peligot in 1834, was derived from the Greek word *methy* meaning wine and *yle* meaning wood or material, and refers to the fact that it is the chief alcohol formed by the destructive distillation of wood. Previous to 1919 it commonly was called *wood alcohol* or *Columbian spirits* in the United States. With the introduction of national prohibition of alcoholic beverages and the advent of the "speakeasy" over which the authorities had no supervisory control, anything called alcohol was used for intoxicating drinks. Since methyl alcohol is highly toxic, the result was an alarming number of deaths and cases of blindness. As one combative measure the use of the Geneva name *methanol* was urged, and it now largely has displaced the older term.

Methyl alcohol now is obtained both by wood distillation and by a synthetic process. In the **wood distillation** process dried hardwood such as beech, birch, hickory, maple, or oak is decomposed in an oven or retort at a temperature increasing from about 160° to 450°. If the wood is dry when placed in the retort the reaction is exothermic, and heat is supplied only to start the reaction. The products are gases, which are burned as fuel, a liquid condensate, and a residue of charcoal. The liquid condensate separates into an aqueous layer called *pyroligneous acid*, and a tarry layer. The pyroligneous acid, of which 200 to 250 gallons per cord of wood is obtained, is mostly water but contains 1 to 6 per cent of methyl alcohol, 4 to 10 per cent of acetic acid, 0.1 to 0.5 per cent of acetone, and smaller amounts of methyl acetate and a number of other organic compounds.

In the oldest process for the separation of the components, the acetic acid is neutralized with lime to produce the nonvolatile calcium acetate, and the mixture is distilled to give a liquid containing 8 to 10 per cent of methyl alcohol and the other volatile constituents. Fractional distillation gives the so-called "82 per cent methyl alcohol" containing 82 per cent organic compounds or 60–65 per cent methyl alcohol, 11–14 per cent acetone, and 6–8 per cent methyl acetate. Further fractionation removes the methyl acetate and acetone as low constant-boiling mixtures with methyl alcohol. This mixture is known as "methyl acetone" and is sold as a solvent [2] without further separation. The next fraction contains 92–95 per cent methyl alcohol. The higher-boiling fractions contain allyl alcohol (p. 517), *n*-propyl alcohol, and methyl ethyl ketone (p. 181). Pure methyl alcohol was obtained through the calcium chloride complex (p. 72).

The **synthetic process** starts with carbon monoxide and hydrogen which combine over a zinc oxide catalyst containing other promoter oxides, for ex-

---

[2] The term *solvent* refers to the use of organic liquids for the purpose of dissolving other organic substances. Solvents are used as reaction media, for extraction of organic compounds from solids or from aqueous solutions, or to provide a means of coating organic materials on other substances or to form them into sheets or fibers. Following the operation the solvent is removed by distillation or evaporation. Hence they usually are low-boiling liquids.

ample 10 per cent chromium oxide, at a temperature of 300°–400° and at pressures from 200 to 300 atmospheres.

$$CO + 2 H_2 \xrightarrow{ZnO-Cr_2O_3} CH_3OH$$

The synthesis frequently is carried out in conjunction with some other operation. For example in one process water gas is mixed with steam and passed over iron oxide, converting most of the carbon monoxide to carbon dioxide which is scrubbed out by water under pressure. The remaining carbon monoxide then is removed by passing over a catalyst for conversion to methyl alcohol leaving hydrogen free of carbon monoxide for the synthesis of ammonia.

$$\underset{\text{Steam}}{H_2O} + \underset{\text{Coke}}{C} \xrightarrow{1200°} \underset{\text{Water}}{H_2} + \underset{\text{Gas}}{CO}$$

$$CO + H_2O \xrightarrow[450°]{Fe_2O_3 + \text{promoters}} CO_2 + H_2 \,(+ 1 \text{ per cent CO})$$

By-product hydrogen from other processes, such as the anaerobic fermentation of starch (p. 70), the electrolytic production of chlorine, or the cracking of hydrocarbons, may be used.

Some higher alcohols also are produced in the synthetic process. The amount can be increased by modifying the catalyst, for example by adding alkalies or by using an iron base-alkali catalyst, and by raising the temperature to 350°–475°.

More recently methyl alcohol has been obtained as one of the products of the controlled air oxidation of natural gas (p. 56). Other alcohols also are formed as well as aldehydes, ketones, and organic acids. The process appears to be one which may become dominant for the production of these compounds.

The total production of synthetic methanol in the United States in 1948 was 990 million pounds, or 155 million gallons, exceeding the production of any other synthetic organic chemical. Its chief uses are for the manufacture of formaldehyde (p. 176), as a denaturant for ethyl alcohol, as a solvent, and as radiator antifreeze. Production of wood alcohol was 2.5 million gallons. Practically all of it was used to denature ethyl alcohol. When pure synthetic methanol sold for 26 cents per gallon, impure wood alcohol sold for 60 cents per gallon, because by law it is a required ingredient of denatured ethyl alcohol (p. 69) used as radiator antifreeze.

Ethyl Alcohol. Although the suffix *yl* was used in 1834 by Dumas and Peligot in the word *methyl* to indicate its derivation from wood, Liebig and Woehler had used the same suffix in 1832 in the term *benzoyl* in the sense of stuff or material. It is in the latter sense that it ordinarily is used. *Ethyl* means the material which gives rise to ether (p. 114).

One important source of ethyl alcohol is the *fermentation of sugars*. **Fermentation** is the decomposition of organic compounds into simpler compounds through the agency of enzymes. **Enzymes** are complex organic compounds secreted by living cells. The name *enzyme* means *in yeast* and was given because the earliest known enzymes were those secreted by yeast cells.

Pasteur,[3] who discovered the nature of fermentation, thought that the living cell was necessary, but this view was disproven by Buchner in 1897. He showed that the juice expressed from yeast cells which had been completely destroyed still was capable of bringing about fermentation.

The chief sources of sugars for fermentation are the various starches and the molasses residue from sugar refining. Corn (maize) is the chief source of starch in the United States, and ethyl alcohol made from corn commonly is known as *grain alcohol*. Potatoes are the chief source of starch in Europe, and rice in Asia. In preparing alcohol from corn the germ first is removed, and the remainder ground and cooked to give the mash. Malt (sprouted barley) or a mold such as *Aspergillus oryzae* containing the enzyme *diastase* is added, and the mixture kept at 40° until all of the starch has been converted into the sugar maltose. This solution is known as the *wort*.

$$2 (C_6H_{10}O_5)_n + n\,H_2O \xrightarrow[\text{in malt}]{\text{Diastase}} n\,C_{12}H_{22}O_{11}$$
$$\text{Starch} \qquad\qquad\qquad \text{Maltose}$$

The wort is cooled to 20°, diluted to 10 per cent maltose, and a pure yeast culture added. The yeast cells secrete two enzymes, *maltase*, which converts the maltose into glucose, and *zymase*, which converts the glucose into carbon dioxide and alcohol.

$$C_{12}H_{22}O_{11} + H_2O \xrightarrow{\text{Maltase}} 2\,C_6H_{12}O_6$$
$$\text{Maltose} \qquad\qquad \text{Glucose}$$

$$C_6H_{12}O_6 \xrightarrow{\text{Zymase}} 2\,CO_2 + 2\,C_2H_5OH$$

Heat is generated and the temperature must be controlled by cooling. At the end of the fermentation the product is run through beer stills (perforated plate type, Fig. 6, p. 10) to remove the alcohol from solid matter. The distillate is fractionated by means of an efficient column of the bubble cap type. A small amount of acetaldehyde (b.p. 21°) distills first and is followed by 95 per cent alcohol. Finally a mixture of fusel oil and water distills. The fusel oil consists of a mixture of higher alcohols, chiefly *n*-propyl, *i*-butyl, *i*-amyl (3-methyl-1-butanol), and active amyl [4] (2-methyl-1-butanol). The exact composition of fusel oil varies considerably, being dependent particularly on the type of raw material that is fermented. These higher alcohols are not formed by fermentation of glucose but arise from certain amino acids (p. 227) derived from the proteins present in the raw material and in the yeast.

Industrial alcohol is ethyl alcohol used for nonbeverage purposes and usually is not produced from starch. Previous to the development of efficient synthetic processes, the chief source of industrial alcohol was the fermentation

---

[3] Louis Pasteur (1822–1895), French chemist and microbiologist whose studies of fermentation led to the germ theory of disease and to immunization by inoculation with attenuated organisms and viruses. The "Life of Pasteur" written by his son-in-law, Vallery-Radot, is a most interesting account of the life and work of an outstanding scientist.

[4] The five-carbon alcohols commonly are referred to as *amyl alcohols*, because they first were obtained from the products of fermentation (L. *amylum* starch). The use of *pentyl* instead of *amyl* is being advocated. The term *active* refers to the effect of the compound on plane-polarized light (p. 259).

of black-strap molasses, the noncrystallizable residue from the refining of sucrose (cane sugar). It contains about 50 per cent of sucrose. Malt is unnecessary in the fermentation, since yeast contains an enzyme, *sucrase* (*invertase*), capable of converting sucrose into glucose and fructose, both of which are fermentable by zymase.

$$C_{12}H_{22}O_{11} + H_2O \xrightarrow{\text{Sucrase}} C_6H_{12}O_6 + C_6H_{12}O_6$$
Sucrose　　　　　　　　　　　　　　Glucose　　Fructose

$$C_6H_{12}O_6 \xrightarrow{\text{Zymase}} 2\,CO_2 + 2\,C_2H_5OH$$
Glucose
or
fructose

The black-strap molasses is shipped from the islands of the Caribbean Sea by tankers to plants located on the Atlantic and Gulf coasts. It is diluted with three to five volumes of water, and sulfuric acid is added to prevent the growth of harmful organisms. After the addition of yeast, the process is the same as for the production of alcohol from starch. Plants may have fermenters of a half million gallons capacity, which are enclosed to collect the carbon dioxide for recovery of alcohol vapors and for the condensation of the carbon dioxide to the liquid or solid form. Storage capacity for molasses may be as high as 6,000,000 gallons.

Glucose formed by the hydrolysis of cellulose (pp. 277, 299) and the sugars present in waste sulfite liquors from the production of wood pulp (p. 298) also are possible sources of carbohydrate for alcoholic fermentation. These sources have been used in Germany. Experimental plants have been built and operated in the United States, but they have not been able to compete with other processes under normal economic conditions.

Several processes for the **synthesis of ethyl alcohol** are possible. The first synthesis was reported by Hennel [5] in 1828, the same year in which Woehler reported the synthesis of urea. In 1826 Hennel had reported the isolation of potassium ethyl sulfate from a sample of sulfuric acid which had absorbed 80 volumes of ethylene, and which had been given to him by Faraday [6] for investigation. In 1828 Hennel reported the hydrolysis of potassium ethyl sulfate to ethyl alcohol. Hennel's discovery was overlooked, however, and the synthesis was rediscovered in 1855 by Berthelot,[7] who absorbed the ethylene from coal gas in concentrated sulfuric acid, and diluted and distilled the solution.

$$CH_2{=}CH_2 + H_2SO_4 \longrightarrow CH_3CH_2OSO_3H$$

$$CH_3CH_2OSO_3H + H_2O \longrightarrow CH_3CH_2OH + H_2SO_4$$

[5] Henry Hennel, English apothecary and contemporary of Michael Faraday. He was killed in 1842 by the explosion of a large quantity of mercury fulminate which he had prepared for the East India Company for military purposes.

[6] Michael Faraday (1791–1867). Although best known for his work on electricity and magnetism, he made outstanding contributions to chemistry as well. He was the first to liquefy a number of gases and was the discoverer of benzene (p. 310). He established the laws of electrolysis and discovered the phenomenon of magnetic optical rotation.

[7] Marcellin Pierre Eugène Berthelot (1827–1907), French chemist and statesman. He is noted especially for his high temperature syntheses of organic compounds, for his study of esterification, and for his work in thermochemistry.

Although the possibility of industrial synthesis by this process was discussed in the following year and a claim made in France in 1862 that the cost of synthetic alcohol was about one-third that of fermentation alcohol, the first continuously successful process was not operated until 1931 in the United States. The ethylene used as the raw material is produced by the cracking of hydrocarbons. It is absorbed in concentrated sulfuric acid at 100° to give a mixture of ethyl hydrogen sulfate and ethyl sulfate. Dilution with water brings about hydrolysis to ethyl alcohol, which is removed by distillation. The dilute sulfuric acid is concentrated for reuse. By 1939, the synthetic process accounted for 25 per cent of the total U. S. production of industrial alcohol and in 1948 for 38 per cent. Ethyl alcohol also is one of the products of the butyl alcohol fermentation of starch (p. 70), of the Fischer-Tropsch synthesis of liquid hydrocarbon fuels (p. 56) and of the controlled oxidation of natural gas (p. 56).

Various grades of ethyl alcohol are produced. **Ordinary alcohol** is 92–95 per cent ethyl alcohol by weight, the remainder being chiefly water. Anhydrous alcohol cannot be obtained by simple distillation because a constant-boiling mixture (also called an *azeotrope*) containing 95.6 per cent alcohol by weight boils lower (78.15°) than pure alcohol (78.3°).

Absolute alcohol (anhydrous, 99.9+ per cent) usually is prepared in the laboratory by removing the water by chemical means, for example by heating with calcium oxide, which reacts with the water, and distilling the dried alcohol from the calcium hydroxide. The 5 per cent water in ordinary alcohol has a marked effect on its solvent properties, and there is a considerable large-scale demand for the anhydrous product. One commercial method of dehydration makes use of the fact that a ternary mixture consisting of 18.5 per cent alcohol, 74.1 per cent benzene (C_6H_6, p. 310), and 7.4 per cent water by weight boils at 64.85°. Since the ratio of water to alcohol is 1:2.5, enough benzene can be added to remove all of the water in the low-boiling distillate, and anhydrous alcohol can be withdrawn from the still pot. A binary mixture containing 80.2 per cent of benzene and 19.8 per cent of ethyl alcohol, and boiling at 68.2°, permits complete removal of any excess benzene. The distillate separates into two layers. The upper layer comprises 84.7 per cent of the total and consists of 11.6 per cent alcohol, 85.6 per cent benzene, and 2.8 per cent water. The lower layer amounts to 15.3 per cent and consists of 51.3 per cent alcohol, 8.1 per cent benzene, and 40.6 per cent water. Redistillation of the upper layer removes all of its water as the ternary mixture, and the residue is returned to the main still. Redistillation of the lower layer removes all of its benzene as the ternary mixture and leaves a dilute alcohol which is rectified to 95 per cent alcohol and returned to the main still. By the use of four stills the process can be made continuous, with 95 per cent ethyl alcohol entering the system and absolute alcohol and water being withdrawn.

Since all countries have derived a sizeable portion of their revenue by taxing alcohol for beverage purposes, ethyl alcohol for industrial use first must be converted into **denatured alcohol** if the payment of tax is to be avoided. Denaturing is the addition of substances which render the alcohol unfit to drink. Many formulas are available to the manufacturer in order that he may choose one suitable for his purpose. Only denatured alcohols containing obnoxious mixtures that are difficult to remove may be sold to the general public without payment of tax. On January 1, 1940, the price of tax-free denatured alcohol was 31 cents per gallon, compared with \$4.55 per gallon for taxed grain alcohol; on January 1, 1950, the prices were 31 cents and \$17.39 respectively. The difference in each case is approximately the tax per gallon. The United States tax is based on "100 U. S. proof" alcohol, which contains half of its volume of absolute alcohol. Since there is a contraction in volume on mixing alcohol and water, one volume of proof spirits contains 0.537 volumes of water. Proof spirits is 42.5 per cent alcohol by weight. Ordinary so-called 95 per cent alcohol is 190 proof. The term **proof spirit** has its origin in an old method of testing whiskey by pouring it on some gunpowder and lighting it. Ignition of the gunpowder after the alcohol burned away was considered proof that the whiskey did not contain too much water.

Production in 1939 was 100 million gallons but rose to 606 million gallons in 1944. In 1948 it was 185 million gallons. The sharp rise during World War II was due to its use for the synthesis of butadiene for the manufacture of synthetic rubber (p. 500). This use required about 55 per cent of the total production. In 1948 about 40 per cent was used for the synthesis of acetaldehyde (p. 179), 15 per cent for the synthesis of other chemicals, 19 per cent as radiator antifreeze, and 26 per cent for solvent and other purposes.

Higher Alcohols. Previous to World War I the chief source of higher alcohols was fusel oil from which *n*-propyl, *i*-butyl, *i*-amyl, and active amyl alcohols were separated by distillation (p. 67). Since then many other alcohols have become available. **n-Butyl alcohol** is made by a special bacterial fermentation process. Corn mash or black-strap molasses is inoculated with a pure culture of *Clostridium acetobutylicum* in closed tanks under anaerobic conditions. The products of fermentation from corn mash are *n*-butyl alcohol, acetone, and ethyl alcohol in the ratio 6:3:1. The strains of the organism capable of fermenting molasses yield about three times as much butyl alcohol as acetone. The evolved gas contains hydrogen and carbon dioxide. The process was developed during World War I as a source of acetone when the supply from the decomposition of calcium acetate from pyroligneous acid was insufficient to meet the requirements of the British for the production of cordite (p. 300). At that time there was no large-scale use for *n*-butyl alcohol, and huge stocks accumulated. Since then uses for *n*-butyl alcohol have been developed, and now it is the most valuable product, and acetone has become the by-product. *n*-Butyl alcohol also is manufactured by a synthetic process starting with acetaldehyde (p. 179). The chief uses of *n*-butyl alcohol are as a solvent, for the manufacture of esters (p. 148), and for the synthesis of *n*-butyraldehyde (p. 180) and *n*-butyric acid (p. 135).

Secondary and tertiary alcohols are manufactured on a large scale from the lower olefins obtained by the cracking of saturated hydrocarbons.

$$CH_3CH{=}CH_2 \xrightarrow{H_2SO_4} CH_3\underset{OSO_3H}{CH}CH_3 \xrightarrow{H_2O} CH_3\underset{OH}{CH}CH_3$$

Propylene   *i*-Propyl alcohol

$$CH_3CH{=}CHCH_3 \text{ (2-Butene)} \text{ and } CH_3CH_2CH{=}CH_2 \text{ (1-Butene)} \xrightarrow{H_2SO_4} CH_3CH_2\underset{OSO_3H}{CH}CH_3 \xrightarrow{H_2O} CH_3CH_2\underset{OH}{CH}CH_3$$

s-Butyl alcohol

$$(CH_3)_2C{=}CH_2 \xrightarrow{H_2SO_4} (CH_3)_2CCH_3 \xrightarrow{H_2O} (CH_3)_3COH$$

Isobutylene $\qquad\qquad$ $\underset{OSO_3H}{|}$ $\qquad$ *t*-Butyl
$\qquad\qquad\qquad\qquad\qquad\qquad\qquad\qquad$ alcohol

Similarly amylenes (pentenes) are converted into secondary and tertiary amyl alcohols. Some of the higher alcohols are obtained also as co-products of methanol synthesis (p. 66), the Fischer-Tropsch synthesis (p. 56), and the controlled air oxidation of natural gas (p. 56). Other methods for synthesizing alcohols are considered after the structures of the compounds from which they are derived have been discussed (pp. 82, 129, 147, 163, 164).

Chemical Properties

From a structural viewpoint an alcohol may be considered as derived from a water molecule by replacement of a hydrogen atom by an alkyl group. Since both contain a hydroxyl group, alcohols would be expected to undergo reactions analogous to those of water, and in many respects this is true.

1. *Formation of Complexes with Metallic Salts.* Alcohols resemble water in that they associate readily, as evidenced by their abnormally high boiling points. Just as water forms hydrates of inorganic salts, alcohols form complexes which might be called alcoholates. Corresponding to $MgCl_2 \cdot 6\ H_2O$ there exist the molecular complexes, $MgCl_2 \cdot 6\ CH_3OH$ and $MgCl_2 \cdot 6\ C_2H_5OH$. Although calcium chloride forms a hexahydrate, the reported complexes with methyl and ethyl alcohols have the composition, $CaCl_2 \cdot 4\ CH_3OH$ and $CaCl_2 \cdot 3\ C_2H_5OH$. Some salts which form hydrates, for example anhydrous calcium sulfate, do not form complexes with alcohols.

In general salts are not as soluble in alcohols as in water, because alcohols have a much lower dielectric constant (methyl alcohol = 34, water = 81) (p. 63). Where a salt such as calcium chloride is highly soluble in alcohols, a definite coordination complex with the alcohol takes place.

2. *Oxonium Salt Formation.* It is well known that when a strong acid is dissolved in water, there is practically complete transfer of the proton from the acid radical to the water molecule as illustrated by the following equation.

$$
\overset{\cdot\cdot}{\underset{\cdot\cdot}{H\!:\!O\!:}} \overset{H}{\vphantom{|}} + H\!:\!\overset{\cdot\cdot}{\underset{\cdot\cdot}{Cl}}\!: \longrightarrow \left[\overset{H}{\underset{\underset{+}{\cdot\cdot}}{H\!:\!O\!:\!H}} \right] \left[\overset{\cdot\cdot}{\underset{\cdot\cdot}{:Cl\bar{:}}} \right]
$$

The product from hydrogen chloride is called *hydronium chloride*, and the $[H_3O^+]$ ion is the *hydronium ion*. The explanation of this reaction is that the negative charge on the larger chlorine atom is more diffuse than that on the oxygen atom. Hence the proton can form a more stable bond with the water molecule than with a chloride ion. The relative ability to combine with a proton or an electron-deficient molecule is called the *basicity* of a group, and the proton is transferred to a water molecule because the water molecule is a stronger base than the chloride ion.

Alcohols also are stronger bases than the anions of strong acids. Hence alcohols will dissolve in strong acids with the formation of alkonium salts.

$$\begin{array}{c} H \\ \cdot\cdot \\ R:O: \ + H:\overset{\cdot\cdot}{\underset{\cdot\cdot}{Cl}}: \ \longrightarrow \\ \cdot\cdot \end{array} \left[\begin{array}{c} H \\ \cdot\cdot \\ R:O:H \\ \cdot\cdot \\ + \end{array}\right] \left[\begin{array}{c} \cdot\cdot \\ :\overset{\cdot\cdot}{Cl}: ^- \\ \cdot\cdot \end{array}\right]$$

The general term for this type of compound is *oxonium salt*. Concentrated sulfuric acid will dissolve practically all organic compounds containing oxygen, frequently without chemical change other than salt formation. This fact is used in qualitative organic analysis *to distinguish alcohols from saturated hydrocarbons.*

Alcohols and all other oxygen-containing compounds are more soluble in aqueous solutions of strong acids than in water because of the competition of alcohol and water molecules for the proton.

$$\begin{array}{c} H \\ \cdot\cdot \\ R:O: \ + \\ \cdot\cdot \end{array} \left[\begin{array}{c} H \\ \cdot\cdot \\ H:O:H \\ \cdot\cdot \\ + \end{array}\right] \rightleftarrows \left[\begin{array}{c} H \\ \cdot\cdot \\ R:O:H \\ \cdot\cdot \\ + \end{array}\right] + H_2O$$

n-Butyl alcohol is miscible with concentrated aqueous hydrochloric acid although it is soluble only to the extent of 8 per cent in water.

Oxonium salt formation differs from proton bonding, since in the latter the proton bonds two molecules together by electrostatic attraction, whereas in the former a proton is transferred completely from one molecule to another, the proton being completely engulfed in the electron shell of the new molecule and carrying a positive charge with it. Alcohols are more soluble in aqueous acids than in water because the charged oxonium ions are considerably more heavily hydrated than the alcohol molecule, which is dependent primarily on proton bonding for hydration. Since the heavier hydration of the oxonium salts can overcome greater van der Waals forces, alcohols of higher molecular weight will dissolve.

3. *Reaction with Metals.* Just as water reacts with metallic sodium to give hydrogen and sodium hydroxide, the alcohols react with sodium to give hydrogen and sodium alkoxide.

$$HOH + Na \longrightarrow \qquad H\overset{-}{O}\ \overset{+}{Na} \qquad + \tfrac{1}{2} H_2$$
Sodium hydroxide

$$CH_3OH + Na \longrightarrow \qquad CH_3\overset{-}{O}\ \overset{+}{Na} \qquad + \tfrac{1}{2} H_2$$
Sodium methoxide

$$ROH + Na \longrightarrow \qquad R\overset{-}{O}\ \overset{+}{Na} \qquad + \tfrac{1}{2} H_2$$
Sodium alkoxide

In these equations the ionic bond between the sodium atom and the hydroxyl, methoxyl, and alkoxyl groups is indicated by (+) and (−) signs. Usually ionic bonds will not be indicated for inorganic salts, because it is assumed that the reader understands that inorganic salts are completely ionized and that although the formula is written NaOH, for example, two types of bonds are involved, the ionic bond between sodium and the hydroxyl group and the covalent bond between the hydrogen atom and the oxygen atom. Also it is assumed that the reader understands that the molecule represented by the formula CH_3OH involves only covalent bonds. However when an organic molecule contains both ionic and covalent bonds, the presence of the ionic bond frequently will be emphasized by indicating the ionic bond with (+) and (−) charges.

Proton transfer reactions frequently will be indicated merely by the symbol [H$^+$] without designating the base with which the proton is associated. Thus the formation of an oxonium salt may be written

$$
\begin{array}{c}
\text{H} \\
\cdot\cdot \\
\text{R} : \text{O} : \\
\cdot\cdot
\end{array}
+ [\text{H}^+] \longrightarrow
\left[
\begin{array}{c}
\text{H} \\
\cdot\cdot \\
\text{R} : \text{O} : \text{H} \\
\cdot\cdot \\
+
\end{array}
\right]
$$

If anhydrous hydrogen chloride is used, [H$^+$] stands for HCl; if an aqueous solution of hydrogen chloride is used, [H$^+$] stands for [H$_3$O$^+$]. If a stronger base than an alcohol is being neutralized with an alcoholic solution of hydrogen chloride [H$^+$] stands for [ROH$_2^+$]. An objection to the use of the symbol [H$^+$] is that it represents a proton, and free protons under ordinary conditions are nonexistent. In organic reactions, however, where a number of bases may be involved, there usually is no point in trying to indicate the base with which the proton is associated.

The reaction with alcohols is slower than with water and decreases with increasing molecular weight of the alcohol.

If a small piece of sodium is dropped into a beaker containing water at room temperature, the reaction is so vigorous that the hydrogen formed bursts into flame; if dropped into methyl alcohol, the reaction is vigorous, but no ignition takes place; if dropped into n-butyl alcohol, only a slow evolution of hydrogen is observed. The decrease in rate probably is caused more by the decrease in solubility of the alkoxide in the alcohol and by the slower rate of diffusion of the ions away from the metal surface in the more viscous medium with resultant coating of the surface of the sodium, than by a decrease in the chemical reactivity of the alcohol.

The reaction product of methyl alcohol with sodium is known as *sodium methoxide*. The term *sodium methylate* also is used but is less satisfactory, since the term alcoholate frequently is used for complexes with inorganic salts analogous to the hydrates.

Other active metals also react at elevated temperatures. For example anhydrous methyl alcohol reacts with magnesium to give hydrogen and magnesium methoxide, Mg(OCH$_3$)$_2$, and amalgamated aluminum reacts with ethyl alcohol, *i*-propyl alcohol, or *t*-butyl alcohol, to give respectively aluminum ethoxide, Al(OC$_2$H$_5$)$_3$, *i*-propoxide, Al(OC$_3$H$_7$-*i*)$_3$, or *t*-butoxide, Al(OC$_4$H$_9$-*t*)$_3$. Since in all cases only one hydrogen atom per mole of alcohol is liberated, this reaction shows that one hydrogen is different from all the rest and must be linked to oxygen.

The reason that hydrogen united to carbon ordinarily is not displaced by metallic sodium is the same as the reason that hydrogen united to carbon does not form proton bonds, namely that the carbon-hydrogen bond is almost completely covalent. The rate of displacement of hydrogen may be greatly increased by the presence of other groups which make the carbon-hydrogen bond more nearly ionic (pp. 111, 174, 202).

Metallic alkoxides are hydrolyzed almost completely by water indicating that alcohols are considerably weaker acids than water.

$$\text{RONa} + \text{H}_2\text{O} \rightleftharpoons \text{ROH} + \text{NaOH}$$

Nevertheless sufficient water and sodium ethoxide are in equilibrium with the alcohol and sodium hydroxide to prevent the formation of completely anhydrous alcohol by treating moist alcohol with metallic sodium. Moreover the reaction can be reversed by removing water by azeotropic distillation with benzene. This method is used commercially to make sodium ethoxide from ethyl alcohol and sodium hydroxide.

   4. **Reaction with Inorganic Acid Halides.** Another typical reaction of water is with inorganic acid halides to give halogen acid and a second inorganic acid.

$$3 \text{ HOH} + \text{PCl}_3 \longrightarrow 3 \text{ HCl} + \text{P(OH)}_3 \tag{1}$$

The alcohols not only behave similarly but react in two different ways. In the above equation the water molecule may split between the oxygen atom and either hydrogen atom. Hydrogen and hydroxyl result in both cases. With alcohol molecules, however, hydrogen and alkoxyl would be obtained in one case and hydroxyl and alkyl in the other. Hence two different reactions may occur.

$$3 \text{ ROH} + \text{PCl}_3 \longrightarrow 3 \text{ HCl} + \text{P(OR)}_3 \tag{2}$$

$$3 \text{ ROH} + \text{PCl}_3 \longrightarrow 3 \text{ RCl} + \text{P(OH)}_3 \tag{3}$$

The relative proportion of reactions 2 and 3 depends on the conditions and the reagent. Phosphorus trichloride with primary alcohols at room temperature gives mostly reaction 2, but phosphorus tribromide at 0° gives mostly reaction 3. Tertiary alcohols invariably give reaction 3, whereas secondary alcohols undergo both reactions simultaneously.

   Compounds of the type P(OR)₃ are *alkyl esters of phosphorous acid* and are named like salts. For example P(OC₂H₅)₃ is *ethyl phosphite.* Compounds of the type RCl are called *alkyl chlorides,* the terminology being carried over from that of salts. They may be considered also as derivatives of hydrocarbons. Thus CH₃CHClCH₃ is called either *i*-propyl chloride or 2-chloropropane.

   The reactions with phosphorus halides are a further chemical proof that the alcohols contain a hydroxyl group, because it appears in phosphorous acid in reaction 3. Since only one mole of hydrogen chloride is obtained from each mole of alcohol in reaction 2, one hydrogen atom in an alcohol must be linked differently than all the rest.

   Other inorganic acid chlorides, for example thionyl chloride, react like phosphorus trichloride.

$$\text{HOH} + \text{SOCl}_2 \longrightarrow 2 \text{ HCl} + \text{SO}_2 \tag{4}$$

$$2 \text{ ROH} + \text{SOCl}_2 \longrightarrow 2 \text{ HCl} + \text{SO(OR)}_2 \tag{5}$$

$$\text{ROH} + \text{SOCl}_2 \longrightarrow \text{ HCl} + \text{RCl} + \text{SO}_2 \tag{6}$$

Here also primary alcohols give chiefly esters (alkyl sulfites, reaction 5), whereas tertiary alcohols give alkyl chlorides (reaction 6).

   5. **Reaction with Inorganic Acids.** Inorganic acids in general react with alcohols with the elimination of water. The products of reaction with halogen acids are alkyl halides.

$$\text{ROH} + \text{HX} \longrightarrow \text{RX} + \text{H}_2\text{O}$$

The rate of this reaction varies with the acid and with the type of alcohol. The order for halogen acids is hydrogen iodide > hydrogen bromide > hydrogen chloride > hydrogen fluoride. The order for the alcohols is tertiary > secondary > primary.

Methyl and *i*-butyl alcohol appear to be exceptions to this rule. In a study of the rate of reaction of alcohols with hydrogen bromide in the presence of water, methyl alcohol reacted as rapidly as *s*-butyl alcohol and more rapidly than *i*-propyl alcohol. It is known that in general methyl derivatives are much more reactive than ethyl and higher alkyl derivatives. *i*-Butyl alcohol reacted at about one tenth of the rate for normal primary alcohols. The nonreactivity of other *i*-butyl derivatives also has been noted (p. 96).

In practice conditions are chosen suitable for the particular compound being prepared. Primary alcohols will react even with aqueous solutions of hydrogen iodide but usually require anhydrous hydrogen bromide or aqueous hydrogen bromide and sulfuric acid. They react with hydrochloric acid at a practical rate only with hot concentrated solutions and zinc chloride as a catalyst. Tertiary alcohols on the other hand react with concentrated aqueous solutions of hydrochloric acid at room temperature.

The *Lucas test* for **distinguishing between primary, secondary, and tertiary alcohols** is based on their relative rates of reaction with hydrogen chloride. The reagent is a solution of zinc chloride in concentrated hydrochloric acid. The lower alcohols all dissolve in this reagent because of oxonium salt formation (p. 71), but the alkyl chlorides are insoluble. Tertiary alcohols react so rapidly that it is difficult to detect solution, the chloride separating immediately. Secondary alcohols give a clear solution at first which becomes cloudy within five minutes with eventual separation into two layers. Primary alcohols dissolve, and the solution remains clear for several hours.

Some oxygen-containing inorganic acids react with alcohols to form alkyl esters in which the alkyl group is linked to the acid radical through oxygen.

$$\text{ROH} + \text{HONO} \longrightarrow \underset{\text{Alkyl nitrite}}{\text{RONO}} + \text{H}_2\text{O} \qquad (7)$$

$$\text{ROH} + \text{HONO}_2 \longrightarrow \underset{\text{Alkyl nitrate}}{\text{RONO}_2} + \text{H}_2\text{O} \qquad (8)$$

$$\text{ROH} + \text{H}_2\text{SO}_4 \longrightarrow \underset{\substack{\text{Alkyl hydrogen}\\\text{sulfate}}}{\text{ROSO}_3\text{H}} + \text{H}_2\text{O} \qquad (9)$$

$$\text{ROH} + \text{HOSO}_2\text{OR} \longrightarrow \underset{\text{Alkyl sulfate}}{\text{ROSO}_2\text{OR}} + \text{H}_2\text{O} \qquad (10)$$

In contrast to hydrochloric acid, these acids react rapidly with the primary alcohols. Esters of tertiary alcohols have not been prepared by the direct action of strong mineral acids, probably because of easy dehydration to the olefin.

6. **Dehydration to Olefins.** If the alcohol is volatile, it can be dehydrated most conveniently by passing the vapors through a hot tube packed with activated alumina.[8]

$$\text{RCHOHCH}_2\text{R} \xrightarrow[350°-450°]{\text{Al}_2\text{O}_3} \text{RCH}{=}\text{CHR} + \text{H}_2\text{O}$$

---

[8] Some forms of solid catalysts are more effective than others. When prepared in such a way that they have the maximum activity, they are called *activated* catalysts. Activated alumina has an optimum porosity or surface structure, and an optimum amount of adsorbed water or water of constitution.

By using pure alumina, molecular rearrangements which frequently take place when acid catalysts are used are largely avoided.

When sulfuric acid is used as a catalyst, it usually is assumed that the alkyl hydrogen sulfate is an intermediate in the reaction.

$$\text{RCHOHCH}_2\text{R} + \text{H}_2\text{SO}_4 \longrightarrow \underset{\overset{|}{\text{OSO}_3\text{H}}}{\text{RCHCH}_2\text{R}} \overset{\text{Heat}}{\longrightarrow} \text{RCH}{=}\text{CHR} + \text{H}_2\text{SO}_4$$

If the boiling point of the alcohol is lower than the temperature of decomposition, it is necessary to use sufficient acid to convert all of the alcohol into the nonvolatile alkyl hydrogen sulfate or the oxonium salt. The process may be made catalytic and continuous by passing the alcohol vapors over pumice impregnated with sulfuric or phosphoric acid and heated to the required temperature.

Although the dehydration of alcohols to olefins in the presence of sulfuric acid usually is indicated as proceeding by way of an intermediate alkyl hydrogen sulfate, and although the formation of alkyl hydrogen sulfates takes place readily at room temperature, other acids such as sulfonic acids that do not esterify readily and nonesterifiable electron-seeking reagents such as zinc chloride also catalyze the dehydration. It appears that the essential step is the formation of the oxonium salt followed by simultaneous loss of water and removal of a proton (p. 100).

The relative ease of dehydration of alcohols is tertiary > secondary > primary. Tertiary alcohols dehydrate so readily that mostly olefin is formed when attempts are made to carry out other reactions in the presence of strong acids. The relative ease with which the hydrogen atom is removed also is tertiary > secondary > primary. Thus the dehydration of *s*-butyl alcohol gives almost exclusively 2-butene.

$$\text{CH}_3\text{CH}_2\text{CHOHCH}_3 \longrightarrow \text{CH}_3\text{CH}{=}\text{CHCH}_3 + \text{H}_2\text{O}$$

Dehydration of alcohols in the presence of strong acids frequently does not yield the expected product. For example when *n*-butyl alcohol is dehydrated in the presence of sulfuric acid, the chief product is 2-butene instead of the expected 1-butene.

$$\text{CH}_3\text{CH}_2\text{CH}_2\text{CH}_2\text{OH} \underset{\text{heat}}{\overset{\text{H}_2\text{SO}_4}{\longrightarrow}} \text{CH}_3\text{CH}{=}\text{CHCH}_3 + \text{H}_2\text{O}$$

This phenomenon, which will be encountered from time to time, is known as **molecular rearrangement**. The rearrangement can be explained by a series of equilibria.

$$\text{CH}_3\text{CH}_2\text{CH}_2\text{CH}_2\text{OH} + \text{H}_2\text{SO}_4 \rightleftarrows \text{CH}_3\text{CH}_2\text{CH}_2\text{CH}_2\text{OSO}_3\text{H} + \text{H}_2\text{O}$$

$$\text{CH}_3\text{CH}_2\text{CH}_2\text{CH}_2\text{OSO}_3\text{H} \rightleftarrows \text{CH}_3\text{CH}_2\text{CH}{=}\text{CH}_2 + \text{H}_2\text{SO}_4$$

$$\text{CH}_3\text{CH}_2\text{CH}{=}\text{CH}_2 + \text{H}_2\text{SO}_4 \rightleftarrows \underset{\overset{|}{\text{OSO}_3\text{H}}}{\text{CH}_3\text{CH}_2\text{CHCH}_3}$$

$$\underset{\overset{|}{\text{OSO}_3\text{H}}}{\text{CH}_3\text{CH}_2\text{CHCH}_3} \rightleftarrows \text{CH}_3\text{CH}{=}\text{CHCH}_3 + \text{H}_2\text{SO}_4$$

The chief product of the reaction is 2-butene because it is thermodynamically more stable than 1-butene. Actually it is not necessary that the intermediate esters be formed since the ionic intermediates of the reaction may undergo rearrangement (p. 100).

Sometimes molecular rearrangement involves also the migration of alkyl groups. For example if methyl-*t*-butylcarbinol is dehydrated in the presence of acids, very little of the expected *t*-butylethylene is formed, the chief products being the result of molecular rearrangement.

$$(CH_3)_2C=C(CH_3)_2 \qquad\qquad 61 \text{ per cent}$$

$$(CH_3)_3CCHCH_3 \xrightarrow[\text{heat}]{H_2SO_4} (CH_3)_2CHC=CH_2 \qquad 31 \text{ per cent}$$
$$\underset{OH}{|} \qquad\qquad\qquad \underset{CH_3}{|}$$

$$(CH_3)_3CCH=CH_2 \qquad\qquad 3 \text{ per cent}$$

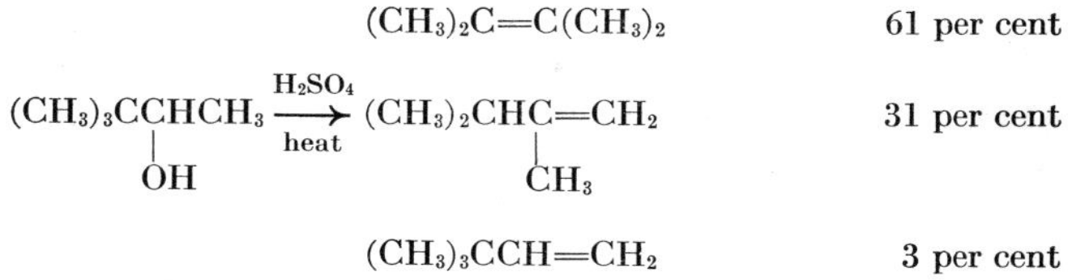

Alcohols may be dehydrated with the formation of olefins by molecular rearrangement when dehydration would not be expected to take place. Thus neopentyl alcohol yields trimethylethylene.

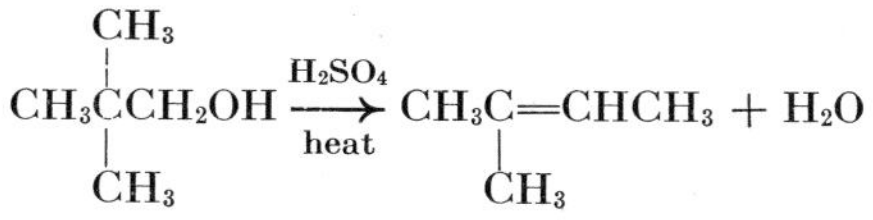

$$\underset{\underset{CH_3}{|}}{\overset{\overset{CH_3}{|}}{CH_3CCH_2OH}} \xrightarrow[\text{heat}]{H_2SO_4} \underset{\underset{CH_3}{|}}{CH_3C}=CHCH_3 + H_2O$$

Because of the possibility of molecular rearrangements, proof of structure should be based on degradative as well as synthetic reactions. The structures of the above olefins can be determined by ozonation, decomposition of the ozonides, and identification of the products (p. 40).

7. Dehydrogenation or Oxidation to Aldehydes and Ketones. Primary and secondary alcohols may be dehydrogenated to aldehydes and ketones respectively by passing the vapors over activated copper, copper-chromium, or copper-nickel catalyst at 300°–325°.

$$RCH_2OH \underset{300°-325°}{\overset{Cu}{\rightleftarrows}} \overset{\overset{H}{|}}{RC}=O + H_2$$
An aldehyde

$$R_2CHOH \underset{300°-325°}{\overset{Cu}{\rightleftarrows}} R_2C=O + H_2$$
A ketone

If air is used along with the alcohol, the hydrogen is converted into water and the reaction goes to completion.

$$RCH_2OH + O_2 \xrightarrow[400°-600°]{Cu \text{ or } Ag} RCHO + H_2O$$

$$R_2CHOH + O_2 \xrightarrow[400°-600°]{Cu \text{ or } Ag} R_2CO + H_2O$$

Tertiary alcohols, which do not have a hydrogen atom on the carbon atom united to the hydroxyl group, do not undergo this reaction but may dehydrate if the temperature is sufficiently high.

The same type of dehydrogenation can be brought about by chemical oxidizing agents. The reagent most commonly employed is dichromic acid in aqueous sulfuric acid (sodium dichromate and sulfuric acid), or chromic anhydride (chromium trioxide) dissolved in glacial acetic acid.

$$3 \text{ RCH}_2\text{OH} + \text{H}_2\text{Cr}_2\text{O}_7 + 3 \text{ H}_2\text{SO}_4 \longrightarrow 3 \text{ RCHO} + \text{Cr}_2(\text{SO}_4)_3 + 7 \text{ H}_2\text{O}$$

$$3 \text{ R}_2\text{CHOH} + 2 \text{ CrO}_3 + 6 \text{ HC}_2\text{H}_3\text{O}_2 \longrightarrow 3 \text{ R}_2\text{CO} + 2 \text{ Cr}(\text{C}_2\text{H}_3\text{O}_2)_3 + 6 \text{ H}_2\text{O}$$

The formation of aldehydes by this method is successful only if the aldehyde is removed rapidly from the oxidizing mixture by distillation; otherwise it is oxidized further to an organic acid (p. 172).

$$\text{RCHO} + [\text{O}] \longrightarrow \text{RCOOH}$$

Strong oxidizing agents such as hot dichromic acid or potassium permanganate may oxidize tertiary alcohols by breaking the carbon chain. The acids so produced always have fewer carbon atoms than the original alcohol.

$$\begin{matrix} \text{CH}_3 \\ | \\ \text{CH}_3\text{COH} \\ | \\ \text{CH}_3 \end{matrix} + 3 \text{ [O]} \longrightarrow \text{CH}_3\text{COCH}_3 + \text{HCOOH} + \text{H}_2\text{O}$$

Under such vigorous conditions these products undergo further oxidation.

$$\text{CH}_3\text{COCH}_3 + 3 \text{ [O]} \longrightarrow \text{CH}_3\text{COOH} + \text{HCOOH}$$

$$\text{HCOOH} + [\text{O}] \longrightarrow \text{CO}_2 + \text{H}_2\text{O}$$

The reactions of alcohols with organic compounds are discussed under the methods of preparation or the reactions of other organic compounds.

ESTERS OF INORGANIC ACIDS

Preparation

Esters of inorganic acids are produced by the reaction of alcohols with inorganic acid halides (reactions 2 and 5 on page 74), or with inorganic acids (reactions *7–10*, on page 75). **Sulfites, phosphites, phosphates, arsenites,** and **silicates** usually are prepared by the first method. Sometimes the sodium alkoxide is used in place of the alcohol to avoid the formation of hydrogen chloride.

$$3 \text{ RONa} + \text{POCl}_3 \longrightarrow (\text{RO})_3\text{PO} + 3 \text{ NaCl}$$

More frequently the alcohol is used together with the calculated amount of a tertiary amine such as pyridine (p. 454) to combine with the halogen acid that is liberated.

Nitrites, nitrates, methyl and **ethyl sulfates,** and **borates** are prepared directly from the alcohol and acid (p. 74). The alkyl nitrites are formed by passing oxides of nitrogen ($\text{NO} + \text{NO}_2 + \text{N}_2\text{O}_3$) into the alcohol, or by adding sulfuric acid to a mixture of the alcohol and an aqueous solution of sodium nitrite.

Properties

In esters the hydrocarbon group always is linked to the acid group through oxygen. Although the esters are named like salts, they are covalent compounds. The lower molecular weight esters are volatile liquids, whereas the higher esters can be distilled under reduced pressure. They are insoluble in water and soluble in organic solvents.

The esters are hydrolyzed by water with varying degrees of ease. Ethyl borate and ethyl silicate, for example, are hydrolyzed readily by water at room temperature.

$$(C_2H_5O)_3B + 3 H_2O \longrightarrow 3 C_2H_5OH + B(OH)_3$$

$$(C_2H_5O)_4Si + 4 H_2O \longrightarrow 4 C_2H_5OH + Si(OH)_4$$

One alkyl group of sulfates and phosphates is hydrolyzed much more readily than a second group. For example at 95° and low concentration the first methyl group of methyl sulfate is completely removed in 3 minutes, whereas only 25 per cent of the second methyl group is removed after 3 hours.

Ethyl nitrate and ethyl perchlorate are hydrolyzed only very slowly by water even at elevated temperatures. Care should be exercised in handling these compounds as they decompose explosively. It is stated that ethyl perchlorate in the anhydrous condition explodes on pouring from one vessel to another.

Uses

Nitrites relax the smooth muscles of the body and produce a rapid lowering of the blood pressure. *i*-**Amyl nitrite** is used for the relief of pain in acute angina pectoris although the normal brevity of the attacks in the absence of medication makes it difficult to determine whether amyl nitrite actually assists in the relief of pain. **Ethyl, butyl,** and *i***-amyl nitrites** are used extensively as a source of nitrous acid in organic reactions when it is necessary or desirable to carry the reaction out in an anhydrous solvent (p. 376). The *sulfites*, *sulfates*, and *phosphates* find important use as alkylating agents, that is as reagents for the introduction of alkyl groups (pp. 115, 382). **Methyl sulfate,** which is used extensively as a methylating agent, is highly toxic and care must be exercised to avoid exposure to its vapors.

When ethyl phosphate reacts with phosphorus oxychloride, a product is obtained which is an effective insecticide, particularly against plant aphids and mites. This material is a mixture of substances of which the active constituent appears to be **ethyl pyrophosphate,** $(C_2H_5O)_4P_2O_3$. Although highly toxic to animals, it hydrolyzes rapidly to harmless phosphoric acid and ethyl alcohol when exposed to moist air. The ready hydrolysis of **ethyl silicate** finds use for the preparation of colloidal solutions of silicic acid and for depositing on porous material films of silicic acid which subsequently dehydrate to silica. Again this chemical must be handled with care, since the vapors cause opacity of the cornea.

REVIEW QUESTIONS

1. What steps are necessary to establish the molecular formula of methyl alcohol? What are the arguments based on the theory of chemical bonding for assigning the structure, CH_3OH? What chemical evidence shows that one hydrogen atom is different from the other three and that a hydroxyl group is present?

2. Write condensed structural formulas for all of the isomeric alcohols having the molecular formula $C_5H_{12}O$ and name as derivatives of carbinol and by the Geneva (I.U.C.) system. Indicate by the Roman numerals I, II, or III, whether the above alcohols are primary, secondary, or tertiary.

3. Write the formulas for all of the alkyl groups that can be derived from the three isomeric pentanes and place them into three divisions according to whether they are primary, secondary, or tertiary.

4. What is the formula for *n*-amyl alcohol; *i*-butyl alcohol; neopentyl alcohol; active amyl alcohol; 4,5-dimethyl-4-ethyl-2-hexanol?

5. Tell why each of the following names is unsatisfactory and give an acceptable name: isopropanol; (1-methylpropyl)carbinol; methyl ethyl carbinol; 2-methylpentanol-1; *s*-butylalcohol?

6. State the conditions necessary for proton bond (hydrogen bond) formation and give an example.

7. Why might methane and water be expected to have nearly the same boiling points? Give and explain the actual facts.

8. Compare the boiling points of alcohols with those of the saturated hydrocarbons having approximately the same molecular weight and explain the differences.

9. Discuss and explain the solubility behavior of hydrocarbons and of alcohols in water.

10. Give reactions illustrating the preparation of the following alcohols from suitable olefins: *i*-propyl alcohol; *t*-butyl alcohol; *s*-butyl alcohol; *t*-amyl alcohol. Why is ethyl alcohol the only primary alcohol obtainable from olefins?

11. Give balanced equations for three reactions suitable for converting *s*-butyl alcohol into *s*-butyl chloride.

12. What is the relative order of reactivity of primary, secondary, and tertiary alcohols (*a*) with hydrochloric acid and zinc chloride, (*b*) with phosphorus trichloride to give phosphorous esters, (*c*) with phosphorus trichloride to give alkyl chlorides, and (*d*) when dehydrated?

13. What is the relative reactivity of hydrochloric, hydrobromic, and hydroiodic acid with primary alcohols?

14. Give balanced equations for preparing from an alcohol (*a*) an aldehyde, (*b*) the ester of an inorganic acid, (*c*) an alkoxide, and (*d*) an alkene.

15. Describe the Lucas test for distinguishing between primary, secondary, and tertiary alcohols.

16. What would be the chief product formed by the dehydration of the following alcohols by means of sulfuric acid: 2-pentanol; 2-methyl-3-pentanol; 1-butanol?

17. Give equations for the conversion of *n*-propyl alcohol into *i*-propyl alcohol; of *i*-propyl alcohol into 1-chloro-2-propanol.

18. Discuss briefly (*a*) the destructive distillation of wood, (*b*) synthetic methanol, (*c*) production of ethyl alcohol by fermentation, and (*d*) the anaerobic fermentation of starch with *Clostridium acetobutylicum*.

19. What is fusel oil and what are its chief components?

20. What is absolute alcohol and how is it prepared? Why is it not possible to prepare it by simple distillation?

21. Give equations for the reaction of (*a*) ethyl alcohol and phosphorus oxychloride; (*b*) ethyl nitrite and aqueous sodium hydroxide; (*c*) ethyl nitrite and dry hydrogen chloride; (*d*) *i*-amyl alcohol and nitrous acid; (*e*) ethyl alcohol and boric anhydride, B_2O_3; (*f*) ethyl alcohol and silicon tetrachloride.

Chapter 6

ALKYL HALIDES. GRIGNARD REAGENTS

ALKYL HALIDES

Alkyl halides are important intermediates for the synthesis of other compounds. Not only do they undergo a variety of reactions, but they are prepared readily in good yields.

Preparation

Alkyl halides are formed when alcohols react with either inorganic acid halides or with hydrogen halides under appropriate conditions (p. 74). These two procedures are the most satisfactory general methods of preparation, although the addition of hydrogen halides to olefins (p. 42) and the direct halogenation of saturated hydrocarbons (p. 84) also may be used. Primary alkyl iodides may be made from primary alkyl chlorides and bromides by the reaction of sodium iodide in acetone solution.

$$RCH_2Cl + NaI \longrightarrow RCH_2I + NaCl$$

The reaction of secondary and tertiary chlorides and bromides is too slow to be practical. Isobutyl chloride is exceptional in that its rate of reaction is too slow to be measurable, in spite of the fact that it is a primary halide (p. 96).

Structure and Nomenclature

The methods of formation from alcohols leave no question as to the structure of the alkyl halides. They usually are named as if they were salts of halogen acids. They may be considered also as halogen derivatives of saturated hydrocarbons and often are so named. Thus ethyl chloride may be called *chloroethane*, and isobutyl bromide may be called *1-bromo-2-methylpropane*.

Physical Properties

In physical properties the alkyl halides resemble the saturated hydrocarbons. They are insoluble in water and are good solvents for most organic compounds. The boiling points of the chlorides are of the same order of magnitude as those of hydrocarbons of the same molecular weight, whereas bromides boil about 60° lower than chlorides, and iodides 70° lower than bromides, again comparing compounds of the same molecular weight (Table 7, p. 82).

The reason for the decrease in boiling points of bromides compared with chlorides, and of iodides compared with bromides probably is the same as the reason for lowering of boiling point with branching of the hydrocarbon chain, since the increase in size of the atom from chlorine to bromine to iodine would be expected to have much the same effect as branching in decreasing the van der Waals forces between the molecules.

Alkyl halides are more dense than hydrocarbons. The densities of the compounds considered so far increase in the order hydrocarbons < alcohols < alkyl chlorides < bromides < iodides, if compounds with the same number of

TABLE 7

COMPARISON OF THE BOILING POINTS OF *n*-ALKANES WITH THOSE OF *n*-ALKYL CHLORIDES, BROMIDES, IODIDES, AND ALCOHOLS OF SIMILAR MOLECULAR WEIGHT

ALKANES			CHLORIDES			BROMIDES			IODIDES			ALCOHOLS		
	Mol. wt.	B.p.		Mol. wt.	B.p.		Mol. wt.	B.p.		Mol. wt.	B.p.		Mol. wt.	B.p.
C_3	44	−45	C_1	51	−24							C_2	46	78
C_4	58	+0.6	C_2	65	+13							C_3	60	97
C_5	72	36	C_3	78	46							C_4	74	118
C_6	86	69	C_4	93	78	C_1	94	5				C_5	88	138
C_7	100	98	C_5	107	108	C_2	108	38				C_6	102	157
C_8	114	126	C_6	121	133	C_3	123	71				C_7	116	177
C_9	128	150	C_7	135	157	C_4	137	102				C_8	130	195
C_{10}	142	174	C_8	149	183	C_5	151	130	C_1	142	42	C_9	144	213
C_{11}	156	194	C_9	163	190	C_6	165	156	C_2	156	75	C_{10}	158	231
C_{12}	170	214	C_{10}	177	223	C_7	179	178	C_3	170	103	C_{11}	172	248

carbon atoms are compared. The density of hydrocarbons increases with increasing length of chain because of the increasing van der Waals forces, but because the hydrocarbon portion of other homologous series is less dense than the usual functional groups, increasing the size of the alkyl group causes a decrease in density.

Reactions

The importance of the alkyl halides lies in the great variety of reactions which they undergo. In all of these reactions, the halogen is removed or replaced by another group. Some of the more important reactions for primary and secondary halides are illustrated by the following equations.

$$RX + AgOH \text{ (or aqueous NaOH)} \longrightarrow ROH \text{ (An alcohol)} + AgX \text{ (or NaX)} \tag{1}$$

$$RX + NaOR \longrightarrow ROR \text{ (An ether)} + NaX \tag{2}$$

$$RX + NaSH \longrightarrow RSH \text{ (A mercaptan, thioalcohol, or alkanethiol)} + NaX \tag{3}$$

$$2\,RX + Na_2S \longrightarrow R_2S \text{ (An alkyl sulfide)} + 2\,NaX \tag{4}$$

$$RX + NaCN \longrightarrow RCN \text{ (An alkyl cyanide)} + NaX \tag{5}$$

$$RX + NH_3 \longrightarrow RNH_3^+X^- \text{ (An alkylammonium halide (amine hydrohalide))} \tag{6}$$

$$RX + Mg \longrightarrow RMgX \text{ (An alkylmagnesium halide (Grignard reagent, p. 85))} \tag{7}$$

$$RX + Zn\text{--}Cu \text{ couple} \longrightarrow RZnX \quad (+ Cu) \qquad (8)$$

An alkylzinc
halide

$$2\,RX + 2\,Zn\text{--}Cu \text{ couple} \longrightarrow R_2Zn \quad (+ Cu) \qquad (9)$$

A dialkylzinc

$$2\,RX + 2\,Na \longrightarrow RR \quad + 2\,NaX \text{ (Wurtz synthesis, p. 106)} \, (10)$$

An alkane

$$RX + Zn + HX \longrightarrow RH \quad + ZnX_2 \qquad (11)$$

(in alcohol) An alkane

The reagents that react with an alkyl halide react even more readily with halogen acids. The reactions for the most part are identical in both cases except that a hydrogen atom takes the place of an alkyl group. For example silver hydroxide and halogen acid give water and silver halide, sodium sulfide gives hydrogen sulfide, sodium cyanide gives hydrogen cyanide, ammonia gives ammonium halide, and sodium gives hydrogen. The principal difference is that the reactions with alkyl halides are slow, whereas those with halogen acids are rapid.

Alkyl iodides react more rapidly than bromides, and bromides than chlorides. Since bromides are cheaper than iodides and usually are sufficiently reactive, they are used most frequently in the laboratory. The specific conditions for carrying out the above reactions and the limitations of the reactions are considered where the methods for preparing the various compounds formed in the reactions are discussed.

For the most part reactions *1* to *10* apply only to primary and secondary halides. Elimination of halogen acid from tertiary halides to form an olefin takes place so much more readily than the replacement of halogen by another group that in the presence of reagents that can react with halogen acids, olefin formation predominates, especially in nonaqueous solvents such as alcohol.

$$\underset{\underset{Cl}{|}}{R_2CHCR_2} + NaOH \longrightarrow R_2C{=}CR_2 + H_2O + NaCl$$

The other reagents behave in the same way. Sodium cyanide, for example, gives olefin, hydrogen cyanide, and sodium chloride. An exception is the reaction with magnesium to give Grignard reagents, but even here special conditions are necessary to obtain good yields with tertiary halides.

A second difference shown by tertiary halides is their easy hydrolysis to alcohols. This reaction is brought about by water alone, and the rate is not affected by either acids or bases.

$$R_3CX + H_2O \longrightarrow R_3COH + HX$$

The ease of removal of halogen acid and ease of hydrolysis with water decrease in the order tertiary > secondary > primary halides, whereas for most displacement reactions the reverse order holds. Hence primary halides give the best yields in reactions *1* to *10*.

Two different orders of activity have been encountered. The order primary > secondary > tertiary holds for the reaction of alcohols with acid halides to form esters (p. 74), and for most of the reactions of alkyl halides. The order tertiary > secondary > primary holds for the reaction of alcohols with acid halides or with halogen acids to give alkyl halides (pp. 74), for the dehydration of alcohols (p. 75), and for the dehydrohalogenation of alkyl halides. Differences in order must be ascribed to differences in mechanism of reaction, a topic considered in Chapter 7.

Alkyl Halides of Commercial Importance

It is evident from the variety of compounds obtainable from them that the alkyl halides are extremely important to the organic chemist for synthesis. Only a few of the simple halides are of industrial importance, however, since only a very small fraction of the known organic compounds are manufactured in large quantities. In the laboratory the chemist is most likely to use bromides or iodides because of their greater reactivity, but industrially the chlorides are used because of their lower cost. Many of the polyhalogen compounds are industrially important, and they are discussed in Chapter 33. **Methyl chloride,** b.p. $-24°$, is made by heating methyl alcohol with hydrochloric acid. It also is formed as one product of the reaction of chlorine with methane (p. 505). Its principal uses are as a refrigerant in mechanical refrigerators, as a low temperature solvent, and as a methylating agent in the preparation of methylcellulose (p. 303), silicones (p. 596), and other organic compounds. **Methyl bromide,** b.p. $4.5°$, is made from methyl alcohol and hydrogen bromide. It is highly toxic and is used as a poison gas for rodent control. It is toxic to other forms of life also and is used as a soil and grain fumigant. Its use in fire extinguishers probably depends on dissociation into free radicals (p. 94) which act as chain breakers and inhibit the propagation of flame. Because of its high toxicity to human beings, it should be used for this purpose only with proper precautions to prevent inhalation of the vapors. The same precautions should be taken when using methyl bromide in chemical reactions. **Ethyl chloride,** b.p. $13°$, is made either from ethyl alcohol and hydrochloric acid in the presence of zinc chloride, or by the addition of anhydrous hydrogen chloride to ethylene at low temperature in the liquid phase, using aluminum chloride or boron trichloride as a catalyst. It is used for the manufacture of tetraethyllead (p. 589) and of ethylcellulose (p. 302), and as a quick acting general anesthetic (footnote, p. 118) for minor operations.

The **amyl chlorides** are made by the direct substitution of the hydrogen atoms of *n*-pentane and *i*-pentane by halogen, a process known as *halogenation*.

$$C_5H_{12} + Cl_2 \longrightarrow C_5H_{11}Cl + HCl$$

This reaction of the hydrocarbons is of limited usefulness and hence was not discussed in Chapter 2. Fluorine reacts with the alkanes spontaneously and so rapidly that the reaction may be explosive. Most combustible compounds will burst into flame when a stream of fluorine is allowed to impinge upon them. Chlorine, bromine, and iodine do not react with alkanes in the dark at room temperature. Chlorine and bromine will react with hydrocarbons photochemically under the influence of light of short wavelength (250–500 mμ [1]) or thermally at high temperatures. The usefulness of the reaction is limited by

---

[1] The abbreviation mμ is used for millimicron, which is equal to 10^{-7} centimeter or 10 Ångstrom units.

the fact that it is not very selective. All types of hydrogen are attacked with almost equal ease, and the introduction of one halogen atom does not appreciably affect the replacement of a second hydrogen atom. The result is that a mixture of almost all of the possible monosubstitution products is obtained, and some polysubstitution products as well.

In the commercial chlorination of pentanes the reaction is carried out in the gas phase at 250°–300° using a volume ratio of pentane to chlorine of 15 to 1 in order to form chiefly monosubstitution products. Even at this ratio about 5 per cent of disubstitution products are formed. The rate of flow of the gases is about 60 miles per hour. This rate is faster than the rate of propagation of the chlorine-hydrocarbon flame, and the unreacted material behind the flame cannot explode. The relative amounts of the various isomers formed from *n*-pentane at 300° are 24 per cent 1-chloropentane, 49 per cent 2-chloropentane, and 27 per cent 3-chloropentane. From *i*-pentane there is obtained 33 per cent 1-chloro-2-methylbutane, 22 per cent 2-chloro-2-methylbutane, 17 per cent 1-chloro-3-methylbutane, and 28 per cent 2-chloro-3-methylbutane. Commercially the mixed monochlorides are hydrolyzed to mixed amyl alcohols (Pentasol). Reaction with ammonia gives amylamines, and with sodium hydrosulfide gives amyl mercaptans and amyl sulfides. It is possible to separate the mixtures by distillation, but for most uses separation is unnecessary.

Substitution Reactions

The direct replacement of hydrogen by a halogen atom or other monovalent group is known as **substitution** and is of considerable importance for other compounds as well as for the saturated hydrocarbons. Substitution of hydrogen by halogen was investigated first by Dumas after an episode at the Tuileries. On the occasion of a ball during the reign of Charles X of France, the guests were driven from the ballroom by choking fumes given off by the burning candles. Brongiart, the chemical advisor to the king, called in his son-in-law Dumas, who found that the candles had been bleached by a new process using chlorine. The bleaching had given rise to chlorinated fat acids, which on burning gave off hydrogen chloride. Dumas then made an extensive investigation of the substitution reaction. One of the *fundamental concepts of substitution and of all replacement reactions* is that the new atom or group takes the position formerly occupied by the replaced atom or group of atoms.

Substitution, chlorination, halogenation, and other terms for analogous reactions should be used only for the direct replacement of hydrogen. For example the reaction of an alcohol with hydrogen bromide should not be spoken of as the bromination of an alcohol or as a substitution reaction, but as the replacement of hydroxyl by bromine. Similarly the reaction of 2-butene and chlorine to give 2,3-dichlorobutane should not be called chlorination, but the addition of chlorine to 2-butene. Although these conventions may seem somewhat arbitrary, they must be observed if chemists are to understand each other without confusion.

GRIGNARD REAGENTS

Zinc or magnesium reacts with alkyl halides to give compounds in which the alkyl group is united to the metal. Such compounds are known as *organo-*

metallic compounds (p. 586). The organozinc compounds found use in early synthetic work but have the disadvantage that only methyl and ethyl iodides give good yields, and that even methylzinc and ethylzinc are difficult to use because they are spontaneously inflammable in air. In 1899 Barbier[2] announced that in many cases the alkylzincs could be replaced by a mixture of alkyl halide and magnesium in ether in the presence of the compound with which the reaction was to take place. This reaction was improved by Grignard,[3] a student of Barbier's, who reported in his doctoral dissertation in 1900 the separate preparation of alkylmagnesium halide solutions and their reaction with a variety of compounds. Subsequent work by Grignard and a large number of other investigators has shown that the use of alkylmagnesium halide solutions, now commonly known as *Grignard reagents*, is of more practical importance for the laboratory synthesis of organic compounds than is any other single synthetic method. The reaction has few commercial applications.

Preparation

Grignard reagents are made by the direct action of alkyl halides on magnesium turnings. Reaction takes place in the absence of a solvent but soon stops because the alkylmagnesium halide is a solid that is insoluble in alkyl halide and coats over the surface of the magnesium. In the presence of a solvent for the alkylmagnesium halide, the reaction goes to completion. Ether is the solvent most commonly used. Sometimes the reaction is slow to start. The drier the reagents and apparatus and the less oxide film on the surface of the magnesium, the easier the reaction starts. Usually a small crystal of iodine is added to initiate the reaction. Alkyl iodides react more readily than bromides, and bromides than chlorides, but the yields are in the reverse order, namely chlorides > bromides > iodides. The higher the dilution and the greater the purity and state of subdivision of the magnesium, the higher the yields.

Several **side reactions** account for decreased yield.

1. The halide may react at the surface of the magnesium in a manner analogous to the Wurtz reaction (p. 106).

$$2\,RX + Mg \longrightarrow RR + MgX_2$$

2. If the halogen is replaced readily, as with tertiary halides, excess halide may react with the Grignard reagent.

$$RMgX + RX \longrightarrow RR + MgX_2$$

3. Halogen acid may be removed, especially from tertiary halides, with the formation of alkene.

$$2\,R_2CHCXR_2 + Mg \longrightarrow 2\,R_2C{=}CR_2 + H_2 + MgX_2$$

---

[2] François Philippe Antoine Barbier (1848–1922), professor at the University of Lyon, France, who is known not only for his discovery of the usefulness of magnesium in organic synthesis but also for his work on the constitution of the terpenes. In his later years he was interested in mineralogy and the analysis of minerals.

[3] Victor Grignard (1871–1935), professor at the University of Nancy and later successor to Barbier at Lyon. He was awarded the Nobel Prize in Chemistry jointly with Paul Sabatier in 1912.

4. All halides in the presence of metallic impurities, especially copper, react with Grignard reagents with the formation of alkene and alkane, an intermolecular oxidation-reduction process known as disproportionation.

$$2 \, RCH_2CHXR + Mg \longrightarrow RCH{=}CHR + RCH_2CH_2R + MgX_2$$

Reactions

1. **With Reactive Hydrogen.** Grignard reagents react with all compounds that evolve hydrogen with alkali metals. The organic product is an alkane.

$$RMgX \begin{cases} + \text{HOH} \longrightarrow \\ + \text{HOR} \longrightarrow \\ + \text{HNH}_2 \longrightarrow \\ + \text{HX} \longrightarrow \end{cases} RH \begin{cases} + \text{Mg(OH)X} \\ + \text{Mg(OR)X} \\ + \text{Mg(NH}_2)X \\ + MgX_2 \end{cases}$$

For simplicity in balancing the equations, the inorganic products usually are written as the mixed compounds $Mg(OH)X$, $Mg(OR)X$, and $Mg(NH_2)X$. Since the molecules are ionic, it is more likely that the solid salts are mixtures of the various possible crystal species, including $Mg(OH)_2$, $Mg(OR)_2$, or $Mg(NH_2)_2$, and MgX_2. The reactivity of Grignard reagents with hydroxyl groups accounts for the necessity for having all materials and apparatus dry and free of alcohol during the preparation of the reagent.

The formation of the alkane is an acid-base reaction, that is a proton-transfer reaction. Hydrogen united to oxygen is lost more readily as proton than hydrogen united to carbon, and hence the weaker acid, the alkane, is liberated. In other words the reaction of a Grignard reagent with water to give alkane and magnesium hydroxide is analogous to the reaction of sodium cyanide with hydrochloric acid to give hydrogen cyanide and sodium chloride.

This type of reaction is valuable for the estimation of groups containing replaceable hydrogen, for example hydroxyl groups. The procedure was proposed first by Tschugaev [4] and further developed by his student Zerevitinov and by others. It commonly is referred to as the *Zerevitinov determination.* A simple form of the apparatus is shown in Fig. 28. A solution of methylmagnesium iodide in a high-boiling ether, such as *i*-amyl ether, is placed in one leg of the bifurcated tube, and a weighed amount of the compound dissolved in a suitable solvent is placed in the other leg. The apparatus is brought to temperature equilibrium with the stopcock open, the cock then is closed, and the height of the mercury column read. The two solutions are mixed, and after again reaching temperature equilibrium, the volume of methane formed in the reaction is determined. From these data and the molecular weight of the compound, the number of active hydrogen atoms in the molecule can be calculated. Various refinements in the above procedure have been introduced to increase the accuracy of the determination.

The concentration of Grignard solutions can be determined by adding water to a known volume of the reagent and titrating the magnesium hydroxide formed. The method is inaccurate to the extent that the reagent has reacted with air, since magnesium alkoxides also react with water to give magnesium hydroxide (pp. 73, 88).

2. **With Halogen.** Halogens react with alkylmagnesium halide to give alkyl halide and magnesium halide.

$$RMgX + X_2 \longrightarrow RX + MgX_2$$

---

[4] Leo A. Tschugaev (1872–1922), professor at the University of St. Petersburg, Russia.

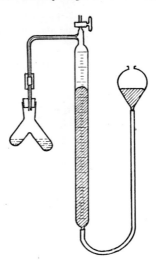

Fig. 28. Zerevitinov apparatus for the determination of reactive hydrogen.

This reaction can be used to determine the concentration of Grignard solutions by titrating with standard iodine solution.

3. **With Oxygen.** Grignard reagents absorb oxygen with the formation of alkoxides, from which the alcohol can be liberated by the addition of water.

$$2\,RMgX + O_2 \longrightarrow 2\,ROMgX$$

$$ROMgX + HOH \longrightarrow ROH + Mg(OH)X$$

Hence it is necessary to exclude air from the reagents to obtain optimum yields.

4. **With Inorganic Halides.** Grignard reagents react with the halides of all elements below magnesium in the electromotive series, usually by replacing the halogen with alkyl groups.

$$HgCl_2 + 2\,RMgX \longrightarrow HgR_2 + 2\,MgX_2$$

$$AlCl_3 + 3\,RMgX \longrightarrow AlR_3 + 3\,MgX_2$$

$$SnCl_4 + 4\,RMgX \longrightarrow SnR_4 + 4\,MgX_2$$

$$PCl_3 + 3\,RMgX \longrightarrow PR_3 + 3\,MgX_2$$

$$SiCl_4 + 4\,RMgX \longrightarrow SiR_4 + 4\,MgX_2$$

If less reagent is used than is required to react with all of the halogens, intermediate reaction products are obtained. For example silicon tetrachloride and methylmagnesium chloride can give rise to methylsilicon trichloride, CH_3SiCl_3, dimethylsilicon dichloride, $(CH_3)_2SiCl_2$, trimethylsilicon chloride, $(CH_3)_3SiCl$, and tetramethylsilicon, $(CH_3)_4Si$. Mercurous chloride and the chlorides of iron, copper, silver, and gold cause chiefly coupling of the alkyl groups.

$$2\,RMgX + CuCl_2 \longrightarrow RR + 2\,MgX_2 + Cu$$

5. With Carbon Dioxide. Grignard reagents add to the carbon-oxygen double bond of carbon dioxide with the formation of the halomagnesium salt of a carboxylic acid.

$$RMgX + O{=}C{=}O \longrightarrow \underset{\underset{R}{|}}{O{=}C{-}OMgX}$$

Addition of a mineral acid liberates the free carboxylic acid (p. 127).

$$RCOOMgX + HCl \longrightarrow RCOOH + MgX_2$$

6. With Other Compounds. The many important reactions of Grignard reagents with other organic compounds are considered as new functional groups are discussed.

REVIEW QUESTIONS

1. Write structural formulas for all the monochloropentanes.
2. Discuss the physical properties of the alkyl halides.
3. Summarize the general methods for the preparation of alkyl halides.
4. Discuss the differences in conditions necessary for the preparation of alkyl chlorides, bromides, and iodides from primary, secondary, and tertiary alcohols using (*a*) halogen acids, and (*b*) phosphorus trihalides.
5. Discuss the direct substitution of hydrogen in a saturated hydrocarbon by halogen. Why is the reaction usually not satisfactory from a preparative standpoint?
6. Give reactions and conditions for the preparation of the following halides starting with any suitable compound: *t*-butyl chloride, *i*-propyl bromide, methyl bromide, *i*-butyl iodide, ethyl chloride.
7. How may primary alkyl chlorides be converted into alkyl iodides?
8. Compare primary, secondary, and tertiary halides in regard to ease of hydrolysis and ease of removal of halogen acid.
9. Compare the ease of displacement of halogen from primary, secondary, and tertiary halides by another group (excluding hydrolysis).
10. Give balanced equations for the reaction of *n*-butyl bromide with each of the following reagents: sodium, magnesium, sodium cyanide, sodium ethoxide, sodium sulfide, and ammonia.
11. What difference in behavior is encountered when tertiary halides react with the above reagents?
12. Discuss the action of aqueous solutions of hydroxides, and of alcoholic potassium hydroxide, on alkyl halides.
13. Give the reasons for and against considering the alkyl halides as belonging to the class of compounds known as esters.
14. What are the differences in the chemical and physical properties of alkali halides and alkyl halides?

NUMERICAL PROBLEMS

15. If a 90 per cent yield is obtained using a 20 per cent excess of sodium bromide and sulfuric acid, how much alcohol and sodium bromide must be used to prepare 200 g. of *n*-butyl bromide?
16. When 0.1 g. of a compound containing hydroxyl groups and having a molecular weight of 87 ± 3 reacted with a solution of methylmagnesium bromide, 50 cc. of methane (S.T.P.) was evolved. How many hydroxyl groups were present in the molecule? (Hint: calculate the equivalent weight of the compound from the Zerevitinov data and compare with the given molecular weight.)

Chapter 7

MECHANISM OF ORGANIC REACTIONS

Two factors are important to chemists in their use of chemical reactions: (1) the position of equilibrium for the reaction, and (2) the rate at which equilibrium is established. The first factor determines the maximum yield of products under the conditions of the experiment, and the second factor determines how fast the reaction goes. The chemist is interested in the latter aspect, not only because a reaction must go at an appreciable rate to be useful, but also because if two or more competing reactions are taking place, as usually is the case in organic reactions, the relative rates of the reactions may be more important in determining the yield of desired product than the relative positions of equilibrium of the competing reactions.

The position of equilibrium depends only on the free energy change of the reaction; that is it is governed only by energy relationships or thermodynamics, and is not concerned with the path by which the reactants are converted into the products. Relative rates of reactions, however, are intimately concerned with the process by which the molecules react. The decomposition of hydrogen iodide to form hydrogen and iodine, and the reaction of hydrogen and bromine to form hydrogen bromide may be cited as illustrations. Both reactions may be represented by simple equations.

$$2\,HI \longrightarrow H_2 + I_2$$

$$H_2 + Br_2 \longrightarrow 2\,HBr$$

The first reaction apparently is as simple as the equation. Two molecules of hydrogen iodide collide and one molecule of hydrogen and one molecule of iodine are formed. The observed rate of decomposition is proportional to the square of the concentration of the hydrogen iodide.

$$\text{Velocity of reaction} = k[HI]^2$$

The rate of formation of hydrogen bromide by the second reaction might be expected to be proportional to the product of the concentration of hydrogen and the concentration of the bromine. Instead the relation found by experiment is

$$\text{Velocity of reaction} = \frac{k[H_2][Br_2]^{\frac{3}{2}}}{[Br_2] - k'[HBr]}$$

Since this complicated rate law cannot be explained by the simple reaction indicated by the over-all equation, the reaction must be complex. Further evidence that balanced equations seldom tell the whole story is the fact that catalysts and solvents markedly affect the rates of reactions but do not even appear in the balanced equations. *The steps that are necessary to account for the effect of various factors on the course and rate of a reaction are known as the* **mechanism** *of the reaction.*

The reactions of molecules involving covalently bound atoms must take place by the breaking and reformation of covalent bonds. It is conceivable that the covalent bond may break in two ways: either one electron goes to each atom joined by the bond as in (*a*), or the pair of electrons stays with one or the other of the two atoms as in (*b*) or (*c*).

If the fragments [*A·*] and [*B·*] could exist with an unpaired electron, they would be known as *free radicals* (p. 424); hence mechanisms in which bonds break by process (*a*) are known as **free-radical mechanisms.** Reactions in the gas phase and reactions catalyzed by free radicals in the liquid phase usually are explainable by this type of mechanism. If the fragments resulting from process (*b*) or (*c*) could exist as such, they would be the ions [*A*⁺] and [: *B*⁻], or [*A* : ⁻] and [*B*⁺]. Positive groups containing a carbon atom that lacks a pair of electrons in its valence shell are called **carbonium ions.** Negative groups containing a carbon atom that has an unshared pair of electrons are called **carbanions.** Mechanisms in which the bonds are assumed to break by process (*b*) or (*c*) during reaction are known as **ionic mechanisms.** Reactions involving polar molecules or ions in the liquid phase usually are believed to take place by way of ionic mechanisms.

It should be emphasized that the theory does not postulate that the formation of free radicals or ions is necessary as an intermediate step in the reaction or that the free radicals or ions represented by [*A · *], [*B · *], [*A*⁺], [: *B*⁻], [*A* : ⁻], or [*B*⁺] are capable of independent existence. There seems to be good evidence that under certain conditions some groups of this type do have independent existence, but under the usual conditions for reactions the energies required for complete dissociation into free radicals or ions are too great for dissociation to take place prior to reaction, and the transition from one covalently bound state to another takes place continuously without the formation of a really free radical or free ion at any time. The arrangement of maximum energy content through which the reacting molecules must pass before the products can be formed is known as the **transition state** or the **transition, critical,** or **activated complex.** The energy that must be supplied to the reacting molecules before they can attain the transition state is called the **activation energy** for the reaction. **Catalysts** are substances that can cause the formation of a transition state having a lower activation energy than one that must be formed in the absence of a catalyst.

In what follows and throughout the text, the difference between fact and theory always should be kept clearly in mind. The composition of a chemical compound, the product of a chemical reaction, the rate of reaction, the position of equilibrium, and the effect of varying conditions on the rate and position of equilibrium can be determined experimentally. Except when errors in observation are made, these facts do not change. The interpretation of these facts and the attempts to find a common basis for the experimental facts are theory. It always should be remembered that theories are inventions of the mind and subject to change in the light of new experimental facts. It is the facts that are of real importance. The theory is valuable only for stimulating the search for new facts and for organizing facts in such a way that they can be remembered more readily. These points should be kept in mind particularly concerning mechanisms postulated for organic reactions. Frequently there may be little or no experimental evidence for the proposed mechanism; it may be merely a likely mechanism consistent with current ideas.

Free-Radical Mechanisms

Pyrolysis of Hydrocarbons. Several of the reactions considered so far are believed to involve free radicals. For example in the thermal decomposition of propane, an initial scission of a carbon-carbon bond is postulated to give two free radicals, each of which has an unshared electron.

$$CH_3CH_2CH_3 \longrightarrow [CH_3 \cdot] + [C_2H_5 \cdot] \tag{1}$$

Propyl radicals may result from the reaction of methyl or ethyl radicals with propane molecules.

$$R \cdot + CH_3CH_2CH_3 \longrightarrow RH + [CH_3CH_2CH_2 \cdot] \tag{2}$$

$$\longrightarrow RH + [CH_3CHCH_3] \tag{3}$$

The propyl radicals may decompose into ethylene and methyl radicals or propylene and hydrogen atoms.

$$\left. \begin{array}{c} [CH_3CH_2CH_2 \cdot] \\ or \\ [CH_3CHCH_3] \end{array} \right\} \longrightarrow \left\{ \begin{array}{c} CH_2{=}CH_2 + [CH_3 \cdot] \tag{4} \\ or \\ CH_3CH{=}CH_2 + [H \cdot] \tag{5} \end{array} \right.$$

The methyl radicals and hydrogen atoms react chiefly by equations *2* and *3* to give methane and hydrogen, and more propyl radicals.

The reason for postulating a primary dissociation into methyl and ethyl radicals in reaction *1* rather than into hydrogen atoms and propyl radicals is that the carbon-carbon bond is weaker than the carbon-hydrogen bond. Thus the energy required to dissociate a hydrocarbon into a free radical and a hydrogen atom is 100 kcal. per mole, whereas that required to form two free radicals is less than 85 kcal. per mole.[1] Therefore when the available energy is limited, the probability of rupture of the carbon-carbon bond is greater than the probability of rupture of the carbon-hydrogen bond. By the same reasoning reaction *4* would be much faster than reaction *5*, and the chief products of the cracking of propane are ethylene and methane rather than propylene and hydrogen.

---

[1] These values for bond strengths are approximately those arrived at by three independent methods and higher than Pauling's values which frequently are given. Calculation of the latter involves the heat of sublimation of graphite which appears to be uncertain by 45 kcal.

Catalytic Reduction. Catalysts capable of bringing about a free-radical type of reaction are those such as metals, nitric oxide, and oxygen that can supply an unpaired electron to a molecule, or those such as organic peroxides and halogen that can dissociate into free radicals, which have an unpaired electron. Catalytic reduction is believed to take place by a free-radical mechanism. Although the equation for the reaction is very simple, the process is rather involved, because it is a multiphase reaction of gases and a solid, or of a gas, liquid, and solid; that is it is a *heterogeneous reaction*. The steps required in the reaction are diffusion of the reactants to the surface of the catalyst, reaction on the catalyst, and diffusion away from the catalyst. The rate of the reaction depends on the slowest of these processes. Even the reaction on the surface is complex. When molecules are adsorbed on the surface of a metallic catalyst such as platinum, palladium, nickel, or copper, they may be dissociated into atoms or free radicals, which have an unshared electron, or a double bond may be broken giving rise to two unshared electrons. For example when hydrogen is adsorbed on platinum, the reaction may be represented as

$$H : H \rightleftarrows 2\,[H \cdot]$$

When ethylene is adsorbed the breaking of one of the carbon-carbon bonds leads to an unpaired electron on each carbon atom.

$$H_2C—CH_2 \rightleftarrows [H_2C—CH_2]$$

These atoms or free radicals undoubtedly are stabilized by a weak pairing of their unpaired electrons with the electrons at the surface of the metal. The process is spoken of as *chemisorption* and leads to a monomolecular layer, in contrast to the physical processes of adsorption which may lead to layers several molecules thick. In the catalytic hydrogenation of ethylene, collision of chemisorbed hydrogen atoms and ethylene diradicals leads to the formation of ethane.

$$[H_2C—CH_2] \xrightarrow{[H\cdot]} [H_2C—CH_3] \xrightarrow{[H\cdot]} H_3C—CH_3$$

Whether or not a reaction takes place between an adsorbed molecule and another molecule depends on whether the orientation and the distances between the parts of the adsorbed activated molecule are such that they fit the shape of the second reactant, allowing reaction to take place on collision. Not only the size and structure of the reactants but also the crystal structure of the surface of the catalyst determines these space relationships. From this limited discussion it is evident that the optimum conditions and type of catalyst will vary for every different pair of molecules reacting, and that the choice of such conditions and catalyst still must be largely empirical. Fortunately hydrogenation catalysts have been developed which show high activity for a wide variety of compounds; hence catalytic hydrogenation is an eminently practical process.

Thermal or Photochemical Halogenation. At elevated temperature or at room temperature in the presence of light of short wavelength chlorine and bromine react with saturated hydrocarbons, replacing hydrogen by halogen and evolving halogen acid (p. 84). In this reaction the energy supplied by the thermal agitation or by light is absorbed by the halogen molecules, which are dissociated into atoms.

$$X : X + \text{thermal energy or} \longrightarrow 2 [X \cdot] \qquad (1)$$
$$\text{light quanta } (h\nu)$$

Collision of the hydrocarbon molecules with halogen atoms produces the hydrocarbon radical and hydrogen halide.

$$[X \cdot] + HR \longrightarrow HX + [R \cdot] \qquad (2)$$

The free radicals collide with halogen molecules producing alkyl halide and more halogen atoms.

$$[R \cdot] + X : X \longrightarrow R : X + [X \cdot] \qquad (3)$$

Although reaction 2 consumes a halogen atom, reaction 3 regenerates one capable of starting a new series of reactions. Thus the presence of a few halogen atoms can start a chain in which reactions 2 and 3 are repeated until all of the reactants are consumed. Such a process is known as a **chain reaction.**

If the chain is broken by the removal of the atoms or free radicals, the reaction will stop before the reactants are entirely consumed. For example combination of two chlorine atoms to give molecular chlorine, or of two alkyl radicals to give saturated hydrocarbon, or of an alkyl radical and chlorine atom to give alkyl halide, would retard or stop the reaction. Collisions between atoms are not very effective because the amount of energy liberated on combination of two atoms is equal to the energy necessary to cause dissociation, and they immediately would fly apart. Only by a simultaneous collision with a third molecule or the wall of the container, which can absorb some of the energy, can the combination of atoms take place. Since statistically such three-body collisions are infrequent, they are not very important in slowing down a reaction. For the reaction of polyatomic free radicals, a three-body collision may not be necessary since some of the energy may be taken up by increased vibrations in other bonds of the molecule. However even here the chain reaction is not greatly retarded, because the low concentration of free radicals makes collisions between them infrequent.

Oxygen and nitric oxide, which have unpaired electrons, appear to be particularly effective in combining with atoms and free radicals. Hence inhibition by the presence of considerable amounts of oxygen or nitric oxide is characteristic of chain reactions. Traces of oxygen or nitric oxide, however, may act as free radicals in initiating chain reactions.

Polymerizations Catalyzed by Free Radicals. The oxygen molecule is unusual in that it contains two unpaired electrons of like spin as evidenced by the fact that it is paramagnetic. Having unpaired electrons, the oxygen molecule behaves to some extent like a free radical. It is thought that in oxygen-catalyzed polymerizations the oxygen molecule combines with one carbon atom of the unsaturated compound by taking one electron from the double bond and leaving a free electron on the other carbon atom.

$$\cdot \ddot{O} : \ddot{O} \cdot \; + CH_2\!\!-\!\!CH_2 \longrightarrow \left[\; \cdot \ddot{O} : \ddot{O} : CH_2\!\!-\!\!CH_2 \cdot \; \right]$$

This intermediate can combine with another molecule of ethylene.

$$[\; \cdot O\!\!-\!\!O\!\!-\!\!CH_2\!\!-\!\!CH_2 \cdot \;] + CH_2\!\!-\!\!\overset{..}{C}H_2 \longrightarrow [\; \cdot O\!\!-\!\!O\!\!-\!\!CH_2\!\!-\!\!CH_2\!\!-\!\!CH_2\!\!-\!\!CH_2 \cdot \;]$$

The process repeats itself until the chain is broken by the union of two free radicals or by taking a hydrogen atom from another molecule. In the latter case a new chain is started. The greater the amount of oxygen used as a catalyst the lower the molecular weight of the polymer, because the larger the number of chains that are started the less the amount of monomer that will be available for each chain, and the more likely a chain will be stopped by colliding with another oxygen molecule or chain. If too large an amount of oxygen is used, polymerization will not take place because the chains are stopped as fast as they are started.

Abnormal Addition of Hydrogen Bromide to a Double Bond. Although this reaction is believed to take place by a free-radical mechanism, it can be discussed better after considering the normal addition of halogen acids (p. 103), which takes place by an ionic mechanism (p. 101).

Ionic Mechanisms

Displacement Reactions of Alkyl Halides. Several reactions that have been considered are believed to take place by ionic mechanisms. All of the common reactions of alkyl halides belong to this class, and some of them take place by the simplest mechanism known. This mechanism is the **displacement reaction,** and the conversion of chlorides to iodides is its simplest form. Here the iodide ion enters the molecule as the chloride ion leaves. For an effective collision, the entering ion must approach from the rear in line with the carbon atom and the ion which is leaving.

$$\left[\; : \ddot{I} : \; \right]^{-} + \; H\!\!-\!\!\underset{R}{\overset{H}{C}}\!\!-\!\!Cl \; \rightleftarrows \; \left[\; : \ddot{I} : \underset{R}{\overset{H \;\; H}{C}} : \ddot{Cl} : \; \right]^{-} \; \rightleftarrows \; I\!\!-\!\!\underset{R}{\overset{H}{C}}\!\!-\!\!H + \left[\; : \ddot{Cl} : \; \right]^{-}$$

When the iodide ion approaches closely enough, bonding with the carbon atom begins, and the chloride ion starts to leave the molecule. At the midstage of the reaction, the three groups that remain bound to the carbon atom lie in a plane which passes through the carbon atom and is perpendicular to the line passing through the two halogen atoms and the carbon atom. This condition together with the associated solvent molecules is the transition state for the reaction (p. 91). As the chloride ion leaves the carbon atom, the other three groups move in a way such that at the end of the reaction the tetrahedral arrangement of the bonds again exists. The process resembles an umbrella being turned inside out and is known as a Walden inversion (p. 271).

With this picture of the mechanism of the reaction, the order of reactivity methyl halide > other primary halides > secondary > tertiary, and the unexpected inertness of primary isobutyl and neopentyl halides can be explained. In order for the transition state to be formed, the three groups attached to the carbon atom must be of such size and shape that they can become planar with the carbon atom and permit a sufficiently close approach of the iodide and chloride ions. Since hydrogen is very small compared to alkyl groups, methyl chloride will react much faster than ethyl chloride, ethyl faster than *i*-propyl, and *i*-propyl faster than *t*-butyl. The kind of alkyl groups replacing hydrogen has little effect, since the blocking is due almost entirely to the atom united to the carbon atom bearing the replaceable group, the rest of the chain being well out of the way most of the time. Exceptions are the *i*-propyl group and the *t*-butyl group present in isobutyl and neopentyl halides. Here scale models indicate that replacement of a single hydrogen atom by these groups makes the formation of the transition complex difficult or almost impossible. Since this effect of alkyl groups and consequent decrease in the rate of a reaction is due to the fact that a group occupies space, that is that the electronic shells of atoms cannot interpenetrate, it is called **steric hindrance.** Most of the reactions of alkyl halides, for example with sodium cyanide, sodium alkoxide, sodium hydrosulfide, sodium sulfide, and ammonia, probably take place in exactly the same way as with sodium iodide. Here the respective ion, or the ammonia molecule with its unshared pair of electrons, takes the place of the iodide ion. This mechanism is a possible one only if the rate of reaction is proportional to the concentration of both reactants.

Hydrolysis of Alkyl Halides. The rate of hydrolysis of methyl halides and primary alkyl halides in alkaline solution is second order, being dependent on the concentration of both hydroxide ion and alkyl halide. It undoubtedly takes place by a simple displacement mechanism, which may be called a *bimolecular mechanism.*

$$\left[H : \overset{..}{\underset{..}{O}} : \right] + H - \overset{H}{\underset{H}{C}} : \overset{..}{\underset{..}{X}} : \longrightarrow HO : \overset{H}{\underset{H}{C}} - H + \left[: \overset{..}{\underset{..}{X}} : \right] \qquad (1)$$

The hydrolysis of tertiary halides, on the other hand, takes place at the same rate in acid, neutral, or alkaline solution and is a first order reaction in which the rate is dependent only on the concentration of alkyl halide. Conceivably the reaction might be a bimolecular substitution by water molecules and appear to be first order because the large excess of water present prevents an appreciable change in the water concentration.

$$H : \overset{..}{\underset{..}{O}} : + R - \overset{R}{\underset{R}{C}} : \overset{..}{\underset{..}{X}} : \longrightarrow \left[H : \overset{+}{\underset{..}{O}} : \overset{R}{\underset{R}{C}} - R \right] + \left[: \overset{..}{\underset{..}{X}} : \right] \qquad (2)$$

If this were the case, however, the reaction should be catalyzed by hydroxide ions, because they have a much greater tendency than water molecules to share a pair of electrons.

In order to explain this behavior, it has been proposed that the rate-controlling step in the reaction is the ionization of the alkyl halide. This ionization is assisted by the energy provided by the solvation of the ions. The second step is the rapid combination of the carbonium ion with solvent molecules.

$$\text{Slow step:} \quad R_3C : \overset{..}{\underset{..}{X}} : \;\rightleftharpoons\; [R_3C^+] + \left[: \overset{..}{\underset{..}{X}} : ^- \right] \text{(with solvation of ions)} \qquad (3)$$

$$\text{Fast step:} \quad [R_3C^+] + : \overset{..}{\underset{..}{O}} : H \longrightarrow \left[R_3C : \overset{+}{\underset{..}{\overset{..}{O}}} : H \right] \qquad (4)$$

Because the rate-controlling step is a unimolecular dissociation, this type of reaction is said to take place by a *unimolecular mechanism.* The second step may take place with or without inversion of the carbon atom since the water molecule may enter from either side.

The reason given for the difference in mechanisms for the hydrolysis of methyl chloride and *t*-butyl chloride is that methyl groups replacing hydrogen on a carbon atom increase the electron density about the carbon atom, making it easier for the halogen atom to leave with the pair of electrons as a chloride ion. That methyl groups have this ability to supply or repel electrons is indicated by observations of the effect of methyl groups on the reactions of a number of types of organic compounds, and more directly by the larger dipole moment of *t*-butyl chloride (2.15) compared to that of methyl chloride (1.56) and by the dipole moments of *p*-disubstituted benzenes (p. 339).

This electron-repelling effect of a methyl group increases the electron density on any atom to which the methyl group is attached, to a greater extent than does a hydrogen atom. Any other alkyl group would have a similar effect. This factor is known as an *inductive effect,* because it behaves like electrostatic induction and induces a greater polarization of the molecule.

The three alkyl groups in *t*-butyl chloride, therefore, cause a greater electron density on the carbon atom bearing the halogen than do the three hydrogen atoms in methyl chloride. A high electron density on this carbon atom would decrease the tendency of a group having an unshared pair of electrons to combine with it as in reactions *1* or *2*. On the other hand a high electron density would favor the ionization of the alkyl halide as in reaction *3*.

Most of the ideas and a great deal of the experimental work on ionic mechanisms have originated in England. The English school, especially Ingold and his collaborators, have couched their ideas in coined terms and phrases which, although they facilitate discussion among the initiated, make an involved subject more difficult for those who do not understand the language. This circumstance may be largely responsible for the slowness with which these ideas were accepted by other chemists. For the same reason it has been considered advisable not to use these terms in this text but to express the ideas in words that already are familiar. Since some of the English terms are finding their way into American usage, however, it is desirable to define the more common ones for reference purposes.

The term *electrophilic* literally means *electron-seeking.* It is applied to a group deficient in electrons, such as a proton. *Cationoid* has been used in the earlier English literature to mean the same thing, because positive cations presumably are deficient in electrons. In the United States, chemists frequently use the very confusing term *electronegative* to describe such groups. The only possible interpretation of why a group or atom that has a tendency to acquire electrons should be called electronegative is that it refers to the state of the atom or group after electrons have been acquired. The terms *electron-deficient, electron-attracting*, or *electron-accepting* are preferable for describing such groups. The *electron affinity* of the group is a measure of this property.

The opposite of electrophilic is *nucleophilic*, meaning *nucleus-seeking*. Even the translation is not immediately clear, since the group to which the term is applied is not actually seeking a nucleus but merely is able to supply electrons to another atom or group. The synonymous terms *anionoid, electropositive*, and *electrodotic* also are objectionable. *Electron-repelling* and *electron-donating* express these ideas much more clearly. This property can be expressed in terms of the *ionization potential* of the group.

Prototropy means the shift of a proton from one portion of the molecule to another, in other words, *proton transfer*. The term, *homolytic fission*, indicates that in a reaction the electron-pair bond is broken in such a way that one electron goes to each of the two parts of the molecule, that is *free radical fission*. *Heterolytic fission* indicates that in a reaction the molecule divides in such a way that one part gets both electrons of the pair and the other part none, or simply *ionic fission*.

The symbol S_N1 applied to a reaction stands for a substitution by a nucleophilic reagent which takes place by a unimolecular mechanism, for example a reaction involving a primary ionization such as reaction *3*, page 97. The symbol S_N2 means a substitution reaction by a nucleophilic reagent which takes place by a bimolecular mechanism, for example a simple displacement reaction such as reaction *1*, page 96.

Change in Relative Order of Reactivity. In the reaction of alkyl chlorides with sodium iodide (p. 81), or in the formation of esters from alcohols (p. 74), the rates of the reaction decrease with the type of alkyl group in the order methyl > primary > secondary > tertiary. On the other hand the rate of hydrolysis of alkyl halides (p. 83), the rate of formation of alkyl halides from alcohols and halogen acid (p. 74) or from alcohols and inorganic acid halides (p. 74), and the rate of dehydration of alcohols (p. 75) decrease in the order tertiary > secondary > primary > methyl. Whenever there is more than one order of reactivity for a given group of structures or functional groups, at least two factors must be involved. One possible factor is the blocking effect of groups to the approach of the replacing group from the back side which is called a steric effect (p. 96). Another possible factor is the inductive effect which may increase or decrease the ease with which a reagent group may approach a molecule or with which a functional group may leave a molecule. The different factors may operate to produce the same effect or to produce different effects. In the reaction of alkyl chlorides with iodide ion the steric effect of the alkyl groups predominates, the order of reactivity being methyl > primary > secondary > tertiary. In the hydrolysis of alkyl halides the inductive effect of the alkyl groups predominates, the order being tertiary > secondary > primary > methyl.

Reaction of Alcohols with Halogen Acids. The formation of alkyl halides from alcohols and halogen acids is the reverse of the hydrolysis of alkyl halides. Hence the mechanism of formation should be the reverse of the mechanism for hydrolysis. The primary reaction of an alcohol with a strong acid is the transfer of a proton from the weakly basic negative ion of the acid to the more strongly basic alcohol to give an oxonium salt (p. 71).

$$\text{CH}_3 : \overset{..}{\underset{..}{\text{O}}} : + \text{H} : \overset{..}{\underset{..}{\text{X}}} : \;\rightleftharpoons\; \left[\text{CH}_3 : \overset{+}{\overset{..}{\underset{..}{\text{O}}}} : \text{H} \right] + \left[: \overset{..}{\underset{..}{\text{X}}} : \bar{} \right]$$
$$\phantom{\text{CH}_3 : }\text{H}\text{H}$$

The addition of a proton to the hydroxyl group weakens the bond between methyl and oxygen. The negative ion then can displace a water molecule from the oxonium ion.

$$\left[:\overset{..}{\underset{..}{X}}:^- \right] + \left[CH_3 : \overset{+}{\overset{..}{O}} : H \atop H \right] \longrightarrow \quad :\overset{..}{\underset{..}{X}} : CH_3 + \quad :\overset{..}{O} : H \atop H$$

If HX is a halogen acid, an alkyl halide is formed; if sulfuric acid, an alkyl hydrogen sulfate.

In view of the fact that the order of reactivity of alcohols to form alkyl halides is the same as that for the hydrolysis of alkyl halides, namely tertiary > secondary > primary > methyl, and that it has been proposed that the hydrolysis of tertiary alkyl halides takes place by a unimolecular mechanism, it is logical to assume an analogous mechanism for the reaction of tertiary alcohols with halogen acid.

$$\text{Fast step:} \quad R_3C : \overset{..}{\underset{..}{O}} : \atop H \quad + H : \overset{..}{\underset{..}{X}} : \rightleftarrows \left[R_3C : \overset{+}{\overset{..}{O}} : H \atop H \right] + \left[:\overset{..}{\underset{..}{X}} :^- \right]$$

$$\text{Slow step:} \quad \left[R_3C : \overset{+}{\overset{..}{O}} : H \atop H \right] \rightleftarrows [R_3C^+] + \quad :\overset{..}{O} : H \atop H$$

$$\text{Fast step:} \quad [R_3C^+] + \left[:\overset{..}{\underset{..}{X}} :^- \right] \rightleftarrows R_3C : \overset{..}{\underset{..}{X}} :$$

Removal of Halogen Acid from Alkyl Halides. Just as a bimolecular and a unimolecular process have been proposed for the hydrolysis of alkyl halides, two mechanisms have been proposed for the removal of halogen acid. The rate in the bimolecular process is dependent on the concentration both of base and of alkyl halide. Removal of a proton by the base is accompanied simultaneously by the elimination of halide ion and formation of a double bond.

$$\left[H\overset{..}{O} :^- \right] + H : CR_2\!\!-\!\!CR_2 : \overset{..}{\underset{..}{X}} : \longrightarrow H : \overset{..}{O} : + R_2C\!\!=\!\!CR_2 + \left[:\overset{..}{\underset{..}{X}} :^- \right] \atop \quad\quad\quad\quad\quad\quad\quad\quad\quad H$$

The curved arrow indicates the migration of the pair of electrons released by the proton to form a double bond between the two carbon atoms.

In the unimolecular process the rate is independent of the concentration of base, the rate-controlling step being the ionization of the halogen.

$$\text{Slow step:} \quad HCR_2\!\!-\!\!CR_2 : \overset{..}{\underset{..}{X}} : \rightleftarrows [HCR_2\!\!-\!\!\overset{+}{C}R_2] + \left[:\overset{..}{\underset{..}{X}} :^- \right]$$

$$\text{Fast step:} \quad \left[H : \overset{..}{\underset{..}{O}} :^- \right] + [H : CR_2\!\!-\!\!\overset{+}{C}R_2] \rightleftarrows H : \overset{..}{O} : + R_2C\!\!=\!\!CR_2 \atop \quad\quad\quad\quad\quad\quad\quad\quad\quad\quad\quad\quad\quad H$$

The presence of a base does, of course, affect the position of equilibrium by combining with the proton liberated in the reaction, thus preventing reversal of the reaction.

Both the loss of halide ion and the removal of proton to give the unsaturated compound are favored by increased substitution of alkyl groups on the respective carbon atoms to which they are attached. For example not only do tertiary halides lose halogen acids more readily than secondary or primary halides, but tertiary hydrogen is lost more readily than secondary or primary hydrogen. Thus dehydrohalogenation of s-butyl bromide gives chiefly 2-butene rather than 1-butene.

$$CH_3CH_2CHBrCH_3 \xrightarrow{\text{NaOH}} CH_3CH{=}CHCH_3 + NaBr + H_2O$$

The reason for the order of the ease with which halide ion is lost has been ascribed to the inductive effect of methyl groups. Consequently the unimolecular mechanism is of greatest importance with tertiary halides. The reason for the order of ease of removal of proton is not obvious since the increase in electron density caused by the alkyl groups should hold a proton more strongly.

Dehydration of Alcohols. The dehydration of alcohols would be expected to take place in a manner analogous to the removal of halogen acid from an alkyl halide. The initial step would be the formation of the oxonium salt.

$$HCH_2{-}CR_2 : \overset{..}{\underset{..}{O}} : \underset{H}{} + H : \overset{..}{\underset{..}{O}} : SO_3H \rightleftharpoons \left[HCH_2{-}CR_2 : \overset{+}{\underset{..}{\overset{..}{O}}} : \underset{H}{H} \right] + \left[: \overset{..}{\underset{..}{O}} : SO_3H \right]$$

In the second step a base removes a proton from the second carbon atom with simultaneous loss of a water molecule.

$$\left[HO_3S : \overset{..}{\underset{..}{O}} : \right] + \left[H : CR_2{-}CR_2 : \overset{+}{\underset{..}{\overset{..}{O}}} : \underset{H}{H} \right] \longrightarrow HO_3S : \overset{..}{\underset{..}{O}} : H + R_2C{=}CR_2 + : \overset{..}{\underset{H}{\overset{..}{O}}} : H$$

$$H_2O + H_2SO_4 \longrightarrow [H_3O^+] + [^-OSO_3H]$$

In the transition state the molecule exists essentially as a carbonium ion and molecular rearrangements may occur, as in the dehydration of 1-butanol (p. 76).

$$[CH_3CH_2CH_2\overset{+}{C}H_2] \rightleftharpoons [CH_3CH_2\overset{+}{C}HCH_3]$$

Addition of Halogens to the Double Bond. The simplest picture of the addition of halogen to the double bond would be the simultaneous addition of both halogen atoms from the same halogen molecule. It seems quite certain, however, from a number of experimental facts that this type of reaction does not take place. Instead a stepwise reaction occurs in which the unsaturated hydrocarbon uses one pair of electrons of the double bond to remove from the halogen molecule a halogen particle having only six electrons, and to form a three-membered ring. The resulting positively charged group (halonium ion) then reacts with a halide ion from the solution with Walden inversion of one of the carbon atoms.

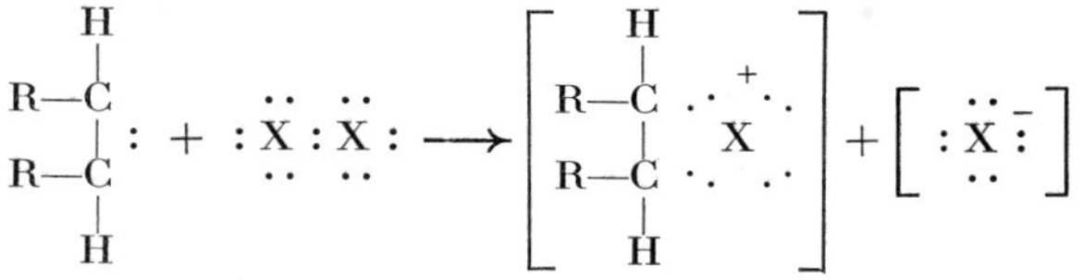

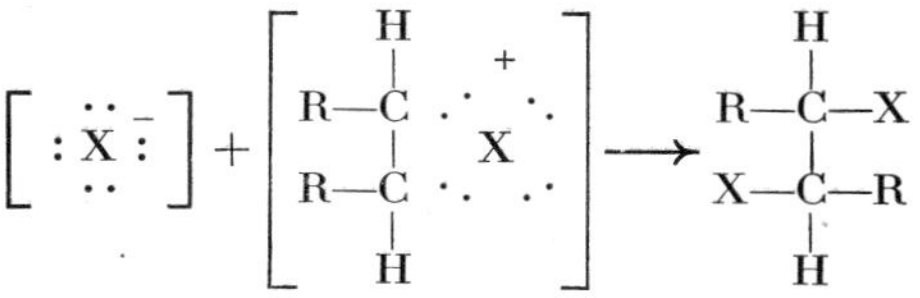

The halide ion removed from the solution need not be, and from a statistical viewpoint usually is not, the same halide ion liberated in the first step of the reaction. Because of the higher concentration of halogen molecules, it is more likely that they react with the intermediate ions.

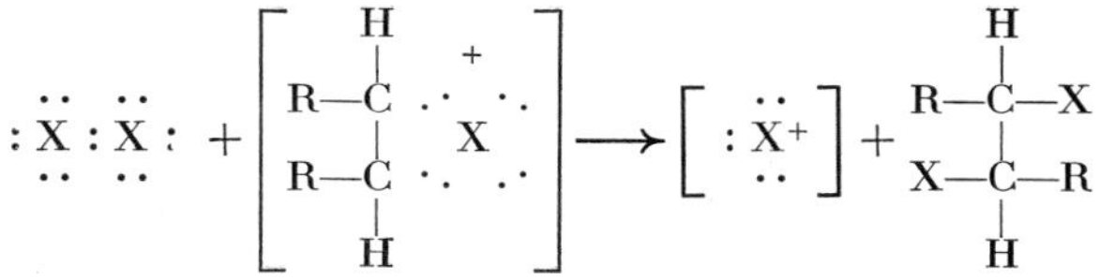

The positive halogen liberated would be available for reaction with an olefin molecule. The positive halogen ion can persist because of the reaction with halogen molecules.

This mechanism looks upon the double bond as a potential electron-donor, which is logical in view of the greater reactivity of the double bond compared with a single bond.

Normal Addition of Acids to the Double Bond. An ionic mechanism for addition of acids to the double bond permits an explanation of the Markovnikov rule, which is based on experimental observation. In the addition of halogen acids and sulfuric acid, it is believed that the first step is the combination of one of the electron pairs of the double bond with a proton derived from the nonionized acid.

$$CH_2{=}CH_2 + H : \overset{..}{\underset{..}{Br}} : \longrightarrow [CH_3{-}\overset{+}{C}H_2] + \left[: \overset{..}{\underset{..}{Br}} : \right]$$

The intermediate positively charged ethyl group (ethonium ion) can combine with a bromide ion to give ethyl bromide. The chance is greater, however, at least initially, that it will collide with a second molecule of hydrogen bromide withdrawing a bromide ion and giving a carbon-bromine covalent bond.

$$[CH_3 \overset{+}{-}CH]_2 \ + \ :\overset{..}{\underset{..}{Br}}:H \longrightarrow CH_3CH_2Br + [H^+]$$

The proton released in the second step may combine with the bromide ion produced in the first step or may add to another molecule of olefin to initiate a repetition of the process.

Ethylene is a symmetrical molecule and the same product results no matter which carbon atom combines with the proton or which with the bromide ion. If the molecule is unsymmetrical, two products are possible, but one predominates, namely that in which the proton has combined with the carbon atom carrying the most hydrogen. The explanation given for this selectivity is that the carbon atom of an alkyl group carries a higher electron density than hydrogen, and increases the electron density on the carbon atom to which it is attached above what this carbon atom would have if it were attached to hydrogen (p. 97). If this carbon atom is united to another by a double bond, the increase in electron density is relieved by a shift of the more mobile electrons of the double bond to the other carbon atom. As a result there is a difference in electron density about the two carbon atoms united by the double bond, and the highest electron density is about the carbon atom bearing the most hydrogen.

$$\begin{array}{ccc} & H \quad H & \\ & \overset{..}{} \quad \overset{..}{} & \\ H_3C & :C \; \overset{..}{\underset{.}{C}} : H & \quad \text{or} \quad \quad H_3C \rightarrow \underset{\delta^+}{CH}\!\!=\!\!\underset{\delta^-}{CH_2} \end{array}$$

The first formula attempts to indicate the relative electron densities on the different carbon atoms. The second formula indicates that the methyl group tends to push electrons into the CH group and that this higher electron density is relieved by a shift of electrons from the double bond to the CH_2 group. The symbols δ^+ and δ^- are used to indicate the fractional difference in charge distribution on the doubly-linked carbon atoms to distinguish it from a difference in charge of one electron which is indicated by the symbols $(+)$ and $(-)$. That such a polarization of the molecule takes place has been shown experimentally; although all saturated hydrocarbons and symmetrical olefins have zero dipole moment (p. 63), moments for the unsymmetrical olefins are observable (for $C_2H_5CH\!\!=\!\!CH_2$, $\mu = 0.37$).

If the double bond in an unsymmetrical olefin is polarized, the Markovnikov rule is explainable, since the more electron-deficient portion of the reagent (H) would add to the carbon atom where the electron density is greater, and the electron-donating portion (X or OSO_3H) would add to the more electron-deficient carbon atom, that is the one with the least hydrogen.

$$CH_3\!\!-\!\!CH\!\!=\!\!CH_2 + HX \longrightarrow CH_3\!\!-\!\!\underset{\underset{X}{|}}{CH}\!\!-\!\!CH_3$$

The polarity of the molecule would explain also the increased reactivity of propylene over ethylene and of isobutylene over propylene, since increased reactivity would be expected with increased polarity of the molecule. From the fact that HOX adds halogen to the carbon atom having the higher electron density, it would appear that the OH portion of the molecule has a higher electron density than the X portion.

$$H_3C \rightarrow \overset{\frown}{CH} = CH_2 + HO - X \longrightarrow CH_3CHCH_2X$$
$$\overset{}{\underset{\delta^+}{}} \quad \underset{\delta^-}{} \quad \underset{\delta^-}{} \quad \underset{\delta^+}{} \qquad \qquad \underset{OH}{|}$$

Actually this reaction is more complex than is indicated by this equation.

Abnormal Addition of Hydrogen Bromide to the Double Bond. Although this reaction is believed to take place by a free-radical mechanism rather than by an ionic mechanism, it is best discussed at this point. The interesting observation has been made that the addition of hydrogen bromide to an olefin takes place contrary to the Markovnikov rule in the presence of peroxides (p. 42). As usual where an exception to a rule is observed, the explanation is a difference in mechanism. The peroxide reacts with the hydrogen bromide and gives bromine *atoms* which initiate the reaction. The addition then proceeds by a free radical chain mechanism.

$$\text{Peroxide} + HBr \longrightarrow \text{Reduced peroxide} + H_2O + [\cdot Br]$$

$$RCH = CH_2 + [\cdot Br] \longrightarrow [R\underset{\cdot}{C}HCH_2Br]$$

$$[R\underset{\cdot}{C}HCH_2Br] + HBr \longrightarrow RCH_2CH_2Br + [\cdot Br]$$

The bromine atom is deficient in an electron and reacts at a point of maximum electron density. Hence it adds to the carbon atom which is least substituted by alkyl groups. Of the halogen acids only hydrogen bromide shows this effect, because hydrogen chloride is not oxidized readily enough for peroxides to produce chlorine atoms, and hydrogen iodide immediately gives molecular iodine.

Acid-Catalyzed Polymerization. Under the influence of acid catalysts, olefins undergo self-addition with the formation of compounds having two, three, four, or many times the molecular weight of the original compound. For example isobutylene polymerizes to give diisobutylenes, triisobutylenes, and on up to polyisobutylenes (p. 43). The probable mechanism of the reaction and the reason for the structures of the products are based on the polarity of isobutylene and the fact that the polymerization is catalyzed by acids. The first step consists of the addition of a proton from the acid catalyst to the carbon atom having the higher electron density, giving a carbonium ion with a free positive charge.

$$\begin{array}{c} H_3C \\ \diagdown \\ \diagup \\ H_3C \end{array} C = CH_2 + HOSO_3H \rightleftarrows \begin{bmatrix} CH_3 \\ \diagdown \\ \diagup \\ CH_3 \end{bmatrix} + [\overset{-}{O}SO_3H]$$
$$\underset{\delta^+ \quad \delta^-}{}$$

This ion could lose a proton and revert to isobutylene, it could combine with the acid sulfate ion to give *t*-butyl hydrogen sulfate, or it could add to a second molecule of isobutylene to give a new carbonium ion. The last alternative is the most likely because of the high concentration of isobutylene.

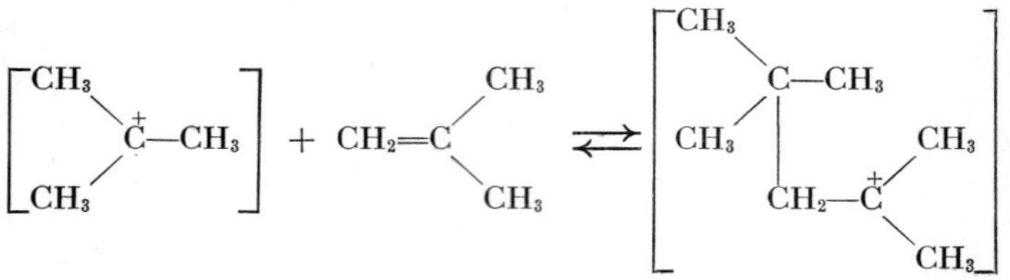

$$\left[\begin{array}{c} CH_3 \\ | \\ C-CH_3 \\ | \\ CH_3 \end{array}\right]^+ + CH_2=C\begin{array}{c} CH_3 \\ \diagdown \\ CH_3 \end{array} \rightleftarrows \left[\begin{array}{c} CH_3 \\ | \\ C-CH_3 \\ CH_3 \diagup \quad \diagdown CH_3 \\ | \\ CH_2-C \\ | \\ CH_3 \end{array}\right]^+$$

This carbonium ion could lose a proton in two ways, either from the adjacent CH_2 group or from one of the adjacent methyl groups, to give the mixture of dimers known as *diisobutylene.*

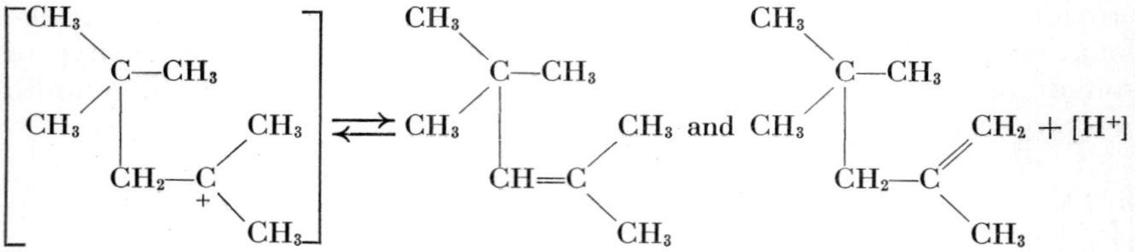

$$\left[\begin{array}{c} CH_3 \\ | \\ C-CH_3 \\ CH_3 \quad CH_3 \\ | \\ CH_2-C \\ | \\ CH_3 \end{array}\right]^+ \rightleftarrows \begin{array}{c} CH_3 \\ | \\ C-CH_3 \\ CH_3 \quad CH_3 \\ | \\ CH=C \\ CH_3 \end{array} \text{and} \begin{array}{c} CH_3 \\ | \\ C-CH_3 \\ CH_3 \quad CH_2 \\ | \\ CH_2-C \\ CH_3 \end{array} + [H^+]$$

Diisobutylene actually has been found to be a mixture of 20 per cent 2,4,4-trimethyl-2-pentene and 80 per cent 2,4,4-trimethyl-1-pentene. Reaction of the polymeric carbonium ion with isobutylene, or of the monomeric carbonium ion with a polymeric product, gives trimers, tetramers, and higher polymers up to the viscous and rubber-like compounds known as polyisobutylenes. In favor of this mechanism is the fact that neutral molecules lacking a pair of electrons in their valence shell, such as boron trifluoride, also are powerful catalysts for polymerization reactions. Moreover the greater the polarization of the double bond by the substitution of methyl groups, the greater the ease of polymerization.

Addition of Grignard Reagents to the Carbon-Oxygen Double Bond. In the organometallic compounds, the carbon-metal bond undoubtedly is highly polarized with the metal the positive end of the dipole.

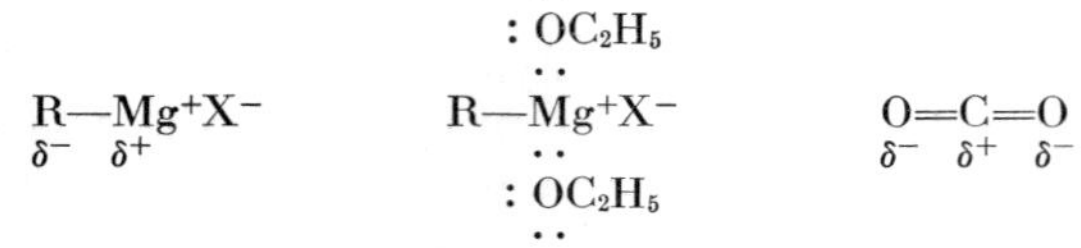

$$\underset{\delta^- \quad \delta^+}{R-Mg^+X^-} \qquad \underset{.. \atop : OC_2H_5 \atop ..}{\overset{.. \atop : OC_2H_5 \atop ..}{R-Mg^+X^-}} \qquad \underset{\delta^- \quad \delta^+ \quad \delta^-}{O=C=O}$$

Therefore in reactions in which the carbon-metal bond is cleaved, it is to be expected that the alkyl group will leave with the pair of electrons. This type of cleavage for organomagnesium compounds is assisted by the solvation of the reagent with ether molecules (p. 117) which supplies electrons to the magnesium atom and permits the alkyl group to leave more readily. In compounds such as carbon dioxide, aldehydes, and ketones (p. 161), the carbonyl group is polarized with the carbon atom at the positive end of the dipole because the oxygen nucleus is more strongly electron-attracting than the carbon nucleus (p. 64). Hence in the addition of Grignard reagents and other reactive organometallic compounds (p. 584) to a carbonyl group, the alkyl group adds to carbon and the metal to oxygen (p. 89).

$$O{=}\underset{\delta^-\ \ \delta^+\ \ \delta^-}{C}{=}O + \underset{\delta^-\ \ \ \delta^+}{R{-}Mg^+X^-} \longrightarrow O{=}\underset{\underset{R}{|}}{C}{-}O^{-+}Mg^{+-}X$$

Often the reaction of the Grignard reagent with carbonyl compounds is preceded by complex formation in which the carbonyl compound displaces ether molecules from the solvated magnesium atom. Although such preliminary complex formation may determine the course of certain Grignard reactions (p. 350), it does not appear to be necessary for reaction since solvates of Grignard reagents with tertiary amines such as pyridine (p. 454) still react with carbonyl compounds. These solvates are so stable that it seems unlikely that the tertiary amine is displaced by the carbonyl compound, a much weaker base, prior to the addition reaction.

Chapter 8

SYNTHESIS OF ALKANES AND ALKENES. ALKYNES (ACETYLENES)

ALKANE AND ALKENE SYNTHESIS

As indicated in Chapters 5 and 6, some of the reactions of alcohols and alkyl halides lead to the production of paraffin and olefin hydrocarbons. It now is possible to summarize some of the general methods for the synthesis of the paraffin hydrocarbons and olefins having a desired structure.

Syntheses of Alkanes

1. *Reduction of an Alkyl Halide.* The direct reduction of alkyl halides may be brought about by a variety of reagents such as zinc and hydrochloric acid in alcoholic solution, sodium and alcohol, sodium amalgam and water, hydrogen iodide, or hydrogen and a catalyst such as platinum. The reaction may be represented by the equation

$$RX + 2 [H] \longrightarrow RH + HX$$

where [H] represents any of the above reducing agents. If hydrogen iodide is used the reaction is

$$RI + HI \longrightarrow RH + I_2$$

In this reaction red phosphorus frequently is used along with aqueous hydrogen iodide. The phosphorus reacts with the iodine to form phosphorus triiodide which is hydrolyzed by the water, regenerating hydrogen iodide. In this way the concentration of hydrogen iodide does not decrease, and only red phosphorus is consumed in the reduction. Because the position of equilibrium favors the formation of hydrocarbon and iodine, the substitution of iodine into a molecule by direct iodination is not possible unless some other reagent is present which will destroy the hydrogen iodide. This reducing action of hydrogen iodide also limits the usefulness of its reaction with alcohols to form alkyl iodides (p. 74).

One of the best methods for preparing pure hydrocarbons is the indirect reduction of halides through the Grignard reagents (p. 87).

$$RX + Mg \longrightarrow RMgX$$

$$RMgX + HOH \longrightarrow RH + Mg(OH)X$$

2. *Wurtz* [1] *Reaction.* The reaction of an alkyl halide with an alkali metal gives a hydrocarbon in which the two alkyl groups have combined.

---

[1] Charles Adolphe Wurtz (1817–1894), successor to Dumas on the latter's resignation from the faculty of the École de Médecine in 1853, and first occupant of the chair of organic chemistry established at the Sorbonne in 1875. He was the first to synthesize amines in 1849. His synthesis of alkanes was published in 1855. Among his many other contributions are the synthesis of ethylene glycol and ethylene oxide in 1859, the reduction of aldehydes to alcohols in 1866, and the synthesis of aldol in 1872. In a work on the history of chemical principles, he antagonized many chemists of other nations with his opening statement, "Chemistry is a French science. It was founded by Lavoisier of immortal memory."

$$2 \text{ RX} + 2 \text{ Na} \longrightarrow \text{RR} + 2 \text{ NaX}$$

The reaction is carried out in an ordinary flask to which a reflux condenser having a wide bore is attached. The metallic sodium is cut into small pieces and placed in the flask, and dry alkyl bromide added through the condenser at such a rate that the reaction always is under control. The surface of the sodium first turns blue and then white with the formation of sodium bromide. When the reaction is complete, the liquid is free of halogen and is distilled. The best yields are obtained with primary halides. Tertiary halides yield almost exclusively olefin.

It should be possible to prepare unsymmetrical hydrocarbons by the reaction of sodium with a mixture of two alkyl halides.

$$\text{RX} + 2 \text{ Na} + \text{R'X} \longrightarrow \text{RR'} + 2 \text{ NaX}$$

This mixed coupling does take place readily if the reactivities of the two halides are approximately the same. However since the other two possible hydrocarbons, RR and R'R', also are formed, the yield of the desired product is small. Mixed coupling takes place to some extent even when there is a marked difference in reactivity, but the greater this difference the greater are the amounts of symmetrical hydrocarbons produced.

3. **Reduction of Olefins.** The double bond of an olefin adds hydrogen quantitatively in the presence of platinum, nickel, palladium, or other hydrogenation catalysts, with the formation of alkanes.

$$\text{RCH}{=}\text{CHR} + \text{H}_2 \xrightarrow[\text{or Pd}]{\text{Pt, Ni,}} \text{RCH}_2\text{CH}_2\text{R}$$

If the unsaturated hydrocarbon is available, for example by the dehydration of an alcohol, this method is an excellent one for alkane synthesis. To convert an alcohol to an alkane, it is easier in general to use the series of reactions alcohol $\longrightarrow$ alkene $\longrightarrow$ alkane, rather than the series alcohol $\longrightarrow$ alkyl halide $\longrightarrow$ alkane.

Syntheses of Alkenes

1. **Pyrolysis of Saturated Hydrocarbons.** Refinery gases from the industrial cracking of petroleum (p. 49) are the chief source of the lower alkenes. Cracking of alkanes is not a useful laboratory procedure, however, because the reaction cannot be controlled to give a single product, and the separation of pure products from the complex mixture that is formed is too difficult in small scale operations.

2. **Dehydration of Alcohols.** Generally the best procedure for converting alcohols to olefins consists of passing them in the vapor state over hot activated alumina (p. 75).

$$\text{RCH}_2\text{CHOHR} \xrightarrow[350°-450°]{\text{Al}_2\text{O}_3} \text{RCH}{=}\text{CHR} + \text{H}_2\text{O}$$

This method is least likely to give rearranged products. For example if highly purified alumina is used, *n*-butyl alcohol will give largely 1-butene with only small amounts of 2-butene.

When acid catalysts are used, molecular rearrangement frequently takes place (p. 76). When rearrangement does not take place, or when the constitution of the rearranged product is known, heating the alcohol to a sufficiently high temperature in the presence of a strong acid such as sulfuric, phosphoric, or *p*-toluenesulfonic acid (p. 356) may be a satisfactory procedure. The last two acids have the advantage that they are relatively nonoxidizing. If the alcohol boils above the temperature required for decomposition, a trace of the acid may be sufficient; otherwise enough acid must be present to keep the alcohol in the form of the nonvolatile oxonium salt. Even a trace of iodine is sufficient to catalyze the decomposition of very easily dehydrated alcohols such as diacetone alcohol (p. 169).

3. Removal of Halogen Acid from Alkyl Halides. The order of ease of removal of halogen acid from alkyl halides is tertiary > secondary > primary for both the halogen atom and the hydrogen atom. The usual reagent is an alcoholic solution of potassium hydroxide.

$$RCH_2CHXR + KOH \text{ (alcoholic)} \longrightarrow RCH{=}CHR + KX + H_2O$$

Alcohol is used as a mutual solvent for the base and the alkyl halide, thus permitting the reaction to take place in a single phase. Potassium hydroxide is preferred to sodium hydroxide because the former dissolves in alcohol much more easily than does sodium hydroxide. Primary halides lose halogen acid so slowly that ether formation becomes the dominant reaction.

$$C_2H_5OH + KOH \rightleftarrows C_2H_5OK + H_2O$$

$$RCH_2X + KOC_2H_5 \longrightarrow RCH_2OC_2H_5 + KX$$

Tertiary alkyl halides lose halogen acid so readily that a higher-boiling organic base such as pyridine (p. 454) or quinoline (p. 458) may be used.

$$R_2CHCXR_2 + C_5H_5N \longrightarrow R_2C{=}CR_2 + C_5H_5NHX$$

4. Removal of Two Halogen Atoms from Adjacent Carbon Atoms. If a compound contains two halogen atoms on adjacent carbon atoms, the halogen may be removed readily by heating with zinc dust in alcohol, leaving a double bond in the molecule.

$$\underset{\underset{X}{|}\quad\underset{X}{|}}{RCHCHR} + Zn \text{ (in alcohol)} \longrightarrow RCH{=}CHR + ZnX_2$$

This reaction is not of much use as a preparative method since the best way to obtain 1,2-dihalides is by adding halogen to an olefin. It occasionally is valuable for the purification of unsaturated compounds if the dihalide can be purified more readily than the olefin itself. The olefin is converted to the dihalide, the dihalide purified, and the olefin then regenerated by means of zinc dust.

ALKYNES (ACETYLENES)

In addition to the olefins, a second homologous series of unsaturated hydrocarbons exists, called **acetylenes** from the first member of the series, or the

alkynes. Acetylene has the molecular formula C_2H_2. The acetylenes add two moles of halogen whereby two halogen atoms are united to each of two adjacent carbon atoms. Using the same arguments advanced for the structure of the olefins, the only logical structure for the acetylenes would be one in which two carbon atoms are joined by a triple bond. Acetylene would have the structure $HC\equiv CH$, and acetylenes in general the structure $RC\equiv CR$.

Physical Properties and Nomenclature

The physical properties of the alkynes closely resemble those of the alkanes and the alkenes, although the boiling points are somewhat higher and the solubility in water is greater. The systems of nomenclature are analogous to those for olefins. Alkynes may be named (*1*) as derivatives of acetylene, and (*2*) by the Geneva system. In the latter the ending is *yne*. These methods are illustrated by the following examples.

$(CH_3)_2CHC\equiv CH$

i-Propylacetylene
or methylbutyne

$$CH_3CH_2CHC\equiv CC_2H_5$$
$$\text{CH}_3$$

Ethyl-*s*-butylacetylene
or 5-methyl-3-heptyne

Preparation

Acetylenes in general may be prepared by two procedures analogous to the preparation of olefins, and by a third that cannot be used for olefins.

1. ***Removal of Two Moles of Hydrogen Halide from Dihalides.*** If a dihalide has the halogen atoms on the same or adjacent carbon atoms, boiling with an alcoholic solution of potassium hydroxide removes two moles of halogen acid with the introduction of a triple bond.

$$RCH_2CX_2R + 2\ KOH\ (alcoholic) \longrightarrow RC\equiv CR + 2\ KX + 2\ H_2O$$

$$RCHXCHXR + 2\ KOH\ (alcoholic) \longrightarrow RC\equiv CR + 2\ KX + 2\ H_2O$$

Since 1,2-dihalides can be prepared easily from olefins, this method can be used to convert olefins into acetylenes.

2. ***Removal of Four Halogen Atoms from Adjacent Carbon Atoms.*** If a tetrahalide has two halogen atoms on each of two adjacent carbon atoms, boiling with zinc dust in alcoholic solution removes the halogen, and an alkyne is formed.

$$RCX_2CX_2R + 2\ Zn\ (in\ alcohol) \longrightarrow RC\equiv CR + 2\ ZnX_2$$

This reaction has the same limitations as the similar one used for the preparation of olefins, namely that the halides of this type are best made by adding halogen to the unsaturated compound.

3. ***From Other Acetylenes.*** This procedure does not produce a triple bond but depends on the fact that hydrogen united to a triply bonded carbon atom is much more acidic than hydrogen united to a singly or doubly bonded carbon atom. Acetylenes of this type form metallic derivatives in which hydrogen is replaced by a metal.

$$RC\equiv CH + Na\ (in\ liquid\ NH_3) \longrightarrow [RC\equiv C^-]Na^+ + \tfrac{1}{2}\ H_2$$

The sodium-carbon bond in acetylides is ionic; that is these metallic derivatives are salts.

The sodium acetylides will react with alkyl halides or alkyl sulfates to give higher homologs of the acetylenes.

$$RC \equiv CNa + R'X \longrightarrow RC \equiv CR' + NaX$$

$$CH_3C \equiv CNa + C_2H_5Br \longrightarrow CH_3C \equiv CC_2H_5 + NaBr$$

Sodium methyl-acetylide   Methylethyl-acetylene (2-pentyne)

Reactions

The acetylenes undergo addition reactions analogous to those of the olefins and are capable of adding two moles of reagent instead of one. Unlike hydrogen united to a doubly bonded carbon atom, however, hydrogen united to a triply bonded carbon is replaced readily by metals.

1. *Addition to the Triple Bond.* Hydrogen can be added to the triple bond in the presence of a suitable catalyst.

$$RC \equiv CR + 2 H_2 \xrightarrow{Pt} RCH_2CH_2R$$

If finely divided palladium or iron is used as catalyst, it is possible to stop the reaction when one mole of hydrogen has been added.

$$RC \equiv CR + H_2 \xrightarrow{Pd \text{ or } Fe} RCH = CHR$$

One or two moles of halogen or halogen acid can be added to the triple bond.

$$RC \equiv CH \begin{cases} + \quad X_2 \longrightarrow RCX = CHX \\ + 2 X_2 \longrightarrow RCX_2CHX_2 \\ + \quad HX \longrightarrow RCX = CH_2 \\ + 2 HX \longrightarrow RCX_2CH_? \end{cases}$$

The addition of nonidentical addenda follows the Markovnikov rule.

Although water does not add directly to the triple bond, the acetylenes react with water in the presence of sulfuric acid and mercurous sulfate. However instead of forming hydroxy compounds, as occurs in the reactions of olefins with water and sulfuric acid, acetylene yields acetaldehyde. A formula enclosed in brackets indicates that the compound is unstable and cannot be isolated.

$$HC \equiv CH + H_2O \xrightarrow[Hg-HgSO_4]{H_2SO_4} [H_2C = CHOH] \longrightarrow CH_3\overset{H}{\underset{|}{C}} = O$$

Acetaldehyde

The initial mercury salt complex probably yields a hydroxyolefin having a hydroxyl group on a carbon atom united to another carbon atom by a double bond. Such structures are known as *enols*. The simple enols are unstable and rearrange to give the more stable isomer having the double bond between the carbon atom and the oxygen atom rather than between the two carbon atoms.

Alkynes other than acetylene yield ketones because addition takes place according to the Markovnikov rule.

$$RC\equiv CH + HOH \xrightarrow[\text{Hg—HgSO}_4]{\text{H}_2\text{SO}_4} \left[\underset{\underset{\text{OH}}{|}}{RC=CH_2} \right] \longrightarrow \underset{\underset{\text{O}}{||}}{RCCH_3}$$

A ketone

2. Replacement of Hydrogen.

If one of the acetylenic carbon atoms bears a hydrogen atom, this hydrogen is replaceable by metals. Acetylene reacts with molten sodium to form a monosodium derivative (sodium acetylide) at 110°.

$$HC\equiv CH + Na \text{ (molten at 110°)} \longrightarrow [HC\equiv C^-]Na^+$$

Sodium acetylide can be formed also by passing acetylene into a dilute solution of sodium in liquid ammonia or into a solution of sodium amide in liquid ammonia.

$$HC\equiv CH + NaNH_2 \longrightarrow [HC\equiv C^-]Na^+ + NH_3$$

If acetylene is passed into sodium at 190°–220°, or if sodium acetylide is heated at this temperature, sodium carbide is formed.

$$HC\equiv CH + 2\ Na \text{ (at 190°–220°)} \longrightarrow Na^+[^-C\equiv C^-]Na^+$$

$$2\ [HC\equiv C^-]Na^+ \xrightarrow{\text{Heat at 200°}} Na_2C_2 + C_2H_2$$

Acetylene reacts readily with aqueous ammoniacal silver nitrate or aqueous ammoniacal cuprous chloride solutions to give water-insoluble carbides.

$$HC\equiv CH + 2\ Ag(NH_3)_2NO_3 \longrightarrow Ag_2C_2 + 2\ NH_4NO_3 + 2\ NH_3$$

$$HC\equiv CH + 2\ Cu(NH_3)_2Cl \longrightarrow Cu_2C_2 + 2\ NH_4Cl + 2\ NH_3$$

Compounds of the type $RC\equiv CH$ yield acetylides, $[RC\equiv C^-]Ag^+$ and $[RC\equiv C^-]Cu^+$, whereas compounds of the type $RC\equiv CR$ do not react. These reactions are useful to distinguish acetylene and monosubstituted acetylenes from olefins and disubstituted acetylenes.

The heavy metal carbides are thermodynamically unstable and may be exploded when dry by heat or shock with the formation of the metal and carbon. Silver carbide, for example, explodes at 140°–150°. Sodium carbide, on the other hand, is stable up to 400°, and calcium carbide, which is made in the electric furnace, melts without decomposition at 2300°.

The acetylides and carbides are salts of the very weak acid, acetylene, and hence are hydrolyzed by water.

$$[HC\equiv \bar{C}]\ Na^+ + H_2O \longrightarrow NaOH + C_2H_2$$

$$Ca^{++}[\bar{C}\equiv \bar{C}] + 2\ H_2O \longrightarrow Ca(OH)_2 + C_2H_2$$

A mineral acid is required to decompose the heavy metal salts.

$$Ag_2C_2 + 2\,HNO_3 \longrightarrow 2\,AgNO_3 + C_2H_2$$

Acetylenic hydrogen (the hydrogen in $HC\equiv CH$ or $RC\equiv CH$) is sufficiently more acidic than alkane hydrogen (the hydrogen in RCH_3) to liberate alkanes from alkyl Grignard reagents with the formation of acetylenic Grignard reagents.

$$RC\equiv CH + R'MgX \longrightarrow RC\equiv CMgX + R'H$$

Since Grignard reagents undergo a great variety of reactions, the acetylenic Grignard reagents are valuable for the preparation of other compounds containing the triple bond.

Industrial Preparation and Use of Acetylene

Acetylene is the only commercially important compound of the series. Although it can be made by any of the general methods, it usually is made by a much cheaper method from calcium carbide.

$$\underset{\text{Coke}\quad\text{Lime}}{3\,C + CaO} \xrightarrow[\text{(2000°)}]{\text{Electric furnace}} \underset{\substack{\text{Calcium}\\\text{carbide}}}{CaC_2} + CO$$

$$CaC_2 + 2\,H_2O \longrightarrow HC\equiv CH + Ca(OH)_2$$

Acetylene can be produced by the decomposition of hydrocarbons at high temperatures. Whereas the order of stability at 25° is ethane > ethylene > acetylene, at 1000° they are about equally stable, and at higher temperatures the order is reversed. If the time of exposure to the high temperature is short enough and the products can be cooled quickly enough, about 50 per cent of the carbon in the feed stock can be converted to ethylene and acetylene. A temperature of around 1350° and a contact time of 0.1 second with as rapid cooling of the products as possible appear to be the optimum conditions.

A process which is being investigated extensively in the United States involves the partial oxidation of methane with oxygen. The temperature used is 1500° and the contact time is 0.01 second with rapid quenching. In addition to acetylene, carbon monoxide and hydrogen also are formed in about the right proportions for the synthesis of methanol.

Acetylene is a colorless gas which boils at −84°. The crude product from calcium carbide has a garlic odor because of the presence of phosphine. Acetylene cannot be liquefied safely, since it is thermodynamically unstable and explodes from shock with the formation of the elements.

$$C_2H_2 \longrightarrow 2\,C + H_2 + 56\,kcal.$$

At atmospheric pressure acetylene is soluble to the extent of one volume of the gas in one volume of water, four volumes in one of benzene (p. 310), six volumes in one of ethyl alcohol, and twenty-five volumes in one of acetone (p. 180). At twelve atmospheres 300 volumes will dissolve in one volume of acetone. Since this solution is stable, acetylene is transported under pressure in tanks filled with a porous material saturated with acetone.

One of the earlier **uses for acetylene** was as an illuminant. When special tips are used which mix it with the proper amount of air, it burns with an intense white flame. Decomposition of the gas gives carbon particles which, because of the high temperature of the flame, are heated to a white incandescence. For the same reason acetylene was mixed with coal gas used for lighting to increase the luminosity of the flame. In 1945 about one fourth of the acetylene produced was used for the welding and cutting of iron and steel by means of the oxyacetylene flame, which has a temperature in the neighborhood of 2800°.

About 70 per cent of the acetylene produced is used for the preparation of other organic chemicals. Acetylene dichloride and tetrachloride are made by the addition of chlorine to acetylene and are used as solvents and for the preparation of other compounds (p. 506). Catalytic addition of water gives acetaldehyde from which acetic acid and a large number of other organic compounds can be made (p. 134). Catalytic addition of acetic acid yields vinyl acetate (p. 516), and addition of alcohols yields vinyl ethers (p. 517), which are used in the preparation of plastics and other useful products. Vinylacetylene (p. 503) and 1,3-butadiene (p. 501), which are starting points for synthetic rubbers, are synthesized from acetylene.

REVIEW QUESTIONS

1. Summarize the general methods discussed thus far for the synthesis of alkanes.
2. Summarize the general methods discussed thus far for the synthesis of alkenes.
3. Butane and 2-butene boil at nearly the same temperature. How could chemical reactions be used to obtain each in a pure form?
4. Give reactions illustrating the preparation of (*a*) *i*-pentane from an alkyl halide; (*b*) 2,5-dimethylhexane from a four-carbon alkyl halide; (*c*) *sym*-methyl-*i*-propylethylene from an alkyl halide; (*d*) 3-ethyl-2-pentene from a dihalide.
5. Give a series of reactions that would lead to the synthesis of (*a*) 3-methylhexane from ethyl-*s*-butylcarbinol; (*b*) dimethylethylmethane from *t*-amyl chloride; (*c*) 2,3-dimethylbutane from *i*-propyl alcohol; (*d*) 2-pentene from 1-pentene.
6. Write structural formulas for all the isomeric alkynes having the molecular formula C_6H_{10} and give a name to each.
7. Write structural formulas for 4-methyl-2-pentyne; sodium methylacetylide; silver carbide.
8. Discuss the similarities and differences in the physical and chemical properties of compounds having the general formulas RCH_2CH_3, $RCH{=}CH_2$, and $RC{\equiv}CH$.
9. If a gas is propane, propylene, or methylacetylene, how may it be identified without resorting to quantitative determinations? Illustrate by equations.
10. How could a mixture of ethane, ethylene, and acetylene be separated by chemical means, recovering each as the pure hydrocarbon? Give equations for the reactions involved.
11. Give reactions for the preparation of (*a*) methylacetylene from *i*-propyl bromide; (*b*) dimethylacetylene from *s*-butyl alcohol; (*c*) methylethylacetylene from methylacetylene; (*d*) 2-butyne from 2-butene.
12. Give reactions for the conversion of (*a*) 1,2-dibromopentane into 2-bromopentane; (*b*) 2,3-dibromobutane into 2,2-dibromobutane; (*c*) ethylacetylene into *s*-butyl bromide.

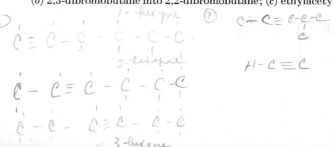

Chapter 9

ETHERS

[handwritten annotations: CH₃CH₂OH, ethyl alcohol, ether —C—O—C—, —C—C—]

The simplest ethers have the general molecular formula $C_nH_{2n+2}O$, and hence are isomeric with the alcohols. Unlike the alcohols, no ether is known containing only one carbon atom, the first member of the series having the molecular formula C_2H_6O. If the formula CH_3CH_2OH is assigned to ethyl alcohol the only other structural formula possible for an isomer would be that in which the oxygen atom joins two carbon atoms, and hence the first ether should contain the structure C—O—C. By placing the hydrogen atoms on the two carbon atoms to give the compound CH_3OCH_3, all of the rules of valence are satisfied. The general formula for the ethers would be ROR. The methods of preparation and chemical properties of the ethers confirm this structure.

Nomenclature

The word *ether* (Gr. *aither*, applied to the material filling heavenly space) was given to ethyl ether because of its volatility. The ethers commonly are divided into two groups, the simple ethers, ROR, in which both R groups are alike, and the mixed ethers, ROR′, in which the R groups are different. They generally are designated by naming the alkyl groups and adding the word *ether*. For the simple ethers no indication need be given that two alkyl groups are present in the molecule; $(CH_3)_2O$ is methyl ether, $CH_3OC_2H_5$ is methyl ethyl ether, and $(C_2H_5)_2O$ is ethyl ether.[1] *[handwritten: C H₃ O C H₃]*

The group RO is known as an *alkoxy group*, and in the Geneva (I.U.C.) system the ethers are named as alkoxy derivatives of hydrocarbons. Methyl ether is methoxymethane, and methyl ethyl ether is methoxyethane. This system usually is used only when other functional groups are present. For example $CH_3OCH_2CH_2CH_2OH$ may be called 3-methoxy-1-propanol.

Physical Properties

Since the ethers do not contain hydrogen united to the oxygen atom, there is no tendency for molecules to associate with each other by proton bonding, and the boiling points are nearly normal. Methyl ether boils at $-24°$ and propane at $-42°$, methyl ethyl ether boils at $6°$ and n-butane at $-1°$, and ethyl ether boils at $35°$ and n-pentane at $36°$.

Ethers have, however, an unshared pair of electrons on oxygen and can form proton bonds with water molecules. As would be expected, the solubilities in water are roughly the same as those of alcohols having the same number of carbon atoms. A saturated solution of ethyl ether in water at 25° con-

---

[1] Since there is no ambiguity in the term methyl ether it is redundant to call it dimethyl ether. The situation is comparable to naming Na_2SO_4 sodium sulfate rather than disodium sulfate. Similarly the addition product of chlorine to ethylene was called ethylene chloride rather than ethylene dichloride (p. 38), just as $MgCl_2$ is called magnesium chloride rather than magnesium dichloride. This same principle will be followed later in naming derivatives of other polyvalent compounds such as the esters of polycarboxylic acids (p. 415) and the alkyl peroxides (p. 573).

tains 6 per cent by weight of the ether, and a saturated solution of *n*-butyl alcohol at 25° contains 7.5 per cent by weight of the alcohol. Water is soluble in both but only 1.5 per cent in ether at 25° compared with 26 per cent in *n*-butyl alcohol at 15°.

Preparation

Ethers usually are made by one of two processes.

1. **The Williamson [2] Synthesis.** This method involves the reaction of a metallic alkoxide with an alkyl halide.

$$RONa + XR' \longrightarrow ROR' + NaX$$

The reaction may be used to prepare mixed ethers as well as simple ethers because it is not reversible. The reaction is important also because it affords synthetic proof of the structure of the ethers. Since an alkyl group has replaced the sodium of an alkoxide made by replacing the hydrogen of the hydroxyl group of an alcohol by sodium, an ether must have two alkyl groups combined with oxygen. Alkyl sulfates resemble alkyl halides in displacement reactions and also may be used to prepare ethers.

$$RONa + (R'O)_2SO_2 \longrightarrow ROR' + NaSO_3OR'$$

2. **The Sulfuric Acid Process.** Just as hydrolysis of alkyl sulfates yields alcohols (p. 68), the alcoholysis of alkyl sulfates yields ethers. Hence ethers can be made from alcohols by reaction with sulfuric acid.

$$ROH + H_2SO_4 \rightleftarrows ROSO_3H + H_2O$$

$$ROSO_3H + HOR \rightleftarrows ROR + H_2SO_4$$

This reaction is carried out by mixing equal moles of alcohol and concentrated sulfuric acid, and heating to a temperature sufficiently high to cause rapid reaction with alcohol but below the temperature for appreciable decomposition of the alkyl hydrogen sulfate to alkene (p. 76). On adding more alcohol to the mixture the ether distills. Yields of ethers are best with primary alcohols because the latter are the least readily dehydrated to olefins. The more volatile the ether, the more readily it is removed from the reaction mixture. If the ether boils above the temperature at which the alkyl hydrogen sulfate decomposes to olefin, the ether must be removed under reduced pressure. It is not possible to prepare ditertiary alkyl ethers by either process, because sodium alkoxides remove hydrogen halide from *t*-alkyl halides, and mineral acids dehydrate tertiary alcohols to give the olefin.

The equations indicate that the sulfuric acid procedure could be used for the preparation of mixed ethers by making the alkyl hydrogen sulfate from one alcohol and allowing the product to react with a second alcohol. Although the second alcohol does react, and some mixed ether is formed, the mixed ether

---

[2] Alexander William Williamson (1824–1904), professor at the University College, London. His synthesis of ethyl ether in 1850 cleared up the confusion existing then concerning the constitution of the alcohols and ethers. He also was the first to assign the correct structure to acetone (p. 180).

always is accompanied by large amounts of both simple ethers because of the easy reversibility of the reactions involved.

It is not necessary that the alkyl hydrogen sulfate be formed as an intermediate for ether formation to take place. As in the dehydration of alcohols, it has been shown that any strong acid such as hydrochloric acid or the sulfonic acids (p. 354), or in fact any strongly electron accepting reagent such as zinc chloride or boron fluoride, will catalyze ether formation. It has been shown also that hydrogen chloride catalyzes ether formation under conditions which do not lead to the formation of ether from ethyl chloride and ethyl alcohol. In general the mechanism undoubtedly is one of acid catalysis and displacement.

$$
\text{R} : \overset{\overset{H}{\cdot\cdot}}{\underset{\cdot\cdot}{O}} : \quad \underset{[B^-]}{\overset{HB}{\rightleftarrows}} \quad \left[\text{R} : \overset{\overset{H}{\cdot\cdot}}{\underset{\underset{+}{\cdot\cdot}}{O}} : H \right] \quad \underset{H_2O}{\overset{ROH}{\rightleftarrows}} \quad \left[\text{R} : \overset{\overset{+}{\cdot\cdot}}{\underset{\underset{H}{\cdot\cdot}}{O}} : R \right] \quad \underset{HB}{\overset{[B^-]}{\rightleftarrows}} \quad \text{R} : \overset{\cdot\cdot}{\underset{\cdot\cdot}{O}} : R
$$

In the above series and in subsequent equilibrium reactions illustrating stepwise mechanisms, it is convenient to adopt a convention which eliminates the necessity of rewriting formulas. The reagent is placed above the double arrow and the minor product which is eliminated is placed below the double arrow. According to the above series of reactions an alcohol molecule picks up a proton from the acid HB eliminating the base [B⁻]. The alkoxonium ion intermediate on collision with another alcohol molecule loses water with the formation of the ether oxonium ion which reacts with the base [B⁻] to regenerate the acid and produce the ether. In the reverse reaction the reagent is the substance below the arrows and the minor product eliminated is above the arrows. For example in the acid catalyzed hydrolysis of ethers, an acid molecule, HB, transfers a proton to the ether molecule forming an ether oxonium ion and eliminating the base [B⁻]. The ether oxonium ion reacts with a water molecule forming the alcohol oxonium ion and eliminating a molecule of alcohol. The alcohol oxonium ion transfers a proton to the base [B⁻] forming a molecule of alcohol and regenerating the acid, HB. It will be observed that the intermediates in brackets disappear and reagents and intermediates that appear both above and below the arrows cancel each other. Hence the over-all reaction is

$$
\text{ROH} + \text{ROH} \rightleftarrows \text{ROR} + \text{H}_2\text{O}
$$

In the sulfuric acid process it is possible that ether formation results from two different reactions that take place simultaneously. The more direct route would be that postulated for acids in general. The second route would involve the alkyl hydrogen sulfate as an intermediate.

$$
\text{R} : \overset{\overset{H}{\cdot\cdot}}{\underset{\cdot\cdot}{O}} : \quad \underset{[\bar{O}SO_3H]}{\overset{H_2SO_4}{\rightleftarrows}} \quad \left[\text{R} : \overset{\overset{H}{\cdot\cdot}}{\underset{\underset{+}{\cdot\cdot}}{O}} : H \right] \quad \underset{H_2O}{\overset{[\bar{O}SO_3H]}{\rightleftarrows}} \text{R} : OSO_3H \quad \underset{[\bar{O}SO_3H]}{\overset{ROH}{\rightleftarrows}} \quad \left[\text{R} : \overset{\overset{+}{\cdot\cdot}}{\underset{\underset{H}{\cdot\cdot}}{O}} : R \right] \quad \underset{H_2SO_4}{\overset{[\bar{O}SO_3H]}{\rightleftarrows}} \text{R} : \overset{\cdot\cdot}{\underset{\cdot\cdot}{O}} : R
$$

The reaction of sulfuric acid with an alcohol is a good example of the way in which the course of an organic reaction may be modified by conditions. If ethyl alcohol is allowed to react at ordinary temperatures with an excess of sulfuric acid, ethyl hydrogen sulfate is formed.

$$
\text{C}_2\text{H}_5\text{OH} + \text{H}_2\text{SO}_4 \longrightarrow \text{C}_2\text{H}_5\text{OSO}_3\text{H} + \text{H}_2\text{O}
$$

If ethyl hydrogen sulfate is heated to the point where it decomposes (above 150°), ethylene is formed.

$$
\text{C}_2\text{H}_5\text{OSO}_3\text{H} \longrightarrow \text{CH}_2{=}\text{CH}_2 + \text{H}_2\text{SO}_4
$$

If sulfuric acid is allowed to react with an excess of alcohol and the mixture heated under reduced pressure, ethyl sulfate distills.

$$C_2H_5OSO_3H + C_2H_5OH \longrightarrow (C_2H_5)_2SO_4 + H_2O$$

If ethyl hydrogen sulfate is heated to 140°–150° and alcohol added below the surface, ethyl ether distills.

$$C_2H_5OSO_3H + C_2H_5OH \longrightarrow (C_2H_5)_2O + H_2SO_4$$

Reactions

Ethers are relatively inert. Because the oxygen atom contains unshared electrons, ethers are capable of forming oxonium salts and addition complexes.

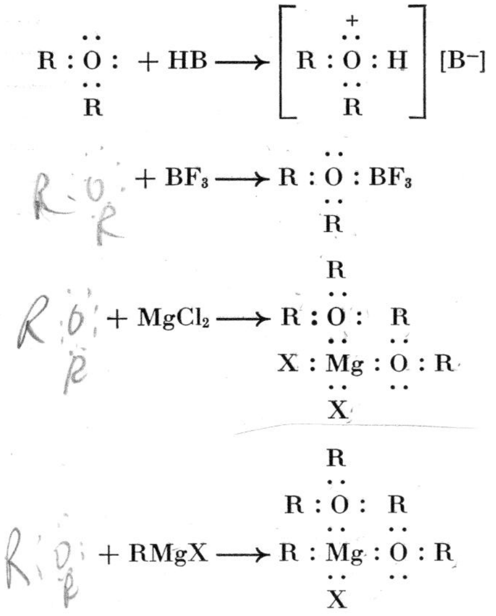

$$\overset{..}{\underset{R}{R : O :}} + HB \longrightarrow \left[\overset{+}{\underset{R}{R : O : H}} \right] [B^-]$$

$$R : \overset{..}{O :}_R + BF_3 \longrightarrow \overset{..}{\underset{R}{R : O : BF_3}}$$

$$R : \overset{..}{O :}_R + MgCl_2 \longrightarrow \overset{R}{\underset{X}{\overset{..}{R : O :} \quad R}} \underset{X}{X : Mg : O : R}$$

$$R : \overset{..}{O :}_R + RMgX \longrightarrow \overset{R}{\underset{X}{\overset{R : O : R}{R : Mg : O : R}}}$$

It is because of the last reaction that ether dissolves alkylmagnesium halides and is used as a solvent in preparing Grignard reagents. Not all ethers are suitable solvents, since the complexes in some cases, for example with *i*-propyl ether and dioxane (p. 522), are insoluble in an excess of the solvent.

All other reactions of the ethers must involve a scission of the carbon-oxygen bond. Because reagents which can split the carbon-oxygen bond in ethers can split the carbon-oxygen bond in alcohols as well, the initial reaction may be followed by a second to give the final product.

$$ROR \xrightarrow[\text{heat}]{H_2SO_4} ROSO_3H + ROH \xrightarrow{H_2SO_4} 2 ROSO_3H + H_2O$$

$$ROR \xrightarrow[\text{(or HI)}]{HBr} RBr + ROH \xrightarrow[\text{(or HI)}]{HBr} 2 RBr + H_2O$$
$$\qquad \text{(or RI)} \qquad\qquad \text{(or 2 RI)}$$

$$ROR + AlCl_3 \longrightarrow ROAlCl_2 + RCl$$

The reaction of ethers and of other compounds containing alkoxy groups with hydrogen iodide is important chiefly because it is the basis of the *Zeisel procedure for the estimation of methoxyl and ethoxyl.* Methyl or ethyl groups linked to oxygen are converted to the volatile methyl or ethyl iodides, which are distilled. The amount of alkyl iodide in the distillate is determined by reaction with alcoholic silver nitrate solution and collecting and weighing the precipitate of silver iodide.

A reaction of ethers which has not found a use but which always should be kept in mind because of its potential danger is the absorption of atmospheric oxygen to form peroxides (p. 579).

$$R_2O + O_2 \longrightarrow R_2O_3$$

These peroxides are unstable and decompose violently on heating. An instance has been reported in which a can containing *i*-propyl ether that had been exposed to air for some time exploded on being moved. Hence ethers should not be exposed to air unnecessarily and always should be tested for peroxides before use and especially before distillation. Peroxides can be detected readily since they liberate iodine from an acidified solution of potassium iodide. A more sensitive test for peroxides is the formation of black mercurous oxide on shaking with a globule of metallic mercury. Peroxides can be removed by shaking the ether with reducing agents (p. 579).

Uses of Ethers

Methyl ether boils at $-24°$ and can be used as a solvent and extracting agent at low temperatures and as a propellant for aerosol sprays. The preparation of **ethyl ether** first was recorded in 1552. Since it was made by the sulfuric acid process, it usually contained sulfur as an impurity, and it was not until 1800 that it was proved that sulfur was not part of the ether molecule. Since 1846 ethyl ether has been used as a general anesthetic [3] and still is the most widely used substance for this purpose. It is used also as a solvent for fats. It frequently is used in the laboratory as a solvent for extracting organic compounds from aqueous solutions, although it is not always the best solvent for this purpose. The disadvantages are that water and ether are appreciably soluble in each other, and ether is very soluble in strongly acid solutions. Moreover it emulsifies readily making separation of the ether and water layers difficult. Finally it usually contains peroxides, which should be removed both for safety and because the peroxides may oxidize the product being extracted. Petroleum ether (p. 54) is free from these disadvantages, and if the distribution coefficient in petroleum ether is unfavorable, benzene (p. 310) or one of the lower boiling chlorinated hydrocarbons, such as methylene chloride (p. 505) or ethylene chloride (p. 506), usually can be used.

Ordinary ether contains some water and alcohol which are detrimental for some purposes such as the preparation of Grignard reagents. Both impurities may be removed by allowing the ether to stand over metallic sodium since sodium hydroxide and sodium ethoxide are insoluble in ether. The pure product is known as **absolute ether.**

---

[3] A general anesthetic is one that acts on the brain and produces unconsciousness as well as insensitivity to pain. In local anesthesia and spinal anesthesia, only portions of the body are rendered insensitive to pain, and the patient retains consciousness.

Methyl propyl ether (*metopryl*) has been reported to be more potent and less irritant than ethyl ether as a general anesthetic. **i-Propyl ether** is a co-product of the manufacture of *i*-propyl alcohol from propylene. **n-Butyl ether** (b.p. 142°) and **i-amyl ether** (b.p. 173°) are made from the alcohols and are used as higher boiling solvents. **β-Chloroethyl ether** (Chlorex), $(ClCH_2CH_2)_2O$, is made by the action of sulfuric acid on ethylene chlorohydrin, $ClCH_2CH_2OH$ (p. 521). It is used as a soil fumigant, as a solvent for refining lubricating oils (p. 54), and in the manufacture of the synthetic rubbers, Thiokol B and Thiokol D (p. 504). Like other β-chloroethers, the halogen is very unreactive. For example it does not react with sodium cyanide to give the cyano ether or with magnesium to give a Grignard reagent.

REVIEW QUESTIONS AND PROBLEMS

1. Write structural formulas for all of the isomeric ethers containing five carbon atoms and name each.
2. Explain the advantages and disadvantages of the Williamson synthesis and the sulfuric acid process for making ethers.
3. Give the probable mechanism for the acid-catalyzed formation of ethers from alcohols. What facts support this view?
4. Why are di-*t*-alkyl ethers difficult to prepare? How may the mixed primary-tertiary alkyl ethers be prepared (*a*) from olefins; (*b*) by the Williamson synthesis?
5. Give equations and conditions for preparing each of the following compounds from the two reagents, ethyl alcohol and sulfuric acid: ethyl hydrogen sulfate; ethylene; ethyl ether; ethyl sulfate.
6. Give equations for the preparation of di-*n*-propyl ether; ethyl *n*-butyl ether; methyl *t*-amyl ether.
7. Why does ethyl ether have about the same solubility in water as *n*-butyl alcohol but a boiling point 82° lower? What normal alkane would be expected to boil approximately where ether boils?
8. Why is ether only slightly soluble in water but miscible with concentrated aqueous hydrochloric acid? Why is dry hydrogen chloride very soluble in both ether and water but not in hexane or carbon tetrachloride?
9. Why does the Grignard reagent dissolve in ether but not in hydrocarbons? Name some inorganic compounds that dissolve in ether.
10. Give equations for the conversion of ether into (*a*) ethyl bromide; (*b*) ethyl alcohol; (*c*) ethylene.
11. What is absolute ether and how may it be prepared? What are some of the common uses of ether?
12. Why is it dangerous to distill ethers that have been exposed to air? What disadvantage may arise if an ether that has been exposed to air is used as a solvent for extraction or for a reaction? What reactions can be used to determine whether an ether is safe to use?
13. What simple chemical tests could be used to distinguish between an alcohol, an ether, an olefin, and a saturated hydrocarbon?
14. Suppose that the molecular formula of a compound is found to be C_3H_8O. How could the structural formula of the compound be determined?
15. Two compounds have the molecular formula $C_4H_{10}O$. One gives ethyl iodide and the other *s*-butyl iodide on treatment with hydrogen iodide. What are the two compounds?
16. Give reactions for the conversion of (*a*) 1-butene into *s*-butyl ether; (*b*) *i*-propyl ether into propylene; (*c*) *i*-amyl ether into 2,7-dimethyloctane; (*d*) *n*-propyl ether into *i*-propyl ether.
17. In a Zeisel determination of methoxyl, 0.1178 g. of substance gave 0.2712 g. of silver iodide. What was the per cent methoxyl in the compound? What was the equivalent weight of the compound?

Chapter 10

CARBOXYLIC ACIDS AND THEIR DERIVATIVES

CARBOXYLIC ACIDS

Numerous types of organic compounds transfer protons to bases more readily than does the water molecule, and these compounds are referred to as organic acids or acidic compounds. The carboxylic acids constitute one of the most important groups of compounds having this property.

Structure

The simplest carboxylic acids have the general formula $C_nH_{2n}O_2$, and since a carboxylic acid having only one carbon atom is known, namely formic acid, CH_2O_2, the number of possible structures is limited. If unlikely structures containing unpaired electrons are omitted, only two formulas, I and II, are reasonable from the theory of electronic structure. Formula I has two oxygen

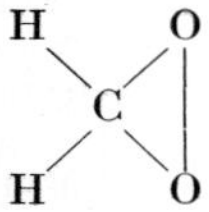

$$
\begin{array}{ccc}
\underset{\text{I}}{\overset{\displaystyle H \diagdown \quad O}{\underset{\displaystyle H \diagup \quad O}{C}}}
&
\underset{\text{II}}{H-\overset{\displaystyle O}{\overset{\|}{C}}-O-H}
&
\underset{\text{III}}{R-\overset{\displaystyle O}{\overset{\|}{C}}-O-H}
\end{array}
$$

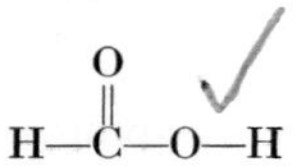

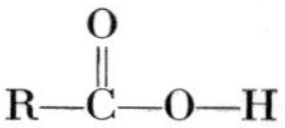

atoms joined to each other; that is it has a peroxide structure. Carboxylic acids, however, do not show any of the properties of peroxides, such as the liberation of iodine from hydrogen iodide solutions. Moreover all monocarboxylic acids contain only one ionizable hydrogen atom. If the hydrogen atoms in formula I ionized, both would be expected to do so. Formula II in which one hydrogen is joined to oxygen and one to carbon accounts for the difference in behavior of the hydrogen atoms. Formula III is the general formula for the homologous series. The methods of synthesis and reactions of carboxylic acids confirm the view that both the doubly bound oxygen atom and the hydroxyl group are combined with a single carbon atom to give the group —COOH, which is known as the *carboxyl group*.

General Methods of Preparation

1. *From the Grignard Reagent and Carbon Dioxide* (p. 89).

$$
RMgX + O{=}C{=}O \longrightarrow R-\overset{\displaystyle O}{\overset{\|}{C}}-OMgX \xrightarrow{\text{HX}} R-\overset{\displaystyle O}{\overset{\|}{C}}-OH + MgX_2
$$

This reaction is not only one of the best general methods for synthesizing carboxylic acids, but it affords good proof of their structure.

120

2. By the Hydrolysis of Alkyl Cyanides (Nitriles).

$$RC\equiv N + 2\,H_2O + HCl \longrightarrow RCOOH + NH_4Cl$$

$$RC\equiv N + H_2O + NaOH \longrightarrow RCOONa + NH_3$$

Both of these reactions are the result of the addition of water to the cyano group, followed by loss of ammonia. The addition is catalyzed both by protons and by hydroxide ions and is a reversible reaction, but the secondary reactions, that is formation of ammonium chloride or of ammonia, are irreversible and the reaction goes to completion. Like the preparation of carboxylic acids from Grignard reagents, the formation by the hydrolysis of nitriles proves that both oxygen atoms in carboxylic acids must be united to a single carbon atom.

3. By the Oxidation of Primary Alcohols.

When primary alcohols are oxidized by an excess of a strong oxidizing agent such as sodium dichromate and sulfuric acid, chromium trioxide in glacial acetic acid, potassium permanganate, or nitric acid, carboxylic acids are produced.

$$RCH_2OH + 2\,[O] \longrightarrow RCOOH + H_2O$$

The symbol [O] merely means any suitable oxidizing agent. The oxidizing agents suitable for the reaction must be remembered. Moreover it is assumed that the student has learned how to balance oxidation and reduction reactions and is able to write balanced equations when necessary (p. 122). For example when sodium dichromate and sulfuric acid is used as the oxidizing agent, the balanced equation is

$$3\,RCH_2OH + 2\,Na_2Cr_2O_7 + 8\,H_2SO_4 \longrightarrow 3\,RCOOH + 2\,Cr_2(SO_4)_3 + 2\,Na_2SO_4 + 11\,H_2O$$

4. By the Oxidation of Unsaturated Compounds.

Controlled oxidation of alkenes with a dilute solution of potassium permanganate yields the dihydroxy derivative (p. 40). The presence of oxygen on two adjacent carbon atoms makes the carbon-carbon bond more susceptible to oxidation, and under the more vigorous conditions of higher temperature, longer time of reaction, and higher concentration of oxidizing agent, the dihydroxyalkane is oxidized to two molecules of carboxylic acid. Since potassium hydroxide is one of the products of oxidation, the salt of the acid is the actual product.

$$3\,RCH{=}CHR' + 2\,KMnO_4 + 4\,H_2O \longrightarrow 3\,\underset{\underset{OH}{|}}{R}CH{-}\underset{\underset{OH}{|}}{C}HR' + 2\,MnO_2 + 2\,KOH$$

$$3\,\underset{\underset{OH}{|}}{R}CH{-}\underset{\underset{OH}{|}}{C}HR' + 6\,KMnO_4 \longrightarrow 3\,RCOOK + 3\,KOOCR' + 6\,MnO_2 + 6\,H_2O$$

Adding these two equations gives

$$3\,RCH{=}CHR' + 8\,KMnO_4 \longrightarrow 3\,RCOOK + 3\,KOOCR' + 8\,MnO_2 + 2\,H_2O + 2\,KOH$$

If one or both of the doubly bound carbon atoms lacks a hydrogen atom, the reaction gives one or two molecules of ketone.

$$R_2C{=}CHR' + 2\ KMnO_4 \longrightarrow R_2C{=}O + KOOCR' + 2\ MnO_2 + KOH$$

Unsaturated compounds having a terminal methylene group give potassium carbonate since the formic acid produced is oxidized further to carbon dioxide and water (p. 133).

$$3\ RCH{=}CH_2 + 10\ KMnO_4 \longrightarrow 3\ RCOOK + 3\ K_2CO_3 + 10\ MnO_2 + 4\ H_2O + KOH$$

Balancing Oxidation-Reduction Equations

By Inspection. When sodium dichromate is reduced to chromic sulfate, three oxygen atoms are available for oxidation. When a primary alcohol is oxidized to an acid, two atoms of oxygen are required.

$$Na_2Cr_2O_7 + 4\ H_2SO_4 \longrightarrow Na_2SO_4 + Cr_2(SO_4)_3 + 4\ H_2O + 3\ [O]$$

$$RCH_2OH + 2\ [O] \longrightarrow RCOOH + H_2O$$

Therefore if the first equation is multiplied by two and the second by three and these equations added, a balanced equation will result.

Potassium permanganate in neutral or alkaline solution is reduced to manganese dioxide. For each two moles of permanganate, three atoms of oxygen are available for oxidation.

$$2\ KMnO_4 + H_2O \longrightarrow 2\ KOH + 2\ MnO_2 + 3\ [O]$$

In acid solution the reduction product is a manganous salt, and five atoms of oxygen are available from two moles of permanganate.

$$2\ KMnO_4 + 3\ H_2SO_4 \longrightarrow K_2SO_4 + 2\ MnSO_4 + 3\ H_2O + 5\ [O]$$

When nitric acid is used as an oxidizing agent, the reduction product ordinarily is considered to be nitrogen dioxide and each two moles of nitric acid provide one atom of oxygen.

$$2\ HNO_3 \longrightarrow 2\ NO_2 + H_2O + [O]$$

If the reduction product is nitrogen trioxide, each mole of nitric acid provides one atom of oxygen.

$$2\ HNO_3 \longrightarrow N_2O_3 + H_2O + 2\ [O]$$

If the reduction product is nitric oxide, two moles of nitric acid provide three atoms of oxygen.

$$2\ HNO_3 \longrightarrow 2\ NO + H_2O + 3\ [O]$$

By Change in Polar Number (Oxidation Number). Since oxidation is the loss of electrons and reduction the gain of electrons, balancing the gain and loss of electrons will lead to the balancing of oxidation and reduction equations. Here certain atoms of the molecules involved are considered to be oxidized or reduced in the reaction. The degree of oxidation or reduction of an atom in a molecule or ion is considered to be proportional to the electron concentration about the atom compared with that of the free atom. Each bond to the atom is assigned a unit polarity, the direction of polarity depending on which atom has the greater attraction for electrons. Hydrogen always is considered positive with respect to other atoms. For other elements the attraction for electrons increases from left to right in a given period and decreases from top to bottom in a given column of the periodic table (cf. Table 6, p. 64). Thus in a primary alcohol the R—C bond is between two carbon atoms and is assigned zero polarity. Each C—H bond and the O—H bond are assigned polarities with the negative end at carbon or oxygen and the positive end at hydrogen. The C—O bond is assigned a polarity with the positive end at carbon and the negative end at oxygen. The same is true for each bond of the double bond in the carboxyl group of acetic acid.

The algebraic sum of the charges on any atom is its **polar number or oxidation number.** Thus the polar number of carbon in a primary alcohol group is $0 - 1 + 1 - 1 = -1$, and that in a carboxyl group is $0 + 1 + 1 + 1 = +3$. If the polar number becomes more positive in a reaction, indicating a decrease in electron density, the atom is oxidized, and if it becomes less positive, indicating an increase in electron density, it is reduced. The change in polar number of an atom in an oxidizing agent must balance the change in the polar number of an atom in the molecule being reduced.

In the unbalanced reaction

$$RCH_2OH + Na_2Cr_2O_7 + H_2SO_4 \longrightarrow RCOOH + Cr_2(SO_4)_3 + Na_2SO_4 + H_2O$$

the atoms undergoing a change in polar number are the carbon atom in the primary alcohol, which changes from -1 to $+3$ or a change of $+4$, and the chromium atoms in the dichromate which change from $+6$ to $+3$ or a change of -3 for each chromium atom, a total change for the two atoms of -6. To balance $+4$ against -6, $+4$ may be multiplied by 6 and -6 by 4, or more simply $+4$ by 3 and -6 by 2. Hence three molecules of alcohol will be oxidized by two molecules of dichromate. The moles of sulfuric acid required and the moles of water formed follow from the number of sulfate ions required and the amount of hydrogen available.

It is unfortunate that the expression *change in valence* sometimes is used in balancing oxidation-reduction reactions when *change in polar number* is meant. The term *valence* should be reserved for the number of covalent bonds by which an atom is united to other atoms or for the number of charges which an ion bears. It is obvious in this example that the valence of carbon has not changed on being oxidized from a CH_2 group to a C=O group but remains four throughout, whereas the polar number has changed from -1 to $+3$.

By Means of Half-Reactions. Oxidation and reduction equations may be balanced by the method of half-reactions. In the present example one half of the reaction is the oxidation of alcohol molecules to acid molecules, and the other half is the reduction of dichromate ion to chromic ion. The source of oxygen for the oxidation half may be considered to be water molecules.

$$RCH_2OH + H_2O \dashrightarrow RCOOH + 4\,[H^+] + 4\,[e^-]$$

$$[Cr_2O_7^=] + 14\,[H^+] + 6\,[e^-] \longrightarrow 2\,[Cr^{+++}] + 7\,H_2O$$

Since the first half-reaction must supply as many electrons as are used by the second half-reaction, the first half-reaction must be multiplied by 3 and the second by 2. Addition then gives

$$3\,RCH_2OH + 2\,[Cr_2O_7^=] + 16\,[H^+] \longrightarrow 3\,RCOOH + 4\,[Cr^{+++}] + 11\,H_2O$$

All of the above schemes for balancing oxidation and reduction equations are empirical and arbitrary and none is more scientific than the others. In the first method oxygen is assumed to be available from the oxidizing agent; in the second method the atoms are assumed to differ in polarity by unit charges; in the third method the reaction is assumed to take place by the elimination of electrons and the consumption of electrons. These assumptions merely are devices for arriving at the desired result, and that method should be used which seems preferable to the individual. The oxidation of organic compounds usually is limited to the addition of oxygen or the removal of hydrogen, and reduction to the addition of hydrogen or the removal of oxygen. Since the oxygen or hydrogen requirement in organic oxidations and reductions can be determined at a glance, the first method given for balancing oxidation-reduction equations is the simplest. Whatever method is used, it should be practiced sufficiently to be carried out correctly and with facility.

Nomenclature

Common Names. Normal carboxylic acids were isolated first from natural sources, particularly from the fats (Chapter 11). Hence they frequently are called *fatty acids*. Since nothing was known about their structure, they were given common names indicating their source. These names and the derivations of the names together with some physical properties are given in Table 8.

TABLE 8

COMMON NAMES OF NORMAL CARBOXYLIC ACIDS

NO. OF CARBON ATOMS	NAME OF ACID	DERIVATION OF NAME	BOILING POINT	MELTING POINT	DENSITY $20°/4°$
			°	°	
1	Formic	L. *formica* ant	100.7	8.4	1.220
2	Acetic	L. *acetum* vinegar	118.2	16.6	1.049
3	Propionic	Gr. *proto* first *pion* fat	141.4	−20.8	0.993
4	Butyric	L. *butyrum* butter	164.1	−5.5	0.958
5	Valeric	valerian root (L. *valere* to be strong)	186.4	−34.5	0.939
6	Caproic	L. *caper* goat	205.4	−3.9	0.936
7	Enanthic or heptylic	Gr. *oenanthe* vine blossom	223.0	−7.5	0.918
8	Caprylic	L. *caper* goat	239.3	16.3	0.909
9	Pelargonic	Pelargonium	253.0	12.0	
10	Capric	L. *caper* goat	268.7	31.3	
11	Undecanoic		280	28.5	
12	Lauric	laurel		43.2	
13	Tridecanoic			41.6	
14	Myristic	Myristica (nutmeg)		53.9	
15	Pentadecanoic			52.3	
16	Palmitic	palm oil		62.8	
17	Margaric	Gr. *margaron* pearl		61.2	
18	Stearic	Gr. *stear* tallow		69.6	
19	Nonadecanoic			69–70	
20	Arachidic	Arachis (peanut)		75.4	
21	Heneicosanoic			74.3	
22	Behenic	behen oil		79.9	
23	Tricosanoic			79.1	
24	Lignoceric	L. *lignum* wood *cera* wax		84.2	
25	Pentacosanoic			83.5	
26	Cerotic	L. *cera* wax		87.7	

Geneva names are given for the odd-carbon acids above C_{10} rather than common names. The reason is that only acids with an even number of carbon atoms have been found in fats, the odd-carbon acids having been prepared synthetically by hydrolysis of the nitriles. The name *margaric* appears to be an exception. However it has been shown that the material isolated from fats and thought to be a C_{17} acid actually is a mixture of palmitic and stearic

CH₃ CH₃ CH COOH

acids. When the true C_{17} normal acid was synthesized, the common name was retained.

As with other homologous series, those compounds having a branching methyl group at the end of the hydrocarbon-chain may be named by adding the prefix *iso* to the common name, for example $(CH_3)_2CHCOOH$, isobutyric acid, or $(CH_3)_2CHCH_2CH_2CH_2CH_2CH_2CH_2COOH$, isocapric acid. If the methyl branch occurs at any other portion of the chain, the designation *iso* may not be used.

As Derivatives of Normal Acids. Acetic acid most frequently is considered as the parent compound, and derivatives are considered as compounds in which the hydrogen atoms of the methyl group are replaced by other groups. For example $CH_3CH_2CH(CH_3)CH(CH_3)COOH$ would be called methyl-*s*-butylacetic acid. This compound also might be considered to be derived from valeric acid and might be called α,β-dimethylvaleric acid or 2,3-dimethyl-valeric acid. When Greek letters are used to designate the positions of the substituents, the α carbon atom of the chain is the carbon atom adjacent to the carboxyl group. When numerals are used, the carbon atom of the carboxyl group is numbered 1.

Geneva System. The final *e* is dropped from the name of the hydrocarbon having the same number of carbon atoms as the longest chain containing the carboxyl group, and *oic* acid is added. The carbon atom of the carboxyl group always is numbered 1 when numbering the atoms of the longest chain. For example $CH_3CH_2CH(CH_3)CH(CH_3)COOH$ would be called 2,3-dimethyl-pentanoic acid.

A second procedure is permitted in which the carboxyl is considered as a substituting group. The longest hydrocarbon chain exclusive of the carboxyl group is chosen, and the acid named as a derivative of this parent hydrocarbon. By this method 2,3-dimethylpentanoic acid would be called 3-methyl-2-pentanecarboxylic acid. In practice the latter method is used only for more complicated polyfunctional compounds in which the application of the usual Geneva rules would not be convenient.

Physical Properties

The **boiling points** of carboxylic acids (Table 8) rise more or less uniformly with increase in molecular weight, the increase for those given averaging about 18° per additional methylene group, the same as for the alcohols. The magnitude of the boiling points, however, is even more abnormal than for the alcohols. Ethyl alcohol boils at 78°, but formic acid having the same molecular weight boils at 101°; *n*-propyl alcohol boils at 98°, but acetic acid boils at 118°. The explanation of the abnormal boiling points of the acids is the same as that for the alcohols, namely association by proton bonds, but the acids are able to form double molecules which are more stable than the association complexes formed by the alcohols.

$$R-C \underset{\overset{..}{OH}}{\overset{\overset{..}{O}:}{\Big\langle}} \qquad \overset{HO}{\underset{:O}{\Big\rangle}} C-R$$

It has been shown by vapor density measurements that the double molecules of acetic acid persist even in the vapor state. Hence it is not surprising that the boiling point of acetic acid (118°, mol. wt. = 60 × 2 = 120) is of the same order of magnitude as *n*-octane (126°, mol. wt. 114).

An interesting characteristic of the normal carboxylic acids is the alternation in **melting points**. Acids with an even number of carbon atoms always melt at a higher temperature than the next member of the series (Fig. 29).

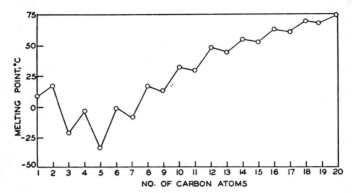

Fig. 29. Melting points of normal carboxylic acids.

X-ray diffraction has shown that in the solid state the carbon atoms of the hydrocarbon chain assume an extended zigzag arrangement in which the carboxyl groups of the odd carbon acids are on the same side of the chain as the terminal methyl groups, whereas those of the even carbon acids are on the opposite side of the chain (see p. 32). Although all of the acids are double molecules, the arrangement of those with an even number of carbon atoms gives a more symmetrical molecule and a more stable crystal lattice.

Because of partial ionization in water, carboxylic acids are somewhat more heavily hydrated than alcohols and hence show somewhat greater **solubility** in water. In general they have about the same solubility in water as the alcohol with one less carbon atom. For example *n*-butyric acid is miscible with water as is *n*-propyl alcohol, whereas *n*-butyl alcohol dissolves only to the extent of about 1 volume in 11 volumes of water. Monocarboxylic acids usually are soluble in other organic solvents.

Odor and Taste

The carboxylic acids which are sufficiently soluble in water to give an appreciable hydrogen ion concentration have a sour taste. The lower members have a sharp acrid odor, and the acids from butyric through heptylic have a disagreeable odor. The odor of rancid butter and strong cheese is due to volatile acids, and caproic acid gets its name from the fact that it is present in the skin secretions of goats. The higher acids are practically odorless because of their low volatility.

General Reactions of Free Acids

1. *Salt Formation.* Alcohols are weaker acids than water, whereas carboxylic acids are stronger than carbonic acid but weaker than mineral acids.

The strength of acids, that is the degree of ionization in water, usually is expressed in terms of the ionization constant, which is related to the equilibrium constant for the reversible reaction

$$HB + H_2O \rightleftharpoons H_3O^+ + B^-$$

The equilibrium constant for this reaction is

$$K = \frac{[H_3O^+][B^-]}{[HB][H_2O]}$$

Since the concentration of the water may be considered as constant, the above expression may be written

$$K_A = \frac{[H_3O^+][B^-]}{[HB]}$$

K_A is called the ionization constant for the acid and is proportional to the extent of ionization. The ionization constants for most simple carboxylic acids vary between 10^{-4} and 10^{-5}, whereas the first ionization constant of carbonic acid is 4.3×10^{-7}. The acid ionization constant of water is 7.3×10^{-20}. Hence carboxylic acids react with bicarbonates, carbonates, or hydroxides to form salts that are not hydrolyzed appreciably by water.

$$RCOOH + NaHCO_3 \longrightarrow [RCOO^-]Na^+ + CO_2 + H_2O$$

$$2\ RCOOH + Na_2CO_3 \longrightarrow 2\ [RCOO^-]Na^+ + CO_2 + H_2O$$

$$RCOOH + NaOH \longrightarrow [RCOO^-]Na^+ + H_2O$$

However carboxylic acids are displaced from their salts by mineral acids ($K_A > 10^{-1}$).

$$[RCOO^-]Na^+ + HCl \longrightarrow RCOOH + NaCl$$

The neutralization of an acid by a standard solution of a base is the customary procedure for estimating acids. When a weak acid is neutralized by a strong base, the equivalence point will be on the alkaline side because of hydrolysis of the salt. Therefore an indicator changing color at the proper acidity is necessary. For carboxylic acids, phenolphthalein usually is satisfactory. The equivalent weight of an acid as determined by neutralization with a standard base is known as the *neutralization equivalent* of the acid.

Since salts are completely ionized, and ions are more heavily hydrated than neutral molecules, the alkali metal salts of carboxylic acids are much more soluble than the acids themselves. For example whereas water solubility of the free normal acids approaches that of the saturated hydrocarbons above C_5, the sodium salts are very soluble up to C_{10} and form colloidal solutions from C_{10} to C_{18}. This fact is used to separate acids from water-insoluble compounds such as alcohols or hydrocarbons. Extraction of the mixture with dilute alkali causes the acid to go into the aqueous layer as the salt. The aqueous layer then can be separated and the free acid liberated from its salt by the addition of a mineral acid. It is necessary to add at least the calculated amount of mineral acid, or if the amount of salt present is unknown, to add mineral acid until a universal indicator, such as Hydrion paper, shows that a pH of 1 or 2 has been reached. Merely making the solution acid to litmus will not completely free the carboxylic acid from its salt because a mixture of the salt and organic acid will be acid to litmus.

Another result of the ionic nature of salts is that they are nonvolatile. The nonvolatility of salts permits volatile acids to be recovered from aqueous solutions or separated from other volatile substances by converting into salts and evaporating to dryness.

2. *Replacement of Hydroxyl by Halogen.* Since the hydroxyl group of alcohols can be replaced by halogen (p. 74), the hydroxyl group of carboxylic acids likewise might be expected to be replaceable. Replacement cannot be brought about with reagents such as the hydrogen halides, however, because the position of equilibrium lies far on the side of the carboxylic and halogen acid. Inorganic acid halides on the other hand react readily, the products being an organic acid halide (acyl halide) and an inorganic acid.

$$3\ RCOOH + PX_3 \longrightarrow 3\ R-\overset{\overset{\displaystyle O}{\|}}{C}-X + P(OH)_3$$
$$\text{An acyl}$$
$$\text{halide}$$

The reactions of other inorganic acid halides are discussed under the preparation of acyl halides (p. 135).

3. *Esterification.* Carboxylic acids react with alcohols to give esters and water. The reaction is catalyzed by hydrogen ion.

$$RCOOH + HOR' \underset{}{\overset{[H^+]}{\rightleftarrows}} R-\overset{\overset{\displaystyle O}{\|}}{C}-OR' + H_2O$$
$$\text{An ester}$$

The mechanism of acid catalysis is discussed on page 142.

4. *Decomposition to Ketones.* Ketones are formed when carboxylic acids are heated in the presence of thoria or manganous oxide to the point where decomposition takes place, or when salts of polyvalent metals such as calcium, lead, or thorium are pyrolyzed.

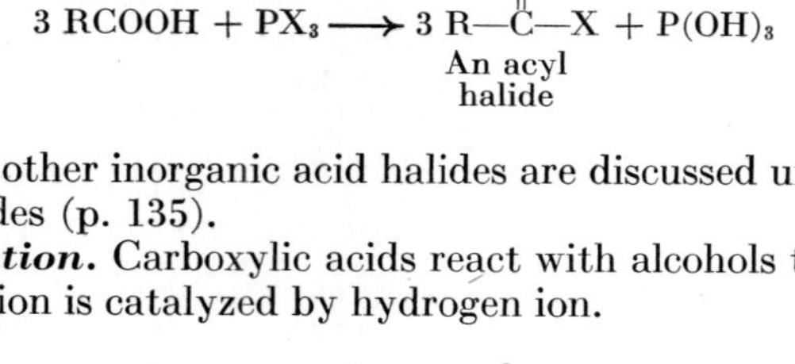

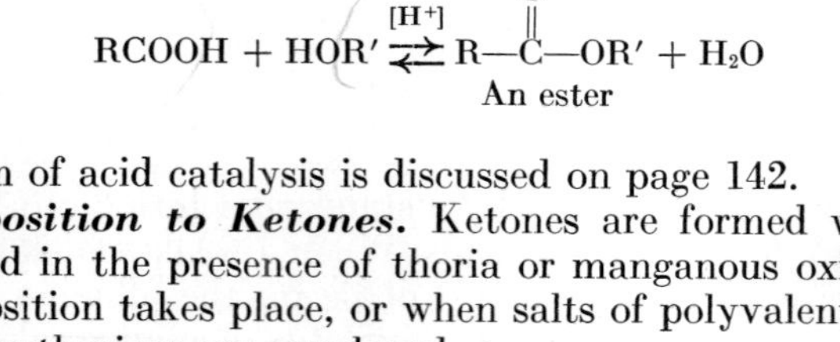

$$\begin{array}{l} R-\overset{\overset{\displaystyle O}{\|}}{C}-OH \\ R-\underset{\underset{\displaystyle O}{\|}}{C}-OH \end{array} \xrightarrow[400°-450°]{ThO_2\ or\ MnO} R-\overset{\overset{\displaystyle O}{\|}}{C}-R + CO_2 + H_2O$$
$$\text{A ketone}$$

$$\begin{bmatrix} R-\overset{\overset{\displaystyle O}{\|}}{C}-O^- \\ R-\underset{\underset{\displaystyle O}{\|}}{C}-O^- \end{bmatrix} Ca^{++} \xrightarrow[\text{decomposition}]{\text{Heat to}} R-\overset{\overset{\displaystyle O}{\|}}{C}-R + CaCO_3$$

In general the vapor-phase decomposition over thoria is the preferred method.

5. *Reduction to Alcohols.* It is possible to reduce acids to primary alcohols with hydrogen in the presence of a zinc-chromium-copper-cadmium catalyst at 350°–400° and 200 atmospheres pressure.

$$RCOOH + 2 H_2 \xrightarrow[350°–400°, \ 200 \ atm.]{Zn—Cr—Cu—Cd} RCH_2OH + H_2O$$

Because of the extreme conditions necessary to bring about the reaction, it rarely is used in the laboratory but has been carried out industrially (p. 159). For converting acids to alcohols on a small scale it is preferable to make first the methyl, ethyl, or butyl esters, and then reduce the esters catalytically, or with sodium and alcohol (p. 147).

In 1947 a very convenient reducing agent was announced, namely lithium aluminum hydride, LiAlH₄. It is soluble in ether and reacts quantitatively with acids, acid chlorides, esters, aldehydes, and ketones to give alcohols. It does not react with carbon-carbon double bonds.

$$4 \ RCOOH + 3 \ LiAlH_4 \longrightarrow LiAl(OCH_2R)_4 + 2 \ LiAlO_2 + 4 \ H_2$$

The reagent is relatively expensive and has been used mainly for research purposes. It is preferable to reduce a salt or the ester or acid chloride rather than the free acid, since less reagent is required (p. 147).

Acidity of Carboxylic Acids and Resonance in the Carboxylate Ion

The question arises as to why the replacement of one hydrogen atom of the water molecule by an alkyl group decreases the acidity, whereas replacement by the acyl group markedly increases the acidity. It is assumed that during ionization a proton leaves the acid; that is the pair of electrons binding the hydrogen and oxygen atoms remains with the oxygen atom. Hence any factors which tend to withdraw the electrons from the hydrogen should facilitate its removal as a proton, but forces tending to make the electrons more readily available should decrease the ease of removal as a proton. Since alkyl groups have a repelling effect on electrons (p. 97), substitution of one hydrogen of the water molecule by alkyl should make the electrons on the oxygen atom more readily available and the hydrogen of the alcoholic hydroxyl group less readily ionized. An acyl group, on the other hand, is an electron-attracting group because the oxygen atom with its greater nuclear charge pulls the electrons away from the carbon atom and makes it deficient in electrons (p. 63). Hence the acyl group facilitates the loss of a proton from a hydroxyl group.

Another factor which makes carboxylic acids lose a proton more readily than water is a phenomenon called **resonance**. If two or more electronic structures of the same or nearly the same stability can be written for the same arrangement of atoms, the most stable electronic structure is not that of any of the conventional structures but is a hybrid of all of the structures. Thus for the carboxylate ion, one electronic structure can be written in which one of the oxygen atoms is doubly bound, and a second structure in which the other oxygen atom is doubly bound. A more stable structure than either, however, is that in which interaction of the unsaturation electrons takes place over all three atoms concerned, that is the carbon atom and both oxygen atoms. This interaction may be represented by placing a double arrow between the conventional electronic structures and enclosing the whole in braces.

The double arrow does not imply an oscillation of electronic structures but symbolizes a hybridization of the conventional structures, and the actual molecule is said to be a *resonance hybrid*. The difference in energy between the conventional structure and that of the hybrid is called **resonance energy** of the molecule.

Two physical properties by which the extent of resonance can be observed are heats of reaction and interatomic distances. Thus the heat of combustion of a resonance hybrid should be less by an amount equal to the resonance energy than the heat of combustion of an isomeric compound containing the same functional groups in isolated positions where no resonance is possible. This effect is observed, although resonance energies as determined by differences in heats of combustion are not very accurate. The numerical values of the latter are large compared with the magnitude of the resonance energies, and small percentage errors in the heats of combustion may cause considerable error in the calculated value of the resonance energy.

Interatomic distances in molecules can be determined with high precision from X-ray diffraction data on crystals, from electron diffraction data on gases, or from spectroscopic data. The double bond shortens the distance between two atoms. Thus the distance between a carbon and oxygen atom linked by a single bond is 1.43 Å, whereas that between doubly linked carbon and oxygen is 1.24 Å. In the resonance hybrid, however, there is neither a single nor a double bond but a bond uniformly encompassing all three atoms. Therefore the distances between the carbon and either oxygen should be identical. Moreover this distance might be expected to be less than the average distance for a double and a single bond, since the resonance energy would cause the atoms to be bound more strongly. The measured distance in the formate ion is 1.27 Å.

To account for the fact that carboxylic acids ionize more readily than water or alcohols, it is necessary only to consider that for a proton to combine with a carboxylate ion, energy equivalent to the resonance energy of the ion must be supplied. Since a hydroxide or alkoxide ion is not stabilized by resonance, less energy is required for combination with a proton. Conversely a proton can leave the carboxyl group of an acid more readily than the hydroxyl group of water or an alcohol. Both the electrostatic (inductive) effect and the resonance effect operate to increase the ease of ionization of the proton. It is not known which effect is the more important.

Two electronic structures can be written for the undissociated carboxyl group, as well as for the carboxylate ion.

The second electronic structure, however, involves a separation of charge within the molecule and hence is much less stable than the first.[1] Since one of the requirements for resonance is that the conventional structures have the same or nearly the same stability, the resonance energy for the undissociated carboxyl group is much lower than that of the carboxylate ion.

The structure R—C—OH is still less stable than that having both charges on the oxygen

---

[1] The charges in these structures sometimes are called *formal charges*. They are arrived at by assuming that each atom possesses all of the unshared electrons placed about it and half of those in each shared pair. The difference between this number and the number of valence electrons in the normal state of the atom is the formal charge. Thus the hydroxyl oxygen possesses two electrons in the unshared pair and half of the three shared pairs or a total of five electrons. Since the oxygen atom has six valence electrons, the hydroxyl oxygen has a deficiency of one electron and bears a formal charge of +1. The carboxyl carbon has half of four shared pairs of electrons, which is the same as the number of valence electrons of the carbon atom, and the formal charge is 0. The second oxygen atom has three unshared pairs and half of a shared pair or a total of seven electrons. Therefore it possesses an excess of one electron and carries a formal charge of −1.

atoms, because the carbon atom does not have a complete octet of electrons. These views are confirmed by electron-diffraction data which show two carbon-oxygen distances in monomeric formic acid or acetic acid, one of 1.43 Å and the other of 1.24 Å, identical within experimental error with the single and double bond interatomic distances.

General Reactions of Salts

1. *Electrolysis* (*Kolbe Hydrocarbon Synthesis*). If an aqueous solution of a water-soluble salt is electrolyzed, the carboxylate ions are discharged at the anode and lose carbon dioxide. The resulting alkyl radicals couple to form a saturated hydrocarbon.

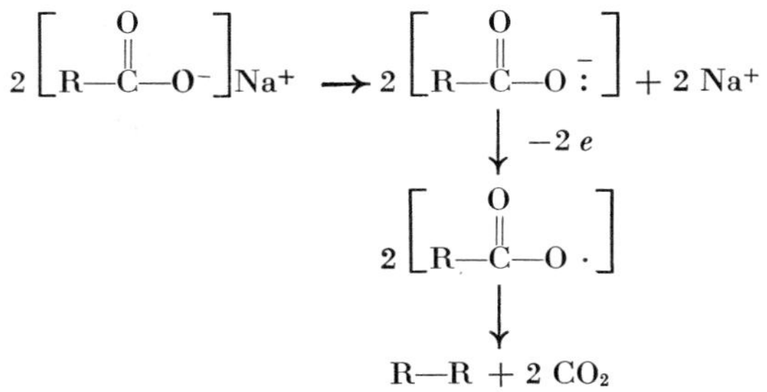

$$2 \left[\begin{array}{c} O \\ \| \\ R-C-O^- \end{array} \right] Na^+ \longrightarrow 2 \left[\begin{array}{c} O \\ \| \\ R-C-O : \end{array} \right]^- + 2\ Na^+$$

$$\Big\downarrow -2\ e$$

$$2 \left[\begin{array}{c} O \\ \| \\ R-C-O\ \cdot \end{array} \right]$$

$$\Big\downarrow$$

$$R-R + 2\ CO_2$$

Actually the reactions at the anode are more complicated than indicated. Hydroxide ions and hydrogen are formed at the cathode.

$$2\ H_2O + 2\ e \longrightarrow 2\ [^-OH] + 2\ [H\ \cdot\ ]$$

$$2\ [H\ \cdot\ ] \longrightarrow H_2$$

2. *Reaction with Alkyl Halides.* Reaction of a metallic salt with an alkyl halide produces an ester and metallic halide.

$$[RCOO^-]M^+ + XR' \longrightarrow RCOOR' + MX$$

Although sodium salts frequently give satisfactory yields, the use of the salt of a metal such as silver or mercury which forms a nonionized halide usually will improve the yield.

3. *Decomposition of Ammonium Salts.* When ammonium carboxylates are heated, two reactions take place: dissociation into the acid and ammonia,

$$[RCOO^-]NH_4^+ \rightleftarrows RCOOH + NH_3$$

and decomposition with the formation of an *amide* and water.

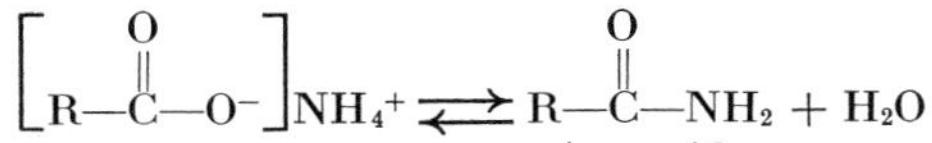

$$\left[\begin{array}{c} O \\ \| \\ R-C-O^- \end{array} \right] NH_4^+ \rightleftarrows \begin{array}{c} O \\ \| \\ R-C-NH_2 \end{array} + H_2O$$
$$\text{An amide}$$

If the ammonium salt is heated with an excess of the free acid or in the presence of ammonia, the dissociation is repressed. Removal of the water by distillation gives good yields of the amide.

4. *Reaction of Silver Salts with Bromine.* When silver salts react under anhydrous conditions with a solution of bromine in carbon tetrachloride, decarboxylation with the formation of an alkyl bromide takes place.

$$RCOOAg + Br_2 \longrightarrow RBr + CO_2 + AgBr$$

Since one carbon atom is lost, this reaction is useful for decreasing the length of a carbon chain.

Industrially Important Acids

Compounds of commercial importance frequently are made by special reactions which are not applicable to other members of the homologous series. The reason for this situation is that industry tries to use low-cost raw materials and to find new ways of reducing the cost of indispensable materials. Hence a compound may be of commercial importance because a special method has been discovered by which it can be made cheaply. On the other hand the intrinsic value of a compound may be such that a great deal of effort and money have been spent to discover new ways of making it more cheaply than by the general procedures.

Formic Acid. **Sodium formate** is made by a special process from carbon monoxide and caustic soda.

$$CO + NaOH \xrightarrow[\text{6–10 atm.}]{200°} [HCOO^-]Na^+$$

This reaction was one of the earliest used commercially for the synthesis of an organic compound from carbon and salt as the raw materials. **Formic acid** can be liberated from the sodium salt by adding a mineral acid. Calcium formate is a co-product in the manufacture of pentaerythritol (p. 526). With the increased uses for pentaerythritol, it appears that more than enough formic acid will be available from this source than is needed to meet the demand.

Because the carboxyl group is united to a hydrogen atom, rather than to a carbon atom as in all subsequent members of the series, formic acid undergoes a number of *special reactions*. When heated with dehydrating agents it decomposes into carbon monoxide and water.

$$HCOOH \xrightarrow[\text{H}_2\text{SO}_4]{\text{Conc.}} CO + H_2O$$

Reaction with phosphorus trichloride gives carbon monoxide and hydrogen chloride because of the instability of formyl chloride at ordinary temperatures.

$$3 \ \underset{\text{H—C—OH}}{\overset{\overset{\text{O}}{\|}}{}} + PCl_3 \longrightarrow P(OH)_3 + 3 \ \underset{\text{H—C—Cl}}{\overset{\overset{\text{O}}{\|}}{}} \rightleftarrows 3 \ CO + 3 \ HCl$$

The latter reaction is reversible and formyl chloride may be obtained from carbon monoxide and hydrogen chloride at the temperature of liquid air. When sodium formate is heated, hydrogen is evolved and sodium oxalate remains.

$$[HCOO^-]Na^+$$
$$[HCOO^-]Na^+ \longrightarrow H_2 + \begin{bmatrix} COO^- \\ | \\ COO^- \end{bmatrix} 2 Na^+$$

Like other compounds containing the —CHO group (p. 172), formic acid is a mild reducing agent.

$$HCOOH + [O] \longrightarrow [HOCOOH] \longrightarrow CO_2 + H_2O$$

Because formic acid is approximately ten times as strong an acid as its homologs, it is used when an acid stronger than acetic acid, but not so strong as a mineral acid, is desired. It is used also for the manufacture of its esters and salts. Sodium formate is used to make formic acid and oxalic acid, and as a reducing agent.

Acetic Acid. This organic acid is by far the most important from the standpoint of quantity used. Production was 185 million pounds in 1940 and 396 million pounds in 1948, exclusive of the amount produced in the form of vinegar. The unit value was 8 cents per pound. It appears in the market largely as *glacial acetic acid* of about 99.5 per cent purity, so-called because on cold days it freezes to an ice-like solid. The melting point of pure acetic acid is 16.7°.

Several methods for the preparation of acetic acid are in use.

1. ENZYME-CATALYZED OXIDATION OF ETHYL ALCOHOL. Acetic acid is the chief component of **vinegar**. The alcohol in fermented fruit juices or fermented malt (beer) in the presence of various species of *Acetobacter* and air is oxidized to acetic acid.

$$CH_3CH_2OH + O_2 \text{ (air)} \xrightarrow{\text{Acetobacter}} CH_3COOH + H_2O$$

In the *barrel process* the fruit juice is contained in barrels exposed to air, and the bacteria form a slimy film on the surface known as *mother of vinegar*. Since the alcohol must come in contact with the oxygen and bacteria by diffusion processes, oxidation is slow, and an acetic acid content of 4–5 per cent is reached only after several months. In the *quick process* a vat is filled with shavings or other porous material which is inoculated with the microorganism. A 12–15 per cent alcohol solution containing nutrient salts for the growth of the bacteria is allowed to trickle over the shavings while a controlled amount of warm air is forced up through the shavings. In this way a vinegar with an acetic acid content of 8–10 per cent may be obtained, which is diluted to 4–5 per cent for use. Vinegar produced by fermentation is used almost exclusively as a preservative and condiment, its value for this purpose being enhanced by flavors present in the cider, wine, or malt.

2. FROM PYROLIGNEOUS LIQUOR. Pyroligneous liquor from the destructive distillation of wood (p. 65) contains 4–10 per cent of acetic acid which may be recovered by neutralizing with lime and distilling to dryness. The **gray acetate of lime** so obtained may be converted to glacial acetic acid by concentrated sulfuric acid. In recent years acetic acid has been recovered from dilute aqueous solutions by extraction from the vapor state with tar oil (*Suida process*), and by azeotropic distillation (p. 69) using ethylene chloride, propyl acetate, or butyl acetate to form a constant-boiling mixture with the

water (*Clarke-Othmer process*). It may be recovered as ethyl acetate by esterifying with ethyl alcohol.

　　3. FROM ACETALDEHYDE. Most glacial acetic acid now is synthesized by the oxidation of acetaldehyde, which may be produced either by the hydration of acetylene (p. 110) or by the catalytic dehydrogenation or air oxidation of ethyl alcohol (p. 77).

$$HC{\equiv}CH + H_2O \xrightarrow[\text{FeSO}_4,\ \text{Fe}_2(\text{SO}_4)_3]{\text{H}_2\text{SO}_4,\ \text{Hg}_2\text{SO}_4,\ \text{Hg},} [H_2C{=}CHOH] \longrightarrow \underset{\text{Acetaldehyde}}{CH_3\overset{\text{H}}{\underset{\|}{C}}{=}O}$$

$$C_2H_5OH \xrightarrow[260°-290°]{\text{Cu—Cr}} CH_3CHO + H_2$$

$$C_2H_5OH + O_2 \xrightarrow[300°-500°]{\text{Ag}} CH_3CHO + H_2O$$

Acetaldehyde absorbs oxygen from the air rapidly to form peracetic acid, a peroxide (p. 581), which in the presence of manganous or cobalt acetate reacts with the acetaldehyde to give acetic acid.

$$\underset{}{CH_3\overset{O}{\overset{\|}{C}}H} + O_2 \longrightarrow \underset{\text{Peracetic acid}}{CH_3\overset{O}{\overset{\|}{C}}{-}O{-}OH}$$

$$CH_3\overset{O}{\overset{\|}{C}}{-}O{-}OH + CH_3CHO \xrightarrow[\text{Co(OCOCH}_3)_2]{\text{Mn(OCOCH}_3)_2 \text{ or}} 2\ CH_3COOH$$

Using 99–99.8 per cent acetaldehyde, 96 per cent acetic acid is obtained, which may be rectified readily to 99.5 per cent.

　　4. OTHER SYNTHETIC PROCESSES. Controlled oxidation of the propane-butane fraction of natural gas with oxygen gives a mixture of alcohols, aldehydes, and acids (p. 56) from which acetic acid and acetaldehyde are isolated. Acetic acid and acetaldehyde also are concomitant products of the Fischer-Tropsch synthesis of liquid fuels (p. 56).

　　Many other processes have been proposed and described in the patent literature. Sodium salts of carboxylic acids in general can be made by the reaction used to prepare sodium formate by replacing the sodium hydroxide with sodium alkoxide.

$$RONa + CO \longrightarrow RCOONa$$

It is possible to obtain the free acids from carbon monoxide and the alcohol in the presence of acid catalysts.

$$ROH + CO \xrightarrow[150°-350° \text{ and } 100-800 \text{ atm.}]{\text{Mineral acids or BF}_3 \text{ at}} RCOOH$$

　　Acetic acid is used where a cheap organic acid is required; for the preparation of metallic salts, acetic anhydride (p. 139), and esters (p. 148); in the manufacture of cellulose acetate (p. 301) and white lead; as a precipitating agent for casein from milk, and for rubber or synthetic rubber from their aqueous emulsions (p. 496); and for numerous other purposes. **Sodium acetate** is used to reduce the acidity of mineral acids. **Lead acetate,** known as **sugar of lead,** and **basic lead acetate,** $Pb(OH)(OCOCH_3)$, are used to prepare other lead salts. **Verdigris** is the basic copper acetate, $Cu(OH)_2 \cdot 2\,Cu(OCOCH_3)_2$, and **Paris green** is a mixed cupric acetate-arsenite. **Aluminum acetate** is used to impregnate cotton cloth or fibers with aluminum hydroxide prior to dyeing, a process known as *mordanting* (p. 477).

Other Acids. **Propionic acid** and **butyric acid** may be made by the oxidation of the corresponding alcohols or by special fermentation processes from starch. They are used in the manufacture of cellulose acetate-propionates and acetate-butyrates (p. 302). **Calcium propionate** is used in bread to prevent molding and ropiness.

The **higher normal acids** having an even number of carbon atoms are obtained by the hydrolysis of fats (p. 151). In Germany during World War II, paraffin from the Fischer-Tropsch synthesis (p. 56) was oxidized by air at $115°–125°$ in the presence of manganese salts to give a complex mixture of higher acids which served as a substitute for acids derived from natural fats.

ACYL HALIDES

Preparation

Since acyl halides result from the replacement of the hydroxyl group by a halogen atom, their structure is represented by the general formula $R\overset{\overset{\displaystyle O}{\|}}{-C}-X$. An inorganic acid halide such as phosphorus trichloride, phosphorus pentachloride, thionyl chloride, or sulfuryl chloride must be used to effect this replacement. These compounds are the acid chlorides of phosphorous, phosphoric, sulfurous, and sulfuric acids, respectively. Their reactions with organic acids take place according to the following equations.

$$3\,RCOOH + PCl_3 \longrightarrow 3\,RCOCl + P(OH)_3$$

$$RCOOH + PCl_5 \longrightarrow RCOCl + POCl_3 + HCl$$

$$RCOOH + SOCl_2 \longrightarrow RCOCl + SO_2 + HCl$$

$$2\,RCOOH + SO_2Cl_2 \longrightarrow 2\,RCOCl + H_2SO_4$$

If the sodium salt of the organic acid is used, phosphorus oxychloride also will react.

$$2\,RCOONa + POCl_3 \longrightarrow 2\,RCOCl + NaCl + NaPO_3$$

Hence when the sodium salt reacts with phosphorus pentachloride, three fifths of the total chlorine is available instead of only one fifth.

$$3\,RCOONa + PCl_5 \longrightarrow 3\,RCOCl + 2\,NaCl + NaPO_3$$

Thionyl chloride, $SOCl_2$, has an advantage over other reagents in that the acyl chloride is obtained in good yield and can be purified readily, the other products of the reaction being gases. For these reasons thionyl chloride is used for small scale preparations even though it is somewhat more expensive than the other reagents.

An equilibrium exists between two different organic acids and their acyl halides.

$$RCOOH + R'COCl \rightleftharpoons R'COOH + RCOCl$$

If R'COCl is so chosen that it boils higher than RCOCl, the latter can be made by the slow distillation of a mixture of RCOOH and R'COCl.

Nomenclature

Acyl halides are named by dropping the ending *ic acid* from the name of the corresponding acid and adding *yl halide*; for example CH_3COCl is acetyl chloride or ethanoyl chloride, and $(CH_3)_2CHCOBr$ is *i*-butyryl bromide or 2-methylpropanoyl bromide. Where confusion may arise between common names for alkyl and acyl halides, systematic names should be used.

Physical Properties

Since the acyl halides do not contain hydrogen united to oxygen, no proton bonding can occur; hence they have normal boiling points. For example acetic acid with a molecular weight of 60 boils at 118°, but acetyl chloride of molecular weight 78.5 boils at 51°. This value is between the boiling points of pentane (mol. wt. 72, b.p. 36°) and hexane (mol. wt. 86, b.p. 69°). Acyl halides are insoluble in water, the covalently-bound halogen atom having the effect of about two or three methylene groups in reducing the water solubility due to the carbonyl group. The acyl halides have a sharp odor and an irritating action on the mucous membranes.

Reactions

1. *With Water, Alcohols, and Ammonia.* The acyl halides may be considered as mixed anhydrides of a carboxylic acid and hydrogen halide and as such react like anhydrides in general with water, alcohols, and ammonia, giving acids, esters, and amides.

$$RCOCl \begin{cases} + HOH \longrightarrow RCOOH + HCl \\ + HOR' \longrightarrow RCOOR' + HCl \quad \text{An ester} \\ + HNH_2 \longrightarrow RCONH_2 + HCl \xrightarrow{NH_3} NH_4Cl \quad \text{An amide} \end{cases}$$

In the last reaction two moles of ammonia are required, since its rate of reaction with hydrogen chloride is greater than its rate of reaction with acyl chloride.

2. *With Salts of Carboxylic Acids.* Acyl halides react with metallic salts of organic acids to give *carboxylic acid anhydrides*.

$$RCOCl + NaO\overset{O}{\overset{\|}{C}}-R' \longrightarrow R\overset{O}{\overset{\|}{C}}-O-\overset{O}{\overset{\|}{C}}R' + NaCl$$

3. With Halogen. Acyl halides halogenate more readily than hydrocarbons and free acids. Moreover only an α hydrogen atom, that is one on the first carbon atom adjoining the carbonyl group, is replaced readily.

$$RCH_2COX + X_2 \longrightarrow RCHXCOX + HX$$

In actual practice free acids are used, the halogenation being carried out in the presence of a small amount of phosphorus trihalide. The reactions then are

$$3\ RCH_2COOH + PX_3 \longrightarrow 3\ RCH_2COX + P(OH)_3$$

$$RCH_2COX + X_2 \longrightarrow RCHXCOX + HX$$

$$RCHXCOX + RCH_2COOH \rightleftarrows RCHXCOOH + RCH_2COX$$

Because of the last reaction a small amount of acid halide is sufficient to permit the direct halogenation of a large amount of acid. This procedure for making halogen acids is known as the *Hell-Volhard-Zelinsky reaction.*

4. With Organomagnesium and Organocadmium Compounds. Acyl halides react at low temperatures with Grignard reagents to give ketones.

$$\underset{R-\overset{\displaystyle O}{\overset{\|}{C}}-Cl}{} + R'MgX \xrightarrow{-80°} \underset{R-\overset{\displaystyle O}{\overset{\|}{C}}-R'}{} + MgX_2$$

A ketone

At room temperature addition to the carbonyl group also takes place to give magnesium tertiary alkoxides from which the alcohol can be obtained by hydrolysis.

$$R-\overset{\overset{\displaystyle O}{\|}}{C}-R' + R'MgX \longrightarrow R-\overset{\overset{\displaystyle OMgX}{|}}{\underset{|}{C}}-R' \xrightarrow{H_2O} R-\overset{\overset{\displaystyle OH}{|}}{\underset{|}{C}}-R' + HOMgX$$

Addition to the carbonyl group is much slower with alkylcadmiums than with Grignard reagents; hence the reaction with alkylcadmiums frequently is preferred for the preparation of ketones.

$$2\ RCOCl + CdR'_2 \longrightarrow 2\ RCOR' + CdCl_2$$

The greater ease of hydrolysis, alcoholysis, and ammonolysis of acyl halides when compared with alkyl halides may be ascribed to the inductive effect of the doubly bound oxygen atom (p. 129), which causes a lower electron density on the carbonyl carbon atom. The rate of reaction with electron-donating reagents is faster for acyl halides than for alkyl halides, even though the same inductive effect decreases the tendency of the chlorine to leave as a chloride ion.

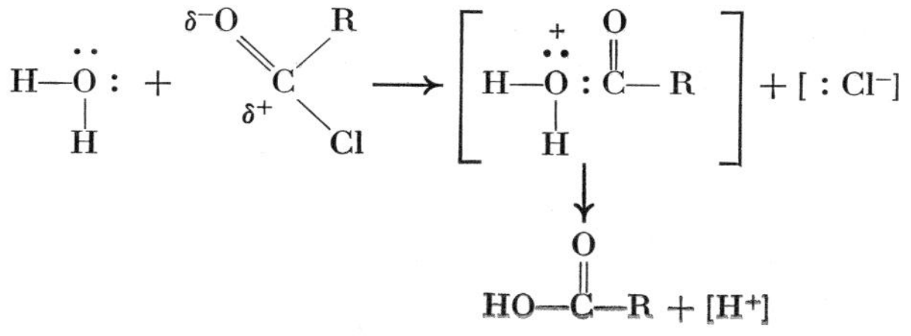

The inductive effect of the oxygen also accounts for the greater ease of substitution of the α hydrogen by halogen, since the positive charge on the carbonyl carbon atom facilitates the loss of a proton from the α carbon atom.

ACID ANHYDRIDES

Preparation

Two general methods for the preparation of acid anhydrides may be used, the first of which, from an acid halide and a salt, clearly defines the structure of carboxylic acid anhydrides.

$$\text{RCCl} + \text{Na}^+\left[\text{-OCR}' \right] \longrightarrow \text{RC—O—CR}' + \text{NaCl}$$

The second method depends on the fact that an equilibrium exists between carboxylic acids and acid anhydrides.

$$2 \text{ RCOOH} + \text{CH}_3\text{C—O—CCH}_3 \rightleftharpoons \text{RC—O—CR} + 2 \text{ CH}_3\text{COOH}$$

Since acetic acid boils at a lower temperature than any other component in the system, it can be removed by careful distillation and the reaction forced to completion. The first reaction may be used for preparing anhydrides in which the R groups are either alike or different. Although the second method is suitable only for the preparation of anhydrides in which both R groups are the same, it is preferred for this purpose because of the availability and low cost of acetic anhydride and the excellent yields.

Nomenclature

A member of this class of compounds is named by adding the word *anhydride* to the name of the acid or acids from which it is derived. For example $(\text{CH}_3\text{CO})_2\text{O}$ is acetic anhydride or ethanoic anhydride, and $(\text{CH}_3\text{CO})\text{O}(\text{CO-CH}_2\text{CH}_2\text{CH}_3)$ is acetic butyric anhydride or ethanoic butanoic anhydride. Those anhydrides having both R groups alike are called *simple anhydrides* whereas those with different R groups are known as *mixed anhydrides*. The former are the more important.

Physical Properties

Anhydrides have higher boiling points than hydrocarbons but lower than alcohols of comparable molecular weight. Acetic anhydride and its higher homologs are insoluble in water. Like the acid halides, the volatile anhydrides are irritating to the mucous membranes.

Acetic anhydride might be expected to be soluble in water because of the relatively large amount of oxygen present. However the resonance energy of the molecule is high (40 kcal.). Consequently there is little tendency for the oxygen atoms to form proton bonds with water molecules.

Reactions

The reactions of carboxylic acid anhydrides are identical with those of acyl halides except that an organic acid replaces halogen acid as a product of the reactions.

$$R-\overset{\overset{\displaystyle O}{\|}}{C}-O-\overset{\overset{\displaystyle O}{\|}}{C}-R \begin{cases} + \text{HOH} \longrightarrow \text{RCOOH} + \text{RCOOH} \\ \\ + \text{HOR}' \longrightarrow \text{RCOOR}' + \text{RCOOH} \\ \qquad\qquad \text{An ester} \\ \\ + \text{HNH}_2 \longrightarrow \text{RCONH}_2 + \text{RCOOH} \xrightarrow{\text{NH}_3} \text{RCOONH}_4 \\ \qquad\qquad \text{An amide} \end{cases}$$

Acetic Anhydride

Acetic anhydride is the only important member of the series. When the chief source of acetic acid was pyroligneous acid, from which it was recovered as calcium or sodium acetate, the anhydride was prepared by the reaction of sodium acetate with one half of the amount of sulfuryl chloride, or of sulfur chloride and chlorine, necessary to form acetyl chloride. The acetyl chloride thus formed reacted with the remainder of the salt to give the anhydride. With the advent of synthetic acetic acid and other methods of recovery from aqueous solutions, new methods of preparation of the anhydride were developed. In one procedure acetic acid is added to acetylene in the presence of mercury salts to give ethylidene acetate, which then is decomposed by heating with acid catalysts such as sulfuric acid or zinc chloride to give acetaldehyde and acetic anhydride.

$$\text{HC}\equiv\text{CH} + 2\,\text{CH}_3\text{COOH} \xrightarrow{\text{Hg salts}} \underset{\displaystyle \text{Ethylidene acetate}}{\text{H}_3\text{C}-\text{CH} \begin{matrix} \nearrow \text{OCOCH}_3 \\ \searrow \text{OCOCH}_3 \end{matrix}} \xrightarrow[\text{or ZnCl}_2]{\text{H}_2\text{SO}_4} \text{CH}_3\text{CHO} + (\text{CH}_3\text{CO})_2\text{O}$$

In a second process the anhydride is formed by the controlled air oxidation of acetaldehyde. Some anhydride always is formed in the synthesis of acetic acid from acetaldehyde, the intermediate peracetic acid (p. 134) apparently reacting with acetaldehyde to give anhydride and water.

$$\text{CH}_3-\overset{\overset{\displaystyle O}{\|}}{C}-O-\text{OH} + \text{CH}_3\text{CHO} \longrightarrow (\text{CH}_3\text{CO})_2\text{O} + \text{H}_2\text{O}$$

By using a cobalt-copper catalyst, reducing the temperature of oxidation, increasing the speed of oxidation, and using a diluent such as ethyl acetate, it is possible to convert two thirds of the acetaldehyde to acetic anhydride while one third is converted to acetic acid. By distillation at reduced pressure the temperature is kept low enough to permit removal of the water and diluent without hydrolysis of the anhydride by the water.

A third process of importance at present is the addition of acetic acid to ketene which takes place rapidly in the absence of a catalyst.

$$\underset{\displaystyle \text{Ketene}}{\text{H}_2\text{C}=\text{C}=\text{O}} + \text{CH}_3\text{COOH} \longrightarrow (\text{CH}_3\text{CO})_2\text{O}$$

Ketene is a gas prepared by the decomposition of acetic acid or of acetone. Acetic acid vapor containing ethyl phosphate is heated to 700°–720°, or acetic acid vapor is passed over aluminum phosphate at 600°–700°. The mixture of ketene, water, and acetic acid vapor is cooled quickly, and the water and acetic acid condense. The ketene then is absorbed in acetic acid in a scrubbing tower. Acetone (p. 180) is converted to ketene by a noncatalytic decomposition at 700°.

$$CH_3COCH_3 \xrightarrow{700°} CH_2{=}C{=}O + CH_4$$

Acetic anhydride is used chiefly to make esters that cannot be made by direct esterification of alcohols with acetic acid. The most important of these is cellulose acetate. Production of acetic anhydride in the United States rose from 250 million pounds in 1940 to 780 million pounds in 1948, when it was valued at 11 cents per pound.

ESTERS

Preparation

Most of the procedures for making esters have been described, namely direct esterification between an acid and an alcohol (p. 128), the reaction of a metallic salt with an alkyl halide (p. 131), the reaction of an acyl halide with an alcohol (p. 136), and the reaction of an acid anhydride with an alcohol (p. 139). A few generalizations should be made about these reactions. In the first place all except direct esterification proceed practically to completion. However side reactions may take place, particularly with tertiary alcohols and tertiary alkyl halides, which make the reactions useless unless special conditions can be found that will produce satisfactory yields. In general the rate of ester formation from alcohols and from alkyl halides follows the order primary > secondary > tertiary, but the ease of loss of water or halogen acid is tertiary > secondary > primary (pp. 76, 83). Therefore when a tertiary alcohol reacts with an acid anhydride, which is a dehydrating agent, or when a tertiary alkyl halide reacts with a sodium salt, which acts as a base, the rate of olefin formation is much greater than the rate of ester formation and only olefin results. The constitution of the carboxylic acid as well as that of the alcohol affects the rate of esterification. Thus the rate of esterification of acetic acid decreases with increasing substitution by alkyl groups. Esters of trimethylacetic acid cannot be formed by direct esterification.

Tertiary alkyl esters are cleaved very readily by hydrogen halides. Hence the action of an acyl halide on a tertiary alcohol usually results in the formation of the alkyl halide and the organic acid. A good method for preparing *t*-butyl bromide is by the reaction of *t*-butyl alcohol and acetyl bromide.

$$(CH_3)_3COH + BrCOCH_3 \longrightarrow (CH_3)_3C{-}O{-}COCH_3 + HBr$$
$$\downarrow$$
$$(CH_3)_3CBr + HOCOCH_3$$

If the halogen acid is removed as fast as it is formed, fair yields of tertiary esters may be obtained. For example when acetyl chloride reacts with *t*-butyl alcohol in the presence of magnesium, the yield of *t*-butyl acetate is 50 per cent.

$$(CH_3)_3COH + ClCOCH_3 + \tfrac{1}{2} Mg \longrightarrow (CH_3)_3C—O—COCH_3 + \tfrac{1}{2} MgCl_2 + \tfrac{1}{2} H_2$$

Similarly a 65 per cent yield can be obtained using an organic tertiary amine base such as dimethylaniline (p. 371) in place of magnesium.

$$(CH_3)_3COH + ClCOCH_3 + C_6H_5N(CH_3)_2 \longrightarrow$$
$$(CH_3)_3C—O—COCH_3 + [C_6H_5\overset{+}{N}(CH_3)_2H]\ Cl^-$$

Direct esterification is a good example of a reversible reaction. The term *reversible reaction* ordinarily is used to mean either that appreciable quantities of the original reactants still are present when equilibrium between the forward and reverse reactions is reached, or that the rate of attaining equilibrium, that is the mobility of the reaction, is so great that the reaction can be reversed readily by altering concentrations.

The esterification reaction has been studied extensively to determine the quantitative laws of reversible reactions, because no by-products are formed in the reaction, the analytical procedures are simple and accurate, the reaction takes place at a convenient rate for measurements, and the position of equilibrium is such that it can be determined accurately. The reaction may be written

$$RCOOH + HOR' \underset{V_2}{\overset{V_1}{\rightleftarrows}} RCOOR' + H_2O$$

The velocities V_1 of the forward reaction and V_2 of the reverse reaction are proportional to the mole fractions of the reacting substances.

$$V_1 = k_1[RCOOH][R'OH]$$
$$V_2 = k_2[RCOOR'][H_2O]$$

At the start of the reaction the concentrations of alcohol and acid are at a maximum and those of the products are zero. Consequently V_1 is at its maximum and V_2 is zero. As the reactants are used and the products are formed, V_1 decreases and V_2 increases. A point eventually will be reached where $V_1 = V_2$, which is the condition for chemical equilibrium. Therefore at equilibrium

$$k_1[RCOOH][R'OH] = k_2[RCOOR'][H_2O]$$
$$\frac{k_1}{k_2} = \frac{[RCOOR'][H_2O]}{[RCOOH][R'OH]} = K_E$$

K_E is known as the *equilibrium constant* for the reaction.

The position of equilibrium is not affected by catalysts, since at this stage catalysts affect the rates of the forward and reverse reactions to exactly the same extent. Catalysts merely change the mobility of the system, that is the time required to attain equilibrium.

Although the mass law holds very well for the esterification reactions, the good agreement probably is fortuitous, because the solution is not ideal, a condition necessary for strict adherence to the mass law. Nonideality also may account for the fact that the position of equilibrium is not always independent of the presence of catalysts. Thus when the number of moles of hydrogen chloride for one mole of ethyl alcohol and one mole of acetic acid is increased from about 0.005 to 0.33, the apparent equilibrium constant changes from 4.3 to 8.8 because of the changes in the environment of the reaction.

The effect of temperature on the position of equilibrium is governed by the principle of Le Chatelier. If heat is evolved in a reaction (*exothermic reaction*), the position of equilibrium will shift to the left as the temperature is increased, whereas if heat is absorbed (*endothermic reaction*), the reaction will go more nearly to completion as the temperature is raised. The esterification reaction is only slightly exothermic (ΔH = ca. -1 kcal.), and hence temperature has practically no effect on the position of equilibrium.

Temperature, like catalysts, has a marked effect on the mobility of the system. Roughly speaking, the rate of a chemical reaction increases from two to three times for each rise of ten degrees in temperature. Pressure affects the position of equilibrium only if a change in volume results during the course of the reaction. Marked changes in volume occur only when one or more of the reactants is a gas under the conditions of the experiment. Where gases are involved, pressure also will affect the rate of attaining equilibrium, since increase in pressure results in an increase in the concentration of the reactants.

The equation for the equilibrium constant indicates that the reaction may be forced in the direction of forming more product by increasing the concentration of either the alcohol or the acid. If the value of the denominator is increased and K_E remains constant, the value of the numerator also must increase. When one reactant is very cheap and the other relatively costly, a large excess of the cheaper compound may be used advantageously to force more complete utilization of the more expensive one. Another way to force complete utilization of the reactants is to remove one or both of the products, since a decrease in the value of the numerator forces a decrease in that of the denominator. The second procedure is the better when it can be employed, since the reactants can be used in stoichiometric proportions and complete conversion can be obtained. When water is one of the products, it often may be removed readily by azeotropic distillation (p. 69).

Superficially the reaction of an alcohol and an acid appears to resemble neutralization of a base by an acid, but nothing could be further from the truth. Neutralization is a reaction between ions, is almost instantaneous at room temperature in the absence of a catalyst, and goes to completion. Esterification is a reaction between molecules, is slow even at elevated temperatures, requiring a catalyst to attain a practical rate, and does not go to completion.

The mechanism of acid-catalyzed esterification is not thoroughly understood, but the following series of equilibria give a picture of the complexity of the reactions taking place in the esterification of a primary or secondary alcohol by a weak acid, and of the function of the catalysts. In the equilibria the convention has been adopted that the reagent is placed above a double arrow and the minor product below the double arrow (p. 116). If reagents are given both above and below the same pair of arrows, the step is one of direct displacement (p. 95), with or without Walden inversion (p. 95), or is one of proton transfer. Using this convention, it is possible to avoid writing each step as a separate equilibrium.

$$
R-\overset{\underset{|}{OH}}{C}=O \underset{B^-}{\overset{HB}{\rightleftarrows}}
\left[R-\overset{\underset{|}{OH}}{C}=\overset{+}{\overset{..}{O}}:H \right]^{II}
\xrightarrow[\;]{R'OH}
\left[R-\overset{\overset{+}{\underset{..}{:}}\overset{H}{\underset{|}{O}}-R'}{\underset{\underset{|}{OH}}{C}}-OH \right]^{III}
\underset{HB}{\overset{B^-}{\rightleftarrows}}
$$

$$
\left[R-\overset{\underset{|}{OH}}{\overset{\overset{|}{O}-R'}{C}}-OH \right]^{IV}
\underset{B^-}{\overset{HB}{\rightleftarrows}}
\left[R-\overset{\overset{|}{OR'}}{\underset{\overset{+}{:}\overset{H}{\underset{|}{O}}-H}{C}}-OH \right]^{V}
\underset{HOH}{\rightleftarrows}
\left[R-\overset{\overset{|}{OR'}}{C}=\overset{+}{OH} \right]^{VI}
\underset{HB}{\overset{B^-}{\rightleftarrows}}
R-\overset{\overset{|}{OR'}}{C}=O^{VII}
$$

It frequently is argued that in writing intermediates of this sort the (+) charge should be indicated outside of the bracket, since the intermediate is a resonance hybrid and the charge is not on one oxygen atom any more than on the other but is distributed over the group as a whole. Although the latter statement is true, in the structure as it is written the charge is certainly on one oxygen atom and not on the other. If the charge is to be placed outside of the bracket the group should be represented by the symbolism for a resonance hybrid (p. 129). The simple electronic valence structure is less cumbersome, however, and is satisfactory for most purposes.

Although a strong acid such as sulfuric acid is the actual material added, an equilibrium at once is established in which all the bases present, sulfate ions, carboxylic acid molecules, water molecules, and alcohol molecules, compete for the available proton. Accordingly the catalyst is indicated as HB, where B is any base and may be a neutral molecule or a negatively charged ion depending on whether HB is a positively charged group such as the ammonium ion, $[NH_4^+]$, or a neutral molecule such as hydrogen chloride, HCl.

The catalysis involves the transfer of the proton from one base to another, and hence the point of attack will be an electron-dense portion of the molecule. The first effective step is the transfer of the proton to the carbonyl group of the acid (I) with elimination of another base. Next the available electrons on an alcohol molecule satisfy the electron-deficient carbon atom of II to give III. A base removes a proton from III to give an intermediate IV, which accepts a proton from a proton donor to give V. Loss of water gives VI, which loses a proton to a base to give the ester VII. The acid-catalyzed hydrolysis of an ester is the exact reverse of this series going from VII to I. From this series of reactions the over-all equation may be obtained by cancelling reagents appearing both above and below the double arrows. The reactants are the initial compound and the reagents remaining above the arrows, and the products are the final compound and the reagents remaining below the arrows. The series of equilibria then reduces to

$$
RCOOH + HOR' \rightleftarrows RCOOR' + H_2O
$$

Besides the equilibria indicated, numerous other proton transfer reactions are taking place simultaneously which do not lead to new products. Moreover since all steps are reversible, not every molecule which reaches an intermediate stage completes the series and ends up as product. The final composition is dependent on the relative thermodynamic stability of the reactants and the products.

This mechanism accounts for the fact that, in the esterification of primary and secondary alcohols by weak acids, the oxygen atom in the eliminated water molecule comes not from the alcohol but from the acid (acyl-oxygen fission). Experimental evidence for this type of fission was obtained first from the esterification of carboxylic acids with mercaptans, the sulfur analogs of alcohols (p. 211). A rigid proof that alcohols behave in the same way results from the esterification of an acid containing ordinary oxygen with an alcohol containing a high percentage of the O^{18} isotope. The labeled oxygen becomes a part of the ester molecule and not of the water molecule.

$$RCOOH + HO^{18}R' \rightleftarrows RCOO^{18}R' + H_2O$$

Moreover alcohols such as neopentyl alcohol which normally rearrange if a hydroxide ion becomes detached from the hydrocarbon radical will esterify without rearrangement. Indications are that the esterifications of tertiary alcohols by weak acids take place by a different mechanism in which the oxygen atom eliminated as water comes from the alcohol (alkyl-oxygen fission). In fact evidence has been presented for four distinct types of acid-catalyzed esterification and hydrolysis.

Nomenclature

Esters are named as if they were alkyl salts of the organic acids, because the early investigators assumed that esterification is analogous to neutralization.

$$\overset{O}{\overset{\|}{CH_3C}}OC_2H_5$$

Thus $CH_3COC_2H_5$ is ethyl acetate or ethyl ethanoate. The beginning student should be careful to recognize the portion of the molecule derived from the acid and that from the alcohol, particularly in condensed structural formulas. For example both $(CH_3)_2CHOCOCH_2CH_3$ and $CH_3CH_2COOCH(CH_3)_2$ are *i*-propyl propionate and not ethyl *i*-butyrate. No difficulty will be encountered if it is remembered that the oxygen of a carbonyl group always follows the carbon atom to which it is attached and that the alkyl group from the alcohol portion of the ester is joined to the carbonyl group through an oxygen atom. If it is necessary to name esters as substitution products the ester is called a *carboalkoxy* or an *alkoxycarbonyl* group. For example $COOCH_3$ is the carbomethoxy group or the methoxycarbonyl group.

Physical Properties

The esters have normal boiling points, but their solubility in water is less than would be expected from the amount of oxygen present. Ethyl acetate with four carbon atoms and two oxygen atoms dissolves to about the same extent as *n*-butyl alcohol, which has four carbon atoms and one oxygen atom (cf. acid anhydrides, p. 138). The volatile esters have pleasant odors which usually are described as fruity.

Reactions

The reactions of the esters depend for the most part on the scission of the linkage between the carbonyl group and the alkoxy group (*acyl-oxygen fission*), or between the alkyl group and the oxygen atom (*alkyl-oxygen fission*). The ease of scission of a carbon-oxygen bond and the type of catalysis which is possible depend on the groups attached to the carbon atoms joined by the oxygen atom. Ethers, R—O—R, having two alkyl groups joined by oxygen are hydrolyzed least readily, and the hydrolysis is subject only to acid catalysis. Esters, RCO—O—R, in which one acyl and one alkyl group are linked through oxygen are more readily hydrolyzed, and both acids and bases catalyze the reaction. Anhydrides, RCO—O—COR, having two acyl groups joined by oxygen are most easily hydrolyzed, water alone bringing about the reaction.

1. *Hydrolysis or Saponification.* Esters may be split by water (hydrolysis) in the presence of either acidic or basic catalysts.

$$RCOOR' + HOH \overset{[H^+]}{\rightleftharpoons} RCOOH + HOR'$$

$$RCOOR' + HOH \overset{[OH^-]}{\rightleftharpoons} RCOOH + HOR'$$

$$\downarrow [OH^-]$$

$$[RCOO^-] + HOH$$

Alkaline hydrolysis frequently is referred to as **saponification,** because it is the type of reaction used in the preparation of soaps (p. 157). The acid-catalyzed reaction is exactly the reverse of acid-catalyzed esterification and either results in the same equilibrium. The base-catalyzed hydrolysis goes to completion and requires one equivalent of alkali for each equivalent of ester, because the acid formed in the base-catalyzed equilibrium reacts irreversibly with the catalyst to form a salt and water. The over-all reaction becomes

$$RCOOR' + NaOH \longrightarrow [RCOO^-]Na^+ + R'OH$$

Because this reaction goes to completion, alkaline saponification is used as a quantitative procedure for the estimation of esters. A weighed sample of the unknown is refluxed with an excess of a standardized aqueous or alcoholic solution of alkali and the excess base at the end of the reaction is titrated with standard acid using a suitable indicator, usually phenolphthalein (p. 492). The equivalent weight as determined by saponification is called the **saponification equivalent** of the ester.

The relative rates of esterification of alcohols by a given acid, namely primary > secondary > tertiary, hold also for the esterification of carboxylic acids by a given alcohol (p. 140). Thus the rates of esterification of *t*-butyl alcohol by acetic acid, or of trimethylacetic acid by ethyl alcohol, are so slow as to be impractical as preparative methods. Similarly *t*-butyl acetate or ethyl trimethylacetate, prepared by procedures other than direct esterification, is very difficult to saponify. This phenomenon is caused by the blocking of the functional group by the branches which prevents effective collision with the catalysts or reagents, and is known as *steric hindrance* (p. 96).

2. *Alcoholysis or Transesterification.* The alkoxy group of an ester of a primary or secondary alcohol and a weak acid may be exchanged readily for that of another alcohol using an acidic or basic catalyst.

$$RCOOR' + HOR'' \overset{[H^+] \text{ or } [R'O^-]}{\rightleftharpoons} RCOOR'' + HOR'$$

Both types of catalysis lead to the same equilibrium, since an acid is not one of the products of reaction. Alcoholate ion, formed by the reaction of an active metal, for example sodium, with the alcohol involved, is used as the basic catalyst rather than hydroxide ion, since the latter would cause saponification of the ester.

Acid-catalyzed hydrolysis of an ester is merely the reverse of esterification (p. 142), and acid-catalyzed alcoholysis is identical except that a second alcohol replaces water. Basic catalysis differs from acid catalysis in that the catalyst is an electron-rich group, and the point of attack will be the carbon atom of the carbonyl group, which is deficient in electrons because of the greater electron-attracting power of the oxygen atom (Table 6, p. 64). The mechanism probably is much simpler than that of acid catalysis, being merely a displacement reaction.

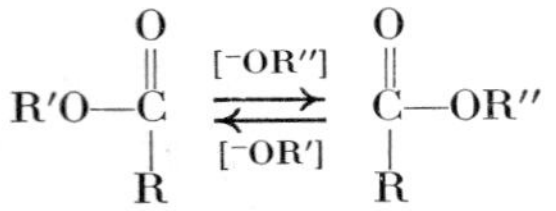

$$R'O-\underset{R}{\overset{\overset{\displaystyle O}{\|}}{C}} \;\underset{[^-OR']}{\overset{[^-OR'']}{\rightleftarrows}}\; \underset{R}{\overset{\overset{\displaystyle O}{\|}}{C}}-OR''$$

Only a small amount of catalyst is necessary because of the very mobile equilibrium.

$$R''OH + [^-OR'] \rightleftarrows [R''O^-] + HOR'$$

For alkaline saponification the reaction is

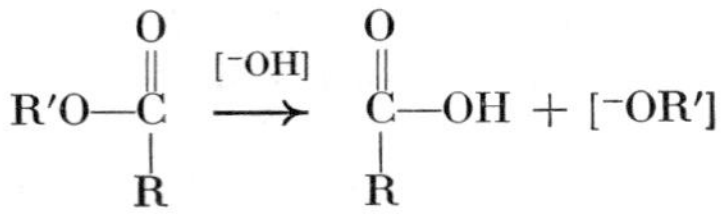

$$R'O-\underset{R}{\overset{\overset{\displaystyle O}{\|}}{C}} \;\overset{[^-OH]}{\longrightarrow}\; \underset{R}{\overset{\overset{\displaystyle O}{\|}}{C}}-OH + [^-OR']$$

followed by the reactions

$$RCOOH + [^-OR'] \longrightarrow [RCOO^-] + HOR'$$

$$RCOOH + [^-OH] \longrightarrow [RCOO^-] + HOH$$

$$HOH + [^-OR'] \longrightarrow [HO^-] + HOR'$$

in all of which the position of equilibrium is far to the right. These mechanisms agree with the fact that in the saponification of an ester with sodium hydroxide in water rich in O^{18}, the isotope enters the acid molecule but does not enter the alcohol molecule formed on hydrolysis.

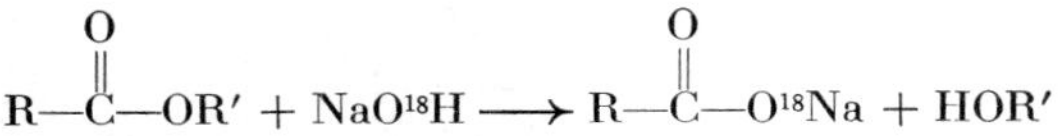

$$R-\overset{\overset{\displaystyle O}{\|}}{C}-OR' + NaO^{18}H \longrightarrow R-\overset{\overset{\displaystyle O}{\|}}{C}-O^{18}Na + HOR'$$

3. *Ammonolysis*. Ammonia splits esters with the formation of amides.

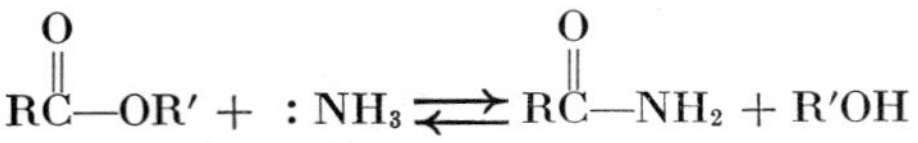

$$R\overset{\overset{\displaystyle O}{\|}}{C}-OR' + \;:NH_3 \rightleftarrows R\overset{\overset{\displaystyle O}{\|}}{C}-NH_2 + R'OH$$

The mechanism of ammonolysis probably is identical with base-catalyzed hydrolysis or alcoholysis, the ammonia molecule taking the place of the hydroxide or alkoxide ion.

4. *Scission by Acids*. Dry hydrogen bromide, hydrogen iodide, and concentrated sulfuric acid split esters just as they do ethers (p. 117), the products being the organic acid and alkyl halide.

$$RCOOR' + HBr \rightleftarrows RCOOH + R'Br$$

The reaction is important principally in the determination of methoxyl and ethoxyl by the Zeisel procedure (p. 118).

5. *Reduction.* The ester group, and thus indirectly the carboxyl group, can be converted into a primary alcohol group by reduction either with sodium and an alcohol, or catalytically. These reactions involve addition of hydrogen to the carbonyl group and elimination of the alkoxyl group.

$$RCOOR' + 4 Na + 3 R'OH \longrightarrow RCH_2OH + 4 NaOR'$$

Ordinarily in the *sodium-alcohol reduction* the methyl, ethyl, or *n*-butyl esters are used along with an excess of the corresponding alcohol as solvent and source of hydrogen. More recently it has been found that improved yields are obtained if an equivalent amount of a higher boiling secondary alcohol, such as the secondary hexyl alcohols or methylcyclohexanols (p. 559), is used as the source of hydrogen in an inert solvent such as toluene or xylene (p. 316). The sodium-alcohol reduction of fats, which are esters of glycerol (p. 159), then becomes competitive with catalytic reduction of acids (p. 129) as a commercial method for the manufacture of higher alcohols. *Lithium aluminum hydride*, $LiAlH_4$, may be used as a reducing agent instead of sodium.

$$4 RCOOR' + 2 LiAlH_4 \longrightarrow LiAl(OCH_2R)_4 + LiAl(OR')_4$$

One half mole or 19 g. of lithium aluminum hydride is equivalent in reducing power to four atoms or 92 g. of sodium. The former is, however, a considerably more expensive reagent, since it is made from lithium hydride.

$$4 LiH + AlCl_3 \longrightarrow LiAlH_4 + 3 LiCl$$

In the *catalytic reduction* of esters, a copper oxide-chromium oxide catalyst is used with hydrogen in the absence of a solvent at 250°.

$$RCOOR' + 2 H_2 \xrightarrow[250°]{CuO—Cr_2O_3} RCH_2OH + HOR'$$

Catalytic reduction of esters is preferred to sodium-alcohol reduction for laboratory preparations if suitable apparatus is available.

The reduction of esters to alcohols is important not only for preparing higher alcohols from natural fat acids, but also because it is the last link in a series of reactions which will permit the continuous increase in length of a hydrocarbon chain one carbon atom at a time.

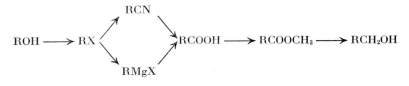

Repetition of the above series of reactions gives the higher homologs.

6. *Reaction with Grignard Reagents.* Grignard reagents will add to a carbonyl group (p. 89). They also will replace an alkoxyl group if the carbon atom to which it is attached carries a second oxygen atom. Therefore the final

product of the reaction of an ester with a Grignard reagent is the magnesium salt of a tertiary alcohol, which yields the alcohol on decomposition with water.

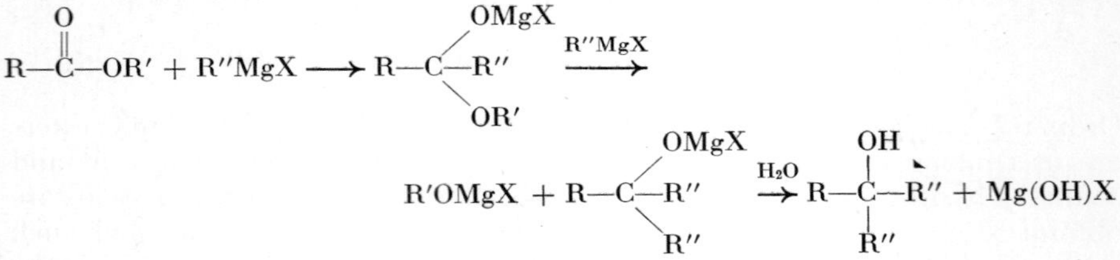

$$
\underset{\substack{\| \\ O}}{R-C-OR'} + R''MgX \longrightarrow R-\underset{\substack{| \\ OR'}}{\overset{OMgX}{C}}-R'' \overset{R''MgX}{\longrightarrow}
$$

$$
R'OMgX + R-\underset{\substack{| \\ R''}}{\overset{OMgX}{C}}-R'' \overset{H_2O}{\longrightarrow} R-\underset{\substack{| \\ R''}}{\overset{OH}{C}}-R'' + Mg(OH)X
$$

Uses

By far the most important general use for esters is as solvents, especially for nitrocellulose in the formulation of lacquers (p. 301). For this purpose ethyl acetate and butyl acetate are used to the greatest extent. Production of these two esters in the United States in 1948 was 60 and 63 million pounds valued at 13 and 18 cents per pound respectively. Ethyl formate is used as a fumigant and larvicide for grains and food products. Higher boiling esters are used as softening agents (plasticizers) for resins and plastics, and a number of the plastics are themselves esters, such as polymethyl methacrylate (p. 557), polyvinyl acetate (p. 516) and cellulose acetate (p. 301).

Some of the volatile esters have specific fruit odors. For example the odors of *i*-amyl acetate, *i*-amyl valerate, butyl butyrate and *i*-butyl propionate resemble the odors of banana or pear, apple, pineapple, and rum respectively. Hence they are used to a limited extent in synthetic flavors or perfumes. Natural odors and flavors are the result of complex mixtures of organic compounds. Very careful blending of synthetic compounds is necessary to imitate the natural product. Table 9 summarizes the results of a careful analysis

TABLE 9

COMPOSITION OF THE VOLATILE OIL OF THE PINEAPPLE

WINTER FRUIT		SUMMER FRUIT	
Constituent	Mg. per kg.	Constituent	Mg. per kg.
Total volatile oil	15.6	Total volatile oil	190.0
Ethyl acetate	2.91	Ethyl acetate	119.6
Ethyl alcohol	0.0	Ethyl alcohol	60.5
Acetaldehyde	0.61	Acetaldehyde	1.35
Methyl *n*-valerate	0.49	Ethyl acrylate	0.77
Methyl *i*-valerate	0.60	Ethyl *i*-valerate	0.39
Methyl *i*-caproate	1.40	Ethyl *n*-caproate	0.77
Methyl caprylate	0.75		

of the substances responsible for the odor and flavor of the pineapple. Both the amount of volatile oil and its components vary with the time of the year at which the fruit is harvested. The bouquet of fine wines has been ascribed to esters produced by the slow esterification of organic acids during the ageing process.

REVIEW QUESTIONS

1. What are the most commonly used names for the normal carboxylic acids having from one to eighteen carbon atoms?

2. Write condensed structural formulas for the isomeric saturated carboxylic acids having six carbon atoms, and name each as a derivative of acetic acid and by the Geneva (I.U.C.) system.

3. Using accepted structural theory, write formulas for all the possible compounds having the formula $C_2H_4O_2$. Indicate which formula represents acetic acid and give chemical evidence that it is the correct one.

4. How does the boiling point of acetic acid compare with that of alcohols and hydrocarbons of approximately the same molecular weight? Explain.

5. Discuss the solubility of carboxylic acids in water and organic solvents; in dilute potassium hydroxide.

6. Give equations for the synthesis of (a) caproic acid from an alkyl halide through a nitrile; (b) 2-methylbutanoic acid from an alkyl halide through a Grignard reagent; (c) n-butyric acid from n-butyl alcohol.

7. Give reactions illustrating the conversion of a carboxylic acid into a salt; a hydrocarbon; a ketone; an acid halide; an acid anhydride; an ester; an amide.

8. Discuss commercial methods for the preparation of formic, acetic, propionic, and butyric acids. What is the chief source of the higher normal carboxylic acids?

9. Give reactions for the general methods for the synthesis of acyl chlorides, acid anhydrides, esters, and amides.

10. What is the chief difference in the preparation of esters by direct esterification and by the use of acyl halides or anhydrides?

11. Compare the reaction of neutralization with that of esterification, and explain the difference.

12. What is meant by the terms *reversible reaction* and *chemical equilibrium*? What factors markedly influence the rate of a chemical reaction? How may the position of equilibrium be shifted?

13. Give equations illustrating the reaction of water, alcohols, and ammonia on acyl halides, acid anhydrides, and esters.

14. Write structural formulas for all the isomeric esters having the molecular formula $C_5H_{10}O_2$ and give two names to each.

15. Write reactions for the synthesis of i-butyryl chloride; acetic butyric anhydride; hexanoyl bromide; valeramide; 4,4-dimethylpentanoic acid; i-amyl propionate.

16. Outline a procedure for converting n-amyl i-caprylate into n-amyl alcohol and i-caprylic acid, obtaining the compounds in a relatively pure state. (Hint: consider the solubilities of the alcohol, the acid, and its sodium salt in water and in organic solvents.)

17. How could a candle made of stearic acid be distinguished from one made of paraffin? (Stearic acid is too insoluble in water to detect with an indicator.)

18. Devise a simple procedure for distinguishing between (a) an ether, an ester, and an acid anhydride; (b) an alkyl halide, an acyl halide, and an acid anhydride; (c) water, n-propyl alcohol, and acetic acid; (d) sodium hydroxide, sodium ethoxide, and sodium acetate.

19. If 0.2 g. of a carboxylic acid required 21.7 cc. of 0.1 N alkali for neutralization to phenolphthalein, what is the equivalent weight of the acid? If one carboxyl group is the only functional group present, what are the possible structures of the compound?

20. The saponification equivalent of an ester is 130, and the neutralization equivalent of the acid regenerated after saponification is 88. What is the equivalent weight of the alcohol with which the acid was esterified?

21. If in problem 20 the acid is monobasic and the alcohol is monohydric, what are the possible structures of the ester?

22. Give reactions that may be used for the preparation of (a) 2-methylbutanoic acid from 2-butene; (b) heptadecanoamide from palmitic acid; (c) triethylcarbinol from propionic acid; (d) dodecane from ethyl hexanoate; (e) 1-heptadecene from ethyl palmitate; (f) tridecyl alcohol from dodecyl alcohol.

Chapter 11

WAXES, FATS, AND OILS

Waxes, fats, and oils are naturally occurring esters of higher straight chain carboxylic acids. They usually are classified on a mixed basis including source, physical properties, and chemical properties.

$$
\text{Waxes} \begin{cases} \text{Vegetable} \\ \text{Animal} \end{cases}
$$

$$
\text{Fats} \begin{cases} \text{Vegetable} \\ \text{Animal} \end{cases}
$$

$$
\text{Oils} \begin{cases} \text{Vegetable} \begin{cases} \text{Nondrying} \\ \text{Semidrying} \\ \text{Drying} \end{cases} \\ \text{Animal} \begin{cases} \text{Terrestrial} \\ \text{Marine} \end{cases} \end{cases}
$$

WAXES

A technical definition of a wax might be that it is anything with a waxy feel and a melting point above body temperature and below the boiling point of water. Thus the term paraffin wax is used for a mixture of solid hydrocarbons, beeswax for a mixture of esters, and Carbowax for a synthetic polyether. Chemically, however, *waxes* are defined as *esters of high molecular weight monohydric (one hydroxyl group) alcohols with the common higher fat acids* (Table 8, p. 124). Hence they have the general formula of a simple ester, RCOOR'. Actually the natural waxes are mixtures of esters and frequently contain hydrocarbons as well.

Carnauba wax is the most valuable of the vegetable waxes. It occurs as a coating on the leaves of a Brazilian palm, *Corypha cerifera*, from which it is removed by shredding and beating of the leaves. It consists of a mixture of the esters of the normal alcohols and fat acids having even numbers of carbon atoms from 24 to 34, the C_{32} and C_{34} compounds predominating. Hydrocarbons having odd numbers of carbon atoms from C_{25} to C_{31} also are present. Because of the high melting point of 80°–87° and its imperviousness to water, carnauba wax is a valuable constituent of automobile and floor waxes and carbon paper coatings. **Beeswax** is the material from which the bee builds the cells of the honeycomb. Its composition resembles that of carnauba wax except that the esters on hydrolysis yield chiefly C_{26} and C_{28} acids and alcohols, and hence it has the lower melting point of 60°–82°. **Spermaceti** is obtained from the head of the sperm whale (Cetaceae). It is chiefly cetyl palmitate, $C_{15}H_{31}COOC_{16}H_{33}$, and melts at 42°–47°. **Degras** or **wool grease** is an extremely complex mixture of waxes, alcohols, and free fat acids recovered from the scouring of wool. It has the unusual property of forming a stable semisolid emulsion containing up to 80 per cent water. A purified product known as **lanolin** or **lanum** finds use as a base for salves and ointments

150

in which it is desired to incorporate both water-soluble and fat-soluble substances.

FATS AND OILS

Both *fats and oils* are *esters of higher fat acids and a trihydric alcohol, glycerol,* $HOCH_2CHOHCH_2OH$. Esters of glycerol frequently are called *glycerides*. They have the general formula $RCOOCH_2CHCH_2OCOR'$ and are dif-

$$OCOR''$$

ferentiated solely by the fact that fats are solid or semisolid at room temperature, whereas oils are liquids. Vegetable fats and oils usually occur in the fruits and seeds of plants and are extracted (*1*) by cold pressing in hydraulic presses or continuous expellers, (*2*) by hot pressing, and (*3*) by solvent extraction. Cold pressing gives the blandest product and is used for producing the highest grade food oils such as olive, cottonseed, and peanut oils. Hot pressing gives a higher yield, but larger quantities of undesirable constituents are expressed, and the oil has a stronger odor and flavor. Solvent extraction gives the highest recovery, and in recent years the process has been so improved that even food oils may be prepared which are free from undesirable odors and flavors. Animal fats are recovered by heating fatty tissue to a high temperature (dry-rendering) or by treating with steam or hot water and separating the liberated fat.

Fat Acids

Since all fats and oils are esters of glycerol, their differences must be due to the acids with which the glycerol is esterified. These acids are both saturated and unsaturated. Of the saturated acids the most important are **lauric acid,** $CH_3(CH_2)_{10}COOH$, **palmitic acid,** $CH_3(CH_2)_{14}COOH$, and **stearic acid,** $CH_3(CH_2)_{16}COOH$. The most important unsaturated acids have eighteen carbon atoms, and one double bond usually is at the middle of the chain. If other double bonds are present they lie further removed from the carboxyl group. **Oleic acid,** $CH_3(CH_2)_7CH{=}CH(CH_2)_7COOH$, has only one double bond; **linoleic acid (linolic acid),** $CH_3(CH_2)_4CH{=}CHCH_2CH{=}CH(CH_2)_7COOH$, has two double bonds separated by one methylene group; **linolenic acid,** $CH_3CH_2CH{=}CHCH_2CH{=}CHCH_2CH{=}CH(CH_2)_7COOH$, has three double bonds each separated by methylene groups; **eleostearic acid,** $CH_3(CH_2)_3{-}CH{=}CH{-}CH{=}CH{-}CH{=}CH(CH_2)_7COOH$, also has three double bonds but they are conjugated;[1] **licanic acid** is 4-ketoeleostearic acid, $CH_3(CH_2)_3{-}CH{=}CH{-}CH{=}CH{-}CH{=}CH(CH_2)_4CO(CH_2)_2COOH$.

Several other unsaturated acids are of interest. **Ricinoleic acid,** $CH_3(CH_2)_5CHOHCH_2CH{=}CH(CH_2)_7COOH$, is 12-hydroxyoleic acid. **Palmitoleic acid,** $CH_3(CH_2)_5CH{=}CH(CH_2)_7COOH$, **petroselenic acid,** $CH_3{-}(CH_2)_{10}CH{=}CH(CH_2)_4COOH$, and **erucic acid,** $CH_3(CH_2)_7CH{=}CH(CH_2)_{11}{-}COOH$, contain sixteen, eighteen, and twenty-two carbon atoms respectively, and the double bond is not at the middle of the chain. Of all the fat acids palmitic acid is the most abundant, and oleic acid is the most widely distributed.

[1] If double bonds and single bonds alternate successively in a molecule, the double bonds are said to be *conjugated.*

TABLE 10

Saponification and Iodine Numbers of Fats and Oils and the Composition of the Fat Acids Obtained by Hydrolysis

FAT OR OIL			Saponification number	Iodine number	Composition of fat acids (per cent)						
					Myristic	Palmitic	Stearic	Palmitoleic	Oleic	Linoleic	Other components
Vegetable fats		Coconut	250–60	8–10	17–20	4–10	1–5		2–10	0–2	a
		Palm	196–210	48–58	1–3	34–43	3–6		38–40	5–11	
Animal fats		Butter	216–35	26–45	7–9	23–26	10–13	5	30–40	4–5	b
		Lard	193–200	46–66	1–2	28–30	12–18	1–3	41–48	6–7	c
		Tallow	190–200	31–47	2–3	24–32	14–32	1–3	35–48	2–4	
Vegetable oils	Nondrying	Castor	176–87	81–90		0–1			0–9	3–7	d
		Olive	185–200	74–94	0–1	5–15	1–4	0–1	69–84	4–12	
		Peanut	185–95	83–98		6–9	2–6	0–1	50–70	13–26	e
		Rape	172–5	94–106	0–2	0–1	0–2		20–38	10–15	f
	Semi-drying	Corn	188–93	116–30	0–2	7–11	3–4	0–2	43–49	34–42	
		Cottonseed	191–6	103–15	0–2	19–24	1–2	0–2	23–33	40–48	
	Drying	Soybean	189–94	124–36	0–1	6–10	2–4		21–29	50–59	g
		Linseed	189–96	170–204		4–7	2–5		9–38	3–43	h
		Tung	189–95	160–80					4–16	0–1	i
		Oiticica	186–94	139–55		11			6		j
Animal oils	Terrestrial	Lard oil	190–95	46–70		22–26	15–17		45–55	8–10	
		Neat's foot	192–7	67–73		17–18	2–3		74–77		
	Marine	Whale	188–94	110–50	4–6	11–18	2–4	13–18	33–38		k
		Fish	185–95	120–90	6–8	10–16	1–2	6–15			l

(a) 5–10 caprylic, 5–11 capric, and 45–51 lauric acids.
(b) 3–4 butyric, 1–2 caproic, 1 caprylic, 2–3 capric, and 2–3 lauric acids.
(c) 2 of C_{20} and C_{22} unsaturated fat acids.
(d) 80–92 ricinoleic acid.
(e) 2–5 arachidic and 1–5 lignoceric acids.
(f) 1–2 lignoceric, 1–4 linolenic, and 43–57 erucic acid.
(g) 4–8 linolenic acid.
(h) 25–58 linolenic acid.
(i) 4–5 saturated acids and 74–91 eleostearic acid.
(j) 70–78 licanic acid.
(k) 11–20 C_{20} and 6–11 C_{22} unsaturated acids.
(l) 24–30 C_{18}, 19–26 C_{20}, and 12–19 C_{22} unsaturated acids.

152

Fats and oils are mixed glycerides and not a mixture of simple glycerides. Occasionally it is stated that a fat contains, for example, tripalmitin, tristearin, and triolein, the tripalmitic, tristearic, and trioleic acid esters of glycerol, but the presence of simple glycerides in fats is rare. The fat acids are combined randomly with the hydroxyl groups of the glycerol, and simple glycerides occur only if more than two-thirds of the acyl groups are of one kind. The approximate relative amounts of the different acids obtained by the hydrolysis of fats are given in Table 10.

In the acids obtained from fats, saturated acids predominate, but in those from oils, unsaturated acids predominate. In other words unsaturation lowers the melting point. Another factor which lowers the melting point is molecular weight. The acids from low-melting fats such as coconut oil, palm oil, and butter contain relatively small amounts of unsaturated acids but considerable amounts of lower fat acids. Although classified as fats because they are solid in temperate zones, coconut oil and palm oil were called oils because they are liquids in the tropics where they are produced.

Reactions of Fats and Oils

The characteristic chemical features of the fats are the ester linkages and the unsaturation. As esters they may be hydrolyzed in the presence of acids, enzymes, or alkali to yield glycerol and free fat acids, or their salts.

$$
\begin{array}{l}
RCOOCH_2 \\
R'COOCH \quad + 3\ H_2O \xrightarrow[\text{enzymes}]{[H^+]\ or} \\
R''COOCH_2
\end{array}
\begin{array}{ll}
RCOOH & CH_2OH \\
R'COOH\ + & CHOH \\
R''COOH & CH_2OH
\end{array}
$$

$$
+ 3\ M^+OH^- \longrightarrow
\begin{array}{ll}
[RCOO^-]M^+ & CH_2OH \\
[R'COO^-]M^+\ + & CHOH \\
[R''COO^-]M^+ & CH_2OH
\end{array}
$$

Since the fat acids differ in molecular weight, and since substances which do not react with alkali, such as high molecular weight alcohols and hydrocarbons, may be present, different fats will require different amounts of alkali for saponification. Hence the amount of alkali required to saponify a given weight of fat may be used as a characteristic of the particular fat. An arbitrary unit known technically as the **saponification value** or **saponification number** is used, which is the *number of milligrams of potassium hydroxide required to saponify one gram of fat*. Table 10 shows that the fats containing chiefly C_{18} acids have almost identical saponification values and the determination is useful only to identify or detect the presence of coconut oil and butter fat, or to determine whether these fats have been adulterated with others having a lower saponification value, or with mineral oils or greases.

The extent of unsaturation likewise is characteristic of a fat and may be determined by the amount of halogen which the double bonds will add. Iodine does not ordinarily form stable addition products with the double bond (p. 39), and chlorine or bromine substitute as well as add. In practice standardized solutions of iodine monochloride (*Wijs solution*) or of iodine monobromide (*Hanus solution*) in glacial acetic acid are used. However the Wijs or Hanus solution is standardized by adding potassium iodide and titrating the liberated iodine with standard thiosulfate solution, and the amount of reagent remaining after reaction with a fat is determined in the same way. *The amount of halogen added expressed in terms of grams of iodine* (as if iodine had added) *per 100 grams of fat* is known as the **iodine number** or **iodine value** of the fat. The increase in iodine number with increasing amounts of unsaturated acids is quite apparent in Table 10.

Thiocyanogen, $(SCN)_2$, shows many of the properties of halogens. It liberates iodine from potassium iodide, and also adds to double bonds. It has been found, however, that whereas one mole will add to monoethylenic acids such as oleic acid, only slightly more than one mole will add to the diethylenic linoleic acid, and somewhat less than two moles to the triply unsaturated linolenic acid. Solutions of thiocyanogen in glacial acetic acid are prepared by adding bromine to lead thiocyanate and are standardized and used like Wijs and Hanus solutions. *The amount of thiocyanogen added expressed in terms of grams of iodine per gram of fat* is known as the **thiocyanogen value.** Since Wijs or Hanus solution will saturate all double bonds, it is possible to estimate the composition of mixtures of oleic, linoleic, and linolenic acids from the iodine and thiocyanogen numbers.

The **hydrogenation of oils** is carried out technically on a large scale by bubbling hydrogen through the oil containing a suspension of finely divided nickel. In this process the double bonds of oleic, linoleic, linolenic, and eleostearic glycerides are hydrogenated and the oils converted into the hard waxy tristearin. By controlling the amount of hydrogen added, any consistency desired may be obtained. Since people of temperate zones prefer fat to oil for cooking purposes, and since fats are more useful than oils as soap stocks, hydrogenation greatly increases the value of an oil.

Rancidity of oils is caused chiefly by air oxidation of the unsaturated acids, which gives a complex mixture of volatile aldehydes, ketones, and acids. In some cases rancidity may be caused by microorganisms. Fats which have been freed of odor and undesirable tastes are now stabilized by the addition of substances which inhibit oxidation (antioxidants, p. 582).

The double bonds of tung oil glycerides are conjugated, that is in alternate positions (p. 494), whereas those of linseed and soybean oils are not. Conjugation confers certain desirable characteristics on a drying oil, particularly increased speed of drying. It is possible to **isomerize** linseed and soybean oils, in which the double bonds are isolated, to oils in which the double bonds are conjugated, and hence make them resemble tung oil in their properties (p. 156).

Castor oil is characterized by the high percentage of ricinoleic acid, which contains a hydroxyl group. The hydroxyl group may be acetylated and the *number of milligrams of potassium hydroxide that is needed to neutralize the acetic acid liberated from one gram of acetylated product* is known as the **acetyl value.** Castor oil has an acetyl value of 142 to 150, but other common fats and oils range from 2 to 20. Substances other than ricinoleic acid, for example high molecular weight alcohols and partially hydrolyzed glycerides, also acetylate and may account for all or part of the acetyl value.

A second double bond may be introduced into the ricinoleic portion of castor oil by dehydration, giving rise to a mixture of linoleic acid and the 9,11-diunsaturated acid in which the double bonds are conjugated, thus changing it from a nondrying to a drying oil. Moreover the high percentage of conjugation that results makes the dehydrated oil resemble tung oil in its properties.

In the laboratory isolation of individual fat acids for use as such or as a means of estimating the relative amounts composing the fat, the methyl or ethyl esters are prepared by transesterification and fractionally distilled under reduced pressure. This procedure is useful only in separating acids differing appreciably in molecular weight, and cannot be used to separate different unsaturated acids having the same number of carbon atoms. The esters are distilled rather than the free acids, since the latter form mixed double molecules which tend to smooth out the differences in boiling points between the individual acids. Commercially the free fat acids are separated by distillation or by solvent extraction processes.

The lead salts of unsaturated fat acids are much more soluble in ether or alcohol than the lead salts of the saturated fat acids. The lead salt method of separation is based on this fact.

Linoleic acid forms a tetrabromide, m.p. 115°–116°, and linolenic acid a hexabromide, m.p. 185°–186°, which can be isolated and purified readily. The linoleic and linolenic acids can be regenerated from their bromides by debromination with zinc dust in alcoholic solution (p. 108).

Oxidation of unsaturated acids with dilute permanganate solutions yields solid polyhydroxy acids, two hydroxyl groups being introduced per double bond (p. 40). These polyhydroxy acids are useful derivatives for identification of the individual unsaturated acids.

Oxides of nitrogen from mercury and nitric acid (Poutet's reagent) convert liquid unsaturated acids into solid isomers (p. 256). Oleic acid is converted into **elaidic acid** and the process is known as *elaidinization*. Oils may be partially solidified by the same reaction.

Uses of Fats and Oils

Food. From 25 to 50 per cent of the caloric intake of man consists of fats. On combustion in animals, fats produce about 9.5 kcal. per gram compared to 4 kcal. per gram for carbohydrates or proteins. Because of their high molecular weight, fats cannot be absorbed directly through the walls of the intestines. They are emulsified in the small intestine by bile and hydrolyzed into fat acids and glycerol in the presence of the enzyme catalyst, *steapsin*, which is secreted by the pancreas. The water insoluble fat acids react with the bile salts (p. 569) to form soluble complexes which, together with the glycerol, are transported through the wall of the intestine. Next they are resynthesized rapidly into fats by means of enzymes and pass into the lymph and then into the blood stream as a highly dispersed emulsion. The blood stream transports them to the tissues where they are burned for energy or stored as fat deposits for future use. From the standpoint of digestion one fat is as useful as another unless its melting point is so high that when mixed with other fats it does not melt or emulsify with the bile at body temperature, in which case it passes into the feces unchanged. However either linoleic or linolenic acid must be supplied by the ingested fats to insure a healthy condition of the skin.

Although some of the fat consumed is mixed with the other foodstuffs, the proteins and carbohydrates, a considerable portion first is isolated in a relatively pure state and consumed as such in bread spreads or used for frying or as salad oils and salad dressings such as mayonnaise. The relatively high cost of butter has led to the development of a substitute generally referred to as **oleomargarin.** Selected vegetable or animal fats and oils, which have been highly refined and properly hydrogenated to give the desired melting point and consistency, are emulsified with about 17 per cent by weight of milk which has been cultured with certain microorganisms to give it flavor. An emulsifying agent such as a monoglyceride (p. 159) or a vegetable lecithin (p. 527) usually is added as well. Butter consists of droplets of water suspended in oil (water-in-oil type emulsion). Oleomargarins may be either water-in-oil or oil-in-water types of emulsions depending on the method of manufacture. Diacetyl, $CH_3COCOCH_3$, and methylacetylcarbinol, $CH_3CHOHCOCH_3$, which account for the characteristic taste of butter, also may be added along with vitamins A and D. For many years oleomargarin manufacturers were not permitted to add color to their product unless an additional Federal tax of ten cents per pound was paid. In many states the sale of colored oleomargarin is prohibited and coloring matter is packaged separately.

Protective Coatings. Glycerides of fat acids containing two or more double bonds absorb oxygen on exposure to air to give peroxides, which catalyze the polymerization of the unsaturated portions. As a result the oils become solid or semisolid and are known as *drying oils.* If exposed in thin layers, tough elastic waterproof films are formed. **Paint** is a mixture of drying oil, pigment, thinner, and drier. The pigment is an opaque material having a refractive index different from that of the oil film, and provides color and covering power. The thinner is a volatile solvent, either turpentine (p. 565) or a petroleum fraction called mineral paint spirits (p. 55), which permits spreading and on evaporation leaves a thin even film of oil and pigment which does not run. The drier is a solution of cobalt, manganese, or lead salts of organic acids, usually naphthenic acids from petroleum (p. 561), which catalyzes the oxidation and polymerization of the oil. The drying oil is known as the *vehicle* because after polymerization it holds or carries the pigment. Linseed oil is the most widely used drying oil, although a certain amount of tung oil in a paint gives it superior properties which seem to be due to the conjugation of the unsaturation. Tung oil has been imported chiefly from China, but the tree can grow in a rather limited belt extending across southern United States, and plantations are in production. Dehydrated castor oil and isomerized linseed and soybean oils (p. 154), which have a certain amount of conjugated unsaturation, have properties resembling tung oil and are used to replace tung oil to a certain extent, especially when supplies from China are not available.

Although soybean oil has in recent years been classed as a drying oil, it formerly was classed as a semidrying oil, and as indicated by Table 10 its composition is such that its properties would be expected to be intermediate between those of cottonseed oil and linseed oil. Its drying properties can be enhanced, a procedure known as *up-grading,* by extraction with solvents which separate the oil into fractions having varying degrees of unsaturation. Another ingenious process is based on transesterification (p. 145) and the higher melting points of the saturated glycerides. The natural oil, which contains mixed glycerides, is treated with a small amount of sodium methoxide and cooled to a temperature at which the glycerides containing chiefly saturated acids crystallize, but at which the glycerides containing the unsaturated acids remain liquid. Thus the saturated acids are removed as the solid glycerides with an increase in unsaturation of the remaining oil. Another method of up-grading an oil consists of liberating the mixed acids by hydrolysis and re-esterifying with alcohols having a larger number of hydroxyl groups such as pentaerythritol, $C(CH_2OH)_4$ (p. 526), or sorbitol, $CH_2OH(CHOH)_4$-CH_2OH (p. 307). In this way molecules having higher molecular weights than the glycerides are formed and less polymerization is necessary to give a solid film. Such "synthetic" vehicles "dry" much faster and may give superior films. Many of the synthetic resins used for baking enamels contain unsaturated acid residues in the molecule and depend on polymerization for the solidification of the film.

Varnish is a mixture of drying oil, rosin (p. 566), and thinner. The rosin imparts hardness and high gloss to the dried film and may be replaced by other natural or synthetic resins. **Oil cloth** is made by coating cotton cloth with a mixture of partially oxidized oil and a pigment, and drying in warm chambers. If the oil is more highly oxidized to a thick viscous mass, mixed with rosin and ground cork or other filler, and rolled into a continuous sheet, **linoleum** is produced. The sheet travels slowly through warm chambers to permit complete polymerization.

Waste containing unsaturated oils is subject to **spontaneous combustion** if air is not excluded, or if not enough ventilation is possible to prevent a rise in temperature as the oil oxidizes and polymerizes. Any rise in temperature increases the rate of polymerization, and the process is accelerated until the material bursts into flame.

Soaps. Oil and water do not mix because the water molecules have a greater attraction for each other than for oil molecules. If a molecule has a large portion which is oil-soluble and a portion which is water-soluble, it will dissolve in water to give a colloidal solution if the effect of the water-soluble portion is sufficiently great. Such a colloidal solution, however, will have an attraction for oil molecules also, and if an oil is shaken with it, the oil will be dispersed into tiny droplets and an oil-in-water type of emulsion results. On the other hand if the effect of the oil-soluble portion of the molecule having mixed functions is sufficiently great, it will dissolve in oil. The water-solubilizing group, however, will have an attraction for water and if the colloidal solution is shaken with water, the latter will be dispersed in the oil to give a water-in-oil type of emulsion. Substances having the property of facilitating the production of emulsions are called *emulsifying agents.*

Dirt adheres to fabric and other surfaces by means of films of oil, and detergent action is largely the result of the action of emulsifying agents on the oil film. In addition the size of the dirt particles may be so small that they are adsorbed by the colloidal detergent, and if this adsorption is stronger than the adsorption to the carrier, the dirt particle is removed.

The alkali metal salts of fat acids having from ten to eighteen carbon atoms qualify as detergents and emulsifying agents, the hydrocarbon chain being oil-soluble and the carboxylate ion water-soluble. Strictly speaking only such salts should be referred to as soaps. If the hydrocarbon chain of the alkali metal salts is less than ten carbon atoms long, it will not cause emulsification of oil. If more than eighteen carbon atoms are present, the salt is too in-soluble in water to form a sufficiently concentrated colloidal solution. Similarly the alkaline earth and heavy metal salts are water-insoluble and hence useless as detergents. Hard water, containing calcium, magnesium, and iron ions, will precipitate insoluble salts when soap solutions are added, and lathering will not take place until these ions are completely removed. Moreover the scum of insoluble salts produced from the soap and inorganic salts may be difficult to remove from the article being washed. The insoluble salts have other uses, however (p. 159), and frequently are called soaps.

Ordinary soaps are usually sodium salts. Stocks containing mostly satu-rated fats give hard soaps, whereas highly unsaturated fats give soft soaps. Low molecular weight soaps, for example from coconut oil, are most soluble in water and give a loose lather consisting of large unstable bubbles, whereas higher molecular weight soaps, such as those from tallow, give a close lather consisting of fine stable bubbles. Potassium soaps are more soluble than sodium soaps but more costly. The fats and hydrogenated oils used in soap manufacture are blended carefully for the particular type of soap desired.

Synthetic Detergents and Emulsifying Agents. In recent years numerous synthetic compounds have become available which meet the gen-eral structural requirements for a detergent or emulsifying agent, namely a water-soluble portion and an oil-soluble portion. The earliest of these were the *sulfated fats and oils* (formerly called sulfonated), which have been in com-mercial use for over one hundred years. The double bonds of the unsaturated portions of the fat will add sulfuric acid to give the hydrogen sulfate of the hydroxy acid. For example the oleic acid portion will react according to the equation

$$\begin{array}{l} CH_2OCO(CH_2)_7CH{=}CH(CH_2)_7CH_3 \\ | \\ CHOCOR \\ | \\ CH_2OCOR' \end{array} + H_2SO_4 \longrightarrow \begin{array}{ll} CH_2OCO(CH_2)_7CH_2CH(CH_2)_7CH_3 \\ | \qquad\qquad\qquad\qquad\quad | \\ CHOCOR \qquad\qquad\quad OSO_3H \\ | \\ CHOCOR' \end{array}$$

Neutralization will give the sodium salt, which provides the water-solubilizing portion of the molecule. In the sulfation of *castor oil*, the hydroxyl group of the ricinoleic acid portion of the molecule reacts more readily than the double bond. If sulfation is carried out at a sufficiently low temperature, the double bond is largely unaffected.

$$C_3H_5\left[OCO(CH_2)_7CH{=}CHCH_2\underset{\underset{OH}{|}}{CH}(CH_2)_5CH_3 \right]_3 + 3\ H_2SO_4 \longrightarrow$$

$$C_3H_5\left[OCO(CH_2)_7CH{=}CHCH_2\underset{\underset{OSO_3H}{|}}{CH}(CH_2)_5CH_3 \right]_3$$

Sulfated castor oil is known as *Turkey Red oil* because it was used in the ap-plication of the dye alizarin to an aluminum mordanted cloth to give the color known as Turkey Red (p. 487). Turkey Red oil should not be confused with *red oil*, which is the technical name given to commercial oleic acid. During 1948 over 35 million pounds of sulfated oils were produced in the United

States, of which approximately 13 million pounds were from fish oils, 7 million pounds from tallow, 3 million pounds from other animal fats, 5 million pounds from castor oil, and 6 million pounds from other vegetable oils.

Since 1930 the catalytic reduction of fat acids (p. 129) or the sodium-alcohol reduction of fats (p. 147), especially coconut oil, has been used to produce mixtures of higher alcohols which can be sulfated to produce detergents.

$$RCH_2OH + H_2SO_4 \longrightarrow RCH_2OSO_3H \longrightarrow RCH_2OSO_3Na$$

Production in the United States in 1948 was about 65 million pounds.

The number of synthetic surface-active agents has increased enormously in recent years. Between 500 and 600 are available commercially. The most widely used synthetic detergents in 1948 were the sodium salts of alkylated aromatic sulfonic acids (p. 355), production of which amounted to over 100 million pounds. The use of products containing synthetic detergents is increasing rapidly. Total sales in 1948 amounted to about 400 million pounds compared to 2500 million pounds of soap products.

In contrast to the triglycerides, monoglycerides have free hydroxyl groups which act as water-solubilizing groups, and hence they become emulsifying agents. They have found extensive use particularly in the manufacture of oleomargarin and in other food industries, and in the preparation of cosmetic creams. They are mixtures prepared either by the partial esterification of glycerol with free fat acids or by the glycerolysis of fats.

Other Uses for Fat Acids. Free fat acids are used as softening agents for rubber. Commercial stearic acid is a mixture of stearic and palmitic acids used in the manufacture of candles, cosmetics, and shaving soaps. The aluminum, calcium, lead, and other metallic soaps when heated with petroleum oils form a gel and are used to thicken oils in the manufacture of lubricating greases. Magnesium and zinc stearates are used in face powders and dusting powders, and as lubricants to prevent sticking in the molding of plastics. Fat acid chains are incorporated into the molecules of antiseptics, drugs, dyes, resins, and plastics to modify their solubility and setting characteristics. Lately, fat acids have been converted on an industrial scale into esters, amides, nitriles, and amines, the last being particularly valuable as a starting point for the synthesis of one type of antiseptic (p. 195).

REVIEW QUESTIONS

1. Define the terms wax, fat, and oil.
2. Give a classification of waxes, fats, and oils and list under each class and subclass the more common representatives.
3. Discuss the composition of fats and oils. Give the names and structures of the more important acids formed on the hydrolysis of carnauba wax, butter, lard, tallow, coconut oil, olive oil, tung oil, and linseed oil. What is unusual about the naturally occurring fat acids?
4. What is meant by the terms saponification number; iodine value; acetyl value? How could cottonseed oil be distinguished readily from lubricating oil; castor oil from olive oil; coconut oil from lard; olive oil from linseed oil; spermaceti from tallow?
5. Discuss the manufacture of soap.
6. Give the principle and the method for converting oils into fats. What volume of hydrogen would be required to convert 500 g. of oil having an iodine value of 105 into the saturated fat?

7. What so-called synthetic detergents are derived from fat acids and how are they made?

8. An unknown compound is insoluble in water but dissolves in dilute sodium carbonate solution. It decolorizes bromine readily without the evolution of hydrogen bromide. No other characteristic groups can be detected. Vigorous oxidation with permanganate gives two acids, a liquid having an equivalent weight of 158 as shown by titration, and a solid having an equivalent weight of 94. Give the likely structure of the original compound and the reactions that it undergoes.

Chapter 12

ALDEHYDES AND KETONES

Both alcohols and ethers have the general formula $C_nH_{2n+2}O$. A less saturated group of compounds is known having the formula $C_nH_{2n}O$. Since the first member of the series, CH_2O, has only one carbon atom, the unsaturation cannot be due to a carbon-carbon double bond. Therefore the only logical structure satisfying the rules of valence is one in which the carbon atom is united to the oxygen atom by a double bond. This functional group, $C{=}O$, which is known as a *carbonyl group*, was present in the carboxyl group of carboxylic acids, but its properties were masked by the presence on the same carbon atom of a hydroxyl group. If only hydrogen or carbon atoms are united to the carbonyl group, the group is characteristic of the compounds known as *aldehydes* and *ketones*. The **aldehydes** have at least one hydrogen atom united to the carbonyl group and are represented by the general formula RCHO. The **ketones** have two carbon atoms united to the carbonyl group and are represented by the formula RCOR. The methods of preparation and reactions are in agreement with these structures.

Preparation

1. *Oxidation or Dehydrogenation of Alcohols.* Aldehydes and ketones are formed by the oxidation or dehydrogenation of primary and secondary alcohols respectively (p. 77).

$$RCH_2OH + [O] \longrightarrow R{-}\overset{\displaystyle O}{\overset{\|}{C}}{-}H + H_2O$$

$$R_2CHOH + [O] \longrightarrow R{-}\overset{\displaystyle O}{\overset{\|}{C}}{-}R + H_2O$$

The oxidizing agent may be air in the presence of a copper or silver catalyst at 550°–600°, or a chemical oxidizing agent such as sodium dichromate and sulfuric acid (dichromic acid). The latter reagent is useful for the preparation of the lower aldehydes only, which because of their low boiling points can be distilled from the reaction mixture as fast as they are formed. Otherwise the aldehyde is retained and oxidized rapidly to acid. The ketones undergo further oxidation less readily, and the reaction is more generally applicable for their preparation. The calculated amount of chromium trioxide, CrO_3, in glacial acetic acid also may be used for the conversion of secondary alcohol groups to ketone groups.

Catalytic dehydrogenation is a convenient process for the preparation of aldehydes and ketones.

$$\underset{\text{(or } R_2CHOH)}{RCH_2OH} \underset{325°}{\overset{\text{Brass spelter}}{\rightleftarrows}} \underset{\text{(or } R_2CO)}{RCHO} + H_2$$

161

Because of the equilibrium the reaction does not go to completion, but the product can be separated by distillation and the alcohol recycled. Copper chromite or alloys of copper and silver, or copper and nickel, also have been recommended as catalysts. It is from this first method of preparation that the name aldehyde is derived (*al*cohol *dehyd*rogenatum).

2. Hydrolysis of Ozonides. Ozonides, prepared by the addition of ozone to the carbon-carbon double bond, can be hydrolyzed to aldehydes and ketones (p. 40).

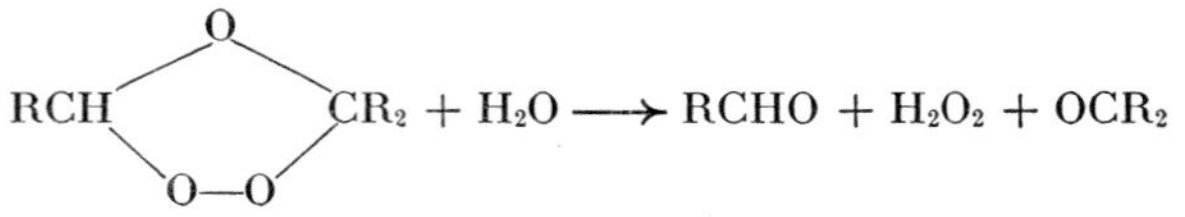

$$\text{RCH} \underset{\text{O—O}}{\overset{\text{O}}{\diamondsuit}} \text{CR}_2 + \text{H}_2\text{O} \longrightarrow \text{RCHO} + \text{H}_2\text{O}_2 + \text{OCR}_2$$

To obtain maximum yields of aldehydes and ketones the decomposition is carried out in the presence of a reducing agent such as zinc dust and acetic acid, or hydrogen and platinum, to destroy the peroxides (p. 577) and prevent the formation of organic acids. Whether aldehydes, ketones, or both are obtained depends on the structure of the olefin from which the ozonide was prepared.

3. Pyrolysis of Carboxylic Acids. Pyrolysis of carboxylic acids over thoria gives ketones (p. 128). The catalyst is deposited on a porous material such as pumice and packed into a tube which is heated to the proper temperature. The organic acid is run into the tube where it vaporizes and passes over the catalyst. The exit gases are condensed and the product separated by distillation.

$$2 \text{ RCOOH} \xrightarrow[400°-450°]{\text{ThO}_2} \text{R}_2\text{CO} + \text{CO}_2 + \text{H}_2\text{O}$$

By using a mixture of organic acids, mixed ketones can be obtained; or if a mixture of formic acid with another organic acid is used, aldehydes can be produced.

$$\begin{array}{c} \text{RCOOH} \\ + \\ \text{R'COOH} \end{array} \xrightarrow[400°-450°]{\text{ThO}_2} \text{RCOR'} + \text{CO}_2 + \text{H}_2\text{O}$$

$$\begin{array}{c} \text{RCOOH} \\ + \\ \text{HCOOH} \end{array} \xrightarrow[400°-450°]{\text{ThO}_2} \text{RCHO} + \text{CO}_2 + \text{H}_2\text{O}$$

The yields of mixed ketones and aldehydes are likely to be poor, because simple ketones and formaldehyde also are produced, and formic acid decomposes into carbon monoxide and water.

Nomenclature

Aldehydes. The **common names** of aldehydes are derived from the acids which would be formed on oxidation, that is the acids having the same number of carbon atoms. In general the *ic acid* is dropped and *aldehyde* added, for example formaldehyde, acetaldehyde, and *i*-butyraldehyde corresponding to the fact that they will yield formic, acetic, and *i*-butyric acids on oxidation. Just as more complex acids may be named as derivatives of acetic acid, aldehydes may be named **as derivatives of acetaldehyde;** thus $C_2H_5CH(CH_3)CHO$ may be called methylethylacetaldehyde. In the **Geneva system** the aldehydes are named by dropping the *e* of the hydrocarbon corresponding to the longest chain containing the aldehyde group and adding *al*. The compound having the above formula would be called 2-methylbutanal. The position of the aldehyde group is not indicated, since it always is at the end of the chain, and its carbon atom is numbered one.

Ketones. The **common names** of ketones are derived from the acid which on pyrolysis would yield the ketone. For example acetone, CH_3COCH_3, may be derived from two molecules of acetic acid, and *i*-butyrone, $(CH_3)_2CHCOCH(CH_3)_2$, from *i*-butyric acid. A second method, especially useful for naming **mixed ketones,** simply names the alkyl groups and adds the word *ketone.* For example $CH_3COC_2H_5$ is methyl ethyl ketone. The name is written as three separate words since the compound is not a substitution product of a substance *ketone.* In the **Geneva system** the ending is *one* and the position of the carbonyl group must be indicated by a number, unless the name is unambiguous without the number. Thus methyl ethyl ketone may be called simply butanone, but ethyl ketone, $CH_3CH_2COCH_2CH_3$, must be called 3-pentanone, since methyl *n*-propyl ketone, $CH_3COCH_2CH_2CH_3$, would be 2-pentanone. Side chains are named and numbered as usual.

Physical Properties

The aldehydes and ketones resemble the ethers in their solubility characteristics and volatility, although aldehydes and ketones do boil somewhat higher than ethers having the same number of carbon atoms. For example methyl ether boils at $-24°$ and acetaldehyde at $+20°$. This higher boiling point is due primarily to the higher permanent dipole moment of aldehydes and ketones (acetaldehyde = 2.5, methyl ether = 1.3; methyl ethyl ketone = 2.8, ethyl ether = 1.1; cf. p. 63).

Reactions

In general aldehydes differ from ketones only in the relative rates of reactions and in the position of equilibrium. Aldehydes usually react faster and the reaction goes more nearly to completion. Since a double bond is present in the carbonyl group, most of the reactions take place by addition. Reactions of both aldehydes and ketones are considered together, attention being called to any important differences. Because of the large number of reactions, it is desirable to group them under simple addition, addition and loss of water, oxidation, and miscellaneous tests and reactions.

SIMPLE ADDITION

1. **Hydrogen.** Aldehydes on reduction yield primary alcohols, and ketones yield secondary alcohols.

$$\underset{\text{H}}{R\overset{|}{C}=O} + 2[H] \longrightarrow RCH_2OH$$

$$R_2C=O + 2[H] \longrightarrow R_2CHOH$$

The reduction may be brought about catalytically with hydrogen and a platinum, palladium, or nickel catalyst, or by chemical reducing agents in neutral or alkaline solution, for example sodium and absolute alcohol, or sodium amalgam and water. Lithium aluminum hydride (p. 147) promises to be a useful reagent for this purpose. Another method known as the *Meerwein-Ponndorf reduction* depends on the equilibrium that exists between alcohols and carbonyl compounds in the presence of aluminum alkoxides.

$Li(alk OH)_4$

$$R'CHO + R_2CHOH \underset{}{\overset{Al(OR)_3}{\rightleftharpoons}} R'CH_2OH + R_2CO$$

If the alcohol used as the reducing agent is so chosen that the aldehyde or ketone formed boils at a lower temperature than any of the other reactants, it may be removed by slow distillation, and the reaction forced to completion. For example if ethyl alcohol and aluminum ethoxide, or *i*-propyl alcohol and aluminum *i*-propoxide, are used, the low-boiling acetaldehyde or acetone is removed. Ketones as well as aldehydes may be reduced. If the reaction is carried out in such a way that it is used to oxidize an alcohol by means of a ketone, it is called an *Oppenauer oxidation.*

2. **Grignard Reagents.** Addition of Grignard reagents takes place as with the carbonyl group of carbon dioxide (p. 89), that is R to carbon and MgX to oxygen. Formaldehyde yields primary alcohols, all other aldehydes yield secondary alcohols, and ketones yield tertiary alcohols. This procedure is one of the most important for the synthesis of complex alcohols, since by choosing the proper R groups in the aldehyde or ketone and in the Grignard reagent almost any desired alcohol may be synthesized, provided the R groups are not too highly branched to cause steric hindrance and prevent addition.

See p 87

$$\underset{}{\overset{O}{\underset{\parallel}{H-C-H}}} + RMgX \longrightarrow \underset{}{\overset{OMgX}{\underset{\underset{R}{\mid}}{H-C-H}}} \overset{H_2O}{\rightarrow} RCH_2OH + HOMgX \ ^{[1]}$$

$$RCHO + R'MgX \longrightarrow \underset{\underset{OMgX}{\mid}}{R-CH-R'} \overset{H_2O}{\rightarrow} \underset{\underset{OH}{\mid}}{RCHR'} + HOMgX$$

$$R_2CO + R'MgX \longrightarrow \underset{\underset{OMgX}{\mid}}{R_2C-R'} \overset{H_2O}{\rightarrow} \underset{\underset{OH}{\mid}}{R_2CR'} + HOMgX$$

Although the above reactions take place readily to give good yields of the products when simple aldehydes or ketones, or simple Grignard reagents are involved, branching of the alkyl groups in either the carbonyl compound or the Grignard reagent or both may permit side reactions to predominate.

3. **Hydrogen Cyanide.** Anhydrous hydrogen cyanide adds to aldehydes and ketones to give α hydroxy cyanides known as **cyanohydrins.**

$$RCHO + HCN \longrightarrow \underset{\underset{H}{\mid}}{\overset{\overset{OH}{\mid}}{R C-CN}}$$

---

[1] Cf. page 87.

$$R_2CO + HCN \longrightarrow R_2\overset{\overset{\displaystyle OH}{|}}{C}\text{—}CN$$

These compounds are named as addition products. For example that derived from acetaldehyde is known as *acetaldehyde cyanohydrin* and that from acetone as *acetone cyanohydrin.* As with any other nitrile, the cyanide group can be hydrolyzed to a carboxyl group (p. 121). Hence the cyanohydrins are intermediates for the synthesis of α hydroxy acids (p. 533).

The reactivity of the carbonyl group depends on the ability of an electron-seeking reagent to attack the oxygen atom or of an electron-donating reagent to attack the carbon atom. Thus it was shown as early as 1903 by Lapworth [2] that the addition of hydrogen cyanide to aldehydes and ketones is accelerated by the addition of bases but retarded by the addition of acids. Therefore the active reagent is cyanide ion and not hydrogen cyanide.

$$\overset{\delta+}{R_2}\overset{\delta-}{C}{=}\ddot{O}: \xrightleftharpoons{[\,:CN^-]} \left[\overset{\overset{\displaystyle R_2C\text{—}\ddot{O}:^-}{|}}{CN} \right] \xrightleftharpoons{HCN} R_2C\text{—}OH + [\,:CN^-]$$

4. Sodium Bisulfite. When shaken with a saturated aqueous sodium bisulfite solution, most aldehydes and methyl ketones will react to form a slightly soluble bisulfite addition compound in which hydrogen has added to oxygen and the sodium sulfonate group to carbon.

$$RCHO + NaHSO_3 \rightleftharpoons \left[\overset{\overset{\displaystyle OH}{|}}{\underset{\underset{\displaystyle H}{|}}{R\text{—}C\text{—}SO_3^-}} \right] \overset{+}{Na}$$

$$RCOCH_3 + NaHSO_3 \rightleftharpoons \left[\underset{HO \qquad SO_3^-}{R\text{—}C\text{—}CH_3} \right] \overset{+}{Na}$$

If both groups attached to the carbonyl group are larger than methyl, the addition compound does not form unless the groups are held out of the way of the carbonyl group, as for example when they are part of a ring as in cyclohexanone (p. 560). As to nomenclature the product from acetaldehyde is known as *acetaldehyde sodium bisulfite* or as the *bisulfite addition compound of acetaldehyde;* that from acetone is *acetone sodium bisulfite* or the *bisulfite addition compound of acetone.*

Since these compounds are salts, they are not soluble in organic solvents and may be freed from other organic compounds such as hydrocarbons or alcohols by filtering and washing with ether. The reactions are reversible and hence anything which will destroy bisulfite will regenerate the carbonyl compound. Either alkali or acid may be used.

[2] Arthur Lapworth (1872–1941), professor at the University of Manchester who held in succession chairs in organic chemistry and in physical chemistry. He was a pioneer investigator of the mechanisms of organic reactions. His ideas were so advanced that his early work received little attention for many years. His investigations of the addition of hydrogen cyanide to carbonyl compounds, of the bromination of ketones, and of acid and basic catalysis now are considered classical.

$$RCHOHSO_3Na + HCl \longrightarrow RCHO + NaCl + SO_2 + H_2O$$

$$R_2COHSO_3Na + Na_2CO_3 \longrightarrow R_2CO + Na_2SO_3 + NaHCO_3$$

Acids have the disadvantage that sulfur dioxide must be removed from the product. Alkalies have the disadvantage that they cause condensation reactions with aldehydes (p. 167). As a result alkalies usually are used to liberate ketones, and acids to liberate aldehydes. An alternate procedure consists of heating the bisulfite addition compound with a slight excess of an aqueous solution of formaldehyde.

$$RCH\begin{matrix} OH \\ \\ SO_3Na \end{matrix} + HCHO \longrightarrow RCHO + H_2C\begin{matrix} OH \\ \\ SO_3Na \end{matrix}$$

$$R_2C\begin{matrix} OH \\ \\ SO_3Na \end{matrix} + HCHO \longrightarrow R_2CO + H_2C\begin{matrix} OH \\ \\ SO_3Na \end{matrix}$$

These exchange reactions take place because the position of equilibrium for the reaction of formaldehyde with bisulfite is farther to the right than it is with the other aldehydes and ketones. The chief importance of the bisulfite addition compounds is their use in separating carbonyl compounds from mixtures with other organic compounds.

5. *Alcohols.* In the presence of acidic or basic catalysts, aldehydes will add one mole of alcohol to form *hemiacetals*.

$$RCHO + R'OH \underset{}{\overset{[H^+] \text{ or } [B^-]}{\rightleftarrows}} RCH\begin{matrix} OH \\ \\ OR' \end{matrix}$$

A hemiacetal

With an excess of alcohol and an acidic catalyst, water is eliminated and an *acetal* is formed.

$$RCH\begin{matrix} OH \\ \\ OR' \end{matrix} + HOR' \underset{}{\overset{[H^+]}{\rightleftarrows}} RCH\begin{matrix} OR' \\ \\ OR' \end{matrix} + H_2O$$

An acetal

Acetal also is the specific name for the product from acetaldehyde and ethyl alcohol. The product from formaldehyde and methyl alcohol has the common name **methylal.** In the reaction of ketones with alcohols, the position of equilibrium is so far to the left that ketals are not formed in significant amounts.

An explanation of the fact that hemiacetal formation is catalyzed by both acids and bases, whereas acetal formation is catalyzed only by acids, is of interest. In the basic catalysis of hemiacetal formation, the alcohol must be the effective point of attack by the catalyst.

$$
ROH \underset{HOH}{\overset{[OH^-]}{\rightleftarrows}} [R'O^-] \overset{RCHO}{\rightleftarrows} \left[\begin{array}{c} \overset{..}{RCH-O} : ^- \\ | \\ OR' \end{array} \right] \underset{[OH^-]}{\overset{HOH}{\rightleftarrows}} \begin{array}{c} RCHOH \\ | \\ OR' \end{array} \tag{a}
$$

When the carbon atom of the carbonyl group of the aldehyde is attacked by the catalyst, as occurs in the alkaline hydrolysis of esters (p. 146), it does not lead to the formation of a hemiacetal, but merely to the hydrated aldehyde.

$$
RCHO \overset{[OH^-]}{\rightleftarrows} \left[\begin{array}{c} \overset{..}{RCH-O} : ^- \\ | \\ OH \end{array} \right] \underset{[OR^-] \text{ or } [OH^-]}{\overset{HOR \text{ or } HOH}{\rightleftarrows}} \left[\begin{array}{c} RCH-OH \\ | \\ OH \end{array} \right] \tag{b}
$$

In acid catalysis, however, the effective point of attack is the carbonyl group.

$$
RCHO \underset{B^-}{\overset{HB}{\rightleftarrows}} \left[\begin{array}{c} .. \\ RCH=O:H \\ + \end{array} \right] \overset{ROH}{\rightleftarrows} \left[\begin{array}{c} H \\ | \\ R-C-OH \\ | \\ + :O-R \\ .. \\ H \end{array} \right] \underset{HB}{\overset{B^-}{\rightleftarrows}} \begin{array}{c} H \\ | \\ R-C-OH \\ | \\ OR \end{array} \tag{c}
$$

The attack by the acid on the alcohol gives $[ROH_2^+]$ which can do nothing but transfer protons to the carbonyl group.

In the conversion of the hemiacetal to the acetal, bases are not effective catalysts, because they can do nothing except attack the hydroxyl of the hemiacetal, which is the reverse of hemiacetal formation (equation *a*). Acid catalysts, however, can initiate continuation of the reaction to the acetal stage. If the acid attacks the alkoxyl group, it merely is catalyzing the reverse of hemiacetal formation (equation *c*). When, however, it attacks the hydroxyl group, acetal formation can result.

$$
\begin{array}{c} H \\ | \\ R-C-OH \\ | \\ OR \end{array} \underset{B^-}{\overset{HB}{\rightleftarrows}} \left[\begin{array}{c} H\ H \\ | \ ..+ \\ R-C-OH \\ | \ .. \\ OR \end{array} \right] \underset{HOH}{\overset{HOR}{\rightleftarrows}} \left[\begin{array}{c} H \\ | \\ R-C-OR \\ | \\ + :O-R \\ .. \\ H \end{array} \right] \underset{HB}{\overset{B^-}{\rightleftarrows}} \begin{array}{c} H \\ | \\ R-C-OR \\ | \\ OR \end{array}
$$

6. ***Aldol Condensation.*** In the presence of dilute aqueous alkalies and acids, aldehydes and ketones having at least one α hydrogen atom undergo condensation reactions. These reactions may be repeated, and under certain conditions complex compounds are formed. In the presence of very dilute alkalies or acids, the product of reaction of two moles of aldehyde or ketone can be isolated. The reaction may be written as the addition of an α hydrogen to a carbonyl group, and carbon to carbon.

$$
RCH=O + R'-CHCHO \overset{[OH^-] \text{ or } [H^+]}{\rightleftarrows} \begin{array}{c} R' \\ | \\ RCHOHCHCHO \end{array}
$$
$$
\begin{array}{c} | \\ H \end{array}
$$

Since the product has both an alcohol and an aldehyde function, it is known as an *aldol*. **Acetaldol** was synthesized by Wurtz in 1872.

$$CH_3CHO + CH_3CHO \underset{[OH^-] \text{ or } [H^+]}{\rightleftarrows} CH_3CHOHCH_2CHO$$
$$\text{Acetaldol or aldol}$$

With ketones the equilibrium is so far to the left that special means of shifting it to the right must be employed to obtain practical amounts.

$$CH_3COCH_3 + CH_3COCH_3 \underset{[OH^-] \text{ or } [H^+]}{\overset{}{\rightleftarrows}} (CH_3)_2COHCH_2COCH_3$$
$$\text{Diacetone alcohol}$$

For the production of diacetone alcohol, the acetone is passed over an insoluble catalyst such as calcium hydroxide or barium hydroxide and the unchanged acetone separated by distillation and recycled.

The alkaline catalysis of aldol condensation introduces a new point of attack for the catalyst in carbonyl compounds, namely the hydrogen atoms on a carbon atom α to a carbonyl group. Since the carbon atom of the carbonyl group is deficient in electrons because of the doubly-bound oxygen atom (p. 129), it has an attraction for electrons on the adjacent α carbon atom. Hence a hydrogen atom on the α carbon atom is removable more readily as a proton than hydrogen in a hydrocarbon, and the base is effective in removing it. The anion thus formed attacks the carbonyl carbon atom of a second molecule, and the product is stabilized by acquiring a proton from a water molecule.

$$\underset{CH_2CHO}{\overset{R}{|}} \underset{HOH}{\overset{[OH^-]}{\rightleftarrows}} \left[\underset{:CHCHO}{\overset{R}{|}} \right]^- \overset{R'CHO}{\rightleftarrows} \left[\underset{:O:^-}{\overset{R}{\underset{|}{R'CH-CHCHO}}} \right] \underset{[OH^-]}{\overset{HOH}{\rightleftarrows}} \underset{OH}{\overset{R}{\underset{|}{RCH-CHCHO}}}$$

In the acid-catalyzed reaction the carbonyl group is the first point of attack, and removal of a proton from the α carbon atom follows.

$$\underset{B^-}{\overset{H}{\underset{|}{RCH_2C=O}}} \overset{HB}{\rightleftarrows} \left[\underset{}{\overset{H}{\underset{|}{RCH_2C=OH}}} \right]^+ \underset{B^-}{\overset{HB}{\rightleftarrows}} \underset{}{\overset{H}{\underset{|}{RCH=COH}}}$$

The product is known as the *enol form* of the carbonyl compound, and the process is called *enolization.* In this process the equilibrium for simple aldehydes and ketones lies far to the left. In the next stage of the reaction, the double bond of the enol form is attacked by the electron-deficient carbon atom of a second molecule of the conjugate acid (p. 192) of the carbonyl compound.

$$\left[\underset{}{\overset{H}{\underset{|}{RCH=COH}}} \right] + \left[\underset{H}{\overset{RCH_2C=OH}{|}} \right] \rightleftarrows \left[\underset{\underset{H}{|}}{\overset{H}{\underset{|}{RCH-C=OH}}} \atop RCH_2COH \right] \underset{HB}{\overset{B^-}{\rightleftarrows}} \underset{RCH_2CHOH}{RCHCHO}$$

The aldols are characterized by the ease with which they lose water. Heating with traces of acid or iodine gives the α,β-unsaturated aldehyde or ketone.

$$CH_3CHOHCH_2CHO \xrightarrow[\text{heat}]{[H^+]} CH_3CH{=}CHCHO + H_2O$$
$$\text{Crotonic aldehyde}$$

$$(CH_3)_2COHCH_2COCH_3 \xrightarrow[\text{heat}]{I_2} (CH_3)_2C{=}CHCOCH_3 + H_2O$$
$$\text{Mesityl oxide}$$

Iodine catalyzes the above dehydrations, because it is an electron-seeking reagent. Familiar evidence for this statement is the greater solubility of iodine in potassium iodide solution than in water because of the formation of triiodide ions by the reaction $I_2 +$

$$\left[\;\; \overset{..}{\underset{..}{:}} I \overset{..}{\underset{..}{:}} \;\; \right]^{-} \longrightarrow [I_3^-].$$ A related phenomenon is the brown color of solutions of iodine in alcohol in contrast to the violet color of solutions in hexane.

Strong sodium hydroxide solutions convert aldehydes having at least two α hydrogen atoms to high molecular weight complex products known as **aldehyde resins.** Aldol condensations, dehydration, and polymerization types of reaction probably play a part in their formation. The product from acetaldehyde is a sticky viscous orange-colored oil with a characteristic odor.

Ketones are not affected appreciably by strong sodium hydroxide solutions. The amide ion, however, is a stronger base than hydroxide ion, and under anhydrous conditions sodium amide converts acetone into a cyclic compound known as isophorone, which again is the result of a combination of aldol addition and dehydration.

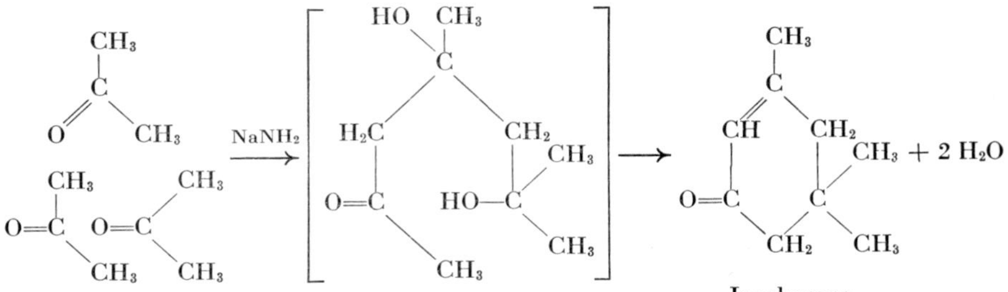

Isophorone

Strong acids favor the trimerization of aldehydes (p. 170) but lead to the condensation and dehydration of ketones. For example acetone yields mesityl oxide directly in the acid-catalyzed reaction.

$$\overset{CH_3}{\underset{CH_3}{\diagdown}}C{=}O + CH_3COCH_3 \underset{}{\overset{[H^+]}{\rightleftarrows}} (CH_3)_2COHCH_2COCH_3 \underset{H_2O}{\overset{[H^+]}{\rightleftarrows}} (CH_3)_2C{=}CHCOCH_3$$

Under more vigorous conditions of catalysis and dehydration, higher condensation products are formed.

$$(CH_3)_2C{=}O + CH_3COCH_3 + O{=}C(CH_3)_2 \xrightarrow[\text{or AlCl}_3]{\text{Dry HCl, ZnCl}_2,}$$
$$(CH_3)_2C{=}CH{-}CO{-}CH{=}C(CH_3)_2 + 2\ H_2O$$
$$\text{Phorone}$$

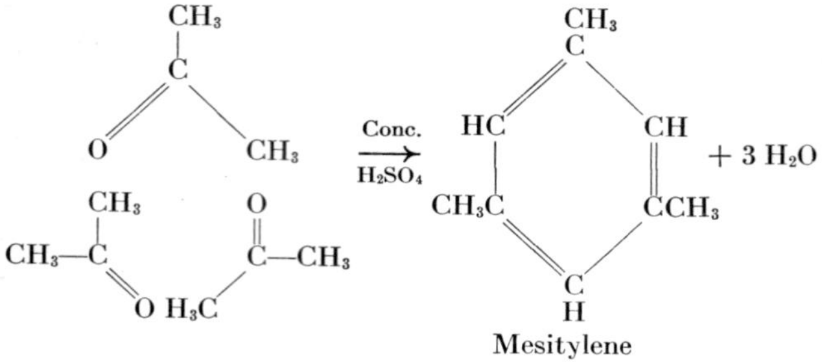

$$CH_3 \underset{H_2SO_4}{\overset{Conc.}{\longrightarrow}} \text{Mesitylene} + 3\ H_2O$$

The formation of mesitylene from acetone is an example of the synthesis of an aromatic type compound (p. 319) from a member of the aliphatic series.

7. *Trimerization*. Aliphatic aldehydes, but not ketones, undergo spontaneous trimerization, or the trimerization may be catalyzed by small amounts of acid. The product is a cyclic compound, that is one in which the atoms are united in a ring.

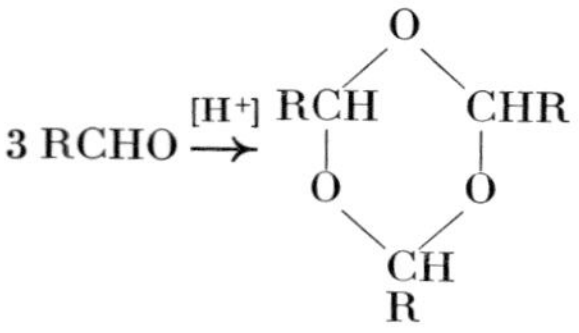

$$3\ RCHO \overset{[H^+]}{\longrightarrow}$$

The reaction can be reversed by heating the trimer with or without a catalyst and removing the lower-boiling aldehyde by distillation. Other types of polymerization are discussed under the individual aldehydes.

The mechanism of the acid-catalyzed trimerization and detrimerization probably is as follows:

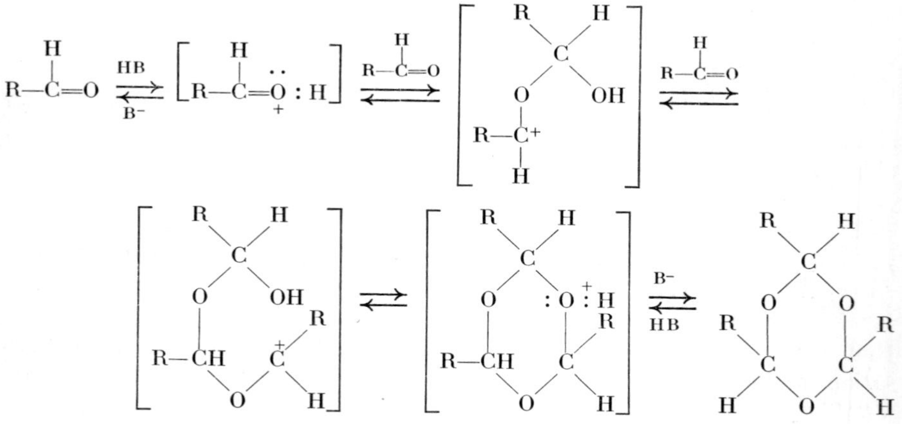

These trimers, which have been classified as **aldals,** resemble the acetals in that there is no effective point of attack for basic catalysts. Hence they are stable in neutral and alkaline solutions.

Addition and Loss of Water

1. *Ammonia.* Addition products with ammonia have been isolated from aldehydes but not from ketones. The structure of the product is uncertain. It is believed that the initial step is simple addition of the amino (NH$_2$) group to carbon, and of hydrogen to oxygen. Monomeric acetaldehyde-ammonia has been isolated.

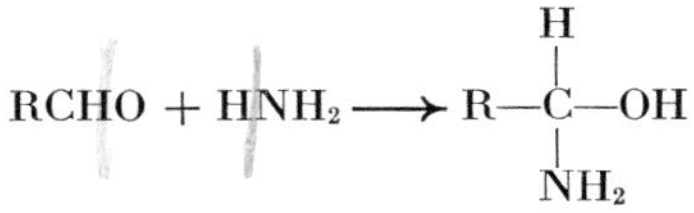

$$\text{RCHO} + \text{HNH}_2 \longrightarrow \text{R}-\underset{\underset{\text{NH}_2}{|}}{\overset{\overset{\text{H}}{|}}{\text{C}}}-\text{OH}$$

The final product, however, is a trimer which may be the trihydrate of the nitrogen analog of the aldehyde trimer.

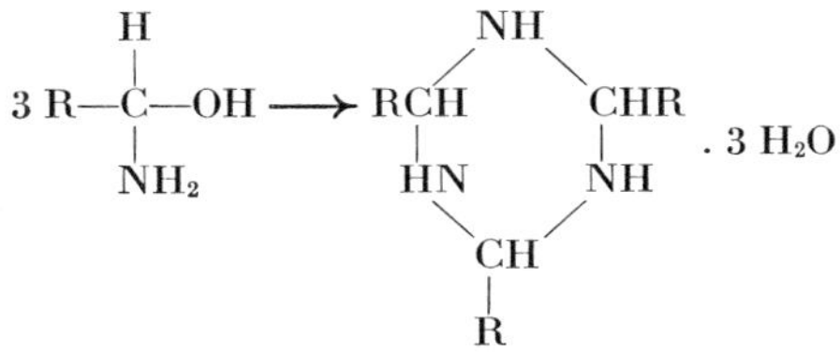

$$3\ \text{R}-\underset{\underset{\text{NH}_2}{|}}{\overset{\overset{\text{H}}{|}}{\text{C}}}-\text{OH} \longrightarrow \begin{array}{c} \text{NH} \\ \text{RCH} \quad \text{CHR} \\ \text{HN} \quad \text{NH} \\ \text{CH} \\ \text{R} \end{array} \cdot 3\ \text{H}_2\text{O}$$

Although analogous compounds have not been isolated from ketones, it seems likely that they are formed as intermediates in certain reactions, since ketones as well as aldehydes undergo the Strecker reaction for the synthesis of amino acids (p. 232).

2. *Hydroxylamine.* When aldehydes and ketones react with hydroxylamine, the hydroxy derivative of ammonia, the initial product undoubtedly is an addition product comparable to aldehyde-ammonia, but loss of water takes place immediately to give a product known as an **oxime.**

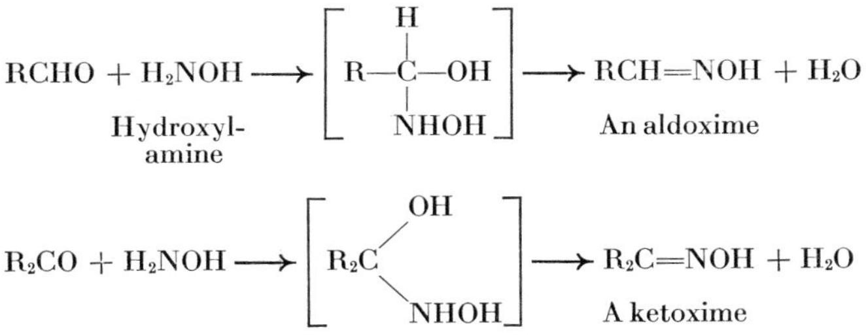

$$\text{RCHO} + \text{H}_2\text{NOH} \longrightarrow \left[\text{R}-\underset{\underset{\text{NHOH}}{|}}{\overset{\overset{\text{H}}{|}}{\text{C}}}-\text{OH} \right] \longrightarrow \text{RCH}{=}\text{NOH} + \text{H}_2\text{O}$$

$$\underset{\text{amine}}{\underset{\text{Hydroxyl-}}{}} \qquad\qquad\qquad \underset{\text{An aldoxime}}{}$$

$$\text{R}_2\text{CO} + \text{H}_2\text{NOH} \longrightarrow \left[\text{R}_2\text{C} \overset{\text{OH}}{\underset{\text{NHOH}}{}} \right] \longrightarrow \text{R}_2\text{C}{=}\text{NOH} + \text{H}_2\text{O}$$

$$\underset{\text{A ketoxime}}{}$$

The product from acetaldehyde, $CH_3CH{=}NOH$, is called **acetaldoxime,** that from acetone is **acetoxime,** and that derived from methyl ethyl ketone, $CH_3(C_2H_5)C{=}NOH$, is **methyl ethyl ketoxime.** Homologous compounds are named in the same way.

When oximes are heated with an excess of aqueous hydrochloric acid, they are hydrolyzed with the regeneration of the aldehyde or ketone and hydroxylamine hydrochloride.

$$\text{RCH}{=}\text{NOH} + \text{HCl} + \text{H}_2\text{O} \dashrightarrow \text{RCHO} + [\text{HO}\overset{+}{\text{N}}\text{H}_3]\ \text{Cl}^-$$

The oxines are both weak bases and weak acids. They are more soluble in cold dilute acids or cold dilute alkali than they are in water.

$$RCH=NOH + HCl \longrightarrow [RCH=\overset{+}{N}HOH]\ Cl^-$$

$$RCH=NOH + NaOH \longrightarrow [RCH=NO^-]\ Na^+ + H_2O$$

However the oximes are much weaker bases ($K_B = 6 \times 10^{-13}$ for acetoxime) than hydroxylamine ($K_B = 1 \times 10^{-8}$). Use is made of this fact in a procedure for the estimation of aldehydes and ketones. After reaction of the carbonyl compound with hydroxylamine hydrochloride, the hydrogen chloride liberated is titrated with standard alkali using a suitable indicator (Bromophenol Blue).

$$RCHO + [H_3\overset{+}{N}OH]Cl^- \longrightarrow RCH=NOH + HCl + H_2O$$

Oximes frequently are crystalline solids and thus are useful derivatives for the identification of aldehydes and ketones. They are useful also for the synthesis of primary amines (p. 186) and alkyl cyanides (p. 199).

3. **Substituted Hydrazines.** Hydrazine has the formula H_2NNH_2, and although it reacts with aldehydes and ketones, the final product may not be typical. The substituted hydrazines having one free amino group (NH_2 group) behave in a regular fashion analogous to hydroxylamine.

$$RCHO + H_2N-NHR' \longrightarrow \begin{bmatrix} RCHNH-NHR' \\ \vert \\ OH \end{bmatrix} \longrightarrow RCH=N-NHR' + H_2O$$
$$\text{An aldehyde hydrazone}$$

$$R_2CO + H_2N-NHR' \longrightarrow \begin{bmatrix} R_2C-NH-NHR' \\ \vert \\ OH \end{bmatrix} \longrightarrow R_2C=N-NHR' + H_2O$$
$$\text{A ketone hydrazone}$$

The hydrazines most commonly used are (*1*) phenylhydrazine, $C_6H_5NHNH_2$, and substituted phenylhydrazines, the products being known as phenyl-hydrazones, and (*2*) semicarbazine (frequently called semicarbazide), $H_2N-NHCONH_2$, the products being known as semicarbazones.

$$(CH_3)_2CO + H_2NNHC_6H_5 \longrightarrow (CH_3)_2C=NNHC_6H_5 + H_2O$$
$$\text{Acetone phenylhydrazone}$$

$$CH_3CH=O + H_2NNHCONH_2 \longrightarrow CH_3CH=NNHCONH_2 + H_2O$$
$$\text{Acetaldehyde semicarbazone}$$

Whereas the simpler aldehydes and ketones usually are liquids, many of the phenylhydrazones and semicarbazones are crystalline solids which can be purified readily and have definite melting points. Like the oximes they are useful derivatives for the identification of aldehydes and ketones.

Oxidation

Aldehydes are oxidized more easily to acids having the same number of carbon atoms than primary alcohols are oxidized to aldehydes. Hence the latter reaction is useful only if the aldehyde produced is volatile and can be removed as fast as it is formed from the oxidizing mixture. Ketones on the other hand are fairly stable to oxidation. When oxidation is forced by using strong oxidizing agents under vigorous conditions, the carbon chain is broken and a mixture of acids having fewer carbon atoms is produced.

$$RCH_2COCH_2R' \xrightarrow[\text{oxidation}]{\text{Vigorous}} \begin{array}{c} RCOOH + HOOCCH_2R' \\ \text{and} \\ RCH_2COOH + HOOCR' \end{array}$$

Because of the difference between the ease of oxidation of aldehydes and ketones, it is possible to choose oxidizing agents which will attack aldehydes and not ketones, and to use the reaction as a distinguishing test. Some mild oxidizing agents used for this purpose are Fehling's solution, an alkaline solution of a cupric complex with sodium tartrate (p. 547); Benedict's solution, a cupric complex with sodium citrate (p. 548); and Tollen's reagent, an ammoniacal solution of silver hydroxide. All behave like solutions of the metallic hydroxides. With Fehling's and Benedict's solutions, the copper is reduced to the cuprous state, which does not form a stable complex with tartrate or citrate ion and precipitates as cuprous oxide.

$$RCHO + 2\ Cu(OH)_2 + NaOH \longrightarrow RCOO^-Na^+ + Cu_2O\!\downarrow + 3\ H_2O$$

If the precipitation of cuprous oxide takes place in the presence of protective colloids, it is finely divided and yellow, but if formed in the absence of protective colloids, it has a larger particle size and is red. With Tollen's reagent, metallic silver is the reduction product.

$$RCHO + 2\ Ag(NH_3)_2OH \longrightarrow RCOO^-NH_4^+ + 2\ Ag\!\downarrow + H_2O + 3\ NH_3$$

If the vessel in which the latter reaction takes place is clean and the rate of deposition slow enough, the silver will deposit as a coherent silver mirror; otherwise it will be a black finely-divided precipitate.

MISCELLANEOUS TESTS AND REACTIONS

1. ***Schiff's Fuchsin Aldehyde Reagent.*** Fuchsin is a magenta dye (p. 481) which can be decolorized in aqueous solution by sulfur dioxide. In the presence of aldehydes, but not ketones, a magenta color reappears. The reaction is not specific for aldehydes, since anything which removes sulfur dioxide, for example mild alkalies, amines, or even heating or exposure to air, will regenerate the color, but in the absence of such interferences it serves to distinguish aldehydes from ketones.

The reaction with aldehydes is not merely a combination with sulfur dioxide and regeneration of the original fuchsin. The color is due to a reaction product of the aldehyde and the dye (p. 481). Thus the hue of the color produced differs with different aldehydes; for example the color produced by formaldehyde is bluer than that produced by acetaldehyde. Moreover strong mineral acids will destroy the color produced by acetaldehyde but not that produced by formaldehyde.

2. ***Replacement of Oxygen by Halogen.*** When aldehydes or ketones react with phosphorus pentachloride or phosphorus pentabromide, the oxygen of the carbonyl group is replaced by two halogen atoms.

$$RCHO + PX_5 \longrightarrow RCHX_2 + POX_3$$

$$R_2CO + PX_5 \longrightarrow R_2CX_2 + POX_3$$

The fact that both halogens in the product are combined with the same carbon atom is further confirmation that the oxygen atom in aldehydes and ketones is attached by a double bond to a single carbon atom. The reaction is of little importance otherwise.

3. **Salt Formation.** The hydrogen atoms on a carbon atom α to a carbonyl group are sufficiently acidic (p. 73) to react with alkali metals and form salts. Thus acetone reacts readily with metallic sodium and hydrogen is evolved.

$$CH_3COCH_3 + Na \longrightarrow [CH_3COCH_2{}^-]\overset{+}{Na} + \tfrac{1}{2} H_2$$

Because the product can act as a basic catalyst, it is accompanied by the alkali-catalyzed condensation products of acetone (p. 169). Acetone is so weak an acid that its salts are completely hydrolyzed by water.

4. **Halogenation and the Haloform Reaction.** The α hydrogen atoms of aldehydes and ketones, like those of acyl halides (p. 137), readily undergo substitution by halogen.

$$RCH_2CHO \xrightarrow{X_2} HX + RCHXCHO \xrightarrow{X_2} HX + RCX_2CHO$$

$$RCOCH_3 \xrightarrow{X_2} HX + RCOCH_2X \xrightarrow{X_2} HX + RCOCHX_2 \xrightarrow{X_2} HX + RCOCX_3$$

In alkaline solution hypohalite ion also acts as a halogenating agent. After one hydrogen is substituted, a second and third on the same carbon atom are substituted with increasing ease. Hence substitution once started continues on the same carbon atom until all of the hydrogen is replaced by halogen. The trisubstitution product is not stable in alkaline solution, and a secondary reaction follows in which the alkali decomposes the trisubstituted molecule to give a trihalogenated methane and the sodium salt of a carboxylic acid.

$$RCOCX_3 + HONa \longrightarrow RCOONa + HCX_3$$

Trihalogenated methanes yield formic acid on hydrolysis, which led Dumas to give them the general name *haloforms* (chloroform, bromoform, and iodoform). To obtain a haloform from a carbonyl compound, at least one group united to the carbonyl group must be methyl. The other group may be hydrogen or any group linked through carbon, provided that any hydrogen atoms remaining on this carbon atom are not substituted more readily than those of the methyl group, and provided that other substituents in the group do not reduce the reactivity of the methyl group by steric hindrance. Acetic acid does not give a haloform because the acetyl group is united to oxygen, which reduces the effect of the carbonyl group on the α hydrogen atoms by resonance (p. 129). Acetoacetic acid, CH_3COCH_2COOH, substitutes on the methylene rather than the methyl group to give CH_3COCX_2COOH, which reacts with alkali to give the sodium salts of acetic acid and a dihaloacetic acid (cf. p. 552).

$$CH_3COCX_2COOH + 2\ NaOH \longrightarrow CH_3COONa + HCX_2COONa$$

Pinacolone (p. 176) gives bromaform but does not give iodoform because the highly branched *t*-butyl group prevents the reaction from proceeding beyond the diiodinated stage.

$$(CH_3)_3CCOCH_3 + 2\ NaOX \longrightarrow (CH_3)_3CCOCHX_2 + 2\ NaOH$$

Occasionally compounds not expected to do so respond to the reaction. The reaction of acetoxime may be explained by the fact that it is a nitrogen analog of a ketone or that hydrolysis to acetone precedes formation of the haloform. 2-Methyl-2-butene probably is converted first to methyl isopropyl ketone during the reaction (cf. p. 520).

Not only do carbonyl compounds meeting the stated conditions undergo the haloform reaction, but all substances which oxidize to such compounds under the conditions of the reaction, for example properly constituted alcohols, also yield haloform.

$$RCHOHCH_3 + NaOX \longrightarrow RCOCH_3 + NaX + H_2O$$

$$RCOCH_3 + 3\ NaOX \longrightarrow HCX_3 + RCOONa + 2\ NaOH$$

The practical importance of the haloform reaction is its use to distinguish between different possible structures. For example acetaldehyde is the only aldehyde, and ethyl alcohol is the only primary alcohol which gives a haloform. The two largest groups of compounds responding to the reaction are the methyl ketones and alkylmethylcarbinols. For conducting such a test, the reaction with alkali and iodine is used since iodoform is a yellow crystalline solid which is identified readily by its melting point.

6. Reduction of the Carbonyl Group to a Methyl or Methylene Group. A carbonyl group may be converted to a methyl or methylene group by reducing first to the alcohol and then converting the alcohol to the halide and reducing the halide to the hydrocarbon (p. 106); or the alcohol might be converted to the olefin and the double bond reduced catalytically (p. 107). However more direct methods are possible. In the *Wolff-Kishner reduction* the aldehyde or ketone is heated with hydrazine in the presence of sodium ethoxide at 200°. The reduction presumably takes place by formation of the hydrazone, which decomposes under the influence of the sodium ethoxide.

$$RCHO + H_2NNH_2 \longrightarrow RCH{=}NNH_2 \xrightarrow[200°]{NaOC_2H_5} RCH_3 + N_2 + H_2O$$

$$R_2CO + H_2NNH_2 \longrightarrow R_2C{=}NNH_2 \xrightarrow[200°]{NaOC_2H_5} R_2CH_2 + N_2 + H_2O$$

The *Clemmensen reduction* consists of refluxing the compound with concentrated hydrochloric acid in the presence of amalgamated zinc.

$$R_2CO + Zn(Hg) + 2\ HCl \longrightarrow R_2CH_2 + ZnCl_2 + H_2O$$

It is easier to carry out than the Wolff-Kishner reduction but is not so satisfactory for the reduction of aldehydes, because they undergo condensation and polymerization reactions too readily in the presence of strong acids.

7. Reduction to Glycols and Pinacols. When an aldehyde reacts with sodium and moist ether, or with amalgamated magnesium, two moles couple with the formation of a 1,2-dihydroxy compound known as a **glycol.**

$$2 \text{ RCHO} + 2 \text{ Na} + \text{H}_2\text{O(moist ether)} \longrightarrow \text{RCHOHCHOHR} + 2 \text{ NaOH}$$

The reduction with magnesium ordinarily is carried out under anhydrous conditions, the salt of the glycol being obtained. The glycol is liberated by a weak acid. Ketones behave similarly, and the ditertiary glycols produced are called **pinacols.**

$$2 \text{ R}_2\text{CO} + \text{Mg(Hg)} \longrightarrow \begin{bmatrix} \text{R}_2\text{C}-\text{O}^- \\ | \\ \text{R}_2\text{C}-\text{O}^- \end{bmatrix} \text{Mg}^{++} \xrightarrow{2 \text{ CH}_3\text{COOH}} \text{R}_2\text{COHCOHR}_2 + \text{Mg(OCOCH}_3)_2$$

The name *pinacol* is derived from the Greek word *pinax* meaning *plate* and refers to the crystalline structure of pinacol itself, the reduction product of acetone.

Strong acids cause dehydration and molecular rearrangement of pinacols to ketones.

$$\text{R}_2\text{COHCOHR}_2 \xrightarrow{[\text{H}^+]} \text{R}_3\text{CCOR} + \text{H}_2\text{O}$$

Pinacol rearranges to the compound known as **pinacolone,** and the general reaction is called a **pinacol-pinacolone rearrangement.**

The mechanism of the reaction may be expressed by the following series of reactions.

$$(\text{CH}_3)_2\text{C}-\text{C(CH}_3)_2 \xrightarrow{\text{HB}} [\text{B}^-] + \begin{bmatrix} (\text{CH}_3)_2\text{C}-\text{C(CH}_3)_2 \\ + : \overset{..}{\text{OH}} \text{ OH} \\ \text{H} \end{bmatrix} \longrightarrow$$

$$\overset{|\ \ \ \ |}{\underset{\text{OH OH}}{}}$$
Pinacol

$$\text{H}_2\text{O} + \begin{bmatrix} (\text{CH}_3)_3\text{CCCH}_3 \\ || \\ + : \text{OH} \end{bmatrix} \xrightarrow{[\text{B}^-]} \text{HB} + \begin{matrix} (\text{CH}_3)_3\text{CCCH}_3 \\ || \\ \text{O} \end{matrix}$$
Pinacolone

Since this reaction is not reversible, it is not desirable to use the convention given on page 116 for the consecutive reactions. To avoid writing several separate reactions, the convention adopted is that only the last compound of an intermediate step is involved in the succeeding step.

Industrially Important Aldehydes and Ketones

Formaldehyde is manufactured by passing a mixture of methyl alcohol and air at 40°–50° over a copper catalyst which maintains itself at 550°–600° by the heat of the reaction. The exit gases are cooled rapidly to prevent side reactions, and the formaldehyde, along with some methyl alcohol, methylal, and methyl formate, is dissolved in water to give a 37 per cent solution known as **formalin.** Formaldehyde also is formed during the controlled oxidation of natural gas or propane-butane mixtures, and it appears that this source will become increasingly important. Methyl alcohol, ethyl alcohol, acetaldehyde, acetone, and acetic acid are produced at the same time (p. 56).

Although formaldehyde may be liquefied readily (b.p. $-21°$) it polymerizes with explosive violence, and large quantities cannot be handled safely in the liquid state. Besides the aqueous solution, formalin, formaldehyde is handled as its polymer, **paraformaldehyde (polyoxymethylene),** which is obtained when aqueous solutions are evaporated, or when gaseous formaldehyde comes in contact with solid surfaces. It is an amorphous solid, insoluble in water or organic solvents, and depolymerizes into gaseous formaldehyde on heating. It is a *linear polymer* of the formula $HO(CH_2O)_nH$ where n may vary from approximately 10 to 100.

When a 60–65 per cent aqueous solution of formaldehyde is distilled with 2 per cent sulfuric acid, the cyclic *trimer* (p. 170), **1,3,5-trioxane,** may be extracted from the distillate. It is a colorless highly refractive crystalline compound melting at 62°, and boiling without decomposition or depolymerization at 115°. It has a pleasant odor resembling that of chloroform, in contrast to the sharp odor of formaldehyde, and is soluble in water and organic solvents. Strong acids initiate depolymerization, as with all compounds of this type, and it promises to be useful as a source of formaldehyde in reactions carried out in nonaqueous solutions.

Formaldehyde undergoes a number of reactions which most other aldehydes do not, because (*1*) it has only hydrogen atoms attached to the carbonyl group and is more reactive than other aldehydes, just as the aldehydes are more reactive than ketones, and (*2*) having only one carbon atom it does not have α hydrogen atoms and cannot undergo aldol-type condensations. For example reaction with ammonia does not lead to an aldehyde-ammonia. Instead the initial addition product condenses further and a compound is obtained which has the formula $(CH_2)_6N_4$ and is called **hexamethylenetetramine.**

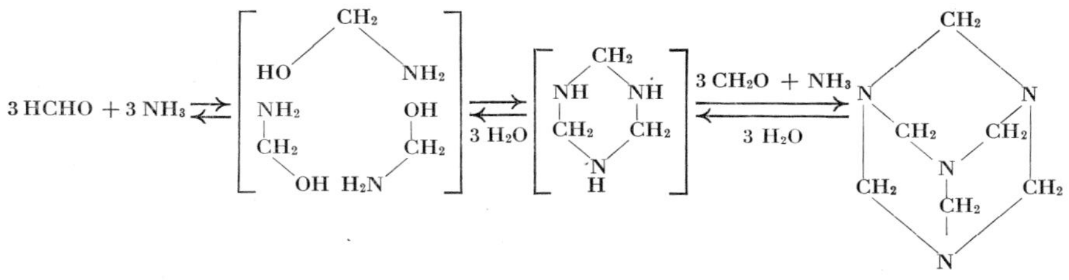

This organic compound was the first whose structure, based on valence theory and chemical reactions, was confirmed by X-ray diffraction.

Hexamethylenetetramine assumed importance during World War II as an intermediate for the manufacture of the high explosive trimethylenetrinitramine (cyclonite, hexogen, RDX). Nitration was carried out in the presence of ammonium nitrate or ammonium sulfate, which permitted utilization of 80–90 per cent of the methylene groups.

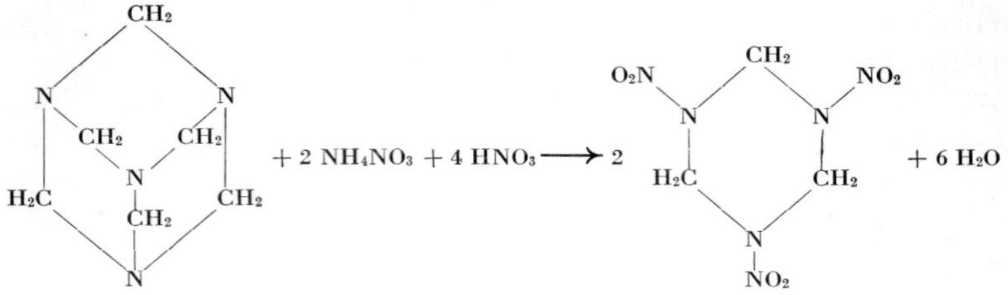

$$\text{[structure]} + 2\ NH_4NO_3 + 4\ HNO_3 \longrightarrow 2\ \text{[structure]} + 6\ H_2O$$

Trimethylenetrinitramine is one of the most powerful modern explosives and has a greater brisance than TNT (p. 351). Up to 30 per cent was mixed with TNT to insure complete detonation of large bombs and to increase the force of the explosion.

Lacking α hydrogen atoms, formaldehyde does not give aldehyde resins with strong alkali, but undergoes the *Cannizzaro reaction*. This reaction consists of an intermolecular oxidation and reduction in which one molecule acts as the reducing agent and is oxidized to formic acid, and another acts as the oxidizing agent and is reduced to methyl alcohol. In the presence of alkali the formic acid appears as the salt.

$$HCHO + HCHO + NaOH \longrightarrow CH_3OH + HCOONa$$

The reaction is not specific for formaldehyde, but is given also by other aldehydes which do not contain α hydrogen atoms, such as trimethylacetaldehyde (pivalic aldehyde). Under certain conditions even aldehydes having α hydrogen atoms will undergo a Cannizzaro reaction rather than aldol condensation. For example, if *i*-butyraldehyde is heated in a sealed tube at 150° with aqueous barium hydroxide, a quantitative yield of *i*-butyl alcohol and barium *i*-butyrate is obtained. Similarly *i*-valeraldehyde or *n*-heptaldehyde, when heated for a few hours with calcium oxide at 100°, gives the corresponding alcohol and calcium salt as the chief products.

With dilute alkalies formaldehyde undergoes a condensation which appears to resemble an aldol condensation, but a hydrogen atom attached to the carbonyl group reacts rather than an α hydrogen atom. A mixture of polyhydroxy aldehydes (carbohydrates, p. 277) results.

$$HCHO + HCHO \longrightarrow HOCH_2CHO \xrightarrow{HCHO} HOCH_2CHOHCHO \xrightarrow{HCHO}$$
$$HOCH_2CHOHCHOHCHO \xrightarrow{HCHO} HOCH_2(CHOH)_xCHO$$

A *specific reaction of formaldehyde* is the formation of a violet color with casein of milk in the presence of ferric chloride and concentrated sulfuric acid. The test is sensitive to one part of formaldehyde in 200,000 parts of milk. This test was important in the enforcement of the law against the addition of formaldehyde as a preservative. It can be used as a general test for formaldehyde simply by adding to milk the material to be tested and then applying the test.

Formaldehyde has some use as a disinfectant and for the preservation of biological specimens, but its chief use is for the manufacture of synthetic resins by condensation with urea (p. 242), melamine (p. 248), or phenol (p. 388). Frequently paraformaldehyde or hexamethylenetetramine may replace formalin for this purpose. Formaldehyde is used also to make *pentaerythritol* which is important for the manufacture of drying oils and the high explosive *pentaerythritol nitrate* (PETN) (p. 526). Another high explosive, *trimethylene trinitramine* (cyclonite, RDX, hexogen), is derived from hexamethylenetetramine (p. 177). Hexamethylenetetramine when taken internally is excreted in the urine and hydrolyzed to formaldehyde when the urine is acid. At one time it was used medicinally as a urinary antiseptic under the name methenamine or urotropin, but has been replaced largely by the sulfa drugs (p. 372) and mandelic acid (p. 420). In the United States the production of formalin (37 per cent) in 1940 was 181 million pounds and it increased to 617 million pounds in 1948. The unit value is around 4 cents per pound.

Acetaldehyde is made commercially by the hydration of acetylene and by the air oxidation of ethyl alcohol over a silver catalyst or dehydrogenation over a copper-chromium catalyst (p. 161). Some acetaldehyde is obtained as a by-product of the fermentation industries (p. 67) and in the oxidation of hydrocarbon gases (p. 56). It boils at 20°, is miscible with water and organic solvents, and behaves typically in all of its reactions. The chief importance of acetaldehyde is its use as an intermediate for the synthesis of other organic compounds, especially acetic acid by air oxidation (p. 134), *n*-butyl alcohol by condensation to crotonic aldehyde followed by catalytic reduction,

$$2\ CH_3CHO \xrightarrow[\text{NaOH}]{\text{Dil.}} CH_3CHOHCH_2CHO \xrightarrow{[H^+]} CH_3CH{=}CHCHO \xrightarrow[\substack{\text{Cu} \\ \text{on pumice} \\ \text{at } 200°}]{H_2} CH_3CH_2CH_2CH_2OH$$

and ethyl acetate made by the Tischenko reaction, an intermolecular oxidation similar to the Cannizzaro reaction. In the presence of aluminum ethoxide, one molecule of aldehyde is oxidized to the oxidation state of acetic acid and the other reduced to that of ethyl alcohol, but instead of appearing as such, ethyl acetate is formed.

$$2\ CH_3CHO \xrightarrow{Al(OC_2H_5)_3} CH_3COOC_2H_5$$

Acetaldehyde also is used in the manufacture of rubber accelerators (p. 498), of the trimer, paraldehyde, and of the tetramer, metaldehyde. **Paraldehyde** is a stable liquid, b.p. 125°, which is depolymerized readily by heating with acids, and hence is a convenient source of acetaldehyde. Paraldehyde first was used medicinally as a sleep-producer (hypnotic or soporific) in 1882. It still is considered to be very efficient and one of the least toxic hypnotics. The chief objections to its use are that it is a liquid with a burning disagreeable taste, and that because it is eliminated largely through the lungs, a patient's breath may smell of paraldehyde for as long as twenty-four hours. **Metaldehyde** is formed when acetaldehyde is treated with traces of acids or sulfur dioxide below 0°. One of the catalysts used commercially is a mixture of calcium nitrate and hydrogen bromide and the temperature of the reaction is −20°. The product is a solid tetramer which, like paraldehyde, has a cyclic structure.

$$
4\ CH_3CHO \xrightarrow[\text{at } -20°]{\text{Ca(NO}_3)_2,\ HBr}
\begin{array}{c}
CH_3 \\
| \\
CH-O \\
O \qquad\qquad CHCH_3 \\
CH_3CH \qquad\qquad O \\
O-CH \\
| \\
CH_3
\end{array}
$$

Like paraldehyde it is depolymerized to acetaldehyde by heat. Since it is a solid and has a fairly high vapor pressure in spite of its high melting point (m.p. 246°, sublimes below 150°), it is used as a convenient solid fuel for heating liquids or foods under unusual conditions when other fuels are not available or not satisfactory. Large quantities are used also in garden baits, the vapors being attractive and yet highly toxic to slugs and snails. The U. S. production of acetaldehyde was 201 million pounds in 1940 and 471 million pounds in 1948. The value is around 9 cents per pound.

n-**Butyraldehyde,** made by the dehydrogenation of *n*-butyl alcohol, is used to manufacture rubber accelerators (p. 498) and polyvinyl butyral (p. 517). Aldehydes having seven to sixteen carbon atoms are used in perfumery. *n*-**Heptaldehyde** is one of the products of the destructive distillation of castor oil (p. 538).

Acetone is by far the most important ketone. It formerly was obtained by the destructive distillation of calcium acetate prepared from pyroligneous liquor (p. 65) but now is produced chiefly by the dehydrogenation of *i*-propyl alcohol. It also is one of the products of the butyl alcohol fermentation of carbohydrates (p. 70). The last process in fact was developed for the production of acetone during World War I, because other sources were inadequate to supply the needs of the British for the manufacture of cordite, their standard smokeless powder (p. 300).[3]

The chief use of acetone is as a solvent for cellulose nitrate in the manufacture of photographic film, lacquer dopes, and explosives (p. 300), and for cellulose acetate in the manufacture of acetate rayon and photographic film (pp. 305, 302). In recent years large quantities have been pyrolyzed to ketene, an intermediate in the manufacture of acetic anhydride (p. 139).

$$
CH_3COCH_3 \xrightarrow{700°} CH_2{=}C{=}O + CH_4
$$
Ketene

$$
CH_2{=}C{=}O + HOCOCH_3 \longrightarrow CH_3CO{-}O{-}COCH_3
$$

Minor uses of acetone are in the manufacture of drugs, e.g. sulfonal (p. 222), and other chemicals such as diacetone alcohol, mesityl oxide, and phorone (p. 169). Production in 1948 amounted to over 450 million pounds of which 94 per cent was made from *i*-propyl alcohol. The unit value was 9 cents per pound.

---

[3] Scientists rarely have influenced directly the decisions of politicians and statesmen, but it has been stated that the Balfour Declaration establishing Palestine as a national home for the Hebrews was the result of Lloyd George's gratitude to Dr. Chaim Weizmann for developing this process for the production of acetone.

Methyl ethyl ketone is made by the dehydrogenation of *s*-butyl alcohol. It is known technically by the initials MEK and is used chiefly as a solvent for dewaxing lubricating oils. **Methyl *i*-butyl ketone** is made by the controlled catalytic reduction of mesityl oxide.

A commercial process for the synthesis of aldehydes and ketones known as the *oxo process* was developed in Germany during World War II. It consists of passing a mixture of olefin, carbon monoxide, and hydrogen over a Fischer-Tropsch catalyst (90 per cent Co_2O_3, 7 per cent ThO_2, and 3 per cent MgO on pumice) at 150°–180° and 150 atmospheres.

$$RCH=CH_2 + CO + H_2 \longrightarrow RCH_2CH_2CHO$$

$$2\ RCH=CH_2 + CO + H_2 \longrightarrow (RCH_2CH_2)_2CO$$

Thus ethylene gives a mixture of 70 per cent propionaldehyde and 30 per cent acetone. The aldehydes prepared from C_{11} to C_{17} olefins were reduced to alcohols which in turn were converted into detergents by sulfation (p. 159). Since 1948, the oxo process has been operated in the United States. By this method diisobutylene (p. 43) is used to produce **3,5,5-trimethylhexanal** (so-called "nonylaldehyde"), which is converted to a variety of other products.

$$(CH_3)_3CCH_2C(CH_3) = CH_2 + CO + H_2 \longrightarrow (CH_3)_3CCH_2CH(CH_3)CH_2CHO$$

REVIEW QUESTIONS

1. What chemical evidence can be given for the presence of a carbonyl group in aldehydes and ketones?
2. Write condensed structural formulas and give two names for each of the isomeric aldehydes having the molecular formula $C_5H_{10}O$; for ketones having the molecular formula $C_6H_{12}O$.
3. Compare the boiling points and solubilities of aldehydes and ketones with those of other types of compounds discussed so far.
4. Give equations illustrating the general methods for the preparation of aldehydes and ketones from alcohols, acids, and olefins.
5. Give equations for the reaction of aldehydes and ketones with the following reagents: hydrogen and a hydrogenating catalyst; hydrogen cyanide; hydroxylamine; semicarbazine; dilute alkali; a Grignard reagent followed by water; phosphorus pentachloride. Give a name to the type of compound formed in each case.
6. Compare the reactions of formaldehyde and acetaldehyde with ammonia and with sodium hydroxide solution.
7. Discuss the polymerization of formaldehyde and acetaldehyde and compare their behavior with that of ketones.
8. Discuss the behavior of aldehydes and ketones to saturated sodium bisulfite solution. Of what value is the reaction?
9. What is the haloform reaction? Which of the following compounds would yield iodoform on treatment with aqueous sodium hydroxide and iodine: methyl alcohol, ethyl alcohol, acetone, ethyl ketone, methyl ethyl ketone, *s*-butyl alcohol, 3-pentanone, acetic acid, trimethylacetaldehyde, acetaldehyde, propionaldehyde, formaldehyde, *i*-butyl alcohol?
10. How could chemical tests be used to distinguish between $(CH_3)_2CHCHOHCH_2CH_3$, $(CH_3)_2CHCH_2CHOHCH_3$, $(CH_3)_2COHCH_2CH_2CH_3$, and $(CH_3)_2CHCH_2CH_2CH_2OH$?
11. Describe three simple tests that may be used to distinguish between aldehydes and ketones.
12. Give chemical reactions that could be used to distinguish between 1-propanol, acetone, and ethyl alcohol?
13. Natural essences frequently are mixtures of alcohols, aldehydes, and hydrocarbons. How could the three classes of compounds be separated and regenerated by chemical means?

14. Give the commercial methods of preparation and industrial uses of formaldehyde, acetaldehyde, acetone, methyl ethyl ketone, and ketene.

15. What is a pinacol and how is it made? Discuss the pinacol-pinacolone rearrangement, including the mechanism of the reaction.

16. The following compounds are produced commercially starting with acetaldehyde: n-butyl alcohol, n-hexyl alcohol, 2-ethyl-1-hexanol, and 2-ethyl-1-butanol. Give reactions showing how this might be done.

17. How could methyl i-butyl ketone, 4-methyl-2-pentanol, and 3,3-dimethyl-2-butanol be prepared starting with acetone?

18. An unknown compound formed a monoxime, reduced Fehling's solution, gave iodoform on treatment with hypoiodite solution, and evolved methane on treatment with methyl-magnesium iodide. Oxidation gave an acid which on purification and titration was found to have an equivalent weight of 116. The acid still formed an oxime and gave a positive iodoform test but no longer reduced Fehling's solution. Write a possible structural formula for the compound and show the reactions it undergoes.

19. A compound containing chlorine did not decolorize bromine solution. On treatment with alcoholic sodium hydroxide solution it gave a chlorine-free compound which on vigorous oxidation gave i-butyric acid as the only organic product. The chlorine-free compound absorbed ozone and after decomposition of the ozonide with zinc dust and acetic acid, formaldehyde was detected. Give the probable structure of the original compound and show the reactions it undergoes.

20. A compound having the molecular formula $C_6H_{12}O$ reacted with hydroxylamine but did not reduce Tollen's reagent. Reduction with hydrogen and platinum gave an alcohol which was readily dehydrated to give a single olefin. Ozonation and decomposition of the ozonide gave two liquid products, one of which reduced Tollen's reagent but did not give a positive iodoform test whereas the other did not reduce Tollen's reagent but did give a positive iodoform test. Give the structure of the original compound and show the reactions it undergoes.

21. A compound having the molecular formula $C_7H_{16}O$ did not react with sodium or phosphorus trichloride. After warming with concentrated sulfuric acid, diluting and distilling, a mixture was obtained which could not be separated satisfactorily by fractional distillation. After the mixture was oxidized by means of dichromic acid, an acidic product was isolated having a neutralization equivalent of 74, and a neutral product which reacted with semicarbazine, but did not reduce Tollen's reagent. Give the structure of the original compound and show the reactions that took place.

22. An alkyl halide A is converted into the corresponding Grignard reagent which is allowed to react with i-butyraldehyde. After decomposition with water a compound B is obtained which reacts readily with hydrogen bromide to give another alkyl halide C. Compound C likewise is converted into the Grignard reagent and decomposed with water to give a fourth compound D. If the original compound A is heated with metallic sodium, a compound identical with D is obtained. Write a structural formula for A and give all of the reactions involved.

23. An unknown compound A reacts with hot hydrogen bromide to form two different halogen compounds B and C, which are separated by fractional distillation. Compound B on treatment with moist silver oxide gives a compound D which does not react at once with a cold mixture of concentrated hydrochloric acid and zinc chloride, but on standing gives an insoluble liquid. Compound C likewise gives a new substance E on treatment with moist silver oxide, but E does not react at all with cold hydrochloric acid-zinc chloride mixture. Both D and E yield iodoform on treatment with iodine in alkaline solution. When E is oxidized under the proper conditions, an aldehyde F is obtained, which on treatment with methylmagnesium iodide solution and decomposition with water gives a compound identical with D. Write the structural formula for A, and illustrate by equations all of the reactions involved.

24. Give reactions for the synthesis of (a) ethyl alcohol from calcium carbide; (b) i-propyl bromide from acetone; (c) 3-pentanone from n-propyl alcohol; (d) i-butyl alcohol from propylene; (e) 2-methyl-2-pentene from n-propyl alcohol; (f) pelargonic aldehyde from a fat acid; (g) n-amyl bromide from n-butyl bromide.

Chapter 13

ALIPHATIC NITROGEN COMPOUNDS *Amines*

Structurally the organic oxygen compounds have been considered as derivatives of the water molecule. Similarly many of the organic nitrogen compounds may be considered as ammonia molecules in which the hydrogen atoms have been replaced by other groups.

H_2O	water	NH_3	ammonia
ROH	alcohols	RNH_2	primary amines
		R_2NH	secondary amines
ROR	ethers	R_3N	tertiary amines
RCOOH	acids	$RCONH_2$	amides
		$RC(NH)NH_2$	amidines
RCOOR	esters	RCONHR	*N*-alkyl amides
		$RCONR_2$	*N,N*-dialkyl amides
		RC(NH)OR	imido esters
RCOOCOR	anhydrides	RCONHCOR	imides
RCH=O	aldehydes	RCH=NH	aldimines
$R_2C=O$	ketones	$R_2C=NH$	ketimines

Since nitrogen has three replaceable hydrogen atoms instead of two as in water, the number of possible combinations is increased. This list is not complete, but contains the types of compounds most frequently encountered. Substituents on nitrogen other than hydrogen, alkyl, and acyl also may be present as for example in the cyanides (p. 198), the isocyanides (p. 200), the oximes (p. 171), the hydrazones (p. 172), and the nitro compounds (p. 201).

AMINES

Nomenclature

Aliphatic amines are alkyl substitution products of ammonia and are named as such, *ammonia* being contracted to *amine*. Thus CH_3NH_2 is methylamine, $(CH_3)_2NH$ is dimethylamine, and $(CH_3)_3N$ is trimethylamine. With mixed amines the alkyl groups frequently are named in the order of increasing complexity, for example $CH_3(C_2H_5)NCH(CH_3)_2$ is methylethyl-*i*-propylamine. The NH_2 group is called the *amino group*, and primary amines having other functional groups conveniently may be named as amino substitution products, for example $CH_3CHNH_2CH_2CH_2OH$ could be called 3-amino-1-butanol. Compounds in which the nitrogen atom is united to one carbon atom, RNH_2, are called *primary amines*; to two carbon atoms, R_2NH, *secondary amines*; and to three carbon atoms, R_3N, *tertiary amines*. The terms *primary, secondary, and tertiary refer to the condition of the nitrogen atom*, whereas when used with alcohols they referred to the carbon atom to which the hydroxyl group was attached. Thus although tertiary butyl alcohol, $(CH_3)_3COH$, is a tertiary alcohol, because the carbon atom is united to three other carbon atoms, tertiary butylamine, $(CH_3)_3CNH_2$, is a primary amine, because the nitrogen atom is directly united to only one carbon atom.

Preparation

MIXED PRIMARY, SECONDARY, AND TERTIARY AMINES

The most direct method for the preparation of amines is the reaction of ammonia with an alkyl halide. In this reaction the more basic ammonia molecule displaces chlorine as a chloride ion, the alkyl group attaching itself to the unshared pair of electrons of the ammonia molecule.

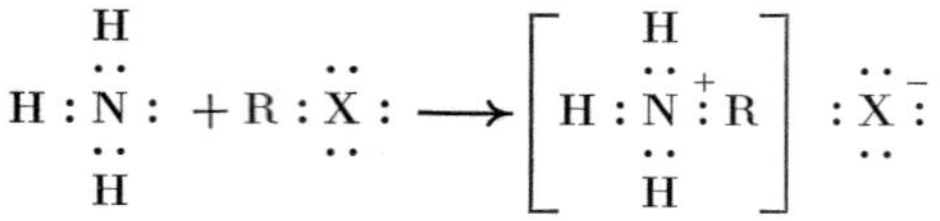

$$H : \overset{\overset{\textstyle H}{..}}{\underset{\underset{\textstyle H}{..}}{N}} : \ + R : \overset{..}{\underset{..}{X}} : \ \longrightarrow \ \left[H : \overset{\overset{\textstyle H}{..}}{\underset{\underset{\textstyle H}{..}}{N}} \overset{+}{\vdots} R \right] \ : \overset{..}{\underset{..}{X}} : \overline{\ }$$

This initial reaction, however, is followed by a series of secondary reactions. Just as ammonia may be liberated from an ammonium salt by reaction with a stronger base,

$$NH_4Cl + NaOH \longrightarrow NH_3 + H_2O + NaCl$$

the free primary amine can be liberated from the alkylammonium salt.

$$RNH_3X + NaOH \longrightarrow RNH_2 + H_2O + NaCl$$

Similarly the excess of ammonia present when the alkyl halide is reacting with ammonia will compete with the primary amine for the hydrogen halide. Since ammonia and the amine have about the same basicity, the reaction does not go to completion, but an equilibrium is established.

$$RNH_3X + NH_3 \rightleftarrows RNH_2 + NH_4Cl$$

Because of its unshared pair of electrons, the primary amine thus formed also can react with a molecule of alkyl halide and give rise to a second pair of reactions to form a secondary amine.

$$RNH_2 + RX \longrightarrow R_2NH_2X$$
$$R_2NH_2X + NH_3 \rightleftarrows R_2NH + NH_4X$$

Immediately a third pair of reactions is possible giving a tertiary amine.

$$RX + R_2NH \longrightarrow R_3NHX$$
$$R_3NHX + NH_3 \rightleftarrows R_3N + NH_4X$$

Finally a single further reaction can take place giving a quaternary ammonium salt.

$$RX + R_3N \longrightarrow R_4NX$$

The reaction stops at this point, because there is no hydrogen attached to nitrogen in the quaternary ammonium salt (nitrogen united to four carbon atoms), and hence no proton can be transferred to another base.

Accordingly the reaction of alkyl halides with ammonia, known as the *Hofmann* [1] *method for preparing amines*, gives rise to a mixture of primary, secondary, and tertiary amines, their salts, and the quaternary ammonium salt. Addition of strong alkali at the end of the reaction liberates a mixture of the free amines from their salts, but the quaternary salt is not affected. Naturally it is possible to control the reaction to a certain extent. If a very large excess of ammonia is used, the chance that the alkyl halide will react with ammonia molecules is greater than that it will react with amine molecules, and chiefly primary amine is produced. If increasing amounts of alkyl halide are used, more of the other products are formed.

The order of reactivity of the alkyl halides with ammonia and amines is iodides > bromides > chlorides, and primary > secondary > tertiary. Alkyl sulfates may replace alkyl halides (cf. p. 115). Because of the ease with which tertiary alkyl halides lose halogen acid, reaction with ammonia yields only olefin and ammonium halide.

$$(CH_3)_3CCl + NH_3 \longrightarrow CH_2{=}C(CH_3)_2 + NH_4Cl$$

PURE PRIMARY AMINES

Since the reaction of an alkyl halide with ammonia gives a mixture of primary, secondary, and tertiary amines, and quaternary salt, reactions yielding only one type of amine are of value. In the following reactions only primary amines are formed.

1. **Hofmann Rearrangement of Amides.** When amides are treated with an alkaline solution of sodium hypochlorite or sodium hypobromite, primary amines are formed which have one less carbon atom than the amide.

$$RCONH_2 + NaOX + 2\ NaOH \longrightarrow RNH_2 + Na_2CO_3 + NaX + H_2O$$

Several steps are involved which are discussed under the reactions of amides (p. 197).

2. **Reduction of Alkyl Cyanides.** If four hydrogen atoms are added to the triple bond of an alkyl cyanide, a primary amine results. The usual reagent is sodium and absolute alcohol, and the reaction resembles the reduction of esters to alcohols.

$$RC{\equiv}N + 4\ Na + 4\ C_2H_5OH \longrightarrow RCH_2NH_2 + 4\ C_2H_5ONa$$

Catalytic reduction may be used,

$$RC{\equiv}N + 2\ H_2 \xrightarrow{\text{Pt or Ni}} RCH_2NH_2$$

---

[1] August Wilhelm Hofmann (1818–1895), German chemist who received his training under Liebig, and who was professor at the Royal College of Chemistry in London from 1845 to 1864, and at the University of Berlin from 1864 until his death. He is noted particularly for his work on amines and for his investigations of aromatic compounds. The latter work laid the basis for the coal tar chemical industry.

but the product is contaminated with secondary and tertiary amines because of the reactions

$$2 \text{ RNH}_2 \underset{}{\overset{\text{Pt or Ni}}{\rightleftarrows}} \text{R}_2\text{NH} + \text{NH}_3$$

$$\text{R}_2\text{NH} + \text{RNH}_2 \underset{}{\overset{\text{Pt or Ni}}{\rightleftarrows}} \text{R}_3\text{N} + \text{NH}_3$$

These side reactions may be suppressed by carrying out the hydrogenation in the presence of a large amount of ammonia.

3. *Reduction of Oximes.* Oximes of aldehydes or ketones also may be reduced by sodium and alcohol to give good yields of primary amines.

$$\text{RCH}{=}\text{NOH} + 4 \text{ Na} + 3 \text{ C}_2\text{H}_5\text{OH} \longrightarrow \text{RCH}_2\text{NH}_2 + \text{NaOH} + 3 \text{ C}_2\text{H}_5\text{ONa}$$

Hence this reaction provides a method for converting aldehydes and ketones into primary amines.

4. *Reduction of Aldehydes and Ketones in the Presence of Ammonia.* Catalytic reduction of aldehydes or ketones in the presence of an excess of ammonia gives good yields of primary amines.

$$\text{RCHO} + \text{NH}_3 \longrightarrow [\text{RCH}{=}\text{NH}] + \text{H}_2\text{O}$$

$$[\text{RCH}{=}\text{NH}] + \text{H}_2 \overset{\text{Pt or Ni}}{\longrightarrow} \text{RCH}_2\text{NH}_2$$

PURE SECONDARY AMINES

Several methods are available which yield only secondary amines.

1. *Reduction of Aldehydes or Ketones in the Presence of Primary Amines.* If primary amines are substituted for ammonia in the last reaction, the product is a secondary amine.

$$\text{RCHO} + \text{H}_2\text{NR}' \longrightarrow [\text{RCH}{=}\text{NR}'] + \text{H}_2\text{O}$$

$$[\text{RCH}{=}\text{NR}'] + \text{H}_2 \overset{\text{Pt or Ni}}{\longrightarrow} \text{RCH}_2\text{NHR}'$$

2. *From Sodium Cyanamide and Alkyl Halides or Sulfates.* Sodium cyanamide (p. 247) reacts with alkyl halides or sulfates like many other salts, the metallic ion being replaced by covalently bound alkyl groups.

$$2 \text{ RX} + \text{Na}_2{}^+[^-\text{N}{-}\text{C}{\equiv}\text{N}] \longrightarrow \text{R}_2\text{N}{-}\text{C}{\equiv}\text{N} + 2 \text{ NaX}$$

The dialkylcyanamide hydrolyzes readily with aqueous acids or bases giving the N,N-dialkylcarbamic acid which loses carbon dioxide.

$$\text{R}_2\text{N}{-}\text{C}{\equiv}\text{N} + 2 \text{ HOH} \overset{[\text{H}^+] \text{ or } [\text{OH}^-]}{\longrightarrow} [\text{R}_2\text{NCOOH}] + \text{NH}_3$$
$$\downarrow$$
$$\text{R}_2\text{NH} + \text{CO}_2$$

In acid solution carbon dioxide is evolved and a mixture of the amine and ammonium salts is obtained, whereas in alkaline solution the free amine, ammonia, and alkali carbonate are formed.

There is no convenient method for preparing pure tertiary amines. In the usual procedure a secondary amine is allowed to react with an excess of alkyl halide, and the tertiary amine is separated from the accompanying quaternary salt.

Physical Properties

Water, ammonia, and methane have very nearly the same molecular weights, but their boiling points are 100°, −38°, and −161°, respectively. The abnormally high boiling point of water is explained by proton bonding between hydrogen united to oxygen, and the unshared pair of electrons on the oxygen atom (p. 60). The boiling point of ammonia indicates that it is not so strongly associated as water. The nitrogen atom is nearer the center of the periodic table than oxygen and hence has less attraction for electrons (p. 64). Therefore the hydrogen atoms attached to nitrogen have less tendency to leave nitrogen as protons or to be shared with other atoms than do those joined to oxygen. On the other hand the unshared pair of electrons on nitrogen is shared more readily with other atoms than those on oxygen. The decrease in tendency to lose a proton accounts for the smaller degree of association.

Primary and secondary amines also are associated. Methylamine (mol. wt. 31) boils at −7° and dimethylamine (mol. wt. 45) boils at +7°, but trimethylamine (mol. wt. 59) boils at +4°. Thus even though its molecular weight is greater than that of dimethylamine, trimethylamine has the lower boiling point. The explanation is that trimethylamine no longer has a hydrogen atom capable of proton bond formation, and hence it is not associated. Its boiling point is comparable to that of other unassociated liquids of the same molecular weight, for example methyl ethyl ether (mol. wt. 60, b.p. +11°) and *n*-butane (mol. wt. 58, b.p. −1°).

There is nothing to prevent the unshared pair of electrons of tertiary amines from forming proton bonds with water molecules, and all types of amines of low molecular weight are soluble in water. Since amines have a greater tendency to share their unshared pair of electrons than do alcohols, they form stronger proton bonds with water and are somewhat more soluble. For example *n*-butyl alcohol dissolves in water to the extent of about 8 per cent at room temperature, but *n*-butylamine is miscible with water; and although less than 1 per cent *n*-amyl alcohol dissolves in water, this degree of insolubility is not reached in the amines until *n*-hexylamine. Like the alcohols and ethers, simple amines are soluble in most organic solvents.

The lower amines have an odor resembling that of ammonia; the odor of trimethylamine is described as "fishy." As the molecular weight increases, the odors become decidedly obnoxious, but they decrease again with increasing molecular weight and decreasing vapor pressure.

Reactions

1. *Basic Properties.* For many purposes it is sufficient to define an acid as a substance which yields hydrogen ions when dissolved in water, and a base as a substance which yields hydroxide ions when dissolved in water. A more general concept is useful in organic chemistry, because acid-base reactions are carried out in many solvents other than water. Usually an acid is considered to be any substance which can lose a proton, and a base is any sub-

stance having an unshared pair of electrons which can combine with a proton (p. 191). Reaction of an acid with a base consists of the transfer of a proton from one base to another. For example when hydrogen chloride dissolves in water, the proton is transferred from the very weak base, chloride ion, to the stronger base, the water molecule.

$$\text{H} : \overset{..}{\underset{H}{\text{O}}} : + \text{H} : \overset{..}{\underset{..}{\text{Cl}}} : \longrightarrow \left[\text{H} : \overset{..}{\underset{H}{\text{O}}} \overset{+}{:} \text{H} \right] \quad : \overset{..}{\underset{..}{\text{Cl}}} \overset{-}{:}$$

Hydronium chloride

If ammonia is added to the water solution of hydrogen chloride, the proton is transferred from the water molecule to the stronger base, the ammonia molecule.

$$[\text{H}_3\text{O}^+] + \; : \text{NH}_3 \longrightarrow [\text{NH}_4{}^+] + \text{H}_2\text{O}$$

Similarly the hydroxide ion displaces the weaker base, ammonia, from the ammonium ion.

$$[\text{NH}_4{}^+] + \left[: \overset{..}{\underset{..}{\text{OH}}} \right] \longrightarrow \text{NH}_3 + \text{H}_2\text{O}$$

In general the aliphatic amines are slightly stronger bases than ammonia and form salts with acids in aqueous solution. They are liberated from their salts by stronger bases such as aqueous solutions of sodium hydroxide.

The amine salts are named either as substituted ammonium salts or as acid addition products; for example $(\text{CH}_3)_3\text{NHCl}$ may be called trimethylammonium chloride or trimethylamine hydrochloride. In the older literature the amine salts frequently are represented by formulas such as $(\text{CH}_3)_3\text{N}\cdot\text{HCl}$, which is equivalent to writing ammonium chloride as $\text{NH}_3\cdot\text{HCl}$.

In the same manner as ammonia forms an insoluble salt with chloroplatinic acid, $(\text{NH}_4)_2\text{PtCl}_6$, so the amine salts, for example $(\text{RNH}_3)_2\text{PtCl}_6$, are insoluble and are used for analytical purposes. To determine the equivalent weight of the compound, it is necessary only to ignite a weighed sample and weigh the residue of platinum.

Calcium chloride may not be used for removing water from amines, because it is solvated by them just as it is by water and ammonia. Amines usually are dried with potassium carbonate, potassium hydroxide, or barium oxide.

2. *Acylation.* Acyl chlorides, acid anhydrides, and esters react with primary and secondary amines, just as they do with ammonia, to give amides. Tertiary amines do not react, because they do not contain a replaceable hydrogen atom.

$$2 \, \text{RNH}_2 + \text{R}'\text{COX} \longrightarrow \text{RNHCOR}' + \text{RNH}_3\text{X}$$

$$\text{RNH}_2 + (\text{R}'\text{CO})_2\text{O} \longrightarrow \text{RNHCOR}' + \text{RCOOH}$$

$$\text{RNH}_2 + \text{R}'\text{COOR}'' \longrightarrow \text{RNHCOR}' + \text{R}''\text{OH}$$

The reaction with acid halides requires two moles of amine, only one of which can be acylated because the second mole combines with the hydrogen halide. Although an acid is formed in the second reaction, it is a weak acid, and the salt of a weak base and a weak acid dissociates sufficiently to produce the acylated amine when heated with an excess of anhydride. Hence all of the amine can be converted into amide by this procedure.

The products formed are known as *N-substituted amides*, the *N* referring to the nitrogen atom of the amide. Thus the reaction product of methylamine with acetic anhydride, $CH_3CONHCH_3$, is called *N*-methylacetamide. Secondary amines in the above reactions yield *N, N*-disubstituted amides. *i*-Butyryl chloride and diethylamine give *N, N*-diethyl-*i*-butyramide, $(CH_3)_2CH_2CON(C_2H_5)_2$.

An important application of the acylation reaction is the separation of tertiary amines from a mixture with primary and secondary amines. After acetylation with acetic anhydride, the unchanged tertiary amine may be separated from the higher boiling amides by distillation, or by extraction with dilute acid. The tertiary amine is basic and forms water-soluble salts whereas the amides are neutral. Similarly acylation can be used to distinguish tertiary amines from primary or secondary amines.

3. *Isocyanide (Carbylamine) Test for Primary Amines.* When a primary amine is heated with chloroform and a few drops of an alcoholic solution of sodium hydroxide, an *isocyanide* (*isonitrile* or *carbylamine*) is formed.

$$RNH_2 + CHCl_3 + 3\ NaOH \longrightarrow RNC + 3\ NaCl + 3\ H_2O$$

The reaction is essentially an alkylation analogous to the reaction of an amine with an alkyl halide. The intermediate alkylation product probably is R—N=C, which in the presence of the alkali loses hydrogen chloride and leaves an unshared pair of electrons on the carbon atom. To stabilize the molecule the unshared pair on the nitrogen atom completes a triple bond between nitrogen and carbon. Hence R ⦂N ⦂C ⦂ is the electronic structure. Since the nitrogen atom now shares with the carbon atom the pair of electrons that it formerly owned exclusively, the nitrogen atom acquires a positive charge and the carbon atom a negative charge, and the formula may be written R—N$^+$≡$^-$C. Sometimes it is written R—N≡C to indicate that one pair of electrons came from the nitrogen atom. *A covalent bond in which one atom has supplied both electrons thus giving rise to a difference in charge of one electron between two atoms in the same molecule* is known as a **semipolar bond, dative bond**, or **coordinate covalence.** The ammonia-boron chloride complex (p. 192) also contains a semipolar bond.

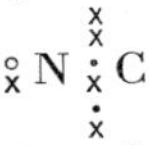

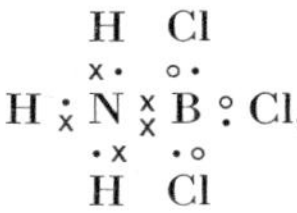

$$H \overset{x}{\underset{x}{⦂}} N \overset{x}{\underset{x}{⦂}} B \overset{\circ}{\underset{\circ}{⦂}} Cl, \quad H_3N\overset{+-}{—}BCl_3, \quad or \quad H_3N \longrightarrow BCl_3$$

However the bond formed when an ammonia or amine molecule combines with a proton is not a semipolar bond, because the proton carries with it a positive charge which neutralizes the negative charge it otherwise would have acquired by sharing half of the pair of electrons belonging to the nitrogen atom.

$$H : \overset{H}{\underset{H}{\overset{..}{N}}} : \ + [H^+] \longrightarrow \left[H : \overset{H}{\underset{H}{\overset{..}{N}}} \overset{+}{:} H \right]$$

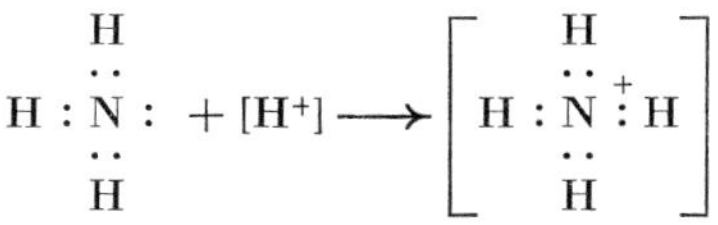

Thus only the nitrogen atom carries a positive charge and the four N—H bonds are all equivalent covalent bonds.

The isocyanides are characterized by a very disagreeable odor which can be detected in minute amounts and which makes the reaction suitable to distinguish primary amines from secondary and tertiary amines. When combined with the acylation reaction, which differentiates primary and secondary amines from tertiary amines, a procedure is available for distinguishing between the three types. Because of the sensitivity of the isocyanide test, secondary amines may contain enough primary amine to give a positive test. If the test is made on a sufficiently small amount of amine (less than 1 mg.), a primary amine will give a positive test, but a secondary amine containing 2 per cent primary amine as impurity will not. The sensitivity of the test naturally depends on the volatility of the isocyanide produced. A more satisfactory method for distinguishing the three types of amines is discussed on page 357.

4. Reactions with Nitrous Acid. The behavior of amines towards nitrous acid depends on the type of amine. In the presence of a strong acid, primary amines react with the evolution of nitrogen. The other products of the reaction depend on the structure of the alkyl group. Usually a mixture of substances is obtained which may contain the expected alcohol or rearranged products, an olefin, an alcohol derivative such as an ether or, if the reaction is carried out in the presence of halogen acid, an alkyl halide.

$$RNH_2 + HONO \xrightarrow{\text{(HX)}} \begin{array}{c}\text{Alcohol, ether,} \\ \text{alkyl halide,} \\ \text{or olefin mixture}\end{array} + N_2 + H_2O$$

Ethylamine, for example, gives 60 per cent ethyl alcohol and traces of ethers; n-propylamine gives 7 per cent n-propyl alcohol, 32 per cent i-propyl alcohol, and 28 per cent propylene; n-butylamine gives 25 per cent n-butyl alcohol, 13 per cent s-butyl alcohol, 8 per cent n- and s-butyl chlorides, and 36 per cent 1- and 2-butenes. Although the complexity of the reaction makes it of little value for preparative purposes, the evolution of nitrogen can be made quantitative, and the reaction is used to estimate primary amino groups.

Secondary amines yield nitrosoamines, which are colored and, since they are amides of nitrous acid, are nonbasic and insoluble in dilute acids.

$$R_2NH + HONO \longrightarrow R_2NNO + H_2O$$

If the reaction of tertiary amines with nitrous acid goes beyond salt formation, it is complex, the chief products being aldehydes and the nitroso derivatives of secondary amines.

5. Oxidation of Tertiary Amines. When tertiary amines react with aqueous hydrogen peroxide, amine oxides are formed.

$$R_3N + H_2O_2 \longrightarrow R_3NO + H_2O$$

The mechanism of this reaction appears to be the simple displacement of hydroxide ion from a molecule of hydrogen peroxide followed by removal of a proton from the hydroxy-ammonium ion.

$$R_3N : \underset{[OH^-]}{\overset{HO-OH}{\rightleftharpoons}} [R_3\overset{+}{N} : OH] \underset{H_2O}{\overset{[OH^-]}{\rightleftharpoons}} R_3\overset{+}{N} : \overset{-}{O}$$

Like the isocyanides (p. 189), the amine oxides contain a semipolar bond or coordinate covalency. Here it is between nitrogen and oxygen, and the formula may be written $R_3N{\overset{+}{\underset{-}{}}}O$ or $R_3N \rightarrow O$. The presence of the semipolar bond gives rise to a high dipole moment which in turn causes the boiling point to be abnormally high. Trimethylamine oxide of molecular weight 75 does not distill at temperatures up to 180°, where it decomposes, whereas dimethylethylamine of molecular weight 73 boils at 38°.

The amine oxides are basic and form salts with acids.

$$R_3N : \overset{..}{\underset{..}{O}} : \; + HX \longrightarrow \left[R_3\overset{+}{N} : \overset{..}{\underset{..}{O}} : H \right] X^-$$

Trimethylamine oxide has been isolated from the muscles of several varieties of marine animals such as the octopus and the spiny dogfish. It undoubtedly is present in the form of its salts.

6. *Alkylation.* Since ammonia reacts with alkyl halides to give a mixture of primary, secondary, and tertiary amines, and quaternary ammonium salt (p. 184), amines also can react with alkyl halides to give secondary or tertiary amines, or quaternary salts.

General Concepts of Acids and Bases

If a base is defined as a substance having an unshared pair of electrons which can combine with a proton (p. 187), then differences in basicity are due to the relative availability of the unshared pair of electrons for filling the valence shell of a proton. The more strongly the pair is held by the base, the weaker the basic properties of the substance; the more loosely the pair is held, the stronger the basic properties of the substance. Conversely if the pair of electrons is shared with a proton, the more strongly the pair is held by the base, the easier it is to lose a proton and the stronger the acidic properties of the substance; the more weakly the electrons are held by the base, the more difficult it is to lose a proton and the weaker the acidic properties of the substance. For example the acidity of the hydrides of carbon, nitrogen, oxygen, and fluorine increases from left to right across the periodic table. For those hydrides having an unshared pair of electrons, the basicity decreases from ammonia to water to hydrogen fluoride. Of the ions CH_3^-, NH_2^-, OH^-, and F^-, methide ion is the strongest base and fluoride ion the weakest. The order of basicity or acidity within a given series is due to the increasing charge on the nucleus of the central atom, which exerts an increasingly stronger pull on the electrons and holds them more strongly. Similarly the ions are more basic than the respective neutral molecules, because the negative charge on the ions makes the electrons less strongly held than in the case of the neutral molecules. In a series H_2O, RCH_2OH, R_2CHOH, R_3COH; or RCH_2O^-, R_2CHO^-, R_3CO^-; or NH_3, RNH_2, R_2NH, R_3N; or NH_2^-, RNH^-, R_2N^-, if R is an alkyl group, which has a repelling effect on electrons (p. 97), it would be expected, in the absence of other effects such as solvation and steric effects, that in each series the basicity would increase and the acidity decrease. That other factors do play a part is shown, for example, by the order of basicity of ammonia and the methylamines in aqueous solutions which is $NH_3 < (CH_3)_3N << CH_3NH_2 < (CH_3)_2NH$. Substituents in the R group affect the acidity depending on whether the substituents are electron-attracting or electron-repelling. A few common types of molecules and ions are listed in the order of increasing acidity and in the order of decreasing basicity.

	Increasing Strength as Acids		Decreasing Strength as Bases
Weakest	CH_4	Strongest	CH_3^-
	R_2NH, RNH_2		R_2N^-, RNH^-
	NH_3		NH_2^-
	R_3COH, R_2CHOH, RCH_2OH		R_3CO^-, R_2CHO^-, RCH_2O^-
	HOH		OH^-
	HCN		CN^-
	R_3NH^+, $R_2NH_2^+$, RNH_3^+		R_3N, R_2NH, RNH_2
	NH_4^+		NH_3
	H_2CO_3		HCO_3^-
	$RCOOH$		$RCOO^-$
	R_2OH^+, ROH_2^+		R_2O, ROH
	H_3O^+		H_2O
	$RCOOH_2^+$		$RCOOH$
Strongest	HX	Weakest	X^-

Acids and bases related to each other, such as ammonia and ammonium ion, or hydroxide ion and water, are said to be *conjugate* to each other. Thus ammonia is the *conjugate base* of ammonium ion, and ammonium ion is the *conjugate acid* of ammonia; hydroxide ion is the conjugate base of water, and water is the conjugate acid of hydroxide ion.

This concept usually is called the Bronsted [2] theory of acids and bases although Lowry [3] had published a paper expressing similar views several months before Bronsted. It is of interest that Lewis [4] in his book on the theory of valence, which was copyrighted in 1923, the same year that the papers of Lowry and Bronsted were published, states that "the definition of an acid or a base as a substance which gives up or takes up hydrogen ion would be more general than the one used before, although it will not be universal." Thus Lewis considered the concept at least as early as Lowry and Bronsted, but discarded it in favor of a more general one.

The fundamental process being considered is the union of a proton lacking a pair of electrons with an ion or molecule that has an unshared pair of electrons.

$$
\begin{array}{c}
\text{H : O :} \\
\ \ \ \ \ \ \ \ddot{} \\
\text{H}
\end{array}
+ [H^+] \longrightarrow
\left[
\begin{array}{c}
\text{H : O : H} \\
\ \ \ \ \ \ \ddot{} \\
\text{H}
\end{array}
\right]
$$

$$
\begin{array}{c}
\text{H} \\
\ddot{} \\
\text{H : N :} \\
\ddot{} \\
\text{H}
\end{array}
+ [H^+] \longrightarrow
\left[
\begin{array}{c}
\text{H} \\
\ddot{} \\
\text{H : N : H} \\
\ddot{} \\
\text{H}
\end{array}
\right]
$$

$$
\left[
\begin{array}{c}
\text{H : O :}^{\ -} \\
\ddot{}
\end{array}
\right]
+ [H^+] \longrightarrow
\begin{array}{c}
\text{H : O :} \\
\ddot{} \\
\text{H}
\end{array}
$$

Entirely analogous processes, however, can take place between any ion or molecule lacking a pair of electrons in its valence shell and any ion or molecule having an unshared pair of electrons. Ammonia, for example, forms a stable complex with boron chloride.

$$
\begin{array}{cc}
\text{H} & \text{Cl} \\
\ddot{} & \ddot{} \\
\text{H : N :} & + \text{B : Cl} \\
\ddot{} & \ddot{} \\
\text{H} & \text{Cl}
\end{array}
\longrightarrow
\begin{array}{cc}
\text{H} & \text{Cl} \\
\ddot{} & \ddot{} \\
\text{H : N : B : Cl} \\
\ddot{} & \ddot{} \\
\text{H} & \text{Cl}
\end{array}
$$

Accordingly Lewis classed boron chloride as an acid and defined an acid as a substance which can fill the valence shell of one of its atoms with an unshared pair of electrons from another molecule. In favor of this concept is the fact that substances such as boron fluoride, aluminum chloride, zinc chloride, or stannic chloride can catalyze the same types of reaction, for example polymerization of olefins (p. 43) or the formation of ethers (p. 116), as can a proton.

Lewis revived his ideas in a paper in 1938, and such compounds are often called Lewis acids. With this definition of an acid it should be remembered that hydrogen chloride, sulfuric acid, acetic acid, and in fact any of the countless number of substances that from the beginning of chemistry have been called acids, are not acids under the Lewis definition. The acid as defined by Lewis is the bare unsolvated proton, which is practically incapable of existence. Moreover substances such as cupric ion, which seldom are considered as acids, are

---

[2] J. N. Bronsted (1879–1947), director of the Fysisk-Kemiske Institute of Copenhagen. His chief contributions were in the fields of electrolytes and reaction kinetics.

[3] Thomas Martin Lowry (1878–1936), professor of physical chemistry at Cambridge University. He is noted for his investigations in the fields of optical rotatory power and of proton transfer reactions.

[4] Gilbert Newton Lewis (1875–1946), professor of physical chemistry at the University of California. He is noted for his development of the electronic theory of valency, for his work in chemical thermodynamics, and for his investigations of deuterium and the absorption spectra of organic compounds.

acids in the Lewis sense, because they can fill their valence shell with unshared pairs from other molecules, as when cupric ion reacts with ammonia molecules to give the cupric-ammonia complex ion.

$$Cu^{++} + 4\ NH_3 \longrightarrow \left[\begin{matrix} NH_3 \\ \overset{..}{H_3N} : \overset{..}{Cu} : NH_3 \\ \overset{..}{NH_3} \end{matrix}\right]^{++}$$

Instead of calling all types of compounds capable of accepting a pair of electrons acids, Sidgwick in his book on valency published in 1927 called them electron-acceptors, thus leaving the term acid for those compounds capable of transferring a proton to a base. Perhaps a better term than electron-acceptor for reagents, such as boron fluoride, aluminum chloride, stannic chloride, or zinc chloride, that behave like a proton would be **protonoid** or **protonoid reagent.** This term would imply properties similar to those of a proton but would not group these compounds with the substances commonly called acids.

Individual Amines

Methylamine, dimethylamine, and **trimethylamine** occur in herring brine and are distributed widely in other natural products, probably as the result of the decomposition or metabolism of nitrogenous compounds. They are manufactured commercially by passing a mixture of methyl alcohol and ammonia over heated alumina.

$$CH_3OH + NH_3 \xrightarrow[400°]{Al_2O_3} CH_3NH_2 \xrightarrow{CH_3OH} (CH_3)_2NH \xrightarrow{CH_3OH} (CH_3)_3N$$
$$\qquad\qquad\qquad +\qquad\qquad +\qquad\qquad +$$
$$\qquad\qquad\qquad H_2O\qquad\qquad H_2O\qquad\qquad H_2O$$

This procedure has not been practical for alcohols that can be dehydrated, since they yield chiefly olefins. Methylamine hydrochloride is formed along with some di- and trimethylamine hydrochlorides when a solution of ammonium chloride in formalin is evaporated to dryness.

$$NH_4Cl + 2\ HCHO \longrightarrow CH_3NH_3{}^+Cl^- + HCOOH$$

This reaction is essentially a Cannizzaro reaction (p. 178). If solid ammonium chloride and paraformaldehyde are mixed and heated, trimethylamine hydrochloride is formed.

$$2\ NH_4Cl + 9\ HCHO \longrightarrow 2\ (CH_3)_3NHCl + 3\ CO_2 + 3\ H_2O$$

Trimethylamine also can be prepared by the dry distillation of beet sugar residues which contain betaine (p. 535).

$$2\ (CH_3)_3N^+CH_2COO^- \longrightarrow 2\ (CH_3)_3N + CH_2{=}CH_2 + 2\ CO_2$$

Methylamine and dimethylamine are used in the tanning industry as dehairing agents. Trimethylamine, when obtained as a by-product, may be utilized by conversion into dimethylamine and methyl chloride, or into ammonium chloride and methyl chloride.

$$(CH_3)_3NHCl + HCl \xrightarrow{Heat} (CH_3)_2NH_2Cl + CH_3Cl$$

$$(CH_3)_3NHCl + 3\ HCl \xrightarrow{Heat} NH_4Cl + 3\ CH_3Cl$$

n-**Butylamines** are prepared commercially from butyl chloride and ammonia, and the **amyl amines** from amyl chlorides and ammonia. All have a wide variety of uses, for example as antioxidants and corrosion inhibitors, absorbents for acid gases, and in the manufacture of oil-soluble soaps. **Higher normal amines** are made by the reduction of nitriles obtained from fat acids through the amides (p. 197).

QUATERNARY AMMONIUM SALTS

The end-product of the reaction of ammonia or of an amine with an alkyl halide is a quaternary ammonium salt (p. 184). The properties of these salts are quite unlike those of the amine salts, since the nitrogen no longer carries a hydrogen atom. They do not dissociate into amine and acid on heating, and strong alkalies have no effect on them. When a solution of a quaternary ammonium halide is shaken with silver hydroxide, or when a quaternary ammonium acid sulfate solution reacts with barium hydroxide, the insoluble silver halide or barium sulfate precipitates leaving the quaternary ammonium hydroxide in solution.

$$[R_4N^+]X^- + AgOH \longrightarrow [R_4N^+]OH^- + AgX$$

$$[R_4N^+]SO_4H^- + Ba(OH)_2 \longrightarrow [R_4N^+]OH^- + BaSO_4 + H_2O$$

The quaternary ammonium hydroxide ionizes completely in aqueous solution, and hence it has the same basic strength in water as sodium or potassium hydroxide. For example glass is etched by solutions of quaternary ammonium hydroxides just as it is by solutions of sodium hydroxide. When a quaternary ammonium salt is decomposed by heat, it dissociates into tertiary amine and alkyl halide. In other words the reaction for the formation of quaternary salts can be reversed at high temperatures.

$$[R_4N^+]X^- \overset{\text{Heat}}{\longrightarrow} R_3N + RX$$

An analogous reaction can be used for the esterification of sterically hindered acids. The acid is converted to the quaternary ammonium salt which is decomposed by heat.

$$[(CH_3)_4N^+][\overline{O}OCCR_3] \longrightarrow (CH_3)_3N + CH_3OCOCR_3$$

When tetramethylammonium hydroxide is heated, the products are trimethylamine and methyl alcohol.

$$[(CH_3)_4N^+]OH^- \longrightarrow (CH_3)_3N + CH_3OH$$

If an alkyl group capable of forming an olefin is present, a tertiary amine, olefin, and water are formed.

$$[(CH_3)_3\overset{+}{N}C_2H_5]OH^- \longrightarrow (CH_3)_3N + C_2H_4 + H_2O$$

This reaction is useful for introducing the double bond into complex compounds and for opening the rings of nitrogen heterocycles (p. 455).

Choline chloride is trimethyl-(2-hydroxyethyl)-ammonium chloride, $[(CH_3)_3\overset{+}{N}CH_2CH_2OH]$ Cl⁻. Its quaternary ammonium ion is an extremely important factor in biological processes, and must be supplied by the diet of the animal organism.

Quaternary ammonium salts in which one of the alkyl groups attached to nitrogen is a long chain hydrocarbon group, such as cetyltrimethylammonium chloride, $[C_{16}H_{33}\overset{+}{N}(CH_3)_3]$ Cl⁻, have properties similar to soaps and are known as *invert soaps*, because the detergent action resides in a positive ion rather than in a negative ion as is the case with ordinary soaps. Many of these invert soaps have high germicidal action.

AMIDES

The monoacyl derivatives of ammonia, primary amines and secondary amines, having the general formula $RCONH_2$, RCONHR, or $RCONR_2$, are known as *amides*. Diacyl derivatives of ammonia, $(RCO)_2NH$, and of primary amines, $(RCO)_2NR$, also are known and are called *imides*. Except for cyclic imides (p. 416) their preparation usually is more difficult because the first acyl group greatly reduces the basicity of the nitrogen. The expected triacylamines are unknown.

Preparation

Most methods for preparing amides have been discussed under the reactions of acids and acid derivatives.

1. *From Acyl Halides and Ammonia or Amines.*

$$RCOCl + 2\ NH_3 \longrightarrow RCONH_2 + NH_4Cl$$
$$+ 2\ H_2NR \longrightarrow RCONHR + RNH_3Cl$$
$$+ 2\ HNR_2 \longrightarrow RCONR_2 + R_2NH_2Cl$$

These reactions go to completion at room temperature. Two moles of ammonia or amine are required per mole of acyl halide because of the inappreciable dissociation of the amine halide at the temperature of reaction.

2. *From Acid Anhydrides and Ammonia or Amines.*

$$(RCO)_2O + 2\ NH_3 \longrightarrow RCONH_2 + RCOONH_4$$
$$+ 2\ H_2NR \longrightarrow RCONHR + RCOONH_3R$$
$$+ 2\ HNR_2 \longrightarrow RCONR_2 + RCOONH_2R_2$$

Although these reactions go as indicated in the presence of an excess of ammonia or amine, it is possible to convert all of the base into amide in the presence of an excess of anhydride because of the ease of dissociation of the ammonium carboxylates.

$$RCOONH_4 \rightleftarrows RCOOH + NH_3$$
$$(RCO)_2O + NH_3 \longrightarrow RCONH_2 + RCOOH$$

3. From Esters and Ammonia or Amines.

$$RCOOR' + NH_3 \longrightarrow RCONH_2 + HOR'$$

$$RCOOR' + H_2NR \longrightarrow RCONHR + HOR'$$

$$+ HNR_2 \longrightarrow RCONR_2 + HOR'$$

4. From Ammonium Salts by Thermal Decomposition.

$$RCOONH_4 \xrightarrow{\text{Heat}} RCONH_2 + H_2O$$

$$RCOONH_3R \xrightarrow{\text{Heat}} RCONHR + H_2O$$

$$RCOONH_2R_2 \xrightarrow{\text{Heat}} RCONR_2 + H_2O$$

Water is removed at the temperature of decomposition, forcing the reaction to completion. The reaction usually is carried out in the presence of an excess of the carboxylic acid to minimize the dissociation of the salt.

$$RCOONH_4 \rightleftharpoons RCOOH + NH_3$$

Nomenclature

The simple amides are named by replacing *ic acid* in the name of the acid or the *e* of the parent hydrocarbon by *amide*. Thus $HCONH_2$ is formamide or methanamide, and $(CH_3)_2CHCONH_2$ is *i*-butyramide or methylpropanamide. Amides derived from amines are named as nitrogen substitution products; for example $CH_3CONHCH_3$ is *N*-methylacetamide, or *N*-methylethanamide.

Physical Properties

All amides are solids with the exception of formamide which melts at 2°. They are associated by proton bonding, which accounts for the high melting and boiling points. Since they also form proton bonds with hydroxylic solvents and other oxygenated molecules, members containing five carbon atoms or less are very soluble in water. Formamide and acetamide are excellent solvents for other organic compounds.

Reactions

1. *Basic and Acidic Properties.* In contrast to ammonia and the amines, the amides do not form salts that are stable in aqueous solution; that is the replacement of a hydrogen atom of the ammonia molecule by an acyl group gives a compound that is a weaker base than water. This effect is in harmony with the effect of replacement of a hydrogen atom of a water molecule by an acyl group. The carbonyl group exerts an electron-attracting effect which increases the ease of ionization of the remaining proton of carboxylic acids and decreases the ability of the nitrogen atom of amides to share its unshared pair. If two hydrogen atoms of ammonia are replaced by acyl groups, the attraction for electrons is sufficient to permit the remaining hydrogen to be removed as a proton by strong bases in aqueous solution. In other words the imides are weak acids.

$$(RCO)_2NH + NaOH \longrightarrow [(RCO)_2N^-]Na^+ + H_2O$$

2. Hydrolysis. The hydrolysis of amides produces the acid and the amine. Like the hydrolysis of esters, the reaction is catalyzed by both acids and bases. However with esters only the basic catalyst reacts with one of the products, whereas in the hydrolysis of the amides both the acid and basic catalyst react with one of the products, thus causing both reactions to go practically to completion.

$$RCONH_2 + NaOH \longrightarrow RCOONa + NH_3$$

$$RCONH_2 + HCl \longrightarrow RCOOH + NH_4Cl$$

3. Dehydration. Distillation of a mixture of an unsubstituted amide with a strong dehydrating agent yields an alkyl cyanide (p. 198).

$$RCONH_2 + P_2O_5 \longrightarrow RC{\equiv}N + 2\ HPO_3$$

$$RCONH_2 + SOCl_2 \longrightarrow RC{\equiv}N + SO_2 + 2\ HCl$$

4. Reaction with Nitrous Acid. Like primary amines, unsubstituted amides react with aqueous nitrous acid with evolution of nitrogen.

$$RCONH_2 + HONO \longrightarrow RCOOH + N_2$$

Mono-N-substituted amides yield nitroso derivatives.

$$RCONHR + HONO \longrightarrow RCON{-}R + H_2O$$
$$\underset{NO}{|}$$

5. Hofmann Rearrangement. One of the methods for the preparation of pure primary amines is the reaction of amides with alkaline solutions of sodium hypochlorite or hypobromite (p. 185).

$$RCONH_2 + NaOX + 2\ NaOH \longrightarrow RNH_2 + Na_2CO_3 + NaX + H_2O$$

Actually several steps are involved, namely halogenation of the amide, removal of halogen acid and rearrangement to the isocyanate (p. 245), and hydrolysis of the isocyanate to the amine and carbonic acid.

$$RCONH_2 + NaOX \longrightarrow RCONHX + NaOH$$

$$RCONHX + NaOH \longrightarrow R{-}N{=}C{=}O + NaX + H_2O$$
$$\text{An isocyanate}$$

$$R{-}N = C = O + 2\ NaOH \longrightarrow RNH_2 + Na_2CO_3$$

Although the series of reactions taking place is rather complex, they can be carried out in a single operation by adding halogen to a mixture of amide and alkali. The reaction is of some importance not only because it can be used to prepare primary amines but because it provides a method for removing one carbon atom from a carbon chain.

The simple aliphatic amides are of little commercial importance, although formamide, N-methylformamide, and acetamide find some use as solvents. Since most amides are solids that can be crystallized readily and have characteristic melting points, they are used as derivatives for the identification of carboxylic acids, esters, acid halides, and nitriles. Of the more complex amides, urea and its derivatives (p. 239) are the most important.

ALKYL CYANIDES (NITRILES)

Nomenclature

The alkyl cyanides, $RC \equiv N$, are alkyl derivatives of hydrogen cyanide and generally are named as if they were salts; for example CH_3CN is called *methyl cyanide*. Organic cyanides also are called *nitriles*. Here the individual nitrile is named from the acid formed on hydrolysis; hence methyl cyanide, which yields acetic acid on hydrolysis, is called *acetonitrile*.

Preparation

The common methods of preparation already have been mentioned in connection with the reactions of alkyl halides, amides, and aldoximes.

1. *From Alkyl Halides (or Sulfates) and Sodium Cyanide.*

$$RX + NaCN \longrightarrow RCN + NaX$$

$$R_2SO_4 + NaCN \longrightarrow RCN + ROSO_3Na$$

$$ROSO_3Na + NaCN \longrightarrow RCN + Na_2SO_4$$

The reactions are carried out in alcoholic or aqueous alcoholic solution. Tertiary alkyl cyanides cannot be prepared by this reaction since tertiary halides lose hydrogen halide to give olefin, sodium halide, and hydrogen cyanide.

In the reaction of alkyl halides with sodium cyanide, a small amount of isocyanide, $R\overset{+}{N}\equiv\overset{-}{C}$, also is formed. The reactive agent is cyanide ion, $(: C \equiv N :)^-$, which has unshared electrons on both carbon and nitrogen. Hence when it displaces the halide ion from the alkyl halide, either the carbon atom or the nitrogen atom may form a bond with the alkyl group. The latter process leads to the formation of isocyanide.

$$(: C \equiv N :)^- + R : \overset{..}{\underset{..}{X}} : \longrightarrow : C \equiv N : R + : \overset{..}{\underset{..}{X}} :^-$$

The isocyanide may be removed from the mixture by making use of the fact that it is more readily hydrolyzed than the cyanide.

2. *Dehydration of Amides.* Amides may be converted to nitriles by heating with dehydrating agents. Either phosphorus pentoxide or thionyl chloride is the usual reagent.

$$RCONH_2 + P_2O_5 \overset{\text{Heat}}{\longrightarrow} RCN + HPO_3$$

$$RCONH_2 + SOCl_2 \overset{\text{Heat}}{\longrightarrow} RCN + SO_2 + 2\,HCl$$

When phosphorus pentoxide is used, the nitrile is distilled from the reaction mixture. If thionyl chloride is used, the mixture is heated under a reflux condenser, and sulfur dioxide and hydrogen chloride are evolved. Amides may be dehydrated also by passing the vapor over a catalyst such as boron phosphate at 350° (p. 544) or alumina at 425°. The higher carboxylic acids or their amides can be converted quantitatively into nitriles by heating at 300° in a stream of ammonia with continuous removal of the water that is formed.

3. **Dehydration of Aldoximes.** The usual reagent for removing the elements of water from an aldoxime is acetic anhydride.

$$RCH{=}NOH + (CH_3CO)_2O \xrightarrow{\text{Heat}} RC{\equiv}N + 2\,CH_3COOH$$

Other dehydrating agents such as phosphorus pentoxide, phosphorus pentachloride, and phosphorus oxychloride may be used.

Physical Properties

Nitriles have abnormally high boiling points. Thus ethyl cyanide of molecular weight 55 boils at 97°, whereas trimethylamine of molecular weight 59 boils at $+4°$.

Cyanides are less soluble in water than amines having the same number of carbon atoms. Hydrogen cyanide and acetonitrile are miscible with water, and propionitrile is fairly soluble, but the higher nitriles are only slightly soluble. The decreased tendency to form proton bonds with water can be ascribed to the reduced basicity of the nitrogen atom (reduced tendency to share the unshared pair of electrons). The cyanides do not dissolve in aqueous acids because they are too weakly basic to form salts.

Physiological Action

Pure alkyl cyanides have a pleasant odor and are only slightly toxic. Usually, however, they are contaminated with the disagreeably odorous and highly toxic isocyanides.

Reactions

The more important reactions of alkyl cyanides already have been used to prepare other compounds.

1. **Hydrolysis to Acids.**

$$RCN + 2\,H_2O + HCl \longrightarrow RCOOH + NH_4Cl$$

$$RCN + H_2O + NaOH \longrightarrow RCOONa + NH_3$$

2. **Alcoholysis to Esters.** To convert nitriles into esters, it is not necessary first to prepare the acid. If the nitrile is refluxed with absolute alcohol and anhydrous acid, the imido ester salt is formed. Addition of water gives the ester.

$$RC{\equiv}N + CH_3OH + HCl \longrightarrow \left[\overset{+NH_2}{\underset{}{RC}{-}OCH_3}\right]Cl^- \xrightarrow{H_2O} \overset{O}{\underset{}{RC}{-}OCH_3} + NH_4Cl$$

Imido ester
hydrochloride

If some water is present in the alcohol or acid, the ester is obtained directly.

3. **Reduction to Primary Amines.** Nitriles may be reduced to primary amines in the same way that esters are reduced to alcohols, that is by adding metallic sodium to a refluxing solution of the nitrile in absolute ethyl alcohol.

$$RC{\equiv}N + 4\,Na + 4\,C_2H_5OH \longrightarrow RCH_2NH_2 + 4\,NaOC_2H_5$$

Catalytic reduction leads to a mixture of primary, secondary, and tertiary amines, but if the reaction is carried out in the presence of an excess of ammonia, good yields of primary amines are obtained (p. 185).

$$RC\equiv N + 2 H_2 \xrightarrow[(+ NH_3)]{Pt \text{ or } Ni} RCH_2NH_2$$

Uses

Nitriles are good solvents but with the exception of hydrogen cyanide and acrylonitrile (p. 537) have not yet found large-scale commercial use. They are important intermediates, however, in the laboratory synthesis of acids, esters, amides, and amines.

ALKYL ISOCYANIDES (ISONITRILES)

As the name implies, the isocyanides or isonitriles are isomeric with the cyanides or nitriles. The structure of the isocyanides and the commonest method of preparation from primary amines are discussed on page 189.

$$RNH_2 + CHCl_3 + 3 NaOH \dashrightarrow R-\overset{+}{N}\equiv\overset{-}{C}: + 3 NaCl + 3 H_2O$$

When an alkyl halide or sulfate reacts with silver cyanide instead of sodium cyanide, the isocyanide, rather than the cyanide, is the main product.

$$RX + AgCN \longrightarrow RNC + AgX$$

Physical Properties

The isocyanides boil about 20° lower than the cyanides. Methyl cyanide boils at 81° and methyl isocyanide at 60°. The corresponding ethyl derivatives boil at 97° and 78°. The isonitriles have an obnoxious odor which can be detected in minute amounts, and are highly toxic.

Reactions

The isocyanides are much more reactive than the nitriles because one of the carbon atoms has an unshared pair of electrons. The initial reaction always involves this unshared pair.

1. *Reduction.* Isocyanides may be reduced catalytically to alkyl-methylamines.

$$R\overset{+}{N}\equiv\overset{-}{C}: \xrightarrow[Pt \text{ or } Ni]{H_2} [RN=CH_2] \xrightarrow[Pt \text{ or } Ni]{H_2} RNHCH_3$$

Thus the reduction of isocyanides leads to secondary amines, whereas nitriles give primary amines (p. 199). The fact that a secondary amine is obtained is proof that the nitrogen must be between a single carbon atom and the alkyl group.

2. *Oxidation.* Mild oxidizing agents such as heavy metal oxides convert isocyanides into isocyanates.

$$R\overset{+}{N}\equiv\overset{-}{C}: + HgO \longrightarrow RN=C=O + Hg$$
Alkyl isocyanate

Sulfur similarly produces an isothiocyanate.

$$R\overset{+}{N}\!\!\equiv\!\!\overset{-}{C}: + S \longrightarrow R\!-\!N\!\!=\!\!C\!\!=\!\!S$$

Alkyl
isothiocyanate

Bromine adds to give a dibromide.

$$R\overset{+}{N}\!\!\equiv\!\!\overset{-}{C}: + Br_2 \longrightarrow RN\!\!=\!\!CBr_2$$

3. **Hydrolysis.** Acid or alkaline hydrolysis leads to the usual scission of the multiple bond to give a primary amine and formic acid. The initial product is the formamide.

$$R\!-\!\overset{+}{N}\!\!\equiv\!\!\overset{-}{C}: + H_2O \longrightarrow [RN\!\!=\!\!CHOH] \longrightarrow RNH\!-\!CHO$$

$$RNHCHO + H_2O + HCl \longrightarrow RNH_3Cl + HCOOH$$

$$RNHCHO + NaOH \longrightarrow RNH_2 + HCOONa$$

The isocyanides have been very important in the development of theories concerning the structure of organic molecules, but as yet have no commercial use.

NITROALKANES

Nitro compounds have the general formula RNO_2 in which the NO_2 group is linked through nitrogen to carbon. In order to maintain an octet of electrons about the nitrogen atom, one of the oxygen atoms is linked by a double bond and the other by a semipolar bond (p. 189).

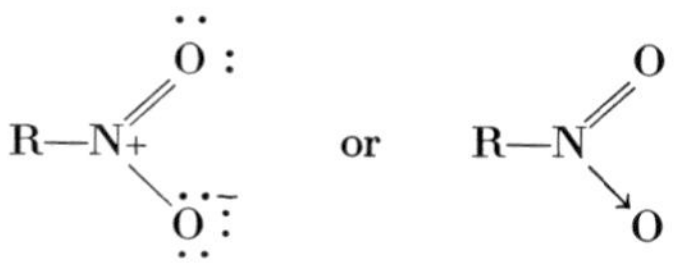

The nitro group resembles the carboxylate ion (p. 129) in that two equivalent electronic structures can be written for it. Hence the actual molecule is a resonance hybrid of the two structures.

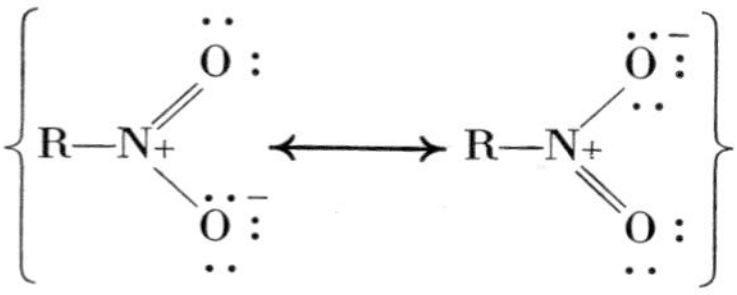

Prior to 1936 the nitroalkanes were largely of theoretical interest. With the advent of the commercial development of vapor phase nitration of propane in 1940, however, the lower nitroalkanes were made available and their numerous reactions became of considerable importance.

Preparation

1. *From Alkyl Halides and Nitrites.* Silver nitrite generally gives the best yield of nitro compound.

$$RX + AgONO \longrightarrow RNO_2 + AgX$$

In this reaction some alkyl nitrite, RONO, (p. 78) also is formed.

The nitrite ion has the electronic structure $\left[\ : \overset{..}{\underset{..}{O}} : N \overset{..}{:} \overset{..}{\underset{..}{O}} \ \right]^{-}$. If the R group becomes attached to the unshared pair on nitrogen, a nitro compound results, whereas if it becomes attached to an unshared pair on oxygen, a nitrite is formed. If an alcoholic solution of sodium nitrite is used the chief product is alkyl nitrite and only a small amount of nitro compound is formed. The chief difference is that silver nitrite is insoluble in alcohol, and the reaction with alkyl halide is a heterogeneous one. Another difference that may be a factor is that silver salts are less ionic than sodium salts. The situation is strictly analogous to the formation of cyanides and isocyanides from sodium cyanide and silver cyanide (p. 200).

Nitromethane is prepared readily in fair yield by the reaction of an aqueous solution of sodium chloroacetate with sodium nitrite and distillation of the mixture. The intermediate sodium nitroacetate decomposes to nitromethane and sodium carbonate.

$$ClCH_2COONa + NaNO_2 \longrightarrow NO_2CH_2COONa + NaCl$$

$$2\ NO_2CH_2COONa + H_2O \longrightarrow 2\ CH_3NO_2 + CO_2 + Na_2CO_3$$

2. *Vapor Phase Nitration of Hydrocarbons.*

$$RH + HONO_2 \overset{420°}{\longrightarrow} RNO_2 + H_2O$$

In the nitration of propane not only 1- and 2-nitropropane are obtained, but also nitroethane and nitromethane formed by the scission of carbon-carbon bonds. These products are separated by distillation and are available commercially. The nitro compounds always are named as substitution products.

Physical Properties

Because of the presence of the semipolar bond in the nitro group, the nitroalkanes have a high dipole moment, which leads to abnormally high boiling points. Moreover the acidity of the α hydrogen probably leads to proton bonding between molecules. Thus nitromethane of molecular weight 61 boils at 101.5°. Nitromethane dissolves in water to about the same extent as *n*-butyl alcohol, but the higher nitroalkanes are practically insoluble. They usually are good solvents for other organic compounds.

Reactions

1. *Salt Formation.* The nitro group has a strong attraction for electrons and decreases the electron-density about an atom to which it is attached. Hence hydrogen is more readily removed from a carbon atom attached to a

nitro group than from an ordinary alkyl group. In fact the aliphatic nitro compounds that have an α hydrogen atom are stronger acids than water and form water-soluble salts with strong bases in aqueous solution.

$$RCH_2NO_2 + NaOH \longrightarrow [R\bar{C}HNO_2]\ Na^+ + H_2O$$

Because of this behavior, the nitro compounds sometimes are called *pseudo acids*. 2-Nitropropane, although practically insoluble in water, will maintain the acidity of water at pH 4.3. Tertiary nitro compounds, R_3CNO_2, in which no hydrogen is united to the carbon atom bearing the nitro group, do not form salts.

This behavior of primary and secondary nitro compounds is analogous to the formation of salts from ketones (p. 174). However when the sodium salt of a ketone reacts with water, the ketone is regenerated at once, but when the sodium salts of certain nitro compounds are acidified, an isomer of the original compound is liberated which is a fairly strong acid. The weakly acidic isomer is believed to have the nitro structure and is called the *nitro* form, whereas the strongly acidic isomer is believed to have an enol structure and is called the *aci* form. The *aci* form rearranges slowly to the *nitro* form.

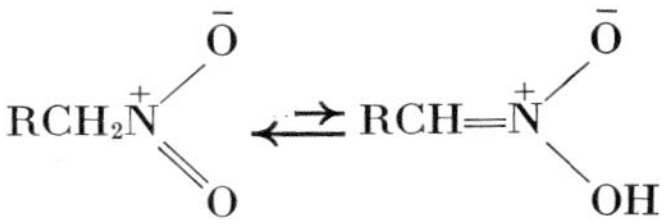

nitro Form   *aci* Form

The phenomenon of relatively stable but readily interconvertible isomers is known as *tautomerism* (p. 553).

Tautomerism is not to be confused with resonance. Resonance does not involve a change in the arrangement of the atoms in the molecule. However the anion of the sodium salt of a nitro compound is a resonance hybrid.

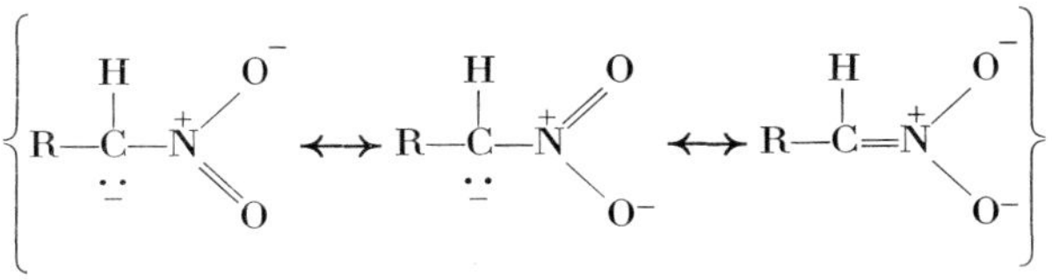

When the sodium salt is acidified, the proton combines more rapidly with an oxygen atom of the resonance hybrid anion than with the α carbon atom. However the *nitro* form is more stable thermodynamically than the *aci* form, and the proton is transferred slowly from oxygen to nitrogen.

2. **Bromination.** Primary and secondary nitro compounds, like aldehydes and ketones (p. 174), brominate easily in alkaline solution.

$$[R\bar{C}HNO_2]N\overset{+}{a} + Br_2 \longrightarrow \underset{\underset{Br}{|}}{R}CHNO_2 + NaBr$$

$$[R_2\bar{C}NO_2]N\overset{+}{a} + Br_2 \longrightarrow \underset{\underset{Br}{|}}{R_2}CNO_2 + NaBr$$

Only hydrogen on the carbon atom adjacent to the nitro group reacts. Hence tertiary nitro compounds are not brominated.

3. **Reaction with Nitrous Acid.** Primary nitro compounds react with nitrous acid to give blue nitroso derivatives, known as *nitrolic acids*, which dissolve in alkali to form red salts.

$$RCH_2NO_2 + HONO \longrightarrow RCH-NO_2 + H_2O$$
$$\underset{NO}{|}$$

Blue, insoluble
in water

$$RCHNO_2 + NaOH \longrightarrow \left\{ \underset{NO}{RC-N} \overset{..}{\underset{O^-}{\overset{+}{N}}}\overset{O}{\diagup} \longleftrightarrow \underset{NO}{RC=N}\overset{+}{\underset{O^-}{\overset{O^-}{\diagup}}} \right\} Na^+$$
$$\underset{NO}{|}$$

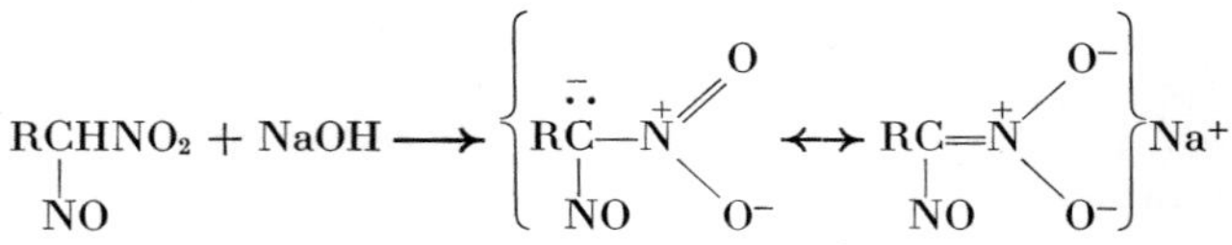

Red solution

Secondary nitro compounds give blue nitroso derivatives which are insoluble in alkali.

$$R_2CHNO_2 + HONO \longrightarrow R_2C-NO_2$$
$$\underset{NO}{|}$$

Blue, insoluble in
water and dilute alkali

These nitroso derivatives are blue only in the liquid monomolecular state. They solidify to white crystalline dimers.

Tertiary nitro compounds do not react with nitrous acid. The difference in behavior of primary, secondary, and tertiary nitro compounds to nitrous acid and alkali may be used to distinguish between the three types and sometimes is referred to as the "red, white, and blue reaction."

4. **Reduction to Primary Amines.**

$$RNO_2 + 6 [H] \longrightarrow RNH_2 + 2 H_2O$$

The reduction may be brought about by hydrogen and a platinum or nickel catalyst, or by an active metal, for example iron, zinc, or tin, and hydrochloric acid.

5. **Acid Hydrolysis.** (a) HYDROLYSIS OF THE NITRO FORM OF A PRIMARY NITRO COMPOUND. When primary nitro compounds are boiled with concentrated aqueous hydrochloric acid, carboxylic acids and hydroxylamine hydrochloride are formed.

$$RCH_2NO_2 + HCl + H_2O \longrightarrow RCOOH + HONH_3Cl$$

By this reaction, which involves an oxidation of the methylene group and reduction of the nitro group, carboxylic acids may be prepared from hydrocarbons. The price of hydroxylamine, which formerly was produced by the reduction of nitrous acid and isolated by way of acetoxime (p. 171), has been reduced greatly because of the above process.

(b) HYDROLYSIS OF THE ACI FORM OF A PRIMARY OR SECONDARY NITRO COMPOUND. If a primary or secondary nitro compound first is converted to the salt of the aci form by alkali and then hydrolyzed by 25 per cent sulfuric acid, aldehydes and ketones are produced with the evolution of nitrous oxide (Nef reaction).

$$2 \text{ RCH=NOONa} + 2 \text{ H}_2\text{SO}_4 \longrightarrow 2 \text{ RCHO} + \text{N}_2\text{O} + 2 \text{ NaHSO}_4 + \text{H}_2\text{O}$$

$$2 \text{ R}_2\text{C=NOONa} + 2 \text{ H}_2\text{SO}_4 \longrightarrow 2 \text{ R}_2\text{CO} + \text{N}_2\text{O} + 2 \text{ NaHSO}_4 + \text{H}_2\text{O}$$

6. *Condensation with Aldehydes.* Primary and secondary nitro compounds undergo an aldol-like condensation with aldehydes in the presence of dilute alkali.

$$\text{RCH}_2\text{NO}_2 + 2 \text{ HCHO} \xrightarrow{[\text{OH}^-]} \text{HOCH}_2 - \underset{\underset{\text{NO}_2}{|}}{\overset{\overset{\text{R}}{|}}{\text{C}}} - \text{CH}_2\text{OH}$$

$$\text{R}_2\text{CHNO}_2 + \text{HCHO} \xrightarrow{[\text{OH}^-]} \text{R} - \underset{\underset{\text{NO}_2}{|}}{\overset{\overset{\text{R}}{|}}{\text{C}}} - \text{CH}_2\text{OH}$$

$$\text{RCH}_2\text{NO}_2 + \text{R'CHO} \xrightarrow{[\text{OH}^-]} \underset{\underset{\text{NO}_2}{|}}{\text{RCH}} - \underset{\underset{\text{OH}}{|}}{\text{CHR'}}$$

These nitro alcohols may be reduced readily to amino alcohols (p. 528).

The aliphatic nitro compounds are excellent solvents, but their chief use has been as intermediates for the synthesis of other organic compounds. **Tetranitromethane** is a valuable reagent for the detection of carbon-carbon unsaturation. When a dilute solution in chloroform is added to a solution of an unsaturated compound, a yellow to red color is produced. The simpler olefins and acetylenes give a yellow color, the tetraalkyl substituted ethylenes and simple conjugated dienes (p. 494) give orange to light red colors, and the alkyl substituted dienes give a deep red color. An advantage of the test is that even unreactive double bonds that do not react with bromine or undergo catalytic reduction give a color with tetranitromethane. α,β-Unsaturated carbonyl compounds do not respond to the test.

Tetranitromethane is prepared by the action of fuming nitric acid on acetic anhydride.

$$4 \text{ HONO}_2 + (\text{CH}_3\text{CO})_2\text{O} \longrightarrow \text{C(NO}_2)_4 + \text{CO}_2 + \text{CH}_3\text{COOH} + 3 \text{ H}_2\text{O}$$

Mixtures of tetranitromethane with organic compounds are violent explosives, and fatal accidents have occurred during its use. Only very dilute solutions should be used, and the solutions should not be heated.

Chloropicrin, Cl_3CNO_2, is made by the reaction of picric acid with sodium hypochlorite (p. 391). It is a powerful lachrymator and is used as a tear gas for dispelling mobs and as a warning agent for toxic gases.

REVIEW QUESTIONS
Amines

1. What are amines?
2. How does the use of the terms primary, secondary, and tertiary as applied to amines differ from their use as applied to alcohols?
3. Compare the number of possible alcohols having the molecular formula $C_4H_{10}O$ with the number of possible amines having the formula $C_4H_{11}N$.
4. Show by equations the complete series of reactions that takes place between ethyl bromide and ammonia, and name each organic product.
5. Give a series of equations for the preparation of a pure primary amine from an ester; from an aldehyde or ketone; from an alkyl halide with one less carbon atom than is desired in the amine.
6. How are amines named?
7. Discuss the solubility and boiling point of amines.
8. What is the most characteristic chemical property of amines? Discuss the physical properties of the product of this reaction.
9. Define the terms acid and base. Arrange the following types of compounds in the order of increasing acidity: water, hydronium ion, ammonia, ammonium ion, carbonic acid, mineral acids, alkanes, alcohols. carboxylic acids. Give the conjugate base of each of these types and list in the order of decreasing basicity.
10. Illustrate by reactions two methods for distinguishing between primary, secondary, and tertiary amines.
11. Outline two methods that might be satisfactory for the estimation of primary amines in the presence of other non-basic nitrogenous compounds.
12. Devise a procedure for obtaining in a relatively pure state each component of a mixture of the following compounds: methyl *n*-butyl ketone, caproic acid, di-*n*-butylamine, and *n*-heptyl alcohol.
13. What conclusions can be drawn concerning the chemical nature of a compound which exhibits the following behavior: (*a*) soluble in water, liberates ammonia with cold alkali; (*b*) insoluble in water, evolves ammonia on boiling with alkali, but does not evolve nitrogen on treatment with nitrous acid; (*c*) insoluble in water, does not evolve ammonia on boiling with alkali, but evolves nitrogen on treatment with nitrous acid; (*d*) insoluble in water but soluble in dilute acid, does not react with alkali or nitrous acid.
14. Discuss the preparation and the physical and chemical properties of quaternary ammonium salts and hydroxides. What is choline chloride and what is its importance?
15. What are amine oxides and how are they prepared?
16. Write electronic formulas for each of the following compounds indicating from which atom the electrons were derived: methyldiethylamine, tetraethylammonium iodide, trimethylamine oxide.
17. Give reactions for the preparation of (*a*) dimethylethylamine from methyl and ethyl alcohols; (*b*) *i*-propylamine from *i*-butyric acid; (*c*) tetraethylammonium hydroxide from ethyl bromide; (*d*) *s*-butylamine from methyl ethyl ketone; (*e*) ethylamine from ethyl ether; (*f*) *n*-hexylamine from *n*-amyl bromide.

Amides

18. Give equations for the general methods of preparation of amides.
19. Why is an excess of acetic acid used in the laboratory preparation of acetamide from ammonium acetate?
20. How are amides named? How is substitution on the nitrogen atom indicated?
21. Discuss the physical properties of amides. Compare the boiling points of acetic acid, acetamide, *N*-methylacetamide, and *N*, *N*-dimethylacetamide and explain.
22. Compare the effect of acyl groups on the basicity of water and of ammonia.
23. Compare the acid- and base-catalyzed hydrolyses of amides to the acid- and base-catalyzed hydrolyses of esters.
24. Give equations for the reaction of butyramide, *N*-methylbutyramide, and *N*, *N*-dimethylbutyramide with nitrous acid.
25. Give the steps for the Hofmann method of converting an amide to a primary amine.
26. Of what use are amides?

27. Two compounds have the molecular formula $C_7H_{15}NO$. Both react on long boiling with hydrochloric acid, one giving a product that reduces Fehling's solution, and the other a product that dissolves in dilute alkali. What can be said concerning the structure of the original compounds?

Alkyl Cyanides and Alkyl Isocyanides

28. Summarize the general methods for the preparation of alkyl cyanides.
29. Compare the nomenclature as cyanides with that as nitriles.
30. Compare the basicity of nitriles with that of tertiary amines. Does this difference have any bearing on the solubility of nitriles in water?
31. Give equations for the more important reactions of alkyl cyanides.
32. How are isocyanides prepared?
33. Compare the electronic structure of isocyanides with that for cyanides.
34. Compare the reduction and hydrolysis of isocyanides with the reduction and hydrolysis of cyanides.
35. Give equations for some other common reactions of the isocyanides.
36. Give reactions for the preparation of (*a*) *n*-butyl isocyanide from *n*-propyl cyanide; (*b*) *n*-butyronitrile from *n*-butyric acid; (*c*) ethyl cyanide from propionaldehyde; (*d*) *n*-propyl isocyanide from *n*-butyramide; (*e*) *t*-butyl cyanide from propionamide.

Nitroalkanes

37. What similarity exists between the reactions for the laboratory preparation of alkyl nitrites and nitroalkanes, and the preparation of alkyl cyanides and isocyanides?
38. Discuss the industrial preparation of nitroalkanes.
39. Discuss the solubility of nitroalkanes in water, dilute acid, and dilute alkali, and give an explanation of the facts.
40. What is the "red, white, and blue reaction"?
41. How may primary nitro compounds be converted into amines; into carboxylic acids; into aldehydes?
42. Discuss the condensation of nitro compounds with aldehydes.
43. Give two simple procedures for distinguishing between a nitroalkane and an alkyl nitrite.
44. Write electronic formulas for ethyl nitrite, ethyl nitrate, and nitroethane.
45. Two compounds have the molecular formula $C_5H_{11}NO_2$. One is fairly soluble in water and the other dissolves in dilute alkali or on treatment with tin and hydrochloric acid. The water-soluble compound evolves ammonia on boiling with alkali, and vigorous oxidation of the hydrolysis product yields an acid having a neutralization equivalent of 66. What can be said about the structures of the two compounds? Give the reactions that they undergo.
46. Give chemical reactions that could be used to distinguish between the following pairs of compounds: (*a*) nitroethane and ethyl nitrite; (*b*) acetonitrile and methyl isocyanide; (*c*) acetamide and ammonium acetate; (*d*) acetamide and acetonitrile; (*e*) trimethylammonium chloride and tetramethylammonium chloride.

Chapter 14

ALIPHATIC SULFUR COMPOUNDS

Since sulfur is the element below oxygen in the periodic table, a series of organic compounds analogous to the oxygen compounds are known. In addition to the oxygen analogs, however, a number of types of tri- and tetracovalent sulfur compounds exist for which there are no oxygen analogs.[1]

OXYGEN ANALOGS—DICOVALENT COMPOUNDS

Bond Formula	Electronic Formula	Name
R—S—H	R : S̈ : H	Mercaptans or alkanethiols
R—S—R	R : S̈ : R	Sulfides or thioethers
R—S—S—R	R : S̈ : S̈ : R	Disulfides
R—C̈(=O)—SH	R : C : S̈ : H (with Ö above)	Thioacids
R—C̈(=S)—SH	R : C : S̈ : H (with S̈ above)	Dithioacids
R—C̈(=S)—H	R : C : H (with S̈ above)	Thioaldehydes or thials
R—C̈(=S)—R	R : C : R (with S̈ above)	Thioketones or thiones

---

[1] Previous to the publication in 1916 of the Lewis theory of electronic structure, compounds of this type were considered to contain tetracovalent and hexacovalent sulfur respectively, the oxygen being bound to sulfur by double bonds. The octet theory of Lewis required that the oxygen-sulfur bond be semipolar (p. 189). During the next twenty years several lines of investigation seemed to confirm this viewpoint, but in 1937 experimental results on bond distances were presented which indicated that in the oxygen acids of sulfur, the oxygen really is linked to sulfur by double bonds. It was not until 1944, however, that the semipolar viewpoint was questioned seriously. Since that time further arguments have been presented both in favor of double bonds and against double bonds for elements other than carbon, nitrogen, and oxygen, although carbon-sulfur double bonds generally are accepted. Because the subject still is controversial, the semipolar structure for sulfoxides, sulfinic acids, sulfones, and sulfonic acids has been retained.

TRICOVALENT AND TETRACOVALENT COMPOUNDS

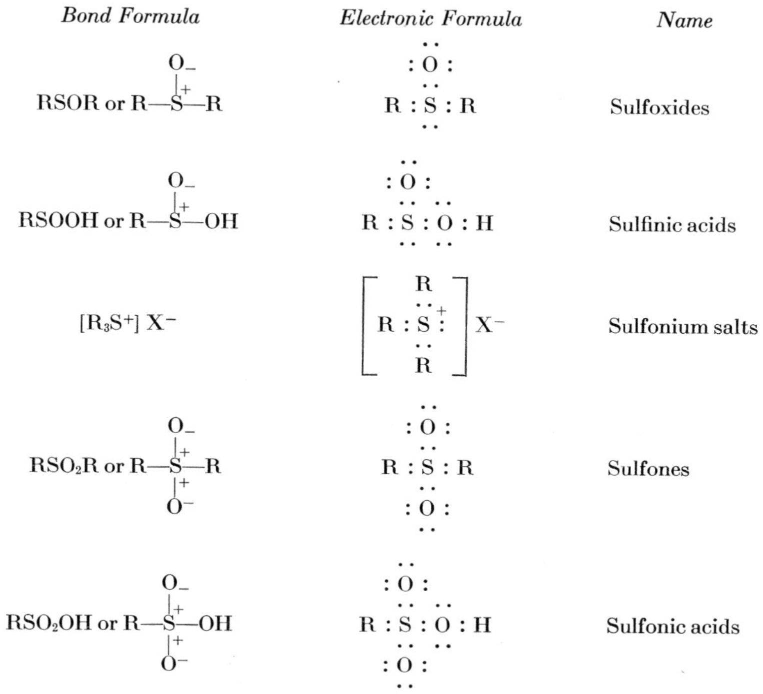

Bond Formula	Electronic Formula	Name

$$\text{RSOR or } R\underset{\underset{+}{|}}{\overset{O_-}{S}}R$$

$$\overset{\cdot\,\cdot}{:\!O\!:} \\ R : \overset{\cdot\,\cdot}{\underset{\cdot\,\cdot}{S}} : R$$

Sulfoxides

$$\text{RSOOH or } R\underset{\underset{+}{|}}{\overset{O_-}{S}}OH$$

$$\overset{\cdot\,\cdot}{:\!O\!:} \\ R : \overset{\cdot\,\cdot}{\underset{\cdot\,\cdot}{S}} : \overset{\cdot\,\cdot}{\underset{\cdot\,\cdot}{O}} : H$$

Sulfinic acids

$$[R_3S^+]\,X^-$$

$$\left[\begin{array}{c} R \\ R : \overset{\cdot\,\cdot}{\underset{\cdot\,\cdot}{S}} : \\ R \end{array}\right] X^-$$

Sulfonium salts

$$\text{RSO}_2\text{R or } R\underset{\underset{+}{|}}{\overset{\overset{O_-}{|}}{\underset{\underset{O^-}{|}}{S}}}R$$

$$\overset{\cdot\,\cdot}{:\!O\!:} \\ R : \overset{\cdot\,\cdot}{\underset{\cdot\,\cdot}{S}} : R \\ \overset{\cdot\,\cdot}{:\!O\!:}$$

Sulfones

$$\text{RSO}_2\text{OH or } R\underset{\underset{+}{|}}{\overset{\overset{O_-}{|}}{\underset{\underset{O^-}{|}}{S}}}OH$$

$$\overset{\cdot\,\cdot}{:\!O\!:} \\ R : \overset{\cdot\,\cdot}{\underset{\cdot\,\cdot}{S}} : \overset{\cdot\,\cdot}{\underset{\cdot\,\cdot}{O}} : H \\ \overset{\cdot\,\cdot}{:\!O\!:}$$

Sulfonic acids

MERCAPTANS

Preparation

1. *From Alkyl Halides or Sulfates, and Sodium Hydrosulfide.* Mercaptans are formed when an alkyl halide is refluxed with an alcoholic solution of sodium hydrosulfide.

$$RX + NaSH \longrightarrow RSH + NaX$$

A more convenient procedure consists of dissolving the alcohol in sulfuric acid, neutralizing with sodium carbonate, and mixing with sodium hydrosulfide solution prepared by saturating sodium hydroxide solution with hydrogen sulfide.

$$ROH + H_2SO_4 \longrightarrow ROSO_3H + H_2O$$

$$2\,ROSO_3H + Na_2CO_3 \longrightarrow 2\,ROSO_3Na + CO_2$$

$$ROSO_3Na + NaSH \longrightarrow RSH + Na_2SO_4$$

Whether alkyl halides or alkyl sulfates are used, some alkyl sulfide always is formed because of the equilibrium

$$RSH + NaSH \rightleftarrows RSNa + H_2S$$

The sodium mercaptide can react with a second mole of alkyl halide or sulfate.

$$RSNa + RX \longrightarrow RSR + NaX$$

The sodium hydrosulfide ordinarily is used in large excess. Because of the alkalinity of sodium hydrosulfide solution, another competing reaction is present, namely loss of mineral acid to give olefins. Hence yields of mercaptans or sulfides are best if the alkyl group is primary, whereas only olefin is formed if it is tertiary.

2. By Reduction of Disulfides. The reduction may be carried out by adding zinc dust to a boiling mixture of disulfide (p. 213) and 50 per cent aqueous sulfuric acid.

$$RSSR + 2 [H] (Zn + H_2SO_4) \longrightarrow 2 RSH$$

Nomenclature

The following examples indicate the usual methods of nomenclature: CH_3SH, methyl mercaptan or methanethiol; $CH_3CH_2CHSHCH_3$, *s*-butyl mercaptan or l-methyl-l-propanethiol. The —*SH* group is known as the *thiol* or *sulfhydryl* group, or more commonly as the *mercapto* group. The last term may be used as a prefix for polyfunctional compounds, for example $HSCH_2$-$COOH$, mercaptoacetic acid.

Physical Properties

If the boiling points of dicovalent sulfur compounds are compared with those of analogous oxygen, nitrogen, and carbon compounds of approximately the same molecular weight (Table 11) it is evident that the boiling points of mercaptans are much more nearly normal than those of alcohols or primary or secondary amines. Although the mercaptans boil somewhat higher than

TABLE 11
BOILING POINTS OF WATER, AMMONIA, HYDROGEN SULFIDE, AND METHANE, AND OF THEIR ALKYL DERIVATIVES

OXYGEN COMPOUNDS			NITROGEN COMPOUNDS			SULFUR COMPOUNDS			CARBON COMPOUNDS		
Compd.	Mol. wt.	B.p. °	Compd.	Mol. wt.	B.p. °	Compd.	Mol. wt.	B.p. °	Compd.	Mol. wt.	B.p. °
H_2O	18	+100	NH_3	17	−38				CH_4	16	−161
CH_3OH	32	+65	CH_3NH_2	31	−7	H_2S	34	−61	C_2H_6	30	−89
C_2H_5OH	46	+78	$C_2H_5NH_2$	45	+17	CH_3SH	48	+6	C_3H_5	44	−42
$(CH_3)_2O$	46	−24	$(CH_3)_2NH$	45	+7						
n-C_3H_7OH	60	+98	n-$C_3H_7NH_2$	59	+49	C_2H_5SH	62	+37	n-C_4H_{10}	58	−1
i-C_3H_7OH	60	+82	$CH_3NHC_2H_5$	59	+32				i-C_4H_{10}	58	−10
$CH_3OC_2H_5$	60	+11	$(CH_3)_3N$	59	+4	$(CH_3)_2S$	62	+38			

hydrocarbons of the same molecular weight, the higher boiling point cannot be ascribed to proton bonding, because ethyl mercaptan and methyl sulfide boil at almost the same temperature. This behavior is in marked contrast to that of the propyl alcohols and methyl ethyl ether, or of methylethylamine and trimethylamine. The rise in boiling points of the series *n*-butane, trimethylamine, methyl ethyl ether, and methyl sulfide can be ascribed to the rise in dipole moment, the measured or estimated values of μ being respectively 0, 0.6, 1.2, and 1.6.

Mercaptans are much less soluble in water than the corresponding alcohols, only 1.5 g. of ethyl mercaptan being soluble in 100 cc. of water at room temperature. This low water solubility also can be ascribed to lack of the ability of sulfur to form proton bonds with water molecules.

Physiological Properties

The volatile mercaptans have an extremely disagreeable odor. Fischer found that the nose can detect one volume of ethyl mercaptan in 50 billion volumes of air. This concentration expressed in terms of weight per cubic centimeter of air is 1/250 of the concentration of sodium which Kirchoff and Bunsen were able to detect by means of the spectroscope. The obnoxious odor of mercaptans decreases with increasing molecular weight, and the odor becomes pleasant above nine carbon atoms. Like hydrogen sulfide, the lower mercaptans are toxic.

Reactions

1. **Salt Formation.** Just as hydrogen sulfide is more acidic than water, the mercaptans are more acidic than alcohols and react with aqueous solutions of strong bases to form salts. Like sodium sulfide these salts are hydrolyzed markedly in aqueous solution.

$$RSH + NaOH \rightleftharpoons RSNa + H_2O$$

The heavy metal salts, such as those of lead, mercury, copper, cadmium, and silver, are insoluble in water. The ease of formation of insoluble mercury salts gave rise to the name mercaptan (*L. mercurium captans* seizing mercury).

2. **Oxidation to Disulfides.** Sodium hypohalite solutions oxidize mercaptans to disulfides at room temperature.

$$2 RSH + I_2 + 2 NaOH \longrightarrow RSSR + 2 NaI + 2 H_2O$$

If a standard iodine solution is used, this reaction is suitable for the quantitative estimation of mercaptans. They are oxidized readily also by air, especially in the presence of ammonia. The oxidation of sulfhydryl groups from the cysteine portion of protein molecules (pp. 229, 235) to disulfide groups and reduction of disulfide to sulfhydryl plays an important part in biological processes.

3. **Oxidation to Sulfonic Acids.** This reaction usually is brought about by heating the mercaptan or a salt such as the lead mercaptide with concentrated nitric acid.

$$RSH + 3 [O] (HNO_3) \longrightarrow RSO_3H$$

$$(RS)_2Pb + 6 [O] (HNO_3) \longrightarrow (RSO_3)_2Pb$$

4. **Ester Formation.** When primary alkanethiols react with carboxylic acids, thioesters and water are formed rather than esters and hydrogen sulfide.

$$RCOOH + HSR \rightleftharpoons RCOSR + H_2O$$

This reaction was the original basis for the assumption that in the esterification of primary alcohols with acids the hydroxyl group is removed from the acid rather than from the alcohol, an assumption which has been proved by the use of the O^{18} isotope (p. 144).

Mercaptans react also with acyl halides to give thioesters.

$$RSH + ClCOR \longrightarrow RSCOR + HCl$$

In contrast to the hydroxyl group, the mercapto group is not replaced readily. For example phosphorus trichloride reacts to give a thioester.

$$RSH + PCl_3 \longrightarrow RSPCl_2 + HCl$$

SULFIDES

Preparation

Sulfides ordinarily are prepared by the reaction of alkyl halides or sulfates with sodium sulfide or sodium mercaptides in alcoholic solution.

$$2\,RX + Na_2S \longrightarrow R_2S + 2\,NaX$$

$$RX + NaSR' \longrightarrow RSR' + NaX$$

The first reaction gives simple sulfides, and the second may be used to prepare mixed sulfides.

Nomenclature

The nomenclature of sulfides is evident from the following examples: $C_2H_5SC_2H_5$, ethyl sulfide or ethylthioethane; $CH_3SCH_2CH(CH_3)_2$, methyl *i*-butyl sulfide or 1-methylthio-2-methylpropane. The Geneva names rarely are used except for polyfunctional compounds. Although names such as diethyl sulfide instead of ethyl sulfide are used, the prefix *di* is unnecessary.

Reactions

1. *Oxidation to Sulfoxides.* At room temperature sulfides react with nitric acid, chromium trioxide, or hydrogen peroxide to give sulfoxides.

$$R-S-R + [O] \ (HNO_3,\ CrO_3,\ or\ H_2O_2) \longrightarrow R-\overset{\overset{\displaystyle O_-}{\underset{+}{|}}}{S}-R \ (RSOR)$$

2. *Oxidation to Sulfones.* Hydrogen peroxide in glacial acetic acid, fuming nitric acid, or potassium permanganate at elevated temperatures oxidizes sulfides to sulfones, which are very resistant to further oxidation.

$$R-S-R + 2\,[O] \ (H_2O_2,\ HNO_3,\ KMnO_4) \longrightarrow R-\overset{\overset{\displaystyle O_-}{\underset{\underset{\displaystyle O^-}{|+}}{|+}}}{S}-R \ (RSO_2R)$$

Oxidation by hydrogen peroxide is catalyzed by strong acids. The mechanism of catalysis appears to be the formation of the conjugate acid of hydrogen peroxide, which, because of the positive charge on one oxygen atom, can transfer $\left[\overset{..}{\underset{..}{OH^+}} \right]$ to the unshared pair of electrons of the sulfur atom more readily than can hydrogen peroxide.

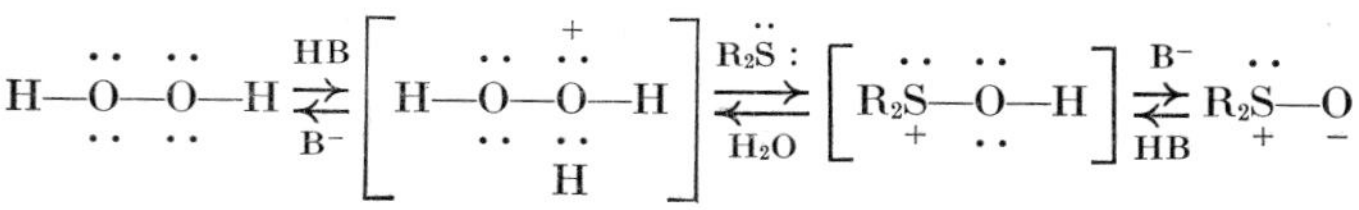

$$H\!-\!\overset{..}{\underset{..}{O}}\!-\!\overset{..}{\underset{..}{O}}\!-\!H \underset{B^-}{\overset{HB}{\rightleftarrows}} \left[H\!-\!\overset{..}{\underset{..}{O}}\!-\!\overset{+}{\overset{..}{\underset{H}{O}}}\!-\!H\right] \overset{R_2\overset{..}{S}:}{\underset{H_2O}{\rightleftarrows}} \left[R_2\overset{+}{S}\!-\!\overset{..}{\underset{..}{O}}\!-\!H\right] \underset{HB}{\overset{B^-}{\rightleftarrows}} R_2\overset{..}{S}\!-\!\overset{..}{\underset{-}{O}}$$

3. *Formation of Sulfonium Salts.* Sulfides react with alkyl halides to give sulfonium salts analogous to the reaction of tertiary amines to give quaternary ammonium salts.

$$R:\overset{..}{\underset{R}{S}}: \,+ R:X \longrightarrow \left[R\!-\!\overset{..}{\underset{R}{S}}\!-\!\overset{+}{R}\right]X^-$$

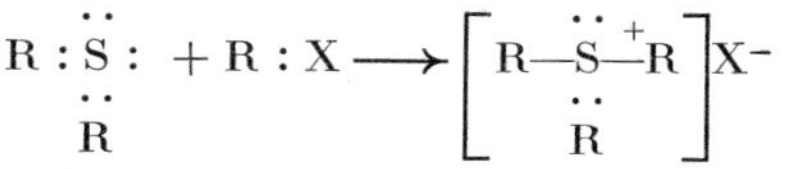

If the R groups are not all alike, this reaction is complicated by the fact that the sulfonium salts dissociate more readily than quaternary ammonium salts. For example the following reactions may occur leading to a mixture of all the possible sulfonium salts.

$$R_2S + R'X \longrightarrow [R_2R'S^+]X^-$$
$$[R_2R'S^+]X^- \rightleftarrows RSR' + RX$$
$$RSR' + R'X \longrightarrow [RR'_2S^+]X^-$$
$$R_2S + RX \longrightarrow [R_3S^+]X^-$$
$$[RR'_2S^+]X^- \rightleftarrows R'_2S + RX$$
$$R'_2S + R'X \longrightarrow [R'_3S^+]X^-$$

Reaction of sulfides with halogen gives dihalides which probably have structures analogous to those of the sulfonium salts.

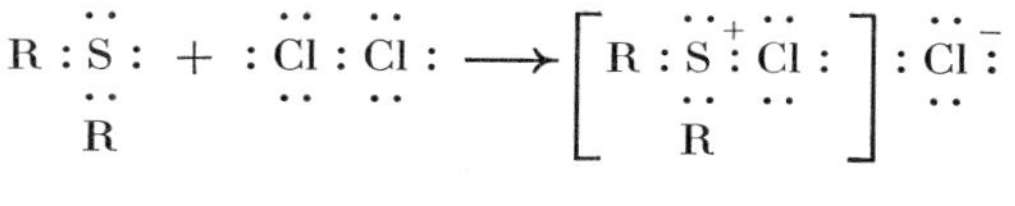

$$R:\overset{..}{\underset{R}{S}}: \,+\, :\overset{..}{\underset{..}{Cl}}:\overset{..}{\underset{..}{Cl}}: \longrightarrow \left[R:\overset{..}{\underset{R}{S}}\overset{+}{:}\overset{..}{\underset{..}{Cl}}:\right] :\overset{..}{\underset{..}{Cl}}\overset{-}{:}$$

DISULFIDES

Preparation

1. ***By Oxidation of Mercaptans*** (p. 211).
2. ***From Alkyl Halides or Sulfates, and Sodium Disulfide.***

$$2\,RX + Na_2S_2 \longrightarrow RSSR + 2\,NaX$$

Sodium disulfide is prepared by dissolving an equivalent amount of sulfur in a concentrated aqueous solution of sodium sulfide. The aqueous solution is diluted with alcohol, heated to boiling, and the alkyl halide added.

Nomenclature

Disulfides are named as such; for example $(CH_3)_2S_2$ is methyl disulfide, and $CH_3SSC_2H_5$ is methyl ethyl disulfide.

Reactions

1. **Reduction to Mercaptans.** The reduction by means of zinc dust and acid has been discussed (p. 210). A second interesting method consists of the scission with metallic sodium.

$$RSSR + 2\ Na \longrightarrow 2\ RSNa$$

The rate of this reaction increases rapidly with increasing molecular weight of the alkyl group. Methyl and ethyl disulfides are very unreactive, whereas the reaction of *n*-butyl disulfide must be controlled by cooling.

2. **Oxidation to Sulfonic Acids.** Like the mercaptans, disulfides may be oxidized to sulfonic acids by heating with strong oxidizing agents such as 50 per cent nitric acid.

$$RSSR + 5\ [O]\ (HNO_3) + H_2O \longrightarrow 2\ RSO_2OH$$

THIOALDEHYDES AND THIOKETONES

The thioaldehydes and thioketones can be prepared from aldehydes or ketones and hydrogen sulfide in the presence of aqueous or alcoholic hydrogen chloride.

$$RCHO + H_2S \xrightarrow{HCl} R\overset{\overset{\displaystyle S}{\|}}{C}H + H_2O$$

$$R_2CO + H_2S \xrightarrow{HCl} R_2C{=}S + H_2O$$

The aliphatic compounds polymerize to trimers $(RCHS)_3$ and $(R_2CS)_3$, which are cyclic trisulfides and can be oxidized to trisulfones. It is said that the odor of thioacetone is so obnoxious that Baumann and Fromm had to abandon their work with the compound because of the protests of the city of Freiburg (Germany).

THIOCARBOXYLIC ACIDS AND DITHIOCARBOXYLIC ACIDS

Thiocarboxylic acids may be prepared by the action of phosphorus penta-sulfide on a carboxylic acid.

$$RCOOH + P_2S_5 \longrightarrow RCOSH + P_2OS_4$$

Structural theory calls for the existence of a second isomer, RCSOH. Only one substance has been isolated, however, because the two forms readily interconvert; that is they are tautomeric (pp. 203, 553).

$$R{-}\overset{\overset{\displaystyle O}{\|}}{C}{-}SH \rightleftarrows R{-}\overset{\overset{\displaystyle OH}{|}}{C}{=}S$$

The esters of the two structures are stable isomers. One isomer may be made from an acid chloride and a mercaptan and the other from an imido ester and hydrogen sulfide.

$$RCOCl + HSR \longrightarrow RC\overset{\overset{\displaystyle O}{\|}}{-}SR + HCl$$

$$RC\overset{\overset{\displaystyle NH}{\|}}{-}OR + 2\,H_2S \longrightarrow RC\overset{\overset{\displaystyle S}{\|}}{-}OR + NH_4SH$$

Thioamides on the other hand are again tautomeric.

$$R-\overset{\overset{\displaystyle S}{\|}}{C}-NH_2 \rightleftarrows R-\overset{\overset{\displaystyle SH}{|}}{C}=NH$$

The dithioacids are made by the reaction of carbon disulfide with Grignard reagents.

$$S{=}C{=}S + RMgX \longrightarrow R-\overset{\overset{\displaystyle S}{\|}}{C}-SMgX \xrightarrow{[H^+]} R-\overset{\overset{\displaystyle S}{\|}}{C}-SH$$

They are colored oils having an unbearable odor and are oxidized by air.

$$2\,RCSSH + [O](air) \longrightarrow R\overset{\overset{\displaystyle S}{\|}}{C}-S-S-\overset{\overset{\displaystyle S}{\|}}{C}-R + H_2O$$

SULFONIUM SALTS

Sulfonium salts, $[R_3S^+]X^-$, ordinarily formed by the reaction of sulfides with alkyl iodides (p. 213), are strongly ionized in aqueous solution. They react with silver hydroxide to give sulfonium hydroxides.

$$[R_3S^+]X^- + AgOH \longrightarrow [R_3S^+]\,OH^- + AgX$$

Sulfonium hydroxides are strong bases analogous to the quaternary ammonium hydroxides' (p. 194). Likewise they decompose in a similar fashion to give sulfides and olefins.

$$[(C_2H_5)_3S^+]OH^- \xrightarrow{Heat} (C_2H_5)_2S + C_2H_4 + H_2O$$

Sulfonium salts dissociate more easily than quaternary ammonium salts.

$$[R_3S^+]X^- \rightleftarrows R_2S + RX$$

Although the sulfur atom in the sulfonium ion still has an unshared pair of electrons, the positive charge holds the pair too strongly to permit reaction with a second molecule of alkyl halide to give a tetraalkylsulfonium ion with two positive charges of the type $[R_4S^{++}]2\,X^-$. Sulfonium salts react with halogen and with some metallic salts to give stable complexes, which probably have this type of structure.

$$[R_3S^+]X^- + X_2 \longrightarrow [R_3SX^{++}]\,2\,X^-$$

Selenium, in which the valence electrons are farther from the nucleus, is able to form tetraalkylselenonium dihalides of the type $[R_4Se^{++}]2\,X^-$.

SULFOXIDES

Sulfoxides ordinarily are prepared by the reaction of sulfides with the theoretical amount of 30 per cent hydrogen peroxide in acetone or acetic acid solution at room temperature.

$$R_2S + H_2O_2 \longrightarrow R_2SO + H_2O$$

They may be prepared also by the hydrolysis of dihalides (p. 213),

$$[R_2\overset{+}{S}Cl]\,Cl^- + H_2O \rightleftarrows R_2SO + 2\,HCl$$

and by the reaction of Grignard reagents with thionyl chloride or with alkyl sulfites.

$$2\,RMgX + SOCl_2 \longrightarrow R_2SO + 2\,MgX_2$$

$$2\,RMgX + SO(OR)_2 \longrightarrow R_2SO + 2\,Mg(OR)_2$$

Sulfoxides may be reduced to sulfides with zinc and acetic acid, or oxidized to sulfones with excess hydrogen peroxide in glacial acetic acid at 100° or with alkaline permanganate or hot fuming nitric acid.

If one of the R groups of a sulfoxide contains hydrogen on the carbon atom α to the sulfoxide group, heating with hydrochloric acid causes a scission of the sulfoxide with the formation of an aldehyde or ketone and a mercaptan.

$$RCH_2SOR + HCl \longrightarrow \left[\begin{array}{c} OH \\ | \\ RCH_2\underset{+}{S}R \end{array}\right] Cl^- \longrightarrow H_2O + [RCH{=}\overset{+}{S}R]Cl^-$$

$$[RCH{=}\overset{+}{S}R]Cl^- + H_2O \longrightarrow RCHO + HSR + HCl$$

Ordinarily sulfoxides are named as such. In the Geneva system the *SO* group is called a *sulfinyl group*. Thus $C_4H_9SOC_4H_9$ is *n*-butyl sulfoxide or 1-butylsulfinylbutane, and $CH_3SOCH(CH_3)_2$ is methyl *i*-propyl sulfoxide or 2-methylsulfinylpropane. They are odorless, colorless solids, insoluble in water and soluble in organic solvents.

SULFINIC ACIDS

Sulfinic acids may be obtained by passing sulfur dioxide into a solution of Grignard reagent and liberating the free acid from the halomagnesium salt by adding mineral acid.

$$RMgX + SO_2 \longrightarrow R\overset{O_-}{\underset{}{\overset{|+}{S}}}{-}OMgX \overset{HX}{\rightarrow} R\overset{O_-}{\underset{}{\overset{|+}{S}}}{-}OH + MgX_2$$

Their salts can be obtained also by reducing sulfonyl chlorides (p. 219) with zinc dust or with sodium sulfite.

$$2\,RSO_2Cl + 2\,Zn \longrightarrow (RSO_2)_2Zn + ZnCl_2$$

$$RSO_2Cl + Na_2SO_3 + 2\,NaOH \longrightarrow RSO_2Na + Na_2SO_4 + NaCl + H_2O$$

The sulfinic acids can be oxidized to sulfonic acids

$$RSOOH + [O] \text{ (air)} \longrightarrow RSO_2OH$$

and reduced to mercaptans.

$$RSO_2H + 4\,[H]\ (Zn + H_2SO_4) \longrightarrow RSH + 2\,H_2O$$

The last reaction affords proof that the sulfur atom in sulfinic and sulfonic acids is united directly to carbon.

SULFONES

Sulfones usually are prepared by oxidizing sulfides or sulfoxides at elevated temperature with an excess of hydrogen peroxide in glacial acetic acid or with fuming nitric acid or potassium permanganate (p. 212). They are formed also by the reaction of alkali sulfinates with alkyl halides.

$$RSO_2Na + RBr \longrightarrow R_2SO_2 + NaBr$$

Alkyl sulfinates might be expected from this reaction, but the alkyl group combines with the unshared pair of electrons on the sulfur atom of the sulfinate ion, $[R\!-\!\overset{..}{S}O_2{}^-]$, rather than with an unshared pair on an oxygen atom.

Reaction of sulfinates with acyl halides yields α-keto sulfones, and with sulfonyl halides, disulfones.

$$RSO_2Na + ClCOR \longrightarrow RSO_2COR + NaCl$$

$$RSO_2Na + ClSO_2R \longrightarrow RSO_2SO_2R + NaCl$$

Sulfones are colorless stable solids usually distillable without decomposition. In contrast to the sulfoxides, they are not readily reduced to sulfides. Some can be reduced to sulfides by heating with sulfur near the boiling point. If heated with Raney nickel containing adsorbed hydrogen, the sulfur is removed completely, yielding saturated hydrocarbons.

$$R_2SO_2 + 3\,H_2 + Ni \longrightarrow 2\,RH + 2\,H_2O + NiS$$

The same type of reaction takes place with sulfoxides, sulfides, and mercaptans.

When sulfones are heated with selenium, alkyl selenides and sulfur dioxide are formed.

$$R_2SO_2 + Se \longrightarrow R_2Se + SO_2$$

When sulfones are heated with metallic sodium, the sodium sulfinate is formed. The alkyl groups that remain combine to give a saturated hydrocarbon, and also undergo disproportionation (p. 87) to alkene and alkane.

$$2\,C_2H_5SO_2C_2H_5 + 2\,Na \longrightarrow 2\,C_2H_5SO_2Na + C_4H_{10}\ (\text{with }C_2H_4 + C_2H_6)$$

The sulfone group has an activating effect on hydrogen attached to an α carbon atom, analogous to that of a carbonyl group (pp. 545, 552).

Disulfones of the type RSO_2SO_2R are cleaved by alkali to give sulfinate and sulfonate.

$$RSO_2SO_2R + 2\ NaOH \longrightarrow RSO_2Na + RSO_3Na + H_2O$$

Sulfones usually are named as such. In the Geneva system the SO_2 *group* is called *sulfonyl*, and sulfones are named as sulfonyl derivatives of saturated hydrocarbons. Thus $CH_3SO_2CH_3$ is methyl sulfone or methylsulfonylmethane, and $CH_3CH_2CH_2CH_2SO_2CH(CH_3)_2$ is *i*-propyl *n*-butyl sulfone or 1-(methylethylsulfonyl) butane.

SULFONIC ACIDS AND DERIVATIVES

Preparation of Sulfonic Acids

1. *By the Oxidation of Mercaptans.*

$$RSH + 3\ [O]\ (HNO_3) \longrightarrow RSO_3H$$

Frequently mercaptans are purified as the lead mercaptides, and the latter are oxidized directly to lead salts of sulfonic acids. The free acid may be obtained by passing hydrogen chloride into an alcoholic suspension of the lead sulfonate.

2. *From Alkyl Halides and Alkali Sulfite.*

$$RX + Na_2SO_3 \longrightarrow [RSO_3^-]Na^+ + NaX$$

This reaction is another example of the tendency for carbon-sulfur bond formation in preference to carbon-oxygen bond formation (cf. sulfones, and alkyl thiocyanates, p. 251). The sulfite ion has an unshared pair of electrons on sulfur as well as on oxygen, but salts of sulfonic acids are formed rather than salts of acid sulfites. The free sulfonic acids can be obtained by passing dry hydrogen chloride into an alcoholic solution of the sodium salt, the sulfonic acid being soluble and the sodium chloride insoluble in alcohol.

3. *From Derivatives of Sulfonic Acids.*
Sulfonyl chlorides and esters of sulfonic acids are purified readily by distillation and may be hydrolyzed to the sulfonic acid.

$$RSO_2Cl + H_2O \longrightarrow RSO_3H + HCl$$

$$RSO_2OR + H_2O \xrightarrow{[H^+]} RSO_3H + HOR$$

Since the sulfonic acids are nonvolatile, the hydrochloric acid, alcohol, and water may be removed by vacuum distillation leaving the pure acid as a residue.

4. *Addition of Bisulfite to Double Bonds.*
Aldehydes and methyl ketones usually add bisulfite to give bisulfite addition compounds, which are the sodium salts of hydroxy sulfonic acids (p. 165).

$$R\overset{\text{H}}{\underset{}{C}}=O + NaHSO_3 \longrightarrow R\overset{\text{H}}{\underset{\underset{SO_3Na}{|}}{C}}-OH$$

If a carbon-carbon double bond is conjugated with the carbonyl group, that is if it is in the α,β position to the carbonyl group, it also will add bisulfite.

$$\underset{\text{Mesityl oxide}}{\overset{\displaystyle CH_3}{CH_3C}\!\!=\!\!CH\!-\!\underset{\displaystyle O}{\overset{\displaystyle \|}{C}}CH_3} + 2\ NaHSO_3 \longrightarrow CH_3\underset{\displaystyle SO_3Na}{\overset{\displaystyle CH_3}{C}}\!-\!CH_2\!-\!\underset{\displaystyle SO_3Na}{\overset{\displaystyle OH}{C}}\!-\!CH_3$$

Although both the double bond and the carbonyl group react, only the sulfonic acid group formed by addition to the carbonyl group is removed readily.

$$CH_3\!-\!\underset{\displaystyle SO_3Na}{\overset{\displaystyle CH_3}{C}}\!-\!CH_2\!-\!\underset{\displaystyle SO_3Na}{\overset{\displaystyle OH}{C}}\!-\!CH_3 + HCl \longrightarrow CH_3\!-\!\underset{\displaystyle SO_3Na}{\overset{\displaystyle CH_3}{C}}\!-\!CH_2\!-\!\underset{\displaystyle O}{\overset{\displaystyle \|}{C}}\!-\!CH_3 + SO_2 + NaCl + H_2O$$

The simple olefins add bisulfite in the presence of oxygen or nitrite. Only in a few cases, however, for example from *i*-butylene, are the yields good.

5. **Sulfonation of Paraffin Hydrocarbons.** Paraffin hydrocarbons do not react appreciably with concentrated sulfuric acid. Fuming sulfuric acid reacts with the higher hydrocarbons, and chlorosulfonic acid, $ClSO_3H$, reacts readily enough with the branched chain hydrocarbons to be used to remove them from normal hydrocarbons. Although sulfonic acids have been reported as products of these reactions, they have not been isolated in a pure state in good yield and the identification is uncertain. It is possible that oxidation has introduced double bonds into the molecule which have added sulfuric acid to give esters of sulfuric acid.

Nomenclature

The Geneva system commonly is used in which the suffix *sulfonic acid* is added to the name of the hydrocarbon, for example CH_3SO_3H, methanesulfonic acid. For higher molecular weight compounds the alkyl group frequently is named, for example $C_{12}H_{25}SO_3H$, laurylsulfonic acid, and $C_{16}H_{33}SO_3H$, cetylsulfonic acid, but this practice should be discontinued. Unobjectionable names are dodecanesulfonic acid and hexadecanesulfonic acid.

Reactions of Sulfonic Acids and Their Derivatives

In contrast to carboxylic acids, the sulfonic acids are strong acids. Because of almost complete ionization, they are very soluble in water, insoluble in saturated hydrocarbons, and relatively nonvolatile.

Methanesulfonic acid reacts with thionyl chloride or phosphorus trichloride to give good yields of methanesulfonyl chloride, and the reactions should be general.

$$CH_3SO_2OH + SOCl_2 \longrightarrow CH_3SO_2Cl + HCl + SO_2$$

$$3\ CH_3SO_2OH + PCl_3 \longrightarrow 3\ CH_3SO_2Cl + P(OH)_3$$

Usually the sulfonyl halides have been prepared by the action of phosphorus pentachloride on the sodium salt.

$$RSO_2ONa + PCl_5 \longrightarrow RSO_2Cl + POCl_3 + NaCl$$

If a high temperature is used, the sulfonyl chloride group is replaced by halogen.

$$RSO_2Cl + PCl_5 \longrightarrow RCl + SOCl_2 + POCl_3$$

Phosphorus trihalides reduce the sulfonyl halide to a disulfide.

$$2 RSO_2X + 5 PX_3 \longrightarrow RSSR + 4 POX_3 + PX_5$$

Sulfonyl chlorides may be prepared also by the action of chlorine and water on a variety of sulfur compounds. One of the best methods starts with disulfides.

$$RSSR + 5 Cl_2 + 4 H_2O \longrightarrow 2 RSO_2Cl + 8 HCl$$

Another good method uses alkyl thiocyanates. Care must be exercised in carrying out this reaction because of the toxicity of the cyanogen chloride produced.

$$RSCN + 3 Cl_2 + 2 H_2O \longrightarrow RSO_2Cl + ClCN + 4 HCl$$

A third procedure starting with alkyl isothioureas no longer is recommended because violent explosions have been reported.

$$RSC\overset{NH}{\underset{NH_2}{\big<}} + 3 Cl_2 + 2 H_2O \longrightarrow RSO_2Cl + ClC\overset{\overset{+}{N}H_2Cl^-}{\underset{NH_2}{\big<}} + 3 HCl$$

All of these oxidations are carried out in the presence of water despite the fact that an acid chloride is produced. The sulfonyl chlorides are very insoluble in water, and their rate of reaction with water is so slow that they may be removed before any appreciable hydrolysis has taken place.

Sulfonic acids do not give satisfactory yields of esters by direct esterification, or of amides by heating ammonium salts. Hence these derivatives always are made from the sulfonyl chlorides. Because of the slow rate of hydrolysis, the reactions may be carried out in the presence of water, usually with the addition of sodium hydroxide (cf. Schotten-Baumann reaction, p. 413).

$$RSO_2Cl + HOR' + NaOH \longrightarrow RSO_2OR' + NaCl + H_2O$$

$$RSO_2Cl + NH_3 + NaOH \longrightarrow RSO_2NH_2 + NaCl + H_2O$$

Sulfonamides are characterized by the relatively high acidity of the hydrogen atoms attached to nitrogen. They are sufficiently acidic to form stable salts with strong alkalies in aqueous solutions.

$$RSO_2NH_2 + NaOH \longrightarrow [RSO_2\overset{-}{N}H]\overset{+}{Na} + H_2O$$

Therefore sulfonamides derived from ammonia or primary amines are soluble in dilute sodium hydroxide solutions.

Sulfonic esters behave more like sulfuric esters than like carboxylic esters. They are hydrolyzed more readily than carboxylic esters by water and like sulfuric esters have an alkylating action. Thus ammonia yields amine salts rather than sulfonamides.

$$RSO_2OR' + NH_3 \longrightarrow [RSO_2O^-][^+NH_3R]$$

When heated with alcohols, ethers are formed.

$$RSO_2OR' + HOR'' \longrightarrow RSO_2OH + R'OR''.$$

Reaction with Grignard reagents gives hydrocarbons.

$$RSO_2OR' + R''MgX \longrightarrow R'R'' + [RSO_2O^-]^+MgX$$

When sodium alkylsulfonates are fused with sodium hydroxide, the products are olefin, water, and sodium sulfite.

$$C_2H_5SO_3Na + NaOH \longrightarrow C_2H_4 + Na_2SO_3 + H_2O$$

INDIVIDUAL SULFUR COMPOUNDS

n-Butyl mercaptan has been isolated as a constituent of the malodorous secretion of skunks. **Mustard gas,** *β-chloroethyl sulfide,* is one of the more powerful vesicants (blistering agents) used in chemical warfare. It is not a gas but a heavy oily liquid boiling at 217°. It is made by the reaction of ethylene and sulfur monochloride.

$$2 CH_2{=}CH_2 + S_2Cl_2 \longrightarrow ClCH_2CH_2SCH_2CH_2Cl + S$$

It may be made also by a process which avoids the presence of sulfur in the final product.

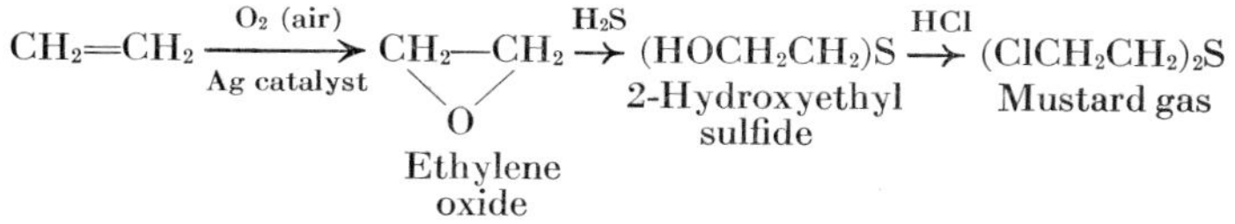

$$CH_2{=}CH_2 \xrightarrow[\text{Ag catalyst}]{O_2 \text{ (air)}} \underset{\substack{\text{Ethylene} \\ \text{oxide}}}{CH_2{-}CH_2} \xrightarrow{H_2S} \underset{\substack{\text{2-Hydroxyethyl} \\ \text{sulfide}}}{(HOCH_2CH_2)S} \xrightarrow{HCl} \underset{\text{Mustard gas}}{(ClCH_2CH_2)_2S}$$

Although not used during World War II, enormous quantities of mustard gas were manufactured in the United States, which possibly acted as a deterrent to its use by the enemy.

A large amount of work has been done in attempts to correlate vesicant action with structure. It has been found that the halogen must be on a carbon atom β to the sulfur atom. For example $ClCH_2CH_2SCH_3$ has properties similar to mustard gas but $ClCH_2CH_2CH_2SCH_3$ and $ClCH_2SCH_3$ do not. These observations have led to the view that the vesicant action is related to the ability to form a sulfonium chloride having a three-membered ring.

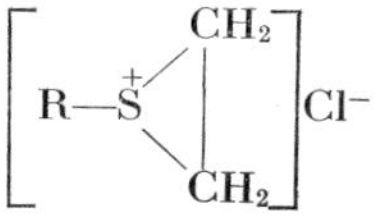

$$\left[R{-}\overset{+}{S} \Big\backslash\!\!\!\Big\langle \begin{matrix} CH_2 \\ | \\ CH_2 \end{matrix} \right] Cl^-$$

Oil of garlic is a complex mixture of which the chief constituent appears to be allyl disulfide, $(CH_2{=}CHCH_2)_2S_2$. **Thiokols** are high molecular weight linear polymeric disulfides and polysulfides having rubber-like properties (p. 503). **Sulfonal** is a soporific which at one time had considerable use, although now it has been replaced almost completely by the barbiturates (p. 462). It is a disulfone and is made from acetone and ethyl mercaptan. Although ketones do not form acetals directly (p. 166), they readily form thioacetals, which can be oxidized to disulfones.

$$\begin{array}{c} CH_3 \\ \diagdown \\ C{=}O + 2\ HSC_2H_5 \longrightarrow \\ \diagup \\ CH_3 \end{array} \qquad \begin{array}{c} CH_3 \quad SC_2H_5 \\ \diagdown \diagup \\ C \\ \diagup \diagdown \\ CH_3 \quad SC_2H_5 \end{array} \xrightarrow{KMnO_4} \begin{array}{c} CH_3 \quad SO_2C_2H_5 \\ \diagdown \diagup \\ C \\ \diagup \diagdown \\ CH_3 \quad SO_2C_2H_5 \end{array}$$

Acetone ethyl thioacetal   Sulfonal

Trional, $\begin{array}{c} CH_3 \quad SO_2C_2H_5 \\ \diagdown \diagup \\ C \\ \diagup \diagdown \\ C_2H_5 \quad SO_2C_2H_5 \end{array}$ **,** and **tetronal,** $\begin{array}{c} C_2H_5 \quad SO_2C_2H_5 \\ \diagdown \diagup \\ C \\ \diagup \diagdown \\ C_2H_5 \quad SO_2C_2H_5 \end{array}$ **,** are increasingly effective, and smaller amounts may be used to produce a given effect. At the time that this type of soporific was used, however, trional and tetronal could not compete with sulfonal because the starting points for their synthesis, methyl ethyl ketone and ethyl ketone, were not easily available.

The salts of many sulfonic acids having large hydrocarbon radicals are used as wetting agents and detergents (p. 355). The Aerosols (not to be confused with aerosols), for example, are manufactured by the addition of sodium bisulfite to long-chain alkyl esters of maleic acid (p. 545).

$$\begin{array}{c} CH{-}COOR \\ \| \\ CH{-}COOR \end{array} + NaHSO_3 \longrightarrow \begin{array}{c} CH_2COOR \\ | \\ CHCOOR \\ | \\ SO_3Na \end{array}$$

Methanesulfonyl chloride is used in research work for the preparation of methanesulfonates, particularly in the field of carbohydrates (p. 287).

REVIEW QUESTIONS

1. List the types of sulfur compounds that have oxygen analogs and give reactions illustrating the methods for preparing them. What types have no common oxygen analogs?
2. (a) Compare the boiling points of water, ammonia, and hydrogen sulfide, and their alkyl derivatives and give an explanation of the facts.
   (b) Compare the solubilities of these compounds in water, and explain.
3. Give balanced equations for (a) the mild oxidation (NaOX), and (b) the vigorous oxidation (HNO_3) of 1-butanethiol.
4. Compare the chemical properties of ethyl ether and ethyl sulfide.
5. Discuss the reaction of acetic acid with ethyl mercaptan and its bearing on the mechanism of esterification. What more direct proof has been given that this view is correct?
6. Compare the chemical properties of thioaldehydes and thioketones with those of aldehydes and ketones.
7. Give equations for the methods of preparing alkanesulfonic acids. How are derivatives of the sulfonic acids prepared?
8. Give a chemical proof that in sulfonic acids, the sulfur is united directly to carbon.

9. What chemical reactions may be used to distinguish between (*a*) ethyl ethanesulfonate and ethyl sulfite; (*b*) *i*-butyl mercaptan and ethyl sulfide; (*c*) butyl sulfoxide and butyl sulfone; (*d*) *n*-propyl sulfide and *n*-propyl disulfide; (*e*) methanesulfonyl chloride and trimethylsulfonium chloride.

10. Write electronic formulas for each of the following compounds indicating from which atom the electrons were derived: sodium ethyl sulfate, methyl methanesulfonate, trimethylsulfonium iodide, methyl ethyl sulfone, *i*-propyl sulfoxide, and ethyl sulfite. For each of these compounds give formulas using the customary methods for indicating covalent, semipolar, and ionic bonds.

11. Give reactions for the preparation of (*a*) 2-propanethiol from *i*-propyl alcohol; (*b*) *i*-butyl sulfone from 2-methyl-1-propanol; (*c*) dithioacetic acid from methyl iodide; (*d*) 2-methylpropanesulfonic acid from methylethylcarbinol; (*e*) trimethylsulfonium hydroxide from dimethyl sulfide; (*f*) ethyl butanesulfonate from butanesulfonic acid.

Chapter 15

PROTEINS, AMINO ACIDS, AND PEPTIDES

Proteins are complex compounds of high molecular weight that yield α-amino acids, RCH(NH₂)COOH, on hydrolysis. Proteins are present in all living tissue, but certain tissues, such as seeds and flesh, contain larger amounts than others, such as fatty and structural tissues. Plants are the ultimate source of all proteins, since plants alone are able to synthesize amino acids from inorganic nitrogen compounds. In this process the plants are aided by soil microorganisms. The nitrite bacteria change ammonia to nitrites, and nitrate bacteria change nitrites to nitrates. The nitrates are converted by the plant first into α-amino acids and then into proteins. Other soil bacteria are able to change organic nitrogen into ammonia, thus completing the cycle. In addition certain soil bacteria in conjunction with the plants on whose roots they grow, namely the legumes, are capable of converting atmospheric nitrogen into amino acids. Some soil organisms can convert nitrogen into ammonium ion nonsymbiotically, and still others are able to carry out the reverse processes of reduction of nitrate and nitrite to nitrogen and ammonia. These various processes, known as the **nitrogen cycle,** are illustrated diagrammatically in Fig. 30.

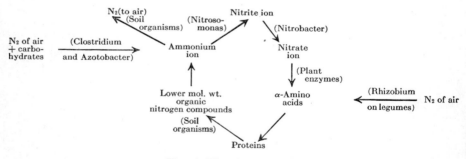

Fig. 30. The nitrogen cycle.

Because of the high molecular weight of the proteins and the similarity in composition of the amino acids, it is not possible to determine the empirical formulas of proteins from the elementary analysis. The elementary composition of all proteins is approximately 50 per cent carbon, 7 per cent hydrogen, 16 per cent nitrogen, 25 per cent oxygen, and 0–2 per cent sulfur. Phosphorus, iron, copper, and other elements also may be present. Proteins, when mixed with non-nitrogenous substances as in foodstuffs, usually are estimated by determining the total nitrogen content and dividing by 0.16.

The proteins are classified into **simple proteins,** yielding only α-amino acids on hydrolysis, and **conjugated proteins,** which yield α-amino acids and one or more groups of a nonprotein nature. The latter are known as **prosthetic groups** (Gr. *prosthesis* an addition). Since the exact structure of individual proteins is unknown, the further classification of proteins is arbitrary and is based largely on their solubility characteristics.

Simple Proteins

Albumins are soluble in water, coagulated by heat and precipitated from solution on saturation with ammonium sulfate. Examples are *serum albumin* from blood serum, *ovalbumin* from egg white, and *lactalbumin* from milk.

Globulins are insoluble in water but soluble in dilute salt solutions, for example 5 per cent sodium chloride solution, and are precipitated by half-saturation with ammonium sulfate. They are soluble also in dilute solutions of strong acids and alkalies. They occur in serum and tissue and make up largely the proteins of seeds and nuts.

Prolamines are insoluble in water and absolute alcohol but soluble in 70–80 per cent ethyl alcohol, and are obtained principally from cereal seeds. Zein from corn is prepared industrially.

Glutelins are insoluble in water and dilute salt solutions but are soluble in dilute solutions of strong acids and alkalies. They occur in cereal seeds and are the proteins that remain after the removal of albumins, globulins, and prolamines.

Scleroproteins (albuminoids) are soluble only in concentrated solutions of strong acids and alkalies. They are the fibrous proteins having a supporting or protective function in the animal organism. Submembers are the *collagen* of the skin, tendons, and bones, the *elastins* of elastic tissues such as tendons and arteries, and the *keratins* from hair, nail, and horn.

Histones are soluble in water but are precipitated by dilute ammonia solution. They are basic compounds and occur combined as salts with acidic substances such as nucleic acids (p. 462) or heme (p. 450) in animal tissues.

Protamines are soluble in water, not coagulated by heat, and precipitated from aqueous solutions by the addition of alcohol. They are more basic than histones and simpler in structure, and are combined as salts with nucleic acids in ripe fish sperm.

Conjugated Proteins

Nucleoproteins are proteins combined with nucleic acids (p. 462), either as salts or by covalent bonds. They occur in the nucleus of every cell, and sometimes in the cytoplasm as well.

Glycoproteins are proteins combined with a carbohydrate but do not contain phosphoric acid, purines, or pyrimidines. They are the *mucins* and *mucoids* (mucus-like substances) of bone, tendons, fish eggs, snails, and other tissue and glandular secretions.

Phosphoproteins have only phosphoric acid as a prosthetic group and occur, for example, in casein of milk and in egg yolk.

Chromoproteins are colored proteins. They contain a metallic element in the molecule, for example iron, magnesium, copper, manganese, vanadium, or cobalt, and may contain a prosthetic group, especially a metalloporphyrin (p. 450). *Hemoglobins* from red blood cells and *hemocyanins* from the blood of invertebrates are examples.

Structure of Proteins

Because of the complexity of the proteins, their high molecular weights, the large number, the complex mixtures that occur naturally, and the similarity in their chemical and physical properties, it is difficult to be certain that a protein is pure, that is a single molecular species. Several proteins have been obtained in a crystalline state but even crystallinity does not guarantee that a protein is homomolecular. Proteins which once were thought to be pure have been separated into a number of fractions by taking advantage of the different rates of migration under an applied electromotive force (*electrophoresis*). Criteria of purity which must be applied, in addition to chemical analysis and crystalline homogeneity, are constancy of solubility at a given temperature regardless of the amount of excess protein present, constancy of diffusion rate, of rate of transfer under an electrical potential (electrophoretic mobility), of rate of sedimentation in the ultracentrifuge, and of dielectric constant.

The complexity of the proteins is indicated by the fact that twenty-odd different α-amino acids have been accepted as being direct products of hydrolysis of proteins, and that the molecular weights of proteins are extremely high. Molecular weights have been determined by osmotic pressure measurements, from rates of diffusion, and from sedimentation data in the ultracentrifuge. If the protein contains a characteristic compound or atom, the equivalent weight can be found by determining the weight of the group or atom in a given weight of protein and calculating the weight of protein associated with one gram molecular weight of the group, or one atomic weight of the atom. For example an equivalent weight can be calculated for hemoglobin from the amount of iron present. Table 12 gives the molecular weights for a number of proteins as determined by several methods. There is fair agreement between the molecular weights calculated from osmotic pressure measurements and those obtained by means of the ultracentrifuge, the latter values being considered the more accurate. The fact that the molecular weights are not integral multiples of the equivalent weights must be ascribed to inexact methods of analysis.

TABLE 12

MOLECULAR WEIGHTS OF PROTEINS

PROTEIN	MOL. WT. BY SEDIMENTATION	MOL. WT. BY OSMOTIC PRESSURE	EQUIVALENT WT. BY CHEM. ANAL.
Ovalbumin	42,000	35,000	28,000 (cystine)
Hemoglobin (horse)	63,000	68,000	16,700 (iron)
Serum albumin (horse)	67,000	72,000	8,000 (cystine)
Serum globulin (horse)	150,000	175,000	9,000 (tryptophan)
Edestin (hemp seed)	303,000		28,000 (cystine)
Thyroglobulin	685,000		
Hemocyanin (octopus)	2,785,000		16,700 (copper)
Hemocyanin (snail)	6,650,000	1,700,000	25,500 (copper)
Tobacco mosaic virus	50,000,000		

Some proteins have been shown by sedimentation in the ultracentrifuge to be definitely polymolecular; that is they are composed of mixtures of molecules having different molecular weights. For example the molecular weights of the molecules of lactalbumin vary from 12,000 to 25,000, of gelatin from 10,000 to 100,000, and of casein from 75,000 to 375,000.

Simple proteins yield only α-amino acids as the ultimate products of hydrolysis. The generally accepted naturally occurring amino acids and their structures are given in Table 13. Since often the only functional groups present

TABLE 13

AMINO ACIDS ACCEPTED AS BEING DIRECT PRODUCTS OF HYDROLYSIS OF PROTEINS

Neutral Amino Acids (equal number of amino and carboxyl groups)
1. Glycine or aminoacetic acid, $CH_2(NH_2)COOH$
2. Alanine or α-aminopropionic acid, $CH_3CH(NH_2)COOH$
3. Valine or α-aminoisovaleric acid, $(CH_3)_2CHCH(NH_2)COOH$
4. Leucine or α-aminoisocaproic acid, $(CH_3)_2CHCH_2CH(NH_2)COOH$
5. Isoleucine or α-amino-β-methylvaleric acid, $CH_3CH_2CH(CH_3)CH(NH_2)COOH$
6. Phenylalanine or α-amino-β-phenylpropionic acid,*

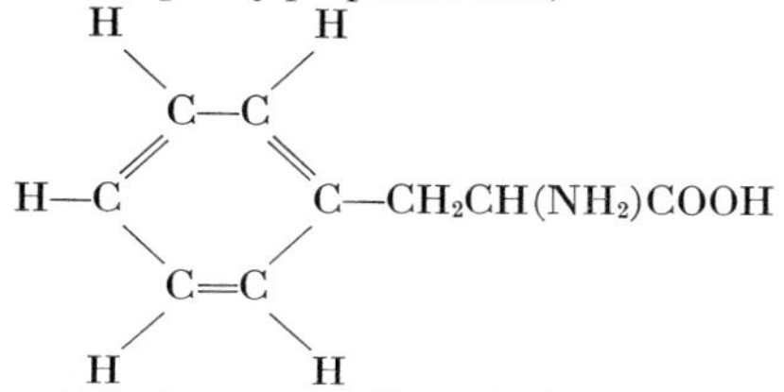

7. Tyrosine or α-amino-β-(4-hydroxyphenyl)propionic acid,*

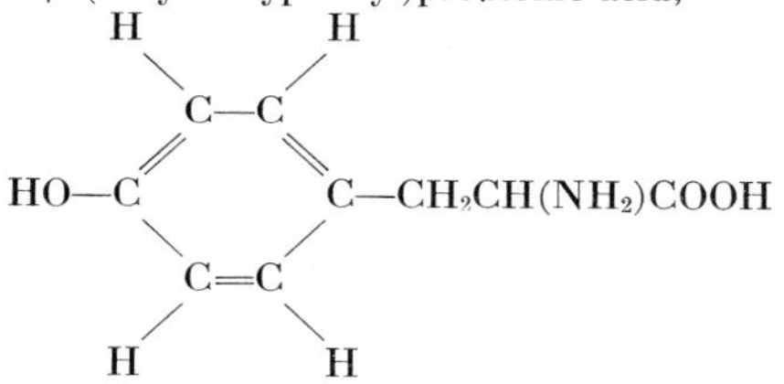

8. Serine or α-amino-β-hydroxypropionic acid, $HOCH_2CH(NH_2)COOH$
9. Threonine or α-amino-β-hydroxybutyric acid, $CH_3CH(OH)CH(NH_2)COOH$
10. Proline or 2-pyrrolidinecarboxylic acid,*

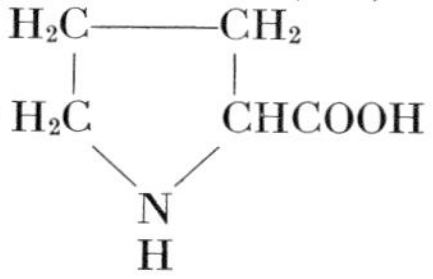

11. Hydroxyproline or 4-hydroxy-2-pyrrolidinecarboxylic acid,*

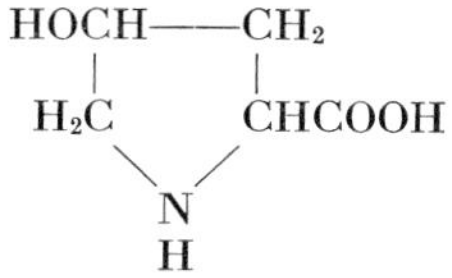

12. Tryptophan or α-amino-β-(3-indolyl)propionic acid,*

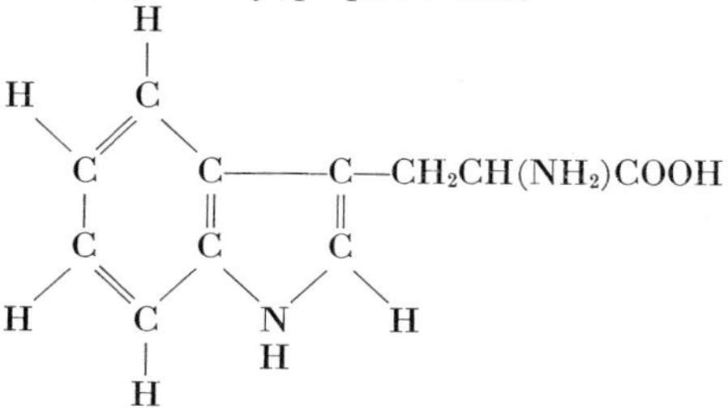

*Compounds containing cyclic structures are discussed in Chapters 19 to 30.

13. Thyroxine or α-amino-β-[3,5-diiodo-4-(3,5-diiodo-4-hydroxyphenoxy)phenyl]propionic acid,*

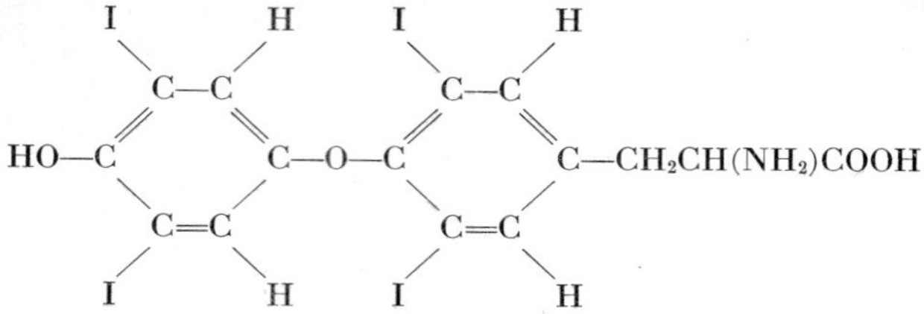

$$\underset{\text{I}}{\overset{\text{I}}{}} \quad \underset{\text{H}}{\overset{\text{H}}{}} \quad \underset{\text{I}}{\overset{\text{I}}{}} \quad \underset{\text{H}}{\overset{\text{H}}{}}$$

HO—C

C—C   C—C

C—O—C   C—CH₂CH(NH₂)COOH

C=C   C=C

14. Iodogorgoic acid or 3,5-diiodotyrosine,*

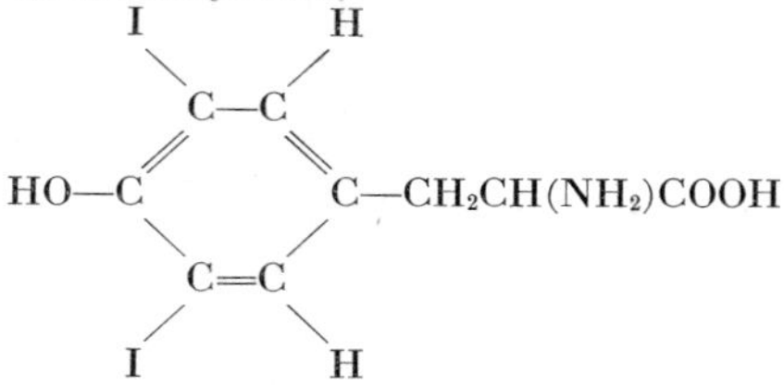

HO—C   C—CH₂CH(NH₂)COOH

C—C

C=C

15. Methionine or α-amino-γ-(methylthio)butyric acid, $CH_3SCH_2CH_2CH(NH_2)COOH$
16. Cysteine or α-amino-β-mercaptopropionic acid, $HSCH_2CH(NH_2)COOH$
17. Cystine or bis-(2-amino-2-carboxyethyl)disulfide,
$$HOOCCH(NH_2)CH_2SSCH_2CH(NH_2)COOH$$

Basic Amino Acids (more basic groups than carboxyl groups)

18. Lysine or α, ϵ-diaminocaproic acid, $H_2NCH_2CH_2CH_2CH_2CH(NH_2)COOH$
19. Arginine or α-amino-δ-guanidinovaleric acid,
$$\overset{\overset{\displaystyle NH}{\parallel}}{H_2NCNHCH_2CH_2CH_2CH(NH_2)COOH}$$

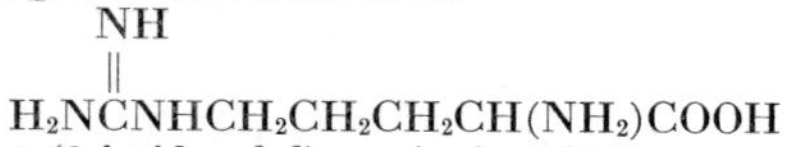

20. Histidine or α-amino-β-(2-imidazolyl)propionic acid,*

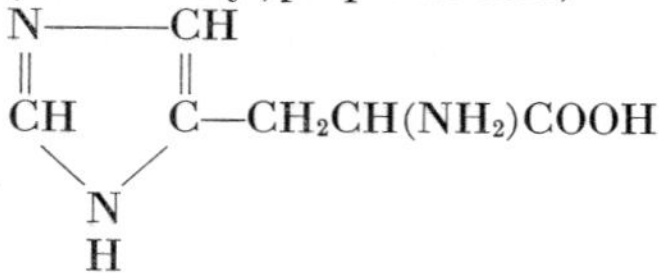

N———CH

CH   C—CH₂CH(NH₂)COOH

N
H

Acidic Amino Acids (more carboxyl groups than amino groups)

21. Aspartic acid or aminosuccinic acid, $HOOCCH_2CH(NH_2)COOH$
22. Glutamic acid or α-aminoglutaric acid, $HOOCCH_2CH_2CH(NH_2)COOH$

are the amino group and the carboxyl group, an amide linkage is the only logical mode of joining the amino acids. If the α-amino acids are represented by the structure, $RCH(NH_2)COOH$, the protein may be represented by the partial structure I.

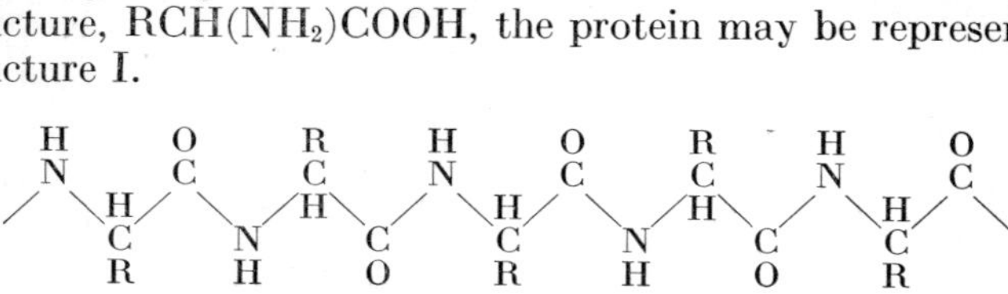

$$\begin{array}{ccccccccc}
H & O & R & H & O & R & H & O \\
N & C & C & N & C & C & N & C \\
& H & H & & H & & H & \\
C & N & C & C & N & C & C \\
R & H & O & R & H & O & R
\end{array}$$

I

However a few of the amino acids have more than one carboxyl group and a few have more than one amino group. Therefore in a molecule such as I some free amino groups and some free carboxyl groups may be expected to be

* Compounds containing cyclic structures are discussed in Chapters 19 to 30.

present. Since ammonia also is a product of protein hydrolysis, some of the carboxyl groups must be combined with ammonia as simple amide groups, $CONH_2$. Hence a section of a protein molecule containing lysine, aspartic acid, and glutamic acid conceivably could have the structure II.

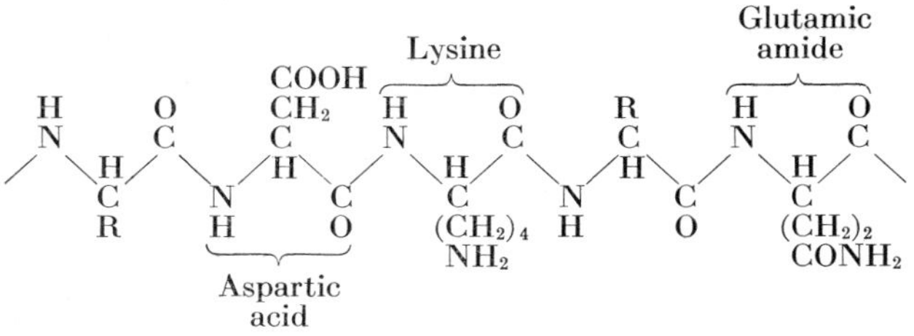

II

Moreover there is some evidence that chains of amino acids may be cross-linked by means of the disulfide linkage in the cystine portions of the molecule as represented in structure III.

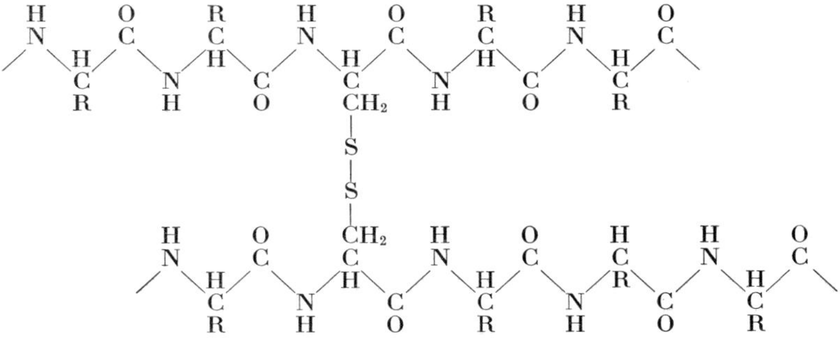

III

Other types of cross linkages, such as the amide or imide linkage, are conceivable, but there is no evidence as yet for their existence.

The fibrous proteins, such as silk, wool, hair, and connective tissues, are notably lacking in the dibasic amino acids, aspartic and glutamic, and probably are best represented by structure I. In fibroin of silk, the molecules are stretched out, but keratin of hair has a folded structure which can be stretched to a linear molecule. Globular proteins also may have their chains folded in an unknown fashion. The forces keeping the molecules in a folded structure probably are proton bonds between NH groups and C=O groups. It is possible to convert nonfibrous proteins such as casein, albumin, or soybean protein into a fibrous form by dissolving in aqueous sodium hydroxide, forcing the solution through fine holes, and coagulating the filament by passing it into an acid formaldehyde bath. The molecules become uncoiled on solution, and are stretched out and oriented parallel to each other during the spinning process. The product is known as *synthetic wool*.

The postulated structural formulas explain one other important physical property of the proteins. The proteins contain potentially free amino groups and carboxyl groups, that is amino groups and carboxyl groups which are not joined to other carboxyl or amino groups by amide linkages. Many of these groups undoubtedly are present in salt form, the protons of the carboxyl groups having been transferred to the basic amino groups. In the presence of strong acids, however, undissociated carboxyl groups exist, and in the presence of strong bases the amino groups are free. Hence the proteins are amphoteric electrolytes. A simple amino acid molecule also contains a free amino group and a free carboxyl group, and can be used to illustrate the equilibria involved.

$$
\begin{bmatrix} R \\ | \\ H_2N-CH-COO^- \end{bmatrix}
\underset{H_2O}{\overset{[OH^-]}{\rightleftarrows}}
\begin{bmatrix} R \\ | \\ \overset{+}{H_3N}-CH-COO^- \end{bmatrix}
\overset{[H^+]}{\underset{}{\rightleftarrows}}
\begin{bmatrix} R \\ | \\ \overset{+}{H_3N}-CH-COOH \end{bmatrix}
$$

Base salt form, as　　　Normal salt form,　　　Acid salt form, as
in the sodium salt　　　as in the free amino　　　in the amino acid
of amino acid　　　　　　acid　　　　　　　　　　hydrochloride

When the amino acid is in its normal salt form, it is a **dipolar ion (zwitter ion)** in which the negative charge on the carboxyl group balances the positive charge on the amino group. If an aqueous solution of the amino acid in this condition is subjected to a potential difference, no migration of the ion takes place. If the solution is made more strongly acid, some of the acid salt is formed and the amino acid will be positively charged and migrate to the negative electrode. If the solution is made more strongly basic, some of the base salt is produced and the amino acid will be negatively charged and migrate to the positive electrode. The acid concentration expressed as pH (log $1/[H^+]$) at which no migration takes place is known as the **isoelectric point.** This point is not necessarily the neutral point (pH 7), because the basicity of the amino group and the acidity of the carboxyl group vary with the structure of the amino acid and need not be the same. Since proteins also contain free amino groups and free carboxyl groups, the same considerations apply to them as apply to the amino acids. Differences in isoelectric point are important particularly in the isolation and purification of amino acids and proteins, because minimum solubility occurs at the isoelectric point, and because direction and rate of migration in an electric field can be controlled by regulating the pH of the solution.

Marked progress has been made since about 1937 in the development of methods for the separation and estimation of amino acids, and the relative amounts of the different amino acids is known with fair accuracy for several proteins, for example β-lactoglobulin and insulin. Little is known about the order of arrangement of the amino acids in the protein molecules, the results of recent attempts at learning this order being controversial. That the molecules of amino acids are not randomly distributed, in which case the differences in proteins might be ascribed to differences in the number and kind of amino acids present, is known from the remarkable specificity of proteins. Thus proteins are not only specific for different tissues but also for different species of animals and even for individual members within a species. For example whole blood of humans must be typed before blood transfusions may be made because not all of the blood proteins of two individuals are necessarily identical, and foreign proteins in the blood stream are toxic to the animal organism.

The number of possible structures for proteins is staggering. Tryptophan has the highest molecular weight (204) of the common amino acids. Therefore a protein such as ovalbumin, with a molecular weight of 42,000, must contain a minimum of 200 molecules of amino acids, and one such as edestin, of molecular weight 303,000, at least 1500 amino acid molecules. β-Lactoglobulin is believed to contain twenty different amino acids and a total of 370 molecules. It has been calculated that if only fifty molecules of nineteen different kinds, apportioned ten of one kind, four of four kinds, two of ten kinds, and one of four kinds, were present in a protein molecule, the number of possible arrangements is 10^{48}. As a comparison the diameter of the Milky Way (300,000 light years) expressed in Ångstrom units (10,000,000 per millimeter) is only 10^{32}. That an organism can synthesize a specific protein for each particular purpose by picking out the desired amino acids from the blood stream and putting them together in the proper order is a striking example of the exactness with which life processes are regulated.

Metabolism of Proteins

The animal organism is unable to synthesize amino acids from inorganic nitrogen and hence must obtain them in its diet from plants or other animals. Protein is ingested and hydrolyzed, the hydrolysis being catalyzed by the enzyme *pepsin* under acid conditions in the stomach, and by *trypsin* and other enzymes under approximately neutral to slightly alkaline conditions in the intestines. By successive stages of hydrolysis amino acids are formed and pass through the walls of the intestine into the blood stream, which transports them to other portions of the body. There under the influence of the body's own specific enzymes, they are resynthesized into the tissues characteristic of the organism.

The organism also is able to convert some amino acids into others. Amino acids that can be so formed need not be ingested. On the other hand it is known that the rat cannot produce valine, leucine, isoleucine, phenylalanine, threonine, tryptophan, methionine, lysine, arginine,[1] or histidine, and hence they have been termed *indispensable* or *essential amino acids*. The term "indispensable" should not be taken to mean that these amino acids are more important than the "dispensable" amino acids, since all natural amino acids undoubtedly are necessary for the development and maintenance of the organism. Indispensable merely means that these amino acids must be supplied in the proteins of the diet, and cannot be synthesized from other amino acids. Studies made so far indicate that the requirements of other species appear to be similar to those of the rat. Arginine, however, is dispensable in dogs and histidine is dispensable in man. For growing chicks glycine is an indispensable amino acid, although it is dispensable in rats. One of the more interesting facts discovered in recent years through the aid of isotopes is that the proteins in the body are being actively built up and torn down continuously, and that there is a fairly rapid turnover of amino acids.

Amino acids not only are incorporated into body proteins, but may be degraded to carbon dioxide, water, and ammonia with the liberation of about 4 kcal. of energy per gram of protein. The ammonia is eliminated chiefly as urea. Amino acids may serve also as precursors of other biologically important compounds or as agents for the elimination of other substances. For example when benzoic acid is ingested, the organism condenses it with glycine and eliminates it in the urine as hippuric acid, $C_6H_5CONHCH_2COOH$.

---

[1] Arginine can be produced but not at a rate sufficient for normal growth.

Synthesis of α-Amino Acids

One of the most general methods for the synthesis of α-amino acids is the reaction of α-halogen acids with ammonia.

$$RCHCOOH + 2 NH_3 \longrightarrow RCH(NH_2)COOH + NH_4X$$
$$|$$
$$X$$

A large excess of ammonia is used to decrease the amount of by-product formed by the reaction of two moles of halogen acid with one mole of ammonia. Bromo acids most commonly are used, since they are prepared readily by the Hell-Volhard-Zelinsky reaction (p. 137). When the nature of the R group does not permit the use of the Hell-Volhard-Zelinsky reaction, a substituted malonic acid (p. 545) may be brominated, since malonic acids brominate much more easily than monocarboxylic acids and lose carbon dioxide on heating (p. 542) to give the bromo acid.

$$\begin{array}{ccc}
COOH & COOH & H \\
| & | & | \\
R{-}CH \xrightarrow{Br_2} R{-}C{-}Br \longrightarrow R{-}C{-}Br + CO_2 \\
| & | & | \\
COOH & COOH & COOH
\end{array}$$

A second method is known as the *Strecker synthesis*, which consists of the reaction of an aldehyde or ketone with a mixture of ammonium chloride and sodium cyanide followed by acid hydrolysis of the amino nitrile. The first stage of the reaction involves the formation of ammonium cyanide which dissociates into ammonia and hydrogen cyanide. Reaction of ammonia with the aldehyde or ketone gives the ammonia addition product, which reacts with hydrogen cyanide to give the amino nitrile.

$$NH_4Cl + NaCN \longrightarrow NH_4CN + NaCl$$

$$NH_4CN \rightleftharpoons NH_3 + HCN$$

$$RCHO \underset{}{\overset{NH_3}{\rightleftharpoons}} RCHOH \underset{H_2O}{\overset{HCN}{\rightleftharpoons}} RCHCN \xrightarrow{H_2O[H^+]} RCHCOOH$$
$$\qquad\qquad | \qquad\qquad | \qquad\qquad |$$
$$\qquad\qquad NH_2 \qquad\quad NH_2 \qquad\quad NH_2$$

Because synthetic amino acids are important to the biochemist and physician, numerous other ingenious syntheses have been devised.

Naturally occurring amino acids are optically active, consisting of a single form of the compound (cf. Chapter 17), whereas the synthetic amino acids are optically inactive, being composed of equal amounts of the naturally occurring form and of a second form that cannot be utilized by the animal organism. Hence when the synthetic amino acids are fed to an animal, they are only half as effective on a weight basis as the natural compounds. Methods are available for separating the synthetic compounds into their active components, but it usually is a difficult process.

Monosodium glutamate is used widely as a condiment and for bringing out the flavor of foods. It is prepared commercially by the hydrolysis of wheat gluten or sugar beet residues. Six million pounds valued at nine million dollars was produced in the United States in 1948. **Tryptophan** is synthesized commercially, because most of that occurring in proteins is destroyed during acid hydrolysis and, as an indispensable amino acid, it must be added to the protein hydrolysates used to treat cases of serious malnutrition. **Methionine** is synthesized for the fortification of protein hydrolysates and for enriching foodstuffs. Small amounts fed to chickens greatly increase their rate of growth.

Synthesis of Peptides

Peptides are polyamides of low molecular weight which yield two or more amino acids on hydrolysis. The terms *di-, tri-, tetra-,* and *pentapeptides* are in use, and products containing many amino acids are known as **polypeptides.** The proteins themselves may be classed as polypeptides. Since the postulation by E. Fischer [2] and by Hofmeister [3] that proteins consist of α-amino acids joined by amide linkages, there has been continued interest in the synthesis of peptides, not only to confirm the theory but also to prepare simple compounds of known constitution for the investigation of the relation between constitution and enzyme activity. It should be possible to heat an amino acid or a mixture of amino acids under conditions which cause the formation of amides from amine salts, and obtain polymeric condensation products. A more convenient method has been devised in which a cyclic amide anhydride is first formed by the reaction of the sodium salt of an amino acid with phosgene.

$$\begin{array}{l} \text{RCHCOONa} \\ \;\;| \\ \;\;\text{NH}_2 \end{array} + \text{COCl}_2 \longrightarrow \begin{array}{l} \text{RCH—C} \\ \;\;| \qquad \text{O} + \text{NaCl} + \text{HCl} \\ \text{NH—C} \end{array}$$

Addition of a trace of moisture initiates a polymeric condensation.

$$\begin{array}{l} \text{RCH—C} \\ \;| \quad \text{O} \xrightarrow{\text{H}_2\text{O}} \left[\begin{array}{l}\text{RCHCOOH}\\ \;| \\ \text{NHCOOH}\end{array}\right] \longrightarrow \text{CO}_2 + \begin{array}{l}\text{RCHCOOH}\\ \;| \\ \text{NH}_2\end{array} \xrightarrow{\qquad} \\ \text{NH—C} \end{array}$$

$$\left[\begin{array}{l} \qquad\quad\text{R} \\ \;\;\;\;| \\ \text{RCHCONHCHCOOH} \\ \;| \\ \text{NHCOOH} \end{array}\right] \longrightarrow \text{CO}_2 + \begin{array}{l}\qquad\quad\text{R}\\ \;\;\;\;|\\ \text{RCHCONHCCOOH}\\ \;|\\ \text{NH}_2\end{array} \xrightarrow[\text{condensations}]{\text{Further}} \begin{array}{l}\text{High}\\ \text{mol. wt.}\\ \text{polymers}\end{array}$$

---

[2] Emil Fischer (1852–1919), professor of organic chemistry at the University of Berlin, and the outstanding director of organic chemical research. He and his coworkers did monumental work in the fields of amino acids and proteins, carbohydrates, and purines, and made important contributions in numerous other fields such as enzymes, stereochemistry, triphenylmethane dyes, hydrazines, and indoles. He was the second recipient of the Nobel Prize in Chemistry in 1902, the first being van't Hoff in 1901.

[3] Franz Hofmeister (1850–1922), professor of biochemistry and experimental pharmacology at the University of Prague, and later at the University of Strassburg.

It is more important, however, to be able to condense the amino acids stepwise to give a product of known constitution. Accordingly it was necessary to devise methods in which only the desired reactions take place. The first general method was devised by Fischer who allowed α-halogenated acid halides to react with amino acids or peptides, and subsequently replaced the α-halogen by an amino group.

$$
\underset{\substack{|\\ \text{XCHCOX}}}{\overset{\substack{\text{R}\\|}}{}} + \underset{\substack{|\\ \text{H}_2\text{NCHCOOH}}}{\overset{\substack{\text{R}'\\|}}{}} \longrightarrow \underset{\substack{|\quad\quad|\\ \text{XCHCONHCHCOOH}}}{\overset{\substack{\text{R}\quad\ \text{R}'\\|\quad\ |}}{}} \overset{\text{NH}_3}{\longrightarrow} \underset{\substack{|\quad\quad\quad|\\ \text{H}_2\text{NCHCONHCHCOOH}}}{\overset{\substack{\text{R}\quad\quad\ \text{R}'\\|\quad\quad\ |}}{}}
$$

The dipeptide thus formed can react with another mole of α-halogenated acid halide, and the product can react with ammonia to give a tripeptide. Making use of these reactions and others which he had devised, Fischer was able to synthesize a peptide containing eighteen molecules of amino acids, which resembled a protein in that it gave the biuret reaction (p. 235) and could be "salted out" of its aqueous solution.

Since Fischer's synthesis is useful only for condensing the simpler amino acids, other methods have been devised. Attempts to protect amino groups by acylation have not been successful, because the amide linkage so formed is no more easily hydrolyzed than that linking the amino acids together, and removal of the acyl group by hydrolysis results in hydrolysis of the peptide linkage as well. This problem was solved by Bergmann [4] by the reaction of the free amino group with benzyl chloroformate (so-called carbobenzoxy chloride). The carbobenzyloxy group can be removed by catalytic reduction.

$$
\underset{\substack{|\\ \text{NH}_2}}{\overset{\text{RCHCOOCH}_3}{}} + \text{C}_6\text{H}_5\text{CH}_2\text{OCOCl} \longrightarrow \underset{\substack{|\\ \text{NHCOOCH}_2\text{C}_6\text{H}_5}}{\overset{\text{RCHCOOCH}_3}{}} \xrightarrow{\text{H}_2(\text{Pd})} \underset{\substack{|\\ \text{NH}_2}}{\overset{\text{RCHCOOCH}_3}{}} + \text{CO}_2 + \text{C}_6\text{H}_5\text{CH}_3
$$

The synthesis of lysylglutamic acid is an example of the use of this reaction. In these reactions the acid with protected amino groups is converted to the azide, rather than the acid chloride, for condensation with the glutamic acid (R = benzyl).

$$
\underset{\substack{|\quad\quad\quad\ |\\ \text{CH}_2(\text{CH}_2)_3\text{CHCON}_3}}{\overset{\substack{\text{NHCOOR NHCOOR}\\|}}{}} + \underset{\substack{|\\ \text{H}_2\text{NCHCOOCH}_3}\\ \text{Methyl glutamate}}{\overset{\text{(CH}_2)_2\text{COOCH}_3}{}} \longrightarrow
$$

$$
\underset{\substack{|\quad\quad\quad\quad|\quad\quad\quad|\\ \text{CH}_2(\text{CH}_2)_3\text{CHCONH CHCOOCH}_3}}{\overset{\substack{\text{NHCOOR NHCOOR (CH}_2)_2\text{COOCH}_3\\|}}{}} \xrightarrow{\text{NaOH}} \underset{\substack{|\quad\quad\quad\quad|\quad\quad\quad|\\ \text{CH}_2(\text{CH}_2)_3\text{CHCONH CHCOOH}}}{\overset{\substack{\text{NHCOOR NHCOOR (CH}_2)_2\text{COOH}\\|}}{}}
$$

$$
\xrightarrow{\text{H}_2,\ \text{Pd}} \underset{\substack{|\quad\quad\quad\quad|\quad\quad\quad|\\ \text{CH}_2(\text{CH}_2)_3\text{CHCONHCHCOOH}}\\ \text{Lysylglutamic acid}}{\overset{\substack{\text{NH}_2\quad\quad\ \text{NH}_2\quad\quad\ (\text{CH}_2)_2\text{COOH}\\|}}{}}
$$

Several naturally occurring peptides are known. Some are of considerable interest and their structure has been determined. For example the **folic acids,**

---

[4] Max Bergmann (1886–1944), German-born chemist who had been an assistant to Emil Fischer. He came to the United States in 1933 and joined the staff of the Rockefeller Institute. He is noted for his work on the analysis of proteins, on the synthesis of peptides, and on the enzymatic synthesis of proteins.

which are valuable in the treatment of pernicious anemia, are polyglutamic acids united to a substituted pterin nucleus and have the structure

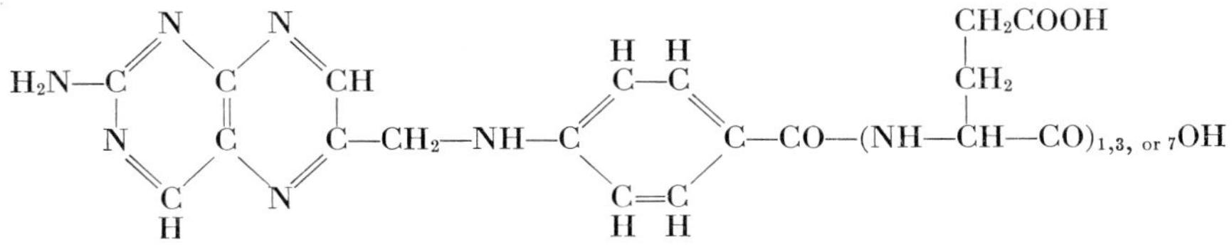

Pteroylglutamic acid (subscript = 1 in the above formula) is the *L. casei* factor isolated from liver and is being synthesized commercially for therapeutic use. **Gramicidin-S,** the antibiotic isolated from the soil organism *Bacillus brevis,* is a cyclopentapeptide or a cyclodecapeptide of the structure

$$[\text{—}(\alpha\text{-valyl-ornithyl-leucyl-phenylalanyl-prolyl})_{1 \text{ or } 2}\text{—}]$$

in which the ends are joined to form a ring. **Glutathion,** which plays an important part in biological oxidations and reductions, is the tripeptide glutamylcysteinylglycine,

$$\underset{\underset{NH_2}{|}}{HOOCCHCH_2CH_2CONHCHCONHCH_2COOH} \quad \underset{\underset{CH_2SH}{|}}{}$$

Tests for α-Amino Acids and for Polypeptides

In the **ninhydrin reaction,** α-amino acids, and proteins or their degradation products that contain a free carboxyl group having an α-amino group, yield a blue color when heated in dilute solution with *triketohydrindene hydrate (ninhydrin).* The reaction is dependent on the oxidizing action of ninhydrin with liberation of ammonia. Subsequent condensation of ninhydrin with its reduction product and ammonia produces the colored compound. Ammonium salts, dilute ammonia solutions, and certain amines also give the reaction under some conditions.

The conditions for the **biuret reaction** and the structure of the products formed are discussed on page 244. Since peptides and polypeptides meet these conditions, they also give a positive test, that is a pink to violet color when dilute copper sulfate solution is added to the alkaline solution of the peptide or protein. The structure of the product of reaction with a section of a polypeptide chain may be represented by the formula

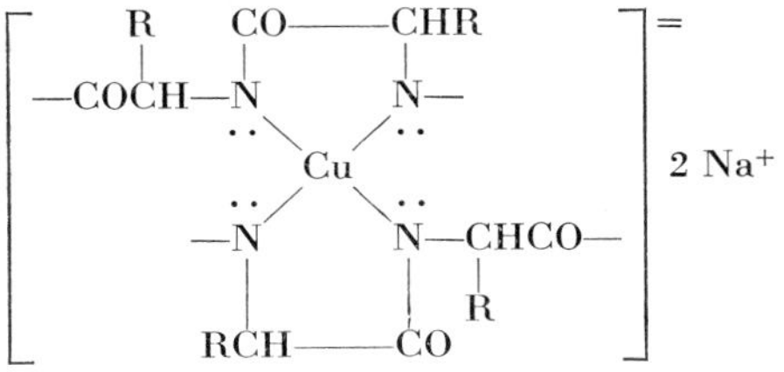

The yellow color produced when concentrated nitric acid comes in contact with skin or other proteins (**xanthoproteic reaction**) presumably is caused

by the nitration of aromatic nuclei to give yellow nitro compounds (Chapter 21). Free amino groups in either amino acids or proteins may be estimated quantitatively by measuring the volume of nitrogen liberated on reaction with nitrous acid (*Van Slyke method*).

$$RCH_2CHNH_2COOH + HONO \longrightarrow RCH{=}CHCOOH + N_2 + 2\ H_2O$$

Although the reaction as usually written indicates the replacement of the amino group by a hydroxyl group, unsaturated and rearranged compounds also may be formed (p. 190). The important point is that one mole of nitrogen is eliminated for each free amino group in the molecule.

REVIEW QUESTIONS

1. Define the term *protein*. What are the sources of proteins? What is the difference between a simple protein and a conjugated protein? What is a prosthetic group?
2. Discuss the elementary composition of proteins and their molecular weights. What methods have been used to determine the molecular weights?
3. What is the generally accepted type of structure for proteins? Why do proteins give the biuret reaction? What is a peptide?
4. Approximately how many naturally occurring amino acids have been isolated? How are they usually classified?
5. Discuss the term *isoelectric point* as applied to amino acids and proteins. Why is it an important property?
6. Discuss the metabolism of proteins in the animal organism. What is meant by the term *essential* or *indispensable* amino acid?
7. Give equations for the synthesis of (*a*) valine from isovaleric acid; (*b*) alanine from acetaldehyde.

Chapter 16

DERIVATIVES OF CARBONIC ACID
AND THIOCARBONIC ACID

DERIVATIVES OF CARBONIC ACID

From the theory of structure the compound $C(OH)_4$ should exist, but the presence of more than one hydroxyl group on the same carbon atom usually results in an unstable molecule that loses water (p. 166). It is not surprising therefore that the hypothetical orthocarbonic acid is nonexistent. Loss of one molecule of water should give ordinary carbonic acid $O=C(OH)_2$. Although it is believed that this compound exists in aqueous solutions of carbon dioxide, all attempts to isolate it result in its decomposition to carbon dioxide and water.

$$[C(OH)_4] \underset{H_2O}{\rightleftarrows} [O=C(OH)_2] \underset{H_2O}{\rightleftarrows} O=C=O$$

Orthocarbonic   Carbonic acid   Carbon dioxide
acid   (hypothetical)
(hypothetical)

In spite of the nonexistence of orthocarbonic acid and carbonic acid, numerous derivatives of these compounds are known, some of which are of considerable importance. Table 14 gives the formulas and names of some of these compounds and of their sulfur analogs. Those compounds with formulas in brackets are not capable of independent existence at room temperature.

TABLE 14
DERIVATIVES OF CARBONIC AND THIOCARBONIC ACIDS

$O=C=O$	Carbonic anhydride, carbon dioxide
$[C(OH)_4]$	Orthocarbonic acid (unknown)
CCl_4	Carbon tetrachloride
$C(OR)_4$	Alkyl orthocarbonates
$[O=C(OH)_2]$	Carbonic acid (unknown)
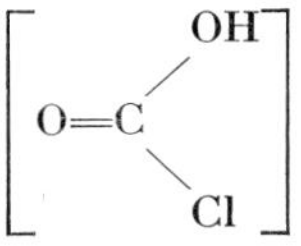 $\left[O=C\diagupfrac{OH}{Cl} \right]$	Chloroformic acid (chlorocarbonic acid) (unknown)
$O=CCl_2$	Carbonyl chloride, phosgene
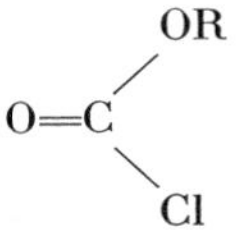 $O=C\diagupfrac{OR}{Cl}$	Alkyl chloroformate (alkyl chlorocarbonate)
$O=C(OR)_2$	Alkyl carbonate

237

TABLE 14 (*Continued*)

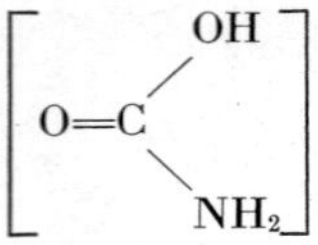

$$\begin{bmatrix} & OH \\ O{=}C & \\ & NH_2 \end{bmatrix}$$

Carbamic acid (unknown)

$$O{=}C \begin{array}{l} OR \\ \\ NH_2 \end{array}$$

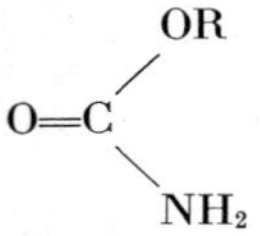

Alkyl carbamates, urethans

$O{=}C(NH_2)_2$ Carbamide, urea

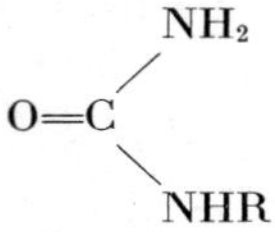

$$O{=}C \begin{array}{l} NH_2 \\ \\ NHR \end{array}$$

N-Alkylureas

$$ROC \begin{array}{l} NH \\ \\ NH_2 \end{array}$$

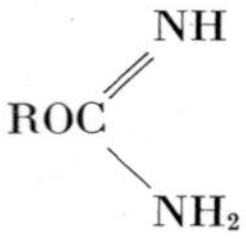

O-Alkylureas

$HN{=}C(NH_2)_2$ Carbamidine, guanidine

$O{=}C{=}NH \rightleftarrows HOC{\equiv}N$ Isocyanic acid $\rightleftarrows$ cyanic acid

$[ROC{\equiv}N]$ Alkyl cyanates (unknown)

$O{=}C{=}NR$ Alkyl isocyanates

$H_2NC{\equiv}N$ Cyanamide

$ClC{\equiv}N$ Cyanogen chloride

$S{=}C{=}O$ Monothiocarbonic anhydride, carbon oxysulfide

$S{=}C{=}S$ Thiocarbonic anhydride, carbon disulfide

$[C(SH)_4]$ Orthothiocarbonic acid (unknown)

$[S{=}C(OH)_2]$ Monothiocarbonic acid (unknown)

$$\begin{bmatrix} & SH \\ S{=}C & \\ & OH \end{bmatrix}$$

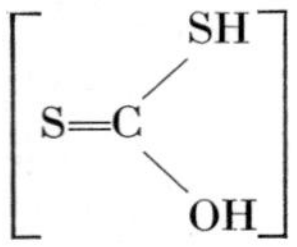

Dithiocarbonic acid (unknown)

$S{=}C(SH)_2$ Thiocarbonic acid

$S{=}CCl_2$ Thiocarbonyl chloride, thiophosgene

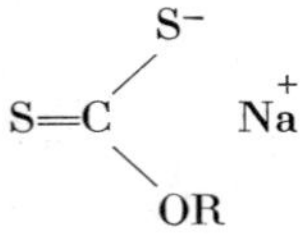

$$S{=}C \begin{array}{l} S^- \\ \quad\quad Na^+ \\ OR \end{array}$$

Sodium alkyl dithiocarbonates, sodium alkyl xanthates

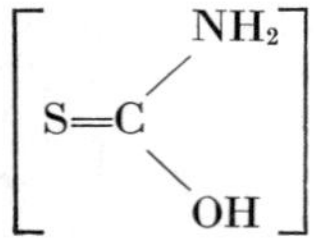

$$\begin{bmatrix} & NH_2 \\ S{=}C & \\ & OH \end{bmatrix}$$

Thiocarbamic acid (unknown)

TABLE 14 (*Continued*)

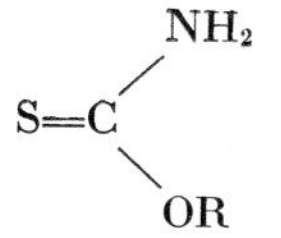

$$S=C\begin{cases} NH_2 \\ \\ OR \end{cases}$$ Alkyl thiocarbamates, thiourethans

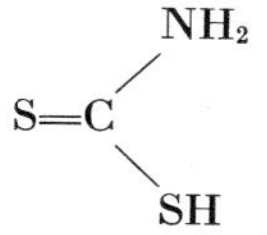

$$S=C\begin{cases} NH_2 \\ \\ SH \end{cases}$$ Dithiocarbamic acid

$S=C(NH_2)_2$ Thiocarbamide, thiourea

$HSC\equiv N$ Thiocyanic acid

$RSC\equiv N$ Alkyl thiocyanates

$S=C=NR$ Alkyl isothiocyanates

$N\equiv CSSC\equiv N$ Thiocyanogen

Phosgene, $COCl_2$, the acid chloride of carbonic acid, first was made by the action of light on a mixture of carbon monoxide and chlorine (Gr. *phos* light *genes* born). In the technical process activated carbon is used as a catalyst.

$$CO + Cl_2 \xrightarrow[\text{carbon}]{\text{Activated}} \underset{\text{Phosgene}}{COCl_2}$$

Phosgene is a sweet smelling gas (b.p. 8°) that is ten times as toxic as chlorine and was the principal offensive battle gas of World War I. The toxic action apparently is due to its ready hydrolysis in the lungs with the liberation of hydrogen chloride.

When phosgene reacts with alcohols, the *alkyl chloroformate* is formed first, and further reaction gives the *alkyl carbonate.*

$$\underset{\text{Phosgene}}{COCl_2} + C_2H_5OH \longrightarrow \underset{\text{Ethyl chloroformate}}{ClCOOC_2H_5} + HCl$$

$$ClCOOC_2H_5 + C_2H_5OH \longrightarrow \underset{\text{Ethyl carbonate}}{OC(OC_2H_5)_2}$$

The chloroformates sometimes are called less correctly *chlorocarbonates.* Phosgene is used for the manufacture of certain ketones that are dye intermediates (p. 407) and for the preparation of **ethyl carbonate,** a useful solvent.

Urea, $CO(NH_2)_2$, is the most important derivative of carbonic acid. It may be considered as the diamide of carbonic acid, the monoamide being the nonexistent carbamic acid, H_2NCOOH. It is because of its relation to carbamic acid, however, that urea frequently is called *carbamide.*

Prior to the development in recent times of technical methods of synthesis and uses, urea was of interest primarily because it is the chief end product of nitrogen metabolism in mammals, being eliminated in the urine. Adult man excretes about 30 g. of urea in 24 hours. It is produced in the liver from ammonia and carbon dioxide. Urea was isolated from urine in 1773, although it was not characterized fully and named urea until 1799. It probably was synthesized first by John Davy, a brother of Sir Humphry Davy, who in 1811 prepared phosgene by the action of sunlight on a mixture of chlorine and carbon monoxide and in 1812 reported that the product reacted with dry ammonia to give a solid which did not evolve carbon dioxide on treatment with acetic acid and hence was not ammonium carbonate. He did not identify his product with urea, however, and credit for the synthesis of urea has been given to Woehler, who in 1828 recognized that the product obtained by boiling a solution of ammonium cyanate with water is identical with urea isolated from urine (p. 3).

$$NH_4OCN \rightleftharpoons CO(NH_2)_2$$

The mechanism of this synthesis is discussed with the chemistry of isocyanic acid (p. 244).

Since its discovery, urea has been isolated as a product of over fifty reactions, two of which have been utilized for its synthesis on a large scale. About the time of World War I, it was prepared by the hydrolysis of calcium cyanamide (p. 248), and sold for $0.60 per pound in 1920. The present commercial synthesis is from dry carbon dioxide and ammonia. Ammonia adds to one of the double bonds of carbon dioxide to yield carbamic acid, which reacts with a second molecule of ammonia to form the ammonium salt. The general method of preparing an amide by heating an ammonium salt converts the ammonium carbamate into urea. Since water is one of the products of the reaction and ammonium carbamate can be hydrolyzed to ammonium carbonate, which dissociates into ammonia and carbon dioxide, exact control of conditions is necessary to obtain the optimum yield of urea. The decomposition of the ammonium carbamate is carried out at 150° and 35 atmospheres pressure in the presence of a 300 per cent excess of ammonia.

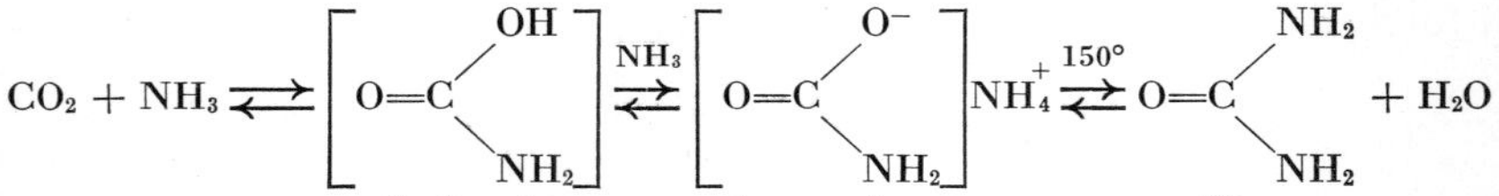

Carbamic acid · Ammonium carbamate · Urea

The high concentration of ammonia suppresses the following side reaction.

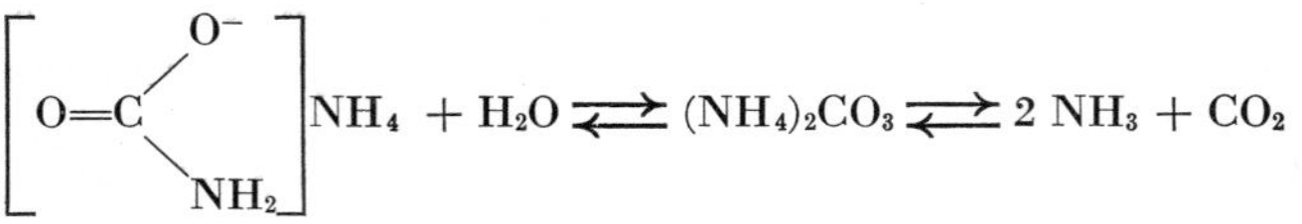

Since the development of this process the price of urea has dropped to about $0.04 per pound. It is used as a fertilizer and for the manufacture of urea-formaldehyde plastics (p. 243). A part of the nitrogen required by ruminants for the synthesis of proteins can be supplied by urea, and it is being added to commercial cattle feeds. A small amount is used in the manufacture of pharmaceuticals (p. 462).

The reactions of urea are those of an amide. It is a very weak base, $K_B = 1.5 \times 10^{-14}$ at 25°, although it appears to be somewhat stronger than acetamide, $K_B = 3.1 \times 10^{-15}$. In spite of this low basicity, the addition of strong nitric acid to a concentrated aqueous solution of urea gives a precipitate of urea nitrate because of the insolubility of the latter in strong nitric acid solution.

Although the nitrogen atom of an amino group ordinarily is more basic than the oxygen atom of a carbonyl group, salt formation of an amide group undoubtedly results from addition of a proton to the oxygen rather than to the nitrogen. If the proton added to nitrogen, the resonance energy of the ion would be very low, whereas if it adds to oxygen considerable stabilization by resonance results. Hence the cation of urea nitrate is best represented as a resonance hybrid (p. 129).

$$\left\{ \begin{array}{ccc} \overset{+}{O}H & OH & OH \\ H_2N-\overset{\|}{C}-NH_2 \leftrightarrow H_2\overset{+}{N}=\overset{|}{C}-NH_2 \leftrightarrow H_2N-\overset{|}{C}=\overset{+}{N}H_2 \end{array} \right\}$$

Hydrolysis of urea yields ammonium carbonate.

$$CO(NH_2)_2 + 2\ H_2O \longrightarrow [CO(OH)_2] + 2\ NH_3 \longrightarrow (NH_4)_2CO_3$$

If the reaction is catalyzed by alkali, the products are the alkali carbonate and ammonia, whereas acid catalysis yields carbon dioxide and the ammonium salt. The hydrolysis also is catalyzed rapidly at room temperature by the enzyme *urease*, which is present in soy bean and jack bean, and is elaborated by certain bacteria. The hydrolysis of urea in the soil liberates the nitrogen as ammonia as part of the nitrogen cycle (Fig. 30, p. 224). Use is made of the urease catalysis for the estimation of urea in biological fluids. After hydrolysis in a suitably buffered solution, the ammonia is liberated and estimated colorimetrically or by titration with standard acid.

Since urea contains NH_2 groups, nitrogen is evolved on reaction with nitrous acid (p. 197).

$$CO(NH_2)_2 + 2\ HONO \longrightarrow CO_2 + 2\ N_2 + 3\ H_2O$$

This reaction is useful as a means of destroying nitrous acid and oxides of nitrogen.

As an amide, urea undergoes the Hofmann rearrangement (p. 197), but the product, hydrazine, is oxidized by hypobromite to nitrogen and water.

$$H_2NCONH_2 + NaOBr + 2\ NaOH \longrightarrow \underset{\text{Hydrazine}}{[H_2NNH_2]} + Na_2CO_3 + NaBr + H_2O$$

$$\downarrow \text{NaOBr}$$

$$N_2 + H_2O + NaBr$$

Amides can be acylated to diacyl derivatives of ammonia, which are known as *imides*. The imides are more acidic than the amides and react with strong bases in aqueous solution to form salts (p. 196). Urea can undergo diacylation, the products being known as **ureids.**

$$CO(NH_2)_2 + 2\ (CH_3CO)_2O \longrightarrow \underset{\text{Diacetylurea}}{CO(NHCOCH_3)_2}$$

Many of the cyclic ureids such as the barbituric acids (p. 462) and alloxan (p. 463) have important physiological properties.

When acetamide is heated with paraformaldehyde, *N*-(hydroxymethyl)-acetamide (methylolacetamide) is formed.

$$CH_3CONH_2 + HCHO \longrightarrow CH_3CONHCH_2OH$$
N-(Hydroxymethyl)-
acetamide
(methylolacetamide)

Similarly urea reacts with formaldehyde to give *N*-(hydroxymethyl)urea, commonly known as **methylolurea.**

$$H_2NCONH_2 + HCHO \longrightarrow H_2NCONHCH_2OH$$
N-(Hydroxymethyl)-
urea
(methylolurea)

When a hydroxymethyl group is united to a nitrogen atom, it readily undergoes further condensation with NH groups with elimination of water (compare the formation of hexamethylenetetramine from formaldehyde and ammonia, p. 177). Hence methylolurea can condense with a second molecule of urea.

$$H_2NCONHCH_2OH + H_2NCONH_2 \longrightarrow H_2NCONHCH_2NHCONH_2$$

Since the amide groups can condense with more formaldehyde, the reaction is capable of yielding high molecular weight chains having the general formula $(-NHCONHCH_2-)_x$. Such a long chain polymer would be expected to be a thick viscous liquid or a thermoplastic solid. It still contains NH groups, however, which can react with formaldehyde to give *N*-hydroxymethyl groups which in turn can react with other NH groups with loss of water. If the second NH group is in a different chain, the chains would be joined together by CH_2 groups and a three-dimensional macromolecule would be formed, resulting in an insoluble nonfusible resin.

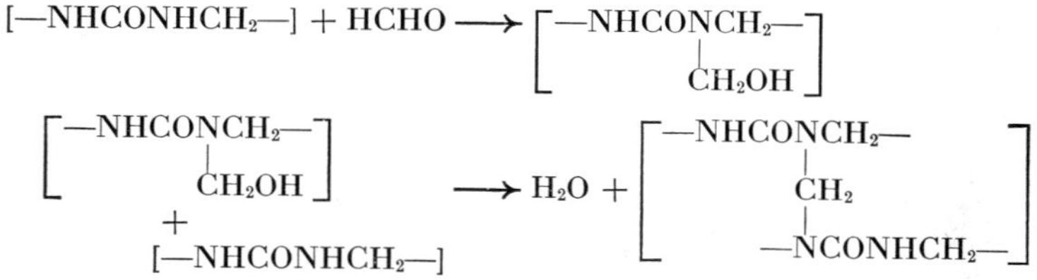

$$[-NHCONHCH_2-] + HCHO \longrightarrow \begin{bmatrix} -NHCONCH_2- \\ | \\ CH_2OH \end{bmatrix}$$

$$\begin{bmatrix} -NHCONCH_2- \\ | \\ CH_2OH \end{bmatrix} \atop + \atop [-NHCONHCH_2-] \quad \longrightarrow H_2O + \begin{bmatrix} -NHCONCH_2- \\ | \\ CH_2 \\ | \\ -NCONHCH_2- \end{bmatrix}$$

Because of the ease of formation of six-membered rings, some of the methylolurea molecules undoubtedly produce cyclic polymers.

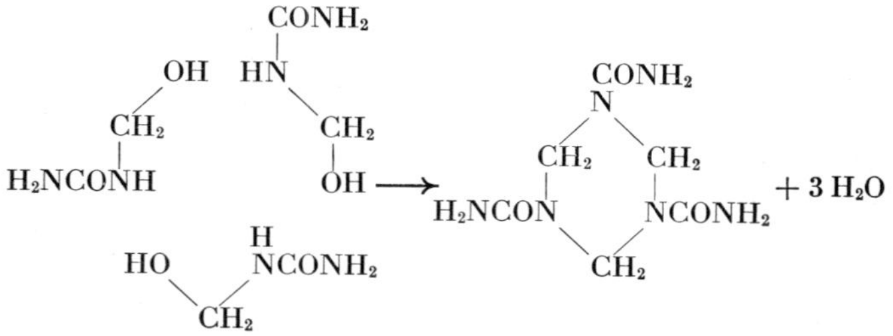

These structures still are polyamides and are capable of undergoing further condensation and entering into the structure of the macromolecule, thus increasing its complexity.

These polycondensation products constitute the commercially important group of plastics known as the **urea-formaldehyde resins.** Three moles of formaldehyde and one of urea are condensed in aqueous solution in the presence of ammonia as an alkaline catalyst. The reaction is stopped at the syrupy stage and mixed with a filler, usually high-grade wood pulp. The mixture is dried and ground and constitutes the thermosetting molding powder. To form an object, the powder is subjected to heat and pressure in a mold. It first flows to fill the mold and then sets to an infusible solid because of completion of the reaction in which cross-linking of the chains takes place. The urea-formaldehyde plastics are colorless, and hence color can be added to produce any desired shade. The intermediate condensation products are used widely also as water-proof adhesives in the manufacture of plywood. Production of urea-formaldehyde resins in the United States amounted to 150 million pounds in 1948.

When urea is heated above its melting point it decomposes into ammonia and isocyanic acid. The isocyanic acid polymerizes at once to a mixture of about 70 per cent of the trimer **cyanuric acid,** and 30 per cent of the linear polymer **cyamelide.**

$$H_2NCONH_2 \longrightarrow NH_3 + HN{=}C{=}O$$
Isocyanic
acid

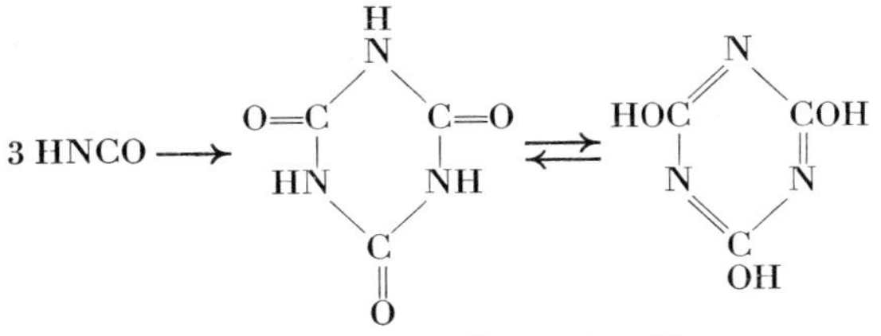

Cyanuric acid

Cyamelide

If cyanuric acid is heated to a high temperature, it depolymerizes to monomeric **isocyanic acid,** which can be condensed below 0° to a colorless liquid. When the liquid is allowed to warm to room temperature it polymerizes spontaneously and explosively to cyanuric acid and cyamelide.

Isocyanic acid is tautomeric with **cyanic acid.**

$$HN{=}C{=}O \rightleftarrows N{\equiv}COH$$

Although the monomeric liquid usually is called cyanic acid, it undergoes addition reactions characteristic of compounds containing a *cumulative* or *twin double bond.* The Raman spectrum also indicates that the *iso* structure prevails. Isocyanic acid is hydrolyzed rapidly to carbon dioxide and ammonia, the intermediate carbamic acid being unstable.

$$HN{=}C{=}O + H_2O \longrightarrow [H_2NCOOH] \longrightarrow CO_2 + NH_3$$

Ammonia and amines add to isocyanic acid to give urea and *N-alkylureas.* Hence in the hydrolysis some urea is formed.

$$HN{=}C{=}O + NH_3 \longrightarrow H_2NCONH_2$$
$$+ H_2NR \longrightarrow H_2NCONHR$$
$$+ HNR_2 \longrightarrow H_2NCONR_2$$

Woehler's synthesis of urea probably is the result of the dissociation of ammonium cyanate into ammonia and cyanic acid, followed by addition.

$$NH_4NCO \rightleftarrows NH_3 + HN{=}C{=}O \longrightarrow H_2NCONH_2$$

Alcohols and isocyanic acid give the *alkyl carbamates (urethans).*

$$HN{=}C{=}O + HOR \longrightarrow H_2NCOOR$$

Urethans can be prepared also by the reaction of alkyl chloroformates with ammonia.

$$2\ NH_3 + ClCOOR \longrightarrow H_2NCOOR + NH_4Cl$$

Amines give *N*-substituted urethans.

$$2\ R'NH_2 + ClCOOR \longrightarrow R'NHCOOR + R'NH_3Cl$$
$$2\ R'_2NH + ClCOOR \longrightarrow R'_2NCOOR + R'_2NH_2Cl$$

The urethans have mild hypnotic properties.

If urea is not heated too strongly, the isocyanic acid first produced adds a molecule of urea to form **biuret.**

$$HN{=}C{=}O + H_2NCONH_2 \longrightarrow H_2NCONHCONH_2$$
$$\text{Biuret}$$

An alkaline solution of biuret gives a violet-pink color when copper sulfate solution is added. The color is due to the presence of a coordination complex with cupric ion in which the four water molecules normally coordinated with the cupric ion are displaced by the amino groups. The alkali removes two protons from the coordinated amino groups to give the neutral insoluble complex, and then two protons from the imide nitrogen atoms to give the water-soluble salt.

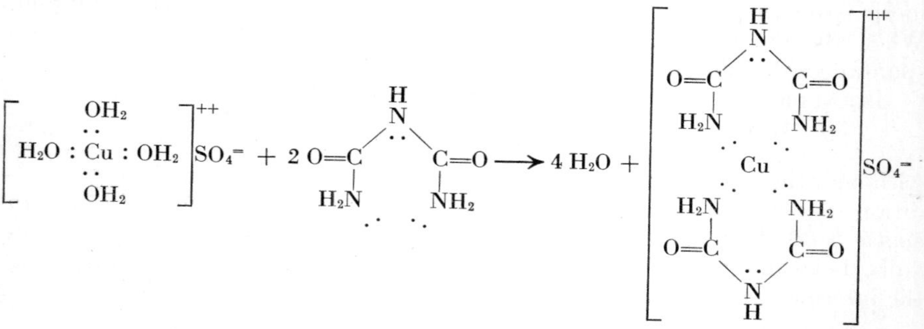

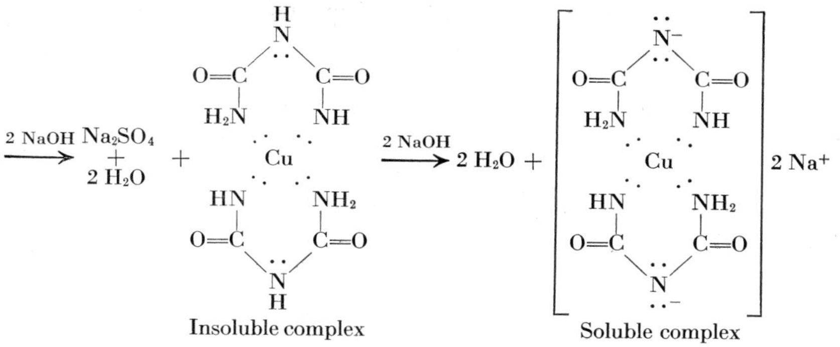

The reaction takes place because of the increased stability that arises when rings are formed. Since only five- and six-membered rings can be formed readily because of the limitations imposed by bond angles, complexes of this sort are formed only when the electron-donating groups, such as the amino groups, are spaced properly in the molecule. The peptide linkage in proteins can lead to a stable complex with copper in which two five-membered rings are formed, and proteins and peptides give the biuret test (p. 235).

If isocyanic acid is tautomeric, two series of alkyl derivatives (or esters) should be possible, the *alkyl cyanates*, $ROC \equiv N$, and the *alkyl isocyanates*, $O = C = NR$. The former are unknown in the monomeric state. When cyanogen chloride reacts with sodium alkoxide, the *alkyl cyanurate* is formed. If the alkyl cyanate is an intermediate, it polymerizes as fast as it is formed.

$$RONa + ClCN \longrightarrow [ROCN] + NaCl$$

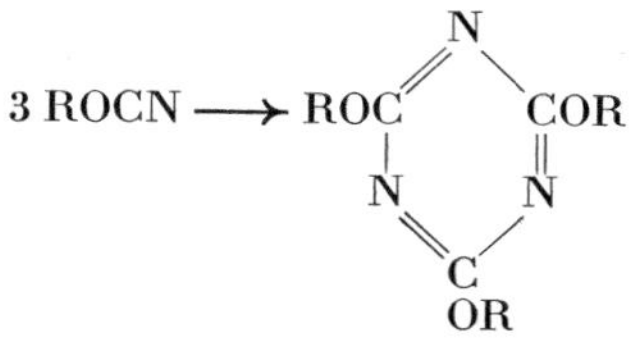

Alkyl cyanurate

The alkyl isocyanates on the other hand are stable compounds. They are formed when potassium cyanate is heated with an alkyl sulfate in the presence of dry sodium carbonate.

$$R_2SO_4 + KNCO \xrightarrow{Na_2CO_3} RN=C=O + RSO_4K$$

Phosgene reacts with primary amines to give alkylcarbamyl chlorides which on heating decompose to alkyl isocyanates.

$$2 RNH_2 + COCl_2 \longrightarrow RNH_3Cl + RNHCOCl \xrightarrow{Heat} RN=C=O + HCl$$

The alkyl isocyanates are intermediates in the Hofmann conversion of amides to amines (p. 197).

Like isocyanic acid, the isocyanates readily hydrolyze with water. The final products are the primary amine and carbon dioxide.

$$RN{=}C{=}O + H_2O \longrightarrow [RNHCOOH] \longrightarrow RNH_2 + CO_2$$

It is of interest that this reaction led to the discovery of amines by Wurtz (p. 106), who first prepared methylamine and ethylamine in 1849 by the hydrolysis of methyl and ethyl isocyanates obtained from potassium cyanate and the alkyl iodides.

Alcoholysis and ammonolysis of isocyanates yield urethans and substituted ureas.

$$RN{=}C{=}O + HOR' \longrightarrow RNHCOOR'$$
$$+ HNH_2 \longrightarrow RNHCONH_2$$
$$+ HNHR' \longrightarrow RNHCONHR'$$
$$+ HNR_2' \longrightarrow RNHCONR'_2$$

Because of the ease of reaction and the formation of solid products, the isocyanates, especially phenyl isocyanate (p. 364), frequently are used to prepare derivatives of alcohols and amines for identification purposes.

Although the alkyl isocyanates and alkyl isothiocyanates (p. 251) usually are considered as having twin double bonds, the dipole moments and electron diffraction data indicate that the molecules are linear. Hence the structure appears to be a resonance hybrid in which the nitrogen-carbon linkage has some triple bond character.

$$\left\{ RN{=}C{=}O \longleftrightarrow R\bar{N}{-}C{\equiv}\overset{+}{O} \longleftrightarrow R\overset{+}{N}{\equiv}C{-}\bar{O} \right\}$$

Fulminic acid is isomeric with the cyanic acids. Its reactions indicate that it is a derivative of carbon monoxide rather than of carbon dioxide or carbonic acid. For example it gives with hydrogen chloride an addition product which on hydrolysis yields formic acid and hydroxylamine hydrochloride. These reactions are explained best by considering fulminic acid to be the oxime of carbon monoxide; that is it contains the $-N{\equiv}C$: grouping present in the isocyanides.

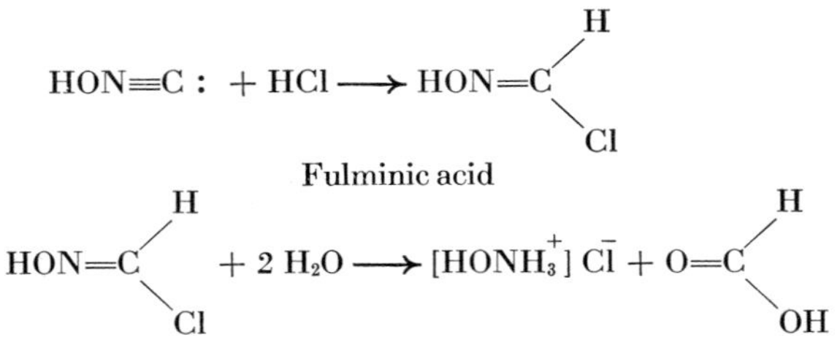

$$HON{\equiv}C: + HCl \longrightarrow HON{=}C\genfrac{}{}{0pt}{}{\diagup H}{\diagdown Cl}$$

Fulminic acid

$$HON{=}C\genfrac{}{}{0pt}{}{\diagup H}{\diagdown Cl} + 2\ H_2O \longrightarrow [HON\overset{+}{H_3}]\ \bar{Cl} + O{=}C\genfrac{}{}{0pt}{}{\diagup H}{\diagdown OH}$$

Attempts to isolate fulminic acid result in complex polymerization products, but its salts are well known. **Mercury fulminate** is prepared by the action of nitric acid on mercury and ethyl alcohol. It is highly explosive and can be detonated by heat or shock. It is used commercially in the manufacture of detonators for explosives. Liebig in 1823 showed that silver fulminate had the same composition as silver cyanate, previously analyzed by Woehler. This instance was the first recognition of the phenomenon which later became known as isomerism.

When urea nitrate is dissolved in concentrated sulfuric acid, **nitrourea** is formed.

$$[H_2NCONH_3^+] \, NO_3^- \xrightarrow[H_2SO_4]{Conc.} H_2NCONHNO_2 + H_2O$$
$$\text{Nitrourea}$$

Electrolytic reduction of nitrourea yields **semicarbazine (semicarbazide),** a valuable reagent for aldehydes and ketones (p. 172).

$$H_2NCONHNO_2 + 6 \, [H](\text{electrolytic}) \longrightarrow H_2NCONHNH_2 + 2 \, H_2O$$
$$\text{Semicarbazine}$$

Various methods are available for the preparation of **N-alkylureas** (pp. 244, 246). Direct alkylation of urea, however, gives **O-alkylureas.**

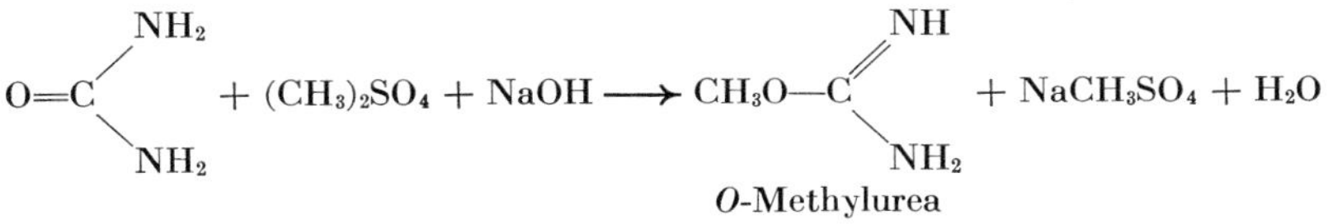

$$O{=}C\begin{matrix} NH_2 \\ \\ NH_2 \end{matrix} + (CH_3)_2SO_4 + NaOH \longrightarrow CH_3O{-}C\begin{matrix} NH \\ \\ NH_2 \end{matrix} + NaCH_3SO_4 + H_2O$$
$$\text{O-Methylurea}$$

The **cyanogen halides** may be regarded as the acid halides of cyanic acid. They are prepared by the reaction of halogens on metallic cyanides.

$$MCN + X_2 \longrightarrow XCN + MX$$

They are highly toxic lachrymators. **Cyanogen chloride** melts at $-6°$ and boils at $15.5°$. **Cyanogen bromide** melts at $52°$ and boils at $61°$. **Cyanogen iodide** sublimes at atmospheric pressure. The cyanogen halides are stable when pure but polymerize readily in the presence of free halogen to give the cyanuric halides.

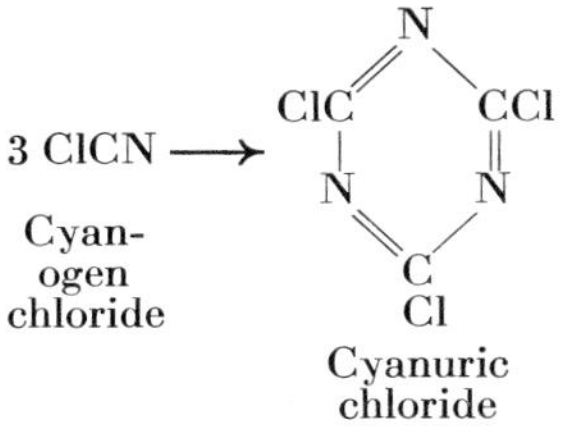

$$3 \text{ ClCN} \longrightarrow$$

Cyanogen chloride

Cyanuric chloride

Cyanamide, $H_2NC{\equiv}N$, may be considered as the amide of hydrocyanic acid and can be prepared by the reaction of cyanogen chloride or bromide with ammonia.

$$2 \text{ NH}_3 + \text{ClCN} \longrightarrow H_2NCN + NH_4Cl$$

It also may be regarded as the nitrile of carbamic acid, since it yields carbamide (urea) on hydrolysis with alkali.

$$H_2NC\!\equiv\!N + H_2O \xrightarrow{\text{[OH}^-\text{]}} H_2NCONH_2$$

Its most important derivative is the calcium salt, **calcium cyanamide,** which is made by passing nitrogen through calcium carbide at about 1100°. Pure calcium carbide does not absorb nitrogen at 1200°, but in the presence of 10 per cent calcium oxide, nitrogen is absorbed readily at 1050°.

$$CaC_2 \,(+\,CaO) + N_2 \longrightarrow CaNCN + C$$

The mixture is brought to reaction temperature by an electrically heated carbon rod, but after the exothermic reaction has been started, the carbon rod may be removed. The cyanamide process was the first important method for the fixation of atmospheric nitrogen, and calcium cyanamide has continued to be an important nitrogen fertilizer.

Cyanamide is stable in aqueous solutions of pH $<$ 5 but dimerizes readily to **dicyanamide** at pH 7–12. Hence dicyanamide is the product formed when calcium cyanamide is heated with water.

$$CaNCN + 2\,H_2O \longrightarrow Ca(OH)_2 + H_2NCN$$

$$H_2NC\!\equiv\!N + H_2NC\!\equiv\!N \longrightarrow \underset{\underset{NH}{\|}}{H_2NCNHC}\!\equiv\!N$$

Dicyanamide

When dicyanamide is heated in the presence of anhydrous ammonia and methyl alcohol, **melamine,** the cyclic trimer of cyanamide, is formed.

$$3\ \underset{\underset{NH}{\|}}{H_2NCNHC}\!\equiv\!N \xrightarrow[\text{heat}]{NH_3,\ CH_3OH} 2$$

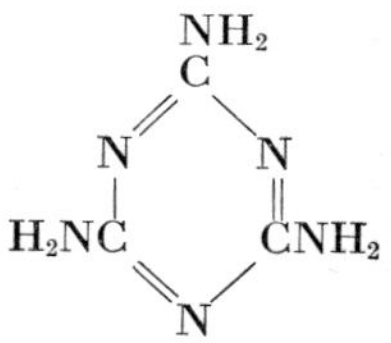

Melamine

The amidine amino groups of melamine, like the amide amino groups of urea, condense with formaldehyde to give high molecular weight products known as **melamine resins.** They are superior to the urea formaldehyde resins in resistance to heat and water.

Guanidine, $HN\!=\!C(NH_2)_2$, is formed when dicyanamide is heated with an excess of ammonia. If dicyanamide is heated with ammonium chloride, guanidine hydrochloride is formed.

$$\underset{\underset{NH}{\|}}{H_2NCNHCN} + 2\,NH_3 \longrightarrow 2\ HN\!=\!C(NH_2)_2$$

Guanidine

$$+\ 2\,NH_4Cl \longrightarrow 2\ [H_2\overset{+}{N}\!=\!C(NH_2)_2]\ Cl^-$$

Guanidine
hydrochloride

Guanidine is the strongest organic base known, having a basic strength comparable to that of hydroxide ion. The high basicity is believed to result from the large amount of resonance energy liberated when a proton adds to guanidine. The high resonance energy is to be expected since the contributing structures are identical (cf. urea, p. 241).

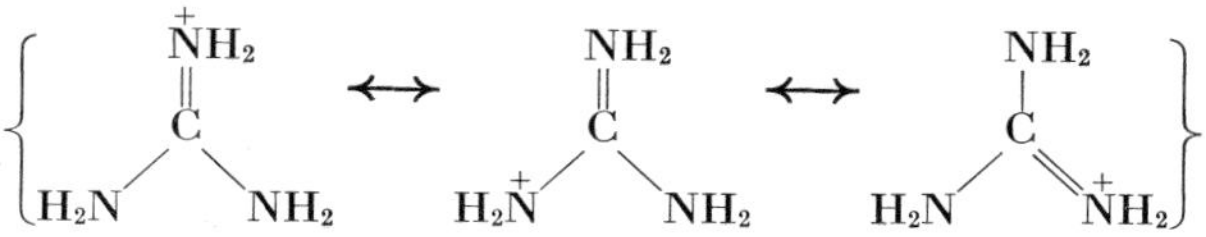

$$\left\{ \begin{array}{ccc} \overset{+}{N}H_2 & NH_2 & NH_2 \\ \| & \| & \| \\ C & \longleftrightarrow \quad C \quad \longleftrightarrow & C \\ H_2N \quad NH_2 & H_2\overset{+}{N} \quad NH_2 & H_2N \quad \overset{+}{N}H_2 \end{array} \right\}$$

Although the salts of guanidine are prepared readily, it is difficult to obtain the free base. If alcoholic solutions of the perchlorate and potassium hydroxide are mixed, potassium perchlorate precipitates. The alcoholic filtrate may be evaporated to give the free base.

When guanidine nitrate is mixed with concentrated sulfuric acid, **nitroguanidine** is formed.

$$[H_2\overset{+}{N}{=}C(NH_2)_2]NO_3^- \xrightarrow{H_2SO_4} HN{=}CNHNO_2 + H_2O$$
$$\underset{NH_2}{|}$$
$$\text{Nitroguanidine}$$

It is used as a component of some explosives. It is about as powerful as TNT and explodes without producing a flash. When mixed with colloided nitrocellulose it gives a flashless propellant powder.

Two derivatives of guanidine are of great importance in biological processes. **Creatine** is methylguanidinoacetic acid. Its phosphoric acid derivative is **phosphagen,** which plays an important part in the muscular activity of vertebrates. Creatine is dehydrated readily to **creatinine,** which is excreted in the urine.

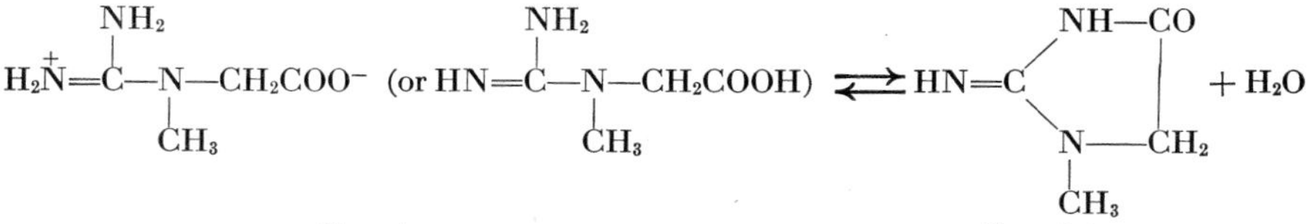

$$\underset{\underset{CH_3}{|}}{H_2\overset{+}{N}{=}C{-}N{-}CH_2COO^-} \text{ (or } \underset{\underset{CH_3}{|}}{HN{=}C{-}N{-}CH_2COOH)} \rightleftarrows HN{=}C\underset{\underset{CH_3}{|}}{\overset{NH{-}CO}{\underset{N{-}{-}CH_2}{\big\langle}}} + H_2O$$

Creatine   Creatinine

The amino acid **arginine** is α-amino-δ-guanidino-n-valeric acid and is involved in nitrogen metabolism in mammals. It takes part also in the muscular processes of invertebrates.

DERIVATIVES OF THIOCARBONIC ACID

Many of the derivatives of carbonic acid have sulfur analogs, some of which are of general interest. Carbon oxysulfide and carbon disulfide are analogs of carbon dioxide. **Carbon oxysulfide** may be prepared by passing a mixture of carbon monoxide and sulfur vapor through a hot iron tube at 500°.

$$CO + S \xrightarrow{500°} COS$$

It is an odorless, toxic gas, boiling at $-47.5°$. **Carbon disulfide** is manufactured on a large scale by reaction of sulfur with charcoal at a high temperature, either in direct-fired retorts or in a continuous type furnace in which the charcoal is heated by the resistance it offers to the electric current.

$$C + 2S \longrightarrow CS_2$$

It can be prepared also by the reaction of methane and sulfur at 700° over an alumina catalyst.

$$CH_4 + 4S \xrightarrow[\text{Al}_2\text{O}_3]{700°} CS_2 + 2H_2S$$

Carbon disulfide is a toxic, low-boiling, highly inflammable liquid that is used to some extent as a solvent, as a toxic agent for rodents, and as an intermediate for the manufacture of carbon tetrachloride (p. 505). The principal uses are in the manufacture of viscose rayon, rubber accelerators, and fungicides.

When solutions of alkali hydroxide or alkoxides in alcohols are mixed with carbon disulfide, the *alkali alkyl dithiocarbonates* are formed. These ester salts commonly are known as **xanthates.**[1]

$$\overset{\text{S}}{\underset{\text{}}{\|}}$$
$$C_2H_5OH + CS_2 + NaOH \longrightarrow C_2H_5OCS^-Na^+$$

Sodium ethyl
xanthate

The alkyl hydrogen dithiocarbonates decompose at room temperature into carbon disulfide and alcohol. Hence the above reaction is reversed by the addition of acid.

$$C_2H_5O\overset{\text{S}}{\overset{\|}{C}}S^-Na^+ + HCl \longrightarrow \left[C_2H_5O\overset{\text{S}}{\overset{\|}{C}}SH \right] + NaCl$$

$$\downarrow$$

$$C_2H_5OH + CS_2$$

The *sodium alkyl xanthates* are used as collecting agents in the flotation process for the concentration of ores. The most important use of the reaction of carbon disulfide with hydroxyl groups is for the production of viscose solutions from cellulose (p. 304). **Zinc butyl xanthate,** or *ZBX*, is a very active accelerator for the vulcanization of rubber (p. 498).

Analogous to the reaction of alcohols with carbon disulfide is the reaction of ammonia and of primary and secondary amines to give the amine salts of **dithiocarbamic acids.**

$$S{=}C{=}S + HNH_2 \longrightarrow \left[H_2N\overset{\text{S}}{\overset{\|}{C}}S^- \right] \overset{+}{N}H_4$$

Ammonium
dithiocarbamate

---

[1] Originally, the reaction product of carbon disulfide, ethyl alcohol, and potassium hydroxide was known as potassium xanthate because it gave a yellow precipitate with copper sulfate (Gr. *xanthos*, yellow). Accordingly xanthic acid should be C_2H_5OCSSH. Since the chief variation in the xanthates is in the nature of the alkyl group, it is preferable to give the common name xanthic acid to the hypothetical dithiocarbonic acid, $HOCSSH$.

$$S=C=S + HNHR \longrightarrow \left[RNH\overset{\overset{\displaystyle S}{\|}}{C}S^- \right] \overset{+}{N}H_3R$$

$$+ HNR_2 \longrightarrow \left[R_2N\overset{\overset{\displaystyle S}{\|}}{C}S^- \right] \overset{+}{N}H_2R_2$$

In the presence of zinc oxide, the product from dimethylamine and carbon disulfide, $[(CH_3)_2NCSS^-]\overset{+}{N}H_2(CH_3)_2$, and the zinc salt, $[(CH_3)_2NCSS^-]_2Zn^{++}$, are powerful rubber accelerators. The zinc salt and iron salts are valuable fungicides and are sold for this purpose under the trade names *Zerlate* and *Fermate*.

Like all thiols, the dithiocarbamates are oxidized readily to disulfides. The products are known as **thiuram disulfides.** Tetramethylthiuram disulfide, $(CH_3)_2NCSS$—$SCSN(CH_3)_2$, is a valuable rubber accelerator known as *Tuads* (p. 498). It is used also in fungicidal preparations for disinfecting seeds and turf. Tetraethylthiuram disulfide (**antabuse**) has been used for the treatment of chronic alcoholism. A patient who has been given the compound orally becomes violently ill on drinking alcoholic beverages.

When the alkali cyanides are heated with sulfur, the thiocyanates are formed.

$$NaCN + S \longrightarrow NaSCN$$

Unlike the cyanates, which react with alkylating agents to give alkyl isocyanates (p. 245), the alkali thiocyanates give the **alkyl thiocyanates.**

$$(CH_3)_2SO_4 + NaSCN \longrightarrow CH_3SCN + NaCH_3SO_4$$
Methyl
thiocyanate

If in the reaction of an alkyl halide or sulfate with an anion there are two possible modes of union of the alkyl group with the anion, that giving rise to the more completely covalent bond takes place. Thus when an alkyl halide reacts with cyanide ion, a carbon-carbon bond is formed to give chiefly the alkyl cyanide rather than a carbon-nitrogen bond to give the isocyanide; the nitrite ion gives the nitro compound having a carbon-nitrogen bond rather than the nitrite having a carbon-oxygen bond. Similarly the cyanate ion gives the isocyanate having a carbon-nitrogen bond rather than the cyanate having a carbon-oxygen bond, the thiocyanate ion gives the thiocyanate having a carbon-sulfur bond rather than an isothiocyanate having a carbon-nitrogen bond, and the sulfite ion gives the sulfonate (p. 218) having a carbon-sulfur bond rather than a sulfite with a carbon-oxygen bond.

The **isothiocyanates,** or **mustard oils,** are obtained by the removal of hydrogen sulfide from *N*-alkyldithiocarbamates by means of a reagent such as lead nitrate that can give an insoluble sulfide.

$$[RNHCSS^-]\overset{+}{N}H_3R + Pb(NO_3)_2 \longrightarrow RN=C=S + PbS + RNH_3NO_3 + HNO_3$$

The isothiocyanates are called mustard oils because **allyl isothiocyanate,** $CH_2=CHCH_2NCS$, is one of the hydrolytic products of a glycoside occurring in black mustard. All of the volatile mustard oils have sharp characteristic odors.

Like the alkyl isocyanates, the alkyl isothiocyanates readily add alcohols and amines, the products being **alkyl thiocarbamates (thiourethans)** and **thioureas.**

$$RNCS + HOR' \longrightarrow RNHCSOR'$$

$$+ HNHR' \longrightarrow RNHCSNHR'$$

$$+ HNR'_2 \longrightarrow RNHCSNR'_2$$

Solid substituted ureas formed from **phenyl isothiocyanate,** $C_6H_5N=C=S$ (p. 366), are useful derivatives for amines. The rate of reaction with amines is so much faster than with water that the reaction can be carried out on aqueous solutions of amines.

Thiocyanogen, $N\equiv CS-SC\equiv N$, is prepared by the action of bromine in ether solution on lead thiocyanate. It is an unstable liquid at room temperature and usually is used in solution. It behaves like the halogens, being intermediate in reactivity between bromine and iodine. It liberates iodine from potassium iodide and adds to the olefinic double bond.

$$RCH=CHR + (SCN)_2 \longrightarrow RCH-CHR$$
$$\qquad\qquad\qquad\qquad | \quad |$$
$$\qquad\qquad\qquad\quad SCN \ SCN$$

Thiourea can be produced from ammonium thiocyanate, a product of the coal gas industry, by a reaction analogous to Woehler's synthesis of urea.

$$NH_4SCN \rightleftharpoons S=C(NH_2)_2$$

In contrast to the production of ammonium cyanate, however, the rate of the reaction is very slow at 100°, and the molten salt must be heated to about 175° for rapid reaction. At this temperature the equilibrium is not very favorable, only one fifth being converted to thiourea. After the melt has cooled the unchanged thiocyanate is dissolved in water, and the insoluble thiourea is removed. The filtrate may be concentrated and the cycle repeated until the conversion is practically complete. Thiourea can be made also by the action of hydrogen sulfide on calcium cyanamide.

$$CaNCN + 2 H_2S \xrightarrow{150°-180°} CaS + H_2NCSNH_2$$

N-Substituted thioureas are obtained by the reaction of amines with alkyl isothiocyanates. The direct alkylation of thiourea gives the salt of the S-alkyl derivative from which the **S-alkylthiourea** (frequently called alkylisothiourea) is obtained by adding alkali.

$$(H_2N)_2C=S + RX \longrightarrow \begin{bmatrix} H_2N-C-SR \\ \underset{+NH_2}{\overset{\|}{}} \end{bmatrix} X^- \xrightarrow{NaOH} RSC \overset{\displaystyle NH}{\underset{\displaystyle NH_2}{\diagup\diagdown}} + NaX + H_2O$$

S-Alkylthiourea
(alkylisothiourea)

S-Substituted thioureas such as *S*-benzylthiourea, $C_6H_5CH_2SC(=NH)NH_2$, react with carboxylic and sulfonic acids to form thiuronium salts that crystallize readily and may be used as derivatives for the identification of the acids.

REVIEW QUESTIONS

1. Write structural formulas for orthocarbonic acid, carbonic acid, and carbon dioxide, indicating by brackets the compounds which cannot be isolated. Write structural formulas for those acid chlorides, esters, and amides, formally derivable from the above three compounds, which are known to exist as individual compounds. Give the common names for each type of derivative.
2. Write equations for a common method of preparation for each type of compound given above.
3. Give equations for all the reactions that should be suitable for the preparation of urea.
4. Which processes for the synthesis of urea have been operated commercially, and which is the present commercial process? What are the commercial uses of urea?
5. Discuss the mechanism of the conversion of ammonium cyanate into urea.
6. Discuss and give equations for the behavior of urea at elevated temperatures.
7. What is the biuret test? Write the electronic formula for the product.
8. Give equations for the reaction of urea with aqueous alkali, nitrous acid, and sodium hypobromite. What is the usual procedure for the quantitative estimation of urea?
9. Discuss the basicity of urea. Why does it form a stable salt with nitric acid?
10. What are ureids? Give an example.
11. What is methylolurea and how is it prepared? Discuss its relation to the urea-formaldehyde resins and indicate the mechanism of thermosetting for this type of resin.
12. What is cyanuric acid?
13. How are alkyl isocyanates prepared? Give equations for their characteristic reactions.
14. How are the *N*-alkyl derivatives of urea prepared? The *O*-alkyl derivatives?
15. How is calcium cyanamide made? What are its uses?
16. Compare the steps in the polymerization of cyanamide to dicyanamide to melamine, with the polymerization of cyanic acid.
17. Give a series of reactions for the preparation of pure secondary amines starting with calcium cyanamide.
18. How is guanidine made? Why is it a much stronger base than urea?
19. Give the formulas for the more common stable sulfur analogs of the derivatives of carbon dioxide.
20. How is carbon disulfide made and what are its more important uses?
21. Discuss the preparation and reactions of alkyl thiocyanates and of alkyl isothiocyanates.
22. What are xanthates, how are they prepared, and what are their uses?
23. How are thiourea and the alkyl substituted thioureas made?
24. Discuss the preparation and importance of the derivatives of dithiocarbamic acid.

Chapter 17

STEREOISOMERISM

The existence of two or more compounds having the same number and kinds of atoms and the same molecular weight has been called *isomerism*; that is isomers have the same *composition* and are represented by the same molecular formulas. Two main types of isomers exist, the most common type being known as **structural isomers,** because it is assumed that the differences between these isomers result from the different ways in which the atoms can be attached to each other. For example butane and isobutane differ in that butane has the carbon atoms linked in a chain, and isobutane has a branched carbon skeleton. Such structural isomers may be called *skeletal isomers*. Structural isomers may arise also from the possibility of more than one position for some other element or group as with 1-chloropropane and 2-chloropropane. These isomers are called *position isomers*. In more complex compounds, greater differences in structure may exist, giving rise to different functional groups in the molecule as with methyl ether and ethyl alcohol. Structural isomers of this type may be called *functional isomers*. The way in which atoms are believed to be joined together is spoken of as the *constitution* of the compound and is represented by structural formulas.

In the second type of isomerism, however, the isomers have the same structural formulas. To explain this type of isomerism it is necessary to postulate a different distribution of the atoms in space, and the phenomenon is known as **stereoisomerism** (Gr. *steros* solid). The subject of stereoisomerism may be divided into two parts, *geometrical isomerism* and *optical isomerism*. The space arrangement of the atoms is referred to as the *configuration* of the molecule, and space models, or perspective drawings, or projections of the space models usually must be used to illustrate the difference between stereoisomers. The three terms *composition*, *constitution*, and *configuration* have definite and distinct meanings. They should not be used interchangeably.

GEOMETRICAL ISOMERISM

Oxides of nitrogen convert oleic acid into elaidic acid, an isomer having the same constitution (p. 155). Although only one 1-butene is known, there are two 2-butenes, one boiling at 0.96° and the other at 3.73°. Similarly 1,1-dichloroethylene exists in only a single form, but two forms of 1,2-dichloroethylene are known, one boiling at 48.3° and the other at 60.5°. The explanation of the increased number of isomers in certain unsaturated compounds is that the two doubly-bound carbon atoms and the four atoms or groups joined to them lie in a plane and that free rotation about the double bond is not possible. Hence if the two groups on each carbon atom are different, two isomers can result (Fig. 31). If the two members of either pair of groups are alike, only one compound is possible. Accordingly in one of the 2-butenes the two methyl groups are on the same side of the molecule, and in the other they

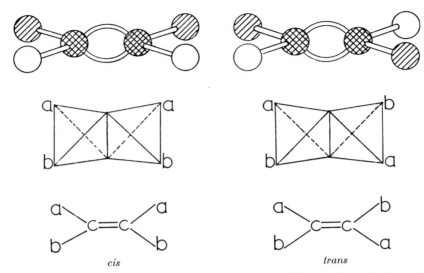

Fig. 31. Representation of *cis* and *trans* forms of geometrical isomers by molecular models, by tetrahedra, and by projection formulas.

are on opposite sides. The isomer with like groups on the same side is known as the *cis* form whereas that in which like groups are on opposite sides is known as the *trans* form (L. *cis* on this side, *trans* across). A similar explanation accounts for the two 1,2-dichloroethylenes.

$$
\begin{array}{cc}
H \qquad\qquad H & CH_3 \qquad\qquad H \\
\diagdown\quad\diagup & \diagdown\quad\diagup \\
C\!=\!C & C\!=\!C \\
\diagup\quad\diagdown & \diagup\quad\diagdown \\
CH_3 \qquad\qquad CH_3 & H \qquad\qquad CH_3 \\
\textit{cis-2-Butene} & \textit{trans-2-Butene}
\end{array}
$$

$$
\begin{array}{cc}
H \qquad\qquad H & Cl \qquad\qquad H \\
\diagdown\quad\diagup & \diagdown\quad\diagup \\
C\!=\!C & C\!=\!C \\
\diagup\quad\diagdown & \diagup\quad\diagdown \\
Cl \qquad\qquad Cl & H \qquad\qquad Cl \\
\textit{cis-1,2-Dichloroethylene} & \textit{trans-1,2-Dichloroethylene}
\end{array}
$$

By a rather complicated procedure it has been proved that *cis*-2-butene is the isomer boiling at 3.73° and *trans*-2-butene is that boiling at 0.96°. The determination of the configuration of the two 1,2-dichloroethylenes was easier, since the dipole moment of the carbon-halogen bond is much larger than that of the carbon-hydrogen bond. An examination of the proposed structures of

$$
\begin{array}{cc}
H \qquad X & X \qquad H \\
\diagdown\quad\diagup & \diagdown\quad\diagup \\
C & C \\
\| & \| \\
C & C \\
\diagup\quad\diagdown & \diagup\quad\diagdown \\
H \qquad X & H \qquad X \\
\textit{cis} & \textit{trans}
\end{array}
$$

the two isomers indicates that the *trans* isomer should have zero dipole moment, because the individual bond moments cancel each other. The *cis* compound on the other hand should have a resultant moment for the molecule as a whole. The arrow represents the direction and magnitude of the moment, the + on the tail indicating the positive end of the moment. The melting points and moments of the 1,2-dihaloethylenes are given in Table 15. The *trans* isomer usually has the higher melting point.

TABLE 15

DIPOLE MOMENTS OF 1,2-DIHALOETHYLENES

	M.p.	μ
1,2-Dichloroethylene (*trans*)	-50	0
(*cis*)	-80	1.85
1,2-Dibromoethylene (*trans*)	-6	0
(*cis*)	-53	1.35
1,2-Diiodoethylene (*trans*)	$+72$	0
(*cis*)	-14	0.75

The configuration of some geometrical isomers can be determined from differences in their chemical reactions. Thus of the maleic and fumaric acids, maleic acid is assigned the *cis* configuration because of the greater ease with which it forms an anhydride (p. 546).

The isomerization of the unsaturated fat acids now is understandable. The naturally occurring compounds exist as one form, which in the presence of the free-radical type catalyst is converted to its geometrical isomer. Thus the liquid *cis* oleic acid is transformed into an equilibrium mixture with its solid *trans* isomer, elaidic acid.

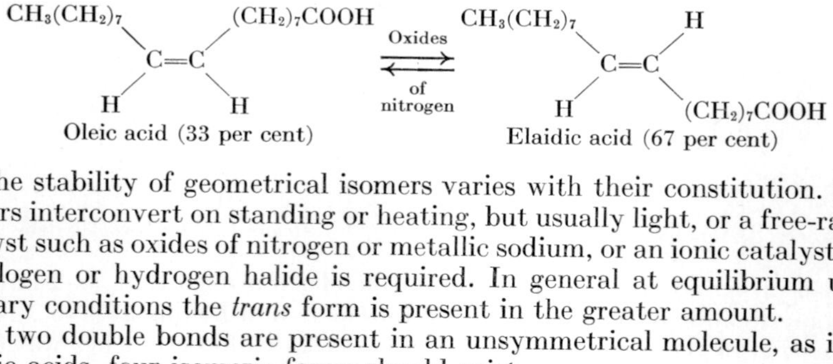

Oleic acid (33 per cent)   Elaidic acid (67 per cent)

The stability of geometrical isomers varies with their constitution. Some isomers interconvert on standing or heating, but usually light, or a free-radical catalyst such as oxides of nitrogen or metallic sodium, or an ionic catalyst such as halogen or hydrogen halide is required. In general at equilibrium under ordinary conditions the *trans* form is present in the greater amount.

If two double bonds are present in an unsymmetrical molecule, as in the linoleic acids, four isomeric forms should exist.

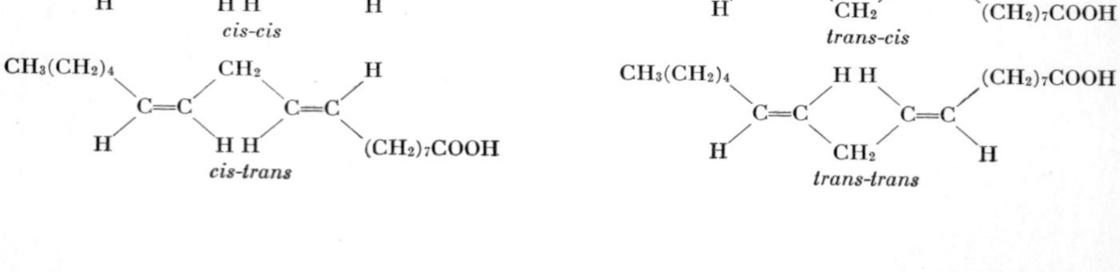

cis-cis   trans-cis

cis-trans   trans-trans

If the molecule is symmetrical, a smaller number of isomers is predicted. For example only three geometrical isomers are possible for 2,4-hexadiene, the *trans-cis* and *cis-trans* forms being identical.

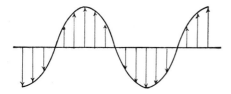

cis-cis   trans-trans   cis-trans

Examples of geometrical isomerism dependent on carbon-nitrogen and nitrogen-nitrogen double bonds also are known (cf. p. 408).

OPTICAL ISOMERISM

Polarized Light

Wave motion may be caused by longitudinal vibrations or transverse vibrations. In a longitudinal vibration, such as a sound wave, the vibrations are parallel to the direction of propagation and symmetrical about the line of propagation. In a transverse vibration, such as an ocean wave, the vibrations are perpendicular to the direction of propagation and there is a lack of symmetry about the line of propagation. The propagation of such a wave may be represented by Fig. 32, which shows the instantaneous magnitude of the vibra-

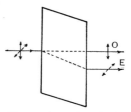

Fig. 32. Propagation of a wave by transverse vibrations.

Fig. 33. Double refraction by a calcite crystal.

tions over a given distance. The behavior of the vibrators during propagation of the wave may be visualized by moving the boundary of the wave along the direction of propagation. Each vector maintains a fixed position and direction but varies continuously in magnitude from zero to $+1$ to zero to -1 to zero.

Ordinary light does not show a lack of symmetry, but in 1669 Erasmus Bartholinus [1] discovered that a properly oriented crystal of iceland spar (calcite, a crystalline calcium carbonate) divides a single ray of ordinary light into two rays. Thus a single line viewed through the crystal appears as two lines. This phenomenon is known as *double refraction*. Eight years later Huygens [2] found that each of the rays formed by double refraction is vibrating

---

[1] Erasmus Bartholinus (1625–1698), Danish professor of mathematics and medicine at the University of Copenhagen.

[2] Christiaan Huygens (1629–1695), Dutch mathematician, astronomer, and physicist. He is known best for his contributions to physical optics.

in a single plane and that the plane of vibration of one ray is perpendicular to the plane of vibration of the other ray (Fig. 33).

Thus the symmetry of a ray of ordinary light about the direction of propagation is caused by transverse vibrations in all directions perpendicular to the direction of propagation. If two mutually perpendicular planes are passed through the ray, each vector will have a component in each plane as indicated in Fig. 34. The action of the calcite crystal is to separate the vectors into their

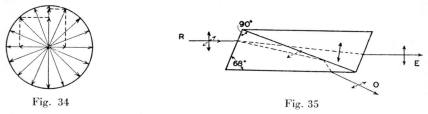

Fig. 34   Fig. 35

Fig. 34. Vibrating vectors along direction of propagation of light ray. Dotted lines indicate how each vector may be considered to be the resultant of two components vibrating at right angles to each other.

Fig. 35. Production of plane-polarized light by a Nicol prism.

components. The emergent rays, each of which is vibrating in a single plane, are said to be *plane-polarized*.

The velocity of light in any material medium is slower than in a vacuum. The ratio of the velocity in a vacuum to the velocity in a material medium is called the *refractive index*. When the velocity of the light is decreased, the path of the ray is bent. The amount of bending is proportional to the amount of retardation. In double refraction the crystal can propagate waves in one plane faster than those vibrating in the plane perpendicular to it. Hence the light is sorted into two rays, one of which is traveling slower than the other and hence is bent more.

The Nicol prism,[3] invented in 1828, is a device for separating one plane-polarized ray from the other. The calcite crystal is a rectangular rhombohedron, the acute angles measuring 71 degrees. In the Nicol prism the two end faces are cut away until these angles are reduced to 68 degrees, and the crystal is divided in a plane perpendicular to the two ends and through the edges of the obtuse angles. The surfaces are polished and the two halves cemented together with Canada balsam, which has an index of refraction less than that of calcite for one of the polarized rays and greater than that of calcite for the other. The action of the Nicol prism is illustrated in Fig. 35. A light ray, *r*, entering the prism parallel to the long axis is doubly refracted. The ordinary ray, *O*, is totally reflected from the surface of the Canada balsam. The extraordinary ray, *E*, is transmitted through the crystal. The reduction in the acute angles of the original calcite crystal from 71 degrees to 68 degrees is for the purpose of securing the proper angle of incidence on the balsam to produce this effect.

If a similarly oriented second Nicol prism is placed in the line of the

---

[3] William Nicol (1768–1851), Scottish physicist who pursued his investigations privately. He devoted himself chiefly to the examination of fluid-filled cavities in crystals, to the manufacture of microscope lenses, and to the microscopic examination of fossil wood.

emergent plane-polarized ray, the ray will pass through the second prism without being affected. If, however, the second prism is rotated about its long axis through 90 degrees, the effect would be the same as if the ray were vibrating at right angles to its original direction, and it would be totally reflected from the Canada balsam layer of the second prism. Two prisms so placed that the plane-polarized ray transmitted by one is not transmitted by the other are spoken of as *crossed Nicols.*

Light may be polarized by processes other than double refraction. In 1808 Malus [4] discovered that light reflected from a glass surface at a particular angle is plane-polarized. When ordinary light passes through a crystal of the mineral tourmaline, the component vibrating in one plane is absorbed much more strongly than that vibrating perpendicular to this plane. This phenomenon is known as *dichroism.* If a dichroic crystal is of the proper thickness, the more strongly absorbed component will be practically extinguished, whereas the other is transmitted in appreciable amount as plane-polarized light. The modern Polaroid operates on the same principle, the absorbing medium being a film containing properly oriented microscopic crystals of a dichroic substance such as the periodide sulfate of quinine. The transmitted light is slightly colored and not completely polarized, but it is possible by this method to make polarizing plates of large area at reasonable cost.

Optical Activity

In 1811 Arago,[5] a pupil of Malus, found that a quartz plate obtained by cutting a quartz crystal perpendicular to the crystal axis will cause the rotation of the plane of polarization of plane-polarized light. This phenomenon can be observed best by placing a plate of quartz between crossed Nicols, the face of one of the Nicol prisms being illuminated from a light source. Before the quartz plate is placed between the two Nicol prisms, no light passes through the second prism. With the quartz plate between them, some light passes through the second prism, which now must be rotated through a definite angle to become dark again. *The ability to rotate the plane of polarization of plane-polarized light* is called **optical activity,** and substances possessing this ability are said to be *optically active.* The number of degrees of arc through which the second crystal must be rotated to restore the original condition is called the *optical rotation* of the optically active substance and is given the symbol α.

Haüy [6] had discovered two kinds of quartz, the crystals differing only in the location of two facets which caused the crystals to be nonidentical mirror images. Because of the mirror image relationships they were called *enantiomorphs* (Gr. *enantios* opposite, *morph* form). In 1815 Biot,[7] another pupil of

---

[4] Etienne Louis Malus (1775–1812), French military engineer. He left the army in 1801 and died of tuberculosis in Paris at the age of 37.

[5] Dominique François Jean Arago (1786–1853), French physicist who, after successfully completing a geodetic survey through Spain, was appointed an astronomer of the French Royal Observatory, a post that he held until his death. He was active in French politics and did much to enhance the prestige of French science.

[6] Rene Just Haüy (1743–1822), French mineralogist who is regarded as one of the founders of the science of crystallography.

[7] Jean Baptiste Biot (1774–1862), French physicist who was associated with Arago in various geodetic surveys. His most important work dealt with optics, especially the polarization of light.

Malus, found that plates of the same thickness from the two kinds of quartz rotate plane-polarized light the same amount but in opposite directions. The form which rotates the plane of polarization to the right when facing the light source is called *dextrorotatory* and that which rotates the plane of polarization to the left is called *levorotatory*. Biot found also that other substances such as sugar solutions and turpentine are optically active, the latter even in the vapor phase.

Measurement of Optical Rotation

The instrument used to measure the extent of rotation of plane-polarized light is called a *polarimeter* or *polariscope* (Fig. 36). It consists of a fixed Nicol

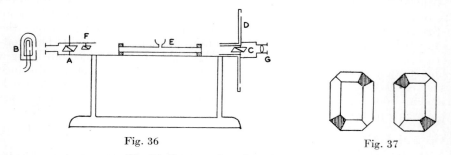

Fig. 36   Fig. 37

Fig. 36. Cross section of a polarimeter.
Fig. 37. Enantiomorphic crystals of the active forms of ammonium acid malate.

prism, *A*, known as the *polarizer*, for polarizing the monochromatic light from the light source, *B*. A second Nicol prism, *C*, known as the *analyzer*, is attached to a disk, *D*, graduated in degrees and fractions of a degree that can be rotated. The container for the sample is a tube, *E*, with clear glass ends, known as a *polarimeter tube*. The polarizer and analyzer are mounted on a suitable stand with a trough between them to hold the polarimeter tube in the path of the polarized light. Since it is easier for the eye to match two adjacent areas to the same degree of brightness than to determine a point of maximum darkness or brightness, a third smaller Nicol prism, *F*, is placed behind the polarizer and rotated through a small angle. In this way the field is divided into two halves of unequal brightness. An eyepiece, *G*, focuses on this field. By rotating the analyzer the fields may be brought to equal brightness which provides a zero point. When an optically active substance is placed in the path of the light, the fields become unequally bright. Rotation of the analyzer returns the two fields to equal intensity. The number of degrees through which the analyzer is rotated measures the activity of the sample.

The extent of rotation varies inversely with the square of the wavelength of the light. This phenomenon is known as *rotatory dispersion*. If white light were used as a source of light, each wavelength would be rotated a different amount while passing through the solution. Accordingly it is necessary to use monochromatic light when measuring optical activity. Usually the *D* line of sodium is used, although frequently it is preferable to use the green line of the mercury arc or the red line of the cadmium arc.

Since the amount of rotation is directly proportional to the length of the path through the active material, this distance must be accurately known. Finally for solutions the extent of rotation depends on the concentration or weight per unit volume of the substance in the solution. These statements are summarized in the equation

$$\alpha = \frac{k\,g\,l}{v}$$

where α = the observed rotation
$\quad g$ = grams of dissolved substance
$\quad v$ = volume of the solution in cubic centimeters
$\quad l$ = length of tube in decimeters
$\quad k$ = a constant characteristic of the compound.

The constant k is called the *specific rotation* of the compound and is designated by the symbol $[\alpha]$, whence $[\alpha] = \frac{\alpha\,v}{g\,l}$. The wavelength used and the temperature of the solution are designated by subscript and superscript. For example $[\alpha]_D^{25}$ indicates that the rotation was determined at $25°$ using the D line of sodium. The *molecular rotation*, $[M]$, is the specific rotation multiplied by the molecular weight and divided by 100.

$$[M] = \frac{M[\alpha]}{100}$$

Usually there is more or less electrical effect between solute molecules and between solvent and solute molecules, which causes the specific rotation to vary somewhat with different concentrations and with different solvents. Hence it is desirable to indicate both the concentration and the solvent used. Thus a proper description of a specific rotation would be

$$[\alpha]_D^{25} = 95.01° \text{ in methyl alcohol } (c = 0.105 \text{ g./cc.})$$

Optical Isomerism

By 1848 two isomeric acids were known which had been isolated from the tartar of grapes. The common acid called tartaric acid had been found by Biot to be dextrorotatory. Its isomer, which had been isolated by Berzelius in 1831 and named racemic acid (L. *racemes* a bunch of berries or grapes), was optically inactive. In the spring of 1848, Pasteur (p. 67) was studying the crystal structure of sodium ammonium tartrate. He noticed that the crystals were characterized by facets which eliminated certain elements of symmetry from the crystal (cf. p. 263). Such facets are known as *hemihedral facets*, since they occur in only half the number required for complete symmetry. As a result of the occurrence of the hemihedral facets, the crystals and their mirror images were not identical; that is the mirror image could not be superimposed on the crystal with coincidence at all points. Figure 37 shows enantiomorphic crystals of the active forms of ammonium acid malate (p. 547). These crystals have fewer faces than those of the sodium ammonium tartrates, and the hemihedral facets can be seen readily. If the hemihedral facets were lacking or if the crystals were holohedral, that is if the facets appeared on all corners, the mirror images would be identical.

Recalling that the active quartz crystals had hemihedral facets and that

Herschel [8] in 1820 had suggested that there may be a connection between the hemihedralism of quartz and its optical activity, Pasteur proceeded to examine crystals of the inactive sodium ammonium racemate, expecting to find them holohedral. He found instead that all of the racemate crystals had hemihedral facets, and that two kinds of crystals were present. One kind was identical with the crystals of sodium ammonium tartrate, and the other kind consisted of mirror images of the tartrate crystals. Pasteur separated the two types of crystals under the microscope and found that the type that looked like sodium ammonium tartrate was indeed dextrorotatory and identical with it, but that the mirror image crystals, when dissolved in water, rotated plane-polarized light exactly the same amount in the opposite direction. When equal weights of the two crystals were mixed, the solution was optically inactive. In other words the reason that racemic acid is inactive is because it is composed of equal quantities of two different kinds of molecules, one dextrorotatory and the other levorotatory.

Quartz and other active crystals such as sodium chlorate and magnesium sulfate lose their optical activity on solution. Similarly amorphous silica is optically inactive. Hence the cause of the activity in the crystal lies in the arrangement of the atoms in the crystal. Tartaric acid, on the other hand, is active in solution. Moreover pinene from oil of turpentine is active in both the liquid and gaseous states. In these compounds the activity must be due to the arrangement of the atoms in the individual molecules. Pasteur himself came to this conclusion, but since the theories of structural organic chemistry were not developed until around 1860 (p. 4), he did not recognize the principle necessary to relate optical activity to molecular structure.

By 1874 the constitution of a number of active compounds was known. In September and November of that year two papers appeared, one by van't Hoff [9] and the other by Le Bel,[10] in which each pointed out that in every case in which optical activity existed, at least one carbon atom was present that was combined with four different groups. The following examples may be cited, the carbon atoms under discussion being marked by an asterisk.

$$\overset{*}{CH_3CH_2CHCH_2OH}$$
$$|$$
$$CH_3$$

Active amyl alcohol

$$CH_3\overset{*}{C}HCOOH$$
$$|$$
$$OH$$

Lactic acid

$$HOOCCH_2\overset{*}{C}HCOOH$$
$$|$$
$$OH$$

Malic acid

$$HOOCCH_2\overset{*}{C}HCOOH$$
$$|$$
$$NH_2$$

Aspartic acid

---

[8] John Frederick William Herschel (1792–1871), noted English astronomer who by inclination was more interested in chemistry and the properties of light and made many valuable contributions in these fields.

[9] Jacobus Hendricus van't Hoff (1852–1911), Dutch physical chemist, professor at Amsterdam University and after 1896 at the Prussian Academy of Sciences and the University of Berlin. He is noted not only for his theoretical contributions to stereoisomerism, but also for his contributions to the theories of solutions and of chemical equilibria. He was the first recipient of the Nobel Prize in Chemistry in 1901.

[10] Jules Achille Le Bel (1847–1930), French chemist who was financially independent and conducted his investigations privately. His experimental work dealt largely with the verification of predictions based on his stereochemical theories.

Wherever a pair of isomers differing in sign of rotation was known, the members of the pair had identical chemical and physical properties with the exception of their action on plane-polarized light, and even here they differed only in the sign of rotation and not in the magnitude of rotation. Accordingly the space relationship between atoms of one isomer must be the same as that between the atoms of the other isomer. van't Hoff and Le Bel pointed out that if the four different groups about the carbon atom are placed at the four corners of a tetrahedron, two arrangements are possible. Two molecules result which are mirror images of each other, but which are not superimposable and hence not identical (Fig. 38). The asymmetry of such arrangements is of

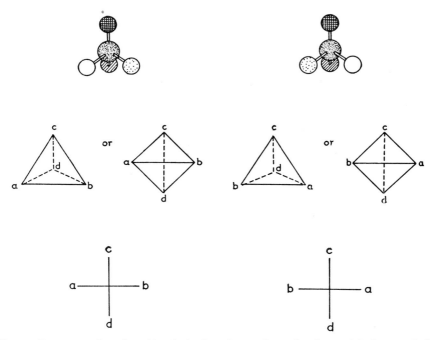

Fig. 38. Representation of nonidentical mirror images by molecular models, by tetrahedra, and by projection formulas.

the same type as the asymmetry of the quartz crystals or of the sodium ammonium tartrate crystals; that is *the condition necessary for the existence of optical activity is that the arrangement of the atoms be such that a crystal or molecule and its mirror image are not superimposable.* A carbon atom joined to four different atoms or groups of atoms is known as an *asymmetric carbon atom.* Two isomers that rotate plane-polarized light equal amounts in opposite directions are known as *active components, optical antipodes, enantiomorphs.* or *mirror images.*

Actually the presence of an asymmetric carbon atom is not necessary for optical activity. Its presence is merely the most frequently encountered condition that removes the elements of symmetry that make mirror images identical. These elements of symmetry are (*1*) a plane of symmetry, (2) a center of symmetry, and (3) an alternating axis of symmetry. A *plane of symmetry* is a plane that divides an object into two halves which are mirror images of each other. The compound C*aabd* (Fig. 39a), for example, has a plane of symmetry, namely that which divides the carbon atom and the groups *b* and *d* into like halves, whereas the compound C*abde* (Fig. 39b) does not have a plane of symmetry.

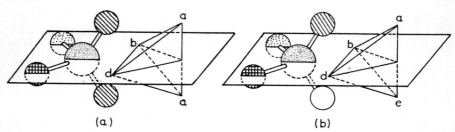

(a)   (b)

Fig. 39. (*a*) Plane of symmetry in compound C*aabd*; (*b*) lack of a plane of symmetry in compound C*abde*.

If an object possesses a plane of symmetry, the object and its mirror image are identical. The same statement holds for the other two elements of symmetry, but since they need to be considered only infrequently, discussion of them is omitted.

Expected Number of Isomers

Molecules containing a single asymmetric carbon atom exist in only two forms. The asymmetric atoms may be designated as $A+$ and $A-$ for the dextrorotatory and levorotatory forms respectively. If a second asymmetric carbon atom is present, the configuration of this atom may be designated as $B+$ or $B-$. Therefore a total of four isomers is possible, namely those in which the four configurations are $A+B+$, $A+B-$, $A-B+$, and $A-B-$. Since $A+$ is the mirror image of $A-$, and $B+$ is the mirror image of $B-$, $A+B+$ is the mirror image of $A-B-$, and the two constitute an enantiomorphic pair and have identical properties except for the sign of rotation. Similarly $A+B-$ and $A-B+$ are enantiomorphic. $A+B+$, however, is not a mirror image of either $A+B-$ or $A-B+$ and has different chemical and physical properties. Similarly any active compound has only one mirror image and all others of its optical isomers differ from it in chemical and physical properties. Optical isomers which are not mirror images are called *diastereoisomers*.

If a third asymmetric atom is present it also may exist in two forms, $C+$ and $C-$, and similarly for a fourth atom, $D+$ and $D-$.

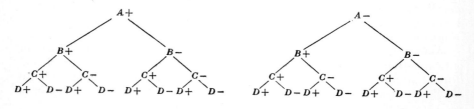

Hence two active forms exist if a single asymmetric carbon atom is present, and the number of active forms is doubled each time a new asymmetric atom is added. The total number of active forms, therefore, is 2^n, where n is the number of asymmetric carbon atoms.

To represent space models on plane paper, perspective drawings of tetrahedra may be used. It is more convenient, however, to use projection formulas.

The convention has been adopted that the two groups at the top and bottom of the projection formulas always are directly over each other and behind

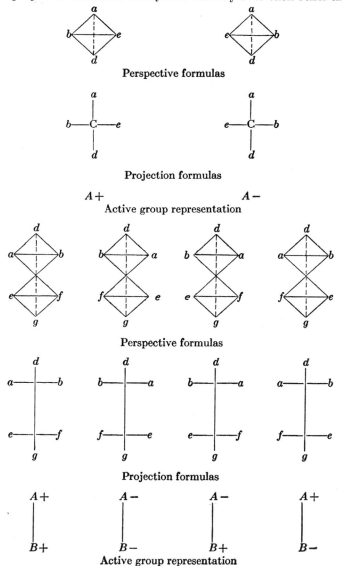

Perspective formulas

Projection formulas

$A+$ $A-$

Active group representation

Perspective formulas

Projection formulas

$A+$ $A-$ $A-$ $A+$

$B+$ $B-$ $B+$ $B-$

Active group representation

the plane of the paper in the corresponding perspective formulas. In any comparison of projection formulas with each other, neither the formula as a whole, nor any portion of the formula may be rotated out of the plane of the paper. Otherwise the top and bottom groups would not bear the same relation to the rest of the formulas as was assumed when they were projected.

In the formulation of the 2^n rule the assumption was made that all of the asymmetric carbon atoms were different, that is that no two of them were attached to the same four kinds of groups. If any of the asymmetric carbon atoms are alike, the number of possible isomers is decreased. Thus if a compound contains two like asymmetric carbon atoms, the possible configurations are $A+A+$, $A+A-$, $A-A+$, and $A-A-$. However since $A+A-$ is identical with $A-A+$, only three optical isomers exist. The tartaric acids investigated by Pasteur may be used for illustration. They have the constitution HOOCCHOHCHOHCOOH. Each of the two asymmetric carbon atoms bears the groups H, OH, COOH, and CHOHCOOH, and hence they are alike. The four possible combinations of active groups are shown by both perspective and projection formulas.

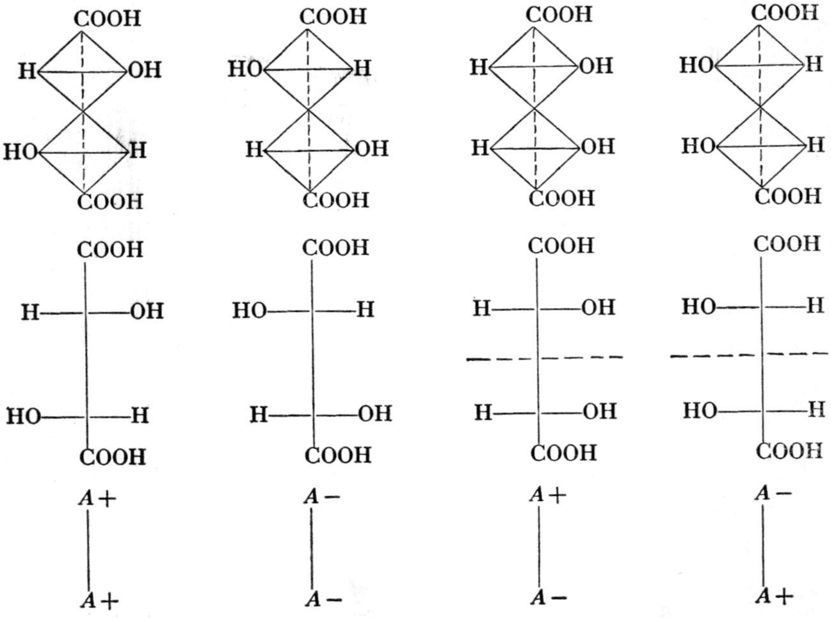

(+)Tartaric acid   (−)Tartaric acid   *meso*-Tartaric acid

The first two forms are nonsuperimposable. The second two arrangements, however, have a plane of symmetry. These structures are not superimposable in the positions shown, but if one or the other is inverted, they become superimposable. In the projection formulas the dotted line indicates a plane of symmetry, and rotation of one or the other formula in the plane of the paper causes the two to coincide. Although it may appear that rotation of a projection formula about a vertical axis also makes it coincide with the other formula, such is not the case since the carboxyl groups are not in the plane of the paper.

Not only is the number of optical isomers reduced from four to three when two like asymmetric carbon atoms are present, but the third form, having a plane of symmetry, is optically inactive. It is known as a *meso form* (Gr. *mesos* middle). Therefore a compound having two like asymmetric carbon atoms has three optical isomers. Two are active enantiomorphs with identical chemical and physical properties. The third is an inactive *meso* form which is a diastereoisomer of the other two and hence differs from them in chemical and physical properties. In addition a fourth form, known as the *racemic* form (after racemic acid), consists of a mixture of equal amounts of the two active forms and hence is optically inactive. It differs from the *meso* form, however, in that it can be separated into active forms whereas the *meso* form cannot. The solid racemic form usually differs in physical properties from the other forms, but in solution it dissociates into the two active forms, and its properties in solution are identical with the properties of the active forms.

If asymmetric carbon atoms are separated by carbon atoms attached to two like groups, the number of optical isomers remains the same. If two like asymmetric carbon atoms are joined to a carbon atom attached to two different nonasymmetric groups, for example *Cabd Cab Cabd*, two active forms and two *meso* forms are possible, each of the latter having a plane of symmetry.

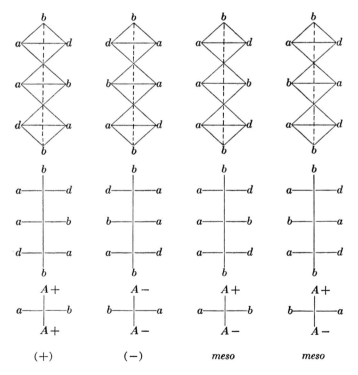

The central carbon atom in such compounds is called a *pseudoasymmetric carbon atom*.

The number of active and *meso* forms can be calculated from the following formulas provided all of the asymmetric carbon atoms can be considered as occurring in a chain of atoms, and none of them in a branch of the chain. In the formulas given below, n = the total number of asymmetric carbon atoms including the pseudoasymmetric carbon atom if present, a = the number of active forms, and m = the number of *meso* forms.

1. If all of the asymmetric carbon atoms are different, $a = 2^n, m = 0$.
2. If the molecule contains like asymmetric carbon atoms and n is even,

$$a = 2^{(n-1)}, m = 2^{\left(\frac{n-2}{2}\right)}.$$

3. If the molecule contains like asymmetric carbon atoms and n is odd,

$$a = 2^{(n-1)} - 2^{\left(\frac{n-1}{2}\right)}, m = 2^{\left(\frac{n-1}{2}\right)}.$$

Separation of Racemic Forms into Active Components (Resolution)

Many naturally occurring organic compounds that contain an asymmetric carbon atom are optically active. For example lactic acid, $CH_3CHOHCOOH$, isolated from muscle is the $(+)$ isomer. Lactic acid produced by fermentation may be $(+)$, or $(-)$, or racemic depending on the fermenting organism. On the other hand, lactic acid produced by synthesis always is racemic. The reason is that when the asymmetric carbon atom is formed by synthesis, there always is an equal chance of producing the $(+)$ or the $(-)$ form, and since the number of molecules involved is very large, equal quantities of both forms are produced. Suppose, for example, that lactic acid is being synthesized by brominating propionic acid to α-bromopropionic acid and hydrolyzing to the hydroxy acid. In the bromination step either of the two α hydrogen atoms may be replaced. Replacement of one gives rise to the $(+)$ form and of the other to the $(-)$ form.

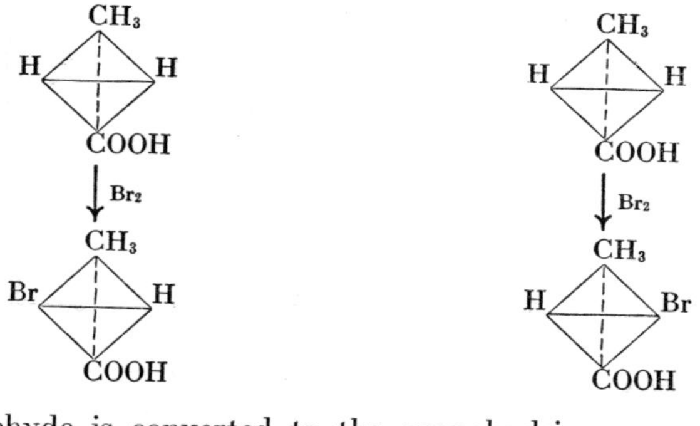

Or if acetaldehyde is converted to the cyanohydrin a racemic mixture is formed, since the double bond of the carbonyl group may be attacked from either side with equal ease during the addition of hydrogen cyanide. Accordingly the separation of racemic mixtures into their active components is of considerable importance. This process is known as *resolution* and the racemate is said to be *resolved* into its active components.

Pasteur's original separation of sodium ammonium racemate into the $(+)$tartrate and the $(-)$tartrate is largely of historical interest only, since not all racemates separate into enantiomorphic crystals. Even sodium ammonium tartrate does so only below 27.7°. Furthermore the mechanical separation is tedious.

Although it has been indicated that enantiomorphs have identical chemical properties, this statement holds only if the reagent itself is not optically active; that is if the reagent is asymmetric, the rates at which two like bonds are broken are no longer equal. Pasteur found, for example, that the enzymes of many organisms destroy one form of a pair of enantiomorphs and not the other. Thus the enzymes of the mold *Penicillium glaucum*, when allowed to act on ammonium racemate, will destroy ammonium (+)tartrate and leave the (−) form unchanged. The general procedure used is to make a solution of the racemate, add nutrient salts, and inoculate with the desired organism. This method has the serious disadvantage that one form is lost and the other form usually is obtained in poor yield. Moreover it is necessary to work with dilute solutions. The method can be applied, however, to a fairly large variety of compounds and frequently provides a simple method for determining whether a compound is capable of resolution.

The differences in behavior of enantiomorphs in living matter are explainable by the fact that reactions in living matter are catalyzed largely by optically active enzymes. A few examples may be given: only one form of an amino acid commonly is present in proteins and is utilizable by the organism in the synthesis of proteins; (+)glucose is the form synthesized by plants and the only form fermentable by yeast or utilizable by living matter; (+)leucine is sweet whereas (−)leucine is faintly bitter; (−)tartaric acid is more toxic than (+)tartaric acid; (−)adrenaline has twelve times the activity of (+)adrenaline in raising blood pressure. These differences merely emphasize the fact that enantiomorphs have identical properties only if they are reacting with nonactive reagents.

By far the most generally practical procedure for the separation of racemic mixtures, also developed by Pasteur, involves the conversion of the enantiomorphs into compounds that are diastereoisomers. Since diastereoisomers are not mirror images, they do not have the same physical properties and may be separated by ordinary physical methods such as fractional crystallization. After the separation of the diastereoisomers, they are converted into the original reactants. If (+) and (−) represent the two active forms present in the racemic mixture and *d* represents a single active form of another compound which will combine with the racemic mixture, the process of separation may be illustrated schematically as follows:

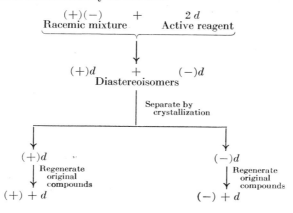

In practice the type of compound formation which takes place most readily and from which the original reactants can be regenerated most easily is salt formation. Thus a racemic acid can be resolved by an active base, or a racemic base by an active acid.

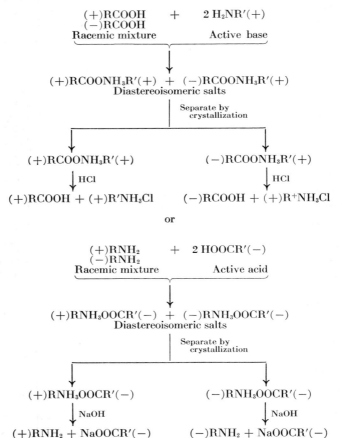

The naturally occurring alkaloids (p. 465) are active bases that give readily crystallizable salts. Those most commonly used for effecting resolution of racemic acids are (−)brucine, (−)strychnine, (−)quinine, (+)cinchonine, (+)quinidine, and (−)morphine. The easily available naturally occurring acids suitable for the resolution of racemic bases are (+)tartaric acid and (−)malic acid. Once a synthetic racemic mixture has been resolved, the active components can be used to resolve other racemic mixtures. Indirect methods and reactions other than salt formation have been used for the resolution of compounds that do not contain acidic or basic groups.

Racemization

Two methods for producing racemic mixtures have been discussed, one by mixing equal amounts of the (+) and (−) forms (p. 262) and the other by producing an asymmetric carbon atom by a synthesis in which none of the reagents is optically active (p. 268). A third method consists in converting either a (+) or (−) form into a mixture of the (+) and (−). This process is known as *racemization*.

Since conversion of a (+) form to a (−) form or a (−) form to a (+) form involves the change in position of at least two groups on the asymmetric atom, bonds must be broken during the racemization, and the molecule must pass through a nonasymmetric intermediate. In the subsequent reformation of the compound equal amounts of the two forms are produced. The most easily racemized compounds and those for which the racemization is most readily explainable are those in which a carbonyl group is α to an asymmetric atom which carries a hydrogen atom. The racemization undoubtedly involves enolization. The enol form does not contain an asymmetric atom, and when ketonization takes place, the double bond may be attacked from either side with equal ease and equal quantities of both (+) and (−) forms are produced. Eventually racemization becomes complete. Thus the racemization of active lactic acid may be represented by the following equilibria.

$$
\begin{array}{ccc}
\underset{\text{C}}{\overset{\text{O}\qquad\text{OH}}{}} & \underset{\text{C}}{\overset{\text{HO}\qquad\text{OH}}{}} & \underset{\text{C}}{\overset{\text{O}\qquad\text{OH}}{}} \\
\text{H—C—OH} \rightleftarrows & \text{C} & \rightleftarrows \text{HO—C—H} \\
\text{CH}_3 & \text{CH}_3 \qquad \text{OH} & \text{CH}_3 \\
(-)\text{Lactic} & \text{Enol form} & (+)\text{Lactic} \\
\text{acid} & & \text{acid}
\end{array}
$$

When an aqueous solution of (+) or (−)tartaric acid or an alkaline solution of its sodium salt is boiled, it is converted into an equilibrium mixture of racemic acid and *meso* tartaric acid, since both asymmetric carbon atoms become racemized.

$$
\begin{array}{ccc}
\text{COOH} & \text{COOH} & \text{COOH} \\
\text{H—C—OH} & \text{HO—C—H} & \text{HO—C—H} \\
\text{HO—C—H} \rightleftarrows & \text{HO—C—H} \rightleftarrows & \text{H—C—OH} \\
\text{COOH} & \text{COOH} & \text{COOH} \\
(+)\text{Tartaric acid} & \textit{meso}\text{-Tartaric acid} & (-)\text{Tartaric acid}
\end{array}
$$

Active compounds that cannot enolize usually are as stable as other organic isomers and do not racemize readily.

Racemization may take place even though enolization is not possible if the active compound is heated to a temperature sufficiently high to cause dissociation of one of the groups attached to the asymmetric atom. The resulting fragment with only three groups attached to the asymmetric atom then may assume a planar configuration. Recombination with the dissociated group can take place from either side and produces equal amounts of both forms (Fig. 40).

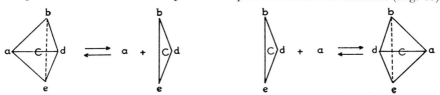

Fig. 40. Racemization without enolization.

Walden Inversion

When active compounds undergo reactions involving the asymmetric atom, the products may be inactive, because racemization can take place when bonds involving the asymmetric atom are broken. Frequently, however, full activity is retained. Retention of activity can be explained only by assuming that the molecule retains its asymmetry during the reaction, which could happen if the entering group merely knocked the group being eliminated out of its position and took its place. However the sign of rotation of the active form produced often depends on the number of steps involved in the reaction. For example aspartic acid can be converted into chlorosuccinic acid either directly or by way of bromosuccinic acid. If the entering groups merely are taking the place of the groups being eliminated, the product should be the same in both cases. Actually one product is levorotatory, and the other is dextrorotatory.

$$
\begin{array}{c}
\text{HOOCCHNH}_2 \\
|\\
\text{HOOCCH}_2 \\
(-)\text{Aspartic acid}
\end{array}
\quad
\underset{+\,2\,\text{HCl}}{\xrightarrow{\text{NaNO}_2}}
\quad
\begin{array}{c}
\text{HOOCCHCl}\\
|\\
\text{HOOCCH}_2\\
(-)\text{Chlorosuccinic acid}
\end{array}
\;+\;\text{NaCl}\;+\;\text{N}_2\;+\;2\,\text{H}_2\text{O}
$$

$$\Big\downarrow \underset{+\,2\,\text{HBr}}{\overset{\text{NaNO}_2}{}}$$

$$
\begin{array}{c}
\text{HOOCCHBr}\\
|\\
\text{HOOCCH}_2\\
(-)\text{Bromosuccinic}\\
\text{acid}
\end{array}
\quad
\xrightarrow{\text{NaCl}}
\quad
\begin{array}{c}
\text{HOOCCHCl}\\
|\\
\text{HOOCCH}_2 \;\;+\;\text{NaBr}\\
(+)\text{Chlorosuccinic}\\
\text{acid}
\end{array}
$$

Therefore a change in configuration must have taken place at one or more steps of the reactions.

It seems reasonable that whatever the mechanism of the replacement of the amino group by halogen, it would be the same whether sodium nitrite and hydrogen chloride, or sodium nitrite and hydrogen bromide, are the reagents. Therefore the chloro- and bromosuccinic acids formed by this reaction would be expected to have the same configuration, and a change in configuration must take place in the conversion of bromosuccinic acid to chlorosuccinic acid. Since the reaction of the amino group with nitrous acid and hydrochloric acid is complex, only the conversion of the bromosuccinic acid to chlorosuccinic acid is considered. This step undoubtedly involves a displacement of bromide ion by chloride ion. As the chloride ion approaches the face of the molecule opposite the bromine atom, the bromide ion leaves, and an inversion of configuration takes place with the formation of a single active form.

$$
\text{Cl} + a \diamond\!\!\!-\!\!\!-\text{Br} \longrightarrow \text{Cl}\!\!\!-\!\!\!\diamond a + \text{Br}
$$

The phenomenon of optical inversion was discovered by Walden [11] in 1895 and is known as the *Walden inversion*. The current interpretation of the mech-

[11] Paul Walden (1863–   ), German physical chemist, whose principal work has been in the field of electrolytes.

anism of inversion was suggested by Werner [12] as early as 1911 and again by Lewis (p. 192) in his book on valence in 1923, and by Lowry (p. 192) in 1924. If the mechanism is correct, replacement of a group on the asymmetric atom by a like group would not produce a new compound but only the enantiomorph. Hence complete racemization eventually should result.

The racemizing action of halide ion was known to Kekulé in 1864, and it was shown in 1913 that the rate of racemization of active bromosuccinic acid was proportional to the bromide ion concentration. It was not until 1935, however, that evidence was presented that this mechanism may be the only one involved in the racemization. It was found by the use of radioactive iodide ions that the rate of introduction of radioactive iodine into 2-iodooctane is the same as the rate of racemization of active 2-iodooctane by the iodide ions. It now is believed that most reactions take place by this mechanism, an inversion of structure taking place at each step of a reaction although the inversion is detectable only with active compounds (p. 95).

Absolute and Relative Configuration

Absolute configuration is the actual configuration of the molecule in space; that is it is the answer to the question, "Which of two enantiomorphic models represents the dextrorotatory form of a compound and which the levorotatory form?" Thus far it does not appear to be possible to answer this question. If, however, the configuration of some reference compound is assumed, it is possible to relate the configuration of other active compounds to this substance and to each other. *The configuration of a compound with reference to the arbitrarily assigned configuration of the reference substance is known as its* **relative configuration.**

At the present time the substance most commonly considered for reference is glyceraldehyde, the (+) form of which is assigned the configuration represented by the perspective formula I on p. 274. In this formula the asymmetric carbon atom is in the plane of the paper, the aldehyde and the hydroxymethyl groups behind the plane of the paper, and the hydrogen atom and the hydroxyl group in front of the plane of the paper. Formula II is a projection of this space formula in the plane of the paper.[13]

---

[12] Alfred Werner (1866–1919), Swiss chemist, professor at the University of Zurich. He was noted for his studies of coordination compounds and for his contributions to stereochemistry. He was awarded the Nobel Prize in Chemistry in 1913.

[13] The results of a special type of x-ray analysis of the sodium rubidium salt of (+) tartaric acid, published in 1951, appear to be consistent with the configuration used by Fischer, and hence, from this evidence, the absolute configuration of (+) glyceraldehyde is the same as that agreed upon by convention.

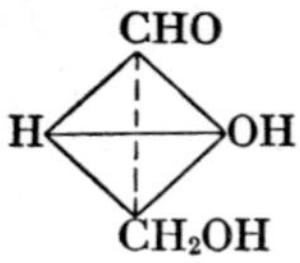

$$\text{I} \qquad \begin{array}{c} \text{CHO} \\ \text{H} \diamond \text{OH} \\ \text{CH}_2\text{OH} \end{array}$$

$$\text{II} \qquad \begin{array}{c} \text{CHO} \\ \text{H—C—OH} \\ \text{CH}_2\text{OH} \end{array}$$

I 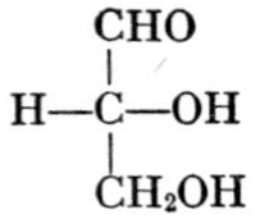   II

(+)Glyceraldehyde

The classical chemical methods for the assignment of relative configuration depend on the assumption that no Walden inversion occurs as long as bonds on the asymmetric atom are not involved. The following series of reactions illustrates how the configurations of a group of compounds have been inter-related. The carbon atom corresponding to that in the reference substance is in bold-face type.

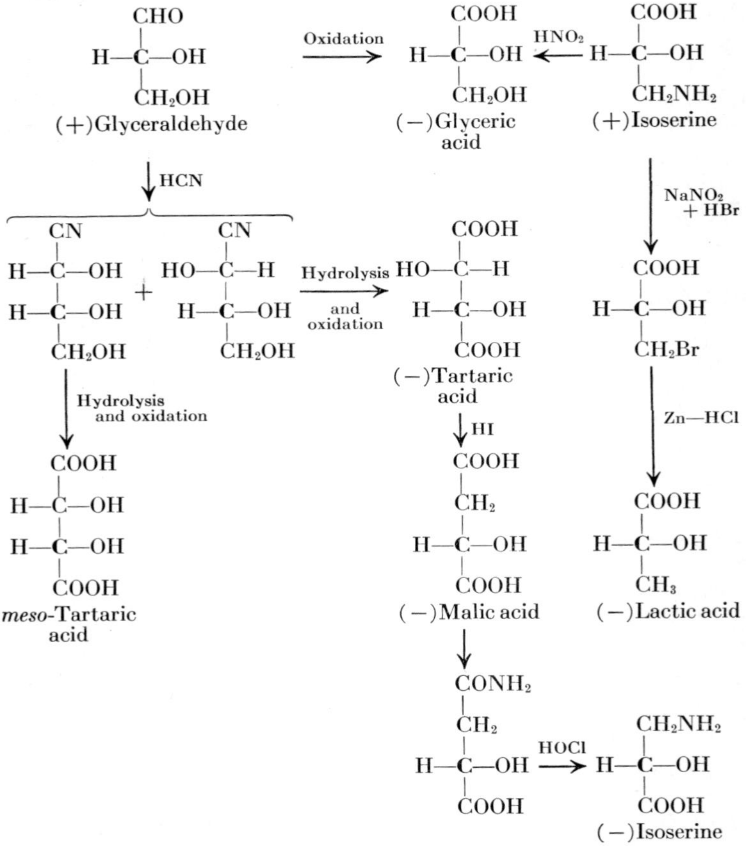

$$\begin{array}{c} \text{CHO} \\ \text{H—C—OH} \\ \text{CH}_2\text{OH} \end{array} \xrightarrow{\text{Oxidation}} \begin{array}{c} \text{COOH} \\ \text{H—C—OH} \\ \text{CH}_2\text{OH} \end{array} \xleftarrow{\text{HNO}_2} \begin{array}{c} \text{COOH} \\ \text{H—C—OH} \\ \text{CH}_2\text{NH}_2 \end{array}$$

(+)Glyceraldehyde   (−)Glyceric acid   (+)Isoserine

$$\downarrow \text{HCN}$$

$$\overbrace{\begin{array}{c} \text{CN} \\ \text{H—C—OH} \\ \text{H—C—OH} \\ \text{CH}_2\text{OH} \end{array} + \begin{array}{c} \text{CN} \\ \text{HO—C—H} \\ \text{H—C—OH} \\ \text{CH}_2\text{OH} \end{array}} \xrightarrow[\text{and oxidation}]{\text{Hydrolysis}} \begin{array}{c} \text{COOH} \\ \text{HO—C—H} \\ \text{H—C—OH} \\ \text{COOH} \end{array}$$

(−)Tartaric acid

$$\downarrow \text{NaNO}_2 + \text{HBr}$$

$$\begin{array}{c} \text{COOH} \\ \text{H—C—OH} \\ \text{CH}_2\text{Br} \end{array}$$

$$\downarrow \begin{array}{c} \text{Hydrolysis} \\ \text{and oxidation} \end{array}$$

$$\begin{array}{c} \text{COOH} \\ \text{H—C—OH} \\ \text{H—C—OH} \\ \text{COOH} \end{array}$$

meso-Tartaric acid

$$\downarrow \text{HI}$$

$$\begin{array}{c} \text{COOH} \\ \text{CH}_2 \\ \text{H—C—OH} \\ \text{COOH} \end{array}$$

(−)Malic acid

$$\downarrow \text{Zn—HCl}$$

$$\begin{array}{c} \text{COOH} \\ \text{H—C—OH} \\ \text{CH}_3 \end{array}$$

(−)Lactic acid

$$\downarrow$$

$$\begin{array}{c} \text{CONH}_2 \\ \text{CH}_2 \\ \text{H—C—OH} \\ \text{COOH} \end{array} \xrightarrow{\text{HOCl}} \begin{array}{c} \text{CH}_2\text{NH}_2 \\ \text{H—C—OH} \\ \text{COOH} \end{array}$$

(−)Isoserine

There is no apparent relationship between the relative configuration and the sign of rotation. Since it is the configuration and not the sign of rotation that is important, active compounds have been divided into two families. Those that are related to (+)glyceraldehyde are said to belong to the D family, and those that are related to (−)glyceraldehyde are said to belong to the

L family. The small capital D and capital L are pronounced *dee* and *ell* respectively and not dextro and levo. They refer to configuration and not to optical rotation. The name D(+)glyceraldehyde reveals both the configuration and the rotation.

A point that frequently is misunderstood is that it is not sufficient to say that a compound is related to (+)glyceraldehyde configurationally without specifying the correspondence of its functional groups to those of (+)glyceraldehyde. Thus the configuration of (+)isoserine is the same as that of (+)glyceraldehyde if the carboxyl group and aminomethyl group of isoserine correspond respectively to the aldehyde and hydroxymethyl groups of glyceraldehyde. If the aminomethyl and carboxyl groups of isoserine correspond to the aldehyde and hydroxymethyl groups of glyceraldehyde, then the configuration of (−)isoserine corresponds to that of (+)glyceraldehyde. For isoserine it is understood that the carboxyl group corresponds to the aldehyde group and the enantiomorphs are called D(+)isoserine and L(−)isoserine.

It is an interesting fact that all of the common naturally occurring amino acids have the same relative configuration. It frequently is stated that they all belong to the L family. By this it is inferred that they are configurationally related to (−)glyceraldehyde rather than to (+)glyceraldehyde. Again this classification is arbitrary, since it merely means that if the carboxyl, amino, hydrogen, and the residual portion R of the amino acids correspond respectively to the aldehyde, hydroxyl, hydrogen, and hydroxymethyl groups of glyceraldehyde, the common natural amino acids have the configuration

REVIEW QUESTIONS

1. Define the term stereoisomerism. What are the two broad classes of stereoisomers?
2. Discuss geometrical isomerism including (*a*) the reason for the isomerism, (*b*) the number of isomers, (*c*) the physical properties and methods of separation of the isomers, and (*d*) the assignment of configuration.
3. What is meant by the term plane-polarized light? Describe two practical methods for producing it and tell how each accomplishes the polarization.
4. What is meant by the term optical activity? How is the extent of optical activity measured? On what factors does the degree of rotation depend? Tell what is meant by the term specific rotation and give a formula for calculating the specific rotation from the observed rotation and other data. What is rotatory dispersion?
5. What are the necessary and sufficient conditions for the existence of optical activity? Why does it necessarily lead to isomerism in organic molecules? What is the commonest cause of optical isomerism? What other terms are used to indicate that two different compounds are mirror images?
6. How does the optical activity of quartz differ from that of organic compounds?
7. Compare the physical and chemical properties of enantiomorphs. How do these properties compare with those of geometrical isomers? Explain the difference.
8. What is a racemic mixture? Why is it not possible to separate a racemic mixture into its components directly by ordinary methods such as fractional distillation or crystallization?
9. When an asymmetric carbon atom is introduced into a molecule by synthesis, and none of the reagents is optically active, a racemic mixture always is formed rather than an active product. Explain.

10. Give the chemical method for the resolution of a racemic mixture into its active components and explain the principle on which the separation is based. What other procedures have been used to resolve racemic mixtures? What are diastereoisomers?

11. If all of the asymmetric carbon atoms in a molecule are different and form part of a chain with none of the asymmetric carbon atoms in side chains, the number of active forms possible is 2^n where n is the number of asymmetric carbon atoms. Explain.

12. What complications arise if a molecule has two like asymmetric carbon atoms? Explain. How can the *meso* forms be separated from each other and from racemic forms?

13. Predict the number and kind of stereoisomers theoretically possible for each of the following structural formulas:

(a) $CH_3CHCOOH$
       |
       NH_2

(b) CH_2CH_2COOH
       |
       NH_2

(c) $C_2H_5CHCH_2OH$
            |
            CH_3

(d) $CH_3CHBrCHBrCH_3$ (e) $CH_3CH_2CHOHCH_3$ (f) $CH_3CH=CHCH_3$

(g) $CH_2=CHCH_2COOH$ (h) $CH_3CH=CHCOOH$ (i) $CH_3CHOHCH_2CHO$

(j) $CH_2OH(CHOH)_4CHO$ (k) $CH_3(CH_2)_7CH=CH(CH_2)_7COOH$

(l) $CH_3(CH_2)_4CH=CHCH_2CH=CH(CH_2)_7COOH$ (m) $CH_3CH=CHCH=CH—CH_3$

(n) $CH_3(CH_2)_5CHOHCH_2CH=CH(CH_2)_7COOH$

14. What is Walden inversion and how is it explained? Does it apply only to optically active compounds?

15. What conventions must be kept in mind when using plane projection formulas to represent stereoisomers?

Chapter 18

CARBOHYDRATES

Carbohydrates are polyhydroxy aldehydes or polyhydroxy ketones or substances which yield such compounds on hydrolysis. They are distributed universally in plants and animals, and are the third important class of animal foods. The combustion of carbohydrates to carbon dioxide and water yields about 4 kcal. of energy per gram. The term *carbohydrate* came into use for these compounds because ordinarily the ratio of hydrogen to oxygen is 2 to 1, for example $C_6H_{10}O_5$, $C_6H_{12}O_6$, $C_{12}H_{22}O_{11}$. For some carbohydrates, however, this ratio does not hold; for example rhamnose has the molecular formula $C_6H_{12}O_5$.

Nomenclature and Classification of Carbohydrates

The simpler carbohydrates commonly are called sugars or saccharides (L. *saccharon* sugar). The ending for sugars is *ose*, for example arabinose, glucose, maltose. Frequently the generic term *glycose* is used from which is derived the prefix *glyc*. The generic terms are used when it is not desired to designate a particular sugar or derivative. The number of carbon atoms may be indicated by a prefix; for example a sugar having five carbon atoms is called a *pentose* and one with six carbon atoms is called a *hexose*. Similarly the prefix may indicate whether the sugar contains an aldehyde group or a ketone group, giving rise to the terms *aldose* and *ketose*. Both the number of carbon atoms and the type of carbonyl group may be indicated by terms such as *aldepentose* and *ketohexose*.

Carbohydrates may be subdivided according to the following classification.

A. Monosaccharides. Carbohydrates that do not hydrolyze.
B. Oligosaccharides. Carbohydrates that yield a few molecules of monosaccharide on hydrolysis.
    1. Disaccharides. One molecule yields two molecules of monosaccharide on hydrolysis.
       (a) Reducing disaccharides. Disaccharides that reduce Fehling's solution.
       (b) Nonreducing disaccharides. Disaccharides that do not reduce Fehling's solution.
    2. Trisaccharides. One molecule yields three molecules of monosaccharides on hydrolysis.
    3. Tetra-, penta-, and hexasaccharides.
C. Polysaccharides. Carbohydrates that yield a large number of molecules of monosaccharides on hydrolysis.

MONOSACCHARIDES

Aldoses

The most important carbohydrate is (+)**glucose** or **dextrose**. Since the naturally occurring isomer always is dextrorotatory, the word *glucose* without indication of sign of rotation always means (+)glucose. Because glucose is typical of the aldoses, it is discussed in considerable detail. Only the characteristic differences of other aldoses are presented.

Glucose is obtained most readily by the hydrolysis of starch or cellulose. It also may be isolated as one of the hydrolytic products of most oligosaccharides and of many other plant products known as glucosides. It occurs free, along with fructose and sucrose, in the juices of fruits and in honey, and to the extent of about 0.1 per cent in the blood of normal mammals. Glucose in free or combined form probably is the most abundant organic compound.

Constitution. Glucose has the molecular formula $C_6H_{12}O_6$. Its constitution may be arrived at from the following chemical behavior.

(a) Reduction with hydrogen iodide and phosphorus yields *n*-hexane. Therefore all of the carbon atoms must be linked in a straight chain.

(b) Glucose reacts with one mole of hydroxylamine to form an oxime, or with one mole of hydrogen cyanide to form a cyanohydrin, indicating the presence of one carbonyl group.

(c) On mild oxidation, for example with sodium hypobromite, glucose yields the monobasic gluconic acid, $C_5H_{11}O_5COOH$.[1] Since no carbon atoms are lost, the carbonyl group must be present as an aldehyde group, which can occupy only an end position of the chain.

(d) On reduction with sodium amalgam, two hydrogen atoms are added to give $C_6H_{14}O_6$, a compound known as *sorbitol* (p. 307). Sorbitol reacts with acetic anhydride to give a hexa-acetate. Accordingly the six oxygen atoms of sorbitol must be present as six hydroxyl groups. Compounds containing two hydroxyl groups on the same carbon atom are rare, and those that are known readily lose water. However sorbitol does not dehydrate easily. Hence one hydroxyl group must be located on each of the six carbon atoms. Since one hydroxyl group was formed by reduction of the aldehyde group of glucose, the constitution of glucose can be represented by $HOCH_2(CHOH)_4CHO$. Most of the isomeric aldohexoses undergo the same reactions, indicating the same constitution. Therefore they are stereoisomers of glucose.

It has been shown by similar methods that the aldopentoses, $C_5H_{10}O_5$, have the structure $HOCH_2(CHOH)_3CHO$. Similarly the aldotetroses have the structure $HOCH_2(CHOH)_2CHO$, and the simplest compound grouped with the aldoses is the triose named glycerose or glyceraldehyde, $HOCH_2CHOH$-CHO.

Configuration. The structural formula for glucose has four different asymmetric carbon atoms, and hence 16 optical isomers are possible, all of which are known. Of these 16 isomers, only two besides (+)glucose are common, namely (+)mannose and (+)galactose. **(+)Mannose** is one of the products of hydrolysis of a number of polysaccharides. It is obtained most readily by the hydrolysis of the vegetable ivory nut, which is the hard endosperm of the seed of the Tagua palm, *Phyletephas macrocarpa*. Vegetable ivory is used for the manufacture of buttons. **(+)Galactose** is formed along with (+)glucose by the hydrolysis of the disaccharide lactose or milk sugar, and is one of the products of hydrolysis of several polysaccharides. The following configurations are assigned to these three sugars.

---

[1] This reaction is general for aldoses, the products being known as *glyconic acids* (or by the less desirable term, *aldonic acids*).

CHO — (+)Glucose; CHO — (+)Mannose; CHO — (+)Galactose structural formulas

For (+)Glucose (Fischer projections):

```
     CHO                CHO
 H ——— OH           H—C—OH
HO ——— H           HO—C—H
 H ——— OH    or     H—C—OH
 H ——— OH           H—C—OH
     CH2OH              CH2OH
```
(+)Glucose

```
      CHO               CHO
HO ——— H           HO—C—H
HO ——— H           HO—C—H
 H ——— OH    or     H—C—OH
 H ——— OH           H—C—OH
     CH2OH              CH2OH
```
(+)Mannose

```
     CHO                CHO
 H ——— OH           H—C—OH
HO ——— H           HO—C—H
HO ——— H     or    HO—C—H
 H ——— OH           H—C—OH
     CH2OH              CH2OH
```
(+)Galactose

(—)Galactose has been isolated from the hydrolytic products of flaxseed mucilage.

Eight aldopentoses are possible and all are known. **(+)Arabinose** and **(+)xylose** may be obtained by the hydrolysis of a wide variety of plant polysaccharides. Thus corn cobs, straw, oat hulls, and cottonseed hulls yield 8 to 12 per cent of (+)xylose. (+)Arabinose is obtained by the hydrolysis of many plant gums. **(—)Arabinose** has been isolated from only two sources, the glycoside *barbaloin* present in aloes, and the polysaccharide of tubercle bacilli. **(—)Ribose** is important because it is one of the products of hydrolysis of the nucleic acids (p. 462). The configurations assigned to these three sugars are

```
      CHO              CHO              CHO
 H—C—OH           H—C—OH           H—C—OH
HO—C—H           HO—C—H            H—C—OH
HO—C—H            H—C—OH           H—C—OH
   CH2OH             CH2OH            CH2OH
(+)Arabinose      (+)Xylose        (—)Ribose
```

D and L Families of Sugars

In his work on the relative configuration (cf. p. 273) of the sugars, Emil Fischer (p. 233) realized that it was not possible to assign an absolute configuration to an active molecule. Accordingly in 1891 he adopted a convention which placed the C-5 hydroxyl group on the right in the projection formula for glucose. He stated that the assignment was arbitrary and that the absolute configuration of this carbon atom remained undecided. He also saw that the determination of relative configurations permitted the assignment of the carbohydrates to two families (p. 274). Those carbohydrates having the hydroxyl group on the right for the asymmetric carbon atom most remote from the carbonyl group were said to belong to the D (*dee*) family, and those having this hydroxyl group on the left were said to belong to the L (*ell*) family. Thus the sugars considered thus far are designated as D(+)glucose, D(+)mannose, D(+)galactose, D(+)xylose, D(—)ribose, and L(+)arabinose. As emphasized on page 275, D and L refer only to configuration and are not concerned with the sign of rotation.

The use of glucose as a reference substance is not convenient for classifying other active compounds into families, and in 1906 Rosanoff suggested that one of the two structures representing the active forms of glyceraldehyde, CHOCHOHCH₂OH, be used for reference. In order to make this reference structure correspond with Fischer's assignment of configuration, Rosanoff proposed that the structure corresponding in configuration to that of C-5 in (+)glucose be called D-glyceraldehyde and that all compounds related to D-glyceraldehyde be placed in the D family. By 1914 Wohl and his coworkers had succeeded in resolving glyceraldehyde and showing that (+)glyceraldehyde has the D configuration. Since then the use of D-glyceraldehyde as the reference substance has been adopted generally.

Desoxyaldoses

Some naturally occurring sugars have a hydrogen atom in place of one or more of the hydroxyl groups. In naming these compounds the prefix *desoxy* is used with the name of the oxygen analog to indicate the lack of oxygen, and the class as a whole is known as the **desoxy sugars**. L(+)rhamnose (6-desoxy-L-mannose) is a hydrolytic product of many glycosides and the most common naturally occurring desoxy sugar. L(—)fucose (6-desoxy-L-galactose) is one of the products of the hydrolysis of the cell walls of marine algae.

CHO	CHO
H—C—OH	HO—C—H
H—C—OH	H—C—OH
HO—C—H	H—C—OH
HO—C—H	HO—C—H
CH₃	CH₃
L(+)Rhamnose	L(—)Fucose

Rhamnose and fucose sometimes are called *methylpentoses*, but this term may cause ambiguity when dealing with the methylated sugars.

Special Reactions of the Aldoses

Oxidation by Cupric Ion in Alkaline Solution. Although the salts of many heavy metals such as copper, silver, mercury, and bismuth are reduced by alkaline sugar solutions, reagents containing copper usually are used for analytical purposes. Cupric hydroxide oxidizes carbohydrates, but its slight solubility in dilute alkali permits only a slow reaction. The rate of oxidation is greatly increased if the copper is kept in solution by the formation of a complex salt with tartrate ion (Fehling's solution) or citrate ion (Benedict's solution) (pp. 547, 548). The former uses sodium hydroxide for alkaline reaction, whereas the latter uses sodium carbonate. Benedict's solution is the more stable and is not affected by substances such as creatine and uric acid. Hence it is preferred for detecting and estimating glucose in urine.

Evidence for reduction is the formation of red cuprous oxide which precipitates because the cuprous ion does not form complexes with tartrates or citrates. If protective colloids are present, as in urine samples, the color of the precipitate may vary from yellow to red depending on the state of subdivision of the particles. In the presence of an excess of carbohydrate, some of the cuprous oxide may be reduced to metallic copper.

The equation for the oxidation of an aldehyde group to a carboxyl group requires a ratio of two moles of cupric salt per mole of aldehyde.

$$\text{RCHO} + 2\ \text{Cu(OH)}_2 \longrightarrow \text{RCOOH} + \text{Cu}_2\text{O} + 2\ \text{H}_2\text{O}$$

Actually one mole of glucose reduces between five and six moles of cupric salt depending on the conditions of the reaction. Moreover ketoses reduce just as well as aldoses, although simple ketones do not reduce Fehling's solution. The explanation lies in the reaction of the sugars with alkali, which not only interconverts aldoses and ketoses but gives degradation products that have reducing properties. Thus acetaldehyde, lactic acid (p. 534), and tartronic acid (p. 547) as well as gluconic acid (p. 278) and glucuronic acid (p. 306) have been identified among the products of oxidation of glucose by Fehling's solution. The ketoses may cause reduction without rearrangement and degradation, since even simple compounds containing the CHOH group adjacent to the carbonyl group are oxidized by alkaline cupric solutions to give dicarbonyl compounds.

$$\underset{\substack{|\\ \text{O \ \ OH}}}{\text{R—C—CH—R}} + 2\ \text{Cu(OH)}_2 \longrightarrow \underset{\substack{|\\ \text{O \ \ O}}}{\text{R—C—C—R}} + \text{Cu}_2\text{O} + 3\ \text{H}_2\text{O}$$

In spite of the complexity of the reaction, it can be used successfully for the quantitative estimation of sugars by standardizing conditions rigidly and by using empirically determined tables relating the amount of sugar to the amount of cupric ion reduced.

Oxidation to Glycaric Acids. When aldoses are oxidized by strong nitric acid, both the aldehyde group and the primary alcohol group are converted to carboxyl groups. The dicarboxylic acids are known as **glycaric acids** (older name *saccharic acids*). By thus making both ends of the sugar molecule alike, it is possible to determine in which aldoses the configurations of the top and bottom pair of asymmetric atoms are enantiomorphic, since the glycaric acids from such molecules have a plane of symmetry, and are *meso* forms and inactive. Thus (+) or (−)galactose gives the inactive galactaric acid (mucic acid), whereas (+) and (−)mannose give active mannaric acids (*mannosaccharic acids*).

CHO	COOH	CHO
H—C—OH	H—C—OH	HO—C—H
HO—C—H	HO—C—H	H—C—OH
HO—C—H	HO—C—H	H—C—OH
H—C—OH	H—C—OH	HO—C—H
CH₂OH	COOH	CH₂OH
(+)Galactose	Galactaric acid (mucic acid) Inactive	(−)Galactose

HNO₃ → ← HNO₃

$$
\begin{array}{ccccc}
\begin{array}{c}
\text{CHO} \\
| \\
\text{HO—C—H} \\
| \\
\text{HO—C—H} \\
| \\
\text{H—C—OH} \\
| \\
\text{H—C—OH} \\
| \\
\text{CH}_2\text{OH} \\
(+)\text{Mannose}
\end{array}
&
\xrightarrow{\text{HNO}_3}
&
\begin{array}{c}
\text{COOH} \\
| \\
\text{HO—C—H} \\
| \\
\text{HO—C—H} \\
| \\
\text{H—C—OH} \\
| \\
\text{H—C—OH} \\
| \\
\text{COOH}
\end{array}
\quad
\begin{array}{c}
\text{COOH} \\
| \\
\text{H—C—OH} \\
| \\
\text{H—C—OH} \\
| \\
\text{HO—C—H} \\
| \\
\text{HO—C—H} \\
| \\
\text{COOH}
\end{array}
&
\xleftarrow{\text{HNO}_3}
&
\begin{array}{c}
\text{CHO} \\
| \\
\text{H—C—OH} \\
| \\
\text{H—C—OH} \\
| \\
\text{HO—C—H} \\
| \\
\text{HO—C—H} \\
| \\
\text{CH}_2\text{OH} \\
(-)\text{Mannose}
\end{array}
\end{array}
$$

Mannaric acids (*manno*-saccharic acids) Active

Formation of Osazones. Fischer in his study of the reaction of phenyl-hydrazine with aldehydes and ketones found that reaction with reducing sugars introduces two phenylhydrazine residues instead of one. A yellow crystalline product known as a **phenylosazone** separates from the hot aqueous solution. The other products of the reaction are aniline (phenylamine) and ammonia. This reaction is characteristic of the grouping RCOCHOHR.

$$
\begin{array}{c}
\text{CHO} \\
| \\
\text{CHOH} \\
| \\
(\text{CHOH})_3 \\
| \\
\text{CH}_2\text{OH}
\end{array}
+ 3\ \text{C}_6\text{H}_5\text{NHNH}_2 \longrightarrow
\begin{array}{c}
\text{CH=N—NHC}_6\text{H}_5 \\
| \\
\text{C=N—NHC}_6\text{H}_5 \\
| \\
(\text{CHOH})_3 \\
| \\
\text{CH}_2\text{OH}
\end{array}
+ \text{C}_6\text{H}_5\text{NH}_2 + \text{NH}_3 + 2\ \text{H}_2\text{O}
$$

A phenylosazone   Aniline

Substituted hydrazines of the general formulas $RNHNH_2$ and R_2NNH_2 may be used to form osazones. Since the osazones from different hydrazines and different sugars differ in melting point, crystal form, and rate of formation, osazone formation is a valuable reaction for the identification of sugars.

When osazones are formed, the asymmetry of the α carbon atom is destroyed. Therefore sugars which differ only in the configuration of the α carbon atom, such as glucose and mannose, yield the same osazone.

$$
\begin{array}{ccccc}
\begin{array}{c}
\text{CHO} \\
| \\
\text{H—C—OH} \\
| \\
\text{HO—C—H} \\
| \\
\text{H—C—OH} \\
| \\
\text{H—C—OH} \\
| \\
\text{CH}_2\text{OH} \\
(+)\text{Glucose}
\end{array}
&
\xrightarrow{\text{C}_6\text{H}_5\text{NHNH}_2}
&
\begin{array}{c}
\text{CH=NNHC}_6\text{H}_5 \\
| \\
\text{C=NNHC}_6\text{H}_5 \\
| \\
\text{HO—C—H} \\
| \\
\text{H—C—OH} \\
| \\
\text{H—C—OH} \\
| \\
\text{CH}_2\text{OH} \\
\text{Glucose phenylosazone} \\
\text{(yellow precipitate)}
\end{array}
&
\xleftarrow{\text{C}_6\text{H}_5\text{NHNH}_2}
&
\begin{array}{c}
\text{CHO} \\
| \\
\text{HO—C—H} \\
| \\
\text{HO—C—H} \\
| \\
\text{H—C—OH} \\
| \\
\text{H—C—OH} \\
| \\
\text{CH}_2\text{OH} \\
(+)\text{Mannose}
\end{array}
\end{array}
$$

An intermediate in this reaction is the hydrazone in which only the carbonyl group has reacted. Although glucose phenylhydrazone is soluble in water, mannose phenylhydrazone is insoluble in water and precipitates as a white solid from aqueous solution even at room temperature. This difference in behavior is used to distinguish between glucose and mannose.

$$
\begin{array}{ccc}
\text{CHO} & & \text{CH=NNHC}_6\text{H}_5 \\
\text{HO—C—H} & & \text{HO—C—OH} \\
\text{HO—C—H} & \xrightarrow{\text{C}_6\text{H}_5\text{NHNH}_2} & \text{HO—C—H} \\
\text{H—C—OH} & & \text{H—C—OH} \\
\text{H—C—OH} & & \text{H—C—OH} \\
\text{CH}_2\text{OH} & & \text{CH}_2\text{OH} \\
\text{(+)Mannose} & & \text{Mannose phenylhydrazone} \\
& & \text{(white precipitate)}
\end{array}
$$

Glycoside Formation. Aldehydes react with alcohols in the presence of acid catalysts to form acetals. Hemiacetals are intermediates in the reaction (p. 166).

$$
\text{RCHO} + \text{HOR}' \underset{[H^+]}{\rightleftarrows} \text{RCH}\begin{array}{c}\text{OH}\\ \diagdown \\ \text{OR}'\end{array} \underset{R'OH,[H^+]}{\rightleftarrows} \text{RCH}\begin{array}{c}\text{OR}'\\ \diagdown \\ \text{OR}'\end{array} + \text{H}_2\text{O}
$$

Hemiacetal   Acetal

When Fischer attempted to prepare an acetal from glucose, methyl alcohol, and hydrogen chloride, definite crystalline products were obtained, but analysis showed that although a molecule of water had been eliminated, only one methyl group had been introduced. Furthermore two isomeric products were obtained. These compounds no longer reduced Fehling's solution, or formed osazones. Moreover they behaved like acetals in that they were hydrolyzed readily in acid solutions but were stable to alkali. This behavior is explainable if it is assumed that the aldehyde group of the sugar first reacts with the alcohol group on the fifth carbon atom to form an internal cyclic hemiacetal having a six-membered ring. The hemiacetal then reacts with methyl alcohol to form the acetal. Since a new asymmetric carbon atom is produced in this process, two diastereoisomers are formed.

These acetals are called *glycosides*, and the two forms are designated α and β. Isomers of this type are known as *anomers* and the carbon atom responsible for the existence of anomers is known as the *anomeric* carbon atom. Hereafter the anomeric carbon atom is indicated by bold-faced type. It can be distinguished readily from the other carbon atoms by the fact that it is united to two oxygen atoms. In the case of glycosides the anomeric carbon atom also is known as the *glycosidic* carbon atom. The designation α is given to the form in which the hydroxyl or substituted hydroxyl group is on the right in the projection formulas for members of the D family and on the left for members of the L family. Hence when indicating the configuration of the anomeric carbon atom, it is necessary to indicate the family of the sugar as well.

$$
\begin{array}{ccccc}
\text{H—C—OCH}_3 & \text{H—C—OH} & \text{CHO} & \text{HO—C—H} & \text{CH}_3\text{O—C—H} \\
\text{CHOH} & \text{CHOH} & \text{CHOH} & \text{CHOH} & \text{CHOH} \\
\text{CHOH} & \text{CHOH} & \text{CHOH} & \text{CHOH} & \text{CHOH} \\
\text{CHOH} & \text{CHOH} & \text{CHOH} & \text{CHOH} & \text{CHOH} \\
\text{H—C} & \text{H—C} & \text{H—C—OH} & \text{H—C} & \text{H—C} \\
\text{CH}_2\text{OH} & \text{CH}_2\text{OH} & \text{CH}_2\text{OH} & \text{CH}_2\text{OH} & \text{CH}_2\text{OH} \\
\text{Methyl } \alpha\text{-D-} & & & & \text{Methyl } \beta\text{-D-} \\
\text{glycoside} & & & & \text{glycoside}
\end{array}
$$

The determination of the ring structure of the methyl glycosides originally was a difficult task. It now is done more easily by means of periodic acid oxidation, which cleaves 1,2-dihydroxy compounds and α-hydroxy aldehydes and ketones between the two oxygenated carbon atoms (p. 520). The dihydroxy compounds give two moles of aldehyde, whereas α-hydroxy aldehydes and ketones give one mole of aldehyde and one mole of acid.

$$RCHOHCH_2OH + HIO_4 \longrightarrow RCHO + HCHO + HIO_3 + H_2O$$
$$RCHOHCHOHR' + HIO_4 \longrightarrow RCHO + OCHR' + HIO_3 + H_2O$$
$$RCHOHCHO + HIO_4 \longrightarrow RCHO + HCOOH + HIO_3$$
$$RCHOHCOR' + HIO_4 \longrightarrow RCHO + R'COOH + HIO_3$$

Five possible ring structures for the methyl glycosides of an aldohexose exist. The number of moles of periodic acid used, and of formic acid and formaldehyde produced are indicated below for each structure. The arrows indicate the points where oxidative fission takes place.

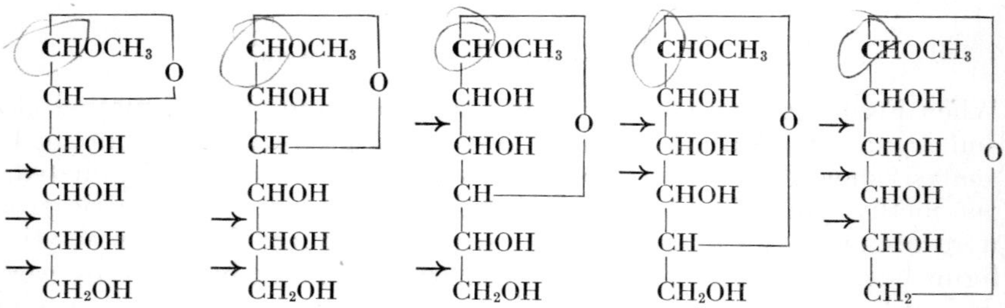

Moles					
HIO_4	3	2	2	2	3
HCOOH	2	1	0	1	2
HCHO	1	1	1	0	0

The reactions are practically quantitative. Hence from the number of moles of periodic acid used and the moles of formic acid and formaldehyde produced, it is possible to determine the ring structure. The ordinary methyl glucosides and most methyl glycosides consume two moles of periodic acid and no formaldehyde is produced, indicating that they have a six-membered ring.

Methylation. Once the sugar is converted into a methyl glycoside, it is stable to alkali, and the remaining hydroxyl groups can be converted to ethers by a modified Williamson synthesis in which the glycoside reacts with methyl sulfate in the presence of sodium hydroxide.

Methyl glycoside — Methyl tetramethylglycoside

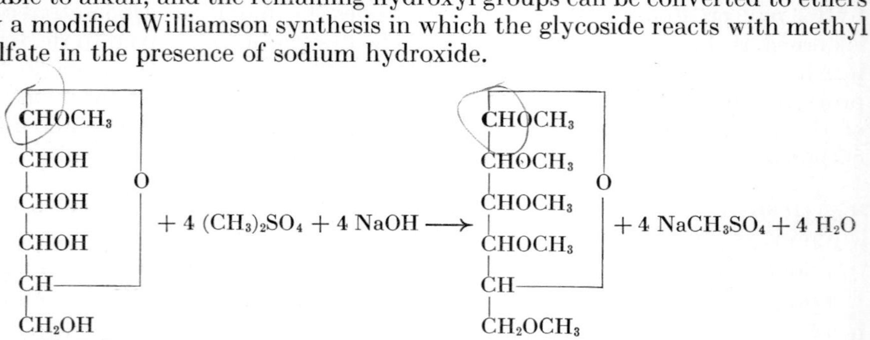

The methoxyl on C-1 differs markedly from the other four in that it is an acetal methoxyl whereas the others are ether methoxyls. The acetal methoxyl can be removed readily by acid hydrolysis to give the 2,3,4,6-tetramethylglycose which, because the ring can open easily, again will reduce Fehling's solution.

$$
\begin{array}{c}
\text{CHOCH}_3 \\
\text{CHOCH}_3 \\
\text{CHOCH}_3 \quad \text{O} \\
\text{CHOCH}_3 \\
\text{CH}\text{---} \\
\text{CH}_2\text{OCH}_3
\end{array}
+ \text{H}_2\text{O} \xrightarrow{[\text{H}^+]} \text{CH}_3\text{OH} +
\begin{array}{c}
\text{CHOH} \\
\text{CHOCH}_3 \\
\text{CHOCH}_3 \quad \text{O} \\
\text{CHOCH}_3 \\
\text{CH}\text{---} \\
\text{CH}_2\text{OCH}_3
\end{array}
\rightleftharpoons
\begin{array}{c}
\text{CHO} \\
\text{CHOCH}_3 \\
\text{CHOCH}_3 \\
\text{CHOCH}_3 \\
\text{CHOH} \\
\text{CH}_2\text{OCH}_3
\end{array}
$$

However the 2,3,4,6-tetramethylglycose can form only a hydrazone and not an osazone, because the hydroxyl group on C-2 is methylated. The methylated sugars played an important part in the determination of ring structures and of the constitution of oligo- and polysaccharides.

Mutarotation. Many optically active compounds give solutions, the rotation of which changes with time. This phenomenon, which is called *mutarotation* (L. *mutare* to change), must result from some chemical change in the molecule. The mutarotation of glucose solutions was reported first in 1846. By 1895 readily interconvertible isomeric modifications of lactose and glucose had been isolated. Three such forms are obtainable from glucose. The form designated α crystallizes as the hydrate from 70 per cent alcohol below 30°. Its freshly prepared aqueous solutions have a specific rotation of +112°. The β form crystallizes from aqueous solutions evaporated at temperatures above 98°. It has a specific rotation of +18.7°. The third form is obtained by adding alcohol to a concentrated aqueous solution and has a rotation of +52.7°. However only α- and β-glucose mutarotate, and each finally attains the value +52.7°. The third form therefore is nothing more than the equilibrium mixture of the α and β forms.

The existence of the two forms of glucose and their mutarotation is explainable if it is assumed that they have cyclic hemiacetal structures analogous to the acetal structures postulated for the methyl α- and β-glycosides. It usually is assumed that their interconversion takes place by way of the open chain form.

$$
\begin{array}{c}
\text{H---C---OH} \\
\text{CHOH} \\
\text{CHOH} \quad \text{O} \\
\text{CHOH} \\
\text{H---C}\text{---} \\
\text{CH}_2\text{OH} \\
\alpha\text{-D-Glycose}
\end{array}
\rightleftharpoons
\begin{array}{c}
\text{CHO} \\
\text{CHOH} \\
\text{CHOH} \\
\text{CHOH} \\
\text{H---C---OH} \\
\text{CH}_2\text{OH}
\end{array}
\rightleftharpoons
\begin{array}{c}
\text{HO---C---H} \\
\text{CHOH} \\
\text{CHOH} \quad \text{O} \\
\text{CHOH} \\
\text{H---C}\text{---} \\
\text{CH}_2\text{OH} \\
\beta\text{-D-Glycose}
\end{array}
$$

That the equilibrium rotation of glucose is not the average of the rotations of α- and β-glucose is not surprising, since they are not enantiomorphs and the equilibrium composition need not be a 50–50 mixture. The anomeric carbon atom of the hemiacetal structure frequently is called the *reducing* carbon atom, since it is involved in the reduction of Fehling's solution.

Ester Formation. The hydroxyl groups of sugars can be converted readily to ester groups. The aldoses acetylate with acetic anhydride in the presence of acidic or basic catalysts. The hexoses yield pentaacetates and the pentoses tetraacetates thus indicating the presence of five and four hydroxyl groups. The acetates, however, do not reduce Fehling's solution and therefore do not contain a free aldehyde group. Moreover two isomeric α and β forms of each acetate are obtained. Hence it is the cyclic form of the sugar which is acetylated. The acid catalysts commonly used are sulfuric acid or zinc chloride, and the basic catalysts are pyridine (p. 454) or sodium acetate (acetate ion).[2]

It is possible by choosing the proper catalyst and conditions to obtain chiefly α- or β-glucose pentaacetates as desired. Acids catalyze the interconversion of α and β forms of the acetates, and the equilibrium mixture of 90 per cent α and 10 per cent β is obtained. Bases catalyze the equilibrium between the free sugars (hemiacetals) but not that between the acetylated products (acetals). Since the β form of the sugar reacts faster than the α form, the base-catalyzed acetylation yields chiefly the β acetate.

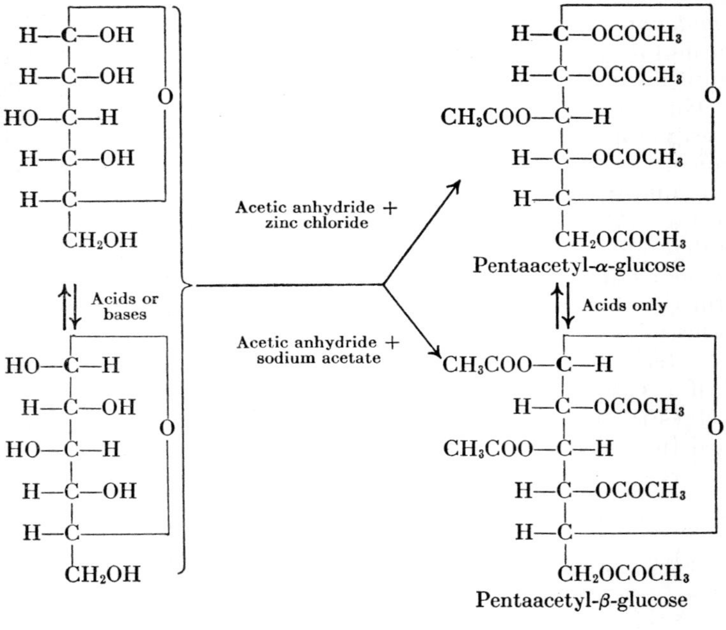

Pentaacetyl-α-glucose

Pentaacetyl-β-glucose

The sugar acetates are saponified readily by alkali. For preparative purposes, however, it is better to remove acetyl groups by transesterification catalyzed by alkoxide ion (p. 145).

---

[2] Zinc chloride is an acid catalyst because the zinc atom lacks two pair of electrons in its valence shell and like the proton can combine with an unshared pair of electrons. Acetate ion in acetic acid solution is a base analogous to the hydroxide ion in water solution (p. 191).

$$\left.\begin{array}{l} \text{CHOCOCH}_3 \\ \text{CHOCOCH}_3 \\ \text{CHOCOCH}_3 \\ \text{CHOCOCH}_3 \\ \text{CH} \\ \text{CH}_2\text{OCOCH}_3 \end{array}\right] \text{O} + 5\ \text{C}_2\text{H}_5\text{OH} \underset{}{\overset{\text{NaOC}_2\text{H}_5}{\rightleftarrows}} \left.\begin{array}{l} \text{CHOH} \\ \text{CHOH} \\ \text{CHOH} \\ \text{CHOH} \\ \text{CH} \\ \text{CH}_2\text{OH} \end{array}\right] \text{O} + 5\ \text{CH}_3\text{COOC}_2\text{H}_5$$

Many other esters of the sugars have been prepared. Among those of importance are the *benzoates* (p. 413) and the *sulfonates* (tosyl and mesyl derivatives, pp. 357, 222). Esters of some inorganic acids such as the *nitrates, carbonates,* and *phosphates* also are important. **Glucose 1-(dihydrogen phosphate)** (Cori ester) and **glucose 6-(dihydrogen phosphate)** (Robison ester) are important intermediates in the alcoholic fermentation of sugars.

Action of Strong Acids. Although dilute acids have little effect on aldoses other than catalyzing α,β interconversion, hot strong acids produce complex changes which involve dehydration. Thus all **pentoses** when distilled with 12 per cent hydrochloric acid give approximately theoretical yields of *furfural* (p. 451). The reaction is used both as a qualitative test for pentoses or sub-

$$\begin{array}{l} \text{CHO} \\ \text{CHOH} \\ \text{CHOH} \\ \text{CHOH} \\ \text{CH}_2\text{OH} \end{array} \overset{\text{Hot}}{\underset{\text{acid}}{\rightarrow}} \left.\begin{array}{l} \text{CHO} \\ \text{C} \\ \text{CH} \\ \text{CH} \\ \text{CH} \end{array}\right] \text{O} \quad \text{or} \quad \begin{array}{c} \text{HC}\!-\!-\!\text{CH} \\ \| \quad\quad \| \\ \text{HC} \quad\ \ \text{C}\!-\!\text{CHO} \\ \diagdown\!\diagup \\ \text{O} \end{array} + 3\ \text{H}_2\text{O}$$

Furfural

stances yielding pentoses on hydrolysis and for their quantitative estimation, by detecting or estimating the furfural that distills (p. 454). The 6-desoxyaldohexoses are converted into 5-methylfurfural.

Hexoses yield 5-(hydroxymethyl)furfural, but this compound is more soluble in water than furfural and is not volatile with steam. Hence it is acted upon further by the hot acid giving **levulinic acid** and considerable amounts of dark insoluble condensation products known as **humins.**

$$\begin{array}{l} \text{CHO} \\ \text{CHOH} \\ \text{CHOH} \\ \text{CHOH} \\ \text{CHOH} \\ \text{CH}_2\text{OH} \end{array} \overset{\text{Hot}}{\underset{\text{acid}}{\rightarrow}} \left.\begin{array}{l} \text{CHO} \\ \text{C} \\ \text{CH} \\ \text{CH} \\ \text{C} \\ \text{CH}_2\text{OH} \end{array}\right] \text{O} \quad \text{or} \quad \begin{array}{c} \text{H}\!-\!\text{C}\!-\!-\!\text{CH} \\ \| 4 \quad 3 \| \\ \text{HOCH}_2\!-\!\text{C}_5 \quad {}_2\text{C}\!-\!\text{CHO} \\ \diagdown\ \ _1\ \ \diagup \\ \text{O} \end{array} \overset{2\ \text{H}_2\text{O}}{\rightarrow} \begin{array}{l} \text{COOH} \\ \text{CH}_2 \\ \text{CH}_2 \\ \text{C}\!=\!\text{O} \\ \text{CH}_3 \end{array} + \text{HCOOH}$$

5-(Hydroxymethyl)furfural   Levulinic
acid

The different furfurals give characteristic color reactions with polyhydric phenols such as resorcinol (p. 393), orcinol (p. 393), and phloroglucinol (p. 394), which may be used to distinguish between pentoses, 6-desoxyhexoses, and hexoses.

Representation of Ring Structures

The formulas used thus far to represent the structure of the sugars do not indicate adequately the space relationships within the molecules, particularly those of the groups on the last two carbon atoms. With a molecular model the open chain formula for glucose can be represented in a coiled manner (III) to portray better the 109.5 degree angle between carbon atoms.

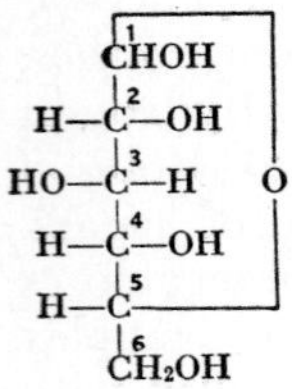

    I 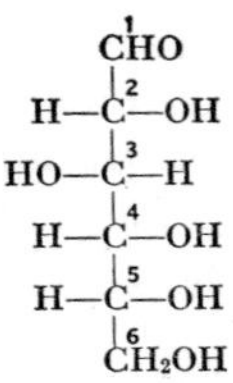   II 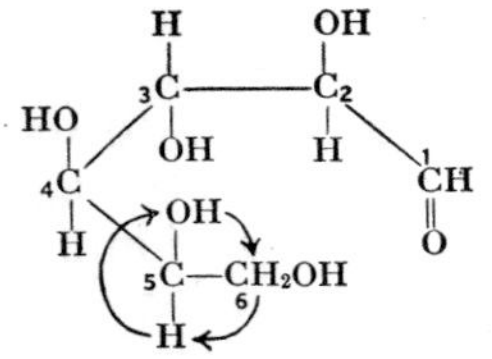   III 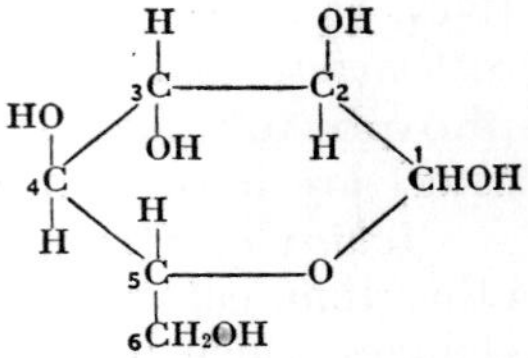   IV

However for the oxygen atom of the hydroxyl group to become a member of the ring, rotation must take place about the bond between the fourth and fifth carbon atoms, with the result that the hydrogen atoms on the fourth and fifth carbon atoms are on opposite sides of the ring instead of on the same side as in the projection representation (I). Formula IV is not a projection formula but is a perspective formula. The ring may be considered as perpendicular to the plane of the paper with the lower portion in front and the groups extending above and below the plane of the ring.

Formula IV does not indicate the configuration of the reducing carbon atom. In the following two formulas for α- and β-glucose these configurations are given. Except for the anomeric carbon atoms the ring carbon atoms are omitted.

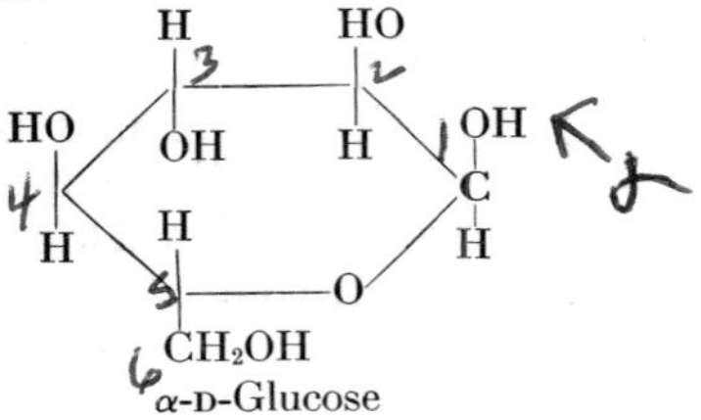

    α-D-Glucose β-D-Glucose

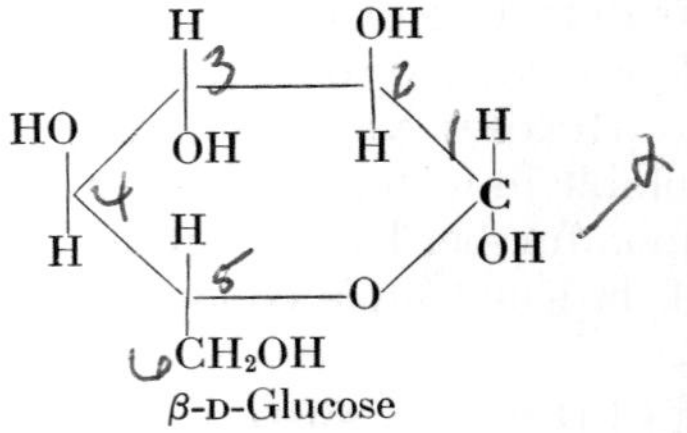

The perspective formulas, frequently called Haworth formulas, are useful also in representing the structures of oligo- and polysaccharides.

Ketoses

Fructose is the most abundant ketose. It occurs free, along with glucose and sucrose, in fruit juices and honey, and combined with other sugars in oligosaccharides. It is the sole product of the hydrolysis of the polysaccharide inulin (p. 297). Naturally occurring fructose has a high negative rotation which gave rise to the common name *levulose*. It is the sweetest of the sugars.

Since individuals vary greatly in their sensory perceptions, it is possible to state only average opinions regarding taste. The results of early workers based on threshold methods, that is the highest dilution that can be tasted, are valueless. When comparing concentrations of equal sweetness, the relative sweetness varies with the concentration. Moreover since α-glucose is sweeter than β-glucose, solutions that have reached equilibrium must be used. When compared with a 10 per cent glucose solution, the relative sweetness of some of the common sugars is lactose 0.55, galactose 0.95, glucose 1.00, sucrose 1.45, and fructose 1.65. Many synthetic compounds are known whose sweetness is from several hundred to several thousand times greater than that of the sugars (p. 416).

Fructose gives the usual addition reactions of carbonyl compounds, but it is not oxidized by hypobromite solutions to give a monocarboxylic acid. Hence it is a ketose and not an aldose. It is oxidized by Fehling's solution and has a reducing power comparable to that of glucose. As a ketone it would not be expected to reduce Fehling's solution. However in the presence of alkali it is in equilibrium with glucose and mannose, which are oxidized readily. Moreover CHOH groups adjacent to a carbonyl group also are oxidized by Fehling's solution (p. 408).

When fructose reacts with phenylhydrazine, a phenylosazone is formed which is identical with that obtained from $(+)$glucose. Hence the carbonyl group must contain C-2, the configuration of the rest of the molecule must be identical with that of $(+)$glucose, and $(-)$fructose must belong to the D family.

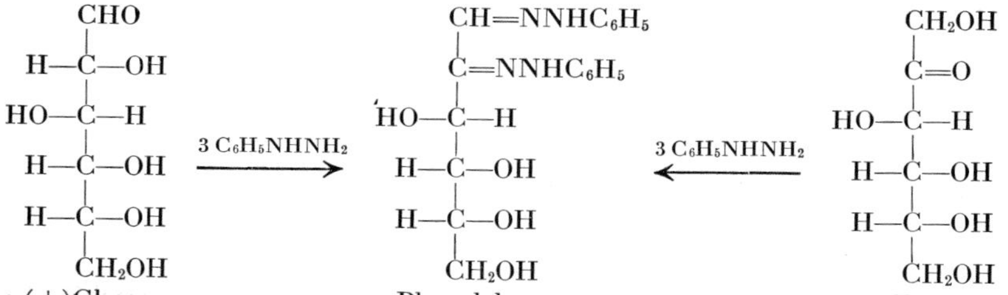

It was the discovery that glucose and fructose give the same osazone, and the realization of its significance, that led Fischer to undertake the unraveling of the configuration of the sugars. α-Methylphenylhydrazine, $C_6H_5N(CH_3)NH_2$, can be used to distinguish fructose from glucose or mannose, since conditions can be chosen such that fructose gives an osazone, whereas glucose and mannose do not.

Sorbose is the only other ketose of importance. It does not occur naturally but is produced by the action of sorbose bacteria (*Acetobacter xylinum* or better *Acetobacter suboxydans*) on L-sorbitol (p. 307).

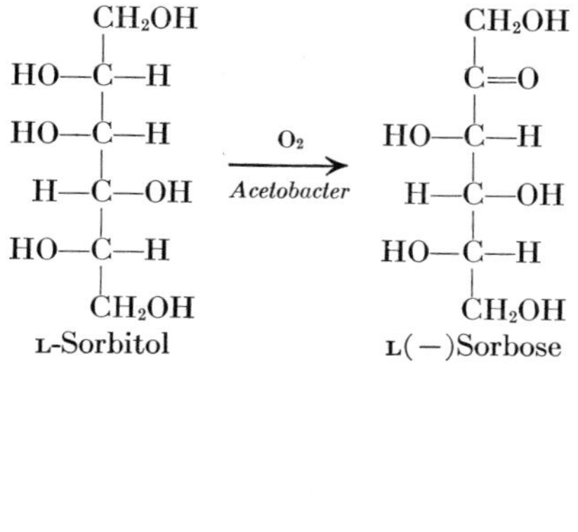

Sorbose is important as an intermediate for the commercial synthesis of **vitamin C,** otherwise known as *ascorbic acid*, which is a necessary dietary factor for the prevention of scurvy. Sorbose can be oxidized with nitric acid to 2-keto-L-gulonic acid, which on heating in water dehydrates to the 1,4-lactone. Because of the acidic properties of ascorbic acid and its ready oxidation, it is believed to exist in the enediol form.

$$
\begin{array}{ccccc}
\text{CH}_2\text{OH} & \text{COOH} & \overset{\text{O}}{\overset{\|}{\text{C}}} & \overset{\text{O}}{\overset{\|}{\text{C}}} \\
\text{C}{=}\text{O} & \text{C}{=}\text{O} & \text{C}{=}\text{O} & \text{HO}{-}\text{C} \\
\text{HO}{-}\text{C}{-}\text{H} \xrightarrow{\text{HNO}_3} & \text{HO}{-}\text{C}{-}\text{H} \xrightarrow{\text{Heat}} & \text{HO}{-}\text{C}{-}\text{H} \rightleftharpoons & \text{HO}{-}\text{C} \\
\text{H}{-}\text{C}{-}\text{OH} & \text{H}{-}\text{C}{-}\text{OH} & \text{H}{-}\text{C} & \text{H}{-}\text{C} \\
\text{HO}{-}\text{C}{-}\text{H} & \text{HO}{-}\text{C}{-}\text{H} & \text{HO}{-}\text{C}{-}\text{H} & \text{HO}{-}\text{C}{-}\text{H} \\
\text{CH}_2\text{OH} & \text{CH}_2\text{OH} & \text{CH}_2\text{OH} & \text{CH}_2\text{OH}
\end{array}
$$

L-Sorbose   2-Keto-L-gulonic acid   Vitamin C (ascorbic acid)

OLIGOSACCHARIDES

Disaccharides

Reducing Disaccharides. **Maltose,** $C_{12}H_{22}O_{11}$, is formed by the enzyme-catalyzed hydrolysis of starch.

$$(C_6H_{10}O_5)_x + \frac{x}{2} H_2O \xrightarrow{\text{Diastase}} \frac{x}{2} C_{12}H_{22}O_{11}$$

Starch   Maltose

Acid or enzyme catalyzed hydrolysis of maltose yields two molecules of glucose.

$$C_{12}H_{22}O_{11} + H_2O \xrightarrow[\text{Maltase}]{\text{[H}^+]\text{ or}} 2\ C_6H_{12}O_6$$

Maltose   (α-glucosidase)   Glucose

Maltose reduces Fehling's solution, forms an osazone and undergoes mutarotation. Hence it contains a potential aldehyde group and a hemiacetal ring structure. The formation of an octaacetate and octamethyl derivative indicates the presence of eight hydroxyl groups.

Hydrolysis to two molecules of glucose points to a linkage through oxygen rather than directly between two carbon atoms, and the ease of hydrolysis by enzymes and acids indicates an acetal linkage rather than an ether linkage. Degradation of methylated derivatives has shown that the two glucose units are linked through the 1 position of the nonreducing half of the molecule and the 4 position of the reducing half. Maltose is hydrolyzed by *maltase*, the α-glucosidase which hydrolyzes methyl α-glucoside, and not by *emulsin*, the β-glucosidase that hydrolyzes methyl β-glucoside. Hence the configuration of C-1 of the nonreducing portion is believed to be α. These conclusions are embodied in the following perspective formulas.

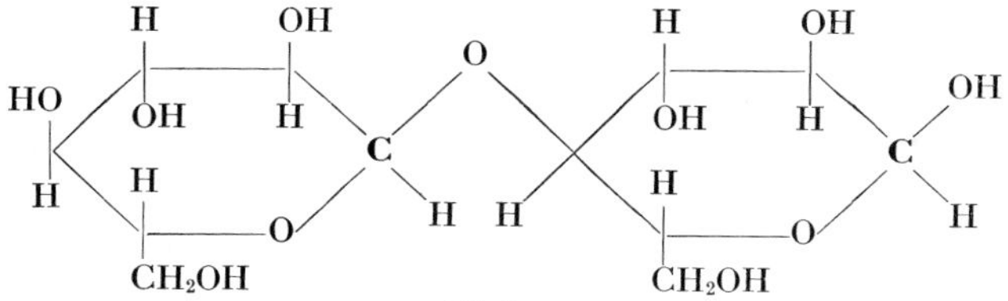

α-Maltose
4-α-Glucosyl-α-glucose
4-α-ᴅ-Glucopyranosyl-α-ᴅ-glucopyranose

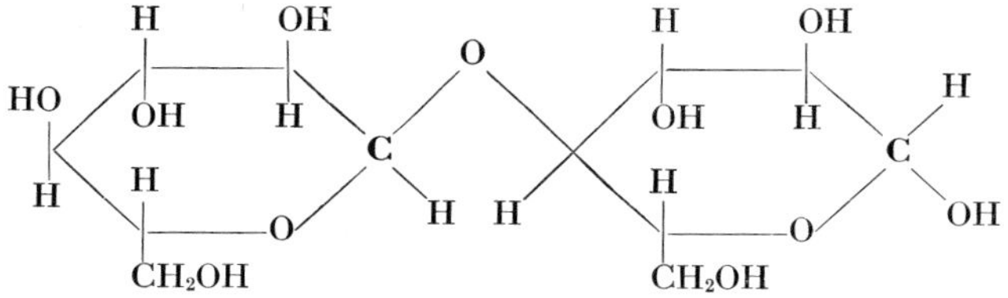

β-Maltose
4-α-Glucosyl-β-glucose
4-α-ᴅ-Glucopyranosyl-β-ᴅ-glucopyranose

α- and β-Maltose differ only in the configuration of the anomeric carbon atom, **C,** of the reducing half of the molecule. The second name given under the formulas is somewhat more descriptive in that it indicates the point at which the nonreducing half of the molecule is attached to the reducing half, and the structure and configuration of both halves. The third name is completely descriptive since it adds the information that the glucose units have the configuration of ᴅ(+)glucose and that they each contain the six-membered pyran nucleus (p. 459).

Cellobiose is a disaccharide formed by the hydrolysis of its octaacetate. The latter compound is obtained in 40 per cent yield when cellulose (cotton or paper) is dissolved in a mixture of acetic anhydride and sulfuric acid, and allowed to stand for one week at 35°. Cellobiose like maltose yields two molecules of glucose on hydrolysis and undergoes all of the reactions of maltose. The results of degradation experiments indicate that it has the same structure as maltose. The only difference in behavior of the two sugars is that cellobiose is hydrolyzed in the presence of emulsin (β-glucosidase) and not in the presence of maltase (α-glucosidase). Hence cellobiose differs from maltose only in that the linkage between the two glucose units has the β-configuration instead of the α-configuration.

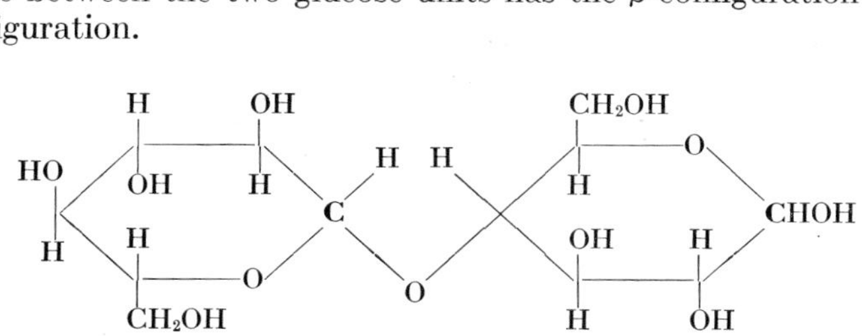

Cellobiose
4-β-Glucosylglucose
4-β-ᴅ-Glucopyranosyl-ᴅ-glucopyranose

Lactose (*milk sugar*) is present in about 5 per cent concentration in the milk of all mammals. It is manufactured commercially from whey, the aqueous solution left after the coagulation of the proteins of milk in the manufacture of cheese. Lactose is a reducing disaccharide, and on acid or enzyme hydrolysis it yields one molecule of galactose and one molecule of glucose. If it first is oxidized to lactonic acid and then hydrolyzed, the products are galactose and gluconic acid. Hence the glucose unit contains the reducing portion of the molecule. Since lactose is hydrolyzed by β-galactosidase, the linkage between the galactose and glucose molecule is believed to be β. Degradation experiments have established its structure as 4-β-D-galactopyranosyl-D-glucose.

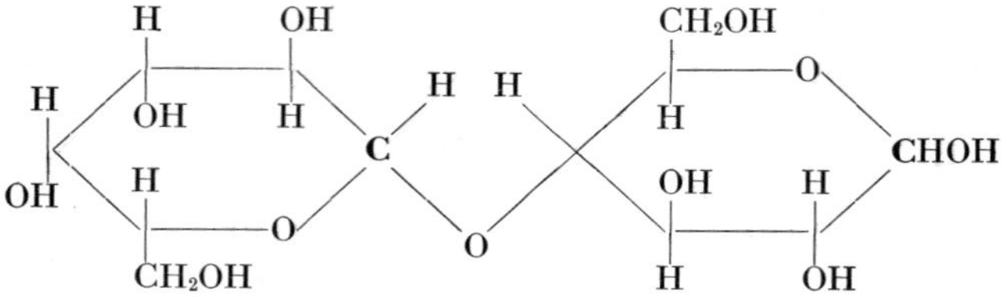

Lactose
4-β-D-Galactopyranosyl-D-glucose

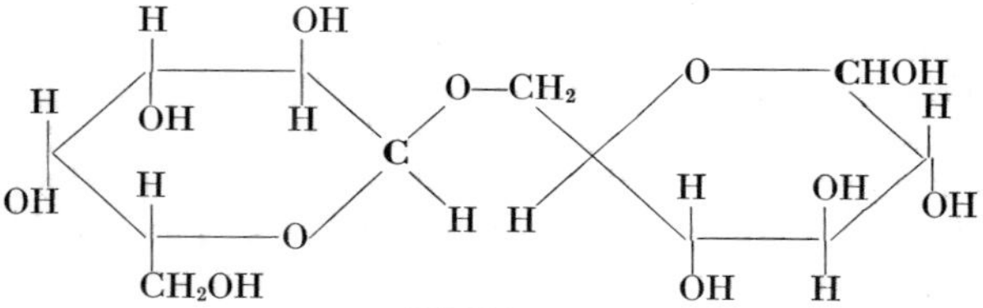

Melibiose
6-α-D-Galactopyranosyl-D-glucose

Melibiose is a reducing disaccharide which can be obtained by the partial hydrolysis of the trisaccharide, *raffinose* (p. 294). It has been found free in plant exudations and has been shown to be 6-α-D-galactopyranosyl-D-glucose.

Although both monosaccharides and reducing disaccharides produce osazones, the reaction can be used to distinguish between them because the osazones of monosaccharides (I) are less soluble than those of disaccharides (II) and crystallize from the hot solution, whereas the osazones of disaccharides crystallize only on cooling.

Nonreducing Disaccharides. Sucrose (*cane sugar, beet sugar*) is the most important disaccharide. It occurs universally in plants and in all portions of the plant. It also is present in honey along with glucose and fructose. The principal sources are sugar cane, sugar beets, and the sugar maple tree. The great ease with which sucrose crystallizes probably accounts for its isolation in a pure state as early as 300 A.D. (p. 2). Sugar cane (*Saccharum officinarum*) belongs to the grass family and probably originated in northeastern India (Skr. *sakara* gravel or sugar). From there it was introduced into China about 400 A.D. and into Egypt by the Arabians in 640 A.D. It is believed that it was introduced into San Domingo by Columbus on his second voyage to America in 1494. Although sucrose was discovered in beet juice in 1747, it was not manufactured from this source until the Napoleonic Wars (1796–1814) made the price of cane sugar prohibitive in Europe.

Sucrose is obtained from cane by grinding the stalk and expressing the juice with rollers. The juice, which contains about 15 per cent sucrose, is made slightly alkaline with lime to prevent hydrolysis. On heating, most of the impurities separate as a heavy scum and a precipitate, which are removed. This process is known as *defecation*. The clear juice is concentrated under reduced pressure and allowed to crystallize. The raw sugar is removed by centrifuging, and the filtrate is reconcentrated and crops of crystals removed until no more can be obtained economically. The final mother liquor is a dark viscous liquid that contains about 50 per cent fermentable sugars and is known as *blackstrap*. It is used for preparing cattle feeds and for the production of alcohol (p. 68).

The raw sugar is shipped to refineries where the brown color is removed by washing and by dissolving in water and passing the solution through decolorizing carbon. Concentration and crystallization yield the pure sugar of commerce. The darker colored crops from the refining operation are sold as brown sugar. If the white crystalline sugar is ground with 3 per cent of starch to prevent caking, the product is known as powdered sugar.

The white sugar beet, a cultivated variety of *Beta maritima*, has been bred to contain up to 18 per cent sucrose. The beet root, free of leaves, is washed and sliced into V-shaped pieces about 1 cm. thick. These pieces are extracted countercurrently by hot water to yield a dark solution containing about 12 per cent sucrose. By diffusing the sugar from the plant cells the amount of protein and high molecular weight impurities extracted is much less than if the beet were crushed and pressed. The warm extract is agitated with 2 to 3 per cent of lime and the mixture then saturated with carbon dioxide. The precipitate carries down most of the impurities and the yellow filtrate is decolorized with sulfur dioxide. After concentrating, crystallizing, and washing, the product is ready for market.

Production of sucrose from the sugar maple (*Acer saccharinum*) is relatively unimportant. Small amounts are prepared also from other sources such as sorghum and palm sap, but sucrose from these sources does not enter the world market.

Sucrose is manufactured in larger amount than any other pure organic chemical. World production in 1949 was 36,646,000 tons of which about one third was from beets and two thirds from cane. Production in the United States in 1949 was 2,100,000 tons of which only one fourth was from cane. Consumption was 7,600,000 tons or 95 pounds per capita.

Hydrolysis of sucrose in the presence of acids or the enzyme invertase yields one molecule of fructose and one molecule of glucose. Sucrose has a positive rotation, $[\alpha]_D^{20} = +66.53$, but during hydrolysis the sign of rotation changes because the high negative rotation of fructose, $[\alpha]_D^{20} = -92.4$ for the equilibrium mixture, more than balances the positive rotation of glucose, $[\alpha]_D^{20} = +52.7$ for the equilibrium mixture. Because of the change in sign of rotation during hydrolysis the process is known as *inversion*, and the mixture of fructose and glucose is known as *invert sugar*. It has about the same sweetening power as sucrose (p. 289) but has much less tendency to crystallize and hence is used in the manufacture of candies and syrups. It is of interest that sucrose octaacetate is extremely bitter.

Sucrose does not reduce Fehling's solution, form an osazone, undergo mutarotation or form methyl glycosides. Accordingly the fructose and glucose portions are linked through the two anomeric carbon atoms. Degradation experiments have shown the presence of a six-membered ring in the glucose portion of the molecule, and a five-membered furan ring (p. 451) in the fructose portion. Sucrose is hydrolyzed by yeast α-glucosidase and not by the β-glucosidase of emulsin. It is hydrolyzed also by sucrase (invertase), an enzyme that hydrolyzes β- but not α-fructofuranosides. Accordingly the anomeric carbon of the glucose portion is assigned the α configuration, and that of the fructose portion the β configuration.

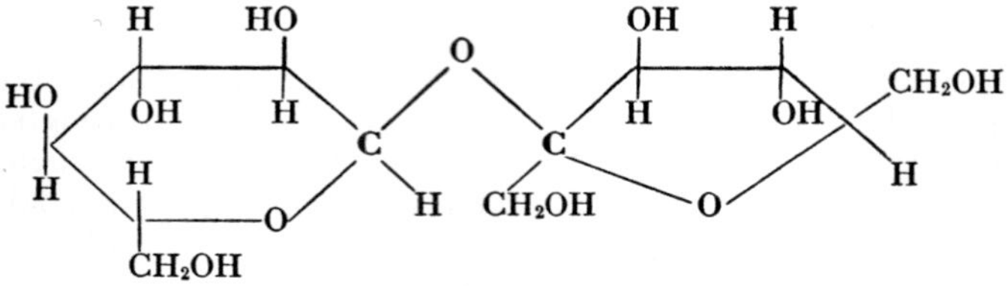

Sucrose
α-D-Glucopyranosyl-β-D-fructofuranoside

All attempts to synthesize sucrose by chemical methods have failed because of the difficulty in obtaining the correct configuration of the glycosidic linkage. The synthesis from glucose and fructose has been accomplished, however, using an enzyme from the microorganism *Pseudomonas saccharophila.*

Trisaccharide

Raffinose is present in small amount in many plants. It accumulates in the mother liquor during the preparation of beet sugar and can be prepared from beet sugar molasses. It may be obtained also by extracting defatted ground cottonseed with water. Complete hydrolysis of raffinose yields one mole each of glucose, fructose, and galactose. Since raffinose is nonreducing, all of the anomeric carbon atoms must be involved in glycosidic links. When raffinose is hydrolyzed in the presence of the α-galactosidase of emulsin, the products are galactose and sucrose, whereas if it is hydrolyzed by sucrase (β-fructosidase) the products are fructose and melibiose. Since the structures of sucrose and melibiose are known, the structure of raffinose is established.

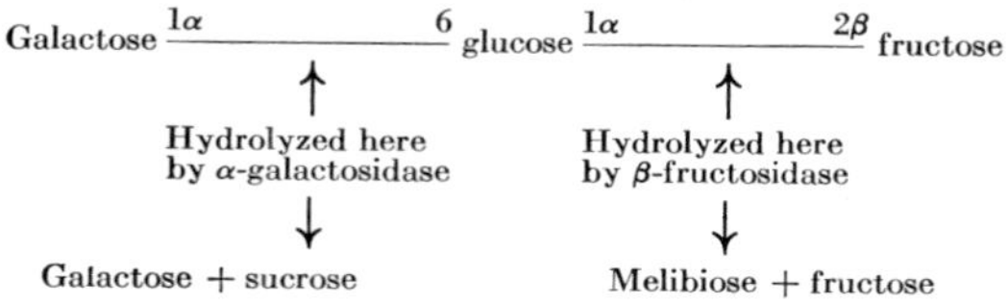

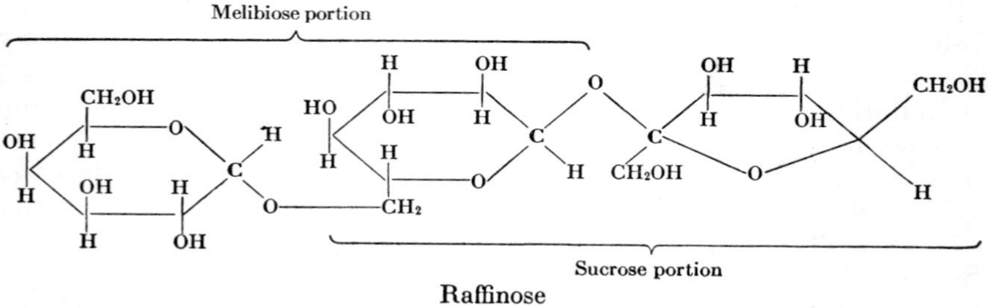

Raffinose

POLYSACCHARIDES

As the name implies, polysaccharides are high molecular weight substances (molecular weights 30,000 to 14,000,000). They are insoluble in liquids and are altered readily by the acids and alkalies required to catalyze their conversion into soluble derivatives. Hence their purification is extremely difficult. Moreover even the purified products are not molecularly homogeneous since the same substance may consist of polymers of varying molecular weight. Nevertheless the polysaccharides are considerably simpler than proteins because frequently only a single type of building unit, for example glucose, is present. Compounds containing a single type of building unit are known as *homopolysaccharides*. Some polysaccharides are derived from several different types of building units and are known as *heteropolysaccharides*. Polysaccharides such as starch, glycogen, or inulin are reserve foodstuffs for the plant or animal; others, as cellulose of plants and chitin of crustacea, have a structural function; for others, such as gums and mucilages, function is unknown.

Homopolysaccharides

Starch. During the growth of a plant, carbohydrate is stored in various parts, such as the roots, seeds, and fruits, in the form of microscopic granules of starch. Seeds may contain up to 70 per cent starch, and roots and tubers up to 30 per cent. Corn, potatoes, wheat, rice, tapioca, sago, and sweet potatoes constitute the chief commercial sources. Starch granules from different sources vary in shape, size, and general appearance.

In the United States most starch is derived from corn (maize). The corn grains are soaked in water containing sulfur dioxide until soft, and then are shredded to free the germ. When the ground mass is mixed with water, the germ floats because of the high oil content and is collected, dried, and pressed to produce corn oil (p. 152). The remainder of the grain sinks and is ground as finely as possible without rupturing the starch granules, and the mixture is washed through screens to remove most of the hull. The starch suspension is passed through long shallow troughs where the starch granules settle, or it is removed by centrifuges. The protein constituents of the grain (gluten) are recovered from the steep water and from the water that leaves the settling tables. Corn steep water now finds an important outlet as a nutrient for the mold used in the manufacture of penicillin (p. 461). In Europe the main source of starch is potatoes, the process of isolation being very similar to the isolation from corn except that no soaking is required since there is no germ to be removed.

When starch is heated with water, the granules burst and a colloidal suspension is produced. This dispersion has been separated into two components. By saturating it with a slightly soluble alcohol, such as butanol or better the commercial mixture of amyl alcohols known as Pentasol (p. 85), a microcrystalline precipitate forms which is known as *A-fraction* or **amylose.** Addition of a water-miscible alcohol such as methanol to the mother liquors precipitates an amorphous material known as *B-fraction* or **amylopectin.**

The two fractions differ markedly in their behavior towards iodine solutions. Amylose gives a deep blue color and absorbs 18 to 20 per cent of its weight of iodine as determined by potentiometric titration. The blue product appears to be an adsorption complex in which iodine molecules fit into the central open spaces of a helix of C_6 units that constitute the amylose molecule. Amylopectin gives a red to purple color and absorbs only 0.5 to 0.8 per cent of iodine. Iodine titration of whole starch may be used to determine the relative amounts of the two components.

Starches from different sources vary greatly in composition. Using the alcohol method of separation, corn starch gives 28 to 29 per cent amylose and tapioca starch about 20 per cent, whereas none is obtained from the starch of waxy maize or sorghum. Iodine titrations give somewhat higher values of amylose, possibly because in the separation method some amylose remains with the amylopectin.

Both fractions give only glucose on hydrolysis, but otherwise they differ considerably in their physical and chemical properties. Amylose is hydrolyzed completely to maltose by malt diastase. Hence it consists entirely of glucose linked through the 1,4 positions, and the configuration of the glucosidic links is α.

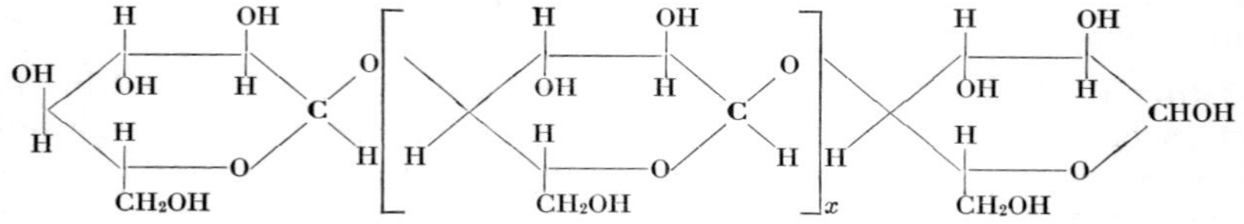

Amylose

Hydrolysis of amylopectin by diastase stops after about 50 per cent has been hydrolyzed to maltose, the remainder being a high molecular weight product that is known as *limit dextrin*. It is believed that amylopectin has

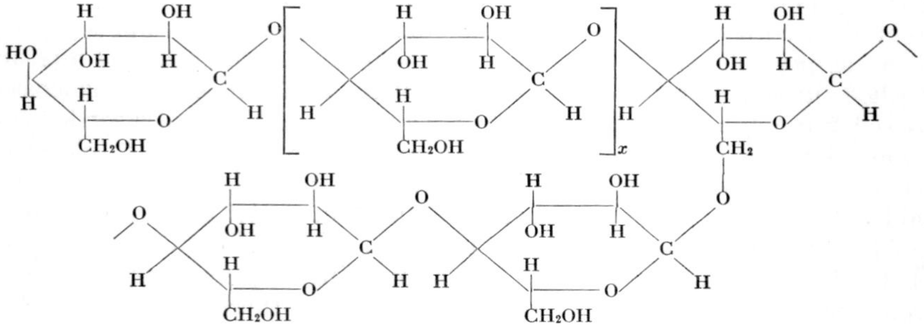

Portion of amylopectin molecule

branching chains, that in enzyme hydrolysis maltose units are cleaved starting with the ends of the branches, and that hydrolysis proceeds until a branch is reached. The residue is the limit dextrin.

The chief use of starch is as food. It is hydrolyzed stepwise by the *salivary amylases*, the final product being maltose if the reaction goes to completion. Since the enzymes are destroyed by strong acid, starch digestion stops as soon as the food is completely mixed with hydrochloric acid of the stomach. Digestion continues, however, in the intestine, where the hydrochloric acid is neutralized and *pancreatic amylase* completes the hydrolysis to maltose. Before passage through the mucous membrane of the intestine, disaccharides such as maltose, sucrose, and lactose are hydrolyzed to the monosaccharides. The latter are converted apparently by the cells of the membrane into the hexose phosphates, which are removed rapidly from the blood by the liver and converted into glycogen.

Industrially starch is converted by acid hydrolysis into **corn syrup** or **crystalline glucose,** both of which are used as food. Large quantities of starch are used as stiffening agents and adhesives, often after modification to dextrins. Starch can be converted to esters and ethers but so far these functional derivatives have not found large-scale uses. Starch nitrates containing 11 to 13 per cent nitrogen (so-called *nitrostarches*) have been used as a demolition explosive to replace TNT.

Glycogen. This reserve carbohydrate of animals does not occur as granules but is distributed throughout the protoplasm. Some of it is water-soluble, but the remainder is bound to protein. The best source is mussels. Glycogen is isolated by hydrolyzing the tissue with hot aqueous alkali, neutralizing, and precipitating with alcohol. Glycogen gives a violet to brown color with iodine. Acid hydrolysis yields only glucose, but diastase gives up to 30 per cent maltose. Glycogen preparations are very heterogeneous and molecular weights vary from 4,000,000 to 14,000,000. It is believed that glycogen is even more highly branched than starch, but that otherwise it has a similar structure.

Inulin. This starch-like substance occurs in many plants, particularly members of the *Compositae*, for example Jerusalem artichoke, goldenrod, dandelion, dahlia, and chicory. It is obtained readily from dahlia tubers or chicory roots. Hydrolysis yields only fructose. Chemical evidence indicates that the chief polymeric units are β-fructopyranose units joined at the 1 and 2 positions.

Inulin

Cellulose. This polysaccharide constitutes the cell membranes of the higher plants. It makes up about 10 per cent of the dry weight of leaves, about 50 per cent of the woody structures of plants, and over 90 per cent of cotton fiber. Pure cellulose is obtained best from cotton by dewaxing with an organic solvent, and removing pectic substances (p. 305) by extracting with hot 1 per cent sodium hydroxide solution.

Like starch, cellulose yields only glucose on hydrolysis. By the ultra-centrifugal method molecular weights of 100,000 to 500,000 (600 to 3000 C_6 units) are indicated, depending on the previous treatment of the cellulose. Since acetolysis yields 40–50 per cent of cellobiose octaacetate which has a β glycosidic linkage (p. 291), it is assumed that the glucose units are linked entirely by a β linkage through the 1,4 positions.

Cellulose

In spite of the fact that cellulose contains five oxygen atoms for each six carbon atoms, it is insoluble in water and alcohols. Evidently because of the high molecular weight and the linear nature of the molecule, van der Waals forces and possibly proton bonding between the molecules provide very strong forces which prevent dispersion in solvents. Cellulose is soluble in strong acids such as concentrated sulfuric acid and strong solutions of zinc chloride, but since a scission of glycosidic links also takes place, the product regenerated by pouring the solution into water has a much lower molecular weight than the original cellulose. Such products are said to be *degraded*. Degradation also takes place on exposure to air in the presence of alkali.

The best solvent for cellulose is an aqueous solution of cupric ammonium hydroxide, $Cu(NH_3)_4(OH)_2$, which is known as *cuprammonium solution* or *Schweitzer's reagent*. Since the viscosity of solutions decreases with the chain length of a molecule, the extent of degradation of cellulose can be estimated by determining the viscosity of solutions in Schweitzer's reagent. Cellulose regenerated by acidifying cuprammonium solutions gives a solution having a lower viscosity than the original cellulose. Hence Schweitzer's reagent itself brings about some degradation. The degradation is greater if the solutions are exposed to air.

Commercial Sources of Cellulose. The technical uses of cellulose are dependent chiefly on its fibrous form and on the strength and flexibility of products prepared from it. Cotton fibers have an average tensile strength of 80,000 p.s.i. compared with 65,000 p.s.i. for medium steel. Fiber length varies with the source. The best fibers, such as flax, jute, and hemp, vary from 20 to 350 cm. in length. Cotton, which is a seed hair, has fibers 1.5 to 5.5 cm. long. Wood fibers vary from 0.2 to 5 mm. in length. The long fibers are used chiefly for making textiles, and cotton is by far the most important for this purpose.

After removal of moisture, wood consists of about 50 per cent cellulose, 15 per cent other polysaccharides and sugars known as *hemicelluloses*, 30 per cent lignin, which acts as a matrix for the cellulose fibers and whose structure is unknown, and 2 per cent of other substances such as fat, resin, and protein. Wood pulp is manufactured by dissolving the lignin with hot solutions of sodium hydroxide, calcium bisulfite, or a mixture of sodium hydroxide and sodium sulfide (made from lime and reduced sodium sulfate). The products, known as soda pulp, sulfite pulp, or sulfate (Kraft) pulp, respectively, consist of impure cellulose that has been more or less degraded. Most wood pulp is used in the manufacture of paper where the length of the fibers and the strength are most important. Fermentable sugars can be recovered from sulfite liquors and used as a source of alcohol. The sulfate process yields for each ton of paper about 50 pounds of **tall oil** (Sw. *tallolja* pine oil), which consists of about 50 per cent unsaturated fatty acids, chiefly oleic and linoleic acids, and 50 per cent resin acids. It is used in the manufacture of soap (p. 157) and synthetic protective coatings (p. 416).

Mercerized Cotton. John Mercer, an English chemist and calico printer, attempted in 1814 to filter a strong solution of sodium hydroxide through cotton cloth and found that the fibers swelled and stopped the filtration. After the cloth was washed free of sodium hydroxide and dried, it dyed more readily than the original cloth. He patented his process in 1850. This treatment, however, shrinks the cloth considerably. Around 1889 Horace Lowe, another English technical chemist, attempted to prevent this shrinkage mechanically by carrying out the whole process with the cloth or yarn under tension. Not only was shrinkage prevented, but the surface irregularities of the fiber were removed giving it a high luster like silk. Moreover the strength of the fiber increased about 20 per cent. This process now is known as *mercerization* and the product is called *mercerized cotton*. It is by far the most widely used chemical finish for cotton in which the fiber is modified. About 45,000,000 pounds of yarn and 800,000,000 yards of cloth are mercerized each year in the United States.

Parchment Paper. When paper is treated for a few seconds with about 80 per cent sulfuric acid, an alteration of the surface of the fiber takes place, and after washing and drying, the paper is stiffer and tougher and does not disintegrate in water. Because of its resemblance to parchment, it is called *parchment paper*.

Glucose. Cellulose can be hydrolyzed to glucose and in this way becomes usable for food or for the production of alcohol or yeast by fermentation. In the technical processes the wood chips are extracted with 40 per cent hydrochloric acid at 20° (Bergius process) or 0.5 per cent sulfuric acid at 130° (Scholler process). The cellulose dissolves leaving the lignin as a solid. Concentration of the extract yields the sugars. Acetic acid also may be recovered from the extracts. The residual lignin can be briquetted and distilled to give charcoal and methyl alcohol. Wood saccharification has been operated in countries with a controlled economy, particularly in Germany before World War II, although even there the operation was not so extensive as generally is believed. Attempts have been made periodically since 1900 to operate plants in the United States, but they have never been feasible economically.

Cellulose Esters. Many important products are derived from cellulose by esterifying the hydroxyl groups, since these derivatives are soluble in organic solvents and thus permit the formation of films or fibers. Formerly the cellulose used for this purpose was chiefly purified cotton linters, the short cotton fibers cut from the cotton seed after the removal of the long fibers by the cotton gin. More recently wood pulp having a high *α-cellulose* content has become the dominant raw material. α-Cellulose is a technical term for the portion of wood pulp that is insoluble in alkali of mercerizing strength (17.5 per cent). The soluble portion consists of the so-called *hemicelluloses* and of sugars and lower molecular weight products.

The **cellulose nitrates** were the first esters to be of technical importance. Dry purified cotton linters are soaked in a mixture of nitric and sulfuric acid. It is desirable to carry out the reaction for as short a time (15–30 minutes), and at as low a temperature (30°–40°) as possible and to keep the water concentration low to reduce degradation. After centrifuging and washing, the nitrated cotton is boiled with water to hydrolyze sulfates and to produce good stability. It is stored wet and dehydrated before use by washing with ethanol or butanol. Three chief types of cellulose nitrate are produced: (*1*) *celluloid pyroxylin* containing 10.5–11 per cent nitrogen, soluble in ethanol-ether mixture and in absolute ethanol; (*2*) *soluble pyroxylin* (*collodion cotton*, or *dynamite cotton*) containing 11.5–12.3 per cent nitrogen and soluble in absolute ethanol; and (*3*) *guncotton*, containing 12.5–13.5 per cent nitrogen. Guncotton containing over 13 per cent nitrogen is insoluble in ethanol-ether and in absolute alcohol. All of the commercial nitrates dissolve in acetone and in the lower molecular weight esters. The dinitrates of cellulose should contain 11.11 per cent nitrogen and the trinitrate 14.15 per cent nitrogen. Hence the commercial products are mixtures rather than pure compounds.

Guncotton is the least degraded, having approximately the chain length of the original cellulose of about 3000 C_6 units. It gives solutions of extremely high viscosity. It is used for making smokeless powder, the chief propellant explosive. The guncotton is *gelatinized* or *colloided* to a dough by mixing with a solvent, and expressed and cut into cylindrical perforated pellets called *grains*. The perforations permit a progressive increase in burning area and hence an increasing rate of combustion as the projectile moves through the barrel of the gun. The United States military forces use a propellant made from guncotton having 12.5 per cent nitrogen and gelatinized with ethanol-ether mixture. The British military forces use a propellant made from guncotton having over 13 per cent nitrogen and gelatinized with acetone. Powders having a higher nitrogen content give a somewhat longer range but are more corrosive on the bore of the gun. **Cordite** and **ballistite** consist of guncotton plasticized with nitroglycerin (p. 525). The equation for the decomposition of cellulose trinitrate may be written as

$$
2 \left[\begin{array}{l} \text{—CH(CHONO}_2)_2\text{—CH—O—} \\ \text{CH———————O} \\ \text{CH}_2\text{ONO}_2 \end{array} \right]_x \longrightarrow 9x\ CO + 3x\ CO_2 + 7x\ H_2O + 3x\ N_2
$$

Sufficient oxygen is present to convert the compound completely to gaseous products, and the large amount of energy liberated in transferring oxygen from nitrogen to hydrogen and carbon raises the gases to a high temperature and produces the pressure necessary to expel the projectile at high velocity.

In 1865 Alexander Parkes, an Englishman, obtained a horn-like mass by mixing cellulose nitrate, alcohol, and camphor. In 1869 the American inventor John Wesley Hyatt obtained a patent for a similar product, which he had developed as a substitute for ivory for billiard balls, and for which he coined the name **celluloid.** It is made by mixing two parts of celluloid pyroxylin with one part of powdered camphor (p. 565) and kneading in a mixer with enough alcohol to form a dough. The soft mass is pressed into various forms or rolled into sheets. In the curing the alcohol evaporates and the articles solidify. Celluloid has many disadvantages, such as undesirable odor and taste, nonresistance to acid and alkali, discoloration in light, and high inflammability. Yet for about fifty years it was the only important plastic, and it still is manufactured and sold under trade names such as *Pyralin, Viscoloid,* and *Fiberloid.*

Thin cellulose nitrate sheet, used chiefly as a base for **motion picture film,** is made by dissolving soluble pyroxylin in a mixture of methanol and acetone together with camphor as a plasticizer, and coating on the highly polished surface of a wheel 20 to 30 feet in diameter. As the wheel rotates slowly, the solvent evaporates sufficiently to permit the film to be stripped continuously from the opposite side and passed through drying rooms where the rest of the solvent is removed.

Large quantities of pyroxylin are used for the manufacture of **artificial leather.** Viscous solutions containing treated castor oil (p. 152) as plasticizer, together with pigment, are coated on cotton fabric in several layers and embossed to resemble leather.

Celluloid pyroxylin and soluble pyroxylin are more degraded than guncotton, having chain lengths of only 500 to 600 C_6 units. It is this smaller molecular size that permits them to give free-flowing solutions at fairly high concentration. Solutions of sufficient concentration to leave a film thick enough to act as a binding agent for pigments and to serve as a protective coating are, however, too viscous to be applied with a brush or spray gun. Further degradation can be brought about by heating the pyroxylin with water in pressure digestors. Pyroxylin giving solutions of almost any desired viscosity thus can be obtained, but the lower the viscosity the shorter the chain length, and hence the lower the film strength and the greater the brittleness of the film. The material commonly used in lacquers is known as **half second cotton,** the viscosity being measured by the time required for a ball of specified size and material to drop through a solution of specified composition under standard conditions. It has a chain length of 150 to 200 C_6 units.

Nitrocellulose lacquers consist of pigment, half second cotton, and a mixture of solvents. The solvents are grouped as *low boilers, medium boilers,* and *high boilers.* The low boilers evaporate rapidly leaving a thick film that still can flow enough to remove brush or spray marks. Evaporation of the medium boilers leaves a dry film. The high boilers remain in the film to plasticize it, that is to keep it flexible. Lacquers were introduced as finishes for automobiles in 1924, to replace varnish, and the ease of application, rapid drying, and durability revolutionized the industry. It is said that the development of chromium plating received its chief impetus because the new body finishes outlasted the nickel plated trim. Nitrocellulose lacquers have been supplanted largely by synthetic alkyd baking enamels (p. 416) for automobile finishes but still are used extensively for refinishing automobiles and for household decoration.

The **cellulose acetates** are next to the nitrates in importance. The maximum amount of acetyl that can be introduced by direct esterification corresponds to the acetylation of one of the three hydroxyl groups, and the product is not soluble in organic solvents and has no commercial use. When cellulose is pretreated by soaking under carefully controlled conditions in a dilute solution of sulfuric acid in glacial acetic acid and then is added to a mixture of acetic anhydride and acetic acid, it dissolves to give a viscous solution. Dilution with water precipitates the **triacetate.** In the past the triacetate was little used, because it was soluble only in the expensive and highly toxic tetrachloroethane (p. 506), or in chloroform containing a small amount of alcohol. Moreover the product was not thermoplastic and films and threads made from it were brittle. Recently, however, a type of triacetate has been developed which is soluble in methylene chloride and which gives flexible films. In 1949 the largest manufacturer of photographic film in the United States started producing all of its safety film base from this triacetate.

The usual commercial material is the so-called **cellulose diacetate.** After acetylation to the triacetate stage, some water is added to the acetylation mixture, and hydrolysis is permitted to take place until approximately the diacetate is formed. The product is precipitated with water, washed, and dried. It is soluble in acetone and gives flexible films and fibers. This material is not molecularly homogeneous but is a mixture having approximately the composition of the diacetate.

Usable diacetates cannot be prepared by stopping the acetylation at the diacetate stage. Those hydroxyl groups that are most readily esterified give the acetate groups that are most readily hydrolyzed. Hence a diacetate formed by the esterification of two of the three hydroxyl groups is a different product from one formed by hydrolyzing one of the three acetate groups.

Cellulose acetate is more expensive than the nitrate. In the first place cellulose nitrate is not soluble in the nitrating mixture, and most of the excess reagents can be recovered without dilution, whereas the acetate must be precipitated by water and large volumes of dilute acetic acid must be concentrated. Secondly the reagents for the preparation of the nitrate are cheaper than those for the acetate. Another disadvantage of the acetate is that it is more highly degraded than pyroxylin, having an average chain length of 175 to 300 units. Hence fibers and films made from it are weaker and more brittle. Nevertheless the lower inflammability of the acetate, its freedom from spontaneous decomposition, and its greater stability to discoloration make it widely used as a base for photographic film and for the manufacture of acetate rayon and plastics.

More recently **acetatepropionates** and **acetatebutyrates** have been prepared by using propionic or butyric acid along with acetic anhydride during the acetylation. These products are thermoplastic without being partially hydrolyzed, and since they contain fewer free hydroxyl groups, they are less permeable to water, weather better, and are more compatible with gums and plasticizers.

Cellulose Ethers. A number of cellulose ethers are of technical importance. **Ethylcellulose** is prepared by soaking high α-cellulose wood pulp or cotton linters with 17 to 18 per cent sodium hydroxide solution and removing the excess solution in a hydraulic press. The product is known as *alkali cellulose* and has the approximate composition $(C_6H_{10}O_5 \cdot 2\ NaOH)_x$, although it does not seem to be a definite compound. The alkali cellulose is shredded to crumbs and treated in an autoclave with ethyl chloride at 120° to 130° for 8 to 12 hours. The ethoxyl content obtained depends on the concentration of the alkali and on the time and number of treatments. Like the acetates, the ethyl celluloses differ in solubility characteristics depending on the extent of reaction. Products containing 0.8 to 1.4 ethoxyl groups per C_6 unit are soluble in water whereas those containing more than 1.5 ethoxyl groups are soluble in most organic solvents. The most widely used commercial product contains 2.2 to 2.6 ethoxyl groups. It is highly compatible with resins and plasticizers and is soluble in mixtures of alcohol and hydrocarbons. Its use is increasing rapidly in the manufacture of coatings, films, and plastics. Unlike the esters, it is very resistant to the action of alkalies.

The **methylcelluloses** of low methoxyl content are soluble in cold water and precipitate on heating. They are used chiefly as thickeners for textile printing, for pastes, cosmetics, sizing, and finish for textile fibers.

The water solubility of the lower acetates and ethers seems anomalous since acylation or etherification of a hydroxyl group ordinarily decreases the solubility in water. The insolubility of cellulose in water, however, may be explained by strong van der Waals forces and proton bonding between chains (pp. 62, 63). Since the replacement of a few hydrogen atoms by hydrocarbon or acyl groups separates the chains and renders these forces inoperative, hydration of the hydroxyl groups becomes more important. In accord with this view, the solubility in water decreases at higher temperatures because the hydrates become less stable.

More recently **carboxymethylcellulose** (CMC) has become technically important. This ether is prepared by the reaction of alkali cellulose with sodium chloroacetate.

$$ROH + ClCH_2COONa + NaOH \longrightarrow R\text{—}O\text{—}CH_2COONa + NaCl + H_2O$$

The commercial product contains about 0.5 carboxymethyl groups per C_6 unit, and the sodium salt is soluble in both cold and hot water. Metallic salts other than those of the alkali metals are insoluble in water. The *sodium salt* is used on a large scale as a thickening agent and protective colloid, as a builder for synthetic detergents, and as a size for textiles.

Oxidized cellulose is not an ether but has properties similar to carboxymethylcellulose because carboxyl groups are present. Nitrogen dioxide, in the presence of sufficient water to form nitric acid, oxidizes the primary hydroxyl group to carboxyl without affecting the rest of the molecule appreciably except for considerable reduction in chain length.

$$3 NO_2 + H_2O \longrightarrow 2 HNO_3 + NO$$

Cellulose $+ 2x$ HNO$_3$ → Oxidized cellulose $+ 2x$ H$_2$O $+ x$ N$_2$O$_3$

Rayon. Synthetic fibers are textile fibers produced from a homogeneous solution or melt, whether the raw material is a synthetic or a natural product. Thus the raw material for some synthetic fibers is coke, but that for others is essentially unmodified cellulose or protein. Synthetic fibers derived from cellulose are known as **rayon.**

World production of rayon reached a maximum in 1941 of 1.4 million tons. Over one third was produced in Germany, one fifth in Japan, and one fifth in the United States. Of this amount over 80 per cent was made by the viscose process, 15 per cent by the acetate process, 4 per cent by the cuprammonium process, and a fraction of 1 per cent by the nitrate process. In the United States viscose rayon accounts for 60 per cent and acetate rayon for 40 per cent of production. Because of the disruption of the industry in Germany and Japan following the war, world production declined about 50 per cent but again reached about 1 million tons in 1947.

In all of the processes the same operations are involved, namely solution of the cellulose or a derivative, forcing the solution through the fine holes of a die called a *spinneret*, and precipitation of the cellulose or evaporation of the solvent to give a thread. The threads have smooth cylindrical surfaces which reflect light and give them a high luster. The strength of the threads can be increased greatly by stretching them, which brings about a linear orientation of the molecules and hence an increase in the attractive forces between the molecules.

Viscose rayon manufacture is based on the reaction of the hydroxyl groups of cellulose with carbon disulfide in the presence of sodium hydroxide to give *xanthates* (p. 250) which are soluble in water. The reaction can be reversed by acidification.

$$\text{ROH} + \text{CS}_2 + \text{NaOH} \longrightarrow \left[\text{RO}\overset{\overset{\text{S}}{\|}}{\text{C}}-\text{S}^-\right]\text{Na}^+ + \text{H}_2\text{O}$$

$$\left[\text{RO}\overset{\overset{\text{S}}{\|}}{\text{C}}-\text{S}^-\right]{}^+\text{Na} + \text{NaHSO}_4 \longrightarrow \text{ROH} + \text{CS}_2 + \text{Na}_2\text{SO}_4$$

Alkali cellulose (p. 302) from high α-cellulose sulfite pulp or from cotton linters is treated in rotating drums with an amount of carbon disulfide equal to 30 to 40 per cent of the weight of dry cellulose (calculated amount for 1 mole of carbon disulfide per C_6 unit is 47 per cent). An orange-colored crumbly product is formed, which is dissolved in 3 per cent sodium hydroxide solution to give the viscous solution known as *viscose*, in which the cellulose molecule has been degraded to an average chain length of 400 to 500 C_6 units. The solution initially is unstable and the viscosity drops rapidly during the first day of standing. A slow hydrolysis of xanthate radicals then takes place with a gradual rise in viscosity for about eight days when it rapidly sets to a gel. Spinning of the solution is carried out after the solution has ripened four to five days when the viscosity is not changing rapidly and after considerable hydrolysis has taken place. The filaments from the spinneret are passed through a bath of sodium bisulfate and additives, where the hydrolysis is completed to give a regenerated cellulose fiber. After coagulation and twisting of the filaments into a thread, the product is thoroughly washed and sometimes bleached. The number of holes in the spinneret depends on the number of filaments desired in the thread and may vary from 15 to 500. The size of the filaments or thread is measured in *denier*, which is the weight in grams of 9000 meters of thread. The common size of the filaments is 2 to 3 denier and of the thread 150 denier, but rayon thread is made as fine as 50 and as coarse as 1000 denier. Ordinary viscose rayon has 50 to 80 per cent of the strength of silk and loses 50 to 60 per cent of its strength when wet. If the spinning is carried out under tension while the filaments still are plastic, orientation of the molecules takes place and the product has a strength equal to that of silk, wet or dry. Since around 1930, filaments of 1 to 20 denier have been cut to lengths of 1 to 6 inches to give **staple fiber.** Here the number of filaments from a single spinneret may be as high as 10,000. Staple fiber is combined with wool, cotton, or linen fibers in spun yarn, or is converted to **spun rayon** by the usual spinning process for cotton or wool.

Viscose solution is converted into **cellophane** by extruding through a slot into the coagulating bath. The addition of glycerol improves the flexibility, and a coating of wax and nitrocellulose lacquer makes it waterproof. Modification of the extruding die gives sausage casings, artificial straw, or filaments containing bubbles. Sealing caps of cellophane are kept moist and pliable in dilute glycerol, and when placed over a bottle top, they dry and shrink to a tight fit. Synthetic sponges are made by incorporating crystals of Glauber's salt ($Na_2SO_4 \cdot 10 H_2O$) of all sizes in the viscose solution and coagulating in blocks. Leaching with warm water dissolves the crystals and leaves the sponge-like mass.

Acetate rayon is made by dissolving cellulose diacetate in acetone and forcing the solution through spinnerets into warm air, where the solvent evaporates. The thread does not require a finishing treatment, and since two thirds of the hydroxyl groups are esterified, it has a higher wet strength than ordinary viscose rayon. The smaller number of hydroxyl groups, however, makes direct dyeing more difficult and special dyes are required (p. 477). Acetate rayon can be distinguished easily from the other rayons by the fact that it still is soluble in acetone. Viscose, cuprammonium, and nitrate rayons are regenerated cellulose and hence insoluble in organic solvents.

Synthetic wool is discussed under proteins (p. 229). Other synthetic fibers such as *Nylon, Orlon, Saran, Dacron* and *Vinyon* are discussed under their specific raw materials (pp. 544, 537, 508, 416, 516).

Pectins and Pectic Acids. Fruits and berries contain water-insoluble complex carbohydrates known as *protopectins*, which on partial hydrolysis yield **pectins** or **pectinic acids.** Pectins have the property of forming gels with sugar and acid under proper conditions and are the agents necessary for the production of jellies from fruit juices. The pectins or pectinic acids contain both carboxyl groups and carbomethoxy groups. Removal of the remainder of the methoxy groups by hydrolysis yields the **pectic acids.** Enzyme hydrolysis of purified pectic acids gives up to 85 per cent of D-galacturonic acid and no other carbohydrates have been identified. The pectic acids contain one free carboxyl group per C_6 unit. These and other experimental data have led to the view that the pectic acids essentially are linear polygalacturonides with α linkages. In the pectins the carboxyl groups are esterified partially with methyl groups.

D-Galacturonic acid

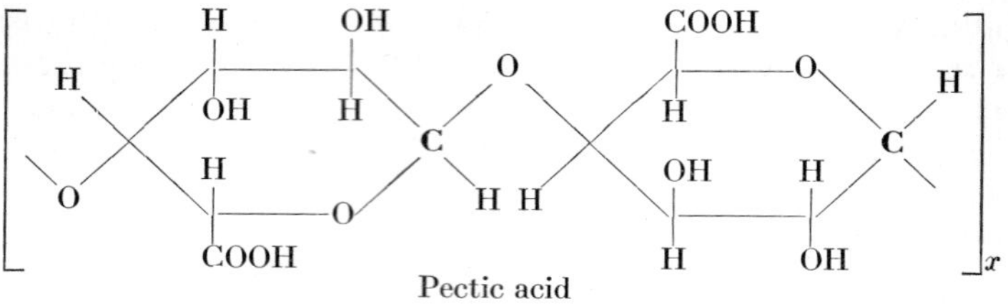

Pectic acid

Galacturonic acid belongs to the group of substances known as **uronic** or **glycuronic acids** in which the end carbon atom of the aldose is present in a carboxyl group, the aldehyde group being unchanged. In the *glyconic acids* (p. 278) the aldehyde group is replaced by the carboxyl group, and in the *glycaric acids* (p. 281) both terminal carbon atoms are in carboxyl groups. The uronic acids and their polymers, when heated with 12 per cent hydrochloric acid, lose one mole of carbon dioxide for each carboxyl group. The other

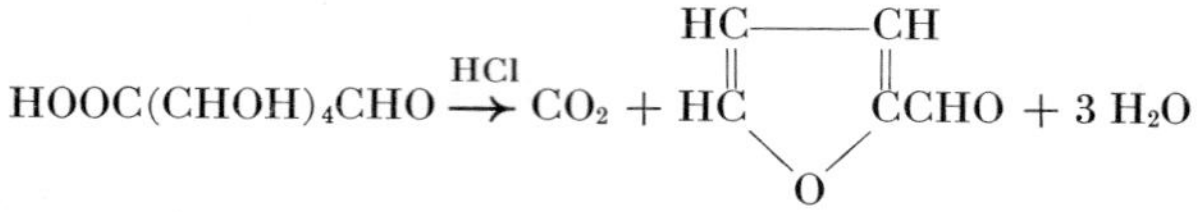

products are furfural and water. The reaction is used for the quantitative estimation of uronic acid and polyuronides by absorbing the carbon dioxide in barium hydroxide solution and weighing the amount of barium carbonate that precipitates.

Heteropolysaccharides

Agar. Among the polysaccharides yielding more than one kind of monosaccharide on hydrolysis, **agar** is the best known. It is the dried mucilaginous substance extracted by hot water from certain East Indian sea weeds (various species of *Gelidium*). Its hot aqueous solutions set to a semisolid gel on cooling, and it is used widely as a support for nutrient media in the growing of microorganisms. The dry product swells in warm water without dissolving and is indigestible, making it useful as a bulk cathartic.

Hydrolysis of purified agar yields D-galactose, L-galactose, and sulfuric acid in the molar ratio of 9 : 1 : 1. The results of degradation indicate that the L-galactose is esterified with sulfuric acid and linked through the 1,4 positions to the D-galactose units, which in turn are linked to each other through the 1,3 positions. The glycosidic links appear to be β.

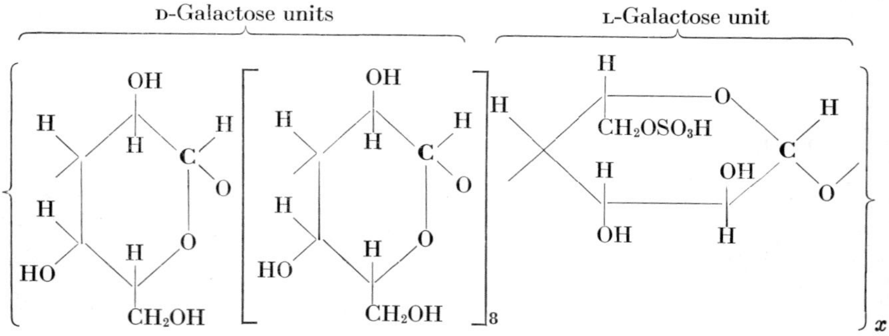

Agar

Plant Gums and Mucilages. Many plants yield water-soluble exudations or extractives that give viscous mucilaginous solutions which are used widely as adhesives and thickening agents. Heteropolysaccharides are the predominant constituents. Among the more common gums and mucilages may be mentioned **gum arabic** from the bark of various species of *Acacia*, **gum tragacanth** from shrubs of the genus *Astragalus*, and **guar flour** from the endosperm of the guar bean.

Immunopolysaccharides. Pneumococci and many other bacteria produce polysaccharides which are responsible for the immunological specificity of the organisms. The polysaccharide of pneumococcus type III has been investigated extensively. It appears to be a linear molecule in which glucose units linked through the 1,4 positions alternate with glucuronic acid units linked through the 1,3 positions.

SUGAR ALCOHOLS

Although sugar alcohols are not carbohydrates in the strict sense, the naturally occurring sugar alcohols are so closely related to the carbohydrates that they are discussed here rather than with other polyhydric alcohols (p. 518).

The sugar alcohols most widely distributed in nature are L-sorbitol (identical with D-glucitol), D-mannitol, and galactitol (dulcitol). They correspond to the reduction products of glucose, mannose, and galactose.

$$
\begin{array}{ccc}
\mathrm{CH_2OH} & \mathrm{CH_2OH} & \mathrm{CH_2OH} \\
| & | & | \\
\mathrm{HO-C-H} & \mathrm{HO-C-H} & \mathrm{H-C-OH} \\
| & | & | \\
\mathrm{HO-C-H} & \mathrm{HO-C-H} & \mathrm{HO-C-H} \\
| & | & | \\
\mathrm{H-C-OH} & \mathrm{H-C-OH} & \mathrm{HO-C-H} \\
| & | & | \\
\mathrm{HO-C-H} & \mathrm{H-C-OH} & \mathrm{H-C-OH} \\
| & | & | \\
\mathrm{CH_2OH} & \mathrm{CH_2OH} & \mathrm{CH_2OH} \\
\text{L-Sorbitol} & \text{D-Mannitol} & \text{Galactitol} \\
\text{(D-glucitol)} & & \text{(dulcitol)}
\end{array}
$$

Since the reduction of the sugars gives compounds in which the end groups are identical, the reduction products of two different sugars frequently will be identical. Thus L-arabitol is identical with L-lyxitol. Similarly D-glucose on reduction gives a sugar alcohol identical with L-sorbitol, one of the two reduction products of L-sorbose. Sorbitol was the name first assigned to the naturally occurring compound and commonly is used rather than D-glucitol. The designation of family for *meso* forms such as erythritol and galactitol is meaningless.

L-Sorbitol first was isolated from the berries of the mountain ash (*Sorbus aucuparia*) in 1872. The red seaweed, *Bostrychia scorpoides*, contains almost 14 per cent sorbitol. It has been isolated in appreciable quantities from many other plants ranging from the algae to the higher orders. **D-Mannitol** also occurs in many plants and in contrast to sorbitol is present frequently in the plant exudates known as *mannas*, for example in the exudates of the manna ash (*Fraxinus ornus*), of the olive, and of the plane trees. Similarly **galactitol (dulcitol)** is present in many plants and plant exudates.

Sorbitol is the most important of the sugar alcohols and is manufactured by the catalytic reduction of glucose. Electrolytic reduction of glucose at pH 10–13 produces a mixture of mannitol and sorbitol because of the epimerizing effect of the alkali on the glucose. Sorbitol is very soluble in water giving thick viscous solutions that can replace glycerol for many purposes.

Related to the sugar alcohols are the polyhydroxycyclohexanes, of which the hexahydroxy derivatives of **inositols** are of most interest. Nine noninterconvertible (cf. p. 562) stereoisomeric forms are possible, two of which are optically active and seven of which are *meso* forms. One of the *meso* forms is distributed widely in nature, and it is this form which is meant by the designation **inositol** or ***meso*-inositol.**

meso-Inositol   Active inositols

It is found in microorganisms, plants, and animals. It occurs both free and combined in many organs of the animal body and in the body fluids. The hexaphosphoric acid ester is called **phytic acid,** and its calcium magnesium salt, known as **phytin,** is present in plants. The best source of phytin is corn steep liquor (p. 295), from which inositol is prepared commercially. *meso*-Inositol is a component of the vitamin B complex and is a dietary requirement for both lower and higher forms of animal life. Hence it is one of the vitamins.

REVIEW QUESTIONS

1. Define the term carbohydrate.
2. Give in outline form a classification of the carbohydrates.
3. Give a group of reactions which establish the accepted open chain structure of glucose. Explain the part of each reaction in the proof of structure.
4. Why is the open chain formula for glucose not an entirely satisfactory representation? How are these phenomena explained?
5. Give equations illustrating the conversion of glucose into gluconic acid, gluconolactone, saccharic acid, glucose pentaacetate, methyl α-glucoside, methyl 2,3,4,6-tetramethyl-α-glucoside, 2,3,4,6-tetramethylglucose.
6. Why can one hydroxyl group of reducing sugars be methylated with methyl alcohol and hydrogen chloride, whereas the other four cannot? Why is one methyl group of 2,3,4,6-tetramethylglucose methyl α-glucoside removed more readily by hydrolysis than the other four?
7. How many aldohexoses are known? What are the configurations of glucose, mannose, and galactose?
8. What is meant by the term *relative configuration*; D-family of sugars?
9. Why do glucose, mannose, and fructose give the same osazone?
10. Why does fructose reduce Fehling's solution? Why must empirical tables be used when estimating sugars by oxidation methods? What is the difference in composition between Fehling's solution and Benedict's solution, and what advantage has one over the other?
11. How can aldohexoses be distinguished from aldopentoses?
12. Explain the difference in structure of maltose, cellobiose, lactose, and sucrose.
13. Write the perspective formulas for 4-β-glucosyl-α-glucose; 6-α-galactosyl-β-glucose.
14. What is the meaning of *pyranose* and *furanose*?

15. Compare the reactions of reducing and nonreducing disaccharides.
16. What differences in the reactions of glucose, mannose, and lactose with phenylhydrazine can be used to distinguish between them?
17. What are the more important differences in the chemical constitution of starch, glycogen, inulin, and cellulose?
18. How is cellulose nitrate made? What is the difference between guncotton, soluble pyroxylin or collodion cotton, and half second cotton? For what are they used?
19. Discuss the preparation and properties of cellulose triacetate, cellulose diacetate, and cellulose acetate-butyrate.
20. How does viscose rayon differ from acetate rayon? How are they made? What is cellophane?
21. What are methylcellulose, ethylcellulose, carboxymethylcellulose, and oxidized cellulose, and for what are they used?

Chapter 19

AROMATIC COMPOUNDS. BENZENE AND ITS HOMOLOGS. COAL PRODUCTS

AROMATIC COMPOUNDS

Most of the compounds considered thus far are classed as aliphatic, since they are related to the fats insofar as the reactions of the hydrocarbon portion of the molecule is concerned (Gr. *aliphatos* fat). It was recognized at an early date that many other compounds had a hydrocarbon portion with a higher ratio of carbon to hydrogen and with distinctly different chemical properties. These substances frequently were pleasantly odorous or derivable from aromatic substances. For example the essential components of the volatile oils of cloves, cinnamon, sassafras, anise, bitter almonds, wintergreen, and vanilla exhibited these properties. The hydrocarbon *benzene* received its name because it was obtained by the decarboxylation of benzoic acid isolated from the aromatic substance *gum benzoin*, and the name *toluene* was assigned to another hydrocarbon because it had been obtained by heating the fragrant *tolu balsam*. Loschmidt [1] in 1861 was the first to state that most of the aromatic compounds could be considered as derivatives of benzene, C_6H_6, just as the aliphatic compounds were considered as derivatives of methane, CH_4. Since then the term *aromatic compounds* has been applied to those compounds having the characteristic chemical properties of benzene.

BENZENE AND ITS HOMOLOGS

Isolation and Structure of Benzene

During the latter part of the eighteenth century an illuminating gas was manufactured in England by the thermal decomposition of whale oil and other fatty oils. When this gas was compressed for distribution in tanks, a light mobile liquid separated. This liquid was brought to the attention of Michael Faraday (p. 68) in 1820, and in 1825 he reported the isolation by distillation and crystallization of a compound which he called *bicarburet of hydrogen*. In 1833 Mitscherlich [2] reported the isolation of the same hydrocarbon by distilling benzoic acid with lime. He named his product *benzin*, but Liebig, as editor

---

[1] Joseph Loschmidt (1821–1895), Austrian physicist and professor at the University of Vienna. He originally was a chemist and published privately in 1861 his views on the use of graphic constitutional formulas in organic chemistry. In this work he proposed formulas for 368 compounds of which 121 belonged to the aromatic series.

[2] Eilhard Mitscherlich (1794–1855), professor of chemistry at the University of Berlin. He first specialized in Oriental languages, particularly Persian, and began the study of medicine because as a physician he would have more freedom than other Europeans to travel in Persia. He soon became so interested in chemical subjects that he gave up his aspirations in the other fields. He is noted chiefly for his work on isomorphism.

of the Annalen der Chemie, added a note to Mitscherlich's paper stating that a more suitable name would be *benzol*, the ending *ol* indicating that it was a liquid (L. *oleum* oil) obtained from the solid benzoic acid. Benzol still is the common term in the German chemical literature and is used in all countries by technicians in the coal tar industry. It has been replaced in the English and French literature by the term *benzene*, the ending *ol* being reserved for alcohols. Although the separation of benzene from the products of the destructive distillation of coal (p. 323) usually is credited to Leigh (1842) and Hoffmann (1845), Liebig's note to Mitscherlich's work indicates that Faraday's compound was recognized then as one of the products of the distillation of coal.

The data of both Faraday and Mitscherlich indicated that benzene has the molecular formula C_6H_6. Since the corresponding alkane has the molecular formula C_6H_{14}, benzene might be expected to be highly unsaturated. On the contrary it is almost as stable to oxidation and to the usual addition reactions as the saturated hydrocarbons. Hydrogen adds catalytically (p. 559) and chlorine or bromine adds in the presence of sunlight (p. 326), but only six atoms add and not eight. Moreover the number of isomers formed on replacing hydrogen atoms by other elements or groups does not correspond to that expected for the aliphatic hydrocarbons. For example only one monosubstitution product is known. Hence each hydrogen atom bears the same relationship to the molecule as a whole as every other hydrogen atom; that is the molecule is symmetrically constituted. This conclusion has been substantiated by a series of reactions in which each of the six hydrogen atoms has been replaced by functional groups in such a way that the equivalence of the six hydrogen atoms was established.

Kekulé, who originated or consolidated most of the views concerning the structure of organic compounds (p. 4), assigned the first definite structural formula to benzene in 1865. He proposed that the six carbon atoms were at the corners of a regular hexagon and that one hydrogen atom was joined to each.

Four years earlier Loschmidt had represented the benzene nucleus by a circle but had made no attempt to indicate the arrangement of the carbon atoms in the nucleus (p. 310). Kekulé's formula accounts also for the fact that if two hydrogen atoms are replaced by other groups, *Y*, three and only three isomers are known. If two adjacent hydrogen atoms are replaced, the resulting compound is known as the *ortho* isomer; if two alternate hydrogen atoms are replaced, the compound is known as the *meta* isomer; and if two opposite hydrogen atoms are replaced, it is known as the *para* isomer (Gr. *ortho* regular or adjacent, *meta* after or the next position beyond, and *para* against or across).

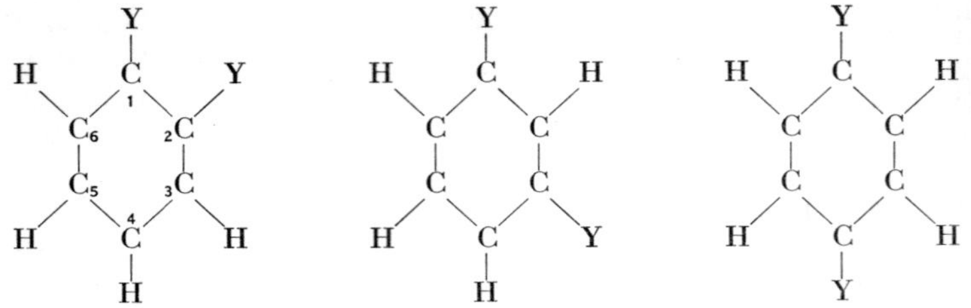

ortho Isomer   meta Isomer   para Isomer

Regardless of which two adjacent hydrogen atoms are replaced the same compound results. For example if hydrogen atoms at positions 3 and 4 are replaced instead of those at 1 and 2, rotation through 120 degrees in the plane of the paper brings the two molecules into coincidence. Similar considerations hold for the *meta* and *para* isomer. Moreover the two groups, *Y*, may be alike or different without changing the number of isomers.

Objections to the simple hexagon formula for benzene are that it violates Kekulé's own advocacy of the tetravalence of carbon, and that it does not explain the addition of six atoms of halogen or six atoms of hydrogen. Both objections are overcome by the introduction of three double bonds in continuous conjugation. Now, however, the objection arises that two *ortho* substitution products would be expected, one in which the two carbon atoms carrying the *Y* groups are linked by a double bond (*a*), and another in which they are linked by a single bond (*b*). To overcome this difficulty, Kekulé proposed in 1872

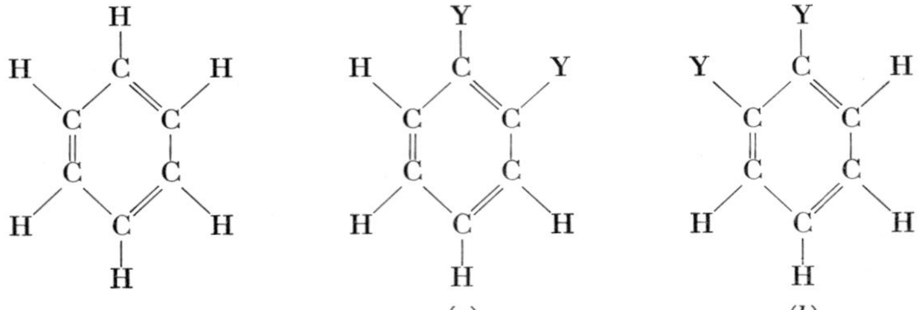

(a)   (b)

that the positions of the double bonds are not fixed, but that an equilibrium exists between two structures which is so mobile that individual isomers such as (*a*) and (*b*) cannot be isolated.

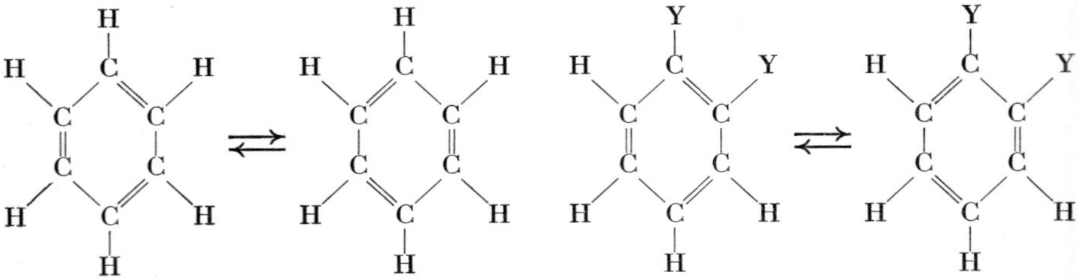

(a)   (b)

The current view is that in neither benzene nor its derivatives do molecules of two structures exist in mobile equilibrium with each other, but that only one kind of molecule is present which is a hybrid of the two structures represented by the symbol

The most direct evidence for this view comes from the measurement of the distances between carbon atoms by means of electron diffraction. In ethane and other saturated compounds the distance between adjacent carbon atoms is 1.54 Å, in ethylene the carbon-carbon distance is 1.34 Å, and in acetylene it is 1.20 Å. In other words the distance is shorter for a double bond than for a single bond and shorter for a triple bond than for a double bond. This result is to be expected since the attraction between atoms increases with the formation of each bond. In compounds containing both single bonds and double bonds, both distances are observed, but for benzene only a single carbon-carbon distance can be detected, namely 1.39 Å, which lies between the single bond and double bond distances. Therefore all of the carbon-carbon bonds in benzene are alike and have properties intermediate between those of a single bond and of a double bond. The problem is the same as that for the carboxylate ion (p. 129) and the nitro group (p. 201). The resonance hybrid structure is more stable than the classical structure by the amount of the resonance energy, which for benzene is about 40 kcal. per mole.

Physical Properties of Benzene

Hexane, C_6H_{14}, boils at 68.8°, and since benzene has a lower molecular weight, its boiling point might be expected to be lower. Actually benzene boils at 80.1°. The higher boiling point can be ascribed to the fact that the benzene molecules have a rigid flat structure, whereas the hexane chains can undergo considerable twisting and bending on thermal agitation. Hence the van der Waals forces can operate more effectively between the benzene molecules. The more symmetrical structure for benzene accounts also for its relatively high melting point of +5.5° compared with −95° for hexane.

Being a hydrocarbon, benzene is practically insoluble in water, but the solubility at 15° of 0.18 g. per 100 g. of water is over ten times that of the 0.014 g. per 100 g. of water for *n*-hexane. The greater attraction of benzene for water molecules would be expected because of the greater polarizability of the unsaturation electrons. The solubility of water in benzene is 0.06 g. per 100 g. of benzene. In general the solubility of highly associated liquids and solids in aromatic hydrocarbons and of aromatic hydrocarbons in associated liquids is greater than the corresponding solubilities of the saturated hydrocarbons. It is for this reason that aromatic hydrocarbons are more useful as solvents and diluents for paints, lacquers, and synthetic enamels than are petroleum fractions. They can be used only with proper precautions, however, because of their high toxicity. Even very low concentrations are dangerous on prolonged exposure. All workers using materials containing volatile aromatic hydrocarbons should be subjected to frequent blood counts to detect signs of poisoning.

Reactions of Benzene

The usual reagents for double bonds do not add readily to benzene. As a measure of the relative reactivity of benzene and olefins to addition, the heat liberated on catalytic hydrogenation may be cited. A doubly substituted olefin such as *cis*-butene liberates 28.6 kcal. per mole on catalytic hydrogenation. If three ordinary double bonds were present in benzene, the heat liberated should be $3 \times 28.6 = 85.8$ kcal. The actual amount of heat liberated is 49.8 kcal. The difference of 36 kcal. is the resonance energy of benzene; that is of the 85.8 kcal. that is liberated on the catalytic hydrogenation of three double bonds, 36 kcal. is used up overcoming the resonance energy of the benzene molecule. Since the heat liberated on hydrogenating 1,3-cyclohexadiene, the cyclic compound with two conjugated double bonds, is 57.2 kcal., the hydrogenation of benzene to cyclohexadiene actually is endothermic by 7.4 kcal. Similarly in other addition reactions, energy must be supplied to get the first mole of reagent to react. In general the reactivity of the unsaturation electrons of benzene is so low that they can be disregarded. Frequently they are not even indicated in the formula for benzene.

In contrast to the nonreactivity of the double bonds, the hydrogen atoms of the aromatic nucleus are substituted more readily than those of the alkanes. The following characteristic reactions of aromatic compounds are the most important ones.

1. *Controllable Halogenation.* Paraffin hydrocarbons react with chlorine or bromine at high temperatures or in the presence of light of short wave length, but the reaction is violent, the position of substitution is random, and considerable quantities of polysubstitution products are formed (p. 85). At ordinary temperatures and in the absence of light, reaction is very slow. Benzene reacts with chlorine or bromine in the presence of light, but addition takes place rather than substitution. On the other hand benzene reacts rapidly with chlorine or bromine in the presence of a catalyst such as iron (or ferric salts) at moderately elevated temperatures to give halogen substitution products.

Chlorobenzene

Since a second halogen substitutes with more difficulty, the reaction can be controlled to give chiefly the monosubstitution product.

2. *Controllable Nitration.* Propane or *n*-butane reacts with oxides of nitrogen at high temperatures. However, not only are all the isomeric monosubstitution products obtained, but also all of the possible nitro compounds resulting from breaking of the carbon-carbon bonds (p. 202). In contrast benzene reacts with fuming nitric acid at moderate temperature, or better

with concentrated nitric acid in the presence of concentrated sulfuric acid, to give good yields of the mono nitro substitution products.

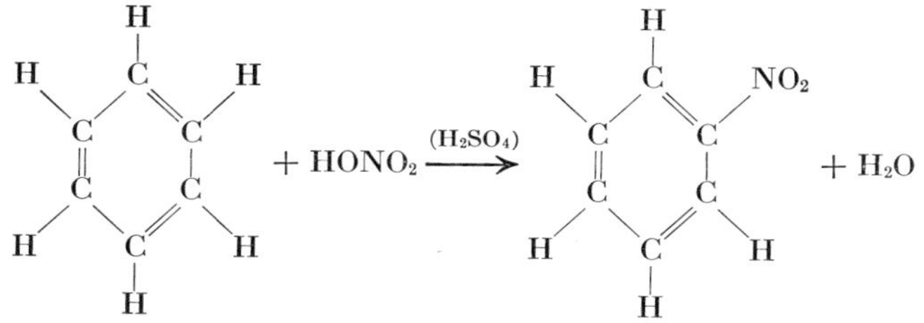

Nitrobenzene

3. *Direct Sulfonation*. Straight chain alkanes do not react with concentrated sulfuric acid, and although branched-chain alkanes react, there is some indication that oxidation to olefins is the first step (p. 219). Sulfonation of benzene takes place readily to give the monosulfonic acid in good yield.

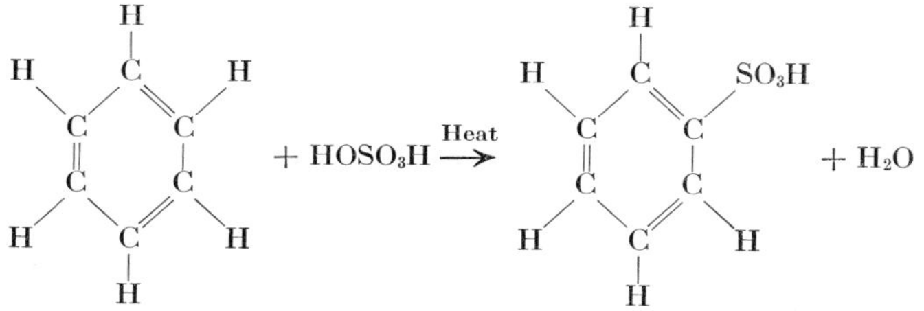

Benzenesulfonic acid

4. *Friedel-Crafts Reaction*. Aromatic hydrocarbons react with acyl halides in the presence of anhydrous aluminum chloride to give good yields of ketones. The reaction is known as the Friedel-Crafts reaction.[3, 4]

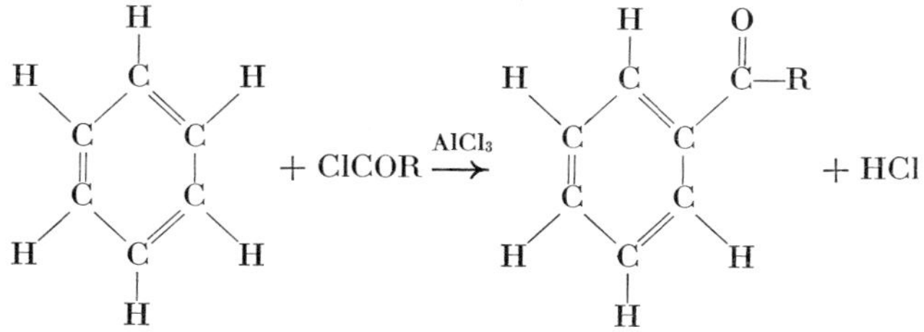

[3] Charles Friedel (1832–1899), successor to Wurtz at the Sorbonne. He was the first to produce isopropyl alcohol by the reduction of acetone, investigated the preparation of organosilicon compounds, and in his later years devoted himself to the chemical aspects of mineralogy.

[4] James Mason Crafts (1839–1917), graduate of Harvard University and student of Bunsen and Wurtz. He became professor of chemistry first at Cornell and then at Massachusetts Institute of Technology but resigned his post in 1874 because of poor health. He revisited the laboratory of Wurtz, planning to stay about a year, and remained there for seventeen years. Much of this time he worked in collaboration with Friedel. He returned to the United States in 1891 and resumed teaching at the Institute. He became head of the chemistry department in 1895 and was president of the Institute from 1897 until he resigned in 1900 to continue his scientific investigations.

It is the ability to undergo these substitution reactions that is characteristic of benzene and its derivatives. Compounds exhibiting these properties constitute the *aromatic compounds*.

5. Oxidation of Side Chains. Although this reaction does not involve the aromatic nucleus, it usually is considered as one of the typical reactions of aromatic compounds. When the alkylbenzenes are subjected to vigorous oxidation with dichromic acid (sodium dichromate and sulfuric acid) or potassium permanganate, or to catalytic air oxidation, the alkyl group is converted to a carboxyl group.

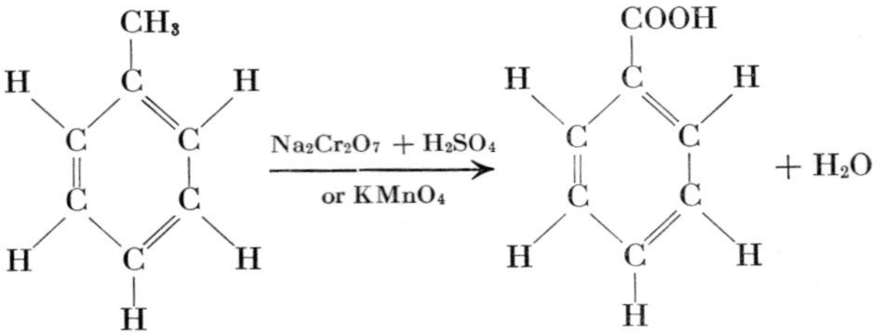

$$\text{Toluene} \xrightarrow[\text{or KMnO}_4]{\text{Na}_2\text{Cr}_2\text{O}_7 + \text{H}_2\text{SO}_4} \text{Benzoic acid} + \text{H}_2\text{O}$$

Since the point of attack is the carbon atom attached to the benzene nucleus, a carboxyl group results regardless of the size of the alkyl group or the type of substituent present in the alkyl group.

Homologs of Benzene

Homologs of benzene are those hydrocarbons which contain an alkyl group in place of one or more hydrogen atoms. **Toluene** is methylbenzene, $C_6H_5CH_3$. The **xylenes** are dimethylbenzenes and three are known. The 1,2-dimethylbenzene is called *ortho* xylene, usually written *o*-xylene, the 1,3 isomer is called *meta* xylene (*m*-xylene), and the 1,4 isomer is called *para* xylene (*p*-xylene).

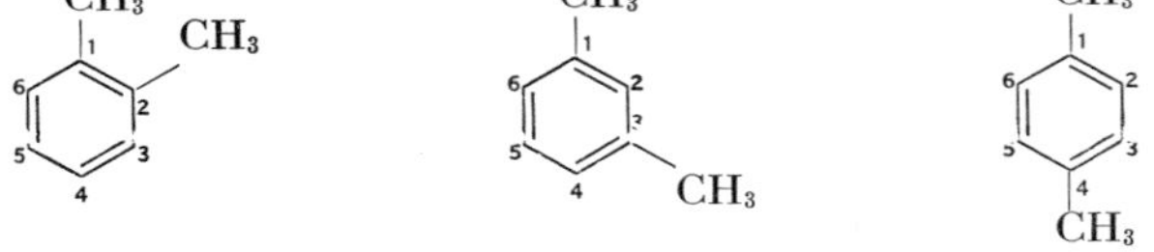

o-Xylene   *m*-Xylene   *p*-Xylene

In these and subsequent formulas the carbon and hydrogen atoms of the benzene ring are represented by the simple hexagon. The double bonds are included to indicate that the ring is aromatic and not alicyclic (p. 557). **Mesitylene** is 1,3,5-trimethylbenzene or symmetrical (*sym-*) trimethylbenzene. **Cumene** is isopropylbenzene, **durene** is 1,2,4,5-tetramethylbenzene, and **p-cymene** is 1-methyl-4-isopropylbenzene.

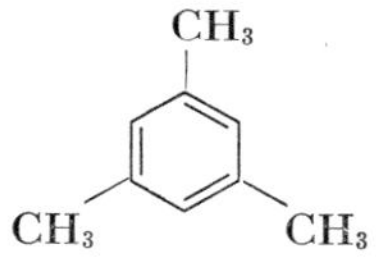

Mesitylene 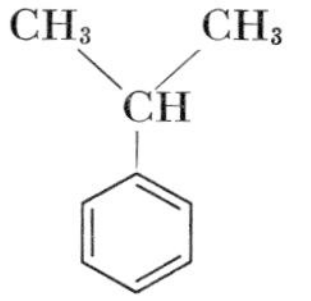 Cumene 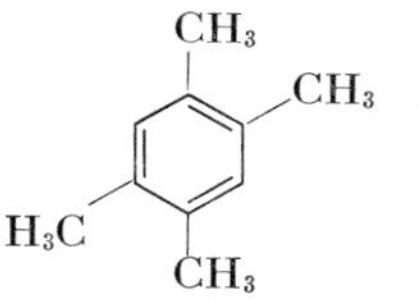 Durene 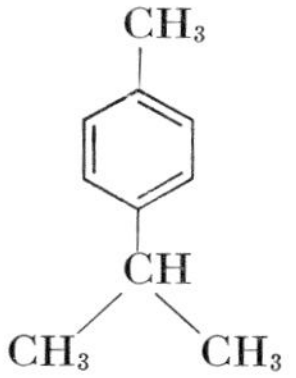 *p*-Cymene

Before 1950 **benzene** had been produced commercially only from coal gas and coal tar (p. 323). Therefore production varied with the utilization of coke, which in turn is linked to the production of steel and hence to the state of general industrial activity. As late as 1940 less than a third of the potential United States supply of 125,000,000 gallons per year was refined to pure benzene for solvent and chemical use, the balance being blended with gasoline and used as motor fuel. During World War II more aniline, phenol, and styrene were required. This demand continued after the war, and in 1946 about 38 per cent of benzene production was used for the manufacture of styrene, 23 per cent for phenol, and 11 per cent for aniline. Intermediates for the production of insecticides, Nylon, synthetic detergents, and maleic anhydride required most of the remaining 28 per cent. Even though benzene production increased to 174 million gallons in 1948, practically all of it was used for chemical purposes. Under such circumstances the price rises, and uses for certain purposes for which cheaper substitutes can be found are eliminated. Thus the price rose from $0.15 per gallon in October, 1946, to $0.19 per gallon in April, 1947. As long as demand exceeded supply the price continued to rise until it became profitable to prepare benzene from petroleum.

The economic picture of **toluene** is exactly the opposite. Prior to World War II, most of the United States production of 30 million gallons per year from coke manufacture was refined, although it was used chiefly as a solvent rather than for chemical purposes. During the war the demand for toluene for the manufacture of TNT required the development of a process for its production from petroleum. A narrow fraction (b.p. 90°–130°) from selected crudes having a high content of methylcyclohexane was dehydrogenated over a molybdena-alumina catalyst at 560° and 300 p.s.i. using a contact time of 15 seconds. The process is called *hydroforming* because the charging vapors are mixed with hydrogen to maintain the activity of the catalyst.

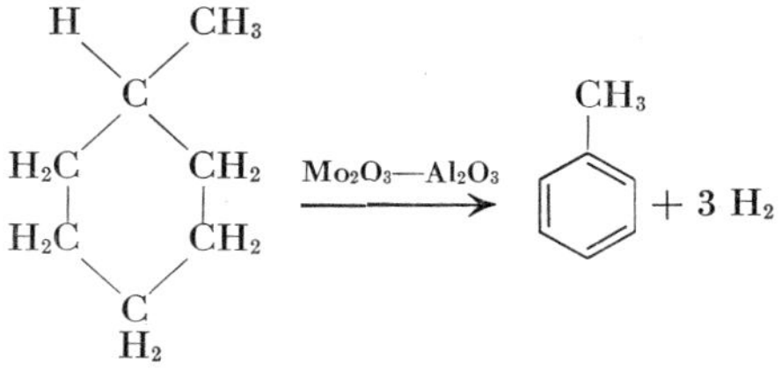

Productive capacity from petroleum reached 175 million gallons annually, giving a total capacity of over 200 million gallons. In 1946, however, the production of toluene was only about 40 per cent of this amount and during the same period when the price of benzene rose from $0.15 to $0.19 per gallon, the price of toluene dropped from $0.27 per gallon to $0.23 per gallon.

Methods have been developed for the high temperature catalytic cyclization and dehydrogenation of alkanes from straight run gasolines to give aromatic hydrocarbons. The preferred catalyst appears to be chromic oxide on alumina. Thus *n*-hexane yields benzene.

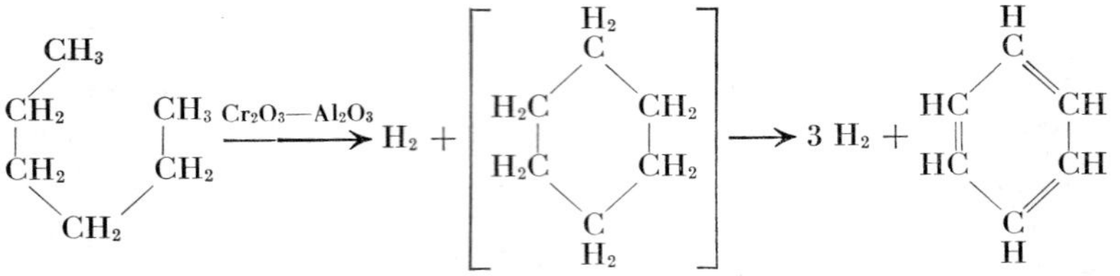

n-Hexane   Cyclohexane   Benzene

Similarly *n*-heptane and *n*-octane yield toluene and *o*-xylene respectively, and branched chain octanes yield other isomers. Thus far practical difficulties have prevented the commercial use of this process. Toluene can be made also from the dimethylcyclopentanes which are present in the distillates from California petroleum. These compounds can be rearranged to methylcyclohexane, which can be dehydrogenated to toluene.

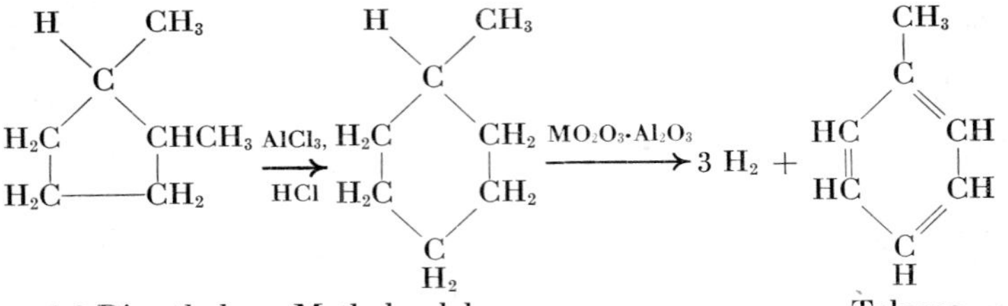

1,2-Dimethyl-   Methylcyclohexane   Toluene
cyclopentane

Since late in 1949, benzene has been produced from the cyclohexane and methylcyclopentane in petroleum by processes analogous to those used for the production of toluene.

A commercial synthesis of benzene homologs involves the addition of benzene to olefins. This reaction is analogous to the addition of alkanes having a tertiary hydrogen atom to olefins (p. 51). With benzene the usual catalysts are anhydrous aluminum chloride, concentrated sulfuric acid, or anhydrous hydrogen fluoride.

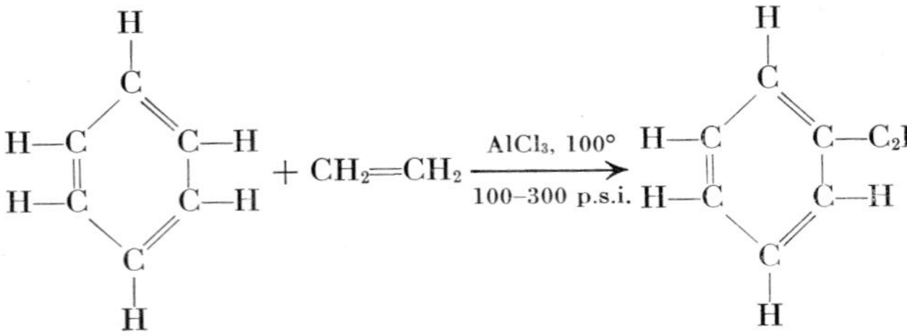

Ethylbenzene

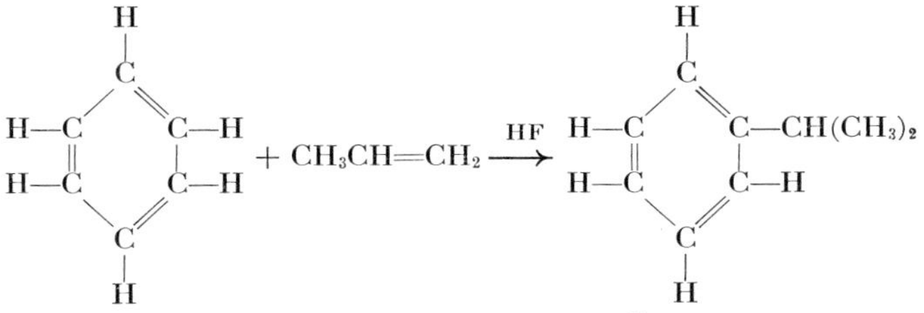

Cumene

A large amount of **ethylbenzene** is made as an intermediate for the production of styrene (p. 425). **Cumene** is used on a large scale for the production of military aviation fuel. The incorporation of 20 to 30 per cent aromatics permits rich-mixture supercharging, which gives extra power for take-off or rapid climb.

In the laboratory alkyl halides or alcohols may be used in place of olefins, hydrogen halide being a product of the reaction. These reactions are variations of the Friedel-Crafts reaction.

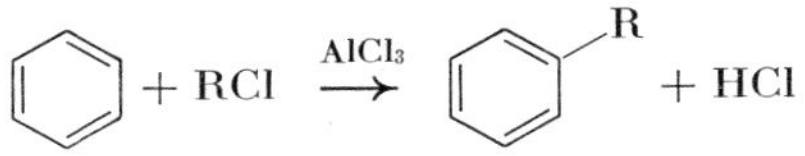

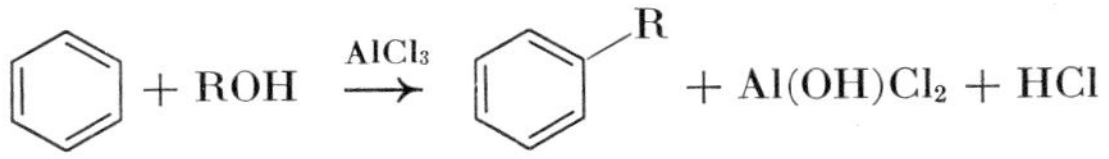

Since an alkylated benzene substitutes even more readily than benzene (p. 332), these reactions lead to mixtures rather than to a single product. Thus in the reaction of benzene with methyl chloride in the presence of anhydrous aluminum chloride, not only toluene but also the xylenes and higher alkylated benzenes are produced.

Mesitylene is made by the condensation of three moles of acetone in the presence of concentrated sulfuric acid.

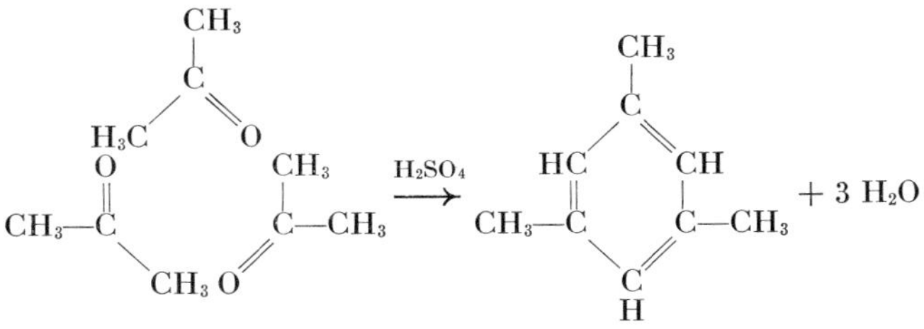

Mesitylene

The reaction illustrates one of a number of syntheses in which aromatic compounds are derived from aliphatic compounds. *p*-**Cymene** is one of the minor products of the sulfite process for making wood pulp (p. 298).

Large quantities of aromatic hydrocarbons are used as solvents and for the synthesis of other aromatic compounds. The homologs of benzene undergo the typical substitution reactions of halogenation, nitration, sulfonation, and Friedel-Crafts reaction. Moreover, the side chains undergo the reactions of the alkanes.

Orientation in the Benzene Nucleus

Three xylenes are known (p. 316). One boils at 138.4° and melts at $+13.4°$, another boils at 139.3° and melts at $-47.4°$, and the third boils at 144.1° and melts at $-25°$. The problem of assigning structures to isomeric benzene derivatives is known as *orientation in the benzene nucleus*. It has been solved in two ways: one way is known as Koerner's absolute method, and the other may be called the interconversion method.

Koerner's [5] *Absolute Method.* If a third group is introduced into each member of any set of three isomeric disubstituted benzenes in which the two original substituents are alike, the *ortho* isomer should yield two trisubstitution products, the *meta* three trisubstitution products, and the *para* only one trisubstitution product. For example, o-xylene on mono-nitration should yield two nitro-o-xylenes, m-xylene should yield three nitro-m-xylenes, and p-xylene should yield one nitro-p-xylene.

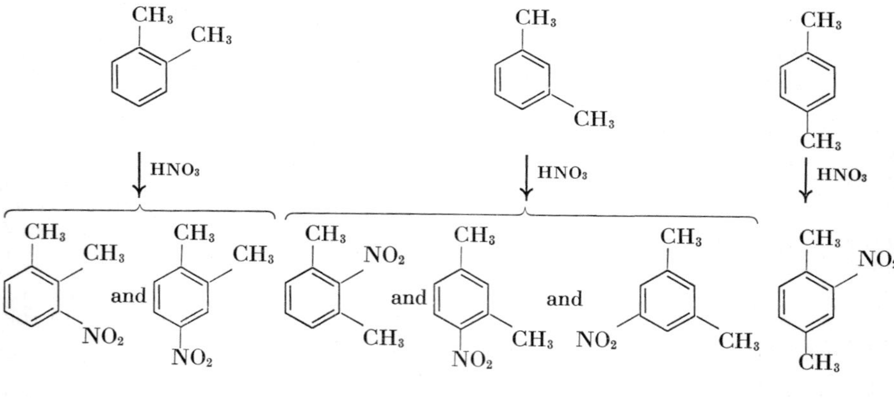

The nitro group has, of course, a larger total number of positions to enter, but more than one position may yield the same compound. For example in p-xylene four hydrogen atoms may be replaced by a nitro group but replacement of any one of them yields the same product.

When the three known xylenes are subjected to monosubstitution, that boiling at 138.4° yields only one compound and hence is the *para* isomer; that boiling at 139.3° yields three compounds and hence is the *meta* isomer; that boiling at 144.1° yields only two compounds and hence is the *ortho* isomer. The constitution of a number of disubstituted benzenes has been determined

---

[5] Wilhelm Guglielmo Koerner (1839–1925), student of Kekulé and professor at the University of Milan. He devised one of the chemical proofs of the equivalence of the six hydrogen atoms of benzene, and first proposed the accepted structural formula for pyridine (p. 454).

by this procedure, and the principle can be extended to other types of substitution products.

   Interconversion Method. Once the orientation of the groups in a substituted benzene has been determined, the orientation is known for all compounds that can be derived from it by converting one or more substituents into other groups. For example three benzenedicarboxylic acids are known. One called *phthalic acid* melts with decomposition at about 200°, another, *isophthalic acid*, melts at 348°, and a third, *terephthalic acid*, sublimes without melting at 300°. These acids can be formed respectively by the vigorous oxidation of *o*-, *m*-, and *p*-xylene and hence are the *o*-, *m*-, and *p*-dicarboxylic acids.

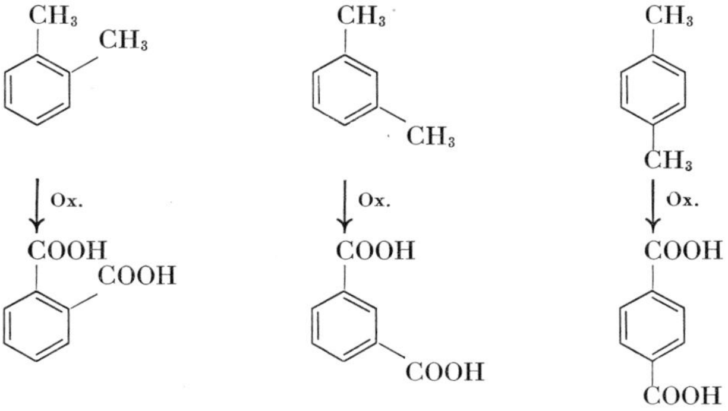

Phthalic acid   Isophthalic acid   Terephthalic acid

Similarly the three toluenemonocarboxylic acids can be obtained by milder oxidation of the three xylenes, and their constitution thereby is established.

Nomenclature

   Kekulé introduced the terms *ring* and *nucleus* to designate the characteristic portion of aromatic compounds. The aliphatic portions he called *side-chains*.

   Common names are used even more extensively for aromatic compounds than for aliphatic compounds. Compounds may be named also as derivatives of benzene, of another parent hydrocarbon, or of some other substitution product of benzene that has a common name. The position of a substituent is indicated by a number. The six carbon atoms of the benzene nucleus are numbered from 1 to 6, the starting point being that which will give the substituents the smallest possible numbers. Usually a formula is written with one group at the top carbon atom which then becomes the number 1 carbon atom of the benzene ring, but such need not be the case. Care should be taken that the name chosen is not ambiguous.

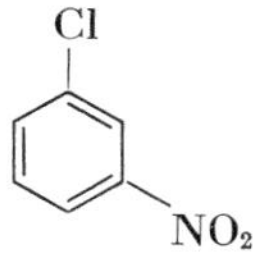

1-Chloro-3-nitrobenzene
3-Chloronitrobenzene
m-Chloronitrobenzene
1-Nitro-3-chlorobenzene
3-Nitrochlorobenzene
m-Nitrochlorobenzene

Groups obtained by dropping a hydrogen atom from an aromatic hydro-carbon are known as *aryl* groups. The group C_6H_5 derived from benzene is known as *phenyl*. This name is derived from *phene*, a name that was proposed by Laurent for benzene, because it is present in illuminating gas (Gr. *phainein* to bring to light). If two hydrogen atoms are dropped, the residue, C_6H_4, is known as a *phenylene* group. Since the two hydrogen atoms may be removed in three ways, there are *o-*, *m-*, and *p*-phenylene groups. If a hydrogen atom is dropped from the methyl group of toluene, the residue is known as a *benzyl* group, but if from the nucleus, three *tolyl* groups, *ortho*, *meta*, and *para*, result. The term *xylyl* appears in the literature, but it should be dropped since some use it to mean $(CH_3)_2C_6H_3{}^-$, whereas others use it to mean $CH_3C_6H_4CH_2{}^-$.

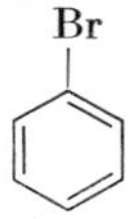

Br

Bromobenzene or
phenyl bromide

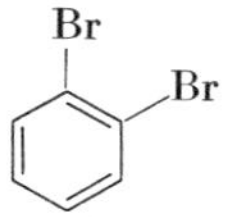

Br
Br

o-Dibromobenzene,
1,2-dibromobenzene, or
o-phenylene bromide

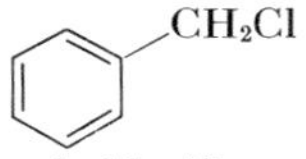

CH₂Cl

Benzyl chloride or
phenylmethyl chloride

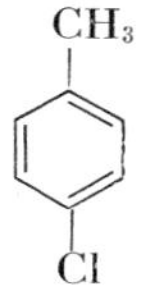

CH_3

Cl

p-Chlorotoluene or
p-tolyl chloride

COAL PRODUCTS

Carbonization of Coal

Coal is a compact stratified mass derived from plants which have suffered partial decay and have been subjected to various degrees of heat and pressure. Most normal banded coals are believed to have originated in peat swamps. The substances peat, lignite, soft or bituminous coal, and anthracite or hard coal are progressive stages of metamorphosis in which the ratio of the amount of carbon to the amount of other elements increases. When coal is heated to a sufficiently high temperature (350°–1000°) in the absence of air, volatile products are formed, and a residue of impure carbon remains which is called *coke.* The process is known as the *destructive distillation* or *carbonization* of coal. When the volatile products cool to ordinary temperature, a portion condenses to a black viscous liquid known as *coal tar.* The noncondensable gases are known as *coal gas.* One ton of coal yields about 1500 pounds of coke, 10 gallons of tar, and 1000 cubic feet of coal gas. About 25 pounds of ammonium sulfate is obtained by removing ammonia from the gas by washing with sulfuric acid.

The principal reason for the commercial carbonization of coal is the production of **coke,** which is used for the reduction of ores in blast furnaces. Coke is used also as a smokeless industrial and household fuel.

Coal Gas

Coal gas varies in composition during the course of the distillation but consists chiefly of hydrogen and methane in about equal volumes, along with some carbon monoxide, ethane, ethylene, benzene, carbon dioxide, oxygen, and nitrogen, and smaller amounts of cyclopentadiene (p. 561), toluene, naphthalene (p. 428), water vapor, ammonia, hydrogen sulfide, hydrogen cyanide, cyanogen, and nitric oxide. After removal of the noxious components the gas is run into mains for use as illuminating gas and as a domestic fuel. When economically desirable, the benzene, toluene, and other less volatile hydrocarbons also are removed by washing (*scrubbing*) with a high-boiling petroleum fraction known as *straw oil*. The hydrocarbons are recovered by heating (*stripping*) the oil and condensing the vapors. Although the benzene and toluene are liquids at room temperature, the coal gas is saturated with them and a larger amount can be obtained by washing the coal gas than can be obtained by distilling the coal tar.

Coal Tar

The composition of coal tar varies with the process used for carbonization. Tar obtained from high temperature distillation is the most useful for chemical purposes. The first step in the separation of the black foul-smelling liquid into its components is distillation. The fractions obtained in a typical procedure are (*1*) *light oil* (so-called because it floats on water) distilling up to 200°, 5 per cent; (*2*) *middle oil* (carbolic oil), 200°–250°, 17 per cent; (*3*) *heavy oil* (dead oil, creosote oil), 250°–300°, 7 per cent; (*4*) *anthracene oil* (green oil), 300°–350°, 9 per cent; and (*5*) *pitch*, the residue, 62 per cent.

The further separation of the fractions depends on a combination of chemical and physical methods. Three main groups of substances are present: (*1*) *neutral compounds*, chiefly hydrocarbons; (*2*) *tar acids*, very weakly acidic substances soluble in sodium hydroxide solution; (*3*) *tar bases*, weakly basic substances soluble in dilute sulfuric acid.

The **light oil** fraction from coal tar is rather small, but about twenty times as much can be recovered by scrubbing coal gas. It usually is separated directly into its components by fractional distillation. The so-called *crude 90 per cent benzol* is a fraction, 90 per cent of which distills between 80° and 100°; *crude 90 per cent toluol*, *solvent naphtha*, and *heavy naphtha* are the fractions, 90 per cent of which distill between the ranges 100° to 120°, 130° to 160°, and 160° to 210° respectively. They consist chiefly of aromatic hydrocarbons and olefins. Most of the tar bases remain behind with the tar acids. The fractions are treated with concentrated sulfuric acid to polymerize the olefins and then are washed with 10 per cent aqueous sodium hydroxide and distilled to give benzene, toluene, and xylenes.

The **middle** or **carbolic oil** is combined with the high-boiling fraction from the light oil and cooled in large shallow pans. The solid hydrocarbon *naphthalene* (p. 428) crystallizes and is removed by centrifuging. The crude naphthalene is distilled, washed while molten with sulfuric acid, water, and aqueous alkali, and distilled again to give refined naphthalene. The oil that is separated from the crude naphthalene is washed with aqueous alkali to remove the tar acids. Steam is passed into the aqueous extract to remove volatile materials and then the solution is cooled and saturated with carbon dioxide which precipitates the weakly acidic tar acids from their salts. The tar acid layer is separated and fractionally distilled to give phenol (p. 380), which is purified further by crystallization. The aqueous sodium carbonate layer is reconverted to sodium hydroxide solution (causticized) by the addition of lime, and the precipitate of calcium carbonate is reconverted to lime and carbon dioxide by heating in lime kilns. The oil remaining after the extraction of acidic substances with alkali is washed with aqueous sulfuric acid, which forms salts with the tar bases and takes them into solution. The tar bases are liberated by the addition of sodium hydroxide and distilled to give chiefly *pyridine* (p. 454). The oil remaining from the acid treatment is distilled to give solvent naphtha and a solid residue of polymerized olefins known as *cumar resin*.

The **heavy oil** may be treated in much the same way to yield naphthalene, the higher tar acids (cresols, p. 380), and the higher tar bases (quinolines, p. 458). The **anthracene oil** is run into tanks and allowed to crystallize over a period of one to two weeks. After filtration the nearly dry cakes are subjected to about 60,000 pounds pressure in a warm hydraulic press to remove more liquid impurities and then ground and washed with solvent naphtha to remove most of the hydrocarbon *phenanthrene* (p. 440), and with pyridine to remove most of a nitrogen-containing compound *carbazole* (p. 451). The residue is sublimed to give the hydrocarbon *anthracene* (p. 437) of 85 to 90 per cent purity.

Over 150 individual compounds have been isolated from coal tar, the first being naphthalene, described in 1820. Anthracene was isolated in 1832, phenol, aniline (p. 360), quinoline, and pyrrole (p. 446) in 1834, and chrysene (p. 441) in 1837. Forty-six components were isolated during the thirty year period 1861–1890 and seventy-nine during the ten year period 1931–1940. The remainder are scattered over the intervening years. The period 1861–1890 was that of the most intensive development of the chemistry of coal tar. The large number of compounds isolated during the period 1931–1940 reflected new techniques in distillation and an exhaustive effort to identify all of the components of coal tar. The more important components are listed in Table 16. The amounts of benzene and toluene given are those present in coal tar and do not include the light oil fraction extracted from coal gas by scrubbing (p. 323).

TABLE 16

CHIEF COMPONENTS OF COAL TAR

COMPOUND	PER CENT	COMPOUND	PER CENT
Benzene	0.1	Phenanthrene	4.0
Toluene	0.2	Anthracene	1.1
Xylenes	1.0	Carbazole	1.1
Naphthalene	10.9	Crude tar bases	2.0
α- and β-Methylnaphthalenes	2.5	(Pyridine 0.1)	
Dimethylnaphthalenes	3.4	Crude tar acids	2.5
Acenaphthene	1.4	(Phenol, 0.7, cresols, 1.1,	
Fluorene	1.6	xylenols, 0.2)	

REVIEW QUESTIONS

1. What is the chief source of aromatic compounds? How are the various components separated?
2. Give the experimental facts on which the accepted structural formula of benzene is based.
3. Discuss and illustrate by equations the more important differences in the chemical behavior of aliphatic and aromatic hydrocarbons and illustrate where possible by equations.
4. Write structural formulas and name all of the isomeric chloronitrobenzenes; trichlorobenzenes; bromodinitrobenzenes.
5. Discuss Koerner's absolute method for distinguishing between *ortho-*, *meta-*, and *para-*disubstituted benzenes. What other procedure may be used?
6. Write structural formulas for toluene, the xylenes, mesitylene, *p*-cymene, cumene. What methods of preparation or sources of these compounds are available other than direct isolation from coal tar?
7. What are the formulas for the phenyl, phenylene, benzyl, and tolyl groups?

Chapter 20

HALOGEN DERIVATIVES OF AROMATIC HYDROCARBONS

In a strict sense aromatic halides are halogen compounds in which the halogen is attached directly to an aromatic nucleus. It is convenient, however, to consider also those halogen compounds formed by addition of halogen to the double bonds of the nucleus, and those in which the halogen is present in a side chain.

Reactions of Aromatic Hydrocarbons with Halogen

Halogen may react with aromatic hydrocarbons in three ways: (*1*) it may add to the double bonds of the nucleus giving a product which no longer has aromatic properties; (*2*) it may replace a hydrogen atom of the benzene nucleus to give an aryl halide; (*3*) if an alkyl side chain is present, it may replace a hydrogen atom of the side chain to give an aralkyl halide.

Addition of Halogen. Exposure of a mixture of benzene and chlorine or bromine to light of short wavelength causes the addition of six atoms of halogen to give a mixture of stereoisomeric benzene hexachlorides or hexabromides.

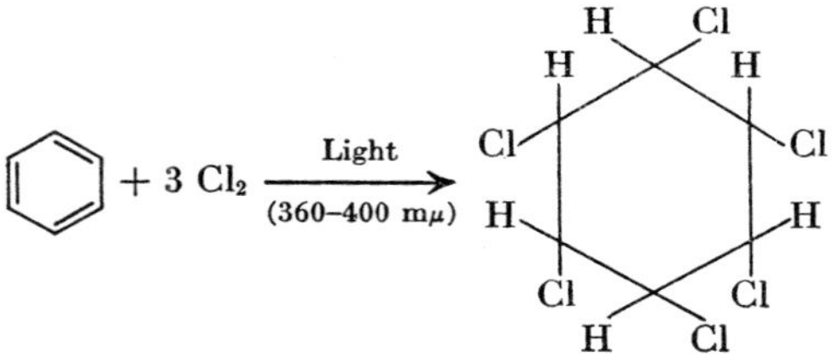

Nine noninterconvertible (cf. p. 562) stereoisomers of benzene hexachloride are possible, corresponding to the nine inositols (p. 308). Five isomers have been isolated and designated α, β, γ, δ, and ϵ.

The mixture of isomers has become of considerable commercial importance because of its insecticidal properties. Production in the United States in 1948 was over 18 million pounds. It is called **BHC** or **666**, abbreviations of its name or the formula $C_6H_6Cl_6$. It must be used at the proper dilution because of its persistent musty odor at higher concentrations. The insecticidal property is due solely to the γ form, which makes up only 12 to 18 per cent of the mixed halides. The insecticidal products are sold on the basis of the content of the γ isomer, which has been given the names *gammexane* and *lindane*.

When the hexachloride or hexabromide is heated with alcoholic potassium

326

hydroxide, three moles of halogen acid are removed to give 1,2,4-trihalo-benzene.[1]

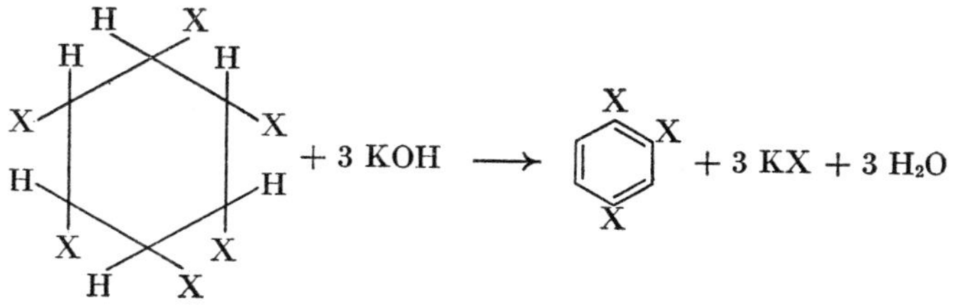

Nuclear Substitution. When aromatic hydrocarbons are warmed with chlorine or bromine in the presence of iron, substitution of nuclear hydrogen takes place with the evolution of halogen acid.

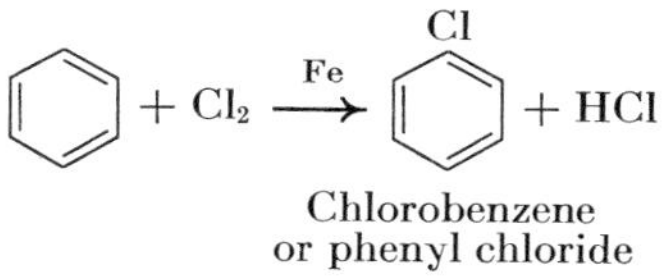

Chlorobenzene
or phenyl chloride

During these reactions some disubstitution takes place, the product being a mixture of the *ortho* and *para* isomers with very little *meta*.

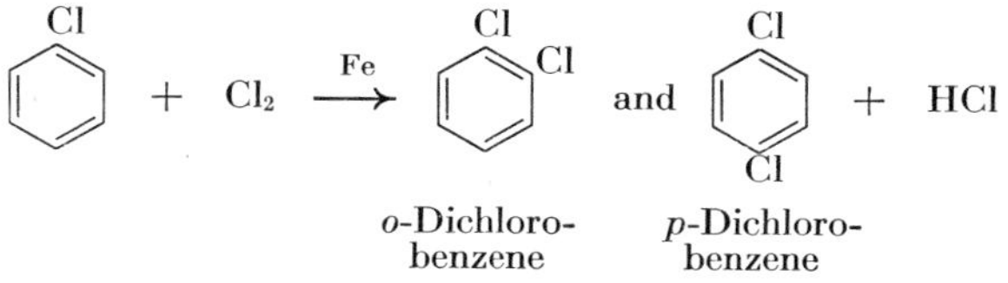

o-Dichloro-
benzene

p-Dichloro-
benzene

The introduction of one halogen atom into the benzene ring makes it more difficult to replace a second hydrogen atom, the relative rates of substitution of benzene and chlorobenzene being about 8.5 : 1. Hence by regulating the amount of halogen and the time and temperature of the reaction, it is possible to produce predominantly mono- or polysubstitution products as desired. Usually in commercial operations, chlorination is carried out until practically all of the benzene has reacted. The composition of the resulting mixture is about 80 per cent chlorobenzene, 17 per cent *p*-dichlorobenzene, 2 per cent *o*-dichlorobenzene, and 1 per cent higher substitution products.

Chlorobenzene is an intermediate in the manufacture of phenol, aniline, DDT, and dyes. *p*-Dichlorobenzene is used as a clothes-moth larvicide, and as a larvicide for the peach-tree borer.

Other aromatic compounds halogenate in a similar manner. For example

---

[1] In the formula for this compound and subsequently, bonds usually are not indicated between the substituent and the aromatic ring.

toluene on chlorination or bromination in the presence of iron yields a mixture of *o*- and *p*-dichloro- or dibromotoluenes.

$$\underset{\text{CH}_3}{\bigcirc} + X_2 \xrightarrow{\text{Fe}} \underset{\text{CH}_3}{\bigcirc}\text{X} \quad \text{and} \quad \underset{\text{CH}_3}{\underset{\text{X}}{\bigcirc}} + HX$$

The active catalyst in these reactions is ferric halide, formed by the action of halogen on the iron. Other metallic halides such as aluminum chloride or bromide also are effective.

As with aliphatic hydrocarbons, iodination does not occur because the position of equilibrium is unfavorable. Iodination of aromatic hydrocarbons can be brought about in the presence of nitric acid, presumably because the equilibrium is shifted by the oxidation of hydrogen iodide.

$$\underset{}{\bigcirc} + I_2 \rightleftharpoons \underset{I}{\bigcirc} + HI$$

$$4\,HI + 2\,HNO_3 \longrightarrow 2\,I_2 + N_2O_3 + 3\,H_2O$$

Direct halogenation is the usual method for the preparation of aryl halides. The replacement of a hydroxyl group by halogen, which is of primary importance in the preparation of alkyl halides, is seldom used, because it is difficult to replace a hydroxyl group attached to a benzene ring (p. 382). Methods for the replacement of the amino group by halogen are discussed on page 371.

Side-chain Substitution. The chemical properties of side chains are for the most part those of aliphatic compounds. Hence if a mixture of toluene vapor and halogen is exposed to light of short wavelength, halogenation takes place in the side chain. Since for aliphatic hydrocarbons the rates of replacement of a second and third hydrogen atom by halogen differ little from the rate of replacement of the first hydrogen atom, approximately equal amounts of mono-, di-, and trisubstitution products are formed.

$$\underset{\text{CH}_3}{\bigcirc} \xrightarrow[\text{+ light}]{X_2} HX + \underset{\text{CH}_2X}{\bigcirc} \xrightarrow[\text{+ light}]{X_2} HX + \underset{\text{CHX}_2}{\bigcirc} \xrightarrow[\text{+ light}]{X_2} HX + \underset{\text{CX}_3}{\bigcirc}$$

	Benzyl halide	Benzal halide or benzylidene halide	Benzo-trihalide

A certain amount of regulation of the ratio of mono- to di- to trisubstitution can be obtained by varying the hydrocarbon-halogen ratio. In the technical preparation of benzyl chloride, reaction takes place at 130°–140°. This temperature is above the boiling point of toluene (111°) but below the boiling point of benzyl chloride (179°). Hence the benzyl chloride condenses as it is formed and further chlorination is prevented. The reaction is carried out in a lead-lined vessel illuminated internally with quartz mercury vapor lamps. At higher temperatures the reaction can be carried out in the absence of light.

Benzyl chloride can be prepared also by the reaction of benzene with formaldehyde and hydrogen chloride in the presence of zinc chloride or phosphoric acid.

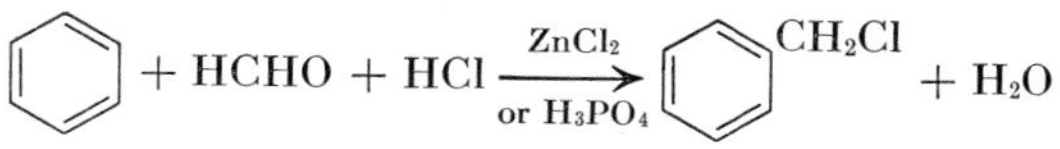

$$\text{[benzene]} + \text{HCHO} + \text{HCl} \xrightarrow[\text{or H}_3\text{PO}_4]{\text{ZnCl}_2} \text{[benzene-CH}_2\text{Cl]} + \text{H}_2\text{O}$$

The process is known as **chloromethylation** and is another substitution reaction that is applicable to aromatic compounds in general. Either the formaldehyde condenses with the aromatic compound to give a benzyl alcohol which then reacts with hydrogen chloride, or the hydrogen chloride adds to the formaldehyde to give chloromethyl alcohol, which reacts with the aromatic compound to give the benzyl chloride.

The relative technical importance of chlorobenzene, *p*-dichlorobenzene, *o*-dichlorobenzene, and benzyl chloride is indicated by the production in the United States in 1948 of 303, 34, 14, and 8 million pounds respectively.

Reactions of Aryl and Aralkyl Halides

Aryl Halides. Unlike the alkyl halides the simple aryl halides are very unreactive. No observable reaction takes place with sodium hydroxide, silver salts, sodium alkoxide, sodium cyanide, sodium sulfide, or ammonia under the ordinary conditions that bring about displacement reactions with the alkyl halides (p. 82). The reactivity may, however, be increased greatly by the presence of other substituents in the benzene ring (p. 348). Aryl bromides and iodides react readily with magnesium in ether solution to give Grignard reagents which undergo all of the usual reactions (p. 586).

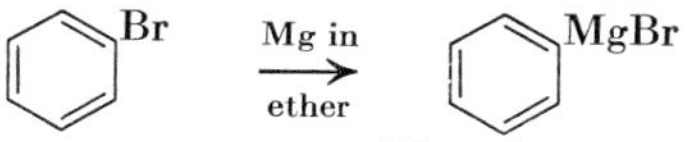

$$\text{[benzene-Br]} \xrightarrow[\text{ether}]{\text{Mg in}} \text{[benzene-MgBr]}$$

Phenylmagnesium
bromide

When the iodides are heated with activated copper powder, coupling of two aromatic nuclei takes place (*Ullmann reaction*).

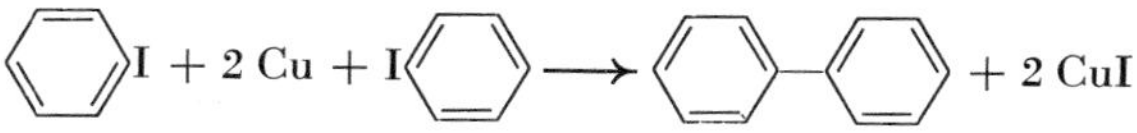

$$\text{[benzene]}\text{I} + 2\text{ Cu} + \text{I}\text{[benzene]} \longrightarrow \text{[benzene-benzene]} + 2\text{ CuI}$$

Biphenyl

When a mixture of aryl halide and alkyl halide is allowed to stand for a long time in the presence of metallic sodium, a mixed coupling takes place (*Wurtz-Fittig* [2] *reaction*).

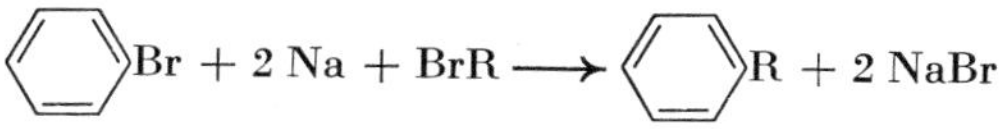

$$\text{[benzene-Br]} + 2\text{ Na} + \text{BrR} \longrightarrow \text{[benzene-R]} + 2\text{ NaBr}$$

---

[2] Rudolph Fittig (1835–1910), professor at the University of Strassburg. He discovered the pinacol reaction in 1858, and applied the Wurtz reaction to mixed alkyl and aryl halides in 1863. He is known also for his synthesis of β-naphthol from benzaldehyde (1883) and his discovery of the interconversion of α,β- and β,γ-unsaturated acids by alkali (1894).

This reaction has been used for the synthesis of benzene homologs. It was particularly valuable as a means of interconverting compounds during the early work on orientation (p. 320).

At temperatures between 200° and 300°, particularly in the presence of copper salts, aryl halides react with aqueous solutions of sodium hydroxide, sodium cyanide, or ammonia to give the corresponding hydroxy, cyano, or amino compounds (pp. 387, 370). The removal of halogen acid with the formation of a triple bond never takes place even in strongly alkaline solutions because the bonds —C≡C— are linear and cannot be combined with 120 degree bond angles in a six-membered ring. Current theory concerning the nonreactivity of unsubstituted aryl halides is discussed on page 349.

Aralkyl Halides. In general halogen in the side chain undergoes the same reactions as that in simple alkyl halides (p. 82). Even the rates of reaction are about the same if the halogen is located beyond the carbon atom attached directly to the ring. If the halogen is located on the carbon atom attached to the ring, the reactivity is greatly increased. For example, although benzyl chloride is a primary halide, it is hydrolyzed readily by aqueous solutions of sodium carbonate, and benzyl bromide reacts with tertiary amines to form quaternary salts about 300 times faster than *n*-propyl bromide. The high reactivity of benzyl halides is explainable by current theory (p. 349).

REVIEW QUESTIONS

1. How does the usual method for the preparation of aryl halides differ from that for alkyl halides and why?
2. Discuss in detail the several aspects of the halogenation of toluene.
3. How can the following compounds be prepared: benzene hexabromide; *o*- and *p*-chloromethyltoluene from toluene; *m*-chloromethyltoluene from *m*-xylene; *o*- and *p*-chlorocumene?
4. Compare the reactivities of chlorobenzene, benzyl chloride, 2-phenylethyl chloride and *n*-butyl chloride.

Chapter 21

AROMATIC NITRO COMPOUNDS. MECHANISM
OF AROMATIC SUBSTITUTION

Although aliphatic nitro compounds have been manufactured commercially only since 1940 (p. 201), aromatic nitro compounds long have been technically important. They have been used as intermediates for the manufacture of dyes since the discovery of mauve by Perkin in 1856. Other technical developments have led to their use as explosives and as intermediates for the manufacture of pharmaceuticals and many other aromatic compounds of commercial importance.

Preparation of Nitro Compounds

The factor contributing most to the widespread use of aromatic nitro compounds is the ease of preparation by direct nitration of aromatic compounds. When benzene is warmed with fuming nitric acid or with a mixture of concentrated nitric acid and sulfuric acid, the chief product is nitrobenzene.

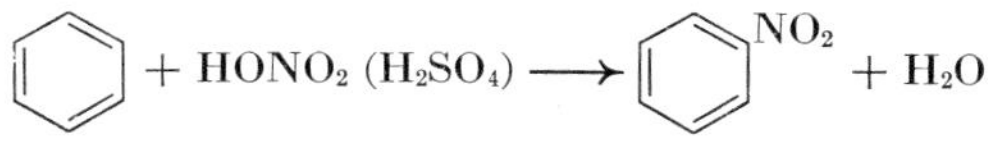

$$\text{C}_6\text{H}_6 + \text{HONO}_2 \ (\text{H}_2\text{SO}_4) \longrightarrow \text{C}_6\text{H}_5\text{NO}_2 + \text{H}_2\text{O}$$

Nitro-
benzene

The presence of a nitro group in a benzene ring decreases the rate of substitution of a second hydrogen atom even more so than does a halogen atom; consequently stronger acids and higher temperatures are needed to obtain appreciable quantities of the dinitrated product. When substitution of a second hydrogen takes place, the nitro group enters chiefly at the *meta* position.

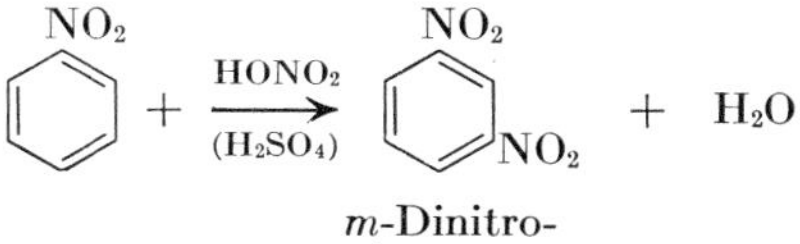

$$\text{C}_6\text{H}_5\text{NO}_2 + \xrightarrow[\text{(H}_2\text{SO}_4)]{\text{HONO}_2} \text{C}_6\text{H}_4(\text{NO}_2)_2 + \text{H}_2\text{O}$$

m-Dinitro-
benzene

It is very difficult to introduce a third nitro group into benzene by direct nitration.

Toluene nitrates more readily than benzene. The principal products are first a mixture of *o*- and *p*-nitrotoluene, then 2,4-dinitrotoluene, and finally 2,4,6-trinitrotoluene (TNT).

331

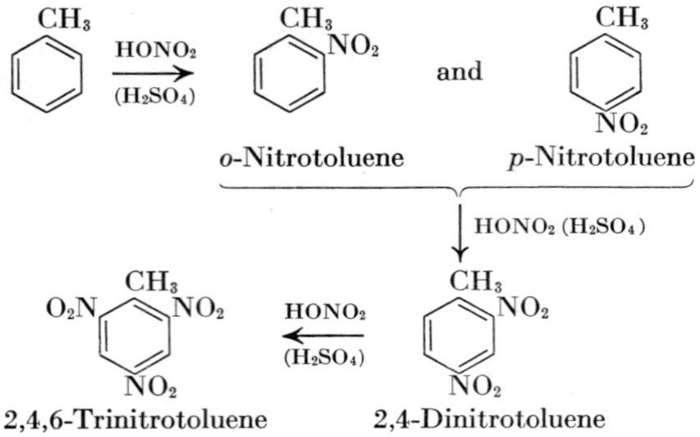

$$\underset{\text{benzene}}{\text{CH}_3\text{—C}_6\text{H}_5} \xrightarrow[\text{(H}_2\text{SO}_4)]{\text{HONO}_2} \underset{o\text{-Nitrotoluene}}{\text{CH}_3,\ \text{NO}_2} \quad \text{and} \quad \underset{p\text{-Nitrotoluene}}{\text{CH}_3,\ \text{NO}_2}$$

$$\underset{\text{2,4,6-Trinitrotoluene}}{\text{O}_2\text{N—CH}_3\text{—NO}_2,\ \text{NO}_2} \xleftarrow[\text{(H}_2\text{SO}_4)]{\text{HONO}_2} \underset{\text{2,4-Dinitrotoluene}}{\text{CH}_3,\ \text{NO}_2,\ \text{NO}_2} \xleftarrow[]{\text{HONO}_2\ (\text{H}_2\text{SO}_4)}$$

Chloro- and bromobenzene nitrate somewhat less readily than benzene and give chiefly a mixture of the *ortho* and *para* isomers.

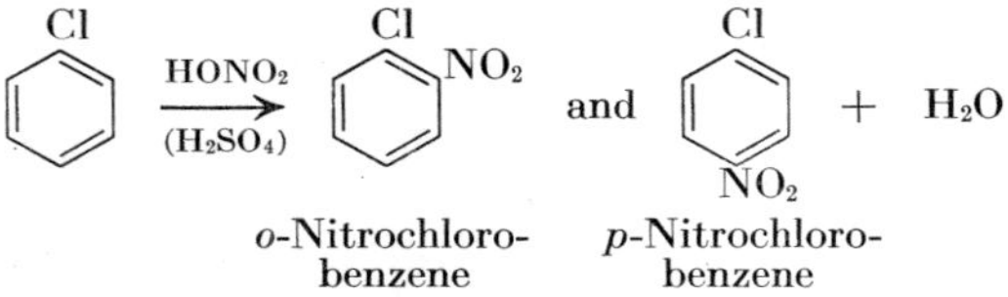

$$\underset{\text{Cl}}{\bigcirc} \xrightarrow[\text{(H}_2\text{SO}_4)]{\text{HONO}_2} \underset{o\text{-Nitrochloro-}\atop\text{benzene}}{\text{Cl},\ \text{NO}_2} \quad \text{and} \quad \underset{p\text{-Nitrochloro-}\atop\text{benzene}}{\text{Cl},\ \text{NO}_2} + \text{H}_2\text{O}$$

On the other hand, chlorination or bromination of nitrobenzene gives chiefly the *meta* isomer.

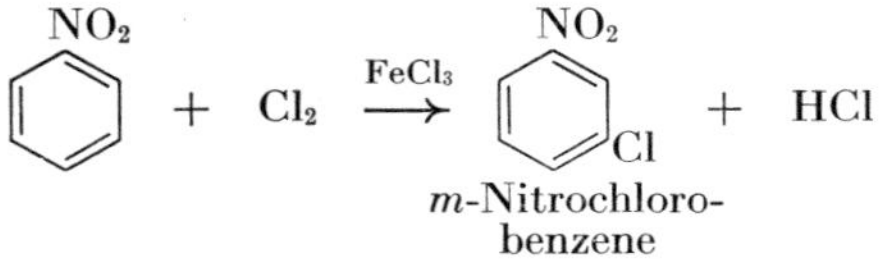

$$\underset{\text{NO}_2}{\bigcirc} + \text{Cl}_2 \xrightarrow{\text{FeCl}_3} \underset{m\text{-Nitrochloro-}\atop\text{benzene}}{\text{NO}_2,\ \text{Cl}} + \text{HCl}$$

Since iron reduces nitro groups (p. 346), anhydrous ferric chloride is the preferred catalyst for the halogenation of nitro compounds.

Rules for Substitution in the Benzene Nucleus

Two striking facts are evident from the substitution reactions discussed so far: (*1*) in some reactions a substituent enters chiefly the positions that are *ortho* and *para* to the group already present in the ring as in the halogenation or nitration of toluene and chlorobenzene, and in other reactions it enters chiefly the *meta* position as in the halogenation or nitration of nitrobenzene; (*2*) the substituent already present, for example a methyl group, may make a second hydrogen more readily substituted than a hydrogen atom of benzene, or a substituent such as a halogen atom or a nitro group may make it more difficult to replace a hydrogen atom.

Many investigations of the products formed in substitution reactions between a variety of reagents and a large number of aromatic compounds have led to the following generalizations:

(*1*) A number of groups, such as halogen (X), nitro (NO₂), sulfonic acid

(SO$_3$H), alkyl (R), and acyl (RCO or ArCO [1]), may be introduced directly into the benzene nucleus, hydrogen being displaced.

(2) When a second substituent is introduced into a benzene nucleus, the relative amounts of the *ortho*, *meta*, and *para* isomers should be 40, 40, and 20 per cent respectively on a statistical basis. Usually this ratio is not obtained. The relative amounts of the isomers depends primarily on the nature of the group already present in the ring.

(3) Groups vary greatly in their directing power, from the [$\overset{+}{N}R_3$] group, which causes substitution almost exclusively in the *meta* position, to the [O$^-$] group which causes substitution almost exclusively in the *ortho* and *para* positions. Other groups fall between these extremes in directing power (Table 17).

TABLE 17

RELATIVE AMOUNTS OF *meta*, *ortho*, AND *para* ISOMERS FORMED
IN THE NITRATION OF MONOSUBSTITUTED BENZENES

GROUP PRESENT IN RING	ISOMERS FORMED ON NITRATION (PER CENT)			
	meta	*ortho*	*para*	*o + p*
OH*	0	73	27	100
I	0	41	59	100
Br	0	38	62	100
Cl	0	30	70	100
F	0	12	88	100
NHCOCH$_3$	2	19	79	98
CH$_3$	4	59	37	96
CH$_2$Cl	16	32	57	88
CH$_2$CH$_2$NO$_2$	13	35	52	87 '
[NH$^+_3$]	33	5	62	67
CHCl$_2$	34	23	43	66
CH$_2$NO$_2$	48			52
COCH$_3$	55	45	0	45
CCl$_3$	64	7	29	36
COOC$_2$H$_5$	72	24	4	32
SO$_3$H	72	21	7	28
CHO	79			21
COOH	80	19	1	20
CN	81			19
NO$_2$	93	7	trace	7
[N(CH$_3$)$_3$$^+$]	100	0	0	0

* In the absence of nitrous acid

Groups causing the production of more than 60 per cent of the *ortho* and *para* isomers combined are called *ortho,para-directing groups*, and those causing the production of more than 40 per cent of the *meta* isomer are called *meta-directing groups*.

(4) *ortho,para*-Directing groups, *with the exception of halogen*, increase the ease with which a second hydrogen can be displaced. Such groups are said to *activate* the ring. *meta*-Directing groups *and halogen* decrease the ease with which a second hydrogen can be displaced; that is they are *deactivating* groups.

Activation and deactivation are reflections of the rates of substitution compared with benzene. The effect of a group on the relative amounts of the three isomers formed reflects the relative rates of substitution at the unsubstituted

---

[1] Ar is used to designate any aryl group, just as R is a general symbol for alkyl groups.

positions. When the group already present is activating and *ortho,para*-direct-ing, it increases the rate of substitution over that of benzene, and at the *ortho* and *para* positions more than at the *meta* positions. When a group is deactivat-ing and *meta*-directing, it decreases the rate of substitution compared with that for benzene, but decreases the rate less at the *meta* positions than at the *ortho* and *para* positions. Halogen, which is deactivating and *ortho,para*-directing, decreases the rate of substitution over that for benzene, but de-creases the rate less at the *ortho* and *para* positions than at the *meta* positions.

From Table 17 an approximate order of directive influence of different groups can be obtained. *These results hold only for nitration and for the par-ticular conditions of the experiment.* For example nitration of chlorobenzene yields 30 per cent *o*-, 70 per cent *p*-, and no *m*-nitrochlorobenzene, but chlorina-tion of chlorobenzene yields 39 per cent *o*-, 55 per cent *p*-, and 6 per cent *m*-dichlorobenzene. Bromination of bromobenzene in the presence of alumi-num chloride yields 8 per cent *o*-, 30 per cent *m*-, and 62 per cent *p*-dibromo-benzene, whereas bromination in the presence of ferric chloride yields 13 per cent *o*-, 2 per cent *m*-, and 85 per cent *p*-dibromobenzene. Nitration of ben-zenesulfonic acid at 20°–30° yields 21 per cent *o*-, 72 per cent *m*-, and 7 per cent *p*-nitrobenzenesulfonic acid, but nitration at 90°–100° yields 29 per cent *o*-, 58 per cent *m*-, and 13 per cent *p*-nitrobenzenesulfonic acid. Thus although the group present in the ring is the dominant factor in determining the position taken by the entering group, the nature of the reagent and the conditions under which the reactions take place also influence the relative amounts of the isomers formed.

Moreover the ratio of *ortho* to *para* is rarely the 2 : 1 expected statistically. Usually the amount of *para* actually exceeds the amount of *ortho* although sometimes the *ortho* isomer is formed to the almost total exclusion of the *para*.

Table 17 does not list the free NH_2, NHR, or NR_2 groups nor the [O⁻] group, because they cannot exist as such in acid solution. These groups are known to direct strongly to the *ortho* and *para* positions from other reactions such as halogenation.

If several groups are all strongly *ortho,para*-directing, it is difficult to de-termine their relative directive power because so little of the *meta* isomer is formed. An answer has been obtained by determining the isomer chiefly formed when a third group enters a *para*-disubstituted compound. For ex-ample chlorination of *p*-hydroxytoluene gives 3-chloro-4-hydroxytoluene, in-dicating that the hydroxyl group is more strongly *ortho,para*-directing than the methyl group.

By such methods the relative order of directive influence has been shown to be [O⁻] > NH_2 > OH > I > Br > Cl > F > CH_3.

When two substituents are present in the benzene ring, the position taken by the entering group is influenced by both groups already present. If these groups direct to the same position, a third group enters almost exclusively at

this position. For example further nitration of either 2-nitrotoluene or 4-nitro-
toluene leads to 2,4-dinitrotoluene (p. 332). In the first compound the 4 position is *para* to the methyl group and *meta* to the nitro group, and in the second compound the 2 position is *ortho* to the methyl group and *meta* to the nitro
group. Similarly two *ortho,para*-directing groups or two *meta*-directing groups
in the *meta* position to each other direct to a single position.

1,3-Dimethyl-
4-nitrobenzene

1,3,5-Trinitro-
benzene

When two *ortho,para*-directing groups or two *meta*-directing groups are *ortho*
or *para* to each other, that with the stronger directive power determines the
predominant isomer. Thus in the chlorination of *p*-hydroxytoluene, the product is 3-chloro-4-hydroxytoluene.

If an *ortho,para*-directing group is *meta* to a *meta*-directing group, the influence of the *ortho,para*-directing group usually predominates over that of the
meta-directing group. For example in the nitration of *m*-nitrotoluene, a third
nitro group enters the 2, 4, and 6 positions but not the 5 position. This result
is to be expected since the methyl group is activating whereas the nitro group is
deactivating.

Many rules have been formulated for remembering whether a group is predominantly *ortho,para*-directing or predominantly *meta*-directing. Some are
purely empirical and others have some theoretical basis, but none is quantitative. Probably the simplest empirical rule is that halogen and groups in which
the atom joined to the ring is united to other elements by single homopolar
bonds or carries a negative charge are chiefly *ortho,para*-directing, whereas
groups in which the atom joined to the ring is united to other elements by
multiple bonds or semipolar bonds or carries a positive charge are chiefly
meta-directing. The principal exceptions to this rule are the trichloromethyl
group (CCl₃), which directs chiefly to the *meta* position, and the vinyl group
(CH=CH₂), which directs chiefly to the *ortho* and *para* positions.

**Mechanism of Substitution in the Benzene Nucleus and the Theory of Directive
Influence**

Mechanism of Substitution in the Benzene Nucleus. Much of the current theory
of the mechanism of organic reactions had its beginnings in attempts to explain aromatic

substitution, particularly the directive influence of groups. Although unsaturation electrons usually are omitted in writing the reactions of aromatic compounds, they undoubtedly are responsible for the characteristic substitution reactions.

In the mechanism proposed for the addition of halogen acids to olefins (p. 110), it is postulated that as the molecule H : X approaches the olefin molecule, the hydrogen atom exerts an attraction for the unsaturation electrons. The olefin becomes polarized and a bond is formed with the transfer of a proton from halogen to carbon and with simultaneous liberation of a bromide ion. The resulting deficiency in electrons of the other carbon atom attracts the halogen atom of another hydrogen halide molecule, which bonds with it to give the addition product and a proton.

$$\text{RCH—CHR} + \text{H} : \overset{\cdot\cdot}{\underset{\cdot\cdot}{\text{X}}} : \longrightarrow [\text{R}\overset{+}{\text{C}}\text{H—CH}_2\text{R}] + \left[: \overset{\cdot\cdot}{\underset{\cdot\cdot}{\text{X}}} : \overline{} \right]$$

$$[\text{R}\overset{+}{\text{C}}\text{H—CH}_2\text{R}] + : \overset{\cdot\cdot}{\underset{\cdot\cdot}{\text{X}}} : \text{H} \longrightarrow \text{RCHX—CH}_2\text{R} + [\text{H}^+]$$

Combination of [H⁺] and $\left[: \overset{\cdot\cdot}{\underset{\cdot\cdot}{\text{X}}} : \overline{} \right]$ gives H : $\overset{\cdot\cdot}{\underset{\cdot\cdot}{\text{X}}}$: , or alternatively $\left[: \overset{\cdot\cdot}{\underset{\cdot\cdot}{\text{X}}} : \overline{} \right]$ may add to $\left[\text{R}\overset{+}{\text{C}}\text{—CH}_2\text{R} \right]$.

Undoubtedly benzene starts to react with proton donors in the same way, the hydrogen atom exerting a polarizing effect on the unsaturation electrons. In order that a pair of electrons may occur at a carbon atom during bond formation with a proton, another carbon atom *ortho* or *para* to the pair of electrons must have an unfilled valence shell and carry a positive charge. The most stable structures for the intermediate are those in which a charge occurs at the *ortho* and *para* positions, since this condition permits two conjugated double bonds to be formed. In the symbolism used in this reaction, the six dots in the first formula represent the six unsaturation electrons of the benzene resonance hybrid.

An intermediate with a positive charge in the *meta* position would be much less stable since two electrons then must remain unpaired.

Therefore if the subsequent steps of the reaction followed the course of the olefins, the intermediate ion would combine with halide ions at the *ortho* and *para* positions to give addition products. Such a course, however, would involve destruction of the resonance of the benzene nucleus. Moreover because of the considerable resonance energy of the intermediate positive ion, it is less reactive than the corresponding alkyl carbonium ion from an olefin. Hence the carbon atom to which the proton becomes attached loses a proton, and the benzene resonance is retained. Thus only an exchange of hydrogen atoms results.

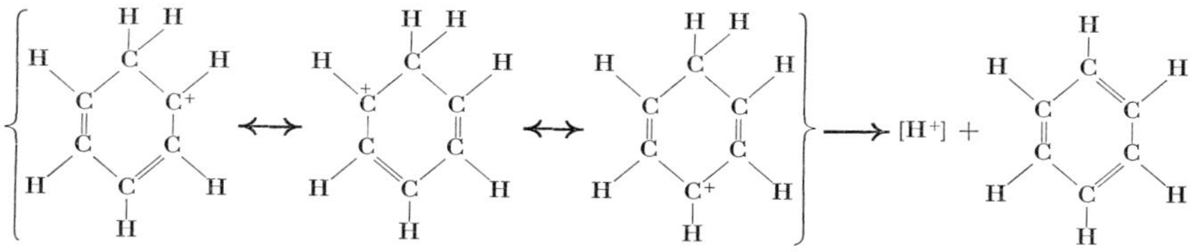

As in other reactions involving the loss of a proton, the removal of the proton is assisted by simultaneous combination with a base, such as a negative ion or a neutral molecule having an unshared pair of electrons. The exchange of hydrogen atoms between benzene and strong acids has been demonstrated by the use of sulfuric or hydrochloric acid containing deuterium.

$$C_6H_6 + DHSO_4 \rightleftarrows H_2SO_4 + C_6H_5D \overset{\text{Etc.}}{\rightleftarrows} C_6D_6$$

$$C_6H_6 + DCl \overset{AlCl_3}{\longrightarrow} HCl + C_6H_5D \overset{\text{Etc.}}{\rightleftarrows} C_6D_6$$

Here then is another type of substitution reaction. The attack is not from the back side with Walden inversion, as was postulated in the simple displacement reaction (p. 95), because the reagent cannot approach from the inside of the ring, and the ring structure could not be maintained if Walden inversion took place. Instead the reagent attacks from one side of the ring, and the displaced group leaves from the other side.

The transfer of hydrogen, however, cannot lead to substitution by another group as actually occurs in nitration and sulfonation. Therefore some simultaneous reaction must take place. There is considerable evidence that the active agent in a mixture of nitric acid and concentrated sulfuric acid is the nitronium ion, $[NO_2^+]$, which arises from the reaction

$$HONO_2 + 2\,H_2SO_4 \longrightarrow [NO_2^+] + [H_3O^+] + 2\,[HSO_4^-]$$

Thus along with the attack of the benzene nucleus by protons, which merely results in hydrogen exchange, attack by $[NO_2^+]$ ions takes place. Again because of the large amount of energy involved in destroying the benzene resonance, and because of the considerable resonance stabilization of the intermediate ion, a negative ion does not add to the positive ion intermediate, but instead a proton is lost simultaneously with the entrance of the $[NO_2^+]$ group.

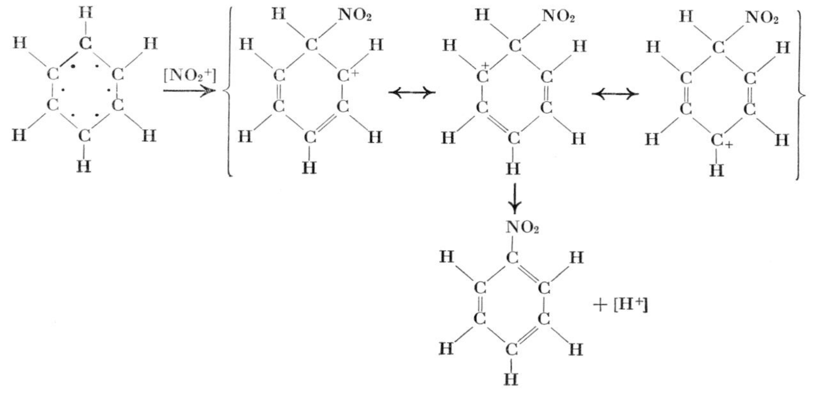

Since the nitronium ion hardly can exist in dilute aqueous solutions of nitric acid, which nevertheless can nitrate reactive aromatic compounds, nitration under these conditions must be by a different reagent. It has been proposed that this agent is the nitricidium ion, $[H_2NO_3^+]$.

$$HONO_2 + HONO_2 \longrightarrow \left[\begin{matrix}HONO_2^+ \\ \ddot{} \\ H\end{matrix}\right] + [ONO_2^-]$$

$$ArH + [O_2NOH_2^+] \longrightarrow ArNO_2 + H_2O + [H^+]$$

Most other aromatic substitutions are believed to follow a course similar to nitration. Thus the catalysis of halogenation appears to involve the formation of halonium salts, the positive halonium ion being the active agent.

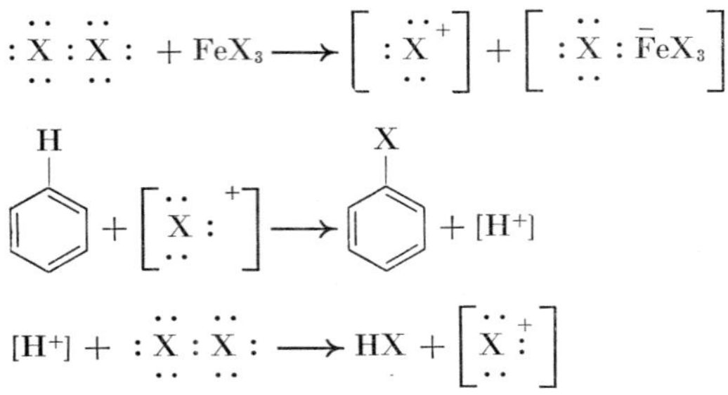

In the Friedel-Crafts reaction and other reactions catalyzed by anhydrous aluminum chloride, the catalyst can exercise its electron-accepting properties with the formation of positive ions that can attack the benzene nucleus.

$$RCl + AlCl_3 \longrightarrow [R^+] + [ClAlCl_3^-]$$

$$CH_2{=}CH_2 + AlCl_3 \longrightarrow [\overset{+}{C}H_2{-}CH_2 : \overset{-}{A}lCl_3]$$

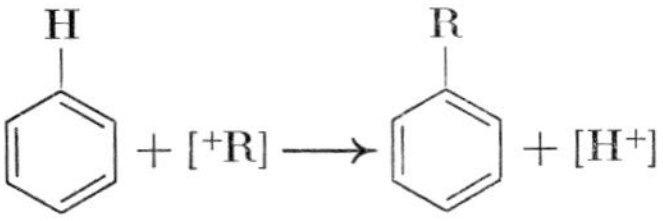

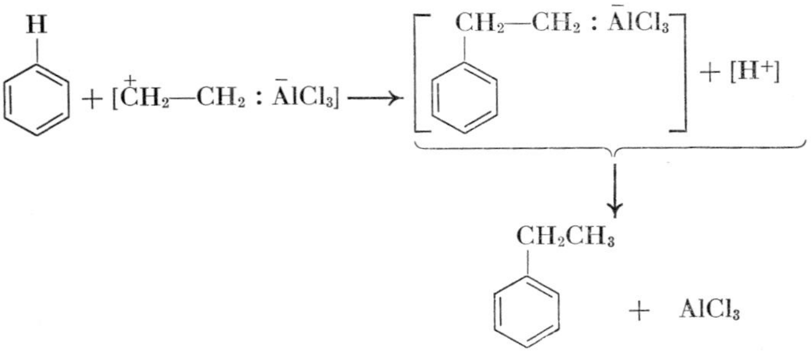

Two mechanisms for direct sulfonation seem reasonable, and it has not been possible to distinguish between them. In one the $[^+SO_3H]$ ion is the sulfonating agent which can arise by the ionization of sulfuric acid.

$$HOSO_3H + 2 H_2SO_4 \longrightarrow [\overset{+}{S}O_3H] + [H_3\overset{+}{O}] + 2 [HSO_4^-]$$

The greater reactivity of sulfuric acid containing dissolved sulfur trioxide (fuming sulfuric acid) may be explained by the reaction

$$SO_3 + H_2SO_4 \longrightarrow [\overset{+}{S}O_3H] + [HSO_4^-]$$

On the other hand the three oxygen atoms in sulfur trioxide undoubtedly greatly decrease the electron density on the sulfur atom. Hence sulfur trioxide may be a strongly electron-seeking reagent in itself and may be the sulfonating agent.

Activation and Deactivation of the Benzene Nucleus. The next question concerns the effect of groups other than hydrogen on the ease of substitution. In the first place the most strongly activating group is the [O$^-$] group which carries a full negative charge of one electron, whereas the most strongly deactivating group is the [NR$_3{}^+$] group which carries a full positive charge equivalent to one electron. This behavior is consistent with the views expressed so far, since a negatively charged group should hold electrons less strongly than a hydrogen atom and increase the availability of the nuclear electrons for the electron-seeking reagent, whereas a positively charged group should hold electrons more strongly than hydrogen and decrease the availability of the nuclear electrons. For groups that do not carry a full negative or positive charge, the relative effectiveness in increasing or decreasing the rate of substitution should depend on the size and direction of the electrical dipole of the monosubstituted benzene.

Electrical Dipole Moments and Their Direction. The methyl group is believed to increase the electron density at a carbon atom over that existing when a hydrogen atom is at the same site (p. 97). If a change in electron distribution takes place when one group replaces another, it should lead to a change in the electrical dipole moment (p. 63) unless the two groups being joined have the same attraction for electrons.

The dipole moment of benzene is zero, as is that of methane, *p*-xylene, and all other symmetrically constituted compounds (p. 63). If there were no difference between the phenyl group and the methyl group in their ability to attract or repel electrons, the moment of toluene would be zero, as is true for ethane or diphenyl. Toluene, however, has a moment of 0.4. Hence there is a shift of the electron density either towards the phenyl group or towards the methyl group.

The direction of the polarization has been determined by comparing the moment of nitrobenzene with that of *p*-nitrotoluene. For nitrobenzene the moment is 3.9. The high dipole moment of nitro compounds is explained by assuming the presence of a semipolar bond in which the nitrogen is positive with respect to the oxygen atoms. Hence the effect of the group must be to decrease the electron density of the ring, which agrees with its deactivating property. Since *p*-dinitrobenzene has zero moment, the moment caused by the nitro groups must be opposed to each other and lie on a line passing through the *para* positions.[2] If now any other group is *para* to the nitro group and the vector representing the

---

[2] Here is direct evidence that the structure of the nitro group is that of a resonance

hybrid of the structures and . If it were unsymmetrically constituted as

electric moment that it induces lies on the line passing through the *para* positions, the moment of the disubstituted benzene will be greater or less than that of nitrobenzene depending on whether the moment is in the same direction as that caused by the nitro group or is opposed to it. Thus if the methyl group has a greater attraction for electrons than a hydrogen atom, the moment of *p*-nitrotoluene should be less than that of nitrobenzene and should approximate $3.9 - 0.4 = 3.5$, but if the methyl group has less attraction for electrons than hydrogen (electron-repelling or electron-donating), the moment of *p*-nitrotoluene should be larger than that of nitrobenzene and should approximate $3.9 + 0.4 = 4.3$. The observed moment for *p*-nitrotoluene is 4.4, and hence the methyl group increases the electron density of the benzene nucleus, which agrees with its activating effect. It is convenient to indicate the direction of the induced moments by the sign $\longmapsto$, the arrow symbolizing the direction in which electron density is increased, the tail being the positive end of the dipole.

O_2N—⬡—CH_3		O_2N—⬡—Cl	
←⊢	←⊢	←⊢	⊢→
3.9	0.4	3.9	1.6
Difference $= 3.5$		Difference $= 2.3$	
Sum $= 4.3$		Sum $= 5.5$	
Experimental $= 4.4$		Experimental $= 2.6$	

Chlorobenzene has a moment of 1.6 and *p*-chloronitrobenzene 2.6. Hence the chlorine atom has a greater attraction for electrons than hydrogen, in agreement with its deactivating effect. The directions of the moments for other groups have been determined by similar methods and are listed in Table 18.

The moments of the amino and substituted amino groups and of all the oxygen-containing groups except the nitro group, the phenoxide ion, and the carboxylate ion, are not collinear with the axis of the benzene ring but make an angle with it (see footnote p. 339).

represented by one of these structures, *p*-dinitrobenzene could have zero moment only when the N $\twoheadrightarrow$ O vectors are opposed to each other. In all other positions the molecule would have a resultant moment. Since isomeric forms cannot be isolated, free rotation about the

$\mu = 0$ $\mu = \text{maximum}$

nitrogen carbon bond must be assumed. Therefore the moments of unsymmetrical nitro groups would not always be opposed, and the molecule would have a resultant electric moment. Hence a zero moment must be ascribed to a symmetrical structure for the nitro group.

$\mu = 0$

Groups known to have unsymmetrical structures, such as the hydroxyl group and the amino group, give rise to electrical moments in the *para* disubstituted compounds.

$\mu = 2.5$ $\mu = 1.5$

Hence for these groups the component affecting the bond to the ring may be considerably different from the observed moment for the molecule.

Directive Influence of Substituents. The general increase or decrease in the availability of the unsaturation electrons of the nucleus does not account for the greater reactivity of one position over another. When an *ortho,para*-directing group is present, polarization by an electron-seeking reagent with an increase in electron density must take place more readily at the *ortho* and *para* positions than at the *meta* positions. The reverse must be true for *meta*-directing groups.

TABLE 18

MAGNITUDE AND DIRECTION OF ELECTRIC MOMENTS OF
BENZENE DERIVATIVES

Group A in C_6H_5-A	Electric Moment of C_6H_5-A	Direction of Moment C_6H_5-A or C_6H_5-A $\longleftarrow +$ $+\longrightarrow$
$N(CH_3)_2$	1.6	
NH_2	1.5	$\longleftarrow +$
CH_3	0.4	
H	0	
$CH=CH_2$	0	
OCH_3	1.2	
SH	1.3	
I	1.3	
Br	1.5	
Cl	1.6	
OH	1.6	
COOH	1.7	$+\longrightarrow$
$COOCH_3$	1.8	
CCl_3	2.0	
CHO	2.7	
$COCH_3$	2.9	
NO	3.1	
$N \rightleftharpoons C$	3.5	
$C \equiv N$	3.9	
NO_2	3.9	

Of the possible polarized structures having an unshared pair of electrons at one of the nuclear carbon atoms of a monosubstituted benzene, the following are the most likely; that is the least amount of energy would be required to form them.

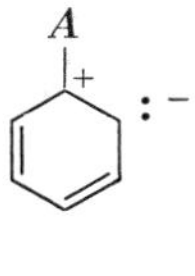

(a) 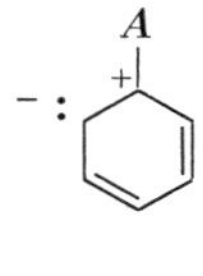   (b) 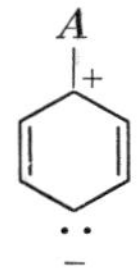   (c) 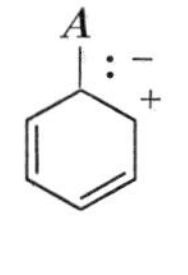   (d) 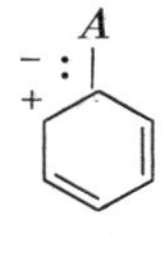   (e) 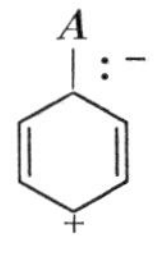   (f)

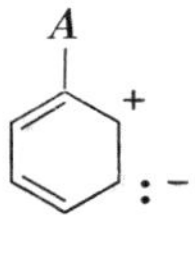

(g) 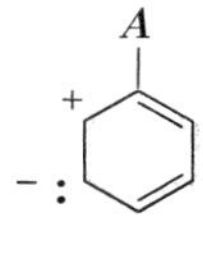   (h) 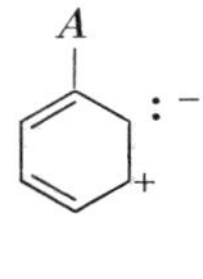   (i) 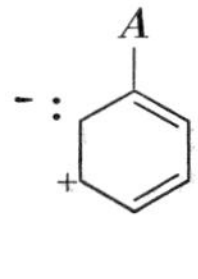   (j) 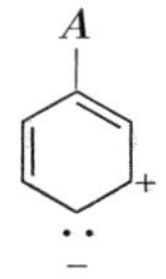   (k) 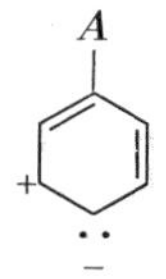   (l)

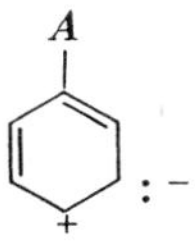

(m) 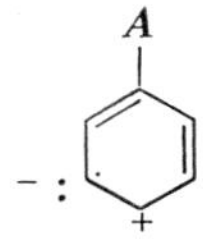   (n) 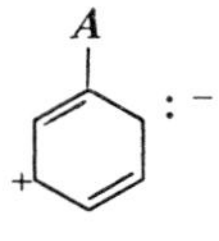   (o) 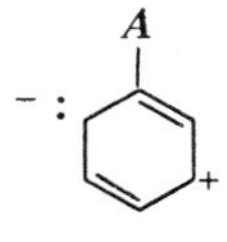   (p) 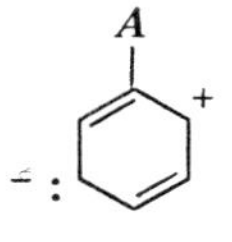   (q) 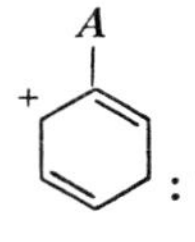   (r)

Structures (d), (e), and (f), however, cannot lead to substitution of hydrogen by an electron-seeking reagent, but only to displacement of A, and need not be considered at this time. If the remaining structures were equally capable of being called into existence by the reagent, the substitution should take place on a statistical basis and lead to an *ortho : meta : para* ratio of 6 : 6 : 3 or 2 : 2 : 1. The ease of formation of structures (a), (b), and (c), however, should be affected markedly by the electrical properties of A, whereas the formation of the remaining structures, in which the charge is more remote, would not be affected appreciably by A. When A is less electron-attracting than hydrogen, structures (a), (b), and (c) can be formed more easily than the remaining structures, which leads to predominantly *ortho* and *para* substitution. When A is more strongly electron-attracting than hydrogen, structures (a), (b), and (c) can be formed less easily than the remaining structures, which leads to predominantly *meta* substitution.

If A is a group that is not complicated by having unshared electrons or multiple bonds on the atom joined to the ring, such as a methyl group, CH_3, or a trichloromethyl group, CCl_3, these considerations hold. Thus when a methyl group is combined with another group, the electron density at the point of union is greater than when a hydrogen atom is joined to the same group (Table 18). Hence structures (a), (b), and (c), or more exactly the transition state structures in which the electron-seeking reagent is bound partially to the unshared pair of electrons, are formed more readily by the reagent than are the remaining structures, and the rate of substitution at the *ortho* and *para* positions is increased over that expected statistically. This type of directive influence of the group A is known as an **inductive effect.** According to Table 18 the trichloromethyl group attracts electrons more strongly than a hydrogen atom; that is it has an inductive effect opposite to that of a methyl group, and by decreasing the electron density tends to prevent the formation of structures (a), (b) and (c). Hence the rate of substitution at the *ortho* and *para* positions is decreased over that expected statistically, resulting in a higher proportion of *meta* substitution.

The series NO_2, CH_2NO_2, and $CH_2CH_2NO_2$ of Table 17, page 333, indicates that the effect of a group rapidly diminishes as saturated hydrocarbon groups are interposed between it and the ring. The series CH_3, CH_2Cl, $CHCl_2$, CCl_3 illustrates the effect of replacing a less strongly electron-attracting group by a more strongly electron-attracting group.

Halogen appears to be anomalous. Since it is more electron-attracting than hydrogen, its inductive effect deactivates the nucleus. Nevertheless it directs *ortho* and *para*. A clue to the problem is afforded by the interatomic carbon-chlorine distances and the dipole moments of *t*-butyl chloride and chlorobenzene. The respective distances are 1.76 Å and 1.69 Å, and the moments are 2.14 and 1.56. Both the shortening of the bond and the lower moment for the aromatic compound can be explained by the interaction of an unshared pair of electrons of the chlorine atom with the unsaturation electrons of the aromatic nucleus as indicated by the resonance hybrid symbolism

The effect of this electronic interaction is opposite to that of the inductive effect, but it is not sufficient to overcome the inductive effect, and the chlorine atom remains deactivating. However on the approach of an electron-seeking reagent, such as a nitronium ion, this type of electronic interaction is sufficient to render the transition states having the nitro group attached to the *ortho* or *para* position (I or II) more stable than that having the nitro group at the *meta* position (III).

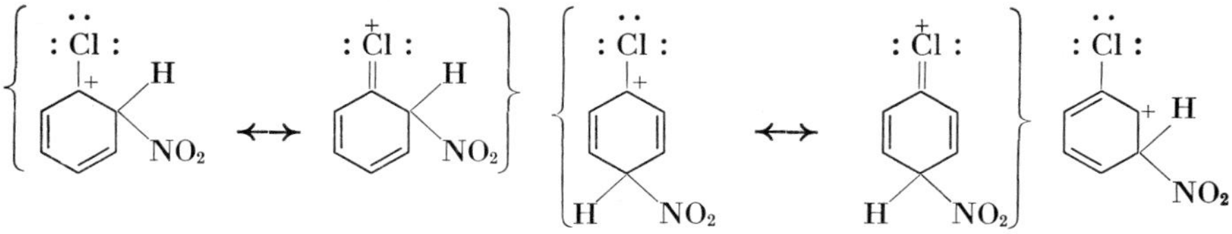

I   II   III

Hence the rate of reaction is greater at the *ortho* and *para* positions than at the *meta* position, although less than the rate of reaction of benzene. This effect has been called the **electromeric, tautomeric, mesomeric, or resonance effect.**

The alkoxyl and hydroxyl groups appear to be still more anomalous than halogen, since they not only are *ortho,para*-directing but are activating as well, despite the fact that they are electron-attracting as shown by the dipole moments of methoxy- and hydroxybenzene (Table 18). The alkoxy group, however, is not as strongly electron-attracting as halogen, and the ability of the oxygen atom to supply electrons to the ring in the transition state is sufficiently greater than that of halogen to make polarization at the *ortho* and *para* positions easier than in benzene.

The hydroxyl group, on the other hand, has about the same electron-attracting power as chlorine (Table 18). Here the activating effect must be due to the presence of a small amount of the strongly activated phenoxide ion in equilibrium with the undissociated hydroxybenzene. In the phenoxide ion the negative charge on the oxygen atom not only reverses the inductive effect; it also increases the resonance effect, since no separation of charge is present in the resonance structures.

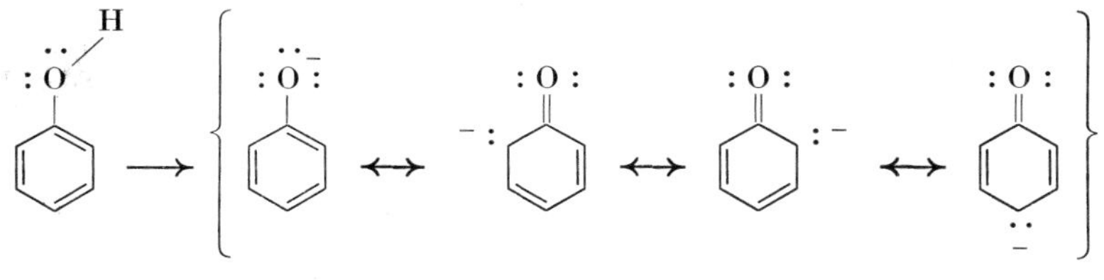

Since the inductive and resonance effects now reinforce each other, the negatively charged oxygen atom is the strongest activating and the strongest *ortho,para*-directing group.

The nitrogen of the amino group is less strongly electron-attracting than oxygen. Moreover it is united to two hydrogen atoms. As a result the group actually is electron-repelling (Table 18). Because the presence of the unshared pair of electrons assists this activating, *ortho,para*-directing effect, the free amino group is only slightly less powerful in this respect than the [O⁻] group. In acid solution the unshared pair of electrons acquires a proton and the group acquires a positive charge so that it becomes deactivating and *meta*-directing.

Although the dipole moment of phenylethylene is zero (Table 18), indicating no polarization of the molecule, the vinyl group is activating and *ortho, para*-directing. The explanation is that the positive charge in the transition state can be distributed over more atoms when the entering group, A, is at the *ortho* or *para* positions (I or II) than at the *meta* position (III).

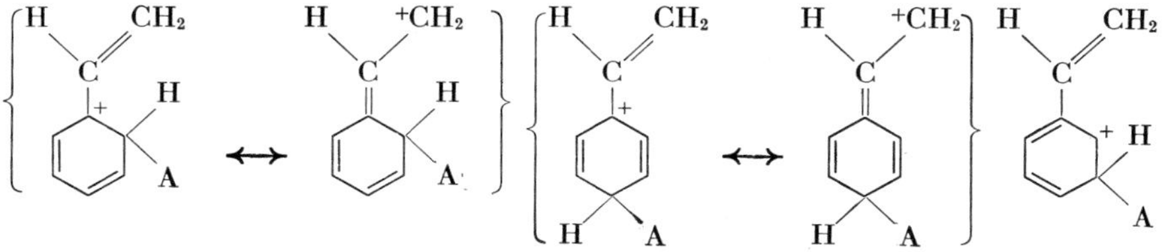

I   II   III

It has been postulated that even the methyl group exerts its activating effect because of a resonance analogous to that of the vinyl group.

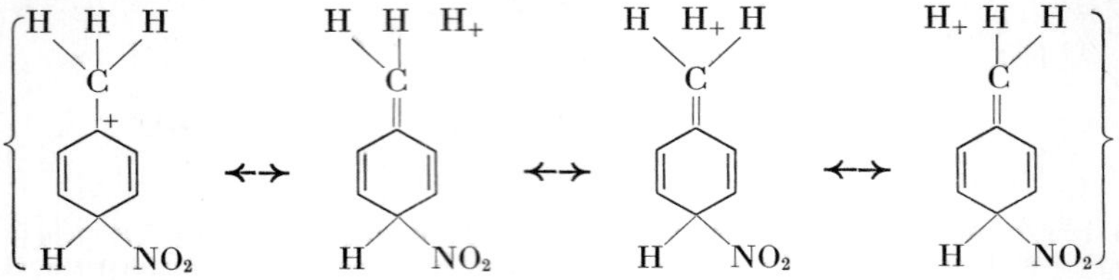

This presumed behavior is called **no-bond resonance** or **hyperconjugation.** It explains the fact that the increase in rate of substitution of toluene over benzene is greater than would be expected from the small dipole moment of toluene.

The discussion thus far applies to substitution by an electron-seeking reagent. Substitutions in the aromatic nucleus are known, however, in which the active agent is electron-donating. An example is the formation of *o*-nitrophenol (*o*-hydroxynitrobenzene) when nitrobenzene is heated with potassium hydroxide in the presence of air.

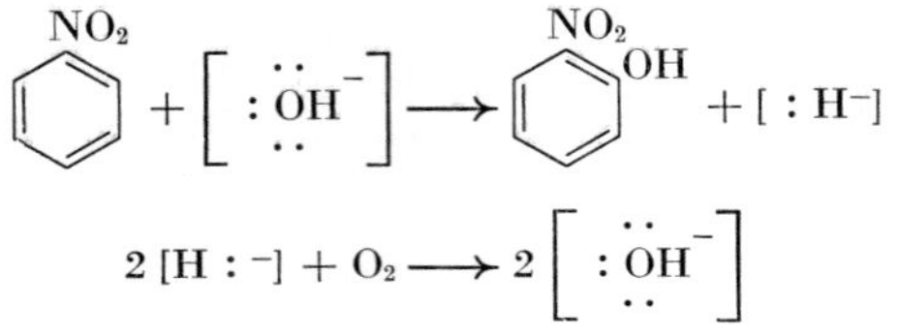

The theory can accommodate these reactions also. Groups that are activating for electron-seeking reagents are those that increase the electron density of the ring nucleus, and hence they are deactivating for electron-donating reagents. Groups that are deactivating for electron-seeking reagents withdraw electrons from the nucleus and are activating for electron-donating reagents. Concerning directive influence, structures (*a*), (*b*), and (*c*) (p. 339) lead to displacement of group *A* by electron-donating reagents, and the relative ease of formation of structures (*d*), (*e*), and (*f*) compared to the remaining structures determines the position taken by the entering group. Thus structures (*d*), (*e*), and (*f*) are favored if *A* is electron-attracting, and lead to predominantly *ortho-para* substitution. Moreover the nitro group is particularly activating because both the inductive effect and the resonance effect favor a positive charge at the *ortho* and *para* positions.

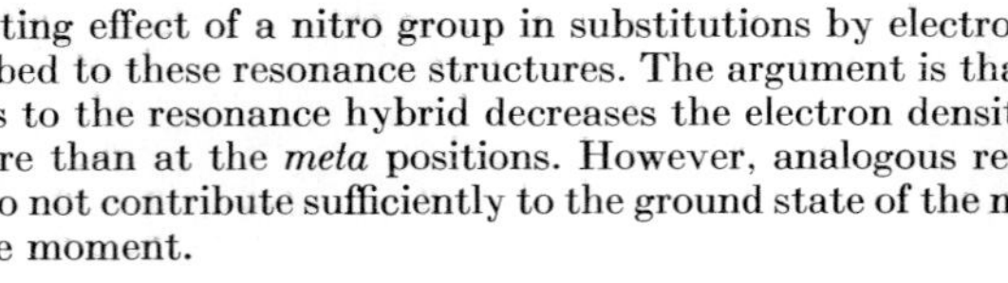

The *meta*-directing effect of a nitro group in substitutions by electron-seeking reagents frequently is ascribed to these resonance structures. The argument is that the contribution of these structures to the resonance hybrid decreases the electron density at the *ortho* and *para* positions more than at the *meta* positions. However, analogous resonance structures for vinylbenzene do not contribute sufficiently to the ground state of the molecule to produce a detectable dipole moment.

Physical Properties of Nitro Compounds

Aromatic nitro compounds usually are solids, either colorless or yellow. Only a few mononitro hydrocarbons are liquids at room temperature. Because of the presence of the semipolar bond, the nitro group has a high dipole moment, and the nitro compounds have high boiling points. The lowest boiling aromatic nitro compound, nitrobenzene, has a dipole moment of 3.9 and boils at 209°. The ability of nitro groups to produce crystallinity and high melting point in aromatic compounds has led to the extensive use of nitro compounds, such as 2,4-dinitrophenylhydrazine (p. 362) and 3,5-dinitro-benzoyl chloride (p. 413), for the preparation of derivatives for identification purposes.

Aromatic nitro hydrocarbons are practically insoluble in water. The liquids are good solvents for most organic compounds and fair solvents for many inorganic salts, especially those such as zinc chloride or aluminum chloride that can accept an unshared pair of electrons and form a complex.

$$C_6H_5\overset{+}{N}\diagup\overset{\bar{O}}{}\diagdown O \ + \ AlCl_3 \longrightarrow C_6H_5\overset{+}{N}\diagup\overset{O:\bar{A}lCl_3}{}\diagdown O$$

Physiological Action

Nitro compounds having a sufficiently high vapor pressure have strong characteristic odors. For the most part they are highly toxic substances. Even those compounds with low vapor pressures are dangerous because they are absorbed readily through the skin, particularly from solutions. Symptoms of poisoning are dizziness, headache, irregular pulse, and cyanosis (blue lips and finger tips caused by a change in the hemoglobin of the blood). Prolonged contact or exposure leads to death.

Reactions of the Aromatic Nitro Group

Reduction. Like the aliphatic nitro compounds, the aromatic nitro compounds are reduced readily to primary amines. The reduction may be brought about by hydrogen and a hydrogenation catalyst at room temperature and atmospheric pressure. Because of the large amount of heat evolved and the speed of the reaction, proper precautions should be taken when hydrogenating large quantities of nitro compounds in a closed system to keep the reaction always under control.

$$C_6H_5NO_2 + 3\ H_2 \xrightarrow[\text{Raney Ni}]{\text{Pt or}} \underset{\text{Aniline}}{C_6H_5NH_2} + 2\ H_2O$$

Ordinarily reduction to the amine is brought about by active metals in acid solution. The reagents commonly used are iron or tin in the presence of hydrochloric acid. When an excess of tin is used, the product is the arylammonium chlorostannite from which the amine is liberated by the addition of alkali.

$$2\ C_6H_5NO_2 + 6\ Sn + 24\ HCl \longrightarrow \underset{\substack{\text{Phenylammonium} \\ \text{chlorostannite}}}{(C_6H_5\overset{+}{N}H_3)_2\overset{=}{S}nCl_4} + \underset{\substack{\text{Chlorostan-} \\ \text{nous acid}}}{5\ H_2SnCl_4} + 4\ H_2O$$

$$\downarrow \text{6 NaOH}$$

$$\underset{\text{Aniline}}{2\ C_6H_5NH_2} + \underset{\substack{\text{Sodium} \\ \text{stannite}}}{Na_2SnO_2} + 4\ NaCl + 4\ H_2O$$

Stannous chloride in the presence of hydrochloric acid reduces nitro compounds to amines, the actual product being the chlorostannate.

$$2\ C_6H_5NO_2 + 6\ SnCl_2 + 24\ HCl \longrightarrow (C_6H_5\overset{+}{N}H_3)_2\overset{=}{S}nCl_6 + 5\ H_2SnCl_6 + 4\ H_2O$$

Phenylammonium   Chlorostannic
chlorostannate   acid

If standardized solutions of stannous chloride are used, the reaction may be used for the quantitative estimation of nitro groups. Zinc and hydrochloric acid is not a satisfactory reducing agent because considerable amounts of chloroanilines are formed (see below).

Commercially nitrobenzene is reduced to aniline by scrap iron and water in the presence of about one-fortieth of the calculated amount of hydrochloric acid. Hence the reduction is brought about essentially by iron and water, the iron being converted to black oxide of iron, Fe_3O_4 (p. 369).

$$4\ C_6H_5NO_2 + 9\ Fe + 4\ H_2O \overset{(HCl)}{\longrightarrow} 4\ C_6H_5NH_2 + 3\ Fe_3O_4$$

If two nitro groups are present in the ring, it is possible to reduce one group without reducing the other. Ammonium or sodium sulfide is the preferred reagent.

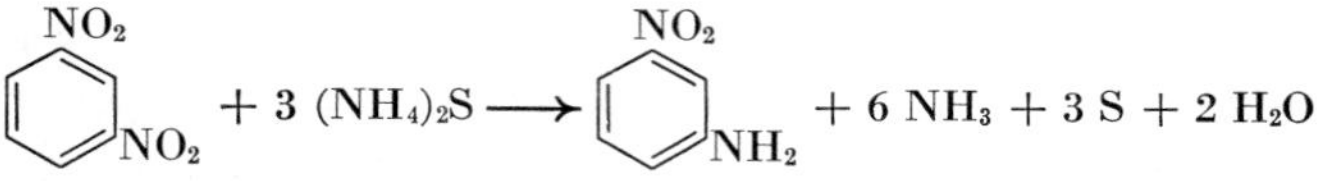

$$+\ 3\ (NH_4)_2S \longrightarrow \qquad +\ 6\ NH_3 + 3\ S + 2\ H_2O$$

This behavior is understandable, since the electron-attracting properties of the nitro groups mutually increase their strength as oxidizing agents and enable one of them to be reduced more easily than if a single nitro group were present. After one nitro group is reduced, the electron-donating property of the amino group decreases the ease of reduction of the remaining nitro group.

Although primary amines are the final reduction products of both aliphatic and aromatic nitro compounds, it is possible with aromatic nitro compounds to isolate a number of intermediate reduction products, which may be obtained in good yield by the use of milder and controlled reducing conditions. Thus nitrobenzene when boiled with an aqueous solution of ammonium chloride and zinc dust gives *N-phenylhydroxylamine* (also called β-phenylhydroxylamine).

$$C_6H_5NO_2 + 2\ Zn + 4\ NH_4Cl \longrightarrow C_6H_5NHOH + 2\ Zn(NH_3)_4Cl_2 + H_2O$$

N-Phenylhydroxylamine
(β-phenylhydroxylamine)

If zinc and hydrochloric acid are used to reduce nitrobenzene, the main product is aniline, but a considerable amount of *p*-chloroaniline is formed, presumably by rearrangement of *N*-chloroaniline produced from *N*-phenylhydroxylamine.

$$C_6H_5NHOH + HCl \longrightarrow H_2O + [C_6H_5NHCl] \longrightarrow$$

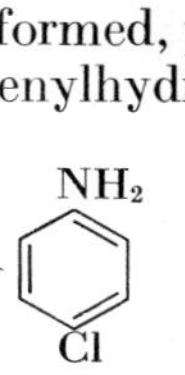

Nitrosobenzene is the first reduction product of nitrobenzene, but it is hard to isolate because it is reduced very rapidly to *N*-phenylhydroxylamine. It can, however, be prepared by oxidation of the latter compound.

$$3 \ C_6H_5NHOH + Na_2Cr_2O_7 + 4 \ H_2SO_4 \xrightarrow{0°} 3 \ C_6H_5NO + Na_2SO_4 + Cr_2(SO_4)_3 + 7 \ H_2O$$
Nitrosobenzene

Sodium methoxide in alcohol, or sodium arsenite solution, gives *azoxybenzene*, in which a coupling of two molecules has taken place.

$$4 \ C_6H_5NO_2 + 3 \ NaOCH_3 \longrightarrow 2 \ C_6H_5N{=}NC_6H_5 + 3 \ NaOCHO + 3 \ H_2O$$

$$\text{(or 6 } Na_3AsO_3) \qquad \overset{|^+}{O^-} \qquad \begin{matrix}\text{Sodium formate} \\ \text{(or 6 } Na_3AsO_4)\end{matrix}$$
Azoxybenzene

The oxygen atom in azoxybenzene is linked to nitrogen by a semipolar bond as in the amine oxides (p. 190). Oxidation of azobenzene with hydrogen peroxide also yields azoxybenzene.

$$C_6H_5N{=}NC_6H_5 + H_2O_2 \longrightarrow C_6H_5N{=}NC_6H_5 + H_2O$$
$$\overset{|^+}{O^-}$$

When nitrobenzene is heated with iron and an aqueous solution of sodium hydroxide, *azobenzene* is formed.

$$2 \ C_6H_5NO_2 + 4 \ Fe + 4 \ H_2O \xrightarrow{\text{(NaOH)}} C_6H_5N{=}NC_6H_5 + 4 \ Fe(OH)_2$$
Azobenzene

Azobenzene can be prepared also by heating azoxybenzene with iron filings,

$$3 \ C_6H_5N{=}NC_6H_5 + 2 \ Fe \longrightarrow 3 \ C_6H_5N{=}NC_6H_5 + Fe_2O_3$$
$$\overset{|^+}{O^-}$$

but the usual laboratory method of preparation is by the oxidation of hydrazobenzene with hypobromite solution.

$$C_6H_5NHNHC_6H_5 + NaOBr \longrightarrow C_6H_5N{=}NC_6H_5 + NaBr + H_2O$$
Hydrazobenzene

The oxidation may be brought about also by passing air through an alkaline alcoholic solution of hydrazobenzene.

When nitrobenzene is heated with zinc dust and aqueous sodium hydroxide, the product is *hydrazobenzene*.

$$2 \ C_6H_5NO_2 + 5 \ Zn + 10 \ NaOH \longrightarrow C_6H_5NHNHC_6H_5 + 5 \ Na_2ZnO_2 + 4 \ H_2O$$

Any of the intermediate reduction products can be reduced to aniline using a strong reducing agent. The reactions of nitrobenzene are summarized in Fig. 41, p. 348.

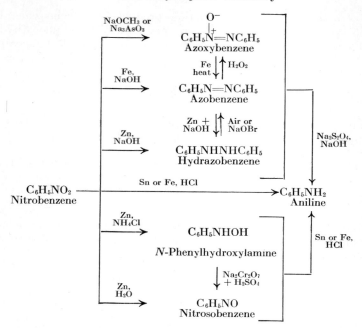

Fig. 41. Reduction products of nitrobenzene.

Effect of the Nitro Group and of Other *meta*-Directing Groups on the Reactivity of Other Nuclear Substituents

Halogen attached to an aryl group is very unreactive in the usual displacement reactions (p. 329). If, however, a nitro group or other *meta*-directing group is in a position *ortho* or *para* to the halogen atom, the reactivity is greatly increased. The reactivity is greater yet when two nitro groups are present in the 2,4 position and reaches a maximum with three nitro groups in the 2,4,6 positions. For example although chlorobenzene reacts with concentrated alkali only at 200°–300° in the presence of copper, 2,4-dinitrochlorobenzene is hydrolyzed by boiling with an aqueous solution of sodium carbonate.

$$\text{2,4-Dinitrochlorobenzene} + H_2O + Na_2CO_3 \xrightarrow{\text{Heat}} \text{2,4-Dinitrophenol} + NaCl + NaHCO_3$$

Similarly aqueous sodium hydrogen sulfide gives 2,4-dinitrothiophenol, sodium sulfide gives 2,4-dinitrophenyl sulfide and ammonia gives 2,4-dinitroaniline.

Other *meta*-directing groups such as carbonyl also have an activating effect when present in the positions *ortho* and *para* to the halogen. If the group is *meta* to the halogen atom it has less effect on reactivity. *meta*-Directing groups in the *ortho* and *para* positions and to a less extent in the *meta* position also increase the acidity of carboxyl and phenolic hydroxyl groups (pp. 412, 381) and decrease the basicity of amino groups (p. 362). *ortho,para*-Directing groups in the *ortho* and *para* positions have the opposite effect (p. 354).

Mechanism of Displacement of Aromatic Halogen

When a halogen atom in an alkyl halide is displaced by an electron-donating group such as a hydroxide ion or an ammonia molecule, the reaction may take place in one of two ways. In the usual bimolecular mechanism (p. 96) the reagent approaches the carbon atom on the side opposite the halogen atom, and as the new bond is formed and the halogen ion leaves, the carbon atom undergoes a Walden inversion. In other reactions, such as the hydrolysis of tertiary halides, a so-called unimolecular mechanism has been proposed in which a slow ionization of the alkyl halide takes place, followed by a rapid combination of the carbonium ion with the electron-donating reagent (p. 97). Since in the carbonium ion the carbon atom is united to only three groups, it must be capable of assuming a planar configuration involving sp^2 hybridization in order to have the requisite stability.

For aromatic halides, neither of these mechanisms is possible. Because of the ring of carbon atoms, the reagent cannot approach from the back side; and if it managed to do so, Walden inversion could not take place without rupture of the ring. Moreover the halogen has less tendency to ionize than that in a primary halide because of the resonance with the benzene ring (p. 342). Hence the only possibility appears to be a direct replacement analogous to substitution by electron-donating reagents (p. 344).

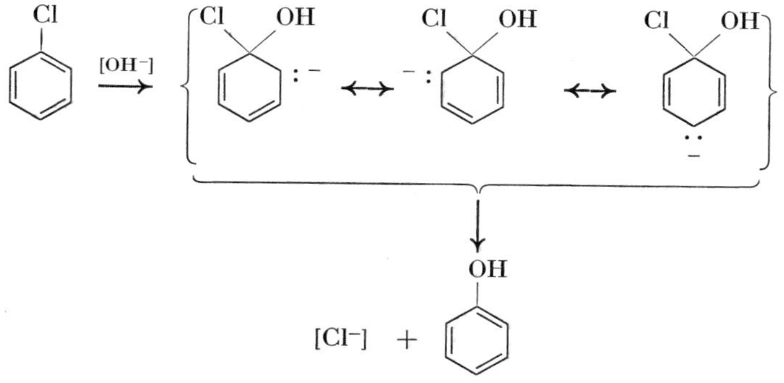

If a *meta*-directing group is present in the *ortho* or *para* positions, the molecule becomes more readily polarizable by the electron-donating reagent to a structure with which the reagent can react. Polarization is particularly easy when a nitro or carboxyl group is present, since either can provide a favorable site for the location of the negative charge.

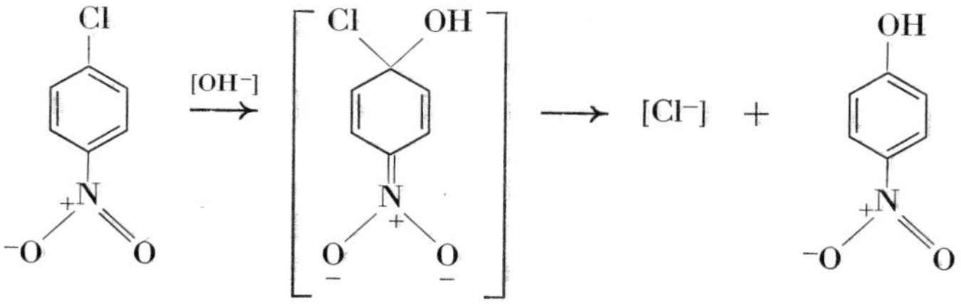

The current explanation of the high reactivity of halogen located on a carbon atom attached to the ring can be illustrated by the phenylmethyl halides (p. 330). Whether the reaction takes place by a bimolecular (p. 96) or a unimolecular mechanism (p. 97), it is facilitated by the stabilization of the phenylmethonium ion by resonance.

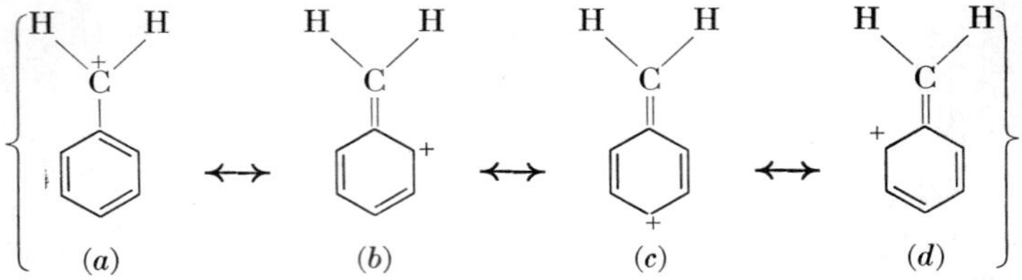

(a)　　　　　(b)　　　　　(c)　　　　　(d)

In the bimolecular mechanism, which is the normal mechanism for benzyl halides, the transition state is halfway between the covalent and the ionic structure. Hence any effect that stabilizes the ionic structure also stabilizes the transition state. In the unimolecular mechanism, which is normal for the triphenylmethyl halides and usual for the diphenylmethyl halides (benzhydryl halides), the halide ion again is lost more readily because of the resonance in the phenylmethonium ion. If ionization precedes reaction, the ion might be polarized by the substituting group to give structures (a), (b), (c), or (d). Since structure (a) does not involve destruction of the benzene resonance, it would be formed most readily. Hence *ortho-* and *para*-substituted toluenes are not obtained. Such abnormal products are formed, however, when benzylmagnesium chloride reacts with certain reagents such as formaldehyde. An intermediate coordination complex with the aldehyde appears to be formed which favors reaction in the *ortho* position.

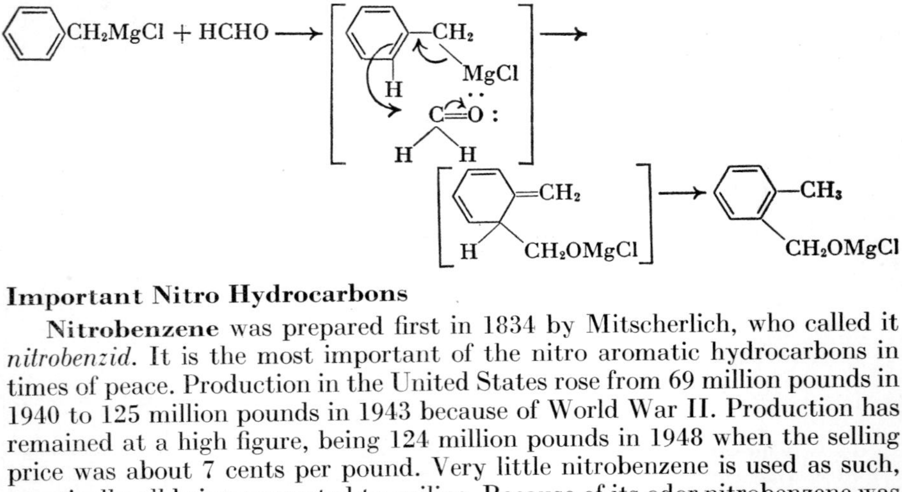

Important Nitro Hydrocarbons

Nitrobenzene was prepared first in 1834 by Mitscherlich, who called it *nitrobenzid*. It is the most important of the nitro aromatic hydrocarbons in times of peace. Production in the United States rose from 69 million pounds in 1940 to 125 million pounds in 1943 because of World War II. Production has remained at a high figure, being 124 million pounds in 1948 when the selling price was about 7 cents per pound. Very little nitrobenzene is used as such, practically all being converted to aniline. Because of its odor nitrobenzene was called *oil of mirbane* or *artificial oil of bitter almonds*. It once was used as a flavoring principle and as a perfume for soaps, and to adulterate oil of bitter almonds. Its high toxicity soon led to a discontinuance of this practice. Because it penetrates leather, it long was used as a solvent for shoe dyes, but here again poisoning occurred by absorption of the vapors through the skin and such formulations now are prohibited in most countries.

Some of the di- and trinitroalkylbenzenes have a musk-like odor and are used in perfumery. They are known as **"synthetic musks"** or **"nitro musks"** although they are not related chemically to the true musks which are cyclic ketones (p. 563).

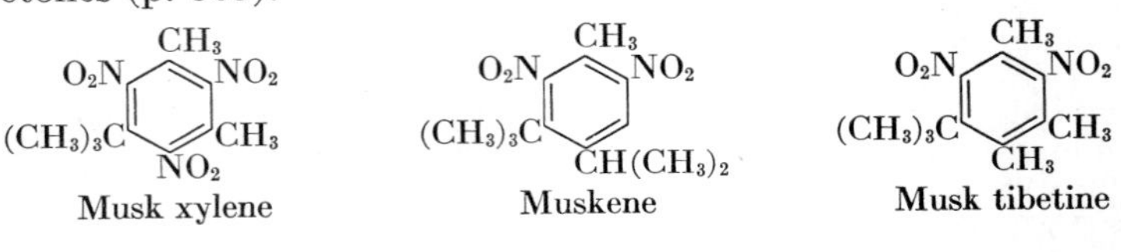

Musk xylene　　　　　　Muskene　　　　　　Musk tibetine

Musk ambrette and *musk ketone* contain a methoxyl group and an acetyl group respectively.

1,3,5-Trinitrobenzene is a more powerful explosive than TNT, but it cannot be made in satisfactory yields by direct nitration of benzene because of the difficulty of introducing a third nitro group unless an activating group also is present. It is prepared on a small scale for reagent purposes by decarboxylating 2,4,6-trinitrobenzoic acid, which is obtained by the oxidation of TNT.

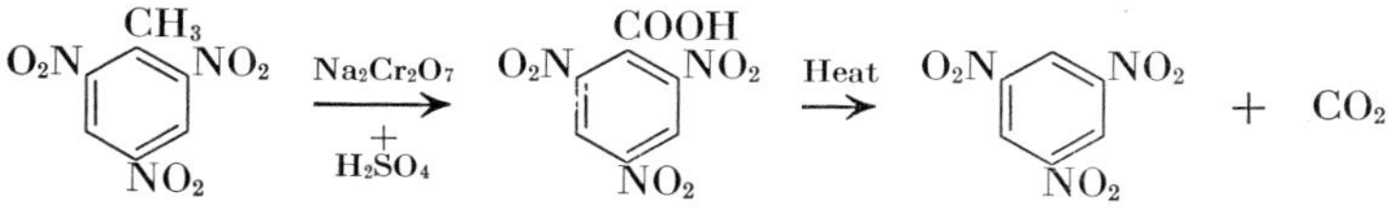

2,4,6-Trinitro-
benzoic acid   1,3,5-Trinitro-
benzene

2,4,6-Trinitrotoluene, commonly known as TNT, is the most important military explosive. It is used for filling bombs, shells, and hand grenades, either alone or with other explosives (pp. 178, 526). Since it melts at 81° and does not explode until 280°, it can be poured into shells in a liquid state and allowed to solidify. It is relatively insensitive to shock and must be exploded by a detonator. Although no figures are available concerning the amount of TNT produced by the United States during World War II, production of toluene in 1946 was only about one fourth of the maximum of 200,000,000 gallons reached in 1944. The difference, assuming an 80 per cent yield, would have permitted a production at the rate of over 2 billion pounds of TNT per year.

REVIEW QUESTIONS

1. Compare the direct nitration of aromatic hydrocarbons with that of aliphatic hydrocarbons.
2. Compare the boiling points of aromatic hydrocarbons, halides, and nitro compounds of approximately the same molecular weight. Compare the melting points of the *ortho, meta,* and *para* nitro derivatives of toluene, chlorobenzene, and nitrobenzene.
3. Give balanced equations for the preparation from nitrobenzene of nitrosobenzene, *N*-phenylhydroxylamine, azoxybenzene, azobenzene, hydrazobenzene and aniline.
4. What is the chief product or products that would be expected when one more group is introduced by the following substitution reactions: (*a*) nitration of chlorobenzene; (*b*) bromination of nitrobenzene; (*c*) nitration of *o*-xylene; (*d*) chlorination of *m*-dinitrobenzene; (*e*) nitration of *m*-nitrotoluene; (*f*) iron-catalyzed chlorination of toluene; (*g*) light-catalyzed chlorination of toluene?
5. What is meant by the terms *activation* and *deactivation* as applied to aromatic compounds? Which of the first six reactions in Question 4 would take place faster than the same reaction with benzene, which slower, and which at about the same rate?
6. Compare the economic importance of benzene and toluene.

Chapter 22

AROMATIC SULFONIC ACIDS AND THEIR
DERIVATIVES

SULFONIC ACIDS

Since aromatic sulfonic acids can be obtained by direct sulfonation, they are more readily available than aliphatic sulfonic acids. The aromatic sulfonic acids are used as intermediates for the introduction of other groups, and to confer water-solubility on aromatic compounds, particularly dyes.

Nomenclature

Sulfonic acids are named by attaching the ending *sulfonic* to the name of the compound that has been substituted and adding *acid*. The positions of the sulfonic acid groups are indicated by numbers or letters.

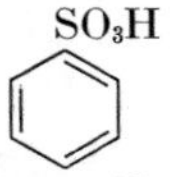

Benzenesulfonic
acid

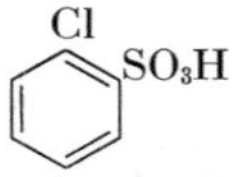

2-Chlorobenzenesulfonic
acid or
o-chlorobenzenesulfonic
acid

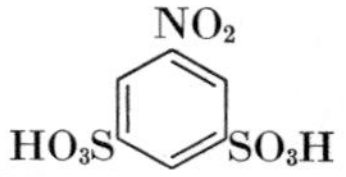

Nitrobenzene-3,5-
disulfonic acid

Physical Properties

Sulfonic acids are strong acids, being ionized completely in aqueous solution. They are very soluble in water but are insoluble or only slightly soluble in nonoxygenated solvents. The pure acids are hygroscopic and difficult to obtain anhydrous. They usually crystallize from aqueous solutions with water of hydration.

Sulfonic acids are relatively nonvolatile, although some can be distilled without decomposition at low pressures. Thus benzenesulfonic acid boils at 135°–137° at a pressure below 0.01 mm. of mercury. The melting points of the anhydrous sulfonic acids are lower than those of the corresponding carboxylic acids.

Preparation

Aromatic sulfonic acids generally are prepared by direct sulfonation. The ease of sulfonation depends on the substituents already present in the ring. Thus if activating groups are present, concentrated sulfuric acid at room temperature may suffice to bring about sulfonation. When deactivating groups are present the use of elevated temperatures and fuming sulfuric acid (oleum) containing varying amounts of dissolved sulfur trioxide may be necessary. Benzene can be converted to the monosulfonic acid using 10 per cent fuming sulfuric acid (100 per cent sulfuric acid containing 10 per cent sulfur trioxide) at room temperature. To convert the monosulfonic acid to the *m*-disulfonic acid a temperature of 200°–245° is used, and to convert the *m*-disulfonic acid to the 1,3,5-trisulfonic acid a temperature of 280°–300° is required.

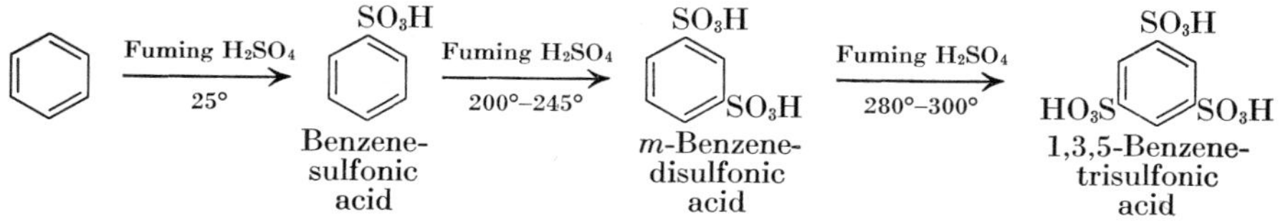

When fuming sulfuric acid is used some *sulfone* (p. 217) may be formed as a by-product. Since the sulfone is insoluble in water, it can be removed after dilution of the sulfonation mixture.

$$C_6H_5SO_2OH \ + \ C_6H_6 \ \xrightarrow{SO_3} \ C_6H_5SO_2C_6H_5 \ + \ H_2SO_4$$
Phenyl
sulfone

In general sulfonation follows the rules for substitution outlined for nitration (p. 332). It appears, however, to be less predictable and more influenced by conditions. Phenol, for example, gives chiefly *o*-phenolsulfonic acid, whereas chlorobenzene gives chiefly *p*-chlorobenzenesulfonic acid. Temperature and catalysts such as mercuric sulfate frequently have a pronounced influence on the position taken by the sulfonic acid group.

Most sulfonic acids are used in the form of their salts. Fortunately the salts can be isolated much more readily than the sulfonic acid. The sodium salts usually are less soluble than the sulfonic acid, particularly in a solution saturated with sodium chloride. Hence they can be isolated by *salting out*. The reaction mixture is poured into water and a brine solution is added.

$$C_6H_5SO_3H \ + \ NaCl \ \longrightarrow \ C_6H_5SO_3Na \ + \ HCl$$
Sodium
benzenesulfonate

The *calcium, barium,* and *lead sulfonates* are soluble in water in contrast to the sulfates. After dilution of the sulfonation mixture with water, the hydroxide, oxide, or carbonate of calcium, barium, or lead can be added to precipitate the sulfate present and leave the sulfonate in solution. Evaporation of the filtrate gives the calcium, barium, or lead sulfonate.

Commercially the **sodium salts** are most useful and are prepared by the *liming out process.* After dilution of the sulfonation mixture, slaked lime is added, and the precipitate of calcium sulfate is removed by filtration. Addition of sodium carbonate to the filtrate precipitates calcium carbonate and leaves the sodium sulfonate in solution. Removal of the calcium carbonate and evaporation give the sodium salt.

Free sulfonic acids can be obtained by adding sufficient sulfuric acid to an aqueous solution of a calcium, barium, or lead salt to precipitate the metallic sulfate, and evaporating the filtrate. Usually it is more convenient to hydrolyze the pure sulfonyl chloride (p. 356).

Reactions of Aromatic Sulfonic Acids and Their Salts

SUBSTITUTION OF THE NUCLEUS

The aromatic ring can be halogenated or nitrated, the SO_3H group being deactivating and *meta*-directing.

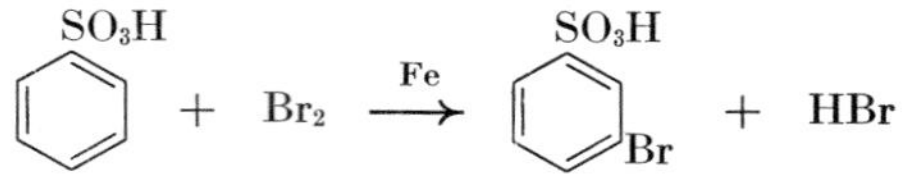

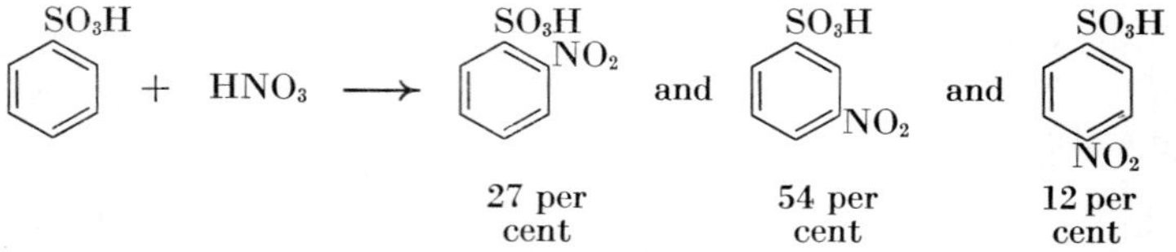

27 per cent   54 per cent   12 per cent

Frequently the sulfonic acid group is displaced, especially when the reaction is carried out in the presence of water.

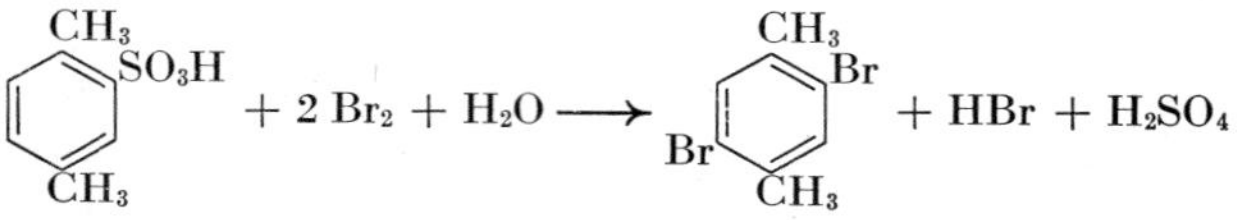

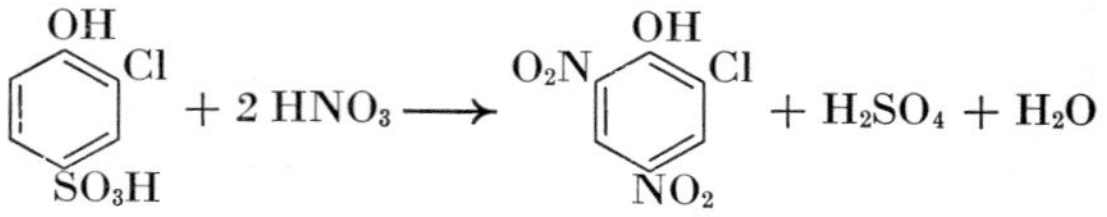

REACTIONS OF FREE SULFONIC ACIDS

1. *Salt Formation and Strength as Acids.* Sulfonic acids react with strong bases to form neutral salts. Salts from weak bases give an acid reaction when dissolved in water. Benzenesulfonic acid is about as strong as sulfuric acid. Electron-attracting groups in the *ortho* and *para* positions increase the acidity, but electron-donating groups decrease the acidity (p. 349). Thus 2,4-dinitrobenzenesulfonic acid is stronger than sulfuric acid, whereas 2,4-dimethoxybenzenesulfonic acid is weaker than sulfuric acid, although it is stronger than nitric acid.

2. *Hydrolysis.* The sulfonation reaction is reversible. Hence if sulfonic acids are boiled with an excess of water, the sulfonic acid group slowly is removed. High concentrations of other mineral acids greatly increase the rate of hydrolysis. The reaction is fairly rapid if carried out in a sealed tube at 150°–170°.

$$C_6H_5SO_3H + H_2O \overset{\text{Heat}}{\underset{\text{HCl}}{\rightleftarrows}} C_6H_6 + H_2SO_4$$

REACTIONS OF SODIUM SULFONATES

1. *Replacement by Hydroxyl.* When a sodium sulfonate is heated with molten sodium hydroxide, the sodium salt of a phenol and sodium sulfite are formed.

$$C_6H_5SO_3Na + 2\ NaOH \xrightarrow{\text{Fusion}} C_6H_5ONa + Na_2SO_3 + H_2O$$
$$\begin{array}{c} \text{Sodium} \\ \text{phenoxide} \end{array}$$

2. Replacement by the Nitrile Group. Fusion of a sodium salt with sodium cyanide yields a nitrile and sodium sulfite.

$$C_6H_5SO_3Na + NaCN \xrightarrow{\text{Fusion}} C_6H_5CN + Na_2SO_3$$
$$\begin{array}{c} \text{Phenyl cyanide} \\ \text{(benzonitrile)} \end{array}$$

Uses of Sulfonic Acids and Their Salts

The free sulfonic acids find very little use. Because they are strong acids and have a much weaker oxidizing action than sulfuric acid, they frequently are used as acid catalysts.

An important use of the sodium sulfonates is for the manufacture of phenols by fusion with sodium hydroxide. The sodium sulfonate group usually is present in direct or substantive dyes (p. 476), its function being to confer water solubility on the dyestuff. Sodium salts of alkylated aromatic sulfonic acids are becoming important also in the field of synthetic detergents. In one process the C_{12} fraction of a polypropylene is condensed with benzene, and the product is sulfonated and converted to the sodium salt.

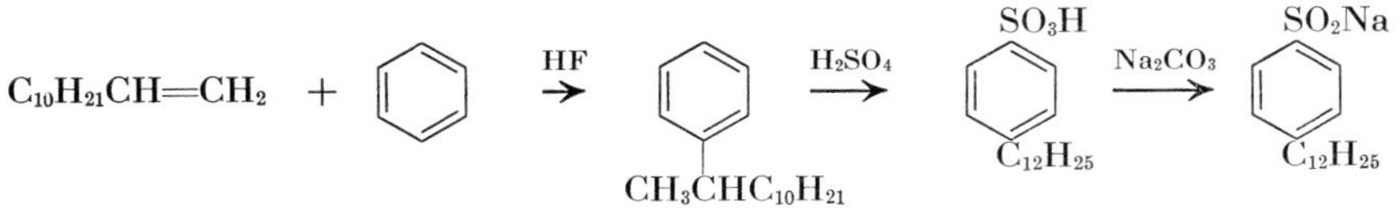

In a second process a kerosene fraction is chlorinated, the product is condensed with benzene, and the alkylated benzene is sulfonated and converted to the sodium salt.

$$RH + Cl_2 \longrightarrow RCl \xrightarrow[\text{AlCl}_3]{\text{C}_6\text{H}_6} C_6H_5R \xrightarrow{\text{H}_2\text{SO}_4} RC_6H_4SO_3H \xrightarrow{\text{Na}_2\text{CO}_3} RC_6H_4SO_3Na$$

In the product made by the first process the aromatic group is near the end of the chain, whereas in the second process chlorination of the aliphatic hydrocarbon takes place at random in the chains. Hence the aromatic ring is located in some molecules at the end of the chain and in others at the middle of the chain and at all intermediate points. Detergents having the water-soluble group at the end of the chain are claimed to be more efficient.

If in the second process a hydrocarbon fraction having an average molecular weight of about 500 is used, and the sulfonic acid is converted to the calcium salt, a product is obtained that is useful as a detergent in lubricating oils to keep internal combustion engines free of carbon. They are valuable particularly in compounding lubricating oils for Diesel engines.

DERIVATIVES OF SULFONIC ACIDS

Derivatives of both the aliphatic sulfonic acids (p. 218) and the aromatic sulfonic acids, such as the amides and esters, are prepared from the acid chlorides. All of the methods used for the preparation of alkanesulfonyl chlorides (p. 219) can be used for the preparation of aromatic sulfonyl chlorides. However the latter usually are prepared by a method applicable only to aromatic compounds, namely direct chlorosulfonation, in which the aromatic compound reacts with chlorosulfonic acid.[1]

$$C_6H_6 + ClSO_2OH \longrightarrow C_6H_5SO_2OH + HCl$$

$$C_6H_5SO_2OH + ClSO_2OH \longrightarrow C_6H_5SO_2Cl + H_2SO_4$$

Two moles of chlorosulfonic acid are required per mole of aromatic compound. The sulfonic acid formed initially is transformed into the sulfonyl chloride by a second mole of chlorosulfonic acid. Toluene yields a mixture of o- and p-toluenesulfonyl chlorides.

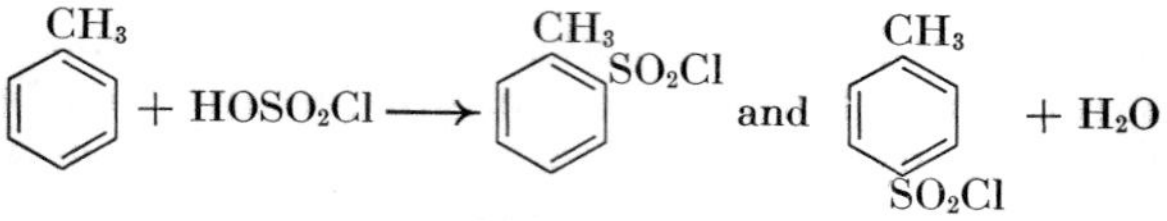

o-Toluene-
sulfonyl
chloride

p-Toluene-
sulfonyl
chloride

The sulfonyl chlorides boil much lower than the sulfonic acids. They are insoluble in water and soluble in organic liquids. Hence they can be isolated more readily than sulfonic acids and can be purified by distillation or crystallization.

Because of the insolubility of sulfonyl chlorides in water, they react only slowly with it. Boiling with water hydrolyzes the sulfonyl chloride to the sulfonic acid and hydrogen chloride, and evaporation at reduced pressure gives the free sulfonic acid. Thus p-toluenesulfonyl chloride gives p-toluenesulfonic acid.

$$p\text{-}CH_3C_6H_4SO_2Cl + H_2O \xrightarrow{\text{Heat}} p\text{-}CH_3C_6H_4SO_3H + HCl$$
$$p\text{-Toluenesulfonic}$$
$$\text{acid}$$

Alcohols and amines react more rapidly than water. Hence the reactions may be carried out in the presence of water, usually with the addition of alkali to remove the hydrogen chloride.

$$ArSO_2Cl + HOR + NaOH \longrightarrow ArSO_2OR + NaCl + H_2O$$

In the absence of alkali, the ester acts as an alkylating agent and undergoes side reactions with the hydrogen chloride and excess alcohol.

$$ArSO_2OR + HCl \longrightarrow ArSO_3H + RCl$$

$$ArSO_2OR + HOR \longrightarrow ArSO_3H + ROR$$

---

[1] Chlorosulfonic acid is manufactured by the reaction of hydrogen chloride and sulfur trioxide.

$$SO_3 + HCl \longrightarrow HOSO_2Cl$$

Pyridine, a tertiary amine (p. 454), frequently is used instead of aqueous alkali in the preparation of sulfonic acid esters. Not only does it combine with the hydrogen chloride formed in the reaction and act as a basic catalyst, but it is a solvent for the sulfonyl chlorides and the alcohol. The reaction of *p*-toluenesulfonyl chloride (*tosyl chloride*) with alcohols frequently is called *tosylation*. It finds important use in preparing the *p*-toluenesulfonyl (*tosyl*) derivatives of carbohydrates (p. 287). The general behavior of sulfonic esters has been discussed (p. 221).

Ammonia and primary and secondary amines, like the alcohols, react with sulfonyl chlorides in the presence of water. Here also an equivalent quantity of a strong alkali is used but for a different reason. The hydrogen chloride produced in the reaction combines at once with unreacted amine. Since the amine salt cannot react with the sulfonyl chloride, only half of the amine can be converted to the sulfonamide.

$$\text{ArSO}_2\text{Cl} + 2 \text{ HNHR} \longrightarrow \text{ArSO}_2\text{NHR} + \text{RNH}_3\text{Cl}$$

If an equivalent quantity of strong base is present, it reacts with the hydrogen chloride, and all of the amine is convertible into sulfonamide.

$$\text{ArSO}_2\text{Cl} + \text{HNHR} + \text{NaOH} \longrightarrow \text{ArSO}_2\text{NHR} + \text{NaCl} + \text{H}_2\text{O}$$

The availability of benzenesulfonyl chloride and of *p*-toluenesulfonyl chloride has made their reaction with amines important as a means of distinguishing between primary, secondary, and tertiary amines, and of separating mixtures of different types of amines. This procedure is known as the *Hinsberg reaction*. It is based on the fact that sulfonamides prepared from primary amines are sufficiently acidic to form sodium salts in aqueous solution and hence are soluble in dilute aqueous alkali (p. 220). Those from secondary amines cannot form a salt and do not dissolve in dilute alkali. Tertiary amines do not react with sulfonyl chlorides in the presence of water.

$$\text{C}_6\text{H}_5\text{SO}_2\text{Cl} + \text{H}_2\text{NR} + 2 \text{ NaOH} \longrightarrow [\text{C}_6\text{H}_5\text{SO}_2\bar{\text{N}}\text{R}]\text{Na}^+ + \text{NaCl} + 2 \text{ H}_2\text{O}$$

Soluble in water; reacts with dilute acid to give water-insoluble sulfonamide

$$\text{C}_6\text{H}_5\text{SO}_2\text{Cl} + \text{HNR}_2 + \text{NaOH} \longrightarrow \text{C}_6\text{H}_5\text{SO}_2\text{NR}_2 + \text{NaCl} + \text{H}_2\text{O}$$

Insoluble in dilute alkali or dilute acid

$$\text{C}_6\text{H}_5\text{SO}_2\text{Cl} + \text{NR}_3 \longrightarrow \text{No reaction; tertiary amine soluble in dilute acids}$$

Sulfonamides having hydrogen on the nitrogen atom react with alkaline hypochlorite solutions to give *N*-halo derivatives.

$$\text{ArSO}_2\text{NHR} + \text{NaOCl} \rightleftarrows \text{ArSO}_2\text{NR} + \text{NaOH}$$
$$\underset{\text{Cl}}{|}$$

If two hydrogen atoms are present, the sodium salt is formed which is soluble in water.

$$p\text{-}CH_3C_6H_4SO_2NH_2 + NaOCl \rightleftarrows [p\text{-}CH_3C_6H_4SO_2\bar{N}Cl]Na^+ + H_2O$$

Sodium salt of N-chloro-
p-toluenesulfonamide
(Chloramine-T)

Since the product is stable when dry and the reaction is reversible in aqueous solution, the N-chlorosulfonamides have the antiseptic properties of hypochlorite solutions. The analogous compound from benzenesulfonamide is known as Chloramine-B. If the chlorination is carried further, a dichloro derivative is formed which is soluble in oils and salves.

$$p\text{-}CH_3C_6H_4SO_2NH_2 + 2\ NaOCl \longrightarrow p\text{-}CH_3C_6H_4SO_2NCl_2 + 2\ NaOH$$

N,N-Dichloro-p-
toluenesulfonamide
(Dichloramine-T)

Since p-toluenesulfonyl chloride is a co-product of the manufacture of saccharin (p. 416), conversion to the amide and to Chloramine-T and Dichloramine-T is one method of utilization.

Sulfonyl chlorides can be reduced to sulfinic acids and to mercaptans (p. 216). These reactions are valuable in the aromatic series as a means of obtaining **sulfinic acids** and **thiophenols.**

$$2\ C_6H_5SO_2Cl + 2\ Zn\ \text{(in ether)} \longrightarrow (C_6H_5SO_2)_2Zn + ZnCl_2$$

Zinc benzene-
sulfinate

$$\downarrow 2\ HCl$$

$$C_6H_5SO_2H + ZnCl_2$$

Benzenesul-
finic acid

$$2\ C_6H_5SO_2Cl + 6\ Zn + 5\ H_2SO_4\ \text{(in water)} \longrightarrow 2\ C_6H_5SH + ZnCl_2 + 5\ ZnSO_4 + 4\ H_2O$$

Thiophenol

Sulfonyl chlorides undergo the Friedel-Crafts reaction with aromatic compounds in the presence of anhydrous aluminum chloride to yield **sulfones.**

$$C_6H_5SO_2Cl + C_6H_6 \xrightarrow{\ AlCl_3\ } C_6H_5SO_2C_6H_5 + HCl$$

Phenyl sulfone

REVIEW QUESTIONS

1. How are aromatic sulfonic acids prepared? What is a common co-product?
2. What is the *liming out process*? How may sulfonic acids be obtained in a pure state?
3. What is fuming sulfuric acid? How is chlorosulfonic acid made?
4. Give reactions for the conversion of a sulfonic acid into (a) the hydrocarbon; (b) the nitrile; (c) the phenol.
5. What is the Hinsberg reaction and of what value is it?

6. Starting with the hydrocarbons, give equations for the preparation of phenyl *p*-tolyl sulfone; *o*-methylthiophenol; 2,4-dimethylbenzenesulfinic acid; *m*-aminobenzenesulfonic acid.

7. Give equations for the various methods by which aromatic sulfonyl chlorides may be prepared.

8. How are amides and esters of sulfonic acids prepared? Why is sodium hydroxide used in these reactions?

9. List some commercial uses for the salts of aromatic sulfonic acids; for sulfonamides.

Chapter 23

AROMATIC AMINES

Compounds classed as aromatic amines have an amino group or an alkyl- or aryl-substituted amino group attached directly to an aromatic nucleus. Usually they are made by a different procedure and undergo different reactions from those of aliphatic amines.

Nomenclature

Aromatic amines may be primary, secondary, or tertiary, and in the secondary or tertiary amines, one or two of the hydrocarbon groups may be aliphatic. Usually the primary amines are named as the amino derivatives of the aromatic hydrocarbon or as aryl derivatives of ammonia, but some are known best by common names such as aniline or toluidine.

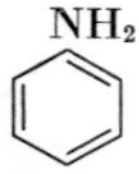

Aniline
(aminobenzene or
phenylamine)

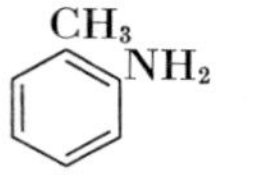

o-Toluidine
(o-aminotoluene or
o-tolylamine)

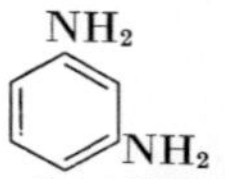

m-Phenylenediamine
(m-diaminobenzene)

Secondary and tertiary amines are named as derivatives of the primary amine, or as derivatives of ammonia.

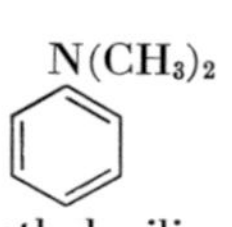

Dimethylaniline

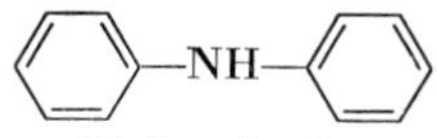

Diphenylamine

Structure

In the structure assigned to the aromatic amines, an amino group is attached to an aromatic ring. If three double bonds are placed in the aromatic nucleus, the amino group is attached to a carbon atom united to another carbon atom by a double bond. Such enamine structures are unstable in the aliphatic series and rearrange to the imine structure which usually polymerizes.

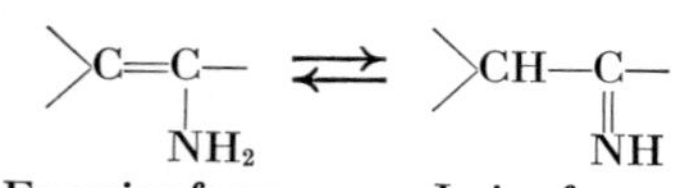

$$\underset{NH_2}{>C=C-} \quad \rightleftarrows \quad \underset{NH}{>CH-C-}$$

Enamine form;
stable structure in
aromatic systems

Imino form;
stable structure in
aliphatic systems

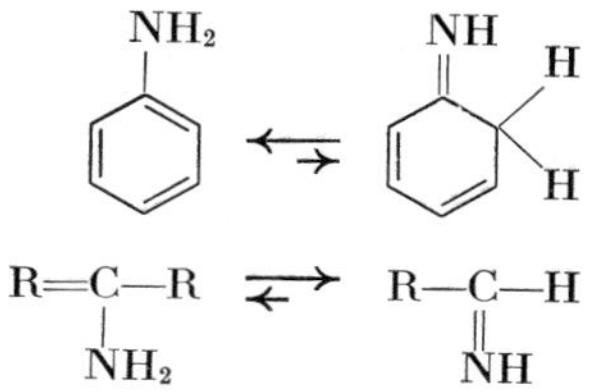

R=C—R $\rightleftarrows$ R—C—H
| NH$_2$ ‖ NH

The stability of the amino structure in aromatic amines is due to the high resonance energy of the aromatic nucleus, which is absent in the dienimine structure.

Physical Properties

The physical properties of the aromatic amines are about what would be expected. Just as benzene (b.p. 80°) boils at a higher temperature than *n*-hexane (b.p. 69°), so aniline (b.p. 184°) has a higher boiling point than *n*-hexylamine (b.p. 130°). The greater difference in the boiling points of the second pair may be ascribed to the fact that aniline has a higher dipole moment ($\mu = 1.6$) than *n*-hexylamine ($\mu = 1.3$). Methylaniline (b.p. 195°) boils at a higher temperature than aniline, but dimethylaniline (b.p. 193°) boils at a lower temperature than methylaniline in spite of the increase in molecular weight, because proton bonding is not possible for dimethylaniline.

Aniline is somewhat more soluble in water (3.6 g. per 100 g. of water) than *n*-hexylamine (0.4 g. per 100 g. of water). Water dissolves in aniline to the extent of about 5 per cent. Aniline is miscible with benzene but not with *n*-hexane.

As is true for all of the disubstituted benzenes, the *para*-substituted anilines, being the most symmetrical, have the highest melting point. Thus *p*-toluidine is a solid at room temperature whereas both the *ortho* and *meta* isomers are liquids.

Physiological Properties

The aromatic amines, like the hydrocarbons and their halogen and nitro derivatives, are highly toxic. The liquids are absorbed readily through the skin, and low concentrations of the vapors produce symptoms of toxicity when inhaled for prolonged periods. Aniline vapors may produce symptoms of poisoning after several hours of exposure to concentrations as low as 7 parts per million. Aniline affects both the blood and the nervous system. Hemoglobin of the blood is converted into methemoglobin with reduction of the oxygen-carrying capacity of the blood and resultant cyanosis. A direct depressant action is exerted on heart muscle. Continued exposure leads to mental disturbances.

The chloro and nitro nuclear-substituted amines, the *N*-alkylated and acylated amines, and the diamines all are highly toxic. The *N*-phenylamines are considerably less toxic than the *N*-alkyl derivatives. The phenolic hydroxyl group also decreases the toxicity somewhat. Toxicity is greatly reduced by the presence of free carboxylic or sulfonic acid groups in the ring.

Preparation

1. *By Reduction of More Highly Oxidized Nitrogen Compounds.* Aromatic nitro compounds yield a series of reduction products, the final product being the primary amine (Fig. 41, p. 348). Therefore aromatic amines may be prepared from nitro compounds, or from the less highly oxidized nitroso, hydroxylamino, azoxy, azo, and hydrazo compounds, by reduction with tin or iron and hydrochloric acid, or by catalytic hydrogenation.

2. *By Ammonolysis of Halogen Compounds.* Halogen attached to an aromatic nucleus usually is very stable to hydrolysis or ammonolysis, and rather drastic conditions are required to bring about reaction (p. 329). If, however, electron-attracting groups are present in the *ortho* and *para* positions, the halogen is more easily displaced. Thus 2,4,6-trinitrochlorobenzene reacts readily with ammonia to yield picramide.

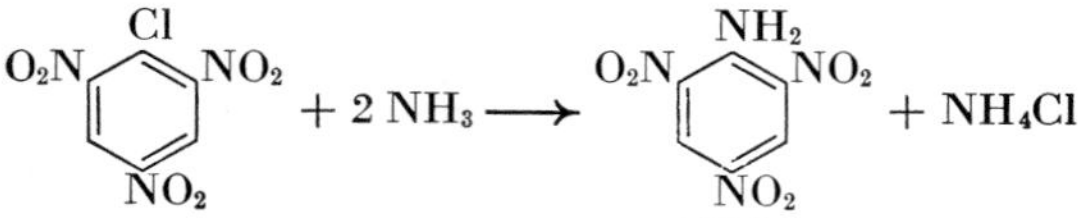

$$\text{2,4,6-Trinitrochlorobenzene} + 2\ NH_3 \longrightarrow \text{2,4,6-Trinitroaniline (picramide)} + NH_4Cl$$

2,4-Dinitrophenylhydrazine, a valuable reagent for aldehydes and ketones, is made from 2,4-dinitrochlorobenzene and hydrazine.

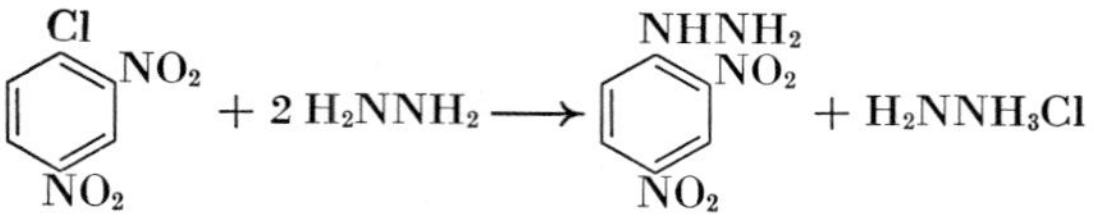

$$\text{2,4-dinitrochlorobenzene} + 2\ H_2NNH_2 \longrightarrow \text{2,4-dinitrophenylhydrazine} + H_2NNH_3Cl$$

Reactions

REACTIONS OF THE AMINO GROUP

1. *Basicity.* An amino group attached to an aromatic nucleus is in general much less basic than one attached to an alkyl radical, although it still is considerably more basic than an amino group attached to an acyl group. Thus the basic dissociation constants of methylamine, aniline, and acetamide are 4.4×10^{-5}, 3.8×10^{-10}, and 3.1×10^{-15} respectively. The presence of electron-attracting groups in the nucleus decreases the basicity still further. For example the basic dissociation constants for *o-*, *m-*, and *p-*nitroaniline are 1×10^{-14}, 4×10^{-12}, and 1×10^{-12} respectively. Similarly the introduction of a second aromatic nucleus on the nitrogen atom greatly decreases the basicity, the basic dissociation constant for diphenylamine being 7.6×10^{-14}. On the other hand the introduction of alkyl groups increases the basicity, the dissociation constants for ethylaniline and diethylaniline being 1.3×10^{-9} and 3.6×10^{-8} respectively. The behavior of methylaniline is anomalous in that it is slightly weaker than aniline.

The decreased basicity of aniline compared with aliphatic amines can be explained by the resonance of the unshared pair of electrons on the nitrogen atom with the unsaturation electrons of the nucleus. This interaction reduces the availability of the unshared pair for bonding with a proton.

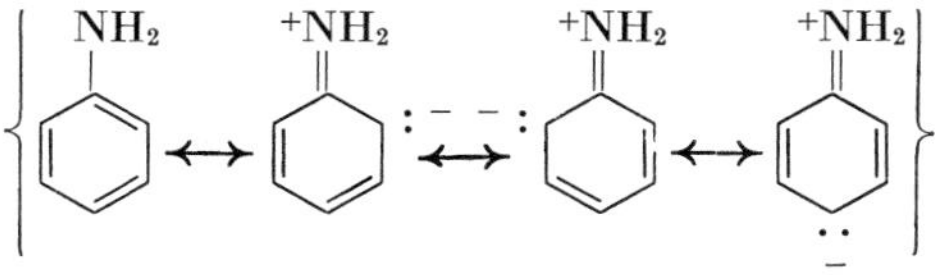

2. Alkylation and Arylation. Like the aliphatic amines, the primary aromatic amines react with alkyl halides to give secondary and tertiary amines and quaternary ammonium salts.

$$C_6H_5NH_2 + RX \longrightarrow [C_6H_5\overset{+}{N}H_2R]X^- \xrightarrow{NaOH} C_6H_5NHR + NaX + H_2O$$
$$N\text{-Alkylani-}$$
$$\text{line}$$

$$C_6H_5NHR + RX \longrightarrow [C_6H_5\overset{+}{N}HR_2]X^- \xrightarrow{NaOH} C_6H_5NR_2 + NaX + H_2O$$
$$N,N\text{-Di-}$$
$$\text{alkylaniline}$$

$$C_6H_5NR_2 + RX \longrightarrow [C_6H_5\overset{+}{N}R_3]X^-$$
$$\text{Phenyltrialkyl-}$$
$$\text{ammonium halide}$$

Simple aryl halides react with difficulty. Although diphenylamine is a minor co-product of the commercial production of aniline from chlorobenzene (p. 370), it is made best by heating aniline with aniline hydrochloride.

$$C_6H_5NH_2 + [C_6H_5\overset{+}{N}H_3]Cl^- \xrightarrow{Heat} (C_6H_5)_2NH + NH_4Cl$$
$$\text{Diphenyl-}$$
$$\text{amine}$$

Triphenylamine is made by heating diphenylamine with iodobenzene, potassium carbonate, and copper bronze.

$$(C_6H_5)_2NH + IC_6H_5 \xrightarrow{K_2CO_3 \ (Cu)} (C_6H_5)_3N + KI + KHCO_3$$
$$\text{Triphen-}$$
$$\text{ylamine}$$

No quaternary salts of either diphenylamine or triphenylamine are known, probably because their low basicity prevents reaction.

3. Acylation. Acid anhydrides and acyl halides convert primary and secondary amines into the amides.

$$C_6H_5NH_2 + (CH_3CO)_2O \longrightarrow C_6H_5NHCOCH_3 + CH_3COOH$$
$$\text{Acetanilide}$$

$$2 \ C_6H_5NHCH_3 + CH_3COCl \longrightarrow C_6H_5N(CH_3)COCH_3 + [C_6H_5\overset{+}{N}H_2CH_3]Cl^-$$
$$\text{Methylaniline} \qquad\qquad\qquad \text{Methylacetanilide} \qquad\qquad \text{Methylaniline}$$
$$\text{hydrochloride}$$
$$\text{(phenylmethylam-}$$
$$\text{monium chloride)}$$

Acylation can be brought about also by heating the amine salts of carboxylic acids.

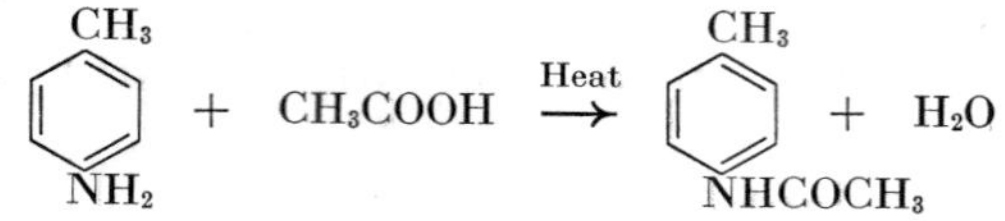

$$\underset{\substack{p\text{-Tolui-}\\ \text{dine}}}{\underset{\text{NH}_2}{\text{CH}_3}} \ + \ \text{CH}_3\text{COOH} \ \xrightarrow{\text{Heat}} \ \underset{\substack{\text{Aceto-}p\text{-}\\ \text{toluidide}}}{\underset{\text{NHCOCH}_3}{\text{CH}_3}} \ + \ \text{H}_2\text{O}$$

When aniline reacts with phosgene, phenylcarbamyl chloride is formed. On heating, hydrogen chloride is lost and *phenyl isocyanate*, a valuable reagent for alcohols and amines (p. 246), is produced.

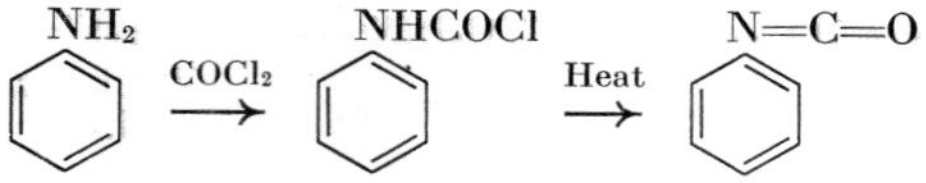

$$\underset{\text{NH}_2}{\bigcirc} \ \xrightarrow{\text{COCl}_2} \ \underset{\text{NHCOCl}}{\bigcirc} \ \xrightarrow{\text{Heat}} \ \underset{\substack{\text{Phenyl}\\ \text{isocyanate}}}{\underset{\text{N=C=O}}{\bigcirc}}$$

Phenyl isocyanate also is useful for the identification of alkyl halides because the latter can be converted to Grignard reagents which add to phenyl isocyanate. Hydrolysis of the addition product gives a solid anilide.

$$\text{C}_6\text{H}_5\text{N=C=O} + \text{RMgX} \longrightarrow \underset{\text{OMgX}}{\text{C}_6\text{H}_5\text{N=CR}} \xrightarrow{\text{H}_2\text{O}} \left[\underset{\text{OH}}{\text{C}_6\text{H}_5\text{N=CR}} \right] \longrightarrow \underset{\text{O}}{\text{C}_6\text{H}_5\text{NHCR}}$$

4. *Reaction with Nitrous Acid.* The behavior of aromatic amines toward nitrous acid, like that of the aliphatic amines, depends on whether the amine is primary, secondary, or tertiary. However the reactions of primary and tertiary aromatic amines differ from those of primary and tertiary aliphatic amines (p. 190).

(*a*) PRIMARY AMINES. At temperatures below 0° in strongly acid solution, nitrous acid reacts with the primary aromatic amine salts to give water-soluble compounds known as *diazonium salts*. The properties and uses of these

$$\underset{\substack{\text{Aniline}\\ \text{hydrochloride}}}{[\text{C}_6\text{H}_5\overset{+}{\text{NH}}_3]\text{Cl}^-} + \text{HONO(NaNO}_2 + \text{HCl)} \longrightarrow \underset{\substack{\text{Benzene-}\\ \text{diazonium}\\ \text{chloride}}}{[\text{C}_6\text{H}_5\overset{+}{\text{N}}_2]\text{Cl}^-} + 2 \text{H}_2\text{O}$$

important compounds are given in Chapter 24.

(*b*) SECONDARY AMINES. Secondary aromatic amines behave like secondary aliphatic amines, yielding *N*-nitroso derivatives.

$$\underset{\substack{\text{Methyl-}\\ \text{aniline}}}{\text{C}_6\text{H}_5\text{NHCH}_3} + \text{HONO} \longrightarrow \underset{\substack{\text{NO}\\ N\text{-Nitroso-}\\ \text{methylaniline}}}{\text{C}_6\text{H}_5\text{NCH}_3} + \text{H}_2\text{O}$$

(*c*) TERTIARY AMINES. Tertiary aromatic amines having an unsubstituted *para* position yield *p*-nitroso derivatives.

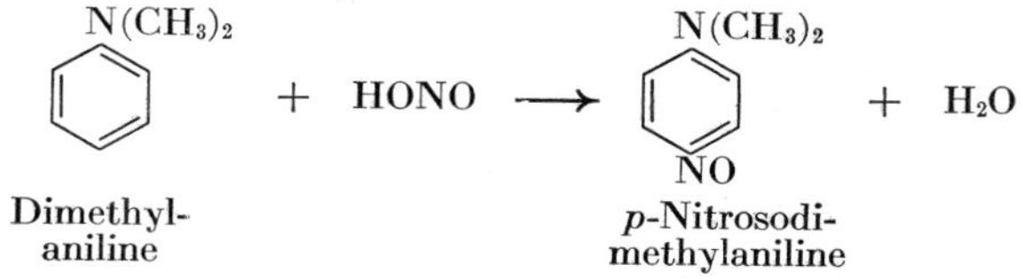

$$\text{Dimethylaniline} + \text{HONO} \longrightarrow \text{p-Nitrosodimethylaniline} + H_2O$$

This reaction takes place because of the strong activating effect of the dimethylamino group. Although most of the dimethylaniline is present as the salt in the acid solution, and the dimethylammonium group is deactivating and *meta*-directing, sufficient free dimethylaniline is in equilibrium with the salt to react with nitrous acid, and the equilibrium shifts until nitrosation is complete. Nitrous acid does not bring about the nitrosation of benzene or even of toluene or mesitylene.

Although both secondary and tertiary aromatic amines yield nitroso derivatives, the reaction still can be used to distinguish between them, because the *N*-nitroso derivatives are amides of nitrous acid. Hence they are not basic and do not dissolve in dilute acids. The *p*-nitroso derivatives, however, form yellow salts with mineral acids. The diazonium salts from primary amines can be detected readily by reaction with aromatic amines or phenols to give highly colored azo compounds (p. 378).

Since nitroso compounds are dark green in color, it appears that salt formation does not take place with the tertiary amino group, but with the nitroso group, stabilization being brought about by resonance with the quinone structure (p. 395).

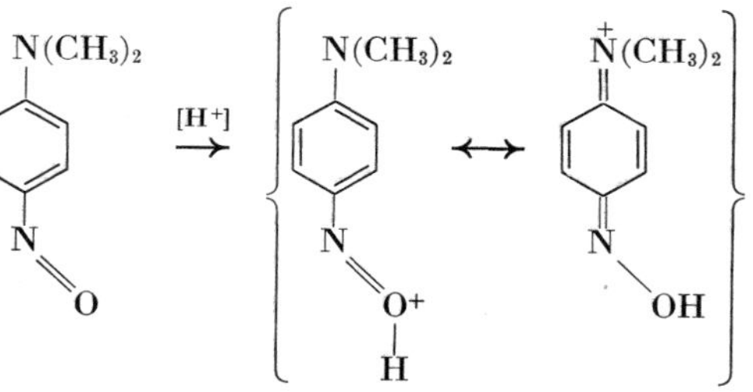

5. *Other Reactions.* Aromatic amines undergo most of the reactions described for aliphatic amines. Thus they give condensation products with aldehydes and ketones. Intermediate condensation products frequently are more stable than those of the aliphatic amines. For example the products of reaction of an aldehyde with one or two moles of aniline can be isolated.

$$C_6H_5NH_2 + OCHR \longrightarrow C_6H_5N{=}CHR + H_2O$$

$$2\,C_6H_5NH_2 + OCHR \longrightarrow (C_6H_5NH)_2CHR + H_2O$$

The products from one mole each of amine and aldehyde are known as *Schiff bases* or *anils*. These intermediates undergo further polymerization and condensation. The condensation products have been used as **rubber accelerators** and antioxidants (p. 498).

Aniline reacts with carbon disulfide in the presence of ammonia to give ammonium phenyldithiocarbamate (p. 250).

$$C_6H_5NH_2 + CS_2 + NH_3 \longrightarrow C_6H_5NHCSS^-{}^+NH_4$$

Hydrogen sulfide can be removed from the dithiocarbamate by reaction with lead nitrate (p. 251) to give **phenyl isothiocyanate** (*phenyl mustard oil*).

$$C_6H_5NHCSS^-{}^+NH_4 + Pb(NO_3)_2 \longrightarrow C_6H_5N{=}C{=}S + PbS + NH_4NO_3 + HNO_3$$

Aniline does not react rapidly with carbon disulfide at room temperature in the absence of ammonia or a metallic oxide, probably because of its low basicity. When aniline is heated with carbon disulfide, the salt of the dithiocarbamate is not formed but hydrogen sulfide is evolved with the production of **thiocarbanilide.**

$$2\ C_6H_5NH_2 + CS_2 \longrightarrow C_6H_5NHCSNHC_6H_5 + H_2S$$
Thiocarbanilide
(diphenylthiourea)

Thiocarbanilide at one time was an important rubber accelerator. It now is used chiefly for the preparation of diphenylguanidine and 2-mercaptobenzothiazole which have supplanted it (pp. 371, 461).

Primary aromatic amines when heated with chloroform and alkali give the *isocyanides* or *carbylamines* (p. 189).

Oxidation

Aliphatic amines are fairly stable to oxidation, but aromatic amines oxidize readily. Unless carefully purified, they soon darken on standing in air. Stronger oxidizing agents produce highly colored products. Even the simplest aromatic amine, aniline, can give rise to numerous and frequently complex oxidation products. It is not surprising that, depending on the oxidizing agent used, azobenzene, azoxybenzene, phenylhydroxylamine, nitrosobenzene, and nitrobenzene have been isolated, since aniline is a further reduction product of these compounds. In addition to the amino group, however, the hydrogen atoms of the benzene ring that are *ortho* and *para* to the amino group are oxidized to hydroxyl groups. Thus when sodium hypochlorite solution is added to aniline, *p*-aminophenol is formed along with azobenzene and other products.

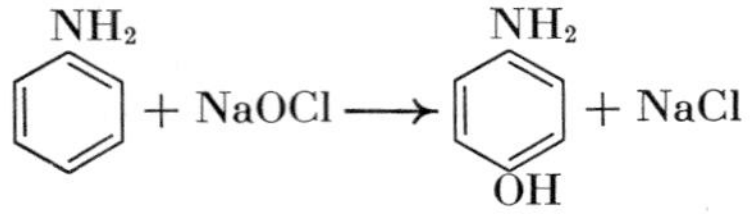

These hydroxy amines are oxidized very readily to quinones (p. 395), which undergo further oxidation and condensation reactions. For example the violet color produced when aniline is mixed with a solution of bleaching powder is due to a series of reactions which form a blue compound known as *indoaniline.*

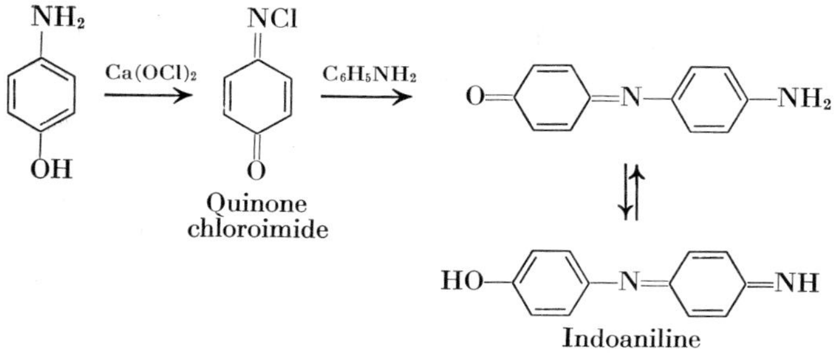

Amine salts are much less readily oxidized than the free amines because the positive charge greatly reduces the electron-donating property of the molecule. Replacement of both hydrogen atoms of the amino group by alkyl groups also hinders some types of oxidation. Lack of hydrogen on the nitrogen atom prevents the formation of compounds such as azobenzene and phenylhydroxylamine. It also prevents oxidation of nuclear hydrogen, since this reaction appears to be dependent on the presence of small amounts of the tautomeric imino forms of the amine (p. 360).

REACTIONS OF THE NUCLEUS

1. *Halogenation.* Because of the strong activating effect of the amino group, no catalyst is required in the halogenation of the nucleus. Furthermore halogenation takes place in aqueous solution and is so rapid that the only product readily isolated is 2,4,6-trichloro- or 2,4,6-tribromoaniline. The three halogen atoms in the *ortho* and *para* positions reduce the basicity of the amino

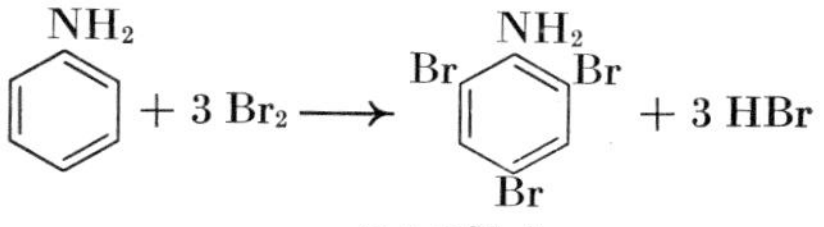

group, and the salt does not form in aqueous solution.

Actually trichloroaniline or tribromoaniline is formed even when chlorine or bromine is added to an aqueous solution of an aniline salt. This behavior seems anomalous at first, since salt formation should lead to deactivation and *meta* orientation. The experimental results can be explained by the presence of free amine formed by hydrolysis of the salt in aqueous solution. This view is confirmed by the fact that aniline dissolved in concentrated sulfuric acid is not chlorinated or brominated at room temperature. At higher temperatures the *meta* substitution product is formed.

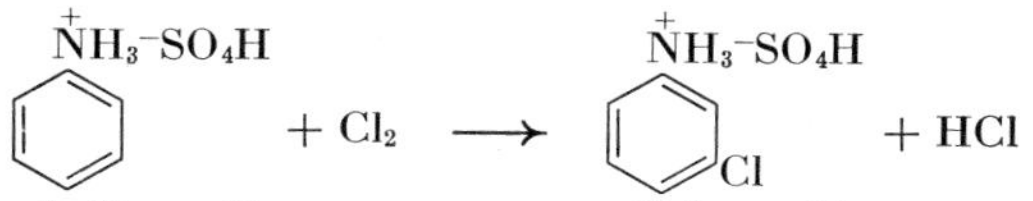

Even the less reactive iodine substitutes aniline directly, the hydrogen iodide combining with unreacted aniline.

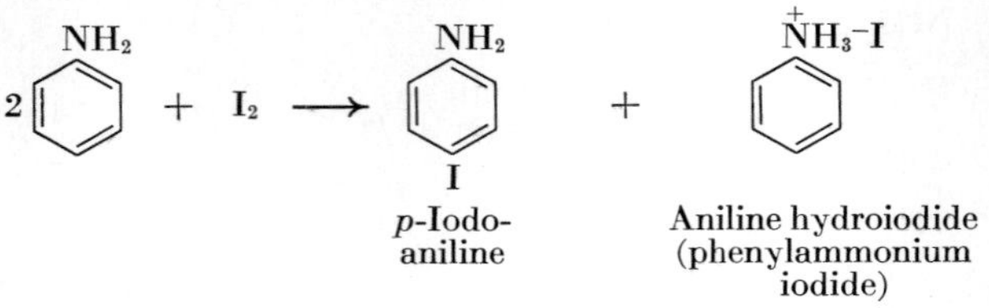

$$2 \underset{\text{NH}_2}{\bigcirc} + \text{I}_2 \longrightarrow \underset{\underset{\text{I}}{\text{NH}_2}}{\bigcirc} + \underset{\overset{+}{\text{NH}_3}\text{-I}}{\bigcirc}$$

p-Iodo-
aniline

Aniline hydroiodide
(phenylammonium
iodide)

If the activating effect of the amino group is reduced by conversion to the acetamino group, monochloro or monobromo derivatives can be obtained.

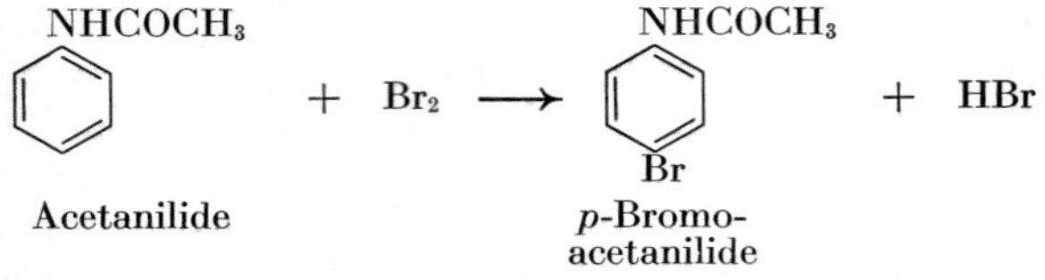

$$\underset{\text{NHCOCH}_3}{\bigcirc} + \text{Br}_2 \longrightarrow \underset{\underset{\text{Br}}{\text{NHCOCH}_3}}{\bigcirc} + \text{HBr}$$

Acetanilide

p-Bromo-
acetanilide

Usually monohalogenated anilines are prepared by reduction of the halogenated nitro compounds.

2. *Nitration.* Because of the ease of oxidation of free aniline (p. 366), only the salt can be nitrated efficiently, and nitration is carried out in concentrated sulfuric acid solution. Hence the chief product is *m*-nitroaniline.

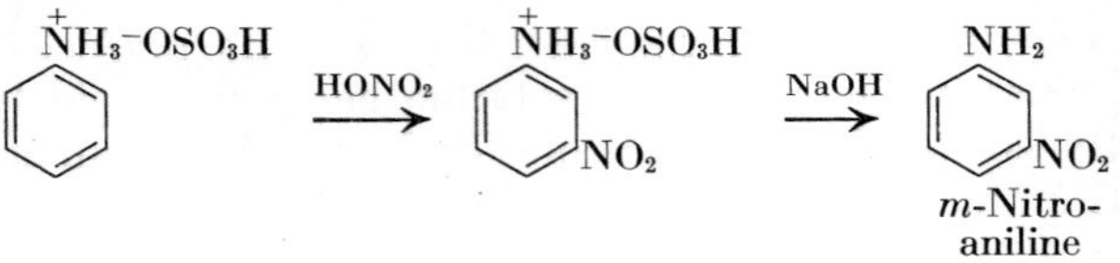

$$\underset{\overset{+}{\text{NH}_3}\text{-OSO}_3\text{H}}{\bigcirc} \xrightarrow{\text{HONO}_2} \underset{\overset{+}{\text{NH}_3}\text{-OSO}_3\text{H}}{\underset{\text{NO}_2}{\bigcirc}} \xrightarrow{\text{NaOH}} \underset{\underset{\text{NO}_2}{\text{NH}_2}}{\bigcirc}$$

m-Nitro-
aniline

Some *o*- and *p*-nitroaniline also are formed, but the amount of *meta* increases with the concentration of the sulfuric acid. The three anilines differ in basicity (p. 362) and can be separated by fractional precipitation from their salts with alkali. The order of precipitation is *ortho*, then *para*, then *meta*. *m*-Nitroaniline usually is made by the partial reduction of *m*-dinitrobenzene (p. 346).

If salt formation is prevented by the conversion of the basic amino group to the neutral acetamido group, nitration in acetic acid takes place almost exclusively in the *para* position. If the nitration is carried out in the presence of acetic anhydride, the *ortho* isomer is the chief product.

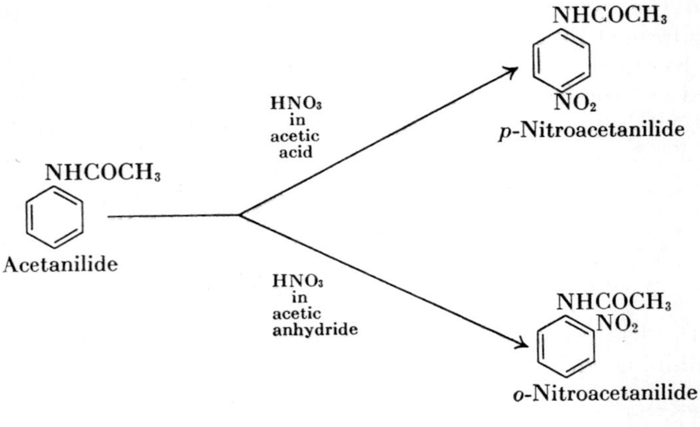

$$\underset{\text{NHCOCH}_3}{\bigcirc} \underset{\substack{\text{HNO}_3 \\ \text{in} \\ \text{acetic} \\ \text{anhydride}}}{\overset{\substack{\text{HNO}_3 \\ \text{in} \\ \text{acetic} \\ \text{acid}}}{\diagup \diagdown}} \begin{matrix} \underset{\text{NO}_2}{\overset{\text{NHCOCH}_3}{\bigcirc}} \\ p\text{-Nitroacetanilide} \\ \\ \underset{}{\overset{\text{NHCOCH}_3, \text{NO}_2}{\bigcirc}} \\ o\text{-Nitroacetanilide} \end{matrix}$$

Acetanilide

Saponification of the nitroacetanilides with sodium hydroxide solution gives the nitroanilines. *p*-Nitroaniline is an intermediate for the manufacture of azo dyes (p. 478).

3. **Sulfonation.** Because of the deactivating effect of the $\overset{+}{N}H_3$ group, aniline does not sulfonate readily. Sulfonation takes place slowly with concentrated sulfuric acid at 180°, or at room temperature with fuming sulfuric acid. Since the $NH_3{}^+$ group is *meta*-directing, the *meta* isomer is expected, but the product is chiefly the *para* isomer. Apparently the sulfamic acid is formed first. Since it does not carry a positive charge, it is *ortho,para*-directing.

Sulfanilic acid

Although the formulas for the sulfonated amines frequently are written as aminosulfonic acids, they actually are inner salts or dipolar ions (cf. p. 230). Thus sulfanilic acid decomposes at 280°–300° without melting, although aniline is a liquid, benzenesulfonic acid is a low melting solid, and both can be distilled. Whereas the amino carboxylic acids are more soluble in either strong base or strong acid than in water, sulfanilic acid is more soluble only in strong bases, because the sulfonic acid group is as strong as any of the mineral acids in aqueous solution.

The common names for *o*-, *m*-, and *p*-aminobenzenesulfonic acids are *orthanilic*, *metanilic*, and *sulfanilic* acids respectively. Metanilic acid is prepared by the reduction of *m*-nitrobenzenesulfonic acid. Orthanilic acid is not readily available but can be obtained by removing the bromine atom in 4-bromoaniline-2-sulfonic acid by reduction.

Technically Important Aromatic Amines and Their Derivatives

Aniline is by far the most important amine from the technical viewpoint. Over 92 million pounds were produced in the United States in 1948, the selling price being about 13 cents per pound. Aniline was discovered in 1826 in the products of the destructive distillation of indigo (p. 484) and given the name *krystallin*, because it readily formed crystalline salts. It was detected in coal tar in 1834 and called *kyanol*, because it gave a blue color with bleaching powder. It was rediscovered in the distillation products of indigo in 1841 and called *aniline* from the Spanish word for indigo, *anil*. In the same year it was produced by the reduction of nitrobenzene with ammonium sulfide and called *benzidam*. Hoffmann (p. 185) proved in 1843 that all four substances are identical.

Both the reduction of nitrobenzene and the ammonolysis of chlorobenzene are used in the commercial production of aniline. In the reduction process scrap cast-iron turnings and water are placed in a cast-iron vessel fitted with a stirrer and a reflux condenser. A small amount of hydrochloric acid or ferric chloride is added, and the mixture is heated to remove oxides from the surface of the iron, the hydrochloric acid or ferric chloride being converted to ferrous chloride. Nitrobenzene then is added with vigorous stirring. The iron is converted to black iron oxide, Fe_3O_4, which is recovered and used as a pigment (p. 346). The aniline is distilled with steam, and the mixed vapors are condensed. The aniline layer of the distillate is separated from the water layer and purified by distillation at reduced pressure. Since aniline is soluble in water to the extent of about 3 per cent, it must be recovered from the aqueous layer of the distillate. In order to avoid extraction with a solvent and recovery of the solvent, the aniline-saturated aqueous layer is returned to the steam generator for processing a subsequent batch. In another procedure the aniline is extracted from the water with nitrobenzene, and the extract put through the reduction process.

The **toluidines, xylidines, phenylenediamines,** and most other primary aromatic amines are prepared by similar procedures involving reduction of the nitro compounds. **m-Nitroaniline** is prepared commercially by the partial reduction of *m*-dinitrobenzene using sodium sulfide as the reducing agent (p. 346).

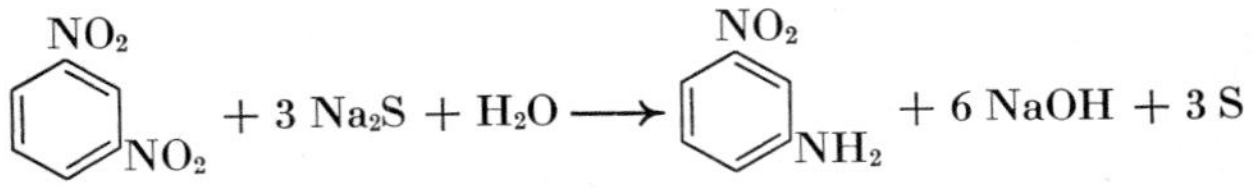

$$\underset{NO_2}{\overset{NO_2}{\bigcirc}} + 3\,Na_2S + H_2O \longrightarrow \underset{NH_2}{\overset{NO_2}{\bigcirc}} + 6\,NaOH + 3\,S$$

Since 1926 aniline has been prepared on a large scale by the reaction of chlorobenzene with ammonia, and this process accounted for about 25 per cent of the total U. S. production in 1948. The chlorobenzene is heated in a pressure system with 28 per cent aqueous ammonia (mole ratio 1 : 6) in the presence of cuprous chloride (introduced as cuprous oxide) at 190°–210°. A pressure of around 900 p.s.i. develops. The process is continuous, the reactants

$$C_6H_5Cl \ + \ 2\,NH_3 \ \xrightarrow[190°-210°]{CuCl} \ C_6H_5NH_2 \ + \ NH_4Cl$$

entering at one end of the system and the products leaving the other end. About 5 per cent of phenol and 1 to 2 per cent of diphenylamine are formed as co-products.

$$C_6H_5Cl \ + \ H_2O \ \xrightarrow{NH_3} \ \underset{Phenol}{C_6H_5OH} \ + \ NH_4Cl$$

$$C_6H_5Cl \ + \ H_2NC_6H_5 \ \xrightarrow{NH_3} \ \underset{Diphenylamine}{C_6H_5NHC_6H_5} \ + \ NH_4Cl$$

These side reactions would take place to a greater extent were it not for the presence of the large excess of ammonia. At the end of the reaction the liquid is expanded into a column. The free ammonia and aniline vaporize and are condensed. Caustic soda is added to the residue to liberate ammonia and aniline from their hydrochlorides, convert the phenol into its sodium salt, and precipitate the copper salts.

o- or *p-*Nitroaniline also may be prepared by the ammonolysis of *o-* or *p*-nitrochlorobenzene. This reaction takes place somewhat more readily than the ammonolysis of chlorobenzene because of the activating effect of nitro groups in the *ortho* or *para* position (p. 348).

The first technical use for aniline was in 1856 for the production of mauve, the first commercial synthetic dye (p. 474). Aniline still is used almost exclusively as an intermediate in the production of other compounds. About half of the total production is used in the manufacture of rubber accelerators and antioxidants (p. 498), about 20 per cent for dyes and dye intermediates, and about 5 per cent for drug manufacture.

Acetanilide was produced to the extent of about 6 million pounds in 1945, but production dropped to about half this amount in 1948 because of the decrease in the production of sulfa drugs (p. 372). A small amount is used as a dye intermediate. Acetanilide was introduced as an antipyretic in 1886 under the name *antifebrine*, and at one time it was used widely for this purpose and as an analgesic. It is highly toxic, however, being similar to aniline in its action, and it has been displaced largely by the relatively safer salicylates (p. 418), especially *aspirin* which was introduced in 1899. Because of its cheapness, however, acetanilide still is used in some proprietary headache and pain-killing remedies.

About 7 million pounds of **dimethylaniline** was produced in 1948. It is made by heating aniline and methyl alcohol in the presence of hydrochloric or sulfuric acid in a pressure reactor at 205°–215°.

$$C_6H_5NH_2 \ + \ 2\,CH_3OH \ \xrightarrow[205°-215°]{H_2SO_4} \ C_6H_5N(CH_3)_2 \ + \ 2\,H_2O$$

It can be made also by passing aniline and methyl ether vapors over activated alumina at 260°.

$$C_6H_5NH_2 \ + \ (CH_3)_2O \ \xrightarrow[260°]{Al_2O_3} \ C_6H_5N(CH_3)_2 \ + \ H_2O$$

Dimethylaniline is used as a dye intermediate (pp. 407, 482) and in the manufacture of tetryl (p. 373).

Diphenylamine is the principal stabilizer for smokeless powder (p. 300), being added in amounts of 1 to 8 per cent of the finished product. Its function is to combine with any oxides of nitrogen that are liberated, which otherwise would catalyze further decomposition. When a solution of diphenylamine in concentrated sulfuric acid reacts with nitrous or nitric acid or with their salts or esters, a deep blue color is formed. The reaction can be used as a *test for diphenylamine* or for the oxidizing agents.

Diphenylguanidine is an important rubber accelerator, production being about 3.8 million pounds in 1948. It is made from thiocarbanilide (p. 366) or by the reaction of aniline with cyanogen chloride.

$$\underset{\substack{\| \\ S}}{C_6H_5NHCNHC_6H_5} + NH_3(aq.) + PbO \longrightarrow \underset{\substack{\| \\ NH}}{C_6H_5NHCNHC_6H_5} + PbS + H_2O$$

Thiocarbanilide   Diphenylguanidine

$$2\ C_6H_5NH_2 + ClCN \longrightarrow C_6H_5NHCN + C_6H_5NH_3Cl$$

Phenyl-
cyanamide

$$\downarrow C_6H_5NH_2$$

$$C_6H_5NHCNHC_6H_5$$

$$\overset{\|}{N}H$$

About 2 million pounds of **sulfanilic acid** (p. 369) and 1 million pounds of *p*-**toluidine** were produced in 1945. Both are used chiefly as dye intermediates.

The production of **sulfa drugs,** which amounted to about 6 million pounds in 1945, dropped to 2.5 million pounds in 1948 because of the increased use of penicillin and other antibiotics. Preparation of the sulfa drugs, however, still consumes a considerable quantity of aniline. The forerunner of the sulfanilamides was *prontosil,* an azo dye patented by I. G. Farbenindustrie in 1932 and definitely established clinically by 1935 as effective against streptococcal infections. Fourneau, a French chemist, and his co-workers showed in 1935 that prontosil is converted into sulfanilamide in the body, and in 1936 that sulfanilamide is equally effective. Sulfanilamide soon was shown to be effective against other cocci infections such as pneumonia and gonorrhea, and other bacterial infections. These results led to the synthesis and testing of hundreds of derivatives of sulfanilamide. *Sulfanilamide* is synthesized from aniline by a series of reactions.

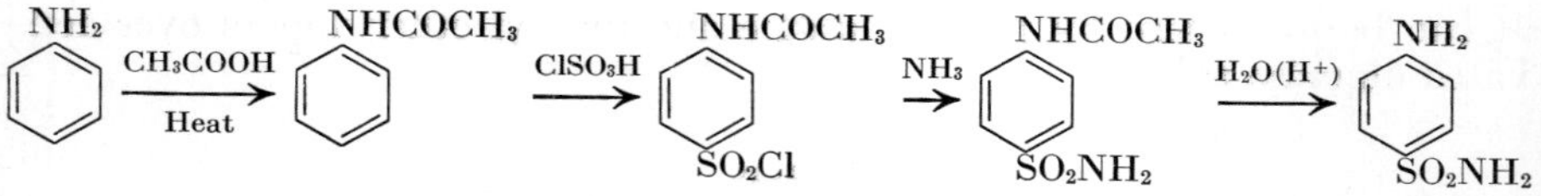

Most of the derivatives of sulfanilamide that have proved to be superior to it differ from it in structure only in that one of the hydrogen atoms of the sulfonamide group is replaced by a more complex organic group. These derivatives are made by substituting another amine for ammonia in the step in which the amide is formed. One exception is *marfanil* in which the nuclear amino group is separated from the benzene ring by a methylene group. It is more effective than the sulfanilamides against anaerobic bacteria such as the anthrax bacillus, and is used for dusting into open wounds.

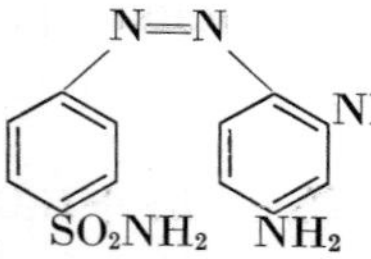

Prontosil
(1932)

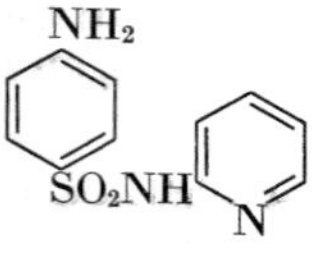

Sulfapyridine
(1938)

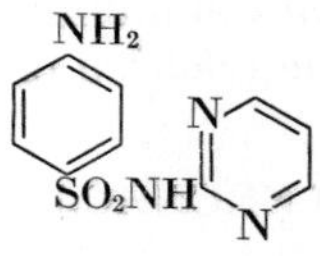

Sulfadiazine
(1941)

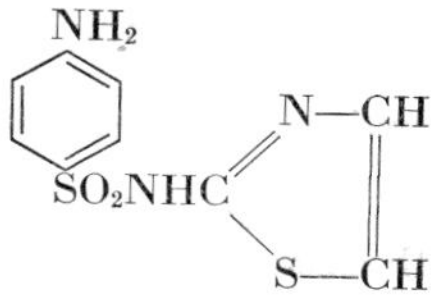

Sulfathiazole
(1940)

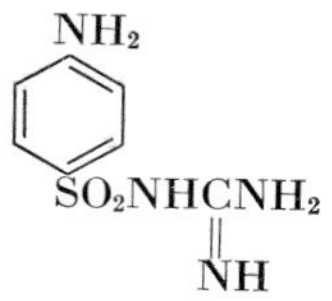

Sulfaguanidine
(1940)

Marfanil

Tetryl, 2,4,6-trinitrophenylmethylnitramide, is the standard booster charge for high explosive shells. The explosion of a shell is initiated by the primary explosive such as mercury fulminate (p. 246) which is sensitive to heat or shock. Detonation of the primary charge causes the explosion of the less sensitive booster charge, which in turn detonates the still less sensitive main charge such as TNT. Tetryl may be made by the reaction of dinitrochlorobenzene with methylamine, followed by further nitration.

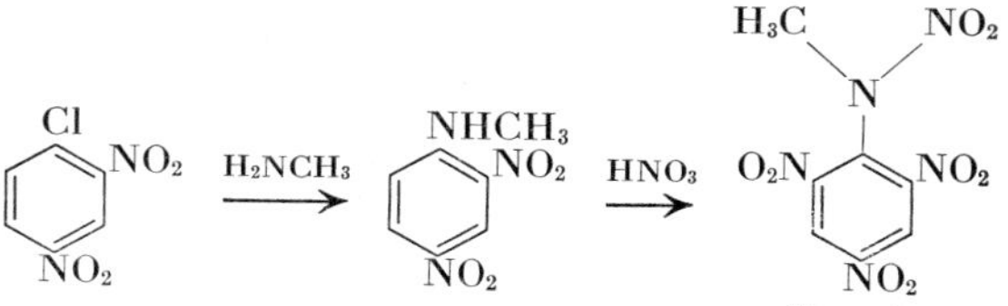

Tetryl

It usually is manufactured by the nitration of dimethylaniline in concentrated sulfuric acid. During the course of the reaction one of the methyl groups is removed by oxidation.

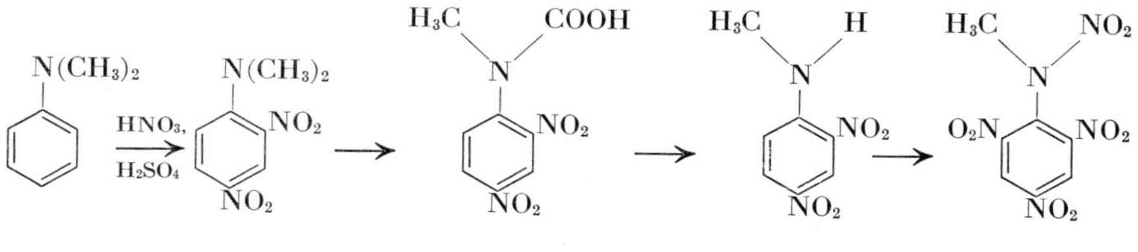

REVIEW QUESTIONS

1. Compare the boiling points of aniline, *n*-hexylamine, methylaniline, and dimethylaniline, and explain.
2. Look up the melting points of the *ortho*, *meta*, and *para* isomers of toluidine, nitroaniline, and chloroaniline, note any regularities, and explain.
3. Discuss the physiological action of aromatic amines.
4. Summarize the methods for preparing primary, secondary, and tertiary aromatic amines.
5. Discuss the bromination, nitration, and sulfonation of aniline.
6. Summarize the methods for the preparation of *o*-, *m*-, and *p*-nitroaniline.
7. Give reactions for preparing (*a*) *p*-chloroaniline and (*b*) *m*-bromoaniline, starting with benzene.
8. Discuss the properties and structure of *p*-aminobenzenesulfonic acid.
9. Compare the basicity of aniline with that of aliphatic amines and of acid amides. Discuss the effect of substituents attached to the nitrogen atom and of substituents in the ring on the basicity of the amino group.

10. Compare the reactions of primary, secondary, and tertiary aromatic amines with those of the corresponding types of aliphatic amines.
11. Give reactions for the preparation of pure ethylamine and pure diethylamine starting with aniline.
12. Compare the ease of oxidation of aromatic amines with that of their salts.
13. What are the sulfanilamides? How is sulfanilamide synthesized, starting with benzene? Why is aniline not chlorosulfonated directly?

Chapter 24

DIAZONIUM SALTS

Diazonium salts and Grignard reagents constitute the two most versatile types of reagents known to organic chemists. The value of Grignard reagents is limited by the fact that for the most part they can be prepared only from the halogen derivatives of aliphatic or aromatic hydrocarbons; that is few other functional groups may be present. This type of limitation does not exist for the formation of diazonium salts. On the other hand the latter can be prepared only if an amino group is attached to an aromatic nucleus.

Diazonium salts were prepared first by Peter Griess [1] in 1858 by the action of nitrous acid on the salt of an aromatic amine.

$$\text{ArNH}_3{}^+\text{Cl}^- + \text{HONO} \longrightarrow \text{ArN}_2{}^+\text{Cl}^- + 2\ \text{H}_2\text{O}$$

The importance of these compounds soon was recognized, and within the course of the next five years, their reactions had been widely investigated and azo dyes derived from them were being manufactured commercially. Moreover the investigations concerning the structure of diazonium salts and of diazo compounds in general have played an important part in the development of the theoretical aspects of organic chemistry.

Physical Properties, Structure, and Nomenclature

In acid solutions the diazo compounds show all of the properties of salts. They are solids, soluble in water, and insoluble in organic solvents. Electrical conductivity measurements show that they are completely ionized in dilute solution. Therefore one of the nitrogen atoms must be quaternary as in ammonium salts. The only reasonable structure is that in which the nitrogen atoms are joined by a triple bond.

$$\left[\text{Ar} \overset{+}{\text{N}} \text{N} : \right] \text{X}^- \quad \text{or} \quad [\text{Ar}\!-\!\overset{+}{\text{N}}\!\equiv\!\text{N}]\text{X}^-$$

In naming these compounds the name of the hydrocarbon from which they are derived is affixed to *diazonium* and the name of the acid radical.

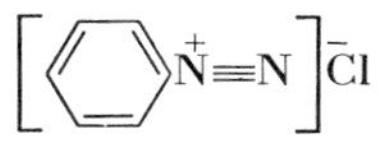

$$\left[\text{C}_6\text{H}_5\overset{+}{\text{N}}\!\equiv\!\text{N} \right]\overset{-}{\text{Cl}}$$
Benzenediazonium
chloride

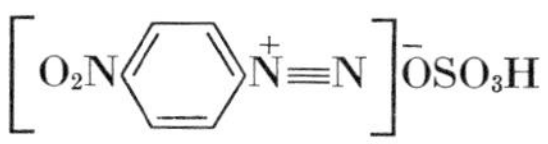

$$\left[\text{O}_2\text{N}\text{-}\text{C}_6\text{H}_4\overset{+}{\text{N}}\!\equiv\!\text{N} \right]\overset{-}{\text{O}}\text{SO}_3\text{H}$$
p-Nitrobenzenediazonium
acid sulfate

---

[1] Johan Peter Griess (1829–1888), German-born chemist for an English brewery. He discovered the diazonium salts while working on a problem suggested by Kolbe and continued his investigations first as an assistant to Hofmann and then throughout his life in whatever time he could spare from his duties at the brewery.

The term *azo* comes from the French word *azote* meaning nitrogen. In compounds such as azobenzene, $C_6H_5N{=}NC_6H_5$, *one* nitrogen atom is present for each aromatic nucleus. In the diazo compounds, *two* nitrogen atoms are present for each aromatic nucleus.

Preparation

In general diazonium salts are not isolated as pure compounds but are prepared and used in aqueous solution. The reaction of the amine salt with nitrous acid is known as *diazotization* and must be carried out in strongly acid solution to prevent the diazonium salt from coupling with unreacted amine (p. 379). The nitrous acid usually is generated *in situ* by the addition of sodium nitrite to the suspension of amine salt in excess mineral acid. The diazonium salts generally are unstable at room temperature. Hence the reaction ordinarily is carried out at 0°, and the solution is used immediately.

Solid diazonium salts may be obtained by dissolving the amine salt in an acid solution of alcohol and adding an alkyl nitrite.

$$[Ar\overset{+}{N}H_3]Cl^- + HCl + C_2H_5ONO \longrightarrow [Ar\overset{+}{N}_2]\overset{-}{Cl} + C_2H_5OH + 2 H_2O$$

In this procedure no inorganic salts are introduced or formed, and the diazonium salt can be precipitated by the addition of ether. The solid salts are crystalline and colorless but darken in air. They explode when heated or subjected to mechanical shock. The stability of diazonium salts varies greatly with the structure of the molecule. *p*-Nitrobenzenediazonium chloride is considerably more stable than benzenediazonium chloride. Some diazonium salts, such as those of 1,5-naphthalenedisulfonic acid (p. 432), are more stable than salts of the mineral acids. Their wet pastes can be kept for some time at room temperature without decomposition, and find use in certain types of dyeing.

Reactions

WITH ELIMINATION OF NITROGEN

1. ***Replacement by Hydrogen.*** Numerous reducing agents can be used to replace the diazonium group by hydrogen. Hypophosphorous acid generally gives the best yields although alkaline formaldehyde may be equally satisfactory.

$$[ArN_2^+]^-OSO_3H + H_3PO_2 + H_2O \longrightarrow ArH + N_2 + H_2SO_4 + H_3PO_3$$

$$[ArN_2^+]^-OSO_3H + HCHO + 3 NaOH \longrightarrow ArH + N_2 + Na_2SO_4 + NaOCHO + 2 H_2O$$

Ethyl alcohol often gives a good yield of the reduction product although other alcohols may replace the diazonium group by alkoxyl (p. 377).

$$[ArN_2^+]^-OSO_3H + C_2H_5OH \longrightarrow ArH + N_2 + H_2SO_4 + CH_3CHO$$

Reductions of this type frequently are valuable, since an amino group can be used to activate the nucleus or bring about a desired orientation and then can be removed by diazotization and reduction. These principles are illustrated by the following series of reactions for the preparation of 1,3,5-tri-bromobenzene.

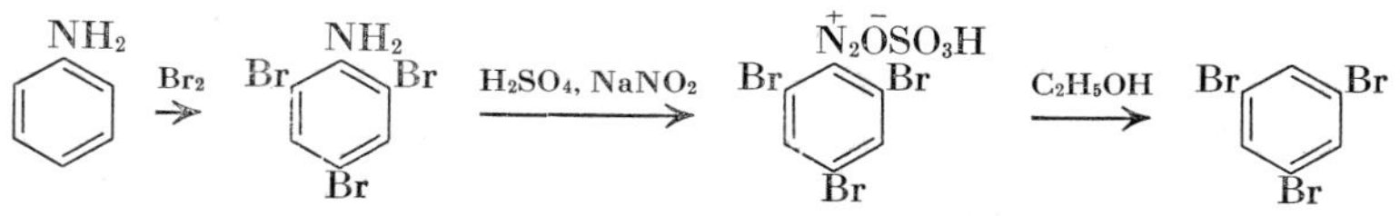

2. Replacement by Hydroxyl. If an aqueous solution of the diazonium salt is heated, nitrogen is evolved and the phenol is formed.

$$[ArN_2^+]^-OSO_3H + H_2O \xrightarrow{\text{Heat}} ArOH + N_2 + H_2SO_4$$

3. Replacement by Alkoxyl. Frequently when a solution of diazonium salt in an alcohol is heated, the diazonium group is replaced by alkoxyl.

$$[ArN_2^+]^-OSO_3H + CH_3OH \longrightarrow ArOCH_3 + N_2 + H_2SO_4$$

4. Replacement by Halogen. The diazonium group can be replaced readily by any of the halogens although different conditions may be required. For replacement by chlorine or bromine the aqueous solution of the corresponding salt is heated either with copper bronze (*Gattermann reaction*) or with cuprous chloride or cuprous bromide (*Sandmeyer reaction*). In general the cuprous halides give better yields.

$$[ArN_2^+]Cl^- \xrightarrow[\text{heat}]{\text{Cu or CuCl}} ArCl + N_2$$

$$[ArN_2^+]Br^- \xrightarrow[\text{heat}]{\text{Cu or CuBr}} ArBr + N_2$$

To replace the diazonium group with iodine it is necessary only to add potassium iodide to the aqueous solution of the sulfate and heat.

$$[ArN_2^+]^-OSO_3H + KI \longrightarrow ArI + N_2 + KHSO_4$$

Fluorine compounds are prepared by diazotizing the aromatic amine in the presence of fluoboric acid, when the fluoborate precipitates. Heating the dry salt yields the fluoro derivative and boron fluoride.

$$ArNH_2 + 2\,HBF_4 + NaNO_2 \longrightarrow [ArN_2^+]^-BF_4 + NaBF_4 + 2\,H_2O$$
$$\downarrow \text{Heat}$$
$$ArF + N_2 + BF_3$$

From these reactions it is evident that for replacement by groups other than halogen, it is preferable to use the diazonium sulfates rather than the diazonium halides since the latter always yield some of the halogen substitution product. Although chlorine and bromine compounds can be prepared by direct substitution, the preparation from the diazonium salt frequently has an advantage since the halogen enters only at the position formerly occupied by the diazonium group. Hence single products are obtained and isomers can be made which cannot be obtained by direct halogenation because of unfavorable directive influences.

5. Replacement by the Cyano (and Carboxyl) Group. If a neutral solution of a diazonium salt is added to a solution of cuprous cyanide-sodium cyanide complex, a precipitate is formed which decomposes to the nitrile on heating.

$$[ArN_2{}^+]^-OSO_3Na + NaCu(CN)_2 \longrightarrow ArCN + N_2 + CuCN + Na_2SO_4$$

Since the nitrile can be hydrolyzed to the acid, the reaction affords a method for replacing the diazonium group by a carboxyl group as well.

Numerous other types of replacement reactions are known which yield, for example, thiophenols, thiocyanates, sulfides, disulfides, sulfinic acids, arsonic and stibonic acids (p. 592), and mercury compounds.

Without Elimination of Nitrogen

1. Reduction to Hydrazines. When a diazonium salt is reduced with zinc dust and acetic acid, with sulfur dioxide, with sodium hydrosulfite, or with stannous chloride, an arylhydrazine is formed.

$$[C_6H_5\overset{+}{N}{\equiv}N]\bar{C}l + 2\,H_2SO_3 + 2\,H_2O \longrightarrow [C_6H_5NHNH_3\overset{+}{}\overset{-}{}]\bar{C}l + 2\,H_2SO_4$$

Since the reaction is general, many of these valuable reagents are easily available. It was the discovery of phenylhydrazine by Emil Fischer in 1877 that led to his work on the structure of the sugars (p. 282).

2. The Coupling Reaction. Diazonium salts react with phenols and tertiary amines in weakly acid, neutral, or alkaline solution, causing substitution in the position *para* to the hydroxyl or amino group with the production of highly colored azo compounds (p. 478).

$$[C_6H_5\overset{+}{N}{\equiv}N]Cl^- + H\!\!\left\langle\!\!\bigcirc\!\!\right\rangle\!\!OH + NaOH \longrightarrow C_6H_5N{=}N\!\!\left\langle\!\!\bigcirc\!\!\right\rangle\!\!OH + NaCl + H_2O$$

p-Hydroxyazobenzene

$$+ H\!\!\left\langle\!\!\bigcirc\!\!\right\rangle\!\!N(CH_3)_2 + NaOH \longrightarrow C_6H_5N{=}N\!\!\left\langle\!\!\bigcirc\!\!\right\rangle\!\!N(CH_3)_2 + NaCl + H_2O$$

p-Dimethylaminoazobenzene

In the coupling reaction the diazonium salt is known as the *primary component*, and the compound with which it couples is called the *secondary component*. If the *para* position of the secondary component is occupied, coupling takes place in the *ortho* position. If the *para* position and both *ortho* positions are blocked, coupling usually does not take place, although occasionally the group in the *para* position is displaced.

Coupling is a substitution reaction analogous to nitration, sulfonation, and halogenation, the active agent being the diazonium ion, $[ArN_2{}^+]$. Like nitrous acid, however, a diazonium salt is a very weak reagent and substitutes only aromatic nuclei that contain a strongly activating group such as an amino or hydroxyl group. Coupling does not take place in strongly acid solution, because the amino groups form salts and become deactivating, and the hydroxyl group is undissociated and not so strongly activating as the phenoxide ion (p. 341).

Coupling takes place with primary and secondary amines to give *diazoamino compounds*.

$$[Ar\overset{+}{N_2}]\overset{-}{C}l + 2\ HNHR \longrightarrow ArN{=}N{-}NHR + RNH_3Cl$$

Some of the primary and secondary aromatic amines also undergo this reaction. For example aniline couples with benzenediazonium chloride buffered with sodium acetate to give diazoaminobenzene.

$$C_6H_5N_2Cl + H_2NC_6H_5 + NaOCOCH_3 \longrightarrow C_6H_5N{=}N{-}NHC_6H_5 + NaCl + CH_3COOH$$
Diazoaminobenzene

It is to prevent this reaction that diazotization is carried out in strongly acid solution, since the amine salt does not couple.

If the diazoamino compound is heated in the presence of an amine salt to catalyze the reaction, rearrangement to the aminoazo compound takes place.

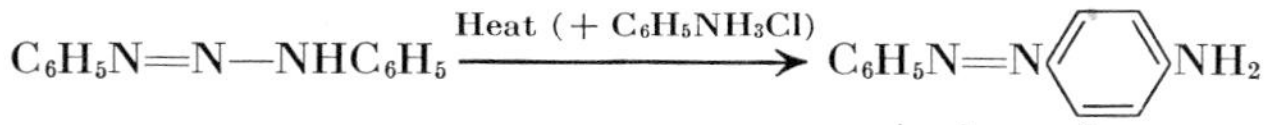

$$C_6H_5N{=}N{-}NHC_6H_5 \xrightarrow{\text{Heat } (+\ C_6H_5NH_3Cl)} C_6H_5N{=}N\text{—}\langle\ \rangle\text{—}NH_2$$
p-Aminoazobenzene

From many primary aromatic amines, for example the naphthylamines (p. 433), the diazoamino compounds cannot be isolated, the nuclear-substituted azo compounds being formed directly.

REVIEW QUESTIONS

1. Discuss the physical properties of diazonium salts and their bearing on the structure of this class of compounds.
2. Give equations and conditions for the replacement of a diazonium group by hydroxyl, hydrogen, halogen, and nitrile groups.
3. How is phenylhydrazine prepared?
4. Discuss the coupling reaction of diazonium salts. Why does coupling take place only in alkaline or weakly acid solutions? Why is it necessary that the reaction mixture contain a large excess of mineral acid during the preparation of diazonium salts?
5. Devise a colorimetric procedure for the estimation of nitrous acid. (Hint: use a diazonium salt as an intermediate.)
6. Give reactions for the preparation of (*a*) *m*-cyanonitrobenzene from *m*-dinitrobenzene; (*b*) *m*-dibromobenzene from benzene; (*c*) *p*-bromophenylhydrazine from bromobenzene; (*d*) *m*-toluidine from *p*-toluidine.

Chapter 25

PHENOLS, AMINOPHENOLS, AND QUINONES

PHENOLS

The phenols are compounds having a hydroxyl group attached directly to an aromatic nucleus. In general their methods of preparation and reactions differ from those of the alcohols.

Occurrence and Nomenclature

The name *phenol* for hydroxybenzene is derived from *phene*, an old name for benzene (p. 403). The hydroxy derivatives of toluene have the common name *cresols*, and those of xylene are called *xylenols*. Phenols in general are named as derivatives of phenol.

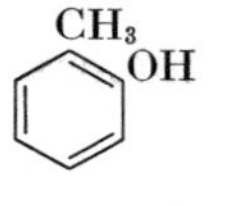

o-Cresol,
o-methylphenol

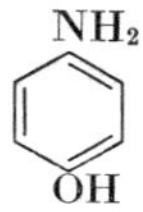

p-Aminophenol

Phenol, cresols, and xylenols occur in coal tar, wood tar, and petroleum distillates along with other phenolic compounds and are known as *tar acids*. The mixed phenols from the cresol fraction is known technically as *cresylic acid*. Derivatives of phenols frequently occur as plant products (pp. 391–393).

Structure

Whereas the enol forms of simple aldehydes and ketones are unstable and pass almost completely into the keto forms, the phenols exist entirely in the enol form. The greater stability of the enol form for the phenols is due to its high resonance energy, compared with that of the keto form. The situation is exactly analogous to that discussed for the aromatic amines (p. 360).

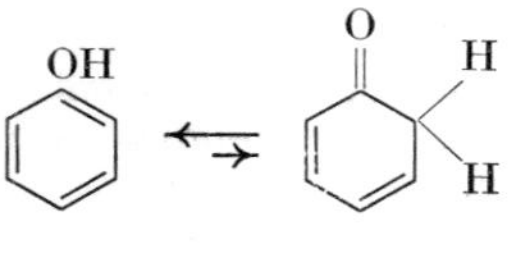

Preparation

This section summarizes methods discussed previously.

1. *From Aromatic Sulfonic Acids* (p. 354).

$$ArSO_3Na + 2\ NaOH \xrightarrow[290°-300°]{Fusion} ArONa + Na_2SO_3 + 2\ H_2O$$

2. *From Aryl Halides* (p. 330).

$$\text{ArCl} + 2\,\text{NaOH} \longrightarrow \text{ArONa} + \text{NaCl} + \text{H}_2\text{O}$$

This reaction goes readily only if the halogen is activated by electron-attracting groups (p. 348), but it is applied industrially to nonreactive halides by using a high temperature (p. 387).

3. *From Diazonium Salts* (p. 377).

$$[\text{Ar}\overset{+}{\text{N}}_2]\overset{-}{\text{O}}\text{SO}_3\text{H} + \text{H}_2\text{O} \overset{\text{Heat}}{\longrightarrow} \text{ArOH} + \text{N}_2 + \text{H}_2\text{SO}_4$$

Physical Properties

The pure phenols are colorless solids or liquids, although as usually encountered they are colored red by oxidation products. Like the aromatic amines (p. 361), they boil higher than the normal aliphatic analogs of the same molecular weight. For example phenol boils at 181° whereas 1-hexanol boils at 157°. Phenol is soluble in water to the extent of 9 g. per 100 g. of water at 25° and becomes miscible at 65°. Water is soluble in phenol to the extent of 29 g. per 100 g. Since the melting point of phenol is only 42°, a small amount of water lowers the melting point below room temperature. This liquid form containing about 5 per cent water is called **carbolic acid.** In the monosubstituted phenols, the *para* isomer has the highest melting point.

Reactions

Reactions Involving the Hydroxyl Group

1. *Acidity.* Phenols are considerably more acidic than alcohols or water, but weaker than carboxylic acids and weaker even than carbonic acid. Thus the acid dissociation constant of acetic acid is 1.8×10^{-5}; carbonic, 4.3×10^{-7}; hydrocyanic, 7.2×10^{-10}; phenol, 1.3×10^{-10}; and water, 1.8×10^{-16}. Hence phenols react with sodium hydroxide solutions to form water-soluble salts but not with aqueous sodium carbonate. Moreover water-insoluble phenols are precipitated from their salts by carbonic acid.

$$\text{ArOH} + \text{NaOH} \longrightarrow [\text{Ar}\overset{-}{\text{O}}]\overset{+}{\text{Na}} + \text{H}_2\text{O}$$

$$[\text{Ar}\overset{-}{\text{O}}]\overset{+}{\text{Na}} + \text{CO}_2 + \text{H}_2\text{O} \longrightarrow \text{ArOH} + \text{NaHCO}_3$$

These reactions are used to distinguish phenols and to separate them from alcohols or carboxylic acids.

These statements apply to phenols which do not contain strongly electron-attracting groups in the nucleus. Thus the acid dissociation constants of some of the nitrophenols are: *o*-nitrophenol, 6.8×10^{-8}; *m*-nitrophenol, 5.3×10^{-9}; *p*-nitrophenol, 6.5×10^{-8}; 2,4-dinitrophenol, 8.3×10^{-5}; and 2,4,6-trinitrophenol (picric acid), 4.2×10^{-1}. In the mononitrophenols, the effect of the nitro group is greater in the *ortho* or *para* positions than in the *meta* position. Two nitro groups in the *ortho* and *para* positions give an acid approximately as strong as a carboxylic acid. The strength of picric acid with three nitro groups in the *ortho* and *para* positions approaches that of the mineral acids.

The greater acidity of phenols compared with alcohols can be explained by the interaction of the unshared pair of electrons of the oxygen atom with the unsaturation electrons of the nucleus (p. 343). This resonance effect decreases the electron density on the oxygen atom and permits loss of a proton more easily from a phenol than from an alcohol. Since the unshared pair of electrons from the oxygen atom does not interact as completely in the phenoxide ion as in the carboxylate ion (the extreme resonance structures are not equivalent in the phenoxide ion, p. 343), the resonance effect is not so pronounced, and the phenols are weaker acids than the carboxylic acids.

The inductive and resonance effects of nitro groups operate the same way in phenols to increase the acidity as they do in aromatic amines to decrease the basicity (p. 362).

2. Colored Complexes with Ferric Chloride. Enols in general give colored water-soluble complexes with ferric chloride. The exact nature of these colored compounds is uncertain, although it seems likely that a coordination compound is formed in which the iron is hexacovalent. The reaction with phenols probably is complicated by the formation of colored oxidation products (p. 383). Whereas with simple enols the color produced is a burgundy red, the phenols give colors that are less pure and usually purplish or greenish. This reaction is a convenient test for phenols and other enols.

3. Ester Formation. Phenols do not esterify directly with carboxylic acids. Esters can be prepared by reaction with anhydrides or acid chlorides.

$$C_6H_5OH + (CH_3CO)_2O \xrightarrow{(H_2SO_4)} C_6H_5OCOCH_3 + HOCOCH_3$$
Phenol   Phenyl acetate

$$C_6H_5OH + CH_3COCl \longrightarrow C_6H_5OCOCH_3 + HCl$$

4. Ether Formation. Phenols form ethers very easily by the Williamson synthesis (p. 115). Since sodium aryl oxides are hydrolyzed only partially in aqueous solution, the reaction can be carried out in this medium.

$$ArONa + XR \longrightarrow ArOR + NaX$$

The methyl ethers are most important, because they can be prepared readily by agitating an alkaline solution of the phenol with methyl sulfate.

$$[C_6H_5\overset{-}{O}]\overset{+}{Na} + (CH_3)_2SO_4 \longrightarrow C_6H_5OCH_3 + CH_3HSO_4$$
Sodium   Anisole,
phenoxide   methyl phenyl
                            ether

Ethyl phenyl ether is known as *phenetole. Phenyl ether* (phenyl oxide) is a coproduct of one of the commercial methods for the synthesis of phenol (p. 387).

5. Replacement by Halogen. The hydroxyl group of phenols, unlike that of alcohols, is difficult to replace by halogen. Halogen acids are without action, and phosphorus trihalides yield only phosphorous esters. If phosphorus pentachloride or pentabromide is used, some replacement occurs, but the reaction is not used for preparative purposes.

$$ArOH + PX_5 \longrightarrow ArX + POX_3 + HX$$

6. *Replacement by Hydrogen.* When phenols are heated with zinc dust the oxygen is removed from the molecule.

$$\text{ArOH} + \text{Zn} \xrightarrow{\text{Heat}} \text{ArH} + \text{ZnO}$$

The reaction, although of no value for synthesis, has been useful in arriving at the fundamental structure of aromatic products.

REACTIONS INVOLVING THE NUCLEUS

1. *Oxidation.* Like the amino group in aromatic amines, the hydroxyl group can supply electrons to the nucleus and permits ready oxidation. Complex mixtures of oxidation products are formed by either air or other oxidizing agents. One of the oxidation products of phenol by air appears to be *quinone* (p. 396), which forms a brilliant red addition product with phenol known as *phenoquinone.*

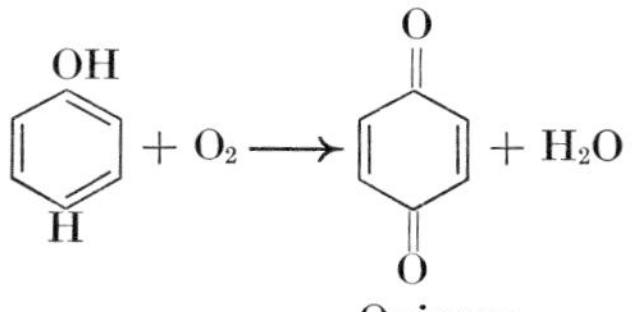

Quinone

$$\text{C}_6\text{H}_4\text{O}_2 + 2\,\text{C}_6\text{H}_5\text{OH} \longrightarrow \text{C}_6\text{H}_4\text{O}_2 \cdot 2\,\text{C}_6\text{H}_5\text{OH}$$
Phenoquinone

2. *Sulfonation.* Because of the strong activating effect of the hydroxyl group, sulfonation takes place very readily. At room temperature concentrated sulfuric acid yields chiefly the *ortho* isomer, whereas at 100° the *para* isomer predominates.

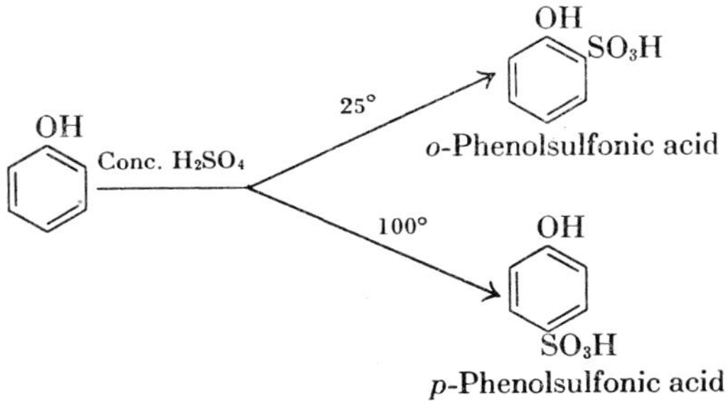

o-Phenolsulfonic acid

p-Phenolsulfonic acid

3. *Halogenation.* By controlled halogenation in anhydrous solvents, it is possible to obtain the monohalogenated phenols in satisfactory yields.

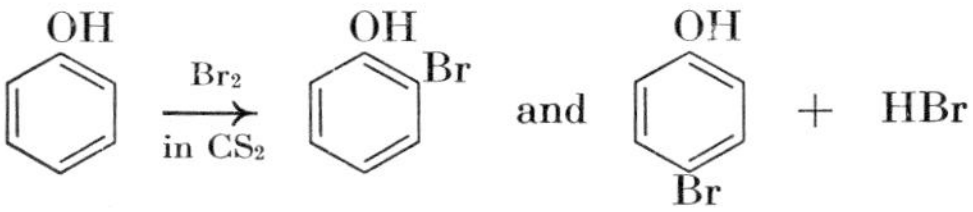

o-Bromo-phenol *p*-Bromo-phenol

When bromine water is added to an aqueous solution of phenol, 2,4,6-tri-bromophenol hypobromite precipitates. Addition of sodium bisulfite produces the tribromophenol.

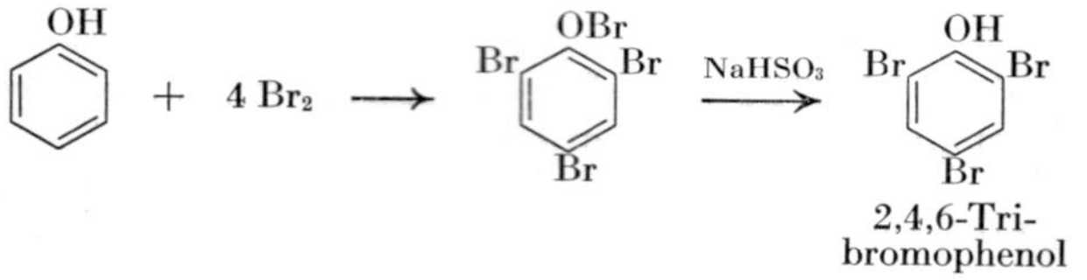

4. *Nitration.* Phenol nitrates so rapidly that if mononitration is desired, dilute nitric acid at room temperature is used.

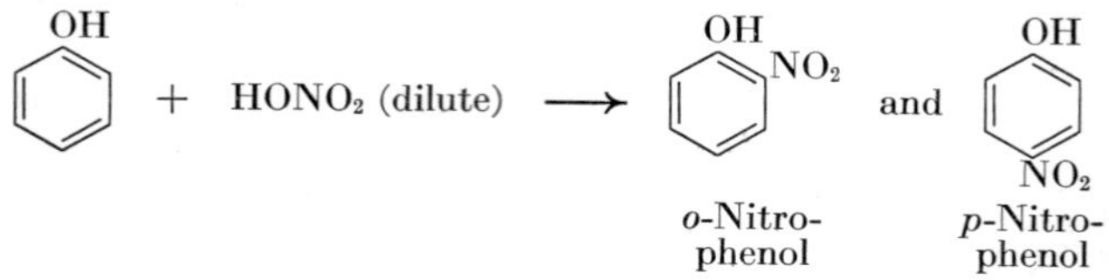

The isomers can be separated by steam distillation, since the *ortho* isomer is much more volatile.

Ortho, meta, and *para* isomers usually boil within 10° of each other, but *o*-nitrophenol boils at 214° and *p*-nitrophenol boils at 245°. The *ortho* isomer also is less soluble in water than the *meta* or *para* compounds. Thus the *ortho* isomer has much less tendency to associ-ate with itself or with other hydroxylic compounds. An explanation of this behavior is that the spatial arrangement of the groups permits the hydrogen atom of the hydroxyl group in the *ortho* isomer to form an internal proton bond with the nitro group in the *ortho* position but not with a nitro group in the *meta* or *para* positions.

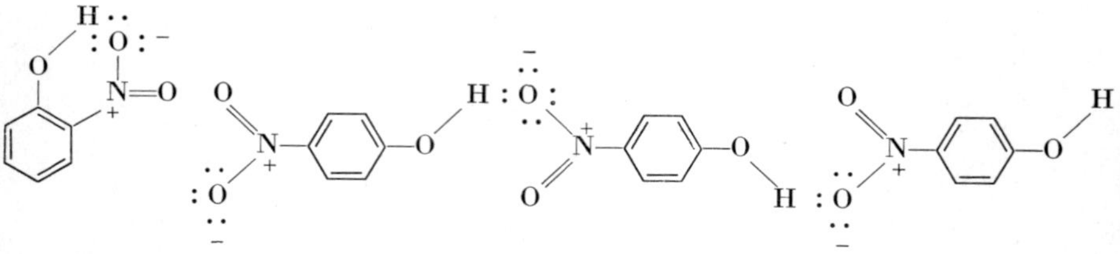

Nonassociated
o-nitrophenol

Associated *p*-nitrophenol

The nitrophenols are colorless or pale yellow. Their salts are deep yellow.

Nitration of phenol with concentrated nitric acid gives **2,4,6-trinitro-phenol (picric acid)**, but the amount of oxidation is excessive, and it is better to sulfonate the phenol first by warming with concentrated sulfuric acid. After some dilution with water, the nitration is carried out by the addition of concentrated nitric acid. The sulfonic acid group counteracts the effect of the hydroxyl group, and hence reduces the rate of the subsequent nitration and of the oxidation reaction. The sulfonic acid group is displaced in the process.

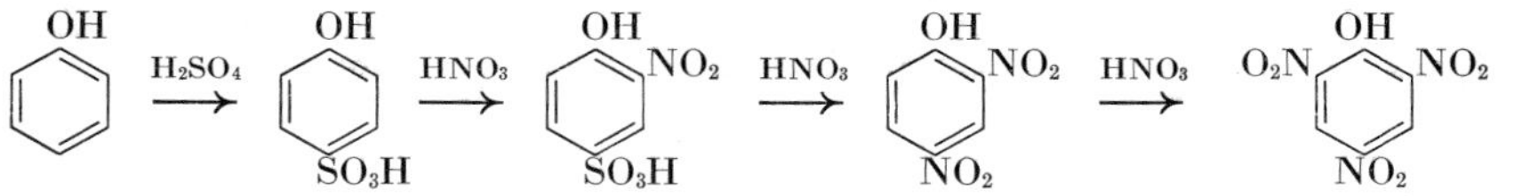

2,4,6-Trinitro-
phenol (picric acid)

5. Nitrosation. The activating effect of the hydroxyl group is so great that phenol reacts with nitrous acid to give **p-nitrosophenol.** This compound is tautomeric with the monoxime of *p*-quinone (p. 396).

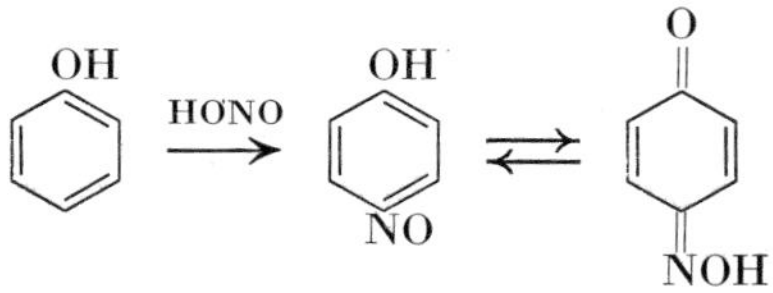

p-Nitroso-   Quinone
phenol   monoxime

If the reaction is carried out in the presence of concentrated sulfuric acid, further condensation with phenol takes place to give a dark green solution of indophenol acid sulfate. When the acid solution is diluted with water and made alkaline, the deep blue sodium salt is formed.

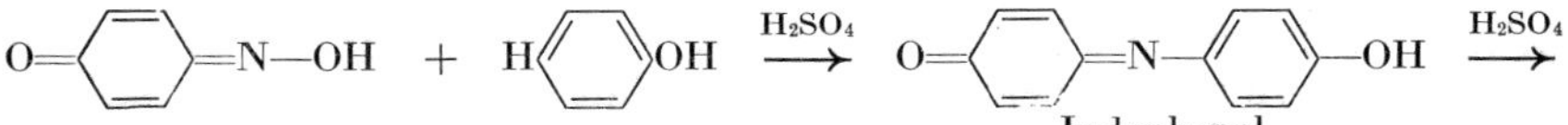

Indophenol

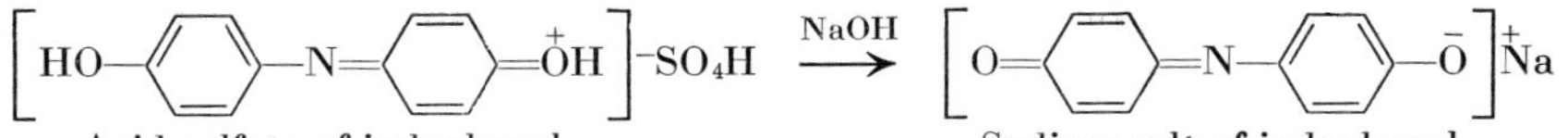

Acid sulfate of indophenol   Sodium salt of indophenol
(deep green)   (deep blue)

The reaction is used as a test for nitrites and is known as **Liebermann's nitroso reaction.**[1] Even some nitrates and aliphatic nitro compounds give the test, since reduction to nitrite takes place in the concentrated sulfuric acid solution.

6. *Condensation with Aldehydes and Ketones.* The activating effect of the hydroxyl group also permits condensation with aldehydes and ketones in the *ortho* and *para* positions. Thus phenol undergoes an aldol-type condensation with formaldehyde in the presence of dilute alkali (*Lederer-Manasse reaction*).

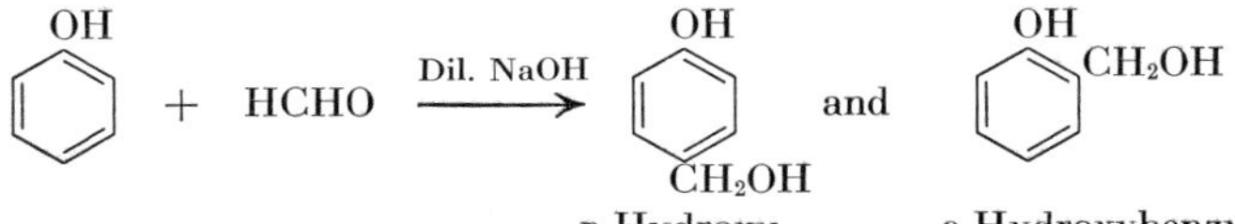

p-Hydroxy-   o-Hydroxybenzyl
benzyl   alcohol
alcohol   (saligenin)

---

[1] Carl Theodor Liebermann (1842–1914), professor at the Berlin Technische Hochschule. His work dealt chiefly with natural dyes and with the chemistry of anthracene (p. 437).

Unless the reaction is controlled carefully, these products undergo further condensation to yield phenol-formaldehyde resins (p. 388).

The condensation with aldehydes is a typical substitution reaction. In alkaline solution the formation of the sodium salt of the phenol greatly increases the probability of reaction of the aldehyde carbon atom at the *ortho* and *para* positions.

Physiological Action

All phenols having a sufficiently high vapor pressure have a characteristic odor. Phenol is highly toxic, killing all types of cells. It precipitates proteins, and when applied to the skin, produces a white spot which soon turns red; later the dead skin sloughs. If allowed to remain in contact with the skin, it penetrates to the deeper tissues and severe burns result. It also is absorbed into the blood stream and acts as a systemic poison.

The phenols in general are toxic to micro-organisms. Although many substances had been discovered empirically to have a preservative and healing action long before the nature of bacterial infection was known, phenol itself was the first compound to be used widely for the avowed purpose of antisepsis. It was introduced by Lister in 1867. Much more effective and less toxic compounds have been developed since then, but antiseptic activity still is reported in terms of the *phenol coefficient*, a number which compares the effectiveness of a preparation with that of a 5 per cent solution of phenol against *Staphylococcus aureus*.

Phenol and Some Important Derivatives

Phenol in 1948 held third place among the synthetic aromatic chemicals, the volume of production being exceeded only by styrene (p. 425) and chlorobenzene (p. 329). The quantity produced in the United States by synthesis was 8 million pounds in 1928, 31 million pounds in 1938, and 274 million pounds in 1948. In the same years the amount of natural phenol obtained from coal tar was 2, 14, and 23 million pounds. Small amounts are obtained also from the refining of petroleum. It has been estimated that the potential demand for phenol was over twice that produced in 1948, production being limited by the supply of benzene.

Production of Phenol. Numerous processes have been developed for the synthesis of phenol. At least four different processes have been competitive in the United States.

1. SULFONATION AND CAUSTIC FUSION. This process is the oldest. It was discovered independently in 1867 by Kekulé, Wurtz, and Dusart. The commercial application originally involved sulfonation with fuming sulfuric acid, conversion to the sodium salt by liming out (p. 353), and fusion with sodium hydroxide. In 1918 a continuous process was developed in which a large excess of benzene runs counter-current to the sulfonating acid, which starts out at a concentration of 98 per cent and ends up as 77 per cent. The sulfonic acid re-

mains dissolved in the benzene at a concentration of 2 per cent and is washed out with water and neutralized with sodium sulfite recovered from the caustic fusion. The solution of sodium salt is concentrated and run into fused sodium hydroxide at 320°–350°. The melt is treated with a minimum of water to dissolve the sodium phenoxide, leaving the sodium sulfite undissolved. The phenol is liberated or *sprung* by passing carbon dioxide into the solution. The sodium carbonate is reconverted to caustic soda by the addition of lime, and the calcium carbonate that precipitates is converted to carbon dioxide and lime in the lime kilns. Alternatively the phenol may be liberated with sulfur dioxide formed when the benzenesulfonic acid is converted to the sodium salt, or the benzenesulfonic acid itself may be used. With the exception of losses, only benzene, sodium hydroxide, and sulfuric acid are consumed in the process, the products being phenol and sodium bisulfite (or sulfur dioxide and sodium sulfite). The over-all process therefore is the oxidation of benzene by sulfuric acid. Since sulfuric acid is made by the oxidation of sulfur dioxide with air, the latter is the ultimate oxidizing agent.

2. HYDROLYSIS OF CHLOROBENZENE (DOW PROCESS). Since 1928 phenol has been manufactured in large quantities by the hydrolysis of chlorobenzene, which is emulsified with 10 per cent sodium hydroxide solution, and then circulated and recirculated with turbulation in copper-lined iron tubes at 320°. The product is bled out of the system at the rate at which the original emulsion enters, making the process continuous. Almost 100 per cent reaction occurs. Besides phenol, about 20 per cent of phenyl ether and smaller amounts of *o*- and *p*-phenylphenol are formed.

$$C_6H_5Cl + 2\ NaOH \longrightarrow C_6H_5ONa + NaCl + H_2O$$

$$C_6H_5Cl + NaOC_6H_5 \longrightarrow C_6H_5OC_6H_5 + NaCl$$
Phenyl ether

$$C_6H_5Cl + C_6H_5ONa + NaOH \longrightarrow \quad \text{and} \quad \text{—ONa} + NaCl + H_2O$$

The phenyl ether is extracted with chlorobenzene and the phenol is liberated with hydrochloric acid. The phenol is purified and separated from the phenylphenols by distillation.

Some phenyl ether is used in the perfume industry, and a large quantity is used to form with diphenyl a eutectic mixture, which serves as a heat transfer medium in industrial operations. This mixture of 74 parts of phenyl ether and 26 parts of diphenyl is stable up to 400° at 135 p.s.i. However if the amount of phenyl ether produced during the manufacture of phenol is greater than the demand, it can be recycled, since at 320° in the presence of sodium hydroxide it is in equilibrium with sodium phenoxide.

$$C_6H_5OC_6H_5 + 2\ NaOH \rightleftharpoons 2\ C_6H_5ONa + H_2O$$
20 per cent \qquad 80 per cent

3. RASCHIG PROCESS. This process was introduced into the United States from Germany about 1940. As in the Dow process two stages are involved, the

chlorination of benzene and hydrolysis. However hydrogen chloride and air replace electrolytic chlorine, water replaces caustic soda, and the process is carried out in the vapor phase. In the first stage benzene, hydrogen chloride, and air are passed over a catalyst.

$$C_6H_6 + HCl + \tfrac{1}{2} O_2 \text{ (air)} \xrightarrow[\text{Cu–Fe cat.}]{230°} C_6H_5Cl + H_2O$$

Although carried out in one step, the process apparently involves the intermediate formation of chlorine by the old Deacon process from hydrogen chloride and air in the presence of cupric chloride. The conversion is about 10 per cent per pass, but the chlorobenzene is separated readily and the unchanged reagents are recycled.

In the second stage the chlorobenzene is hydrolyzed with water. Here again the conversion is about 10 per cent.

$$C_6H_5Cl + H_2O \xrightarrow{425° + \text{cat.}} C_6H_5OH + HCl$$

The recovery of hydrogen chloride for use in the first stage is about 97 per cent. About 10 per cent of co-products are formed including 6 per cent of dichlorobenzene in the first stage. This process like the first is an indirect air oxidation of benzene.

4. DIRECT AIR OXIDATION. Phenol has been produced by passing a mixture of air and benzene (or toluene) over a brick checkerwork coated with boron oxide glass and heated to 700°–800°. The purpose of the boron oxide is to act

$$C_6H_6 + \tfrac{1}{2} O_2 \longrightarrow C_6H_5OH$$

not as a catalyst for the oxidation, but as a free-radical chain breaker to cut down the amount of oxidation to carbon dioxide and water (p. 582).

Uses of Phenol and Its Derivatives. The chief use for phenol is for the manufacture of phenol-formaldehyde resins and plastics. Production of these *phenolics* in the United States amounted to 376 million pounds in 1948. Although the reaction of phenol and formaldehyde to give resins was reported by Baeyer in 1872, it was not until 1909 that a commercially useful product was developed by Baekeland, a Belgian-born American chemist, who was looking for a substitute for shellac. For a long time the term *Bakelite* was synonymous with phenol-formaldehyde plastics. The trade name now is owned by the Union Carbide and Carbon Corporation and is used to designate all of their plastics except the vinyl polymers (p. 516).

Two general processes of manufacture are in use. The *one-step process* produces cast phenolics, which usually are converted into useful objects by machining. Phenol and somewhat more than one molecular equivalent of aqueous formaldehyde are heated for a short time with a basic catalyst such as ammonia or sodium hydroxide. A *resole* or *A-stage resin* is formed which is fusible and soluble in organic solvents. It is a linear polymer, condensation having taken place in the *ortho* and *para* positions. This molten resin is drawn off and cast into molds which then are heated at 75°–85° until the reaction is complete. During this stage the linear polymeric chains are cross-linked by the excess formaldehyde, and the infusible, insoluble resin is formed.

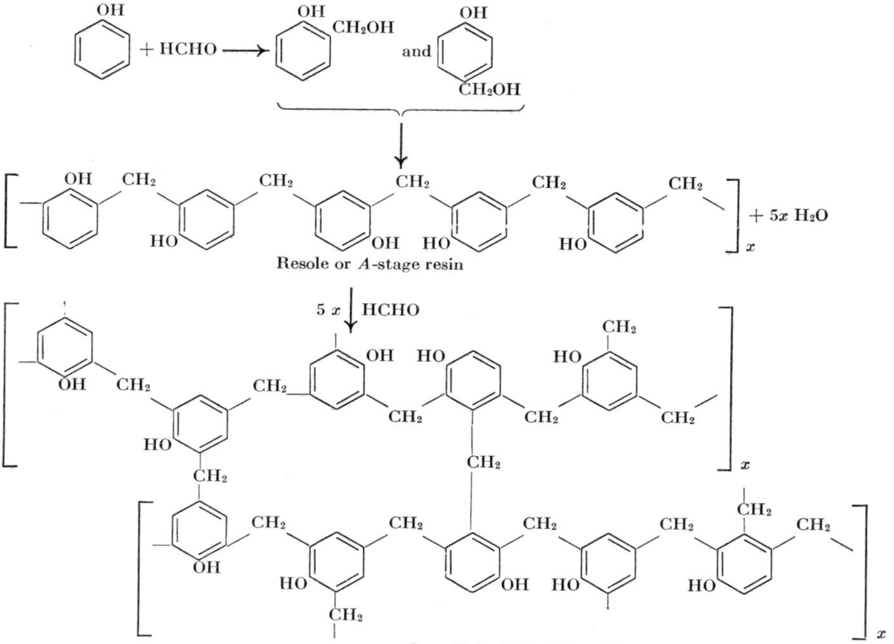

Resole or *A*-stage resin

Cross-linked infusible resin

The above formulas merely indicate possible modes of linkage. In the actual resin these various types of linkage undoubtedly are distributed randomly.

The *two-step process* is used for the compression molding of objects. Phenol and about 0.8 molecular equivalent of formaldehyde is heated with about 0.1 per cent of hydrogen chloride as an acid catalyst. After two hours the water is removed by distillation at reduced pressure, and the resole is run into pans or onto the floor, where it is cooled to a glassy solid. It is broken into pieces which are ground in ball mills with lime to neutralize the acid. It then is mixed with hexamethylenetetramine (p. 177), a mold lubricant such as zinc stearate, a filler such as sawdust, and a brown or black coloring matter. After compacting and granulating, it is known as *molding powder*. When the proper amount of the powder is placed in a mold and subjected to heat and pressure, the material flows to fill the interstices of the mold, and the hexamethylenetetramine supplies the additional formaldehyde and ammonia necessary to produce cross-linkage and setting of the resin.

The phenol-formaldehyde plastics usually are dark colored. They are brittle, the strength of the finished product being dependent largely on the filler. However they are cheap, have a good finish, high heat resistance and high dielectric strength. If *para*-substituted phenols are used, for example *p*-cresol or *p-t*-butylphenol, the cross-chain reaction is blocked and the product is thermoplastic. About half of the phenolic resin production is used for molding purposes. Most of the remainder is used as a bonding agent in the manufacture of plywood and other laminated materials, and as water-proof adhesives for other purposes.

If a phenolsulfonic acid is condensed with formaldehyde and phenol, the resulting resin contains sulfonic acid groups and can act as an ion-exchange material. The chief use is for softening water. Hard water contains alkaline earth and heavy metal salts which form insoluble precipitates with soaps (p. 158) and deposit insoluble salts in water heaters and boilers. When such water is passed over the sodium salt of an ion-exchange material, these undesirable ions are replaced by sodium ions, the salts of which are more soluble.

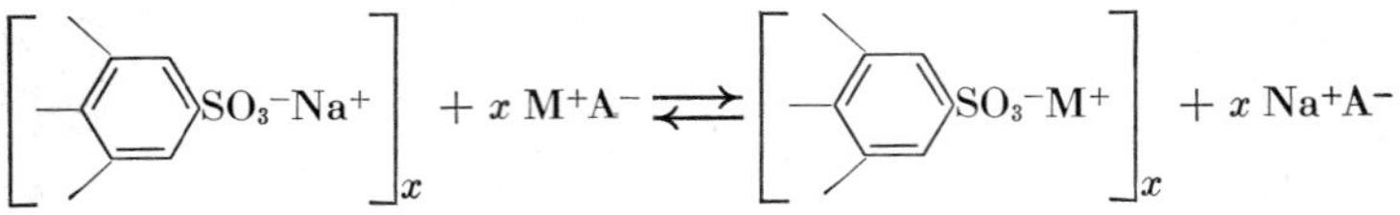

$$\left[-\!\!\bigcirc\!\!-SO_3{}^-Na^+ \right]_x + x\,M^+A^- \rightleftarrows \left[-\!\!\bigcirc\!\!-SO_3{}^-M^+ \right]_x + x\,Na^+A^-$$

In the above equilibrium M^+ is any cation and A^- any anion, which need not be monovalent. When exchange has taken place to the extent that the undesirable cations no longer are removed sufficiently from solution, the ion exchanger is regenerated by allowing it to stand with a concentrated salt solution, which shifts the equilibrium to the left. Sulfonated polystyrenes (p. 425) behave in the same way.

If the ion-exchange resin is used as the free acid, it exchanges hydrogen ions for other cations and can be regenerated with concentrated hydrochloric acid.

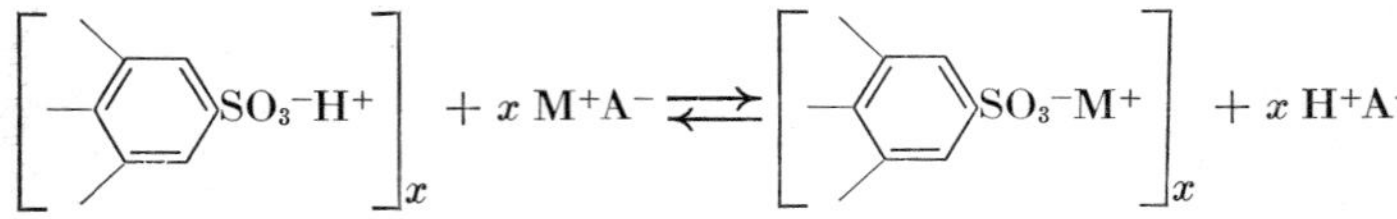

$$\left[-\!\!\bigcirc\!\!-SO_3{}^-H^+ \right]_x + x\,M^+A^- \rightleftarrows \left[-\!\!\bigcirc\!\!-SO_3{}^-M^+ \right]_x + x\,H^+A^-$$

A solution which has exchanged its metallic ions for hydrogen ions can be passed over a basic resin, such as one produced by condensing *m*-phenylenediamine (p. 360) with formaldehyde, to give substantially ion-free water.

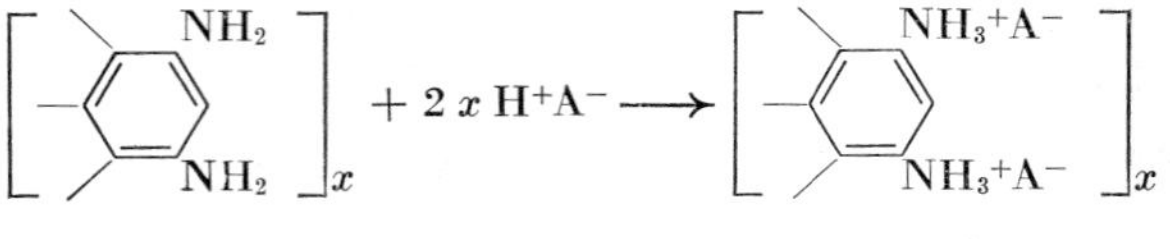

$$\left[-\!\!\bigcirc\!\!\begin{smallmatrix}NH_2\\NH_2\end{smallmatrix} \right]_x + 2\,x\,H^+A^- \longrightarrow \left[-\!\!\bigcirc\!\!\begin{smallmatrix}NH_3{}^+A^-\\NH_3{}^+A^-\end{smallmatrix} \right]_x$$

When the basic resin is converted fully to its salt, it can be regenerated with sodium hydroxide solution.

Since the aromatic amino groups are only weakly basic (p. 362), these resins are not very efficient for removing weak acids. To provide groups that are more basic, dibasic aliphatic amines such as ethylenediamine are condensed with the aromatic diamine and formaldehyde, or a tertiary aromatic amine is used which can be converted to a quaternary hydroxide.

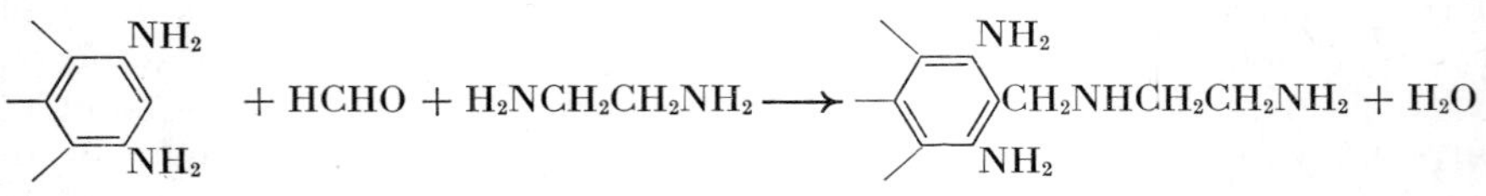

$$-\!\!\bigcirc\!\!\begin{smallmatrix}NH_2\\NH_2\end{smallmatrix} + HCHO + H_2NCH_2CH_2NH_2 \longrightarrow -\!\!\bigcirc\!\!\begin{smallmatrix}NH_2\\CH_2NHCH_2CH_2NH_2\\NH_2\end{smallmatrix} + H_2O$$

$$\underset{\text{N(CH}_3)_2}{\overset{\text{N(CH}_3)_2}{\bigcirc}} \longrightarrow \underset{\text{N(CH}_3)_3{}^+\text{OH}^-}{\overset{\text{N(CH}_3)_3{}^+\text{OH}^-}{\bigcirc}}$$

Large quantities of phenol are used for the refining of lubricating oils (p. 54). **Pentachlorophenol** dissolved in oil is used extensively for treating wood to prevent the growth of fungi. The sodium salt is used to treat industrial water to prevent the growth of slime and algae. **2,4-Dichlorophenoxyacetic acid (2-4-D)** has become an important selective weed killer. It is made from sodium 2,4-dichlorophenoxide and sodium chloroacetate.

$$\underset{\text{Cl}\quad\text{Cl}}{\overset{\text{ONa}}{\bigcirc}} + \text{ClCH}_2\text{COONa} \longrightarrow \underset{\text{Cl}\quad\text{Cl}}{\overset{\text{OCH}_2\text{COONa}}{\bigcirc}}$$

2,4,6-Trinitrophenol, because of its high acidity and its bitter taste, was given the name **picric acid** (Gr. *pikros* bitter). At times it has been used as a yellow dye for silk and as a military explosive. Besides the procedure given on page 384, other processes of manufacture have been developed. For example if chlorobenzene is nitrated to 2,4-dinitrochlorobenzene, the halogen can be removed readily by hydrolysis and the nitration completed in good yield.

$$\underset{}{\overset{\text{Cl}}{\bigcirc}} \xrightarrow{\text{HNO}_3 + \text{H}_2\text{SO}_4} \underset{\text{NO}_2}{\overset{\text{Cl}\quad\text{NO}_2}{\bigcirc}} \xrightarrow{\text{H}_2\text{O} + \text{Na}_2\text{CO}_3} \underset{\text{NO}_2}{\overset{\text{OH}\quad\text{NO}_2}{\bigcirc}} \xrightarrow{\text{HNO}_3 + \text{H}_2\text{SO}_4} \underset{\text{NO}_2}{\overset{\text{OH}}{\underset{}{\text{O}_2\text{N}\bigcirc\text{NO}_2}}}$$

The aromatic ring of trinitrophenol is oxidized by alkaline hypochlorite to give **chloropicrin** (trichloronitromethane, p. 205).

$$\underset{\text{NO}_2}{\overset{\text{OH}}{\text{O}_2\text{N}\bigcirc\text{NO}_2}} + 11\,\text{NaOCl} \longrightarrow 3\,\text{Cl}_3\text{CNO}_2 + 3\,\text{Na}_2\text{CO}_3 + 3\,\text{NaOH} + 2\,\text{NaCl}$$

The *aryl phosphates* are made by the reaction of the phenol with phosphorus oxychloride.

$$3\,\text{ArOH} + \text{POCl}_3 \longrightarrow (\text{ArO})_3\text{PO} + 3\,\text{HCl}$$

They are used extensively as plasticizers and flame retarders. **Phenyl phosphate** (triphenyl phosphate) is used in photographic film base to increase flexibility, to produce flat sheets, and to decrease flammability. Technical **tricresyl phosphate,** prepared from the mixed cresols, is one of the most important of the plasticizers, particularly for vinyl polymers. It is used also as a nonflammable hydraulic fluid and as an additive for lubricating oils. Production in the United States in 1948 was 15 million pounds.

Creosote oil, a coal, wood, or petroleum tar fraction boiling at 225°–270°, contains considerable amounts of the **cresols** and is used on a large scale for wood preservation. **Thymol,** *3-hydroxy-4-isopropyltoluene,* occurs in thyme oil. In the absence of a sufficient supply of the natural product, it is synthesized from *m*-cresol and propylene.

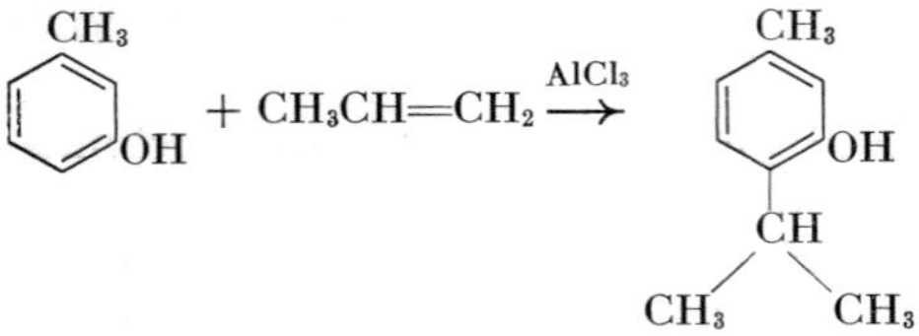

$$\text{(structure)} + CH_3CH=CH_2 \xrightarrow{AlCl_3} \text{(structure)}$$

Thymol is antiseptic in high dilutions. It has a more pleasant aromatic odor than phenol or the cresols, and frequently is used in proprietary antiseptic preparations. Thymol is the starting point for the synthesis of menthol (p. 565). **Carvacrol,** *2-hydroxy-4-isopropyltoluene,* also occurs in some essential oils. Many other phenols or phenol ethers are responsible for the aromatic properties of essential oils. **Anethole,** the chief constituent of anise oil, is 4-propenylanisole.

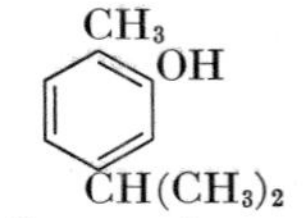

Carvacrol

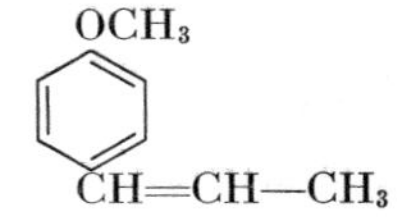

Anethole

POLYHYDRIC PHENOLS AND AMINOPHENOLS

The *o*-, *m*-, and *p*-dihydroxybenzenes are known as *catechol* (or *pyrocatechol*), *resorcinol*, and *hydroquinone* respectively. **Catechol** is so named because it is one of the distillation products of *gum catechu*, obtained from certain Asiatic tropical plants. It can be prepared by the general method of synthesis, namely the fusion of sodium *o*-phenolsulfonate with caustic soda, or by the acid hydrolysis of its monomethyl ether (guaiacol). **Guaiacol** occurs in the

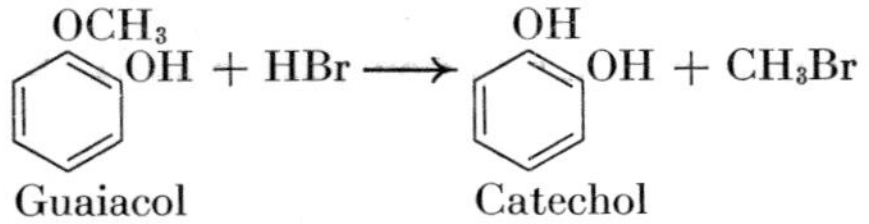

$$\text{(structure)} + HBr \longrightarrow \text{(structure)} + CH_3Br$$

Guaiacol   Catechol

distillation products of guaiac, the resin from American tropical trees of the genus *Guaiacum*, but is produced commercially from wood tar. Methylation of guaiacol with methyl sulfate and sodium hydroxide (p. 382) gives the dimethyl ether of catechol, which is known as **veratrole.** Veratrole also is formed on decarboxylation of veratric acid obtained from plants of the genus *Veratrum*. **Eugenol** from oil of cloves is 2-methoxy-4-allylphenol, and **safrole** from oil of sassafras and from camphor oil is the formaldehyde acetal of 4-allylcatechol. Being an acetal, safrole is hydrolyzed easily by dilute acids.

Eugenol

Safrole

The toxic irritants of poison ivy, poison oak, and related plants of the *Anacardiaceae* are catechols having long unsaturated side chains, for example **3-geranylcatechol** with a 10-carbon doubly unsaturated side chain and **urushiol** with a 15-carbon triply unsaturated side chain.

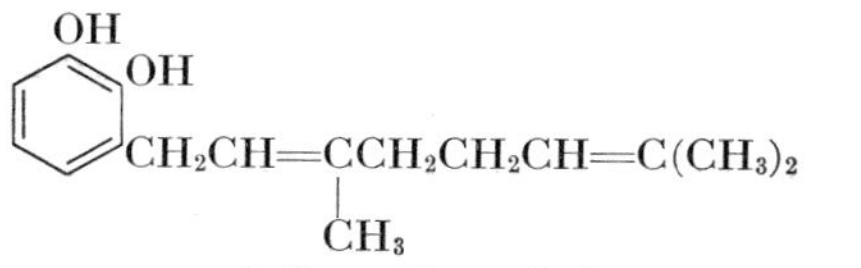

OH
OH
CH₂CH=CCH₂CH₂CH=C(CH₃)₂
|
CH₃
3-Geranylcatechol

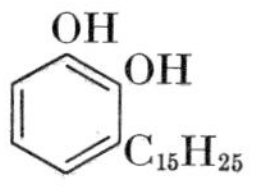

OH
OH
C₁₅H₂₅
Urushiol

Resorcinol is a product of the distillation of natural resins but is manufactured by the fusion of sodium *m*-benzenedisulfonate with caustic soda. It undergoes substitution reactions readily in the 4 position. The condensation products with formaldehyde are used as cold-setting adhesives. Resorcinol also is an intermediate for the preparation of azo dyes (p. 478), fluorescein (p. 483), and **n-hexylresorcinol**. The last compound is a popular antiseptic and is synthesized by the following reactions (cf. pp. 407, 175).

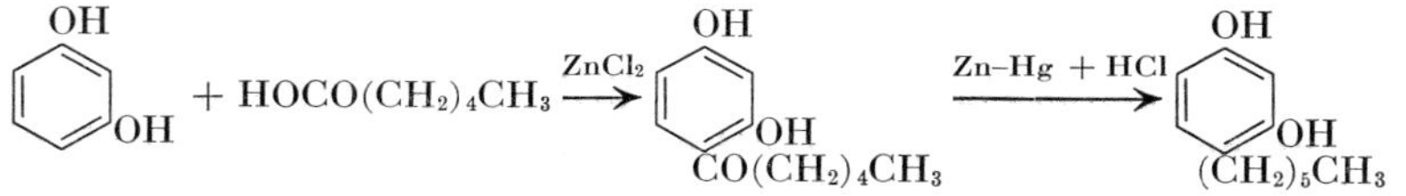

OH
OH + HOCO(CH₂)₄CH₃ $\xrightarrow{ZnCl_2}$ OH OH CO(CH₂)₄CH₃ $\xrightarrow{Zn-Hg\ +\ HCl}$ OH OH (CH₂)₅CH₃

The antiseptic power of phenol is increased greatly by the substitution of alkyl groups into the nucleus. Thus the cresols are nearly as toxic as phenol, but their phenol coefficients are about 3. As the length of the alkyl group is increased the effectiveness increases up to six carbon atoms, and then decreases. *n*-Hexylphenol is 500 times more effective than phenol. Evidently a hydrocarbon chain of six carbon atoms corresponds to the optimum solubility in water and in fats, both of which are present in cells. The effect of the compound in lowering the surface tension of water also is important. **2,4,6-Trinitroresorcinol** is known as **styphnic acid** and like picric acid is used to prepare derivatives of organic compounds. **Orcinol,** which can be obtained from certain lichens and aloes, is *5-methylresorcinol*. It is used as a reagent to distinguish between pentoses, methylpentoses, and hexoses (p. 288).

Hydroquinone is manufactured by the reduction of quinone (p. 396) with sulfurous acid.

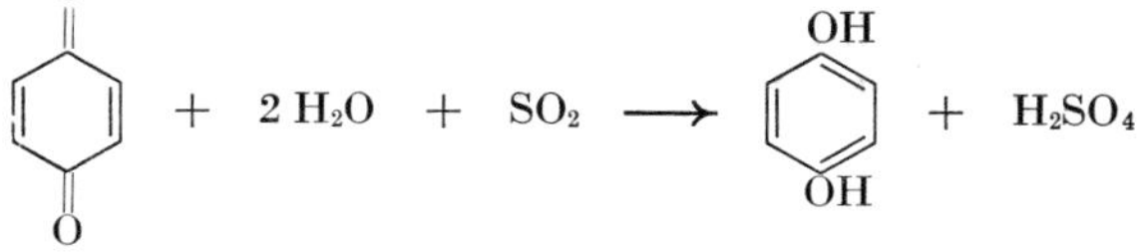

O
O + 2 H₂O + SO₂ ⟶ OH OH + H₂SO₄
Quinone   Hydroquinone

Pyrogallol (pyrogallic acid) is *1,2,3-trihydroxybenzene* and is prepared by decarboxylating gallic acid, obtained by hydrolysis of gallotannin (p. 419).

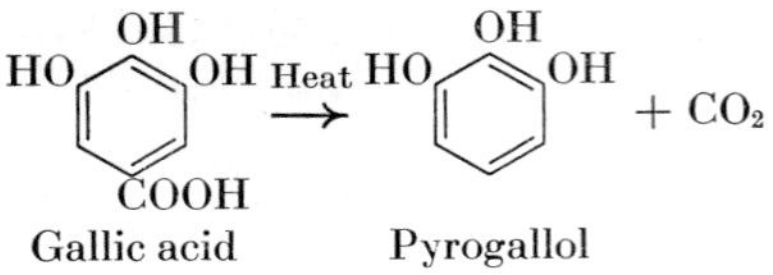

Gallic acid　　　　Pyrogallol

Hydroquinone and pyrogallol are important photographic developers (p. 395). Alkaline pyrogallol solutions absorb oxygen very readily and are used to remove oxygen from mixtures with other gases. Hydroquinone is used extensively to prevent unwanted autoxidation and polymerization of organic compounds (p. 582).

Phloroglucinol (*sym. trihydroxybenzene, 1,3,5-trihydroxybenzene*) is a useful reagent for the estimation of furfural and hence of pentoses (p. 454). It is made most conveniently by a series of reactions starting with trinitrotoluene.

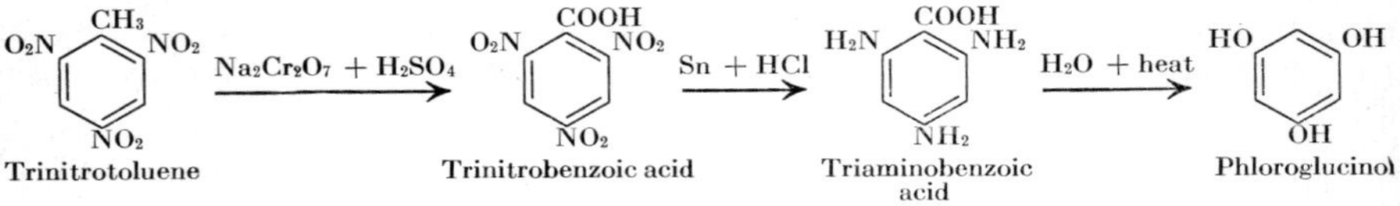

Trinitrotoluene　　　Trinitrobenzoic acid　　　Triaminobenzoic acid　　　Phloroglucinol

Whereas simple ketones behave as if very little of the enol form is present and simple phenols behave as if very little of the keto form is present, phloroglucinol reacts as if both forms are present or are in very mobile equilibrium with each other.

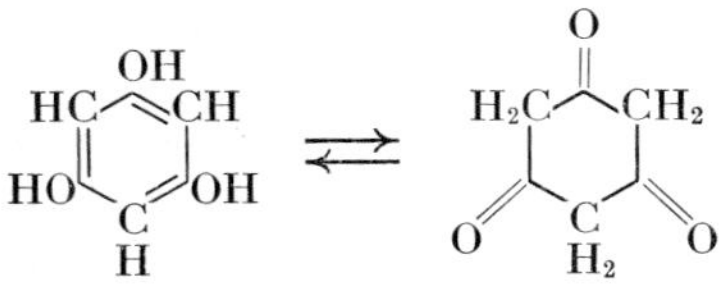

Of the aminophenols, **p-aminophenol** (P.A.P.) is the most important because of its use as a photographic developer. It is made by the nitrosation of phenol followed by reduction. It also can be made by the electrolytic reduction

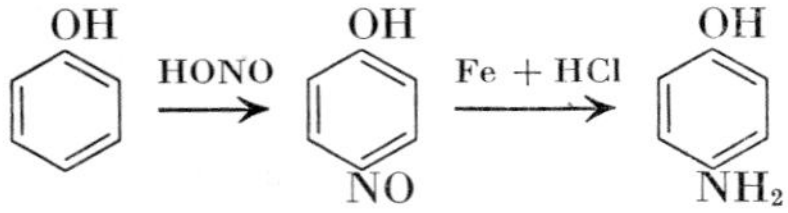

of nitrobenzene in acid solution. *N*-Phenylhydroxylamine is formed which rearranges in acid solution to the salt of *p*-aminophenol.

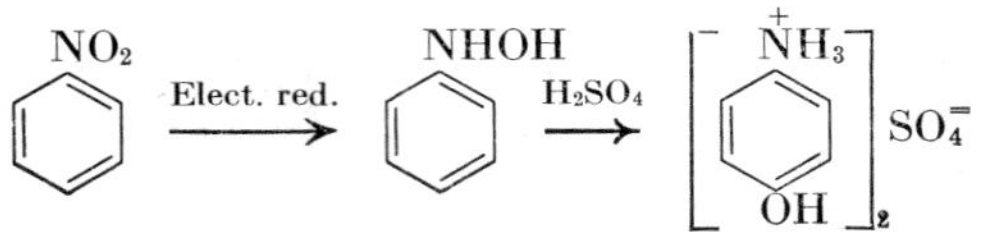

p-Hydroxyphenylglycine (photographer's *Glycine*) is made by the condensation of *p*-aminophenol with sodium chloroacetate.

NH₂ + ClCH₂COONa ⟶ NHCH₂COOH + NaCl
(OH)   (OH)

When *p*-hydroxyphenylglycine is heated in a mixture of cresols, decarboxylation takes place to give **p-(methylamino)phenol.** This compound can be made also by heating an aqueous solution of methylamine and hydroquinone in an autoclave at 100° (cf. p. 433). The sulfate, known as **Metol** or **Elon,** is another commercial photographic developer.

The common black and white photographic plate, film, or printing paper consists of a support on which is coated an emulsion of mixed silver bromide and iodide in gelatin solution. Silver halides darken on exposure to light. The light energy dissociates the silver halide into silver and halogen atoms, the number of silver atoms formed depending on the intensity of the light falling on the silver halide and the time of exposure. If a photographic plate were exposed long enough to a light image, enough silver would be formed to produce a silver image on the plate. A more satisfactory procedure is to give a short exposure and produce an invisible latent image on the plate. Each silver particle thus formed then can act as a nucleus for the deposition of more silver when the plate is subjected to mild chemical reduction. During this reduction a visible image develops because the density of the silver deposited is proportional to the number of silver nuclei which in turn is proportional to the intensity of the light which fell on the plate. After the desired amount of development, the unreduced silver halide is removed by dissolving with sodium thiosulfate solution (photographer's *hypo*) leaving the silver image on the plate, film, or print.

The most important developers are hydroquinone, pyrogallol, and *p*-aminophenol and its derivatives, because they bring about the chemical reduction of the silver halide at the desired rate. The introduction of amino and hydroxyl groups into the benzene nucleus increases the ease of oxidation by increasing the availability of the unsaturation electrons (pp. 366, 383). Since the ease of oxidation increases with increasing numbers of electron-donating groups, the polyhydric phenols, polyaminobenzenes, and the aminophenols oxidize more readily than phenol and aniline. The ease of oxidation is increased greatly in alkaline solution and decreased in acid solution because the electron-donating power of an oxide ion or of an amino group is much greater than that of a hydroxyl group or an ammonium ion. Different developers produce different types of deposition of silver and hence influence the characteristics of the developed image. Usually a combination of developers is used to produce the desired effect.

QUINONES

Of the three dihydroxybenzenes, or the diamines, or the aminophenols, the *ortho* and *para* isomers oxidize much more easily than the *meta* isomers. The reason is that the *ortho* and *para* isomers can lose two hydrogen atoms from oxygen or nitrogen to give stable compounds known as **quinones.**

OH
( )OH --[O]--> ( )=O + H₂O
                  O

o-Benzoquinone

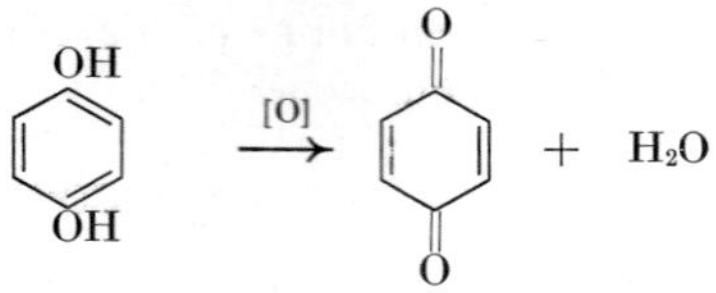

p-Benzoquinone

This type of oxidation is not possible for the *meta* isomers, since no stable structure can be written for a *meta* quinone. Quinones are formed also by the oxidation of aminophenols and diamines, because the intermediate quinonimines and quinonediimines are hydrolyzed rapidly in aqueous solution.

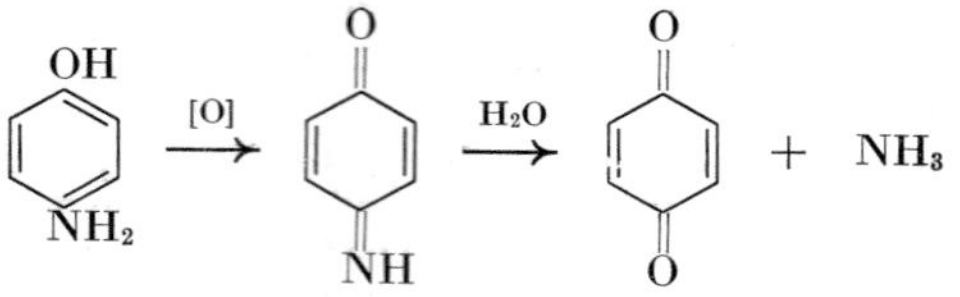

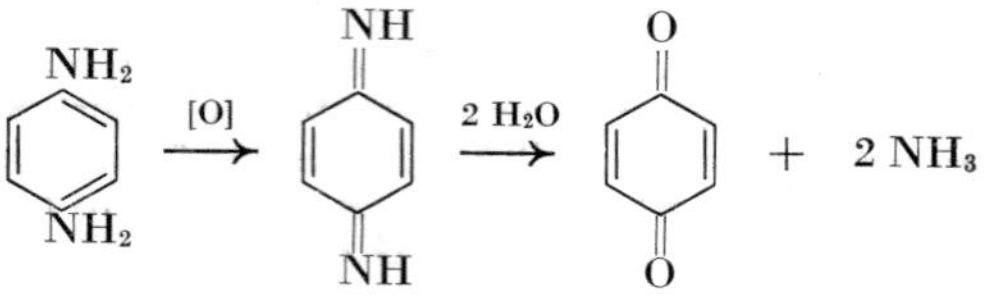

Quinone is a generic term for the above class of compounds but frequently is used as a specific name for *p*-benzoquinone. The name *quinoyl* was assigned to this compound when it first was obtained by the oxidation of quinic acid extracted from cinchona bark. Berzelius later changed the name to *quinone*. It is a bright yellow solid with a sharp odor and is prepared commercially by the oxidation of aniline with manganese dioxide and sulfuric acid.

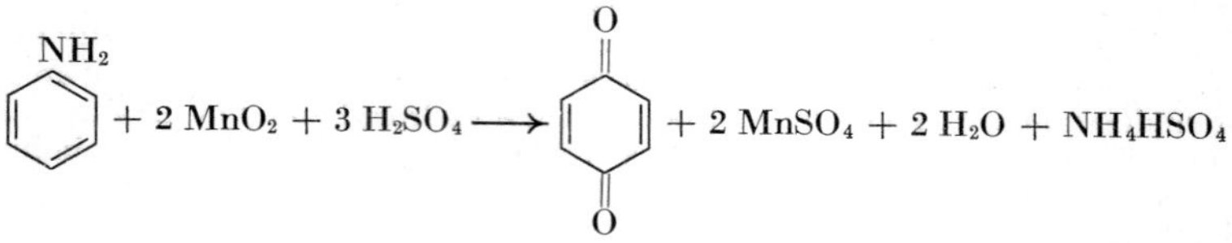

Quinone and hydroquinone combine directly in equimolecular proportions to give **quinhydrone,** which is an almost black crystalline solid and gives deeply colored solutions. The association appears to be due to proton bonding (p. 63). In aqueous solution it behaves like an equimolar mixture of quinone and hydroquinone, and since the interconversion of the two compounds is quantitative and readily reversible, a platinum electrode in a saturated solution can be used instead of a hydrogen electrode for measuring hydrogen ion concentration.

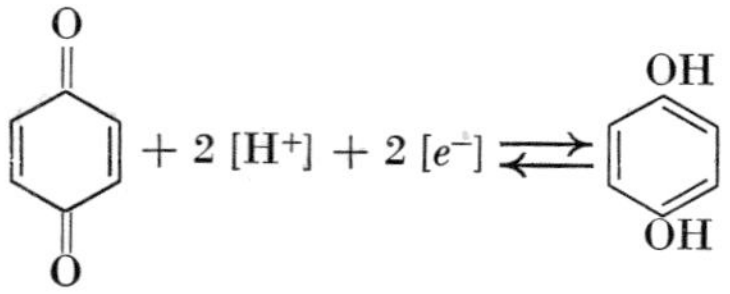

However both the hydrogen electrode and the quinohydrone electrode have been supplanted almost entirely by the glass electrode.

When a salt of 2,6-dichloro- or 2,6-dibromo-4-aminophenol reacts with hypochlorite solution, the **quinone chloroimide** is formed.

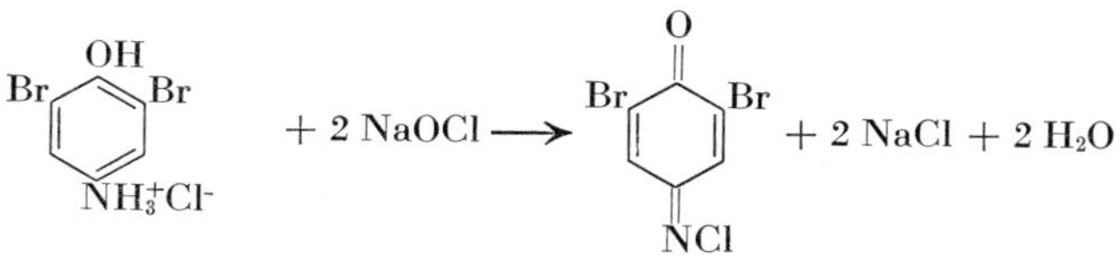

These compounds are valuable reagents for the detection of small amounts of phenol in water, since reaction in alkaline solution gives the intensely colored indophenols (p. 385).

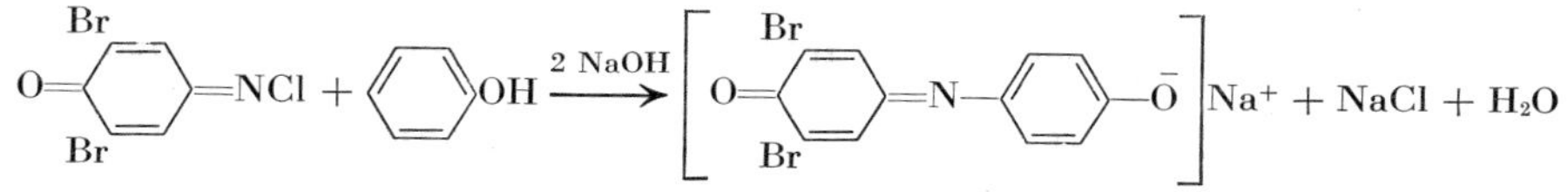

REVIEW QUESTIONS

1. Give reactions for the general methods for the synthesis of phenols.
2. Compare the reactions of the hydroxyl group in phenols with the reactions of alcoholic hydroxyl groups and explain the differences.
3. Give three reactions of phenol which illustrate the marked effect of the hydroxyl group on the ease of substitution in the benzene ring.
4. What is Liebermann's nitroso reaction? What other reaction discussed in this chapter resembles it?
5. Give two practical methods for the synthesis of picric acid. Why is direct nitration of phenol unsatisfactory?
6. Give reactions for the commercial processes for the synthesis of phenol. What are its chief uses?
7. What are the formulas and sources of the cresols; thymol; catechol; resorcinol; quinone; hydroquinone; pyrogallol; phloroglucinol?
8. Give reactions, other than the specific methods mentioned in the text, that might be used for the synthesis of thymol, catechol, hydroquinone, and phloroglucinol, starting with a readily available compound.
9. Give reactions suitable for the synthesis of *t*-butylphenol. What is meant by the term *phenol coefficient?*
10. Why are catechol, hydroquinone, and *p*-aminophenol useful as photographic developers whereas resorcinol and *m*-aminophenol are not?
11. Write a balanced equation for the conversion of aniline to quinone by oxidation with acid potassium permanganate solution.
12. Give reactions for the preparation of (*a*) *m*-nitrophenol from nitrobenzene; (*b*) *p*-cyanophenol from phenol; (*c*) *p*-methoxybromobenzene from phenol; (*d*) 1,2,4-trihydroxybenzene from resorcinol.

Chapter 26

AROMATIC ALCOHOLS, ARALKYLAMINES, ALDEHYDES AND KETONES. STEREOCHEMISTRY OF THE OXIMES

ALCOHOLS AND ARALKYLAMINES

The methods for preparing compounds containing hydroxyl or amino groups in alkyl side chains of aromatic nuclei and the reactions of these groups are the same as the methods of preparation and reactions of aliphatic alcohols and amines. The chief difference is a considerably greater reactivity of the groups that are attached to the carbon atom adjacent to the ring.

Benzyl alcohol is made by the hydrolysis of benzyl chloride (p. 328).

$$C_6H_5CH_2Cl + H_2O + Na_2CO_3 \longrightarrow C_6H_5CH_2OH + NaHCO_3 + NaCl$$

When benzyl alcohol is mixed with sulfuric acid, a high molecular weight insoluble hydrocarbon is formed by self condensation in the *ortho* and *para* positions.

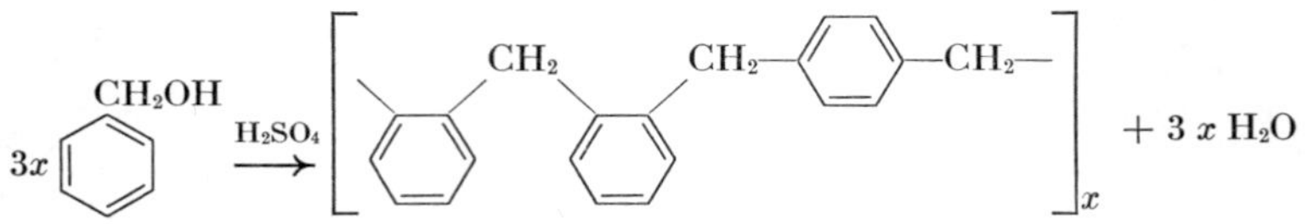

Benzyl acetate is used for the preparation of perfumes of the jasmine or gardenia type, and **benzyl benzoate** is used as a miticide. The antipyretic (fever-reducing) power of willow bark (*Salix alba*) was known to the ancients and is due to the bitter glucoside **salicin,** first isolated in 1827. Hydrolysis yields glucose and **saligenin** (*o-hydroxybenzyl alcohol*, p. 385).

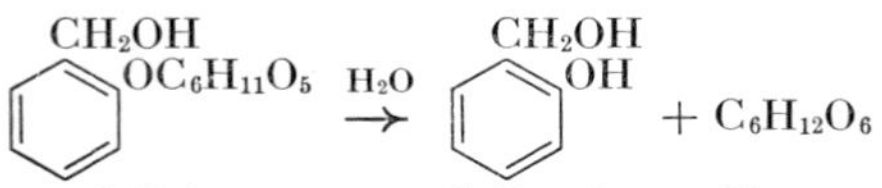

Diphenylcarbinol (*benzhydrol*) is made by the reduction of phenyl ketone (benzophenone, p. 407).

$$C_6H_5COC_6H_5 + Zn + 2 NaOH \longrightarrow C_6H_5CHOHC_6H_5 + Na_2ZnO_2$$

It dehydrates with extreme ease to form **benzhydryl ether,** dilute acids being sufficient to cause reaction.

$$2 (C_6H_5)_2CHOH \longrightarrow (C_6H_5)_2CHOCH(C_6H_5)_2 + H_2O$$

398

Benadryl, $(C_6H_5)_2CHOCH_2CH_2N(CH_3)_2$, the β-dimethylaminoethyl ether of benzhydrol, was one of the first synthetic chemicals to be used widely in the treatment of histamine allergies (p. 460). It also is one of the more effective preventives and cures for seasickness.

Triphenylcarbinol usually is prepared by the action of phenylmagnesium bromide on ethyl benzoate.

$$C_6H_5COOC_2H_5 + 2\ C_6H_5MgBr \longrightarrow (C_6H_5)_3COMgBr + MgBr(OEt)$$
$$\downarrow H_2O$$
$$(C_6H_5)_3COH + MgBr(OH)$$

The carbinol reacts with concentrated aqueous hydrochloric acid to give **triphenylmethyl chloride** (*trityl chloride*).

$$(C_6H_5)_3COH + HCl \longrightarrow (C_6H_5)_3CCl + H_2O$$

Triphenylmethyl chloride in the presence of pyridine (p. 454) reacts with the primary alcohol groups of sugars to give triphenylmethyl ethers, a process frequently called *tritylation*.

$$RCH_2OH + ClC(C_6H_5)_3 + C_5H_5N \longrightarrow RCH_2OC(C_6H_5)_3 + C_5H_5NHCl$$

The remaining hydroxyl groups can be methylated or acetylated. The triphenylmethyl group then can be removed selectively, since triphenylmethyl ethers are hydrolyzed more readily in acid solution than are methyl ethers or esters.

β-Phenylethyl alcohol is an important component of oil of roses. The synthetic product is made either by the sodium-alcohol reduction of ethyl phenylacetate, or by the reaction of phenylmagnesium chloride with ethylene oxide (p. 521).

$$C_6H_5CH_2COOC_2H_5 + 4\ Na + 3\ C_2H_5OH \longrightarrow C_6H_5CH_2CH_2OH + 4\ NaOC_2H_5$$

$$C_6H_5MgCl + CH_2CH_2 \longrightarrow C_6H_5CH_2CH_2OMgCl \xrightarrow{H_2O} C_6H_5CH_2CH_2OH + MgCl(OH)$$
$$\underset{O}{\diagdown\diagup}$$

Benzylamine, dibenzylamine, and **tribenzylamine** are formed when ammonia reacts with benzyl chloride. They are only slightly less basic than the aliphatic amines. The benzyl-nitrogen bond is cleaved readily by catalytic hydrogenation. Hence the benzyl group can be used to protect an amino group during condensation reactions of other portions of the molecule, and then can be removed.

$$R_2NCH_2C_6H_5 + H_2 \xrightarrow{\text{Raney Ni}} R_2NH + CH_3C_6H_5$$

β-Phenylethylamine may be regarded as the parent substance of a large group of medicinally important compounds known as *sympathomimetic amines*.

The name was coined to indicate that they have an action like that of the sympathetic nervous system. For example they dilate the pupil of the eye (*mydriatic action*), strengthen the heart beat, and increase blood pressure (*pressor activity*). It now is believed that the sympathetic system performs these functions by the elaboration of epinephrine (Adrenalin), itself a substituted β-phenylethylamine. Formulas for only a few of these important compounds are given.

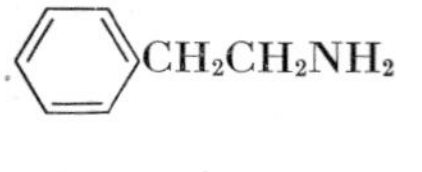

$CH_2CH_2NH_2$

β-Phenylethylamine

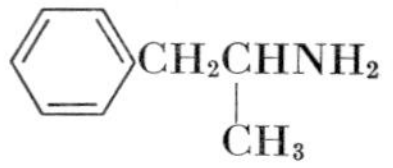

CH_2CHNH_2
CH_3

Benzedrine

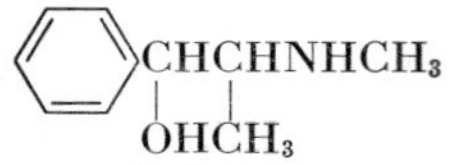

$CHCHNHCH_3$
$OHCH_3$

Ephedrine

$CHCHNH_2$
$OHCH_3$

Propadrine

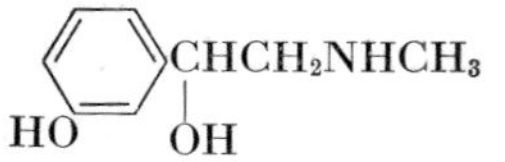

$CHCH_2NHCH_3$
HO OH

Neosynephrine

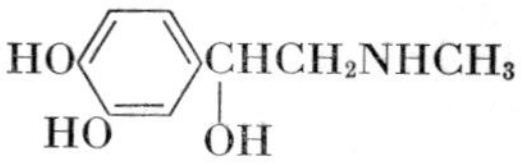

HO $CHCH_2NHCH_3$
HO OH

Epinephrine
(Adrenalin)

Benzedrine (*amphetamine*) can be synthesized by the application of a series of general reactions.

$$C_6H_5CH_2COOH + HOCOCH_3 \xrightarrow{ThO_2, 400°} C_6H_5CH_2CCH_3 \xrightarrow{H_2NOH} C_6H_5CH_2CCH_3 \xrightarrow{Red.} C_6H_5CH_2CHCH_2$$

Phenylacetic acid

Benzyl methyl ketone
O

Benzyl methyl ketoxime
NOH

Benzedrine
NH_2

It has a powerful action on the central nervous system leading to temporary increase in alertness, lessened fatigue, and increased irritability and sleeplessness. This action is followed by fatigue and mental depression; hence considerable danger lies in promiscuous use of the drug.

The closely related compound **ephedrine** is present in the herb *Ma Huang* (*Ephedra vulgaris*) used medicinally by Chinese physicians for thousands of years. The active principle was isolated by Japanese workers in 1885, but it did not become well known in the western world until about 1925 after the investigations of Chen and Schmidt in the United States. It is administered for the treatment of bronchial asthma, and for a few years was used in nose drops for contracting the capillaries and relieving nasal congestion caused by colds. For the latter purpose it has been replaced largely by other synthetic arylethylamines such as **Neosynephrine. Propadrine** is used orally for this purpose. It is of interest that Propadrine differs from Benzedrine only in having an additional hydroxyl group; yet it is much less likely to cause central stimulation.

Epinephrine (**Adrenalin**) was the first hormone to be isolated in crystalline form (Abel, 1897) and the first hormone to be synthesized (Stolz, 1904, and Dakin, 1905). Hormones (Gr. *hormaein* to excite) are chemical substances produced by the cells of one part of an organism and transported by the fluids of the organism to another site where they exert their specific action. Adrenalin is the active principle of the adrenal medulla. A minute amount (therapeutic dose 0.2–0.5 mg.) injected into the blood stream increases the blood pressure, accelerates the heart beat, and counteracts the effect of excessive amounts of insulin. It is believed to be the excitatory substance elaborated by the sympathetic nerve endings. When administered with local anesthetics (p. 418), it prolongs their action by constricting the blood vessels locally and preventing the anesthetic from being carried away from the site of injection. Adrenalin contains an asymmetric carbon atom and the naturally occurring $(-)$ form is 20 times more active than the $(+)$ form. Numerous methods have been developed for its synthesis, but it still can be prepared most economically in the United States from the adrenal glands of cattle.

Chloromycetin (chloramphenicol), isolated from an unidentified species of *Streptomyces*, a soil organism, is the first antibiotic to be synthesized by a practical procedure. It is a relatively simple molecule and contains an aromatic nitro group and a dichloroacetyl group. Neither structural feature had been found previously in a natural product.

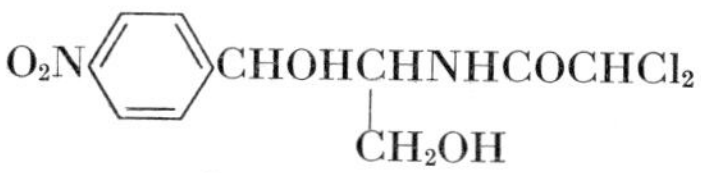

$$O_2N\text{—}\langle\bigcirc\rangle\text{—}CHOHCHNHCOCHCl_2$$
$$\underset{\displaystyle CH_2OH}{|}$$

Chloromycetin

Chloromycetin is especially effective against typhus and Rocky Mountain fever.

ALDEHYDES

Preparation

The aromatic aldehydes can be prepared by any of the general methods used to prepare aliphatic aldehydes. Additional methods are available that are applicable only to aromatic compounds. Usually some one procedure is preferable for a particular aromatic aldehyde. The more commonly used procedures are summarized below.

1. *Hydrolysis of Dihalides.* Usually it is preferable to oxidize a methyl group indirectly by halogenating to the dihalide (p. 328) and hydrolyzing.

$$ArCH_3 + 2\,Cl_2 \longrightarrow ArCHCl_2 + 2\,HCl$$

$$ArCHCl_2 \xrightarrow{H_2O(Na_2CO_3)} HCl + [ArCH(OH)Cl] \longrightarrow ArCHO + HCl$$

2. *Oxidation of Unsaturated Side Chain.* If the side chain contains a double bond adjacent to the ring, it can be oxidized to give aromatic aldehydes. The latter are less easily oxidized to acids by chemical reagents such as potassium permanganate than are aliphatic aldehydes.

$$ArCH{=}CHCH_3 \xrightarrow{KMnO_4} ArCHO + CH_3COOH$$

3. *Gattermann's[1] Hydrogen Cyanide Synthesis.* This procedure is used chiefly on phenols and phenol ethers which substitute with greater ease than hydrocarbons. It again is a Friedel-Crafts type of reaction (p. 407), an addition product of hydrogen chloride and hydrogen cyanide probably being the active reagent.

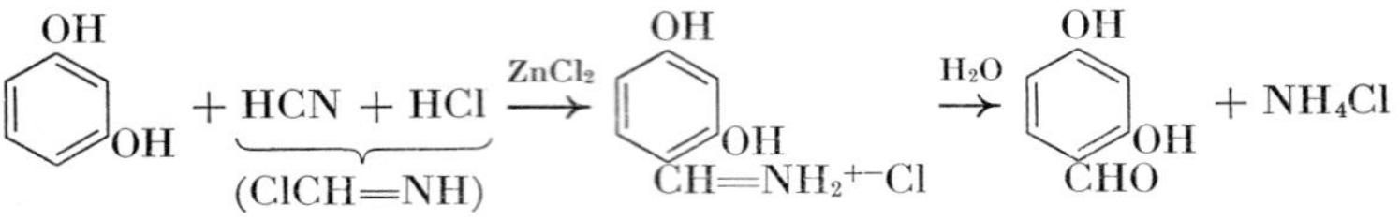

Zinc chloride is a sufficiently active catalyst for resorcinol. Zinc cyanide and hydrogen chloride may be used in place of anhydrous hydrogen cyanide, or the hydrogen cyanide may be replaced by bromocyanogen. Formerly the reaction was believed to be useful only with phenols and phenol ethers, but it has been shown to give 85 to 100 per cent yields with toluene or xylene if carried out at 100°.

4. *Reimer-Tiemann Reaction.* This reaction takes place only with phenols.

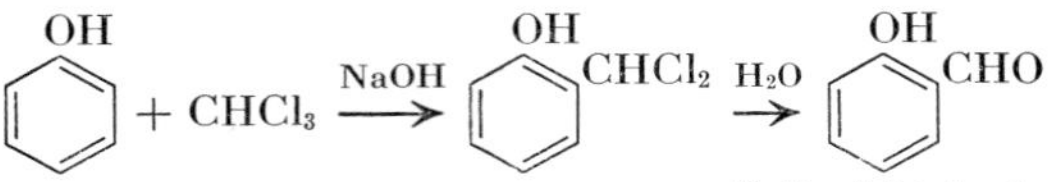

It involves both substitution and hydrolysis. *Ortho* substitution usually predominates unless the *ortho* positions are occupied, when *para* substitution takes place.

Reactions

Aromatic aldehydes undergo most of the general addition reactions of aliphatic aldehydes such as reduction and oxime formation. They are oxidized by air to the acid, by way of the peroxide (p. 581). However they are not oxidized by solutions of oxidizing agents as readily as aliphatic aldehydes. For example benzaldehyde does not reduce Fehling's solution. Moreover they do not polymerize. Special consideration of some of the more important reactions is of value.

1. *Halogenation of the Aldehyde Group.* The hydrocarbon portion of the molecule of aliphatic aldehydes is halogenated in the position α to the carbonyl group more rapidly than is the aldehyde group itself. Since no α hydrogen is present in aromatic aldehydes, and the aromatic ring does not substitute in the absence of special catalysts, it is possible to bring about the direct substitution of the hydrogen atom of the aldehyde group by halogen, the product being an acid halide.

$$C_6H_5CHO + Cl_2 \longrightarrow C_6H_5COCl + HCl$$

Benzalde-   Benzoyl
hyde   chloride

---

[1] Ludwig Gattermann (1860–1920), professor at Heidelberg. He is best known for his work with diazonium salts (p. 377), for his syntheses of aromatic aldehydes, and for his popular laboratory textbook.

2. **Cannizzaro Reaction.** Like all aldehydes that do not have hydrogen on an α carbon atom, aromatic aldehydes undergo the Cannizzaro reaction (p. 178).

$$2\ C_6H_5CHO + NaOH \longrightarrow C_6H_5CH_2OH + C_6H_5COONa$$

Benzyl   Sodium

alcohol   benzoate

Since formaldehyde is oxidized more easily than the aromatic aldehydes, the latter can be converted completely to the alcohol by a *crossed Cannizzaro reaction.*

$$C_6H_5CHO + HCHO + NaOH \longrightarrow C_6H_5CH_2OH + HCOONa$$

If hydroxyl groups are present in the *ortho* or *para* positions, the Cannizzaro reaction takes place only when catalyzed by finely divided metals, especially silver.

3. **Reaction with Ammonia.** Acetaldehyde reacts with ammonia in the mole ratio 1 : 1 to give an addition product, acetaldehyde-ammonia, which dehydrates to ethylidenimine or its polymer (p. 171). With formaldehyde the mole ratio of the reactants is 6 : 4 and the dehydration is spontaneous to give hexamethylenetetramine having a cage structure (p. 177). Benzaldehyde reacts with ammonia in the mole ratio of 3 : 2 with spontaneous dehydration to give a product known as **hydrobenzamide.**

$$3\ C_6H_5CHO + 2\ NH_3 \longrightarrow C_6H_5CH{=}NCHN{=}CHC_6H_5 + 3\ H_2O$$

$|$

C_6H_5

Hydrobenzamide

Actually the product is not an amide but is the dibenzylidene derivative of benzylidenediamine. In the reactions of all aldehydes with ammonia, the aldehyde-ammonia undoubtedly is the initial product.

4. **Condensation with Primary Amines.** Aromatic aldehydes condense with primary aliphatic or aromatic amines to give imino derivatives known as *Schiff bases.* The products from aromatic amines are known also as *anils.*

$$C_6H_5CHO + H_2NCH_3 \longrightarrow C_6H_5CH{=}NCH_3 + H_2O$$

N-Methylbenzyli-

denimine

(benzalmethyl-

amine)

$$C_6H_5CHO + H_2NC_6H_5 \longrightarrow C_6H_5CH{=}NC_6H_5 + H_2O$$

Benzylidenaniline

(benzalaniline)

Schiff bases do not polymerize and in general are more stable than *N*-alkyl-alkylidenimines, $RCH{=}NR$, because the conjugation of the double bond with the aromatic nucleus greatly reduces its reactivity.

Schiff bases can be reduced easily by hydrogen and Raney nickel to the secondary amines. It is not necessary to isolate the Schiff bases, but only to shake an alcoholic solution of aromatic aldehyde and primary amine with hydrogen in the presence of the catalyst.

5. Aldol-Type Condensations with Aliphatic Aldehydes and Ketones. Aromatic aldehydes condense with other aldehydes and ketones having two α hydrogen atoms. However the intermediate aldols lose water even more readily than the aliphatic aldols (p. 168), because the double bond formed by loss of water is conjugated not only with the carbonyl group but also with the aromatic ring.

$$C_6H_5CHO + CH_3CHO \xrightarrow{\text{Dil. NaOH}} C_6H_5CH{=}CHCHO + H_2O$$
$$\text{Cinnamaldehyde}$$

$$C_6H_5CHO + CH_3COCH_3 \xrightarrow[\text{10 per cent}]{\text{NaOH}} C_6H_5CH{=}CHCCH_3 + H_2O$$
$$\overset{\|}{O}$$
$$\text{Benzylidenacetone}$$
$$\text{(benzalacetone)}$$

$$C_6H_5CH{=}CHCCH_3 + OCHC_6H_5 \xrightarrow[\text{10 per cent}]{\text{NaOH}} C_6H_5CH{=}CHCCH{=}CHC_6H_5 + H_2O$$
$$\overset{\|}{O} \qquad\qquad\qquad\qquad\qquad \overset{\|}{O}$$
$$\text{Dibenzylidenacetone}$$
$$\text{(dibenzalacetone)}$$

The yield of cinnamaldehyde is not as good as those of benzyliden- and dibenzylidenacetone because of the polymerizing action of the alkali on the aliphatic aldehyde. Aldehyde condensations with ketones brought about by the use of 10 per cent sodium hydroxide are known as *Claisen reactions*.

6. Perkin Synthesis. A reaction analogous to those with aldehydes and ketones, but taking place with anhydrides at higher temperatures, was discovered by Perkin (p. 474). The basic catalyst for the reaction usually is the sodium salt of the acid corresponding to the anhydride used.

$$ArCHO + (RCH_2CO)_2O \xrightarrow[100°]{\text{NaOCOCH}_2R} \left[\begin{matrix} R & O & O \\ | & \| & \| \\ ArCH{=}C{-}C{-}O{-}C{-}CH_2R + H_2O \end{matrix} \right]$$
$$\downarrow$$
$$\overset{R}{\underset{|}{ArCH{=}CCOOH}} + RCH_2COOH$$

The final product is an α,β-unsaturated acid formed by the hydrolysis of the intermediate anhydride.

7. Benzoin Condensation. When benzaldehyde is shaken with an aqueous alkali cyanide solution, two molecules condense to give a keto alcohol known as **benzoin.**

$$2\ C_6H_5CHO \xrightarrow{\text{KCN}} C_6H_5CCHOHC_6H_5$$
$$\overset{\|}{O}$$
$$\text{Benzoin}$$

Formally this reaction appears to take place by the addition of the hydrogen of one aldehyde group to the carbonyl group of the other and union of the carbon atoms. That the reaction is not simply an aldol-type condensation, however, is indicated by the fact that it is not catalyzed by ordinary bases but specifically by alkali cyanides. Lapworth (p. 165) proposed that the first step is the addition of cyanide ion followed by proton transfer to give the cyanohydrin. The cyanohydrin contains a hydrogen α to a nitrile group and hence can undergo a base-catalyzed condensation with a second molecule of aldehyde. The resulting cyanohydrin of benzoin then loses hydrogen cyanide.

$$\text{ArCHO} \rightleftharpoons \left[\underset{\text{CN}}{\text{ArCHO}} {}^{\overline{\ :}} \right] \xrightarrow[\text{[: OH}^-]]{\text{H}_2\text{O}} \underset{\text{CN}}{\text{ArCHOH}} \xrightarrow[\text{H}_2\text{O}]{\text{[: OH}^-]} \left[\underset{\text{CN}}{\text{Ar}\overset{..}{\text{C}}\text{OH}} \right] \rightleftharpoons \xrightarrow{\text{ArCHO}} \left[\underset{\text{CN}}{\text{Ar}}-\overset{\text{O}\,^{\overline{\ :}}}{\underset{\text{OH}}{\text{C}}}-\text{CHAr} \right] \xrightarrow[\text{[: OH}^-]]{\text{H}_2\text{O}}$$

$$\underset{\text{CN}\quad\text{OH}}{\text{Ar}-\text{C}-\text{CHOHAr}} \xrightarrow[\text{H}_2\text{O}]{\text{[: OH}^-]} \left[\underset{\text{CN}\quad\text{O}\,^{\overline{\ :}}}{\text{Ar}-\text{C}-\text{CHOHAr}} \right] \xrightarrow[\text{[: CN}^-]]{} \underset{\text{O}}{\text{ArCCHOHAr}}$$

Important Aromatic Aldehydes

Benzaldehyde is one of the products of hydrolysis of the cyanogenetic glycoside, *amygdalin* (Gr. *amygdalon* almond), which is present in the seeds of members of the prune family. It once was called *oil of bitter almonds*.

$$\underset{\underset{\text{Amygdalin}}{\text{OC}_{12}\text{H}_{21}\text{O}_{10}}}{\text{C}_6\text{H}_5\text{CHCN}} \xrightarrow{\text{H}_2\text{O}} \underset{\text{Glucose}}{2\,\text{C}_6\text{H}_{12}\text{O}_6} + \underset{\substack{\text{Benzaldehyde}\\\text{cyanohydrin}}}{\text{C}_6\text{H}_5\text{CHOHCN}} \longrightarrow \underset{\text{Benzaldehyde}}{\text{C}_6\text{H}_5\text{CHO}} + \text{HCN}$$

Benzaldehyde played an important part in the work which laid the foundations of structural organic chemistry, because Liebig and Woehler showed that the radical benzoyl, C_6H_5CO, could be transported intact through a large number of chemical transformations. Benzaldehyde is prepared commercially by the hydrolysis of benzylidene chloride, one of the products of the side-chain chlorination of toluene (p. 328). It is used to some extent as a flavoring agent and as a perfume, but chiefly in the synthesis of other organic compounds.

Cinnamaldehyde, $C_6H_5CH{=}CHCHO$, is the chief component of cassia oil and oil of cinnamon, the volatile oils of the bark of *Cinnamonium cassia* and *Cinnamonium ceylonicum*. It is synthesized by the aldol condensation of benzaldehyde with acetaldehyde (p. 404).

Anisaldehyde is prepared by the oxidation of anethole (p. 392).

$$\underset{\text{Anethole}}{\text{CH}_3\text{O}{-}\!\!\!\bigcirc\!\!\!{-}\text{CH}{=}\text{CHCH}_3} + 2\,\text{KMnO}_4 \longrightarrow \underset{\text{Anisaldehyde}}{\text{CH}_3\text{O}{-}\!\!\!\bigcirc\!\!\!{-}\text{CHO}} + 2\,\text{MnO}_2 + \text{CH}_3\text{COOK} + \text{KOH}$$

Anisaldehyde is used in perfumery under the name *aubepine*. It has the odor of hawthorn flowers with no resemblance to the odor of anisole, benzaldehyde, or anethole. The floral character of the odor is completely lacking in the *ortho* and *meta* isomers.

Vanillin is the principal odorous constituent of vanilla beans, the long podlike capsules of a tropical climbing orchid, *Vanilla planifolia*. It probably is the most widely used flavoring material with the exception of salt, pepper, and vinegar. Annual production of the synthetic product in the United States is over half a million pounds. Besides being used to produce a desired odor or flavor of vanilla, it has a pronounced effect in masking undesirable odors. For example one part in 2000 will mask the undesirable odor of fresh paint. The masking and neutralizing of the odors of articles manufactured from rubber, textiles, and plastics is an important phase of the perfumer's art.

Numerous processes have been developed for the synthesis of vanillin. One of the earliest was the use of the *Reimer-Tiemann reaction* on guaiacol.

$$\underset{\text{Guaiacol}}{\text{(OH, OCH}_3\text{ ring)}} + \text{CHCl}_3 + 3 \text{ KOH} \longrightarrow \underset{\text{Vanillin}}{\text{(OH, OCH}_3\text{, CHO ring)}} + 3 \text{ KCl} + 2 \text{ H}_2\text{O}$$

In another process guaiacol is condensed with formaldehyde in the presence of an arylhydroxylamine such as 4-hydroxylaminotoluene-2-sulfonic acid, and the resulting product is hydrolyzed.

$$\underset{}{\text{(OH, OCH}_3\text{ ring)}} \xrightarrow{\text{HCHO}} \underset{}{\text{(OH, OCH}_3\text{, CH}_2\text{OH ring)}} \xrightarrow{\text{HONHC}_7\text{H}_6\text{SO}_3\text{H}}$$

$$\underset{}{\text{(OH, OCH}_3\text{, CH=NC}_7\text{H}_6\text{SO}_3\text{H ring)}} \xrightarrow{\text{H}_2\text{O}} \underset{}{\text{(OH, OCH}_3\text{, CHO ring)}} + \text{H}_2\text{NC}_7\text{H}_6\text{SO}_3\text{H}$$

For many years the cheapest synthetic method started with eugenol from natural oil of cloves. The eugenol was isomerized to isoeugenol in which the double bond is conjugated with the benzene ring, and the side chain then oxidized with permanganate under controlled conditions.

$$\underset{\text{Eugenol}}{\text{(OH, OCH}_3\text{, CH}_2\text{CH=CH}_2\text{ ring)}} \xrightarrow{\text{NaOH}} \underset{\text{Isoeugenol}}{\text{(OH, OCH}_3\text{, CH=CHCH}_3\text{ ring)}} \xrightarrow{\text{KMnO}_4} \underset{\text{Vanillin}}{\text{(OH, OCH}_3\text{, CHO ring)}}$$

Currently vanillin is being obtained from a natural raw material, namely the lignin dissolved in waste sulfite liquors (p. 298). On heating lignin with alkali, vanillin is formed to the extent of 6–7 per cent of the lignin content. **Ethavan** is the trade name of a synthetic product containing an ethoxy group in place of the methoxy group. It has 3.5 times the flavoring power of vanillin.

Methylation of vanillin with methyl sulfate and alkali yields **veratral** (3,4-dimethoxybenzaldehyde), a material useful in organic synthesis. **Piperonal** (*heliotropin*) is 3,4-methylenedioxybenzaldehyde and is made from safrole (p. 392) by a process analogous to the production of vanillin from eugenol. It has a pleasant odor and is used in perfumery. It also is valuable in organic synthesis. In contrast to benzaldehyde and cinnamic aldehyde, which rapidly oxidize in air to the acids, anisaldehyde, vanillin, and piperonal are highly stable to autoxidation (p. 581).

KETONES

Ketones that do not have the carbonyl group adjacent to an aromatic ring are prepared by the general procedures described for aliphatic ketones (p. 161). Those ketones having a carbonyl group adjacent to the ring usually are prepared by the Friedel-Crafts reaction (p. 315). Either an acyl halide or an acid anhydride may be used. With acyl halides one equivalent of anhydrous aluminum chloride is required because a stable addition product of the ketone and catalyst is formed. With acid anhydrides two moles of aluminum chloride are required because the carboxylic acid formed also reacts with aluminum chloride.

$$ArH + ClCOR \text{ (or } Ar) + AlCl_3 \longrightarrow ArCR \text{ (or } Ar) + HCl$$
$$\underset{O : AlCl_3}{\overset{\|}{}}$$
$$\downarrow H_2O$$
$$ArCOR \text{ (or } Ar) + H_2O : AlCl_3$$

$$ArH + (RCO)_2O + 2\ AlCl_3 \longrightarrow ArCR + RCOOAlCl_2 + HCl$$
$$\underset{O : AlCl_3}{\overset{\|}{}}$$
$$\downarrow 2\ H_2O$$
$$ArCOR + RCOOH + 2\ H_2O : AlCl_3$$

Only one acyl group substitutes, because the carbonyl group is sufficiently deactivating to prevent a second substitution. For the same reason halogen and *meta*-directing groups prevent the Friedel-Crafts reaction from taking place. Nitrobenzene frequently is used as a solvent for these reactions. On the other hand, activating groups permit reactions of the Friedel-Crafts type to take place that do not occur with aromatic hydrocarbons. Resorcinol for example gives ketones by condensation with carboxylic acids in the presence of zinc chloride.

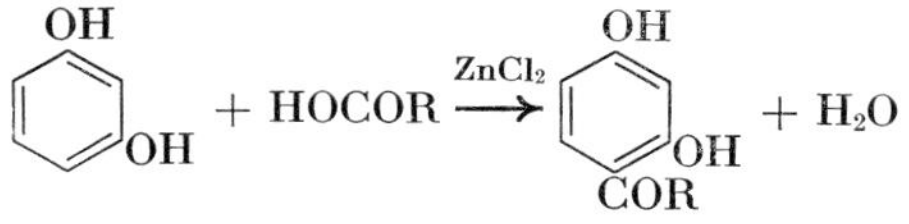

Acetophenone is methyl phenyl ketone and **benzophenone** is phenyl ketone. Both have some use in perfumery and are valuable intermediates for organic synthesis. The Claisen reaction of benzaldehyde with acetophenone (p. 404) gives **benzalacetophenone,** $C_6H_5COCH\!\!=\!\!CHC_6H_5$. Benzalacetophenone was given the name *chalcone* because its hydroxy derivatives have a reddish yellow color (Gr. *chalkos* copper). **Michler's ketone,** *p*-dimethylaminophenyl ketone, is made from dimethylaniline and phosgene. It is used as a dye intermediate (p. 482).

$$4\ (CH_3)_2NC_6H_5 + COCl_2 \xrightarrow{\ ZnCl_2\ } (CH_3)_2N\text{—}C_6H_4\text{—}CO\text{—}C_6H_4\text{—}N(CH_3)_2 + 2\ C_6H_5\overset{+}{N}H(CH_3)_2\bar{C}l$$
$$\text{Michler's ketone}$$

Chlorination or bromination of acetophenone gives **ω-chloro-** or **ω-bromoacetophenone** (*phenacyl chloride* or *phenacyl bromide*). Both are relatively harmless but potent lachrymators, and chloroacetophenone is used extensively as a tear gas for dispelling mobs. The phenacyl chlorides and bromides react with the sodium salts of carboxylic acids to give solid esters which serve as derivatives for the identification of carboxylic acids. **p-Nitrophenacyl bromide** is particularly useful for this purpose.

$$p\text{-}NO_2C_6H_4COCH_2Br + NaOCOR \longrightarrow p\text{-}NO_2C_6H_4COCH_2OCOR$$
p-Nitrophenacyl ester

Benzil, a 1,2-diketone, is obtained easily by the oxidation of benzoin (p. 404). Even mild oxidizing agents such as Fehling's solution or copper sulfate in pyridine (p. 454) bring about the reaction.

$$C_6H_5COCHOHC_6H_5 + 2\ CuSO_4 + 2\ C_5H_5N \longrightarrow C_6H_5COCOC_6H_5 + Cu_2SO_4 + (C_6H_5NH)_2SO_4$$
Benzoin   Pyridine   Benzil

The cupric sulfate can be regenerated by passing air into the cuprous solution. Benzil on heating with aqueous or alcoholic alkali undergoes the **benzilic acid rearrangement** to give sodium benzilate.

$$C_6H_5COCOC_6H_5 + NaOH \longrightarrow (C_6H_5)_2COHCOONa$$

STEREOCHEMISTRY OF THE OXIMES

Aromatic aldoximes and mixed ketoximes exist in isomeric forms. Thus α-benzaldoxime melts at 34° and does not dehydrate readily, whereas β-benzaldoxime melts at 130° and can be converted easily into the nitrile. The existence of these isomers is explained by the angular distribution of the bonds to nitrogen and the lack of free rotation about the double bond, analogous to the *cis-trans* isomerism of unsaturated compounds (p. 254). The form having the hydroxyl and hydrogen on the same side is known as the *syn* form and is assigned to α-benzaldoxime. The form having hydroxyl and hydrogen on opposite sides is called the *anti* form and is assigned to β-benzaldoxime.

C₆H₅   H   C₆H₅   H
\\C//   \\C//
N   N
OH   HO

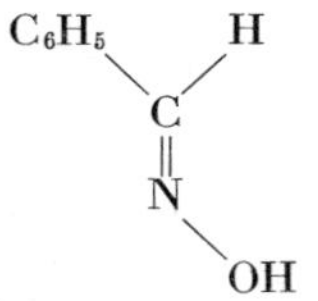

α- or *syn*-Benzaldoxime 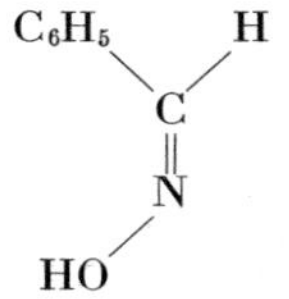   β- or *anti*-Benzaldoxime

Similarly two forms of phenyl-*p*-tolyl ketoxime are known, the α form melting at 154° and the β form at 116°.

When ketoximes are treated with a variety of acidic reagents such as concentrated sulfuric acid, acetyl chloride, or phosphorus pentachloride in ether solution, rearrangement to an amide takes place.

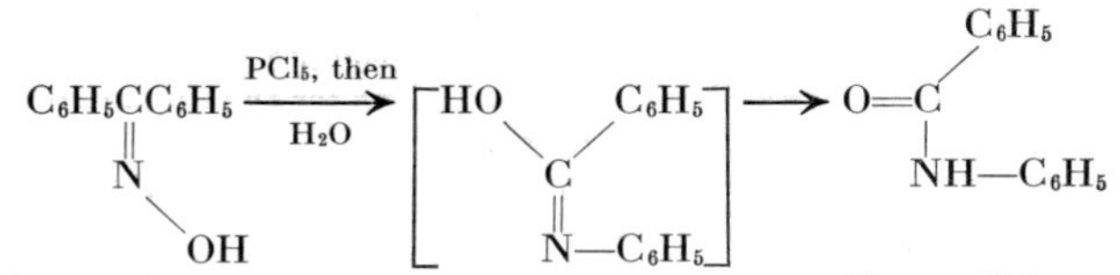

$$C_6H_5CC_6H_5 \xrightarrow[\text{H}_2\text{O}]{\text{PCl}_5, \text{ then}} \left[HO \diagdown_{\underset{\underset{N-C_6H_5}{|}}{C}}\diagup^{C_6H_5} \right] \rightarrow O=C \diagup^{C_6H_5}_{NH-C_6H_5}$$

Benzophenone
oxime

Benzanilide

This reaction is known as the **Beckmann** [2] **rearrangement.** The isomeric ketoximes rearrange to different products, the groups which are *anti* to each other changing places during the rearrangement. Since these products can be identified readily by hydrolysis, this procedure can be used to determine the configuration of the ketoximes.

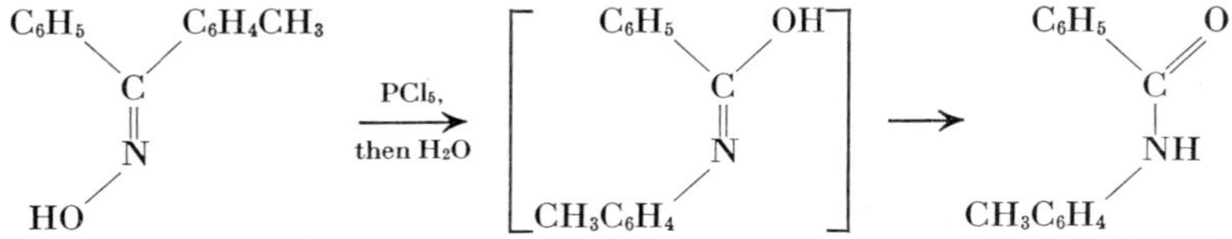

syn-Phenyl *p*-tolyl
ketoxime

Benz-*p*-toluidide

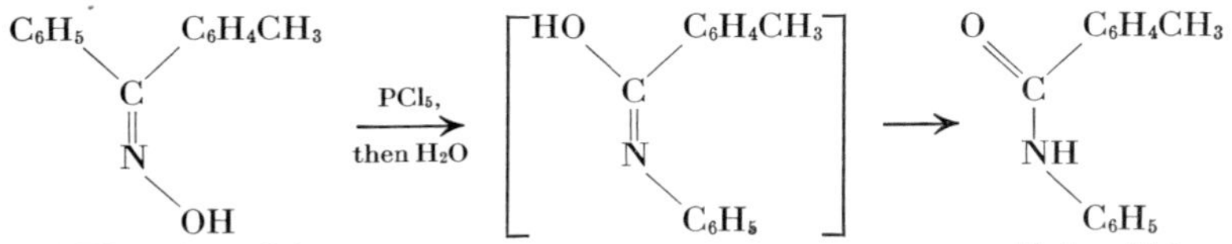

anti-Phenyl *p*-tolyl
ketoxime

p-Toluanilide

REVIEW QUESTIONS

1. Give reactions for the conversion of benzyl chloride into β-phenylethyl alcohol.
2. Compare the chemical behavior of benzyl chloride, benzylamine, and benzyl alcohol with that of chlorobenzene, aniline, and phenol.
3. Give equations for the synthesis of diphenylcarbinol, triphenylcarbinol, and triphenylchloromethane.
4. Give equations for the synthesis of benzaldehyde, cinnamic aldehyde, salicylaldehyde, anisaldehyde, vanillin, and piperonal.
5. What is the Gattermann hydrogen cyanide synthesis; the Reimer-Tiemann synthesis?
6. Give equations for the reaction of benzaldehyde with concentrated aqueous sodium hydroxide; ammonia; dilute potassium cyanide solution.
7. Discuss the mechanism of the benzoin condensation and compare with the aldol condensation.

---

[2] Ernst Beckmann (1853–1923), first director of the Kaiser Wilhelm Institut fuer Chemie. He was trained as a pharmacist and then studied under Kolbe and Wislicenus. He first observed the rearrangement of benzophenone oxime in 1886. Beckmann had a wide range of interests and occupied chairs in organic, physical, and pharmaceutical chemistry, and in food technology and nutrition. He developed many pieces of laboratory apparatus such as the sodium press, the differential thermometer, electromagnetic stirrers, and electrical heating apparatus. Beckmann redesigned the laboratories at Leipzig, and the Kaiser Wilhelm Institut was built largely according to his plans.

8. Discuss the Friedel-Crafts reaction for the preparation of alkyl aryl ketones and diaryl ketones, including reagents and limitations of the reaction.
9. What is the Claisen reaction? Illustrate by reactions for the preparation of benzyliden-acetophenone, benzylidenacetone, and dibenzylidenacetone.
10. What are *anils* or *Schiff* bases and how are they prepared? What is formed on acid hydrolysis of anils; on catalytic reduction?
11. Discuss the isomerism of the aldoximes and the ketoximes. What is the Beckmann rearrangement and how may it be used to determine the configuration of ketoximes? What method is available for determining the configuration of aldoximes?

Chapter 27

AROMATIC CARBOXYLIC ACIDS AND DERIVATIVES

The effect of an aromatic nucleus on the properties of a carboxyl group attached to it is less pronounced than the effect on other groups such as halogen, amino, and hydroxyl groups. Nevertheless the effect is sufficient to warrant special attention being given to some of the methods of preparation and reactions of aromatic carboxylic acids. Many of the derivatives of carboxylic acids are important compounds.

Preparation

Strictly aromatic acids, in which the carboxyl group is attached to the ring, can be prepared by the general methods available for aliphatic carboxylic acids. Some of these general methods become particularly important in the aromatic series.

1. **Hydrolysis of the Trichloromethyl Group.** Since the trichloromethyl group frequently can be formed by direct chlorination (p. 328), hydrolysis of this group becomes an important procedure for preparing aromatic acids.

$$C_6H_5CCl_3 + 2\ Na_2CO_3\ (aqueous) \longrightarrow C_6H_5COONa + 3\ NaCl + 2\ CO_2$$
$$\text{Benzotrichloride} \qquad\qquad\qquad \text{Sodium benzoate}$$

2. **Hydrolysis of Nitriles.** Although aryl cyanides usually cannot be prepared by the reaction of aryl halides with sodium cyanide, they can be prepared from sulfonates by cyanide fusion or from amines through the diazonium salts. Acid- or base-catalyzed hydrolysis yields the acid.

$$\text{ArCN} \begin{cases} \xrightarrow{\ NaOH + H_2O\ } ArCOONa + NH_3 \\ \xrightarrow{\ HCl + 2\ H_2O\ } ArCOOH + NH_4Cl \end{cases}$$

3. **Oxidation of Side Chains.** Although only primary alcohols and aldehydes are oxidized to acids without loss of carbon in the aliphatic series, even a methyl group attached to an aromatic nucleus can be oxidized to a carboxyl group in good yield.

$$ArCH_3 \xrightarrow[\text{or KMnO}_4]{Na_2Cr_2O_7 + H_2SO_4,} ArCOOH + H_2O$$

The aryl group makes the carbon atom attached to the ring more easily oxidized than atoms further away from the ring. Once this carbon is oxidized further oxidation takes place still more readily; hence side chains longer than methyl also give aromatic acids.

$$ArCH_2R \xrightarrow{Ox.} ArCHOHR \longrightarrow ArCOR \longrightarrow ArCOOH + HOOCR$$

411

Therefore most side chains in which a carbon atom is attached to the nucleus are converted to a carboxyl group on strong oxidation. The reaction is useful not only for preparing aromatic acids, but also for locating the position of side chains in the aromatic nucleus, since the constitutions of the more common aromatic acids are known. The reaction is limited to compounds that do not contain hydroxyl or amino groups in the nucleus, because the latter increase the ease of oxidation of the ring.

4. *Carbonation of Grignard Reagents.* Arylmagnesium halides react with carbon dioxide to give salts of carboxylic acids.

$$ArMgX \xrightarrow{\text{CO}_2} ArCO_2MgX \xrightarrow{\text{HX}} ArCOOH$$

Reactions

For the most part the reactions of aromatic acids are identical with those of aliphatic acids, the more important differences being in degree rather than in kind.

1. *Acidity.* The unsubstituted benzene ring gives rise to a slightly stronger acid than an unsubstituted alkyl group (benzoic acid, $K_a = 6.6 \times 10^{-5}$, acetic acid $K_a = 1.8 \times 10^{-5}$). The effect of substituents in the nucleus on the ionization of benzoic acid has been studied extensively. Ionization constants for a few compounds are listed in Table 19.

TABLE 19

Ionization Constants of Benzoic Acid and Derivatives

SUBSTITUENT	POSITION		
	ortho	*meta*	*para*
H	6.6×10^{-5}	6.6×10^{-5}	6.6×10^{-5}
CH$_3$	1.2×10^{-4}	5.3×10^{-5}	4.2×10^{-5}
OH	1.1×10^{-3}	8.3×10^{-5}	3.3×10^{-5}
OCH$_3$	8.0×10^{-5}	8.2×10^{-5}	3.4×10^{-5}
Br	1.4×10^{-3}	1.5×10^{-4}	1.0×10^{-4}
Cl	1.2×10^{-3}	1.5×10^{-4}	1.0×10^{-4}
NO$_2$	6.7×10^{-3}	3.1×10^{-4}	3.7×10^{-4}

2. *Esterification.* If no substituents are present in the *ortho* positions, direct esterification of the carboxyl group proceeds as with straight chain aliphatic acids. If, however, one of the *ortho* positions is substituted, the rate of esterification is greatly decreased, and if both *ortho* positions are occupied, esterification does not take place. This behavior was noted first by Victor Meyer (p. 16) and sometimes is called the *Victor Meyer esterification law.* The esters of *ortho*-substituted benzoic acids can be prepared by the reaction of the silver salts with alkyl halides. However once they are formed, they cannot be hydrolyzed easily.

These effects are observed regardless of the nature of the substituents. Apparently a **steric effect (steric hindrance,** p. 96) is involved analogous to that noted for secondary and tertiary aliphatic carboxylic acids (p. 140.)

Groups larger than hydrogen so effectively occupy the space surrounding the carbon atom of the carboxyl group that there is insufficient room to form the intermediate or transition state necessary for the formation or the saponification of the ester.

3. *Decarboxylation*. When the salt of an aromatic carboxylic acid is fused with alkali, the carboxyl group is replaced by hydrogen. The usual reagent is *soda lime,* a mixture of sodium hydroxide and calcium hydroxide.

$$\text{ArCOONa} + \text{NaOH} \xrightarrow{\text{Heat}} \text{ArH} + \text{Na}_2\text{CO}_3$$

This reaction takes place with aliphatic carboxylic acids also, but except for sodium acetate which yields methane, the side reactions are so complex that the reaction has no practical value.

4. *Acyl Halide Formation*. In general the hydroxyl group of aromatic acids is replaced with more difficulty than that of aliphatic acids, and phosphorus pentachloride is the preferred reagent instead of phosphorus trichloride.

$$\text{ArCOOH} + \text{PCl}_5 \longrightarrow \text{ArCOCl} + \text{POCl}_3 + \text{HCl}$$

Thionyl chloride also can be used. Sometimes the acid chloride can be prepared conveniently by the chlorination of the aldehyde (p. 402).

The aromatic acyl chlorides (frequently called aroyl chlorides) are insoluble in water and hence react with it very slowly. As a result alcohols and amines can be acylated in aqueous solution. When dilute alkali is used to combine with the hydrogen chloride formed, the reaction is called the *Schotten-Baumann reaction.*

$$\text{ArCOCl} + \text{ROH} + \text{NaOH} \longrightarrow \text{ArCOOR} + \text{NaCl} + \text{H}_2\text{O}$$

$$\text{ArCOCl} + \text{H}_2\text{NR} + \text{NaOH} \longrightarrow \text{ArCONHR} + \text{NaCl} + \text{H}_2\text{O}$$

A more recent procedure uses a tertiary amine such as pyridine (p. 454) as both solvent and base.

$$\text{ArCOCl} + \text{HOR} + \text{C}_5\text{H}_5\text{N} \cdot \longrightarrow \text{ArCOOR} + \text{C}_5\text{H}_5\text{NHCl}$$

Important Aromatic Acids and Derivatives

Benzoic acid was described in 1560 as a product of the distillation of Siam gum benzoin, an aromatic resin. The term *benzoin* is a corruption of the Arabic *luban jawi* which means the *frankincense of Java.* Its composition was established by Liebig and Woehler in 1832. It has been manufactured technically by the oxidation of toluene, by the hydrolysis of benzotrichloride, and by the partial decarboxylation of phthalic acid (p. 416). The benzoyl derivative of glycine, $\text{C}_6\text{H}_5\text{CONHCH}_2\text{COOH}$, occurs in the urine of horses and other herbivora and is known as **hippuric acid** (Gr. *hippos* horse). When benzoic acid is ingested by animals, including humans, it is detoxified by combination with glycine and eliminated in the urine as hippuric acid. Benzoic acid frequently is incorporated to the extent of 0.1 per cent as a preservative for foods.

Benzoyl chloride is made by the chlorination of benzaldehyde. It is a liquid having a characteristic odor and strong lachrymatory action, and is used as a benzoylating agent. When benzoyl chloride is shaken with sodium peroxide in water, **benzoyl peroxide** is formed.

$$2\ C_6H_5COCl + Na_2O_2 \longrightarrow C_6H_5\overset{O}{\overset{\|}{C}}-O-O-\overset{O}{\overset{\|}{C}}C_6H_5 + 2\ NaCl$$
Benzoyl peroxide

Benzoyl peroxide has been used as a bleaching agent for flour and is used as a catalyst for polymerization reactions. When it reacts with sodium methoxide, methyl benzoate and sodium perbenzoate are formed. Removal of the methyl benzoate, acidification, and extraction with chloroform gives a chloroform solution of **perbenzoic acid.**

$$(C_6H_5COO)_2 + NaOCH_3 \longrightarrow CH_3OOCC_6H_5 + C_6H_5\overset{O}{\overset{\|}{C}}-O-ONa \overset{HCl}{\longrightarrow} C_6H_5\overset{O}{\overset{\|}{C}}-O-OH$$
Perbenzoic acid

Perbenzoic acid reacts quantitatively with nonconjugated double bonds to form the oxide, a valuable preparative procedure.

$$RCH{=}CHR + C_6H_5CO_3H \longrightarrow RCH\underset{\diagdown O \diagup}{-}CHR + C_6H_5COOH$$

Since the perbenzoic acid liberates iodine from potassium iodide, the chloroform solution can be standardized and the reaction used for the *quantitative estimation of double bonds.*

3,5-Dinitrobenzoic acid is made by the nitration of benzoic acid. Reaction with phosphorus pentachloride gives **3,5-dinitrobenzoyl chloride,** a valuable reagent for the identification of alcohols. The latter react with it even in aqueous solution by the Schotten-Baumann reaction to give solid 3,5-dinitrobenzoates.

The *o*-, *m*-, and *p*-benzenedicarboxylic acids are known as *phthalic, isophthalic,* and *terephthalic acids.* **Phthalic acid** on heating above 180° rapidly loses water to form the cyclic anhydride.

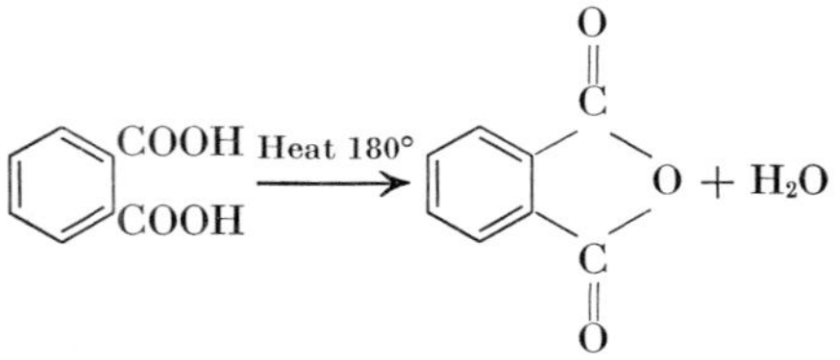

Phthalic acid   Phthalic anhydride

Hence in the usual methods for synthesizing phthalic acid, namely the high temperature oxidation of *o*-xylene or naphthalene (p. 428), it is the anhydride that is obtained.

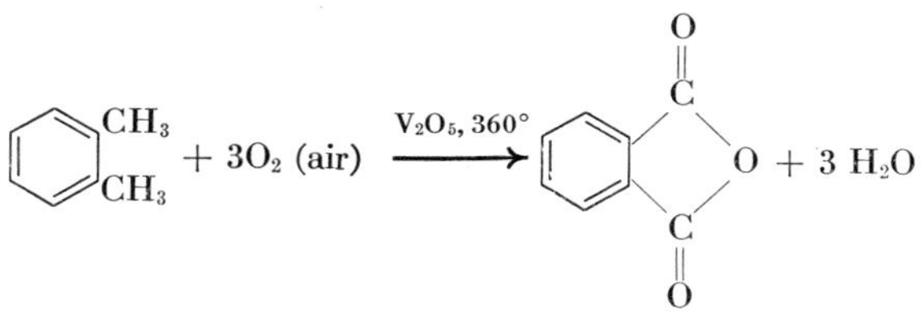

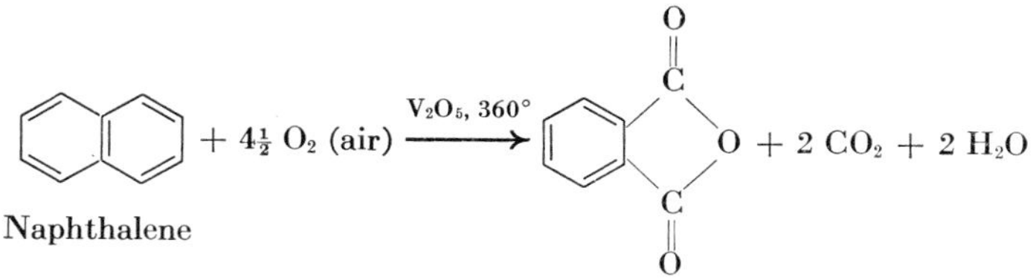

$$\text{(o-xylene)} + 3 O_2 \text{ (air)} \xrightarrow{V_2O_5,\ 360°} \text{(phthalic anhydride)} + 3 H_2O$$

Naphthalene $+ 4\frac{1}{2} O_2 \text{ (air)} \xrightarrow{V_2O_5,\ 360°} \text{(phthalic anhydride)} + 2 CO_2 + 2 H_2O$

Prior to the development of this process by Gibbs in 1918, sulfuric acid in the presence of mercuric sulfate had been used as the oxidizing agent (p. 484).

About 159 million pounds of phthalic anhydride was produced in 1948 at a price of about $0.20 per pound. In 1949 production capacity in the United States was approaching 200 million pounds per year. About half of the phthalic anhydride is used to produce the **methyl, ethyl, butyl,** and **higher alkyl esters** of phthalic acid, which are used as plasticizers of synthetic resins and polymers. **Methyl phthalate** (dimethyl phthalate, DMP) is an effective insect repellent.

About a third of the phthalic anhydride is used for the manufacture of protective coatings of the **glyptal** (glycerol and phthalic anhydride) type. Since both phthalic acid and glycerol are polyfunctional, heating the two together gives polymeric esters. If three moles of phthalic anhydride to two of glycerol are used, a fusible resin first is obtained which on further heating gives an infusible solid, insoluble in organic solvents. The cross-links occur not only between two polymeric chains as indicated, but between large numbers of chains.

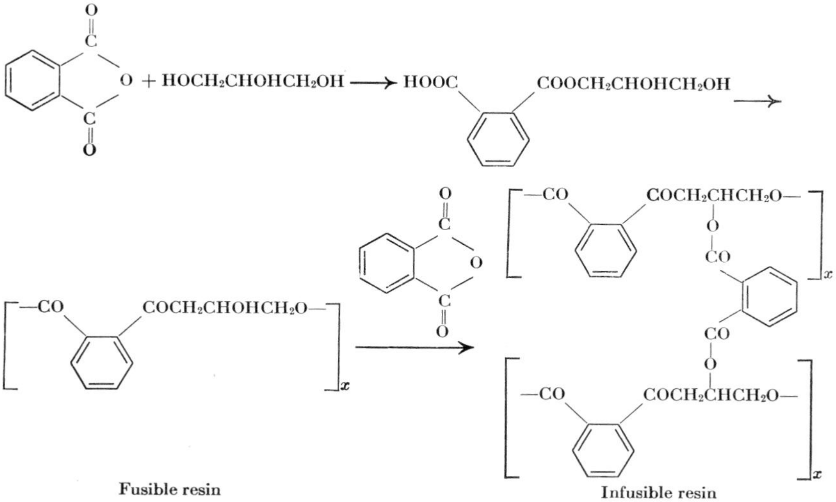

Fusible resin   Infusible resin

If one mole of phthalic anhydride, one mole of glycerol, and one mole of a monocarboxylic acid (a modifying agent) is heated, one of the hydroxyl groups is esterified with the monocarboxylic acid and cross-linking is prevented, thus forming a fusible solid, soluble in organic solvents. If unsaturated monocarboxylic acids such as those from the drying oils are used, the resin after coating on a surface can undergo further oxidative polymerization like a drying oil to give very tough, elastic, weather-resistant films. It is these synthetic enamels that are used so extensively for the finishing of automobiles and household appliances. The glyptal resins belong to a more general class of polymeric substances derived from polyhydric alcohols and polybasic acids known as **alkyd resins.**

A considerable quantity of phthalic anhydride is used for the manufacture of anthraquinone (p. 438), an intermediate for the synthesis of anthraquinone dyes (p. 487). Smaller amounts are used for miscellaneous purposes such as the manufacture of phthalein (p. 482) and xanthene dyes (p. 483), benzoic acid, and phthalimide.

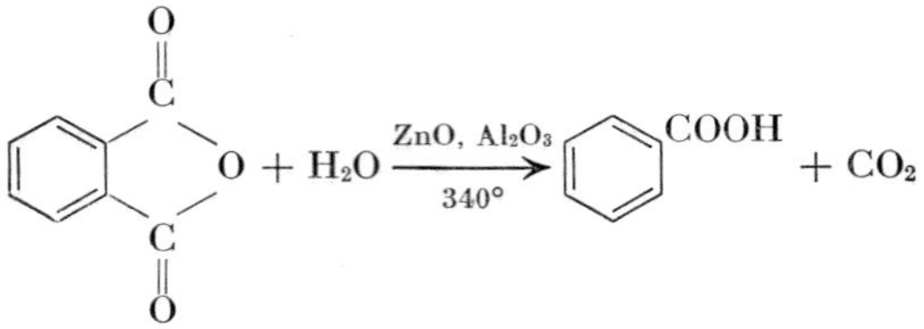

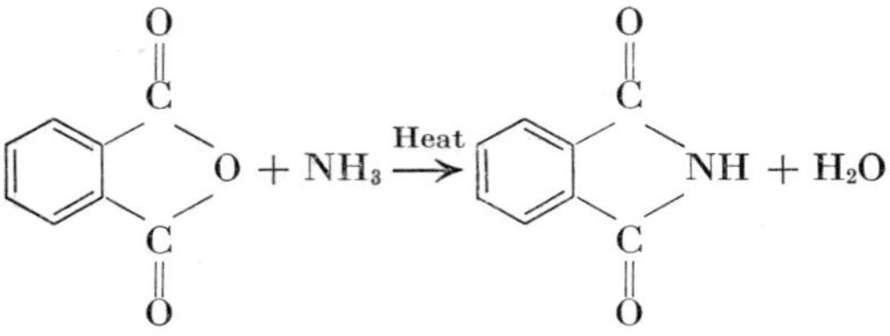

Phthalimide

Isophthalic acid has no special use, but British investigators have found that **terephthalic acid** yields a polymeric ester with ethylene glycol that can be spun into a textile fiber. The product has been named *Terylene, Fiber V* and *Dacron.*

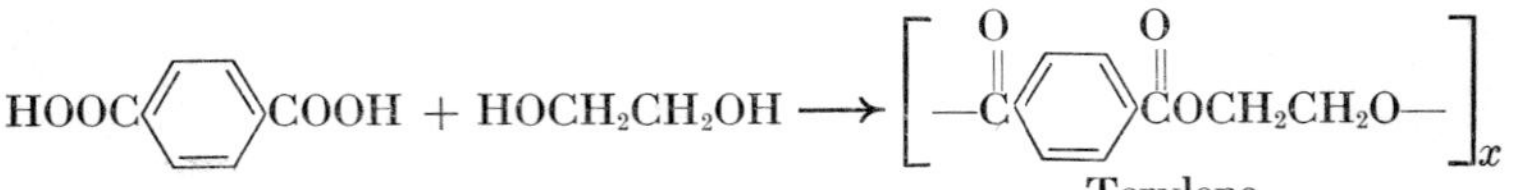

Terylene

Saccharin, discovered by Remsen,[1] is the imide of the mixed anhydride of *o*-carboxybenzenesulfonic acid. It usually is stated to have a sweetness from

[1] Ira Remsen (1846–1927), professor of chemistry at Johns Hopkins University, later president of the university. He established the first adequate graduate school in chemistry in the United States. He was an outstanding teacher, and his textbooks in both inorganic and organic chemistry were used throughout the world. He established in 1879 the American Chemical Journal, which later was combined with the Journal of the American Chemical Society. Remsen always was interested in the effect of substituents on the reactivity of other groups and it was while investigating the effect of substituents on the oxidation of side chains that he discovered saccharin.

550 to 750 times that of cane sugar. Relative sweetness, however, depends on the method of determination and the individual (p. 289). For most tastes a $\frac{1}{2}$ grain (0.03 gram) tablet replaces a heaping teaspoon (10 grams) of sucrose, indicating a sweetening power about 300 times that of sucrose. Saccharin has no food value and is used only when it is desirable to reduce the consumption of sugar. Saccharin is made from toluene by a series of reactions.

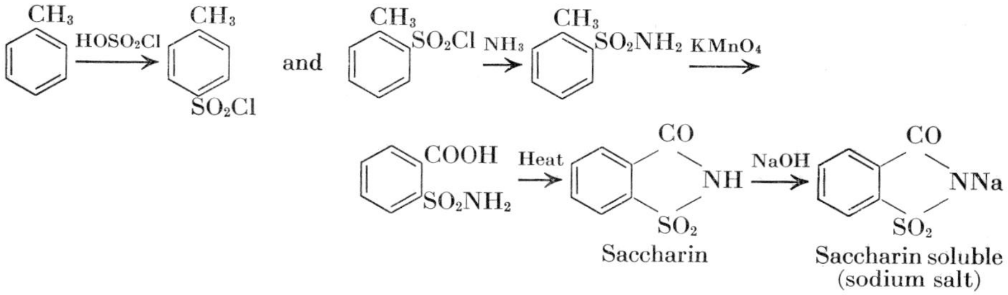

The imide is converted to the sodium salt to increase the solubility in water.

Anthranilic acid, *o*-aminobenzoic acid, is made by the action of alkaline sodium hypochlorite on phthalimide. The reaction involves hydrolysis to the sodium salt of phthalamic acid and a Hofmann rearrangement.

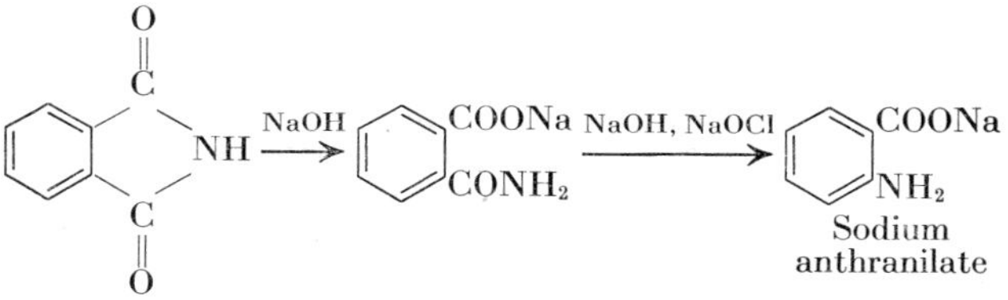

At one time a large quantity of anthranilic acid was used for the synthesis of indigo (p. 484). **Methyl anthranilate** is present in several odorous oils and contributes to the odor and flavor of grape juice. The synthetic product is used in grape flavors.

Although ***p*-aminobenzoic acid** is present in the mixture of substances known as the vitamin B complex, its necessity in the human diet has not been established. Bacteria, however, must be supplied with it for the proper functioning of certain enzyme systems, and apparently this fact accounts for the effectiveness of sulfanilamide in combating bacterial infections. Bacteria absorb the closely related sulfanilamide in place of *p*-aminobenzoic acid. Sulfanilamide, however, cannot function in the enzyme system; hence the growth of the bacteria is inhibited.

Since *m*-nitrobenzoic acid is the chief product of the nitration of benzoic acid, *p*-aminobenzoic acid is made by the oxidation of *p*-nitrotoluene followed by reduction.

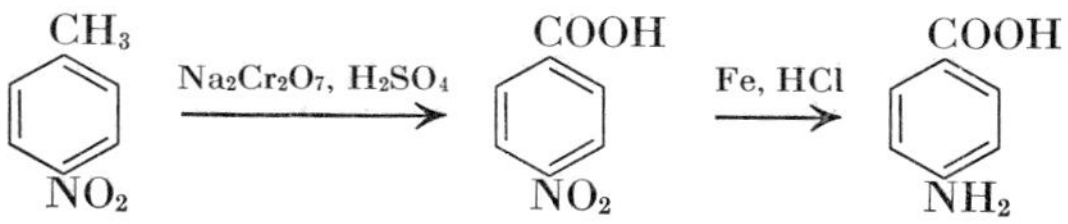

Certain *p*-aminobenzoic esters have a local anesthetic action. The ethyl ester is known as **anesthesin** and the butyl ester as **butesin.** They are used for relieving the pain of burns and open wounds. The most important derivatives are the aminoalkyl *p*-aminobenzoates, which on injection at the proper site block the transmission of pain by the nerve trunks. Their development resulted from attempts to find agents less toxic than cocaine, the first local anesthetic (p. 466). The function of the tertiary amino group is principally to form a salt that is water soluble and does not hydrolyze appreciably. **Novocain** (*procaine*, β-diethylaminoethyl *p*-aminobenzoate hydrochloride) was synthesized by Einhorn in 1905. It still is the most frequently used local and spinal anesthetic, although hundreds of related compounds have been synthesized and many placed on the market. Its method of synthesis is that generally used for all of the compounds of this type.

$$O_2N\langle\ \rangle COCl + HOCH_2CH_2N(C_2H_5)_2 \longrightarrow$$

$$\left[O_2N\langle\ \rangle COOCH_2CH_2\overset{+}{N}H(C_2H_5)_2 \right]Cl^- \xrightarrow{\text{Fe, HCl}} \left[H_2N\langle\ \rangle COOCH_2CH_2\overset{+}{N}H(C_2H_5)_2 \right]Cl^-$$

Novocain
(procaine)

Of the hydroxy acids, the *ortho* isomer, **salicylic acid,** is by far the most important. It is prepared by the action of carbon dioxide on sodium phenoxide at 150° (*Kolbe synthesis*).

Sodium salicylate

If potassium phenoxide is used instead of sodium phenoxide, the chief product is the *para* isomer. Salicylic acid was prepared first by Piria in 1838 from salicylaldehyde, which derived its name from the fact that it could be obtained by the oxidation of saligenin from the glucoside salicin (p. 398). Salicylic acid also was known as *spirsaeure* in the older German literature because salicylaldehyde is present in the volatile oil from the blossoms and leaves of various species of *Spiraea*.

The importance of salicylic acid and its derivatives lies in its antipyretic and analgesic action. **Sodium salicylate** was used first for this purpose in 1875 and in the following year for the treatment of rheumatic fever. The irritating action of sodium salicylate on the lining of the stomach led to the investigation of the action of various derivatives.

Phenyl salicylate (*Salol*) was introduced in 1886. It passes unchanged through the stomach and is hydrolyzed to phenol and salicylic acid in the alkaline juices of the intestines. Since, however, the weight of phenol liberated is almost equal to that of salicylic acid, there is considerable danger of phenol poisoning. Salol now is used only as an enteric coating for medicinals that otherwise would be destroyed by the secretions of the stomach. When the pill reaches the alkaline intestines the salol is hydrolyzed and dissolved, and the medicinal is liberated. Salicylic acid now is administered almost exclusively as the acetyl derivative, which is known as *aspirin* (from the German *acetyl-spirsaeure*). Like salol it passes through the stomach unchanged and is hydrolyzed to salicylic acid in the intestines.

OH
COOC₆H₅

Salol

OCOCH₃
COOH

Aspirin

Salicylates lower body temperature rapidly and effectively in subjects having fever (antipyretic action) but have little effect if the temperature is normal. They are mild analgesics relieving certain types of pain such as headaches, neuralgia, and rheumatism. The threshold for cutaneous pain by heat is raised about 35 per cent when 2 grams of aspirin is taken orally. The extensive use of aspirin is indicated by the production in the United States in 1948 of about 11 million pounds, enough for one hundred 5-grain pills for every member of the entire population. Although the toxic dose is large, promiscuous use of salicylates is not without danger. Single doses of 5 to 10 grams have caused death, and 12 grams taken over a period of twenty-four hours causes symptoms of poisoning. Moreover in some persons salicylates cause skin rashes.

The chief component of oil of wintergreen (*Gaultheria procumbens*) was identified as **methyl salicylate** in 1843. It is used to a considerable extent as a flavoring agent and in rubbing liniments. It has a mild irritating action on the skin and acts as a counter-irritant for sore muscles.

p-Aminosalicylic acid (2-hydroxy-4-aminobenzoic acid) can be made by the Kolbe synthesis (p. 418) from *m*-aminophenol. It is being used along with streptomycin in the treatment of tuberculosis.

Gallic acid (3,4,5-trihydroxybenzoic acid) is found free in sumach, tea, and many other plants. It is prepared by the hydrolysis of the **tannin** (**tannic acid**) present in oak galls (gall nuts or nutgall), which are the excresences on young twigs of oaks caused by parasitic insects. This particular tannin, called *gallotannin*, is a mixture of gallic acid esters of glucose. One product isolated by E. Fischer was shown to be a *pentadigalloylglucose*. The digallic acid is itself an ester, *m*-galloylgallic acid.

HO   O   HO   OH
HO—⟨ ⟩—C—O—⟨ ⟩
HO   COOH

m-Galloylgallic acid

Compounds of this type are known as **depsides** (Gr. *depsein* to tan) because many of them have tanning properties. Tannins in general are substances that have the property of rendering the gelatin of hides insoluble, thereby converting the hide to leather.

Gallic acid and tannic acid are used in the manufacture of permanent writing inks. They form colorless water-soluble ferrous salts, which on oxidation by air give blue-black insoluble ferric salts. The latter are more permanent to light than the dye used to make the ink initially visible. Gallic acid is decarboxylated to produce pyrogallol (p. 394).

Cinnamic acid is made by the Perkin synthesis (p. 404).

$$C_6H_5CHO + (CH_3CO)_2O \xrightarrow{NaOCOCH_3} [C_6H_5CH{=}CHCOOCOCH_3 + H_2O] \longrightarrow$$

$$C_6H_5CH{=}CHCOOH + HOOCCH_3$$
Cinnamic acid

When salicylaldehyde is subjected to the Perkin reaction, the resulting free acid is unstable and cyclizes spontaneously to the lactone known as **coumarin.** Coumarin is present in the tonka bean, the seed of a tropical South

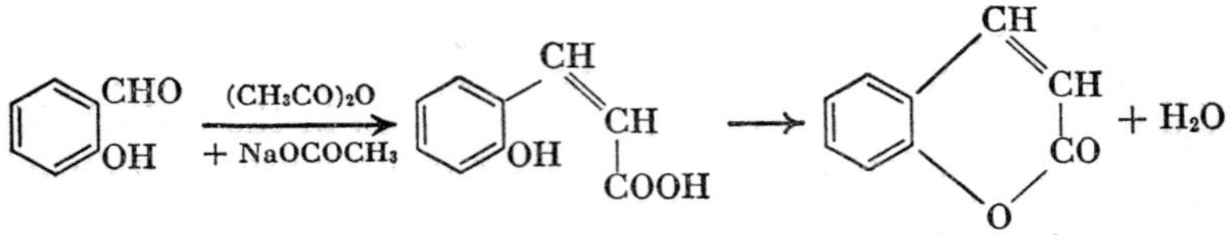

Coumarin

American tree (*Dipteryx odorata*) known to the natives as *cumaru*. It has been isolated also from numerous other plants. It has the odor of newly mown hay and is used in perfumery. It was the first natural perfume to be synthesized from a coal tar chemical (p. 475).

Dicoumarol (dicoumarin) is the agent responsible for the hemorrhagic disease that results when cattle eat spoiled sweet clover. It now is used in surgery to prevent the clotting of blood. Another coumarin derivative, called *Warfarin*, promises to be an effective rat poison.

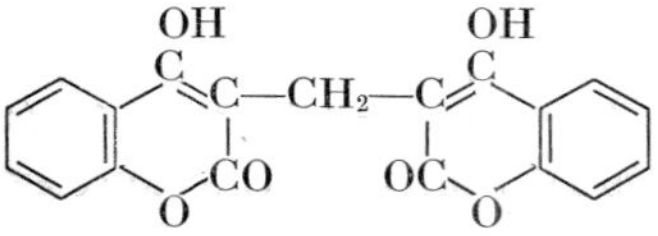

Dicoumarol (dicoumarin) 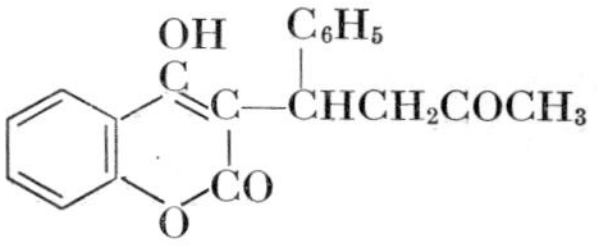   Warfarin

Mandelic acid (α-hydroxyphenylacetic acid) is prepared by the hydrolysis of benzaldehyde cyanohydrin (mandelonitrile).

$$C_6H_5CHO \xrightarrow{HCN} C_6H_5CHOHCN \xrightarrow{HCl} C_6H_5CHOHCOOH$$
Mandelonitrile   Mandelic acid

Its name arises from the fact that it first was obtained by heating an extract of bitter almonds (Ger. *mandel* almond) with hydrochloric acid (p. 405). Mandelic acid administered orally is excreted unchanged in the urine. Since it is bactericidal in acid medium, it is used in the treatment of urinary infections.

REVIEW QUESTIONS

1. Give reactions for four procedures for the synthesis of *p*-toluic acid (*p*-methylbenzoic acid) starting with toluene or *p*-xylene.
2. Compare the reactions of aromatic carboxylic acids with those of aliphatic acids. What

is the effect of *ortho* substitution on the rate of esterification of aromatic acids and on the ease of hydrolysis of esters?

3. What are the raw materials for the commercial synthesis of phthalic anhydride? What are its principal uses?

4. How is benzoyl chloride made commercially? In what other way may it be prepared? What is the Schotten-Baumann reaction and why is it not applicable with acetyl chloride?

5. Give reactions for the preparation of benzoyl peroxide and perbenzoic acid. Of what use is the latter reagent and what are its limitations?

6. Give equations for the synthesis of anthranilic acid, *m*-aminobenzoic acid, and *p*-aminobenzoic acid starting with coal tar hydrocarbons.

7. Give equations for the synthesis of Novocain starting with air, water, salt, sulfur, petroleum, and coal tar. (Hint: satisfactory intermediates are *p*-nitrobenzoic acid, ethylene chlorohydrin, and diethylamine.)

8. What is the Kolbe synthesis of salicylic acid? What is oil of wintergreen; aspirin?

9. Give equations for the synthesis of saccharin starting with toluene. What is the chief co-product of the synthesis and how is it used?

10. Give a practical procedure for the separation of *n*-butyl alcohol, phenol, benzoic acid, and benzenesulfonic acid.

11. Arrange the following compounds in the order of increasing acidity: water, phenol, *p*-nitrophenol, carbonic acid, ammonia, methane, acetic acid, benzoic acid, ammonium chloride, benzenesulfonic acid, ethyl alcohol, phthalimide, benzenesulfonamide, aniline, acetamide, diphenylamine, nitroethane, sulfuric acid, *n*-butyl mercaptan, *o*-nitroaniline. Where two or more compounds have approximately the same acidity, bracket them together.

Chapter 28

ARYLALKANES. FREE GROUPS. ARYLALKENES.
BIPHENYL AND ITS DERIVATIVES

ARYLALKANES

The simplest of the arylalkanes is **toluene** (p. 316). **Diphenylmethane** can be synthesized by the Friedel-Crafts reaction either from benzyl chloride or methylene chloride and benzene.

$$C_6H_5CH_2Cl + C_6H_6 \xrightarrow{\text{AlCl}_3} C_6H_5CH_2C_6H_5 + HCl$$

$$CH_2Cl_2 + 2\ C_6H_6 \xrightarrow{\text{AlCl}_3} C_6H_5CH_2C_6H_5 + 2\ HCl$$
Diphenylmethane

Oxidation of diphenylmethane yields benzophenone, which is more stable to further oxidation than aliphatic ketones because further oxidation requires rupture of a benzene ring.

$$C_6H_5CH_2C_6H_5 \xrightarrow{\text{Na}_2\text{Cr}_2\text{O}_7,\ \text{H}_2\text{SO}_4} C_6H_5\overset{\overset{\displaystyle O}{\|}}{C}C_6H_5 + H_2O$$

Triphenylmethane may be prepared from chloroform and benzene.

$$3\ C_6H_6 + CHCl_3 \xrightarrow{\text{AlCl}_3} (C_6H_5)_3CH + 3\ HCl$$

A better method is from benzene and carbon tetrachloride. The intermediate complex of triphenylmethyl chloride and aluminum chloride is reduced with ether to triphenylmethane.

$$CCl_4 + 3\ C_6H_6 \xrightarrow{\text{AlCl}_3} (C_6H_5)_3CCl \cdot AlCl_3 + 3\ HCl$$

$$(C_6H_5)_3CCl \cdot AlCl_3 + (C_2H_5)_2O \longrightarrow (C_6H_5)_3CH + CH_3CHO \cdot AlCl_3 + C_2H_5Cl$$

The accumulation of phenyl groups in triphenylmethane increases the acidity of the CH group sufficiently to permit reaction with potassium amide in liquid ammonia to give a potassium salt; that is triphenylmethane is a stronger acid than ammonia.

$$(C_6H_5)_3CH + KNH_2 \longrightarrow (C_6H_5)_3CK + NH_3$$

The solution of the potassium salt in liquid ammonia is red.

Direct oxidation of triphenylmethane yields triphenylcarbinol. The reaction stops at this point because the tertiary alcohol cannot be oxidized further without destroying a benzene ring.

$$(C_6H_5)_3CH \xrightarrow{\text{Na}_2\text{Cr}_2\text{O}_7,\ \text{H}_2\text{SO}_4} (C_6H_5)_3COH$$
$$\text{Triphenyl-}$$
$$\text{carbinol}$$

Tetraphenylmethane is difficult to prepare because the replacement of a halogen atom by a fourth bulky group is slow. A yield of about 5 per cent is obtained by the reaction of triphenylmethyl chloride and phenylmagnesium bromide.

$$(C_6H_5)_3CCl + C_6H_5MgBr \longrightarrow (C_6H_5)_4C + MgBrCl$$

Derivatives of **1,1-diphenylethane** are important insecticides. The first to be used for this purpose was 1,1-bis-*p*-chlorophenyl-2,2,2,-trichloroethane, known as **DDT.** It is manufactured by the action of sulfuric acid on a mixture of chlorobenzene and chloral (trichloroacetaldehyde, p. 518).

$$2\ ClC_6H_5 + OCHCCl_3 \xrightarrow{\text{H}_2\text{SO}_4} (p\text{-}ClC_6H_4)_2CHCCl_3 + H_2O$$
$$\text{Chloral} \qquad\qquad \text{DDT}$$

Although prepared in 1874, the insecticidal properties did not become known until 1942. During World War II it was used in delousing powders to prevent the spread of typhus, and as a mosquito larvicide to render swampy areas habitable. Since then it has been used widely as an agricultural insecticide and in household sprays. Production in the United States reached over 33 million pounds in 1945 but declined to 20 million pounds in 1948. A large number of related compounds have been prepared and their properties investigated. Some, such as **Methoxychlor** (1,1-bis-*p*-methoxyphenyl-2,2,2-trichloroethane), have been reported to be equally effective and less toxic.

Hexaphenylethane was prepared by Gomberg [1] in 1900 by the action of finely divided metals on a benzene solution of triphenylmethyl chloride.

$$2\ (C_6H_5)_3CCl + 2\ Ag\ (or\ Zn) \longrightarrow (C_6H_5)_3CC(C_6H_5)_3 + 2\ AgCl$$
$$\text{Hexaphenylethane} \quad \text{(or ZnCl}_2\text{)}$$

Hexaphenylethane is a colorless crystalline solid, but its solutions are deep yellow. The solutions rapidly absorb oxygen from the air to give triphenylmethyl peroxide.

$$(C_6H_5)_3CC(C_6H_5)_3 + O_2 \longrightarrow (C_6H_5)_3C\text{—}O\text{—}O\text{—}C(C_6H_5)_3$$

They decolorize iodine with the formation of triphenylmethyl iodide and react with alkali metals to give brick red metallic salts.

[1] Moses Gomberg (1866–1947), Russian-born American chemist who obtained both undergraduate and graduate training at the University of Michigan and then worked with Baeyer and Victor Meyer. After synthesizing tetraphenylmethane, he returned to Michigan and attempted to synthesize hexaphenylethane with the result that he discovered stable free radicals.

$$(C_6H_5)_3CC(C_6H_5)_3 + I_2 \longrightarrow 2 \ (C_6H_5)_3CI$$

$$+ \ 2 \ K \longrightarrow 2 \ (C_6H_5)_3CK$$

None of these reactions would be expected from the structure of the hydrocarbon. The explanation lies in the dissociation of hexaphenylethane in solution into two free **triphenylmethyl** groups, each with an unpaired electron.

$$(C_6H_5)_3C : C(C_6H_5)_3 \rightleftharpoons 2 \ [(C_6H_5)_3C \cdot]$$

These unpaired electrons can pair with the unpaired electrons of the oxygen molecule or with that of an iodine atom to form covalent bonds, or can accept an electron from a metallic atom to form an ionic bond.

Solutions of hexaphenylethane in benzene do not conduct an electric current, but solutions in liquid sulfur dioxide have a high conductivity, and the equivalent conductance increases with dilution. Evidently hexaphenylethane can dissociate in an ionizing medium into the triphenylmethonium ion and the triphenylmethide ion.

$$(C_6H_5)_3C : C(C_6H_5)_3 \xrightleftharpoons[]{\text{Liquid SO}_2} [(C_6H_5)_3C^+] + [: \overset{-}{C}(C_6H_5)_3]$$

Triphenyl-   Triphenyl-
methonium   methide
ion   ion

Thus three types of free groups in which carbon has an abnormal valence are possible. Neutral groups having an unpaired electron are known as *free radicals*; groups positively charged because they lack a pair of electrons in the valence shell of a carbon atom are known as *carbonium ions*; groups negatively charged because a carbon atom has an unshared pair of electrons are called *carbanions*.

The markedly greater stability of the triphenylmethyl free radical compared to the methyl free radical can be ascribed to the large resonance energy of the former. This resonance may be indicated by the hybrid symbolism.

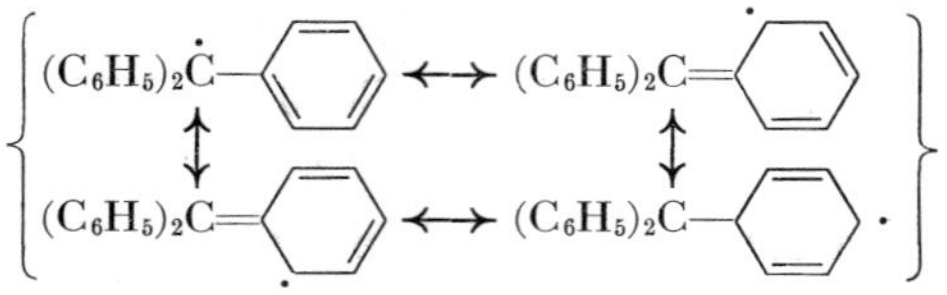

Since electronic interaction takes place with all three benzene nuclei, a total of ten important resonance structures contribute to the stability of the free radical. If more aromatic nuclei are conjugated with the system, the possibility for resonance increases and the free radicals become still more stable. Thus replacement of the phenyl groups of hexaphenylethane successively by *p*-biphenyl groups (xenyl groups) increases the degree of dissociation. In 3 per cent solutions in benzene, triphenylmethyl exists to the extent of about 2 per cent in equilibrium with its dimer, xenyldiphenylmethyl 15 per cent, dixenylphenylmethyl 79 per cent, and trixenylmethyl 100 per cent.

ARYLALKENES

From a practical viewpoint the simplest of the arylalkenes, **phenylethylene,** is a very important substance. Over 378 million pounds was produced in the U. S. in 1948, exceeding the production of any other synthetic aromatic chemical. The common name **styrene** arises from the fact that it was obtained first in 1831 by the distillation of *storax*, a fragrant resin from *Styrax officinalis.* It arises from the cinnamic acid present, which decomposes on slow distillation.

$$C_6H_5CH{=}CHCOOH \xrightarrow{\text{Heat}} C_6H_5CH{=}CH_2 + CO_2$$
$$\text{Styrene}$$

Styrene also is present in coal tar, which was the first commercial source. At present it is made by converting benzene to ethylbenzene, which then is dehydrogenated catalytically.

$$C_6H_6 + CH_2{=}CH_2 \xrightarrow{\text{AlCl}_3} C_6H_5CH_2CH_3 \xrightarrow[500°-600°]{\text{Cr}_2\text{O}_3-\text{Al}_2\text{O}_3} C_6H_5CH{=}CH_2 + H_2$$
$$\text{Ethylbenzene} \qquad\qquad \text{Styrene}$$

The importance of styrene lies in its easy polymerization, which was observed as early as 1839. As late as 1930, however, polystyrene had little commercial use because the product was very brittle. Subsequently the brittle polymers were avoided by proper purification of the monomer to remove the small amounts of impurities which cause cross-linking. Very pure styrene polymerized at room temperature gives a fibrous tough solid having a molecular weight of about 500,000, which is a thermoplastic linear polymer, soluble in benzene.

$$x\, C_6H_5CH{=}CH_2 \longrightarrow \left[\begin{array}{c} -CH_2CH- \\ | \\ C_6H_5 \end{array}\right]_x$$

If as little as 0.01 per cent of divinylbenzene, $CH_2{=}CHC_6H_4CH{=}CH_2$, is present, the product no longer is thermoplastic and only swells in benzene, because cross-linking of the linear chains has taken place.

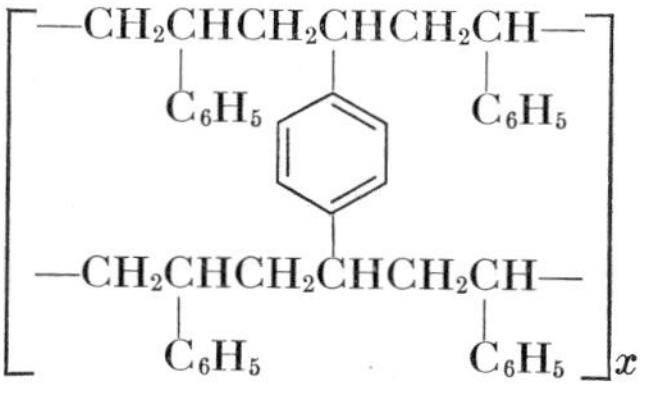

$$\left[\begin{array}{c} -CH_2CHCH_2CHCH_2CH- \\ \quad | \qquad\qquad\qquad | \\ \quad C_6H_5 \qquad\qquad C_6H_5 \\[2pt] \bigcirc \\[2pt] -CH_2CHCH_2CHCH_2CH- \\ \quad | \qquad\qquad\qquad | \\ \quad C_6H_5 \qquad\qquad C_6H_5 \end{array}\right]_x$$

Polystyrene has high transparency and strength and, being a hydrocarbon, it is a good electrical insulator, is chemically resistant, and is light in weight.

The copolymer of styrene and divinylbenzene is sulfonated to give cation-exchange resins (p. 390). Styrene also is copolymerized with butadiene to give the most important type of synthetic rubber, Buna-S or GRS (p. 502). Polymerized 2,4-dichlorostyrene has still better electrical properties than polystyrene, and the copolymer with butadiene has certain advantages over the styrene-butadiene copolymer.

Three diphenylethylenes are possible. **1,1-Diphenylethylene** can be made by the reaction of acetophenone and phenylmagnesium bromide. The intermediate carbinol can be dehydrated readily to the olefin.

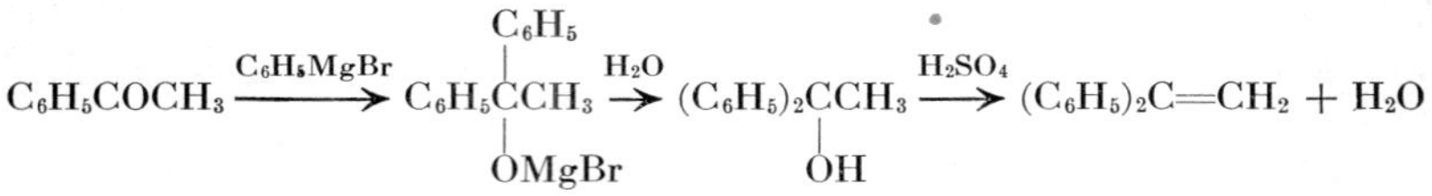

$$\underset{}{C_6H_5COCH_3} \xrightarrow{C_6H_5MgBr} \underset{\underset{OMgBr}{|}}{\overset{\overset{C_6H_5}{|}}{C_6H_5CCH_3}} \xrightarrow{H_2O} (C_6H_5)_2\underset{\underset{OH}{|}}{C}CH_3 \xrightarrow{H_2SO_4} (C_6H_5)_2C{=}CH_2 + H_2O$$

The two *1,2-diphenylethylenes* are known as **cis-** and **trans-stilbene** (p. 255). *Trans*-stilbene is the stable isomer and is obtained by the dehydration of benzylphenylcarbinol.

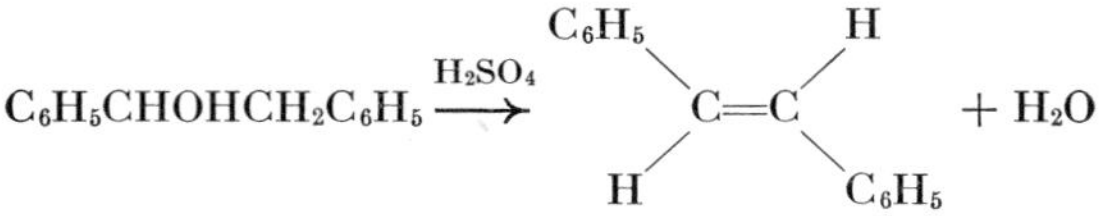

$$C_6H_5CHOHCH_2C_6H_5 \xrightarrow{H_2SO_4} \underset{trans\text{-Stilbene}}{\overset{C_6H_5 \qquad H}{\underset{H \qquad C_6H_5}{C{=}C}}} + H_2O$$

Irradiation with ultraviolet light converts it to *cis*-stilbene.

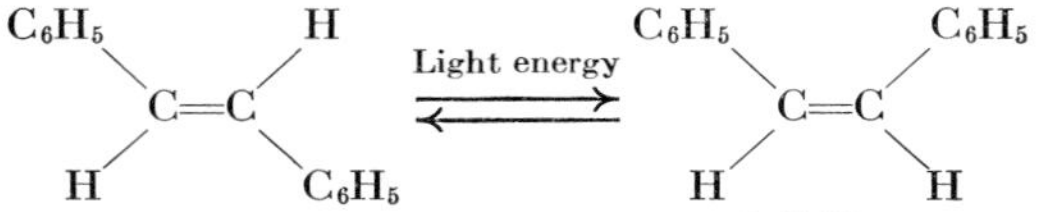

$$\underset{H \qquad C_6H_5}{\overset{C_6H_5 \qquad H}{C{=}C}} \underset{\text{Light energy}}{\rightleftarrows} \underset{\underset{cis\text{-Stilbene}}{H \qquad H}}{\overset{C_6H_5 \qquad C_6H_5}{C{=}C}}$$

Triphenylethylene may be prepared by dehydration of diphenylbenzyl-carbinol or phenylbenzhydrylcarbinol. **Tetraphenylethylene** is formed when diphenyldichloromethane, prepared by the action of phosphorus pentachloride on benzophenone, is heated with zinc dust.

$$2\,(C_6H_5)_2CO \xrightarrow{2\,PCl_5} 2\,(C_6H_5)_2CCl_2 \xrightarrow{2\,Zn} (C_6H_5)_2C{=}C(C_6H_5)_2 + 2\,ZnCl_2$$

BIPHENYL AND ITS DERIVATIVES

Biphenyl and its derivatives form the largest group of compounds having benzene rings directly united. **Biphenyl** is obtained when benzene is heated to a high temperature. In the laboratory preparation the vapor from refluxing benzene is allowed to come in contact with a spiral of electrically heated Nichrome wire, but in the commercial method the vapor is passed through molten lead.

$$2\,C_6H_6 \xrightarrow{700°-800°} C_6H_5C_6H_5 + H_2$$

Since the initial stage in the formation of biphenyl undoubtedly is the decomposition of benzene into phenyl radicals and hydrogen atoms, it is not surprising that small amounts of the terphenyls, *m-* and *p-diphenylbenzene,* also are produced.

Besides the use of biphenyl in the eutectic with phenyl ether as a heat transfer medium (p. 387), some of its substitution products are important. The halogenated biphenyls (Arochlors) are used as transformer oils, and some of the aminobiphenyls are used as dye intermediates. Direct substitution reactions lead to *ortho* and *para* monosubstitution products, but since the groups introduced usually are deactivating, a second substitution takes place in the second ring.

The most important derivative of biphenyl, *p,p'*-diaminobiphenyl or **benzidine,** is not made from biphenyl but by the benzidine rearrangement of hydrazobenzene (p. 347). It is an important intermediate for the synthesis of direct dyes for cotton (p. 479).

$$\langle\!\!\!\!\bigcirc\!\!\!\!\rangle\text{NHNH}\langle\!\!\!\!\bigcirc\!\!\!\!\rangle + 2\text{ HCl} \xrightarrow{\text{Heat}} \left[\text{H}_3\overset{+}{\text{N}}\langle\!\!\!\!\bigcirc\!\!\!\!\rangle\!\!\!-\!\!\!\langle\!\!\!\!\bigcirc\!\!\!\!\rangle\overset{+}{\text{NH}}_3\right]2\text{ Cl}^-$$

Benzidine hydrochloride

o-**Tolidine** (*p,p'*-diamino-*m,m'*-dimethylbiphenyl) is made similarly from *o*-hydrazotoluene.

Benzidine is oxidized under certain conditions to give an intensely blue colored product known as Benzidine Blue. This reaction has been used as the basis of tests for peroxidases and of sensitive spot tests for manganese, cerium, copper, molybdenum, lead, and cyanide ion.

Biphenyl derivatives can be prepared by heating iodobenzenes with finely divided copper (*Ullmann reaction*). The reaction is valuable because it permits the synthesis of derivatives of known constitution and of compounds that cannot be prepared readily in other ways.

$$2\,\underset{\text{COOH}}{\overset{\text{NO}_2}{\langle\!\!\!\bigcirc\!\!\!\rangle}}\!\!\text{I} + 2\text{ Cu} \longrightarrow \underset{\text{COOH}\ \ \text{COOH}}{\overset{\text{NO}_2\ \ \ \ \text{NO}_2}{\langle\!\!\!\bigcirc\!\!\!\rangle\!\!-\!\!\langle\!\!\!\bigcirc\!\!\!\rangle}} + \text{Cu}_2\text{I}_2$$

2,2'-Dinitro-6,6'-
biphenyldicarboxylic
acid

REVIEW QUESTIONS

1. Give equations for the synthesis of diphenylmethane and triphenylmethane. What is the initial product of oxidation in each case?
2. Discuss the method of preparation and chemical properties of hexaphenylethane. How are these properties explained? What are the three classes of *free groups*?
3. How is styrene made and of what use is it?
4. Give reactions for the synthesis of stilbene, triphenylmethane, and tetraphenylethylene.
5. What is biphenyl and how is it made? Of what use is it? In the direct substitution reactions of diphenyl, what positions are taken by the entering groups and why?
6. What is the common name for *p,p'*-diaminobiphenyl and how is it made?
7. Give reactions for the preparation of (*a*) styrene from benzaldehyde; (*b*) triphenyl-methyl from benzophenone; (*c*) stilbene from benzyl alcohol; (*d*) 1,1-bis-*p*-methoxy-phenyl-2,2,2-trichloroethane from phenol; (*e*) *p,p'*-biphenyldicarboxylic acid from toluene.

Chapter 29

CONDENSED NUCLEAR HYDROCARBONS
AND THEIR DERIVATIVES

Condensed nuclear compounds are compounds in which two or more carbon atoms are shared in common by two or more aromatic rings. The most common compounds of this type are naphthalene and anthracene and their derivatives. Numerous systems that are more complex are known.

NAPHTHALENE

Occurrence and Structure

Naphthalene, isolated some time before 1820, was the first pure compound to be obtained from the distillation products of coal. The reason for its early discovery is that it is a beautiful crystalline solid that sublimes readily. It was noticed first as a deposit in the condensers during the distillation of the naphtha fraction and hence was called naphthalene. Naphthalene is obtained chiefly by allowing the carbolic and creosote fractions of coal tar to crystallize (p. 323).

The empirical formula, $C_{10}H_8$, was established by Faraday in 1826 by the analysis of barium naphthalenesulfonate, but it was not until after Kekulé propounded his theory of aromatic structure that Erlenmeyer [1] proposed a satisfactory structural formula for naphthalene in 1866. Erlenmeyer's formula contains two aromatic nuclei having two carbon atoms in common.

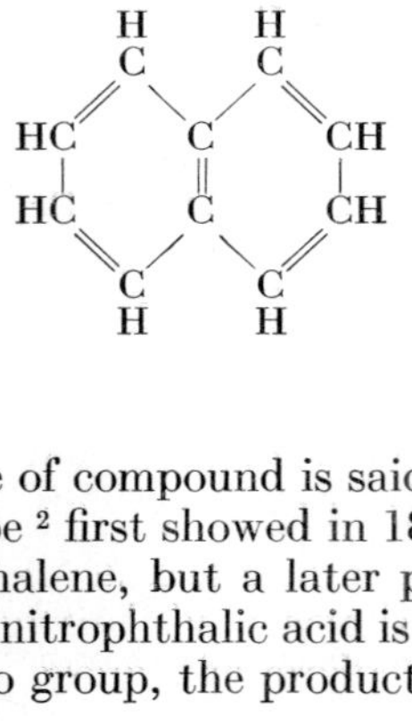

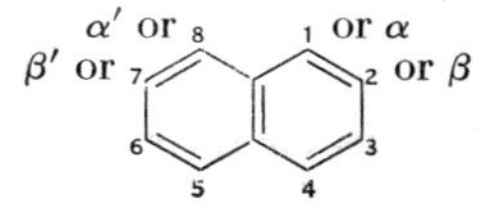

Naphthalene

This type of compound is said to have a *fused* or a *condensed* ring system.

Graebe [2] first showed in 1869 that two different benzene rings are present in naphthalene, but a later proof is more direct. When nitronaphthalene is oxidized, nitrophthalic acid is formed, but if the nitro group first is reduced to the amino group, the product of subsequent oxidation is phthalic acid.

---

[1] Richard August Karl Emil Erlenmeyer (1825–1909), professor at the University of Munich. He is well known for the still popular conical flask which he devised.

[2] Carl Graebe (1841–1927), student of Bunsen and Baeyer and later professor at the University of Geneva. He is known chiefly for determining the structure of alizarin and synthesizing it but did important work in the fields of polynuclear compounds and dyes in general.

428

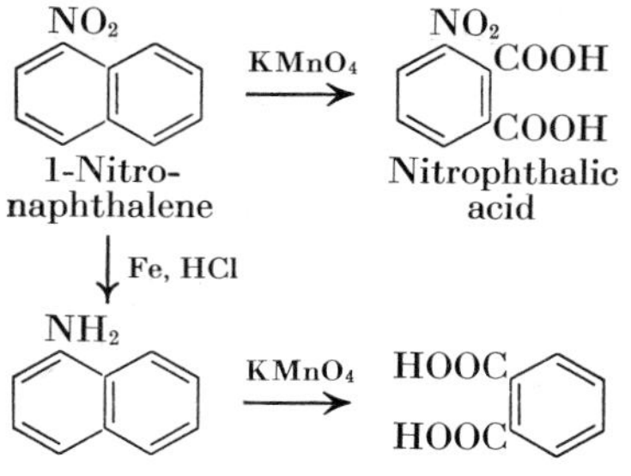

1-Nitro-
naphthalene

Nitrophthalic
acid

The reason for the difference in behavior on oxidation is that the nitro group makes an aromatic ring harder to oxidize than an unsubstituted benzene ring, whereas the amino group increases the ease of oxidation of the ring to which it is attached (p. 366).

Several syntheses of naphthalene substantiate Erlenmeyer's formula. One of the more unequivocal syntheses is that of Fittig which involves the cyclization of β-benzylidenepropionic acid to 1-naphthol and reduction to naphthalene.

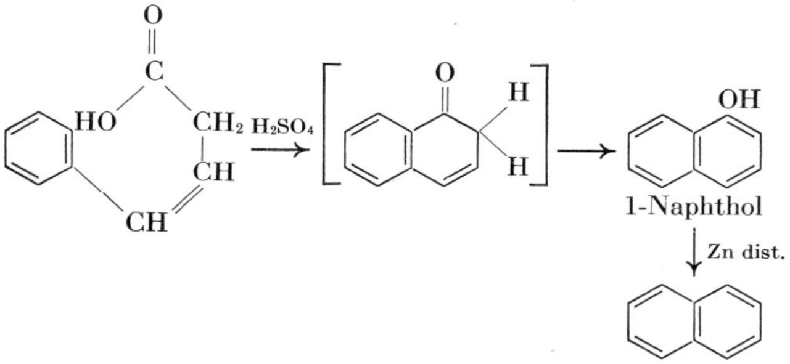

1-Naphthol

The formula accounts for the existence of two monosubstitution products, frequently designated as α and β, and ten disubstitution products when both groups are alike. Up to ten hydrogen atoms can be added to naphthalene indicating five potential double bonds.

As with benzene, the unsaturation electrons of naphthalene are in a closed conjugated system (p. 313). This condition can be represented as a resonance hybrid of the conventional bond structures.

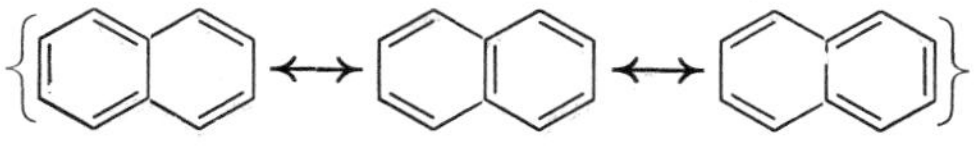

Reactions

Addition Reactions. One ring of naphthalene undergoes addition reactions more readily than benzene. Reaction with sodium and ethyl alcohol produces a 1,4-dihydro derivative. At the higher temperature of boiling *i*-amyl alcohol, the 1,2,3,4-tetrahydro derivative (tetralin) is formed.

Catalytically the reduction may be carried to the tetrahydro or the decahydro stage.

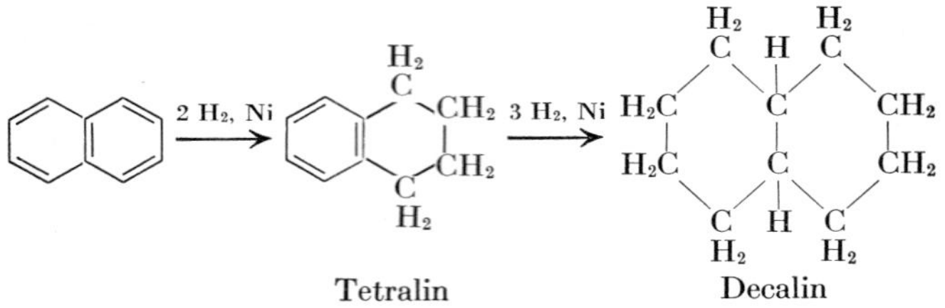

Tetralin   Decalin

Tetralin and **decalin** find some use as solvents. Decalin is of interest in that it exists in two stereoisomeric configurations, *cis*-decalin in which the methine or methylidyne (CH) hydrogen atoms are on the same side of the ring union, and *trans*-decalin in which they are on opposite sides (p. 561).

 Naphthalene adds one or two molecules of chlorine more easily than does benzene. The addition products on heating lose hydrogen chloride.

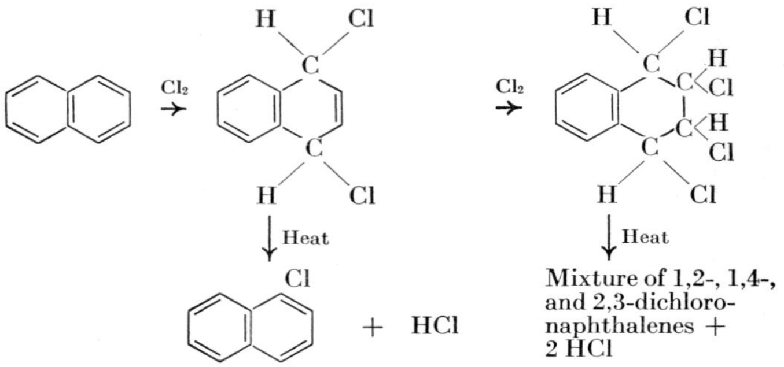

Because of this behavior **naphthalene tetrachloride** is used as a component of soldering pastes, the hydrogen chloride generated on heating being available for removing metallic oxide films.

 Substitution Reactions. Naphthalene undergoes all of the substitution reactions of benzene, using the same reagents and catalysts. **Direct halogenation** in the presence of iron gives 95 per cent of α-chloronaphthalene and about

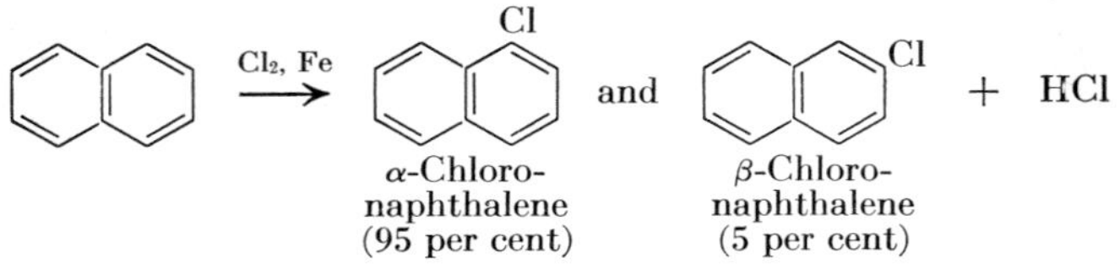

α-Chloro- β-Chloro-
naphthalene naphthalene
(95 per cent) (5 per cent)

5 per cent of the β isomer. Similarly nitration with a mixture of nitric and sulfuric acids yields 95 per cent of α-nitronaphthalene together with about 5 per cent of β-nitronaphthalene. Sulfonation of naphthalene below 80° gives chiefly the α-sulfonic acid, whereas above 120° the β-sulfonic acid is the main product.

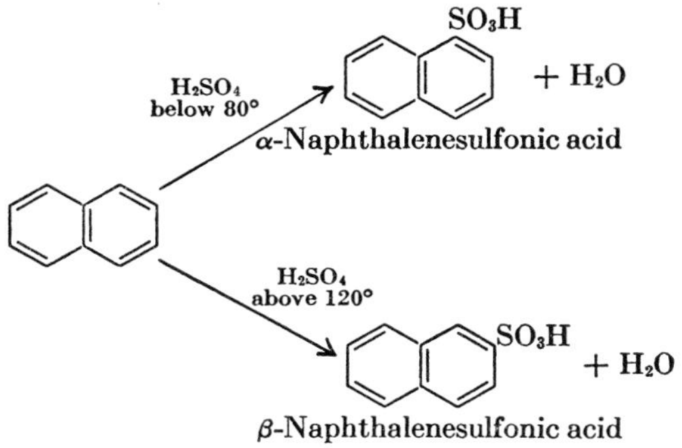

α-Naphthalenesulfonic acid

β-Naphthalenesulfonic acid

This behavior is important because it provides the principal method for introducing a functional group into the β position. Most β-substituted naphthalenes are prepared by way of the β-sulfonic acid. The reason for this behavior appears to be that the rate of sulfonation in the α position is very much faster than in the β position, but the stability of the β-sulfonic acid is greater. Since the reaction is reversible, the β isomer eventually predominates. Mixtures of the α and β acids are separated by crystallization of the calcium salts, the calcium salt of the α isomer being the more soluble.

The Friedel-Crafts reaction also gives mixtures of α and β substitution products, the relative amounts of which can be controlled by varying the conditions of the reaction. Reaction with acetyl chloride in carbon disulfide gives about three-fourths α and one-fourth β substitution, whereas in nitrobenzene solution the β isomer is formed almost exclusively.

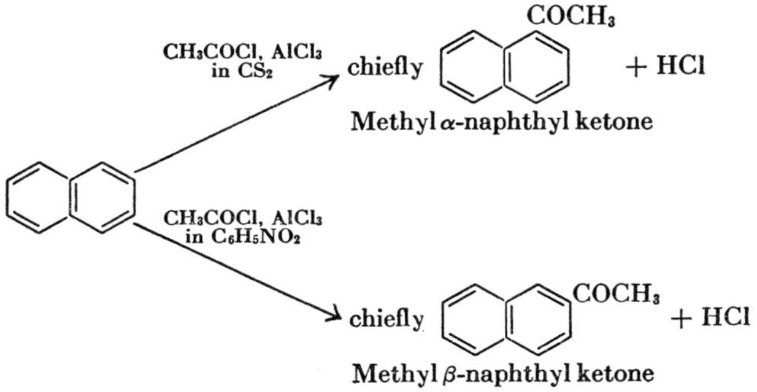

Methyl α-naphthyl ketone

Methyl β-naphthyl ketone

Disubstitution follows essentially the same rules as for benzene, although the reversibility of some reactions frequently permits rearrangement of the initial product to a more stable isomer. If the group in a monosubstituted naphthalene is deactivating, a second substituent will enter the second ring usually in one of the α' positions, except for sulfonation which can take place in a β' position.

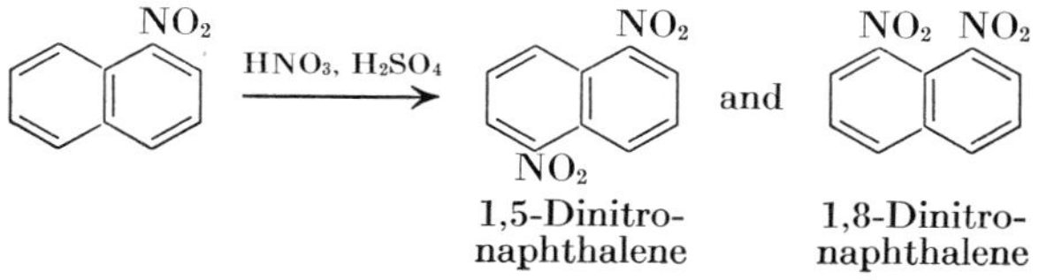

1,5-Dinitro-
naphthalene

1,8-Dinitro-
naphthalene

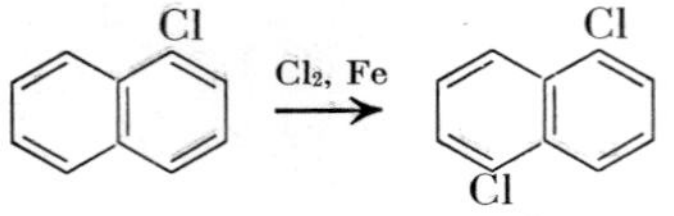

1,5-Dichloro-
naphthalene

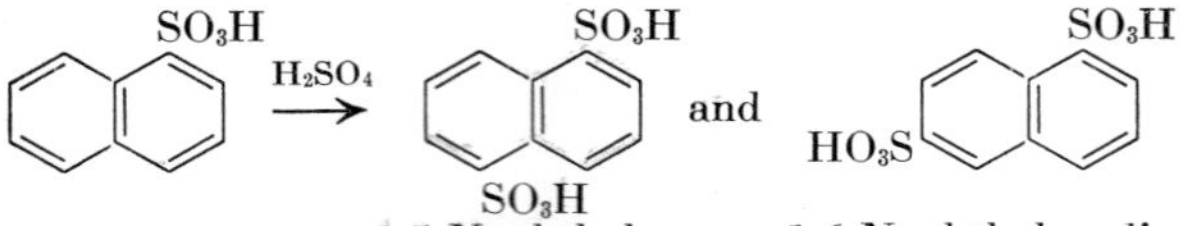

and

1,5-Naphthalene-   1,6-Naphthalenedi-
disulfonic acid   sulfonic acid

and

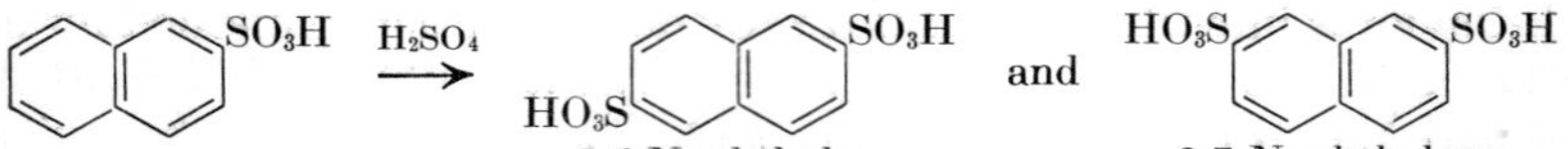

2,6-Naphthalene-   2,7-Naphthalene-
disulfonic acid   disulfonic acid

If the group present is activating and in the α position, a second substituent will enter the 4 (*para*) position, except that in sulfonation a rearranged product may result (p. 431). If an activating group is in the β position, a second substituent enters the α position. Again sulfonation may give anomalous products. Preference for the 1 position over the 3 position in the second reac-

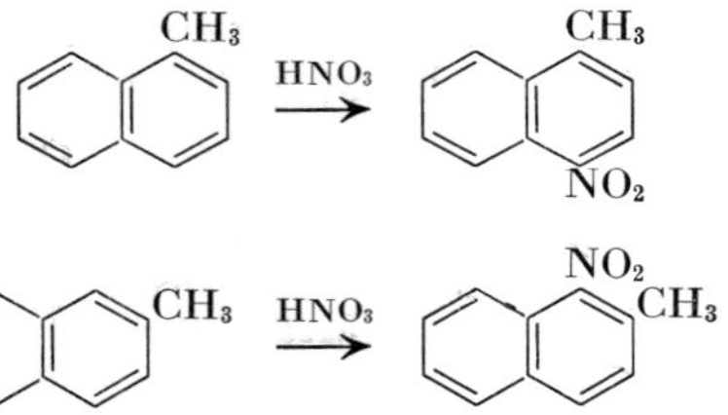

tion is to be expected, since both the methyl group and the second ring activate the 1 position.

Naphthalene Derivatives

Alkyl Derivatives. α- and β-Methylnaphthalene are isolated commercially from coal tar. **α-Methylnaphthalene** has been selected as the standard fuel with zero rating in testing Diesel fuels, because of its poor burning characteristics in the Diesel engine (p. 53). The sulfonated methylnaphthalenes (trade name *Nekals*) are used as wetting agents. Sulfonated butylnaphthalenes (trade name *Tret-o-lites*) are used to break water-oil emulsions obtained from oil wells.

Naphthols. α- and β-Naphthol are prepared from the corresponding sodium sulfonates by fusion with sodium hydroxide. They not only are important dye intermediates themselves but are used for the synthesis of other dye intermediates. Their relative importance is indicated by the production in this country in 1945 of about a half-million pounds of the α isomer and over twenty million pounds of the β isomer. Pure α-naphthol is made by the hydrolysis of α-naphthylamine (p. 433).

Halogenated Naphthalenes. α-Chloro- and α-bromonaphthalene are made by direct halogenation. The β isomers are only of research interest. They can be made by the action of phosphorus pentahalides on the naphthol or by the Sandmeyer reaction from diazotized β-naphthylamine.

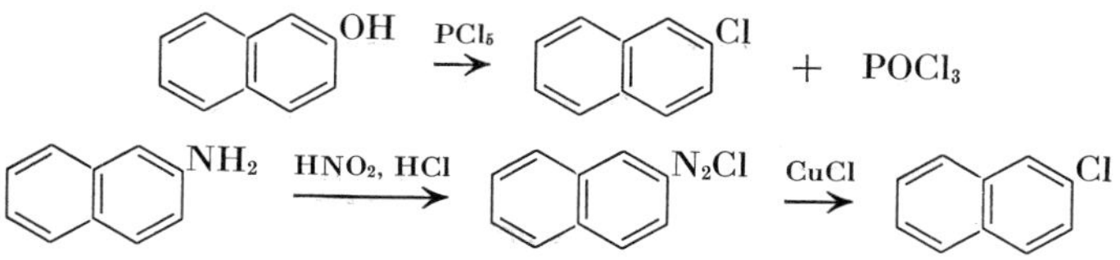

The polychloronaphthalenes made by direct chlorination are solids which find use as impregnating agents under the trade name *Halowax*.

Naphthylamines. α-Naphthylamine is made by the iron reduction of α-nitronaphthalene. β-Naphthylamine is made by the ammonolysis of β-naphthol. This reaction, which is slow in the benzene series, can be brought about easily in the naphthalene series by aqueous ammonia and ammonium sulfite, and is known as the **Bucherer reaction.**

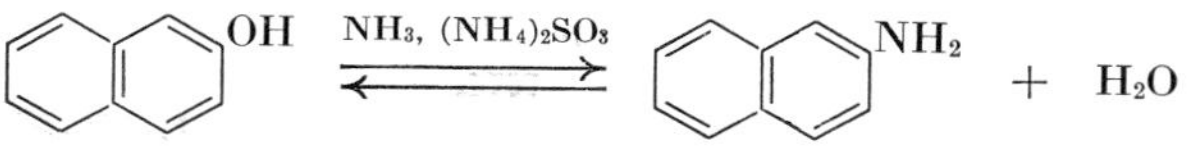

Amines other than ammonia can be used to give substituted aminonaphthalenes. The reaction is reversible and is used to prepare naphthols from naphthylamines if the naphthylamine is more readily available. For example pure α-naphthol is obtained best from pure α-naphthylamine.

It usually is assumed that the Bucherer reaction proceeds through the keto form and that the function of the sulfite is to stabilize this form by converting it to the bisulfite addition compound.

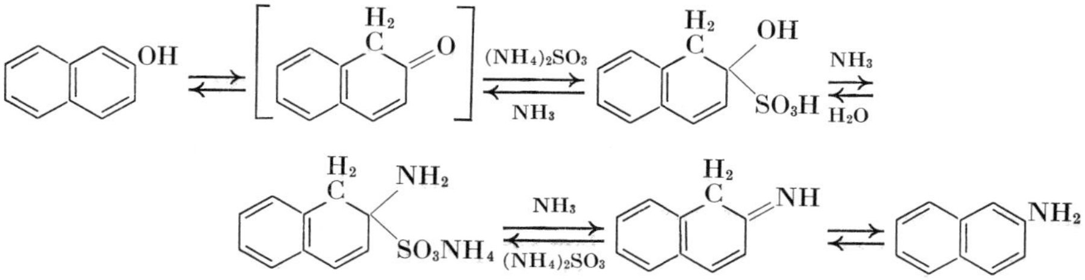

Sulfonated Naphthols and Naphthylamines. Naphthols and naphthylamines couple with diazonium salts to give azo compounds which absorb light of longer wavelength than the simpler azo compounds derived from benzene derivatives, because of increased opportunity for resonance. In order that these colored compounds be water-soluble, however, strongly water-solubilizing groups must be present. Hence azo dyes for direct dyeing always contain sulfonic acid groups, and the sulfonated naphthols and naphthylamines are used widely as dye intermediates. Usually these intermediates have common names which were assigned by dye manufacturers because the constitution of the compound was unknown when it first came into use, or because the originator did not care to be overly helpful to his competitors.

Naphthionic acid is made from α-naphthylamine by the baking process described for the preparation of sulfanilic acid (p. 369).

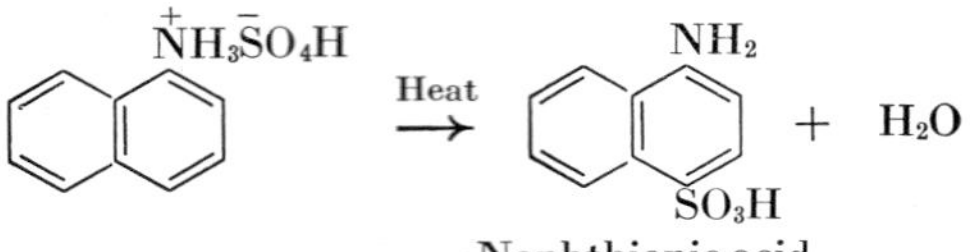

$$\overset{+}{N}H_3\overset{-}{S}O_4H \xrightarrow{\text{Heat}} \quad NH_2 \;,\; SO_3H \quad + \quad H_2O$$

Naphthionic acid

When β-naphthalenesulfonic acid is nitrated, the nitro group enters the 5 and 8 positions. Reduction gives rise to the corresponding aminosulfonic acids which are known as **Cleve's acids.**

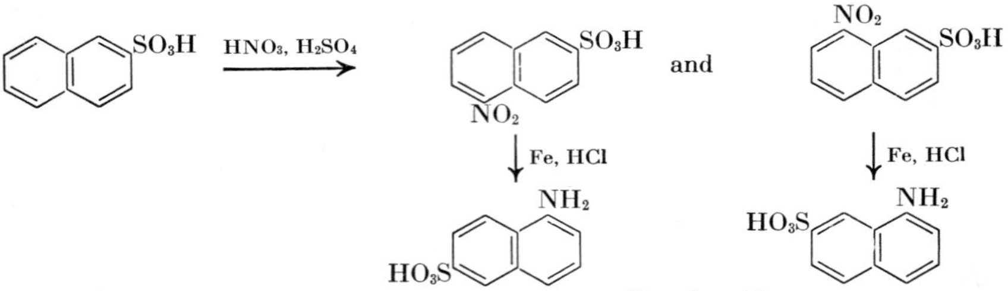

$$SO_3H \xrightarrow{HNO_3,\ H_2SO_4} \quad SO_3H,\ NO_2 \quad \text{and} \quad NO_2,\ SO_3H$$

$$\Big\downarrow \text{Fe, HCl} \qquad\qquad \Big\downarrow \text{Fe, HCl}$$

$$HO_3S,\ NH_2 \qquad\qquad HO_3S,\ NH_2$$

Cleve's acids

Naphthionic acid is hydrolyzed to 1-naphthol-4-sulfonic acid (**Neville-Winther acid**) by boiling with aqueous sodium bisulfite.

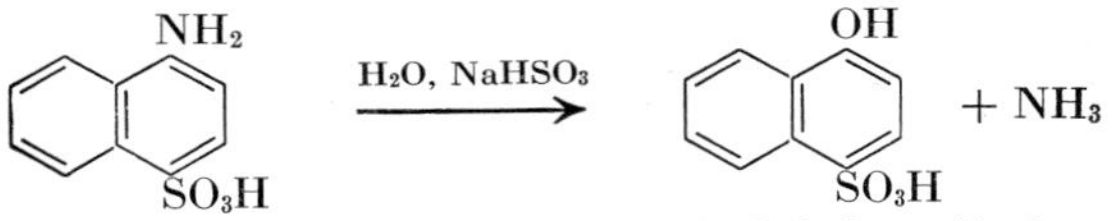

$$NH_2,\ SO_3H \xrightarrow{H_2O,\ NaHSO_3} \quad OH,\ SO_3H \quad + \quad NH_3$$

1-Naphthol-4-sulfonic acid
(Neville-Winther acid)

This reaction was known but not openly published eight years before Bucherer discovered it in 1904, but Bucherer demonstrated the general usefulness and the reversibility of the reaction.

Sulfonation of β-naphthol at a low temperature gives the 1-sulfonic acid, which rapidly rearranges to the 8-sulfonic acid, and at higher temperatures to the 6-sulfonic acid (**Schaeffer's acid**). With an excess of sulfuric acid the 3,6- and 6,8-disulfonic acids (**R-acid** and **G-acid**) are formed.

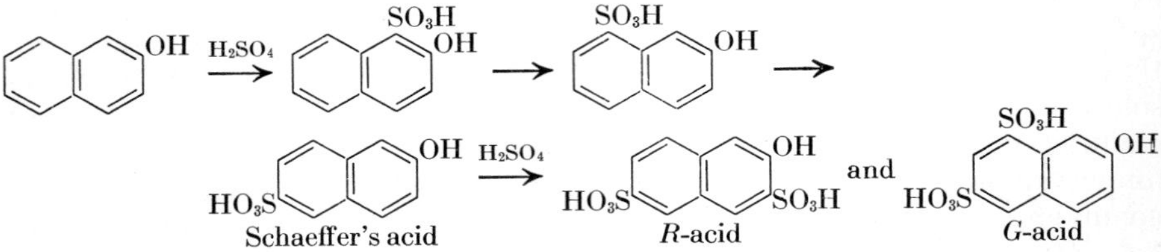

$$OH \xrightarrow{H_2SO_4} SO_3H,\ OH \rightarrow SO_3H,\ OH \rightarrow$$

$$HO_3S,\ OH \xrightarrow{H_2SO_4} HO_3S,\ OH,\ SO_3H \quad \text{and} \quad HO_3S,\ OH,\ SO_3H$$

Schaeffer's acid   R-acid   G-acid

The designations R and G come from the German words *rot* and *gelb* which refer to the red and yellow shades of the azo dyes produced by coupling. The acids are isolated as the sodium salts which are known as Schaeffer's salt, R-salt, and G-salt.

Aminonaphthols. 4-Amino-1-naphthol and 1-amino-2-naphthol are prepared best by coupling α- or β-naphthol with diazotized sulfanilic acid and reducing the azo dye with sodium hydrosulfite.

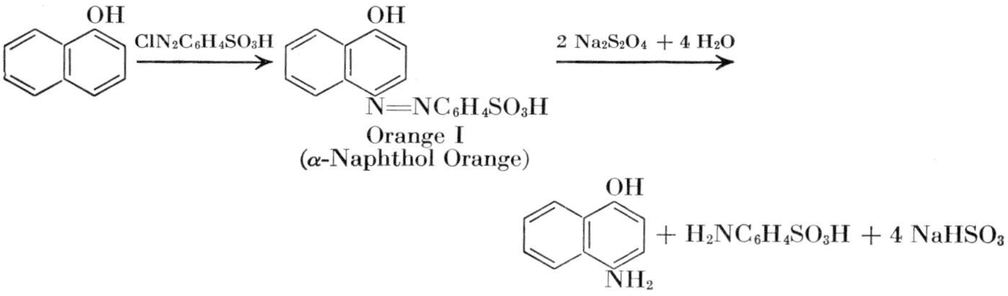

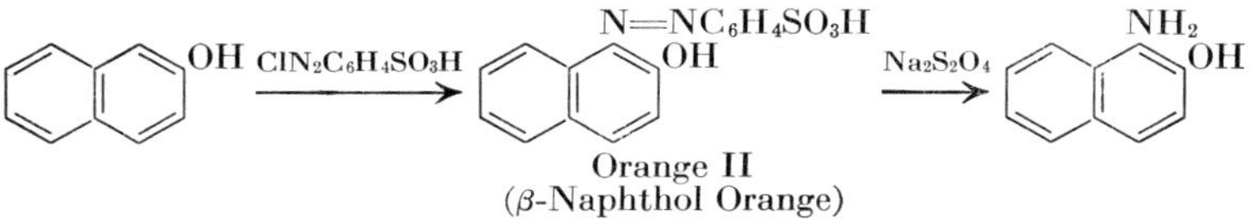

Orange I
(α-Naphthol Orange)

$+ H_2NC_6H_4SO_3H + 4 NaHSO_3$

Orange II
(β-Naphthol Orange)

The most important derivative of an aminonaphthol is **H-acid,** which is made by the controlled sodium hydroxide fusion of 1-naphthylamine-3,6,8-trisulfonic acid (**Koch's acid**).

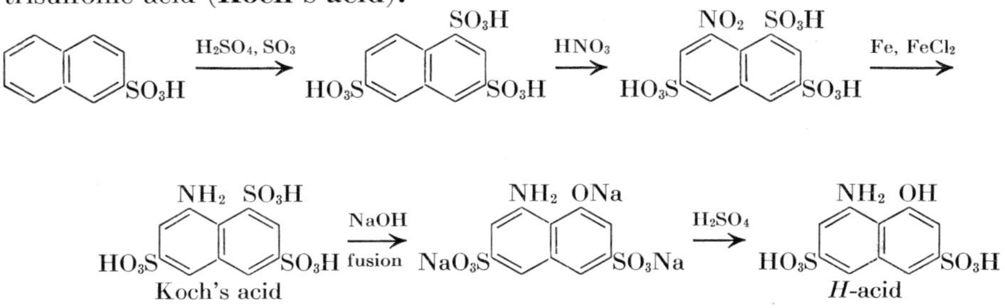

Koch's acid

H-acid

Sulfonation of β-naphthylamine gives a mixture of 2-aminonaphthalene-6,8-disulfonic acid and 2-aminonaphthalene-1,5,7-trisulfonic acid. Controlled caustic fusion of the disulfonate gives γ-**acid,** 2-amino-8-hydroxynaphthalene-6-sulfonic acid.

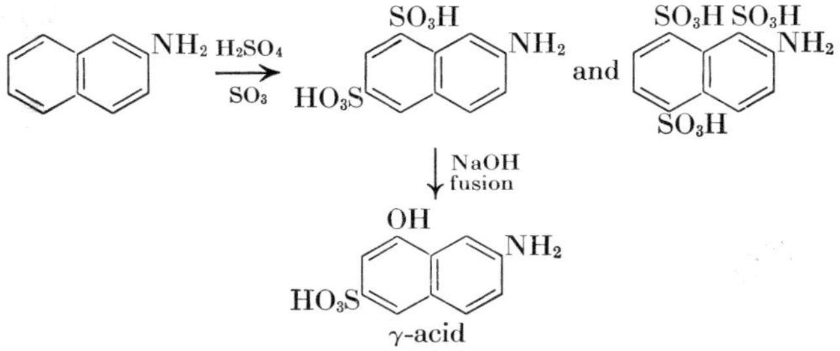

γ-acid

Naphthoquinones. Whereas the benzene ring permits the existence of only two benzoquinones, the *ortho* and *para*, the naphthalene ring system permits a third. α- and β-Naphthoquinones are prepared by the oxidation of 4-amino-1-naphthol and 2-amino-1-naphthol respectively. The latter are obtained more readily than the dihydroxy or diamino derivatives. The third naphthoquinone, called *amphi*, is obtained by the oxidation of 2,6-dihydroxynaphthalene.

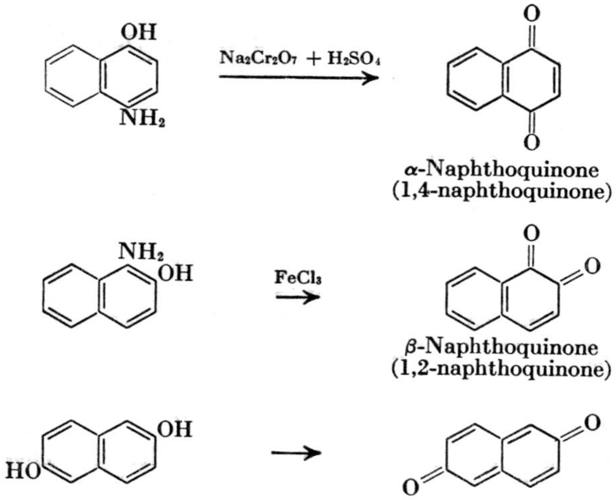

α-Naphthoquinone
(1,4-naphthoquinone)

β-Naphthoquinone
(1,2-naphthoquinone)

Amphi-naphthoquinone
(2,6-naphthoquinone)

The most interesting of the naphthoquinones are the two forms of **vitamin K.** Vitamin K_1 is found in green plants such as alfalfa and K_2 in putrefied fish meal. One of the K vitamins must be supplied by the diet for the adequate clotting of blood, and so they are termed *antihemorrhagic factors*. Although

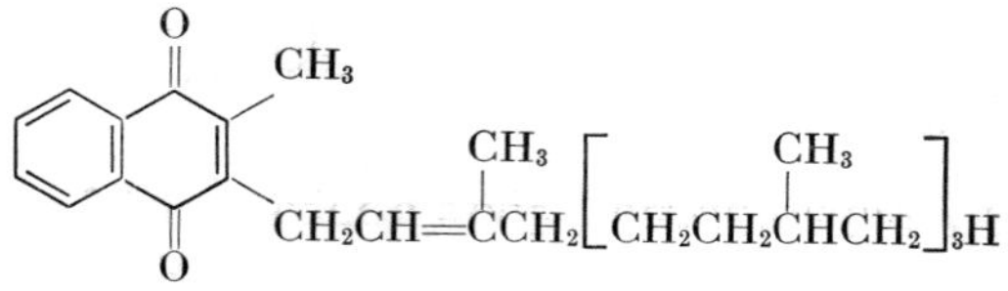

Vitamin K_1

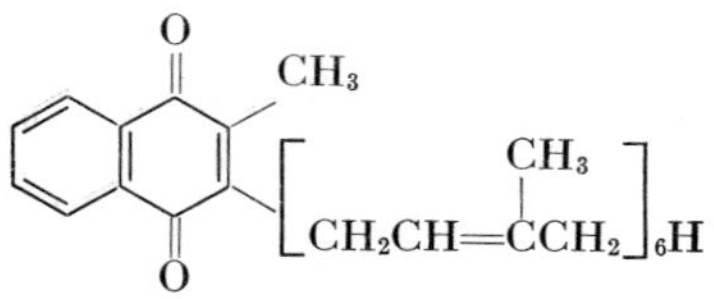

Vitamin K_2

modifications in the structure of vitamin K_1 usually decrease its activity, it has been found that 2,3-dimethyl-α-naphthoquinone is more potent on a weight basis and almost as potent on a mole basis.

Carboxylic Acids. α- or β-Naphthoic acid can be made by hydrolysis of the corresponding nitrile. The latter is prepared from the sulfonic acid by fusion with sodium cyanide, or from the amine through the diazo reaction. α-Naphthoic acid can be obtained also from α-bromonaphthalene through the Grignard reagent.

The most important dibasic acid is **naphthalic acid** prepared by the oxidation of acenaphthene, a component of coal tar.

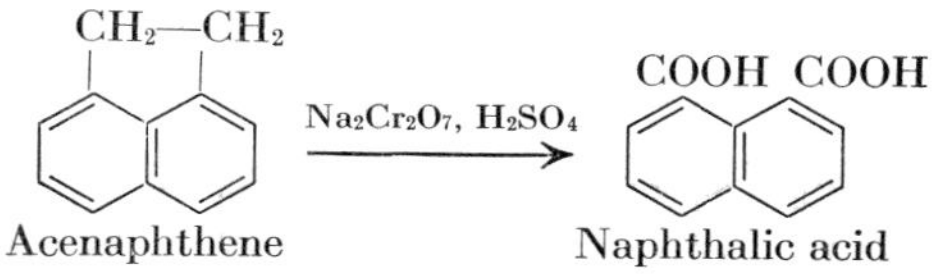

Acenaphthene Naphthalic acid

The spatial relation of the two carboxyl groups is such that naphthalic acid closely resembles phthalic acid in its properties. On heating, it yields an anhydride which can be converted to the imide.

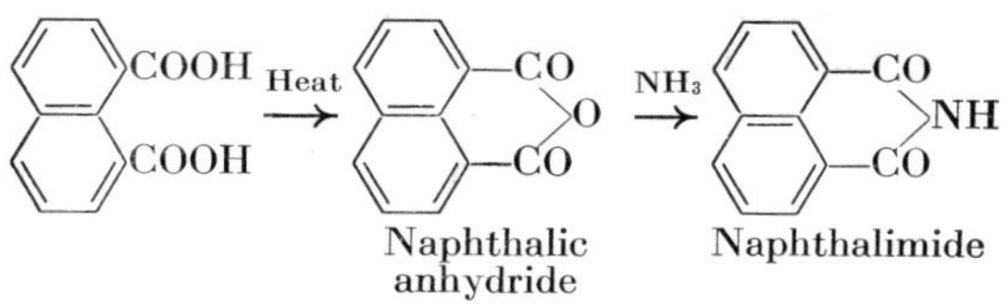

Naphthalic anhydride Naphthalimide

Certain chemicals present in plants accelerate the growth of cells and are known as **auxins**. Many synthetic compounds have similar properties and are used by nurserymen to increase the ease of rooting of cuttings and by orchardists to prevent premature bud formation and premature dropping of fruit. One of the more widely used substances for this purpose is α-**naphthylacetic** acid which can be made by the chloromethylation of naphthalene, conversion to the nitrile, and hydrolysis.

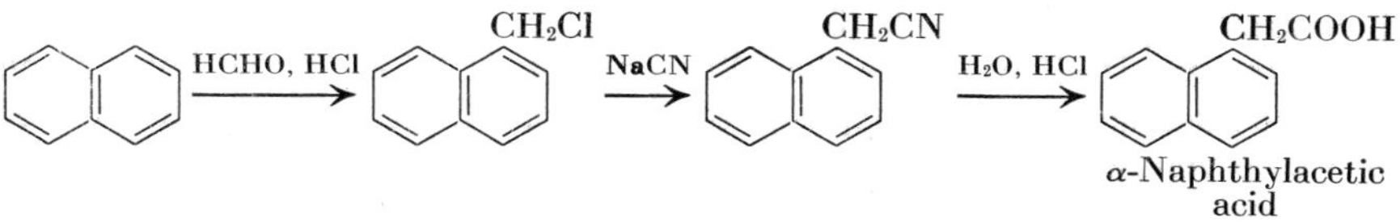

α-Naphthylacetic acid

ANTHRACENE AND DERIVATIVES

The coal tar fraction boiling at 300°–350° is known as **anthracene oil,** or as **green oil** because of its dark green fluorescence. It is run into tanks and allowed to crystallize over a period of one to two weeks and filtered. The nearly dry cakes are hot-pressed at 50,000 to 70,000 pounds pressure to give a mixture of anthracene, phenanthrene, and carbazole. The press cake is ground and washed with coal tar naphtha to remove most of the phenanthrene and then with pyridine to remove the carbazole. Anthracene was the second compound to be isolated from coal tar (p. 324) although less than 1 per cent is present. At first it was believed to be an isomer of naphthalene and was called paranaphthalene, but later the name was changed to anthracene (Gr. *anthrax* coal). At one time anthracene was the sole source of the anthraquinone dyes, but intermediates for the latter now are synthesized from benzene.

Anthracene has the molecular formula $C_{14}H_{10}$. It has both unsaturated and aromatic properties. Thus it readily adds one mole of hydrogen. It also sulfonates directly and can be oxidized to anthraquinone, $C_{14}H_8O_2$. Its structure is arrived at from the rational synthesis of some of its derivatives. Thus when o-bromobenzyl bromide reacts with metallic sodium, a dihydroanthracene is formed, identical with that obtained by the reduction of anthracene. Mild oxidation converts it to anthracene.

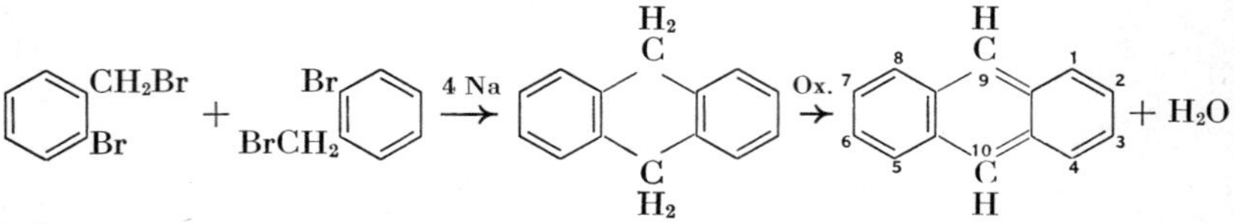

9,10-Dihydro-anthracene   Anthracene

Anthraquinone is obtained in good yield by condensing benzene with phthalic anhydride and cyclizing with sulfuric acid.

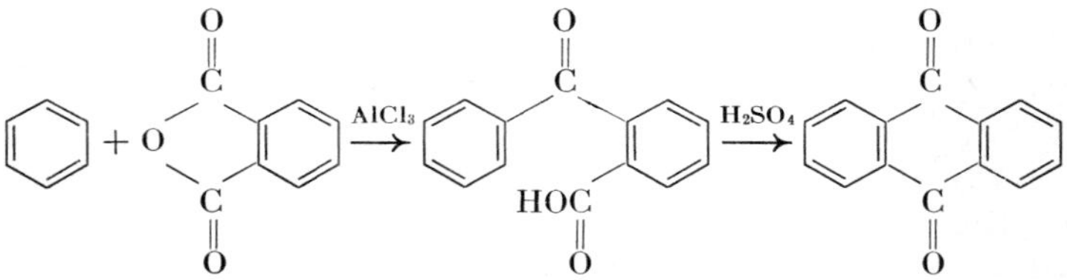

o-Benzoylbenzoic acid   Anthraquinone

From these syntheses it is clear that anthracene contains three fused rings, and that addition and oxidation take place at the two central carbon atoms which are designated as the 9,10 positions.

Anthracene itself has little use. When pure it is colorless and has a strong pale blue fluorescence when exposed to ultraviolet light. Ordinary anthracene has a pale yellow color and exhibits a strong greenish-yellow fluorescence.

Derivatives of anthraquinone are of great importance in the dye industry (p. 487). Formerly **anthraquinone** was made by the oxidation of anthracene, but now it is made by the cyclization of o-benzoylbenzoic acid. Since halogen or nitro groups may be introduced into phthalic anhydride by direct substitution, and since it or its derivatives may be condensed with any aromatic derivative capable of undergoing the Friedel-Crafts reaction, the general method of synthesis can lead to a large number of derivatives of anthraquinone.

Anthraquinone closely resembles naphthalene in its substitution reactions. Thus sulfonation catalyzed by mercuric sulfate at 120° gives chiefly α-**anthraquinonesulfonic acid,** whereas the uncatalyzed sulfonation at 140° gives chiefly β-**anthraquinonesulfonic acid.** The technical sodium salt of the β isomer, obtained by the liming out process (p. 353), is known as **silver salt** because of its silvery gray appearance.

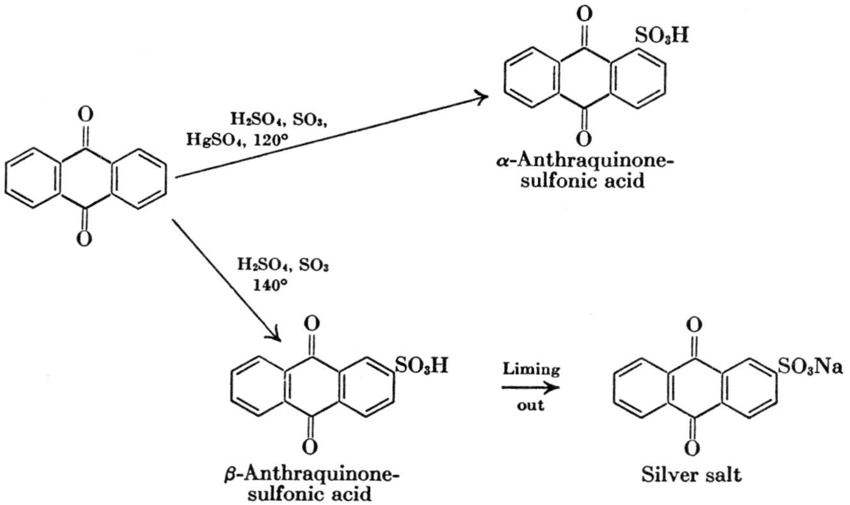

α-Anthraquinone-
sulfonic acid

β-Anthraquinone-
sulfonic acid

Silver salt

Nitration of anthraquinone yields only **α-nitroanthraquinone.**

α-Aminoanthraquinone can be made by reduction of α-nitroanthraquinone or by the action of ammonia on the salt of the α sulfonate in the presence of barium chloride.

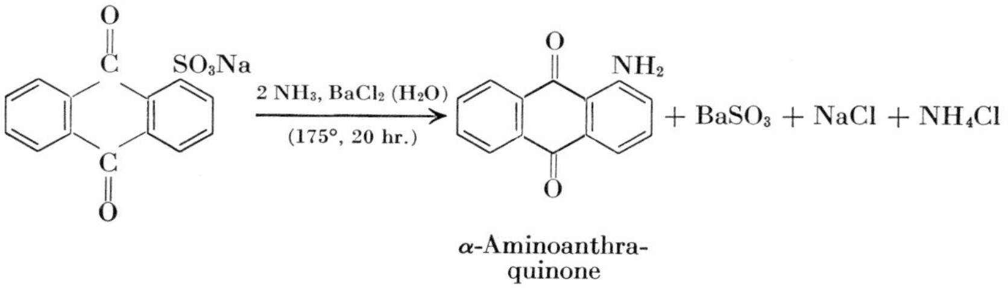

α-Aminoanthra-
quinone

β-Aminoanthraquinone is made from silver salt by a similar process using calcium chloride instead of barium chloride at 195°. A second technical process for this important dye intermediate is the ammonolysis of 2-chloroanthraquinone made from 4-chlorophthalic anhydride.

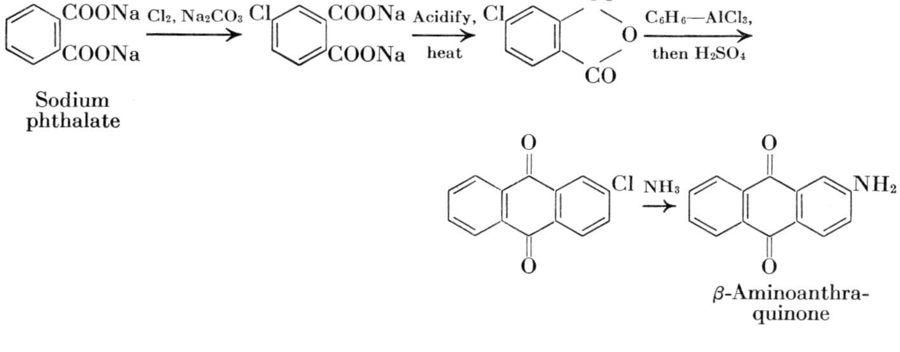

Sodium
phthalate

β-Aminoanthra-
quinone

The aminoanthraquinones do not couple with diazonium salts, presumably because of the deactivating effect of the carbonyl groups. The dihydro derivatives, in which the carbonyl groups are converted to hydroxyl groups, couple readily.

When silver salt is fused with sodium hydroxide not only is the sulfonate group replaced by hydroxyl but the hydrogen in the α position is oxidized to hydroxyl. To prevent the simultaneous reduction of the anthraquinone, an oxidizing agent is added.

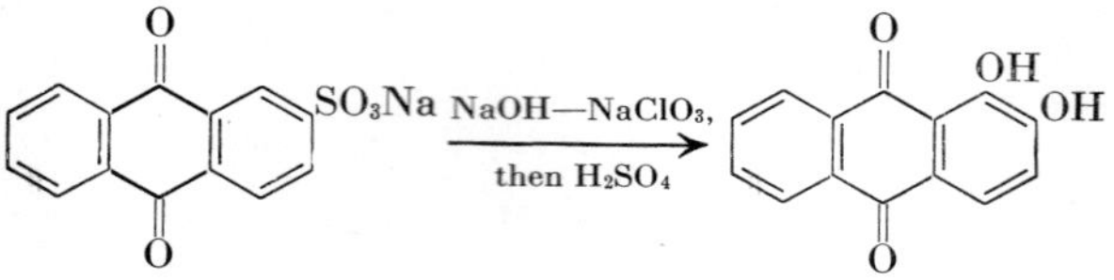

Alizarin

The product is **alizarin,** formerly an important mordant dye (p. 487).

About fifty anthraquinone derivatives have been identified as pigments in plants, fungi, lichens, and insects. Many are hydroxymethylanthraquinones. **Emodin** has strong cathartic properties and is an active principle of cascara, senna, aloes, and rheum (rhubarb). **Physcion** occurs widely in molds and lichens.

Emodin

Physcion

The most important reaction of anthraquinones is their easy reduction to dihydro derivatives. The latter are phenols and are soluble in alkali. The reduced form on exposure to air is reoxidized to the water-insoluble anthraquinone.

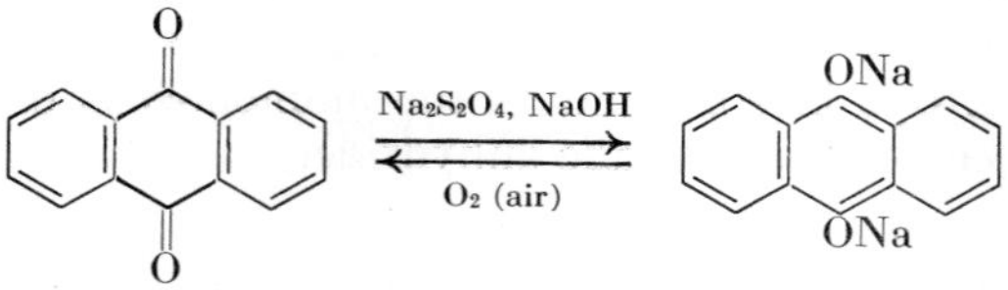

Water-insoluble anthraquinone

Water-soluble sodium salt of dihydroanthraquinone

These reactions are the basis for the application of the anthraquinone vat dyes to cotton cloth (p. 487).

OTHER CONDENSED RING SYSTEMS

Phenanthrene is isomeric with anthracene. Its structure can be deduced from its oxidation to phenanthraquinone and diphenic acid (2,2'-biphenyldicarboxylic acid).

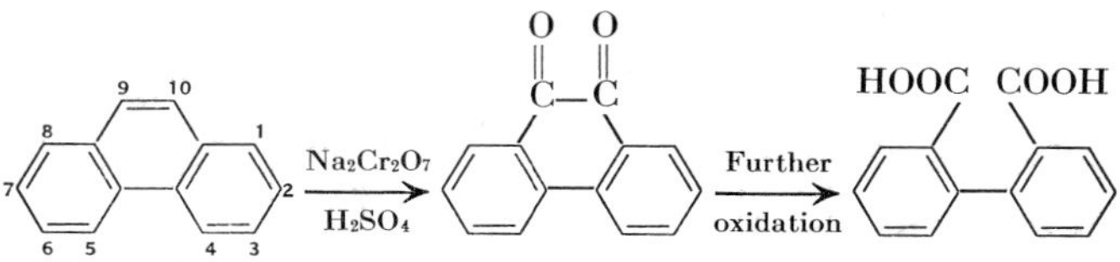

Phenanthrene → (Na₂Cr₂O₇, H₂SO₄) → Phenanthra-quinone → (Further oxidation) → Diphenic acid

The carbon skeleton of phenanthrene is present as a nonaromatic ring system in many natural products. When these products are heated with sulfur or selenium, dehydrogenation takes place and phenanthrene derivatives are formed. Since the aromatic hydrocarbon usually can be purified easily and its constitution determined more readily than that of the original compound, these dehydrogenation products have played an important part in elucidating the constitution of complex natural products. For example the ring system in abietic acid, the chief constituent of pine rosin (p. 566), was identified by the isolation of **retene,** 1-methyl-7-isopropylphenanthrene, from the dehydrogenation products.

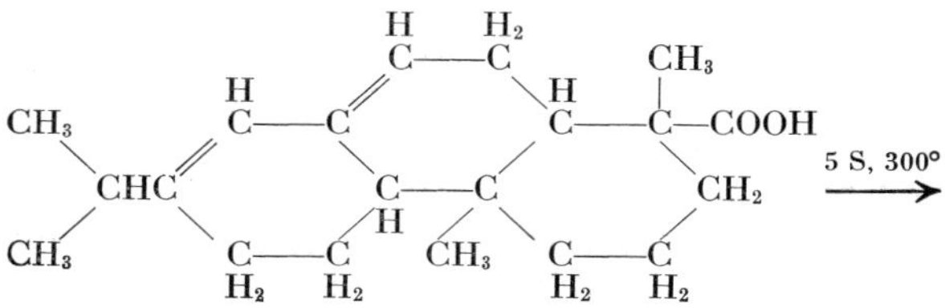

Abietic acid — (5 S, 300°) →

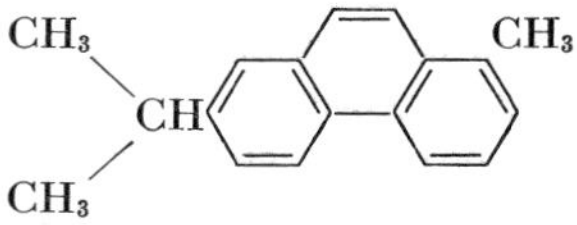

Retene $+ CO_2 + CH_3SH + 4 H_2S$

The following formulas illustrate the structures of other interesting aromatic hydrocarbons with condensed nuclei.

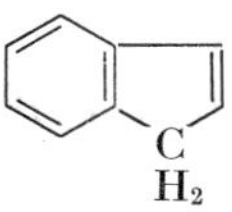

Indene

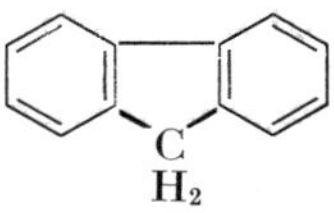

Fluorene

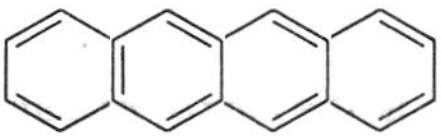

2,3-Benzanthracene (naphthacene)

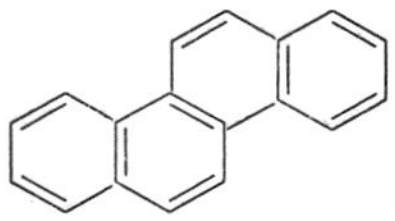

1,2-Benzophenanthrene (chrysene)

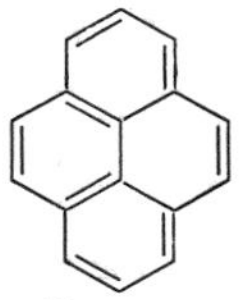

Pyrene

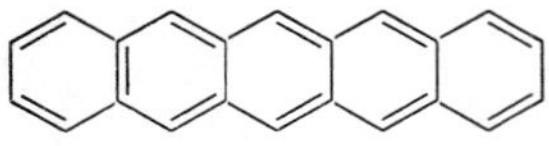

2,3:6,7-Dibenzanthracene
(pentacene)

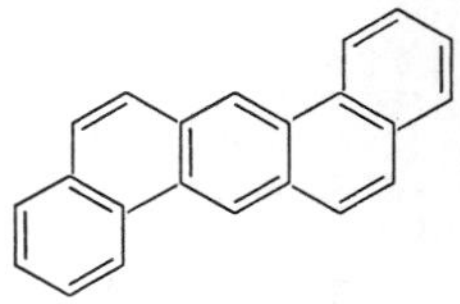

1,2:5,6-Dibenzanthracene

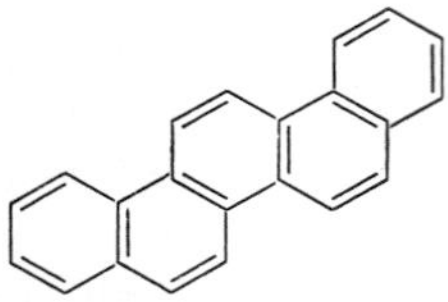

1,2:7,8-Dibenzophenanthrene
(picene)

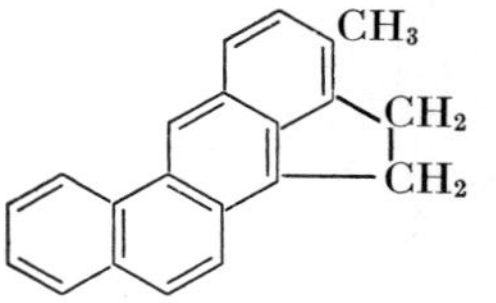

Methylcholanthrene

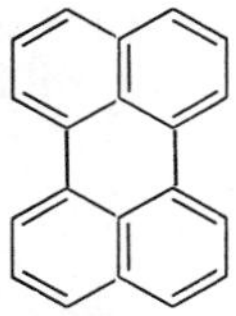

Perylene    Coronene 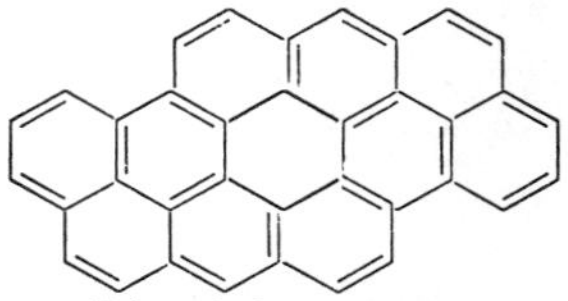   Dinaphthocoronene

Anthracene has an absorption band in the near ultraviolet and is colorless, but naphthacene is orange-yellow and pentacene is purple. 1,5-Dibenzanthracene and methylcholanthrene are powerful carcinogenic hydrocarbons; that is they produce skin cancers when applied over a considerable period of time. Derivatives of picene are obtained by dehydrogenating many natural products belonging to the triterpene group (p. 567). Dinaphthocoronene, $C_{36}H_{16}$, contains 96.4 per cent carbon.

Condensed nuclear hydrocarbons, such as phenanthrene and chrysene, for which structures can be written having three double bonds in all rings are much less reactive than those, such as anthracene and naphthacene, for which the structures of one or more rings must be written with less than three double bonds.

REVIEW QUESTIONS

1. What is the source of naphthalene? Compare its abundance with that of other compounds which accompany it.
2. Give a proof of the structure of naphthalene, including evidence from analysis, reactions, synthesis, and the number of monosubstitution products.
3. What monosubstitution products are formed by the direct halogenation, nitration, and sulfonation of naphthalene?
4. Give reactions for the synthesis from naphthalene of α-naphthylamine; β-naphthylamine; α-naphthoic acid; 4-amino-1-naphthol.
5. How many naphthoquinones are known and how are they prepared? What are the vitamins K_1 and K_2?
6. Give a reaction for the conversion of acenaphthene into naphthalic acid.
7. Give equations for the synthesis of anthraquinone starting with benzene and naphthalene.
8. What product is formed on reduction of anthraquinone; nitration; sulfonation?

9. How is β-aminoanthraquinone made; alizarin?
10. What is emodin?
11. What is the structure of phenanthrene? Give reactions for its conversion into phenanthraquinone and diphenic acid.
12. What happens when phenanthraquinone is heated with alkali? (Hint: compare the structure of phenanthraquinone with that of benzil.)
13. What are the structural formulas for indene; fluorene; chrysene; 1,2 : 5,6-dibenzoanthracene?

Chapter 30

HETEROCYCLIC COMPOUNDS. ALKALOIDS

Compounds in which three or more atoms are joined to form a closed ring are known as cyclic compounds. If all of the ring atoms are carbon, the compound is said to be *carbocyclic*, but if different kinds of atoms constitute the ring, the compound is said to be *heterocyclic*. Theoretically any atom capable of forming at least two covalent bonds can be a member of a ring, but the heterocyclic compounds encountered most frequently contain nitrogen, oxygen, and sulfur as the hetero atoms.

RING COMPOUNDS CONTAINING ONE HETERO ATOM

Three- and Four-membered Rings

The members of this group that are of most importance are the ethylene oxides. Their methods of preparation and reactions are discussed on page 522.

Five-membered Rings

Thiophenes. In 1879 Baeyer reported that when benzene is mixed with isatin and concentrated sulfuric acid a blue color is produced. This behavior was called the *indophenin reaction* and was believed to be characteristic of benzene until Victor Meyer in 1882 attempted to demonstrate the reaction on a sample of benzene that had been prepared by the decarboxylation of benzoic acid. The lecture demonstration failed, and the resulting investigation as to the cause of the failure led to the discovery that the indophenin reaction is not characteristic of benzene, but of a sulfur compound with physical and chemical properties resembling those of benzene so closely that the few tenths of a per cent present in coal tar benzene had not been detected previously. This compound was named *thiophene*. Subsequent development of thiophene chemistry was so rapid that five years after its isolation in 1883, Meyer published a 300-page book on the subject.

Thiophene has the molecular formula C_4H_4S and forms two monosubstitution products. It has been assigned a cyclic structure with two double bonds, which is supported by the methods of synthesis. Until 1946 thiophene was synthesized by heating sodium succinate (p. 540) with phosphorus heptasulfide (sometimes called phosphorus trisulfide).

$$2 \underset{\substack{\displaystyle | \\ \text{Sodium succinate}}}{\overset{\displaystyle \text{CH}_2\text{—CH}_2}{\underset{\displaystyle \text{ONa} \quad \text{ONa}}{\overset{\displaystyle | \qquad\quad |}{\text{O=C} \qquad \text{C=O}}}}} + P_4S_7 \longrightarrow 2 \underset{\substack{\displaystyle | \\ \text{Thiophene}}}{\overset{\displaystyle \overset{4}{\text{H}}\text{C} \text{——} \overset{3}{\text{C}}\text{H}}{\underset{\displaystyle \underset{5}{\text{H}}\text{C}\alpha' \quad \alpha\text{C}\underset{2}{\text{H}}}{\overset{\displaystyle \beta' \qquad\quad \beta}{\underset{\displaystyle \underset{1}{\text{S}}}{}}}}} + 4\,NaPO_2S + S$$

444

Renewed interest in the chemistry of thiophene and its derivatives has developed with the commercial production of thiophene from butane and sulfur.

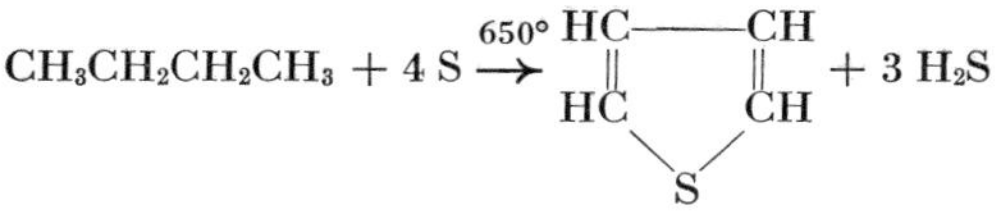

$$CH_3CH_2CH_2CH_3 + 4 S \xrightarrow{650°} \underset{S}{\overset{HC{-\!\!\!-}CH}{\underset{HC\quad CH}{||\quad\quad||}}} + 3 H_2S$$

The butane and sulfur vapor are preheated separately to 600° and mixed in the reaction tube at 650° for a contact time of 0.07 second, after which the exit gases are cooled rapidly. The unreacted materials are recycled. A longer reaction time leads to a more complex mixture of products.

Thiophene boils at 84°, and the boiling points of its homologs and derivatives also are close to those of the benzene analogs. The replacement of a benzene ring in physiologically active compounds by a thiophene ring has little effect on their activity. Thus the thiophene analogs of cocaine or atropine (p. 467) have similar local anesthetic or mydriatic action. 2-Thiophenecarboxylic acid when ingested is eliminated in the urine as the amide of glycine, just as benzoic acid is eliminated as hippuric acid (p. 413).

Thiophene undergoes the typical substitution reactions of aromatic compounds and is considerably more reactive than benzene. The sulfur atom has much the same effect as oxygen or sulfur attached to the benzene nucleus; that is it is activating and *ortho,para*-directing. The 3 and 5 positions in thiophene correspond to the *ortho* and *para* positions in thiophenol, but since the 2 and 5 positions are identical as are the 3 and 4 positions, all positions in thiophene substitute with considerable ease. When possible, substitution usually takes place almost exclusively in the 2 or 5 position.

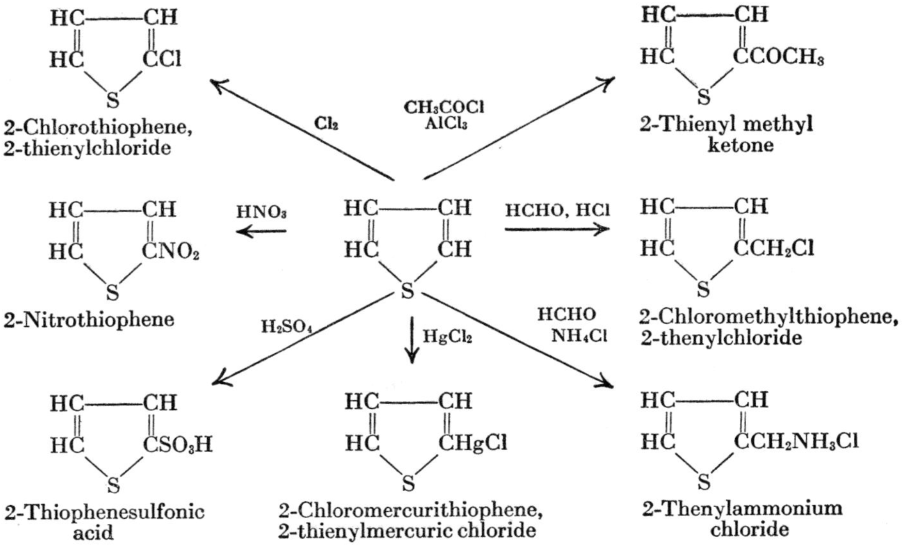

2-Chlorothiophene, 2-thienylchloride

2-Thienyl methyl ketone

2-Nitrothiophene

2-Chloromethylthiophene, 2-thenylchloride

2-Thiophenesulfonic acid

2-Chloromercurithiophene, 2-thienylmercuric chloride

2-Thenylammonium chloride

An exception to exclusive 2 substitution is the alkylation with isobutylene which yields about equal amounts of the 2- and 3-*t*-butylthiophenes.

$$
\underset{S}{\overset{HC-CH}{\underset{HC\quad CH}{\|\quad\|}}} + CH_2{=}C(CH_3)_2 \xrightarrow[60°-65°]{75\%\ H_2SO_4} \underset{S}{\overset{HC-CH}{\underset{HC\quad CC(CH_3)_3}{\|\quad\|}}} \text{ and } \underset{S}{\overset{HC-CC(CH_3)_3}{\underset{HC\quad CH}{\|\quad\|}}}
$$

The greater reactivity of thiophene over benzene permits the reactions to be carried out under milder conditions that are more nearly like those used for phenols. Thus halogenation takes place without a catalyst. Unless special conditions are observed, direct nitration gives 2,5-dinitrothiophene. Concentrated sulfuric acid reacts at room temperature, preferably in an inert solvent. The Friedel-Crafts reaction is carried out in petroleum ether solution, or a milder catalyst such as stannic chloride is used rather than aluminum chloride. The greater ease of sulfonation is the basis for the removal of thiophene from benzene by shaking with concentrated sulfuric acid.

If either a *meta-* or an *ortho,para*-directing group is present in the 2 position, a second group enters the 5 position. Hence the deactivating effect of a *meta*-directing group on the 5 (*para*) position is overbalanced by the activating effect of the sulfur atom. When substituents are in the 3 (or 4) position mixtures of isomers usually are formed.

Thiophene and its homologs do not behave like sulfides. For example oxidation does not produce the sulfoxide or the sulfone, and alkyl halides do not give sulfonium salts.

Although some derivatives of thiophene behave like the corresponding benzene analogs, most of them are too reactive to give satisfactory yields of simple products. Thus the halogen derivatives form Grignard reagents, and 2-acetylthiophene can be oxidized to 2-thiophenecarboxylic acid. On the other hand reduction of 2-nitrothiophene to the amine is difficult because the ring also is reduced with the production of hydrogen sulfide. 2-Aminothiophene can be obtained as the chlorostannate by careful reduction with tin and hydrochloric acid. The free amine darkens and solidifies on exposure to oxygen. It couples with benzenediazonium chloride to give the azo derivative, but does not itself undergo a true diazotization.

The resemblance of thiophene to benzene can be ascribed to similar molecular weights, similar shapes of the molecules, and most of all to the similar electronic interactions. On the approach of electron-seeking reagents, transition complexes can be formed readily at the 3 and 5 (= 4 and 2) positions.

$$
\left\{\ \underset{S^+}{\overset{H}{\underset{HC\quad CH}{\overset{HC-C:^-}{\|\quad\|}}}}\quad \longleftrightarrow\quad \underset{S^+}{\overset{HC=CH}{\underset{H-C\quad CH}{\|\qquad\|}}}\ \right\}
$$

Pyrroles. Pyrrole, C_4H_5N, is the nitrogen analog of thiophene. It is present in coal tar and in the tars obtained by the distillation of waste animal matter such as bones (*bone oil* or *Dippel's oil*), horn, and scrap leather. Its presence in bone oil was detected in 1834 by the red color which is produced when its vapors come in contact with a pine splint dipped in concentrated hydrochloric acid (Gr. *pyrros* red). It was not isolated in a pure state from these sources until 1858.

The **structure** of pyrrole is most obvious from its formation by distilling succinimide (p. 543) with zinc dust (cf. p. 383).

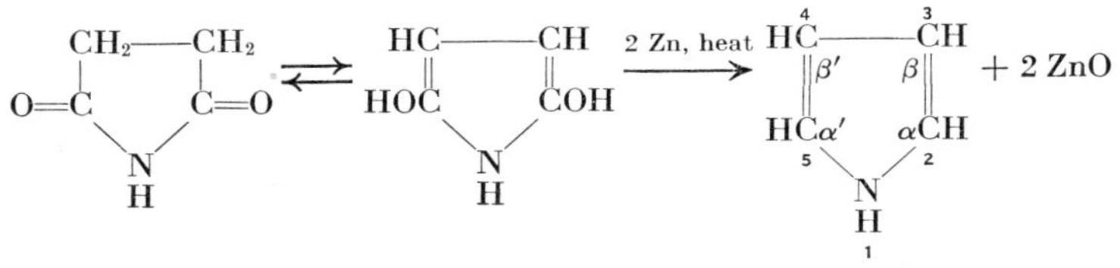

Succinimide   Pyrrole

It is **prepared** best by heating ammonium salts of glycaric acids (p. 281) in a stream of ammonia. Ammonium saccharate gives the best yield, but ammonium mucate is more readily obtainable. At the high temperature used, the ammonium salt undoubtedly dissociates into the free acid, which dehydrates, decarboxylates, and reacts with ammonia.

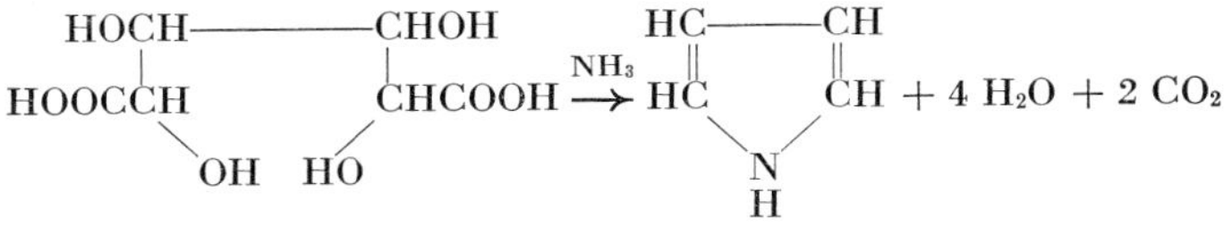

The **physical properties** of pyrrole are distinctly anomalous. It has the exceptionally high boiling point of 131° compared with 78° for *n*-butylamine. It is practically insoluble in water, whereas *n*-butylamine is miscible with water. The dipole moment of 1.83 is high, but it is lower than the moment of 2.11 for pyridine, C_5H_5N, which boils lower and is miscible with water (p. 454).

In regard to their **chemical properties,** pyrrole and its simple derivatives are characterized by their ease of oxidation by air to give dark-colored resins, and by their sensitivity to strong acids, which produce polymeric red substances. Pyrrole is a considerably weaker base than aniline. By the same token it is a stronger acid than aliphatic secondary amines and its metallic derivatives are less easily hydrolyzed. Thus it forms a potassium salt by reaction with solid potassium hydroxide.

$$C_4H_4NH + KOH \rightleftarrows [C_4H_4N^-]K^+ + H_2O$$

The weaker basicity and the higher acidity of pyrroles compared to secondary amines is understandable in terms of the resonance picture. Since the unshared electrons on nitrogen are interacting with the other unsaturation electrons, they are less available for bonding with a proton, and the low electron density on nitrogen permits the hydrogen to leave more readily as a proton.

Methylmagnesium bromide reacts with pyrrole to give methane and an *N*-magnesium bromide derivative. These derivatives behave as if the magnesium were combined at the 2 position, since reagents yield 2-substituted pyrroles.

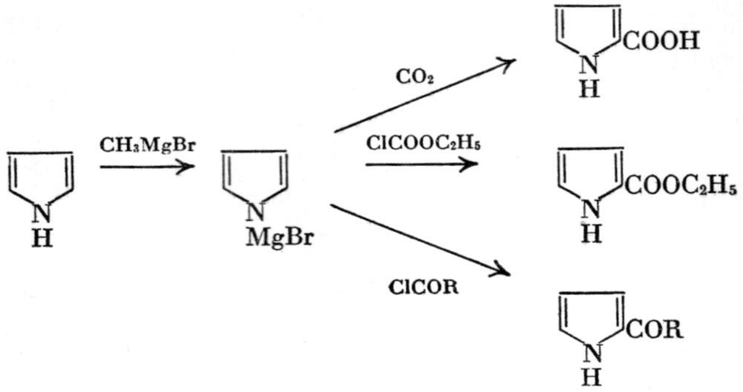

This behavior resembles that of the benzylmagnesium halides (p. 350) and can be explained by a similar mechanism.

The pyrrole nucleus undergoes many reactions characteristic of aromatic compounds. Since it is destroyed by strong acids, however, halogenation, nitration, sulfonation, and Friedel-Crafts reactions under the usual conditions are not applicable. On the other hand the NH group, like the amino group in aromatic amines, strongly activates the ring, and many substitution reactions take place under mild conditions. Halogenation is conducted under alkaline conditions, when even iodine gives tetraiodopyrrole.

$$C_4H_4NH + 4 I_2 + 4 NaOH \longrightarrow C_4I_4NH + 4 NaI + 4 H_2O$$

3-Nitropyrrole results from reaction with amyl nitrate and sodium ethoxide.

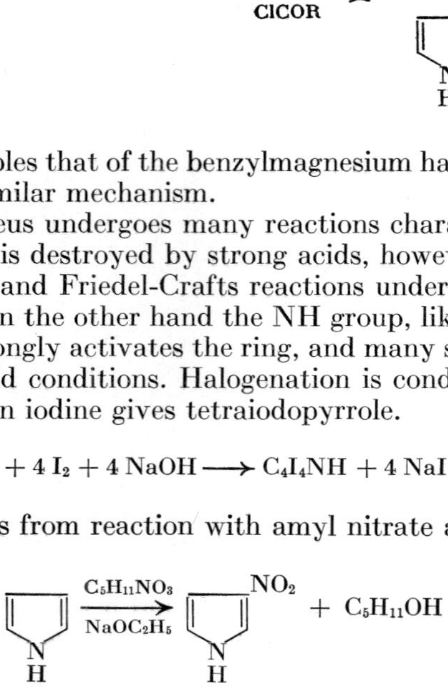

Other nuclear reactions resemble those of phenol (pp. 402, 385).

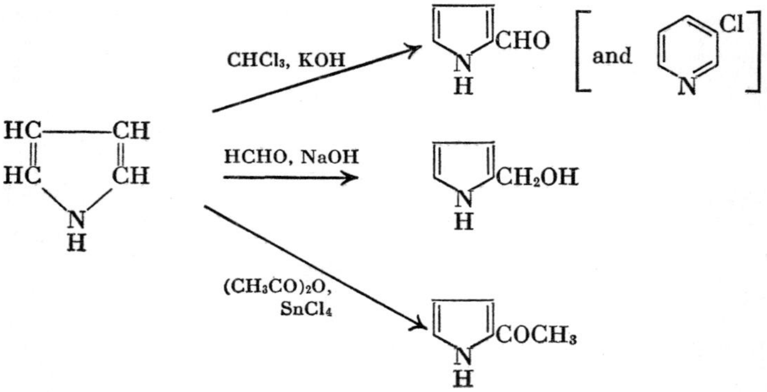

Pyrrolecarboxylic acids lose carbon dioxide on heating, a behavior characteristic of phenolcarboxylic acids (p. 394).

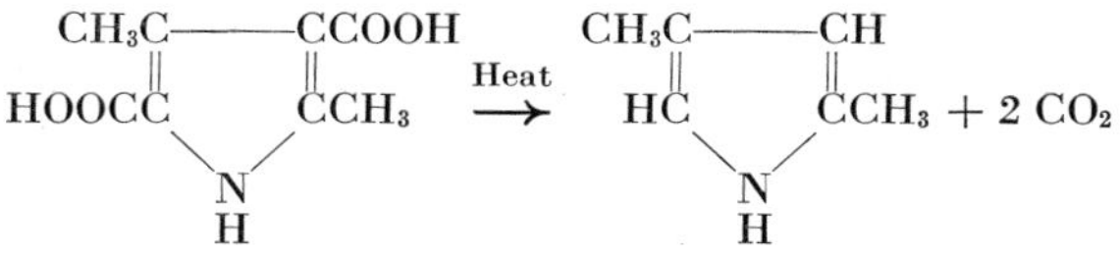

$$CH_3C\text{------}CCOOH \quad CH_3C\text{------}CH$$
$$HOOCC \qquad CCH_3 \xrightarrow{\text{Heat}} HC \qquad CCH_3 + 2\ CO_2$$

Reduction of pyrrole with zinc and acetic acid yields 2,5-dihydropyrrole (**pyrroline**), and catalytic reduction yields the tetrahydro derivative, **pyrrolidine**. The formation of pyrrolidine hydrochloride when 1-chloro-4-aminobutane is heated is a proof of the structure of pyrrolidine.

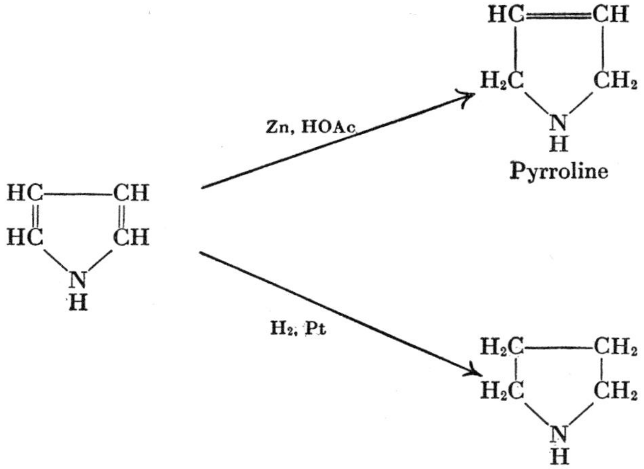

Pyrroline

Pyrrolidine

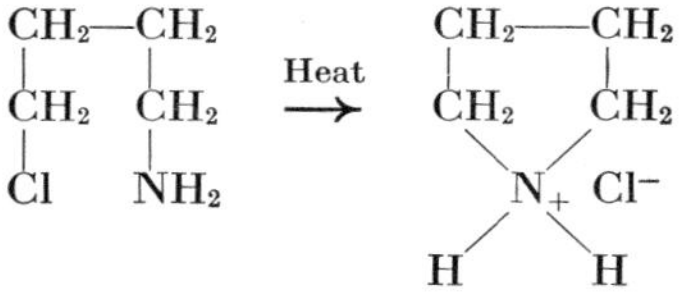

$$CH_2\text{---}CH_2 \qquad CH_2\text{---}CH_2$$
$$CH_2 \quad CH_2 \xrightarrow{\text{Heat}} CH_2 \quad CH_2$$
$$Cl \quad NH_2 \qquad\qquad N_+\ Cl^-$$

Pyrrolidine
hydrochloride

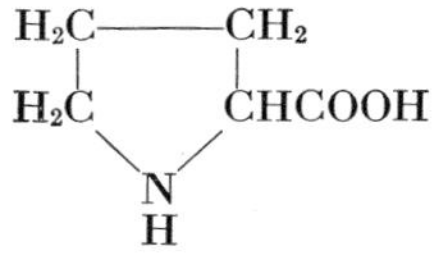

Proline

Pyrrolidine is a typical secondary aliphatic amine. It is miscible with water, its basic dissociation constant is 1.3×10^{-3}, and it boils at 88°. **Proline,** a natural amino acid (Table 13, p. 227), is α-pyrrolidinecarboxylic acid.

Porphin Derivatives. Alkylated pyrrole nuclei form the building units for many biologically important pigments, for example those of bile, blood, and the green coloring matter of plants. Hence pyrrole and the alkylated pyrroles are present in bone oil (p. 446), which arises from the decomposition of bone marrow, the source of the blood pigments. These pigments have a basic structure known as the **porphin nucleus** which contains a flat 16-membered strainless ring. The **porphyrins** derived from natural pigments (Gr. *porphyra* purple) have substituents in the eight β positions of the pyrrole nuclei. The

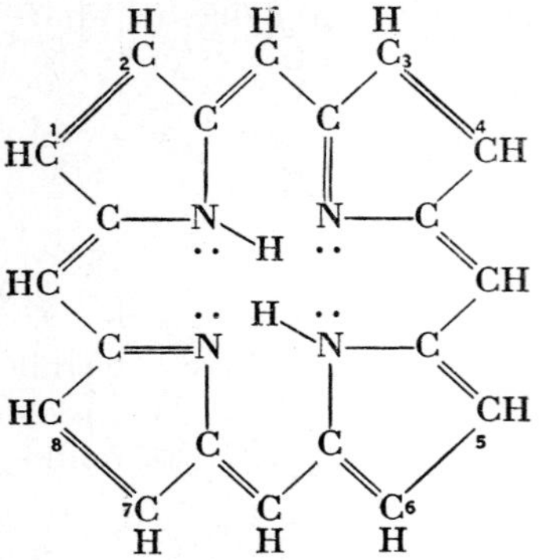

Porphin nucleus

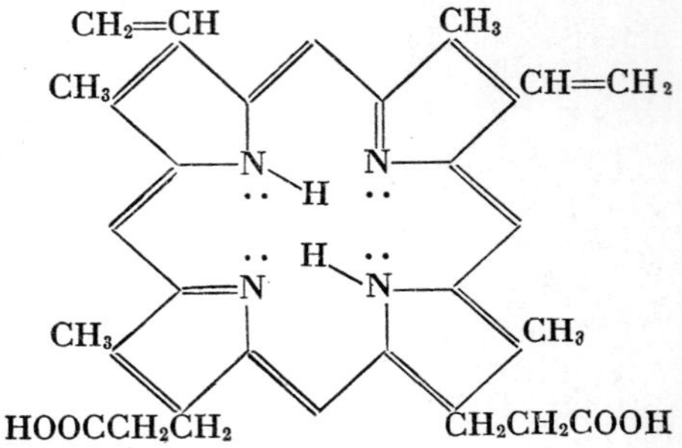

Protoporphyrin

natural pigments themselves are metal chelate complexes (p. 520) of the porphyrins. Thus reaction of **protoporphyrin** with ferric chloride in alkaline solution gives **hemin.** The reduced compound lacking the chloride ion is the **heme** of hemoglobin (p. 225).

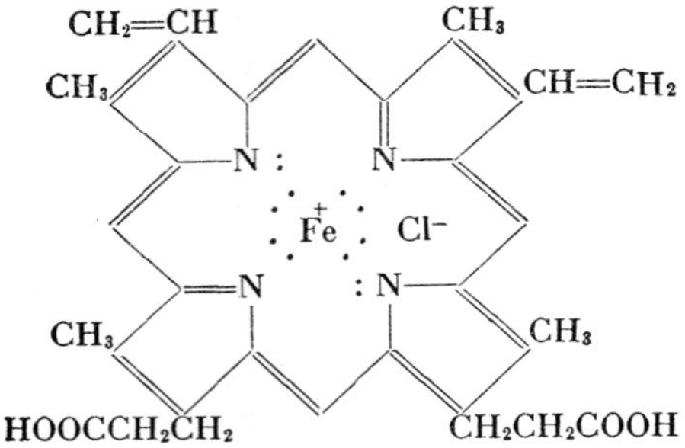

Hemin

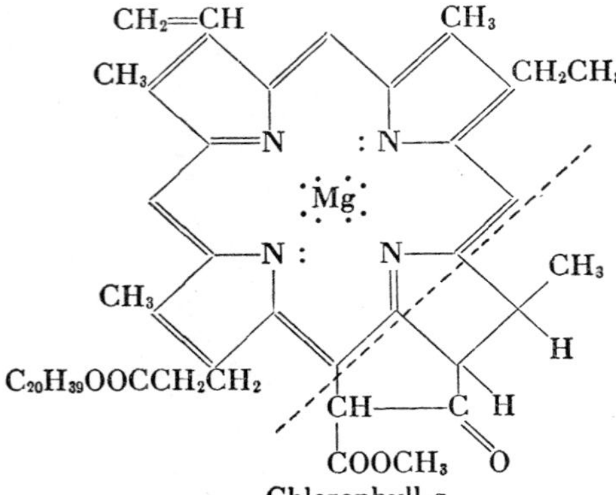

Chlorophyll *a*

The **chlorophylls** are magnesium complexes of porphyrins esterified with the long-chain alcohol phytol, $C_{20}H_{39}OH$ (p. 566). Chlorophyll *b* differs from chlorophyll *a* in that it has an aldehyde group replacing the methyl group in the 3 position. The structure of the portion of the molecule below the dotted line is considered to be uncertain. The synthesis of hemin has been reported, but the method of synthesis is not sufficiently rational to be an unequivocal proof of structure.

Benzopyrroles. 2-Benzopyrrole is known as **indole** because it was obtained first by Baeyer [1] in 1866 by distilling oxindole, a degradation product of indigo (p. 484), with zinc dust. It first was synthesized in 1869 and was not found in coal tar until 1910. Numerous syntheses of indole and its derivatives have been developed. One which clearly indicates the structure of indole is the intramolecular condensation of formo-*o*-toluidide.

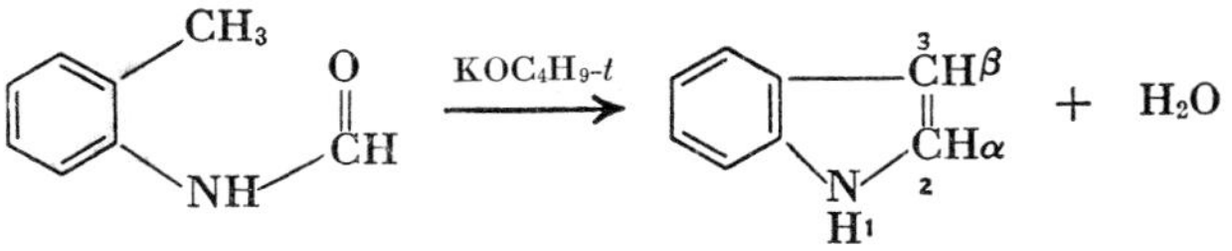

Indole and 3-methylindole (skatole) are formed during the putrefaction of proteins. They contribute to the characteristic odor of feces. In contrast pure indole in high dilution has a flowery odor and is used in preparing jasmine, orange blossom, and lilac blends. In fact it is present in natural jasmine, orange blossom, and jonquil extracts.

The most important derivative of indole is **tryptophan,** an essential amino acid (p. 231). The name arises from the fact that it is destroyed by the acid hydrolysis of proteins, but can be obtained by enzymic hydrolysis with trypsin.

Tryptophan

Carbazole

Carbazole, 2,4-dibenzopyrrole, is present to the extent of over 1 per cent in coal tar. It is isolated from the anthracene fraction as the potassium salt. The chief use is in the preparation of blue sulfur dyes (p. 489).

Furans. Furan, C_4H_4O, is the oxygen analog of thiophene. The most available derivative of furan is the α aldehyde, **furfural,** from which most other furans are prepared. Furfural first was obtained in 1840 by the distillation of bran (L. *furfur*) with dilute sulfuric acid. It results from the dehydration of pentoses formed by the hydrolysis of the pentosans in the bran.

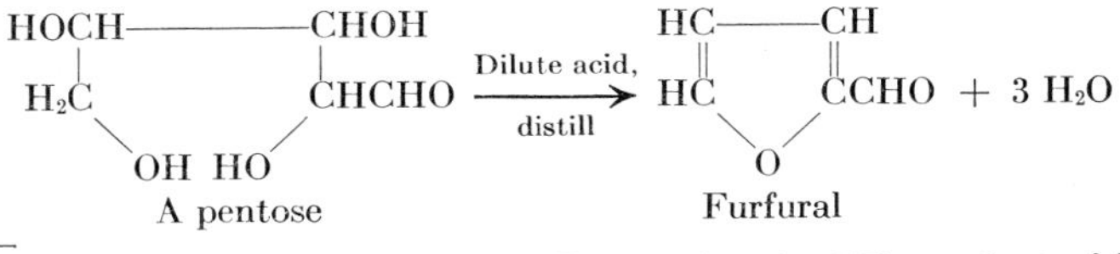

A pentose

Furfural

---

[1] Johann Friedrich Wilhelm Adolf von Baeyer (1835–1917), student of Bunsen and Kekulé and successor to Liebig at the University of Munich. He was awarded the Nobel Prize in Chemistry in 1905. Of the many who studied under Baeyer may be mentioned O. Fischer, Perkin Jr., Friedlaender, Bamberger, Curtius, Rupe, and Willstaetter.

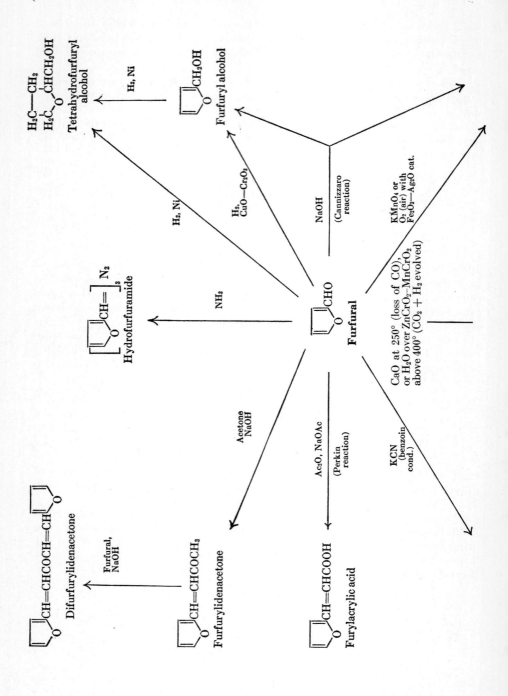

Furfural

CHO

Tetrahydrofurfuryl alcohol

H₂C—CH₂
H₂C   CHCH₂OH
     O

Furfuryl alcohol

CH₂OH

H₂, Ni

H₂, CuO—Cr₂O₃

H₂, Ni

NaOH (Cannizzaro reaction)

KMnO₄ or O₂ (air) with Fe₂O₃—Ag₂O cat.

CaO at 250° (loss of CO), or H₂O over ZnCrO₂—MnCrO₂ above 400° (CO₂ + H₂ evolved)

NH₃

[CH=   ]₃ N₂

Hydrofurfuramide

Acetone NaOH

Ac₂O, NaOAc (Perkin reaction)

KCN (benzoin cond.)

Difurfurylidenacetone

CH=CHCOCH=CH
                O

Furfural, NaOH

Furfurylidenacetone

CH=CHCOCH₃
   O

Furylacrylic acid

CH=CHCOOH
   O

452

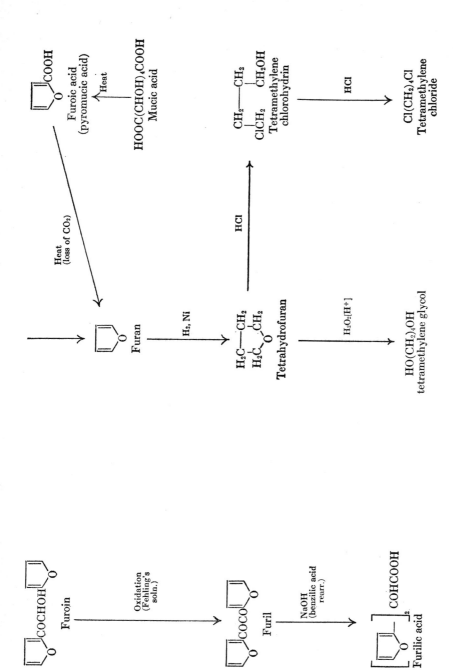

Fig. 42. Reactions of furfural and derived products.

453

The commercial production since 1922 by the hydrolysis of oat hulls stemmed from an attempt to produce an improved cattle feed from them. The availability of cheap furfural led to several large-scale applications, and now it is made also from other agricultural wastes that contain pentosans, such as corn cobs and straw. Because of increased use and technical improvements in the process, the price has dropped from $1.00 per pound in 1922 to 10 cents per pound in 1948.

Furfural is a colorless liquid with a pleasant characteristic odor. It is oxidized by air, the color changing through shades of yellow and brown to almost black. The initial products after peroxide formation appear to be formic acid and β-formylacrylic acid, $OCHCH{=}CHCOOH$. The latter undergoes condensation reactions to give high molecular weight polymers. These changes can be prevented by storing in the absence of oxygen or by adding an antioxidant (p. 582).

Furfural can be detected by the brilliant red color that it gives with aniline in the presence of acetic acid. Reaction of furfural with an acid solution of phloroglucinol (p. 394) gives a dark green precipitate of unknown and probably variable composition. The weight of precipitate formed has been related empirically to the weight of furfural from which it was produced; hence the reaction can be used for the quantitative estimation of furfural, and indirectly of pentoses and pentosans (p. 288).

Furfural and furans in general undergo ring scission by acids, which is followed by complex condensation reactions. In alkaline or neutral solution, furfural gives all of the reactions of benzaldehyde. The more commonly used reactions are summarized in Fig. 42, p. 453.

Furfural is used on a large scale as a solvent for refining lubricating oils (p. 54), and for removing butadiene from its mixtures with butene and butane (p. 501). With the developing shortage of benzene, a process has been developed to use furfural as an alternate raw material for the preparation, through tetramethylene chloride and tetramethylene cyanide, of hexamethylenediamine, $H_2N(CH_2)_6NH_2$, one of the components of Nylon salt from which Nylon is made (p. 544). α-**Furfuryl mercaptan,** the thiol corresponding to furfuryl alcohol, is one of the essential constituents of the aroma of roasted coffee. At high concentrations the synthetic product has an intense odor of onions, but at high dilution $(1 : 10^6)$ it has the aroma of roasted coffee and is used in perfumes and flavoring agents. **Tetrahydrofuran** has been synthesized on an industrial scale from acetylene (p. 501), as well as from furfural.

Six-membered Rings

Pyridines. **Pyridine,** C_5H_5N, was isolated first from bone oil in 1851 and then from coal tar in 1854. Coal tar is the sole commercial source, although less than 0.1 per cent of pyridine is present (Table 16, p. 324).

Pyridine boils at 115° and is miscible with water. It also is a good solvent for most organic compounds, and dissolves many inorganic salts. Like most of the higher amines, it has a disagreeable odor.

Pyridine is a typical tertiary amine. It reacts with alkyl iodides to give quaternary ammonium salts.

$$C_5H_5N : \quad + \quad CH_3I \quad \longrightarrow \quad [C_5H_5N : CH_3^+]I^-$$

N-Methylpyridinium
iodide

It is considerably weaker as a base ($K_b = 2.3 \times 10^{-9}$) than aliphatic tertiary amines ($K_b =$ ca. 10^{-4}) but stronger than aniline ($K_b = 3.8 \times 10^{-10}$). Reduction with sodium and alcohol gives a hexahydro derivative known as *piperidine*. Since three monosubstitution products are known, pyridine can be represented best as an analog of benzene in which a CH group is replaced by nitrogen.

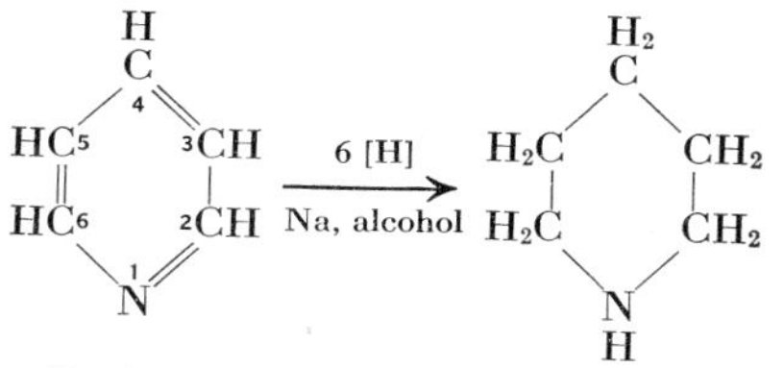

Pyridine   Piperidine

Piperidine is a typical secondary amine having a basicity ($K_b = 1.6 \times 10^{-3}$) and other properties resembling those of secondary aliphatic amines. The assigned structure is supported by its synthesis from pentamethylenediamine hydrochloride.

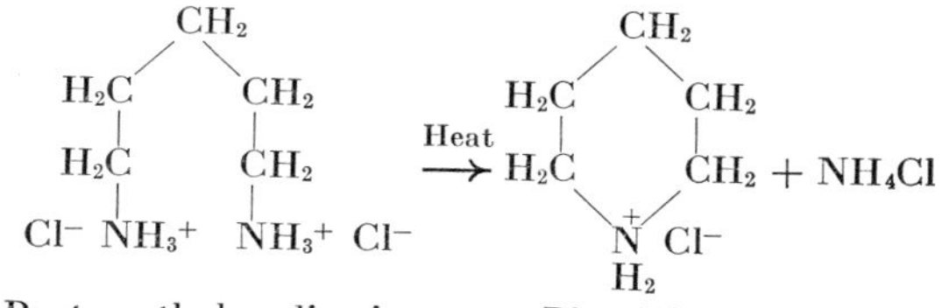

Pentamethylenediamine   Piperidine
hydrochloride   hydrochloride

Piperidine can be converted to a quaternary ammonium hydroxide which decomposes on heating with opening of the ring (p. 194).

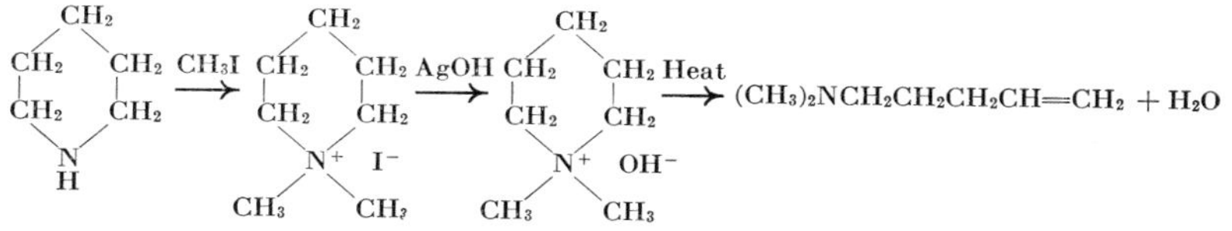

This method of opening nitrogen rings, known as **Hofmann's exhaustive methylation** procedure, has been valuable in determining the structure of alkaloids (p. 465) and other nitrogen heterocycles of unknown constitution.

Excluding its basic properties, pyridine is less reactive than any type of compound with the exception of the saturated hydrocarbons. It is not affected by boiling with alkaline permanganate, concentrated nitric acid, or dichromic acid. The action of chlorine on pyridine hydrochloride at 120° for several weeks yields a complex mixture containing di-, tetra-, and pentachloropyridines. Bromine reacts with the hydrobromide to give **3-bromo-** and **3,5-dibromo-pyridine.** Bromination in the vapor phase at 300° gives **3-bromopyridine,** but at 500° the product is **2-bromopyridine.** Distillation of pyridine sulfate with concentrated sulfuric acid in the presence of vanadium sulfate gives a 50 per cent yield of **3-pyridinesulfonic acid. 3-Nitropyridine** is obtained in a 22 per cent yield by heating with concentrated sulfuric and fuming nitric acids at 300° in the presence of iron salts. On the other hand the amino group can be introduced directly into pyridine by heating with sodium amide (*Chichibabin* [2] *reaction*). The main product is **2-aminopyridine,** although some **4-aminopyridine** and several other products also are formed.

$$\text{(pyridine)} \xrightarrow{\text{NaNH}_2} \text{(2-aminopyridine)} \quad \text{and} \quad \text{(4-aminopyridine)}$$

The inertness of pyridine to substitution reactions with acidic reagents and the comparative ease of substitution by amide ion, as well as the positions taken by the substituents, is understandable. In the first place the nitrogen atom, having a greater positive charge on the nucleus, has a greater attraction for electrons than a carbon atom and decreases the availability of the unsaturation electrons. What is more important, combination with a proton or other electron-seeking reagent gives it a positive charge which holds the electrons still more strongly. Hence the rate of substitution by electron-seeking reagents is very low (cf. p. 339). Moreover the positive charge on nitrogen prevents the formation of structures analogous to (*a*), (*b*), and (*c*) on page 341, and when substitution does take place, the rate is fastest at position 3.

The chief commercial use for crude pyridine has been as a denaturant for ethyl alcohol. More recently it is being used as an intermediate for the manufacture of certain pharmaceuticals. α-**Aminopyridine** for example is used in the manufacture of sulfapyridine (p. 372). Pyridine finds important use in organic synthesis as a basic solvent whereby it not only can exert a catalytic action but also combines with acids produced in reactions. For example acetylations and benzoylations take place smoothly in pyridine solution.

$$\text{ROH} + \text{ClCOC}_6\text{H}_5 + \text{C}_5\text{H}_5\text{N} \longrightarrow \text{ROCOC}_6\text{H}_5 + \text{C}_5\text{H}_5\text{NHCl}$$

For this purpose the pyridine must be anhydrous since water in the presence of pyridine hydrolyzes the reagent. The presence of interfering amounts of water in pyridine can be detected easily by adding pure benzoyl chloride free of benzoic acid. If water is present an immediate precipitate of the slightly soluble benzoic anhydride is formed.

$$\text{C}_6\text{H}_5\text{COCl} + \text{H}_2\text{O} + \text{C}_5\text{H}_5\text{N} \longrightarrow \text{C}_6\text{H}_5\text{COOH} + \text{C}_5\text{H}_5\text{NHCl}$$

$$\text{C}_6\text{H}_5\text{COOH} + \text{ClCOC}_6\text{H}_5 + \text{C}_5\text{H}_5\text{N} \longrightarrow (\text{C}_6\text{H}_5\text{CO})_2\text{O} + \text{C}_5\text{H}_5\text{NHCl}$$

The three methylpyridines are known as α-, β-, and γ-**picolines** (L. *pix, picis* pitch). They occur in bone oil, but the commercial source is coal tar.

---

[2] Aleksei Eugenievitsch Chichibabin (1871–1945), professor of chemistry at the Imperial College of Technology of Moscow until 1929. From 1931 until his death he worked at the Collège de France in Paris. He is noted chiefly for his studies of the chemistry of pyridine compounds.

The α isomer is present in largest amount and was isolated first in 1846. The β isomer was isolated in 1879, and the γ isomer, which is present in smallest amount, in 1887. Oxidation of the three isomers with permanganate yields the three carboxylic acids.

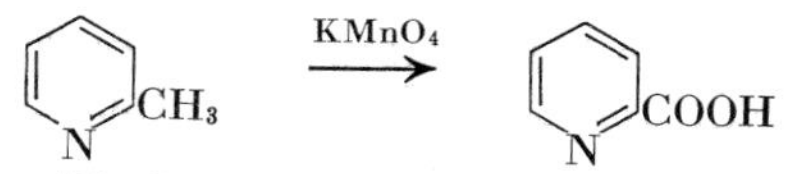

α-Picoline → α-Picolinic acid (picolinic acid)

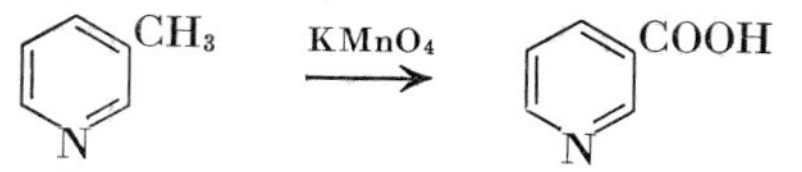

β-Picoline → β-Picolinic acid (nicotinic acid)

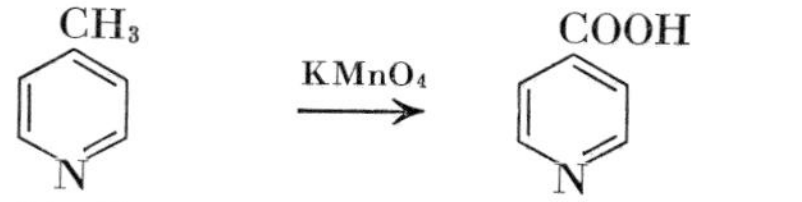

γ-Picoline → γ-Picolinic acid (isonicotinic acid)

The name *nicotinic acid* for the β isomer arises because it first was obtained in 1867 by the oxidation of nicotine. This reaction elucidated the structure of half of the nicotine molecule.

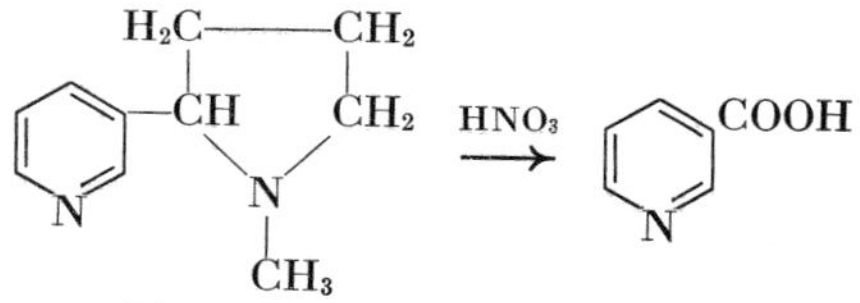

Nicotine

It was not until 1937 that it was recognized that the absence of nicotinic acid or its amide from the diet resulted in the deficiency disease known as *pellagra* in humans and *black tongue* in dogs. Over one million pounds of the acid and amide valued at over 3 million dollars was manufactured in the United States in 1948 for use in fortified wheat flour and vitamin preparations. The names *niacin* and *niamide* have been coined for the acid and its amide because they are considered to be more acceptable to the public.

Pyridoxine (*vitamin B₆*) and **pyridoxal** function in certain enzyme systems that can bring about the decarboxylation of amino acids.

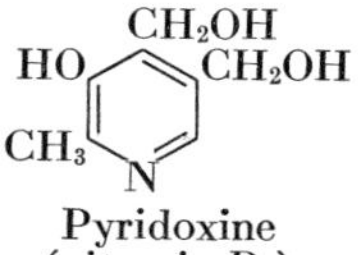

Pyridoxine (vitamin B₆)

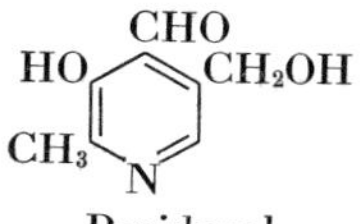

Pyridoxal

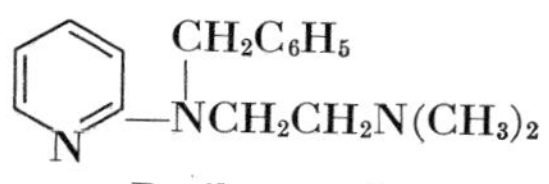

Pyribenzamine

Pyribenzamine is one of the more widely used antihistaminics (p. 461).

Quinolines. **Quinoline** is 2,3-benzopyridine. It first was isolated from coal tar in 1834. It was obtained also by the distillation of quinine alkaloids with alkali in 1842. However both products were accompanied by impurities that gave different color reactions, and they were not proven to be identical until 1882.

The structure of quinoline is indicated clearly by *Friedlaender's synthesis* from *o*-aminobenzaldehyde and acetaldehyde in the present of dilute alkali.

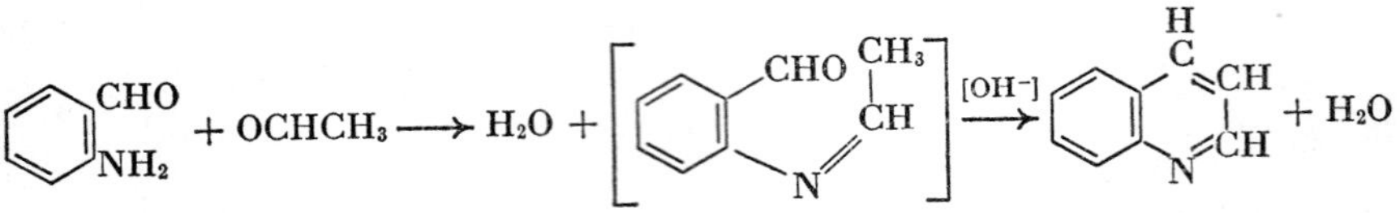

Although the reaction goes well and is general, it is not very useful for preparative purposes because the *o*-aminobenzaldehydes are difficult to obtain.

The presence of the pyridine ring in quinoline can be demonstrated by oxidation with permanganate. Because of the greater stability of the pyridine ring, the benzene ring is oxidized preferentially. The chief product is α, β-pyridinedicarboxylic acid (**quinolinic acid**) which can be decarboxylated to pyridine.

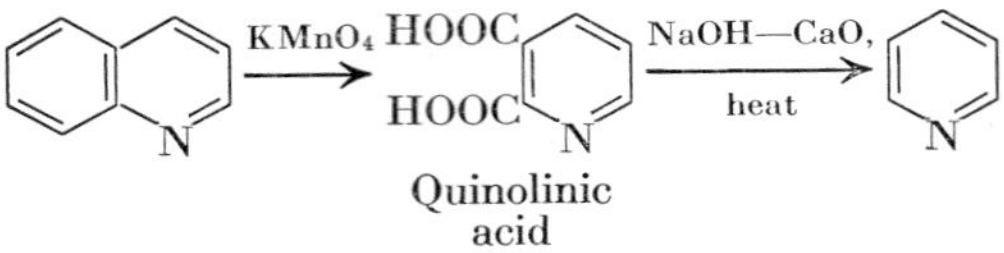

Quinolinic
acid

Pure quinoline is obtained best by the *Skraup synthesis*, which results when a mixture of glycerol and aniline is heated with concentrated sulfuric acid and a mild oxidizing agent such as arsenic acid or nitrobenzene. Ferrous sulfate and boric acid usually are added to moderate the reaction. Presumably the first stage is the dehydration of the glycerol to the unsaturated aldehyde, acrolein. Aniline then adds 1,4 to the conjugated unsaturated aldehyde. Subsequent ring closure and oxidation yields the quinoline. The method can be used also for the synthesis of quinoline derivatives.

2-Methylquinoline, known as **quinaldine,** occurs in coal tar. 4-Methylquinoline (**lepidine**) accompanies quinoline in the decomposition products of quinine alkaloids.

8-Hydroxyquinoline is made from *o*-aminophenol by the Skraup reaction. The space relationship of the hydroxyl group and the unshared pair of electrons on the nitrogen atom is such that insoluble chelate (p. 520) coordination complexes are formed with metallic ions, making it a valuable reagent in analytical chemistry.

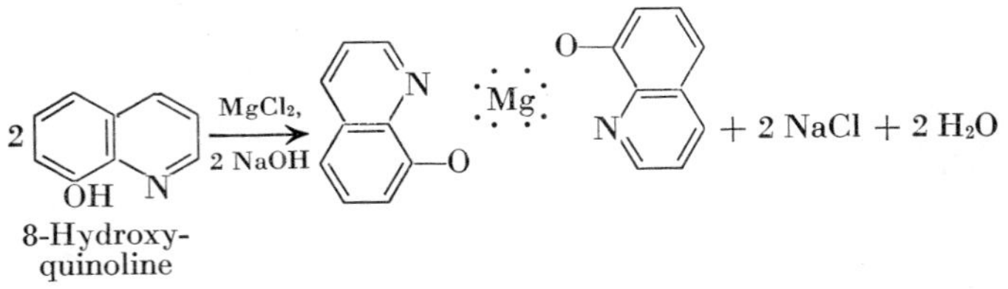

8-Hydroxy-
quinoline

3,4-Benzopyridine is known as **isoquinoline.** It accompanies quinoline in coal tar and is available commercially from this source. Oxidation with permanganate yields both phthalic acid and **cinchomeronic acid** (3,4-pyridinedicarboxylic acid).

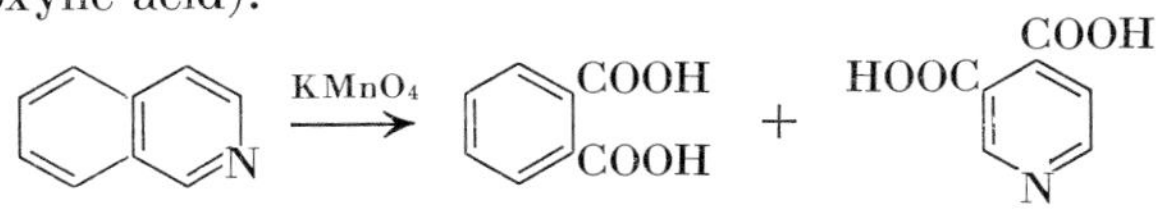

Isoquinoline   Cinchomeronic acid

The most general synthesis of isoquinolines is the *Bischler-Napieralski reaction* which starts with phenylethylamines.

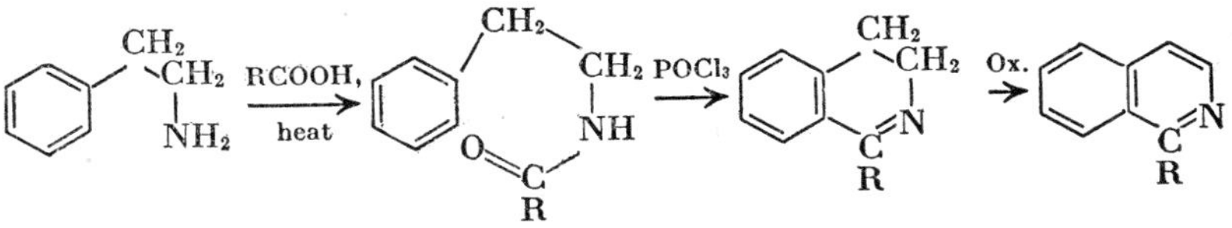

Several natural alkaloids are benzylisoquinolines (p. 467).

Acridine is 2,3:5,6-dibenzopyridine. It received its name from its irri-

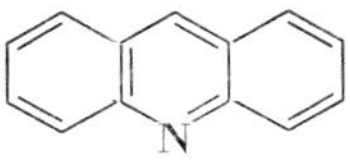

Acridine 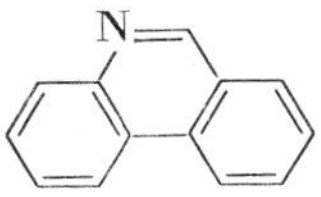   Phenanthridine 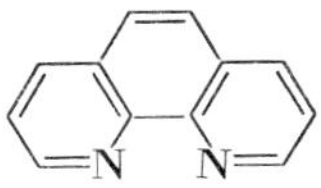   *o*-Phenanthroline

tating action on the skin and mucous membranes. 2,3:4,5-Dibenzopyridine is known as **phenanthridine** because of its relation to phenanthrene.

o-Phenanthroline contains two nitrogen atoms replacing two CH groups of the phenanthrene nucleus. The position of the nitrogen atoms is such that *o*-phenanthroline can form stable complex cations with metal ions. The *iron chelate complex* (p. 520), in which iron has a coordination number of six, is a valuable oxidation-reduction indicator, being intensely red in the reduced form and faintly blue in the oxidized form.

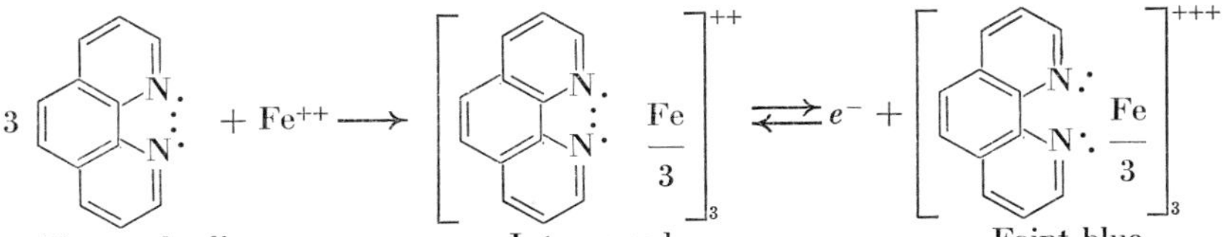

o-Phenanthroline   Intense red   Faint blue

Pyrans. The six-membered ring containing a single oxygen atom and two double bonds is known as the *pyran ring*. The oxonium salts containing an aromatic system are known as *pyrylium salts*.

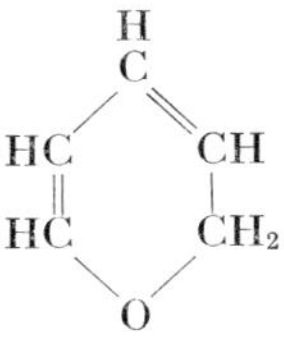

α-Pyran γ-Pyran 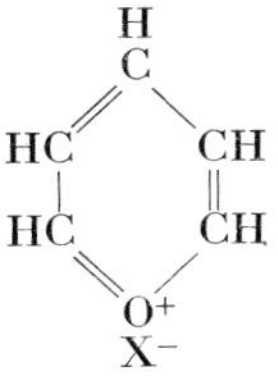   Pyrylium salt

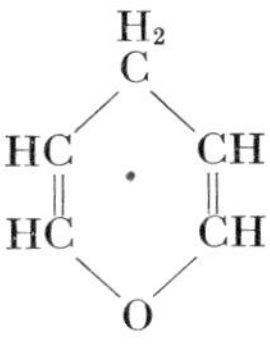

No simple pyran or benzopyrylium salt is known but **benzopyrans** frequently are present in plants, and many are of considerable interest. Thus the germ oil of seeds, especially wheat germ oil, contains substances designated as *vitamin E* which are necessary for the growth and normal reproduction of the rat. At least four compounds are present that have this activity and they have been called the *tocopherols* (Gr. *tokos* childbirth, *pherein* to bear). The most active is *α*-**tocopherol,** the racemic form of which has been synthesized from trimethylhydroquinone and phytyl bromide (p. 566).

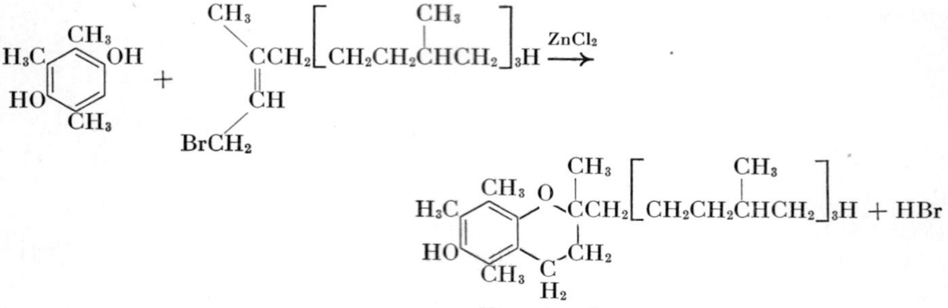

$$H_3C \underset{\underset{CH_3}{HO}}{\overset{\overset{CH_3}{\,}}{\bigcirc}} OH \; + \; \underset{\underset{BrCH_2}{\overset{\|}{CH}}}{\overset{\overset{CH_3}{|}}{CCH_2}}\left[CH_2CH_2CHCH_2\right]_3 H \xrightarrow{ZnCl_2}$$

$$H_3C\underset{\underset{CH_3}{HO}}{\overset{\overset{CH_3\;O}{\,}}{\bigcirc}}\overset{\overset{CH_3}{|}}{CCH_2}\left[CH_2CH_2CHCH_2\right]_3 H \; + \; HBr$$

α-Tocopherol

The tocopherols are distributed widely in food, and their use as a supplement to the diet of man and animals for therapeutic purposes has been controversial. The tocopherols have a marked antioxidant action and decrease the rate at which rancidity develops in foods containing fats (p. 582).

Many of the brilliant coloring matters of flowers contain a pyran ring. These **anthocyanin coloring matters** are discussed in Chapter 31.

RING COMPOUNDS CONTAINING TWO OR MORE HETERO ATOMS

The number of possible compounds falling into this group is very large. Only a few of the more important ones are considered.

Five-membered Rings

Pyrazole and **imidazole** each contain two hetero nitrogen atoms. **Histidine,** which contains the imidazole ring, is an essential amino acid (p. 231).

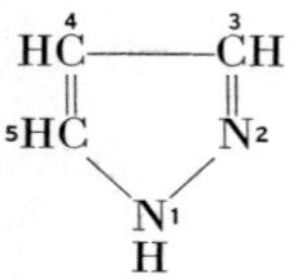

Pyrazole	Imidazole	Histidine	Histamine

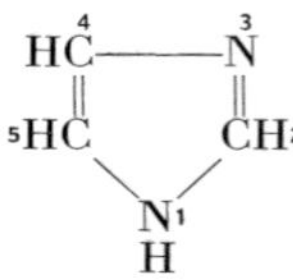

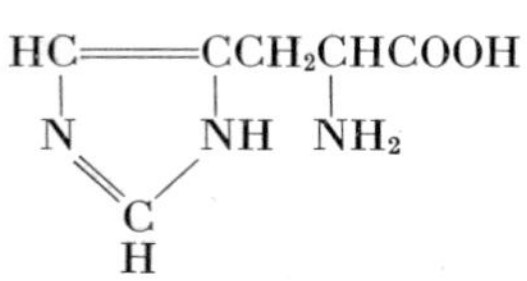

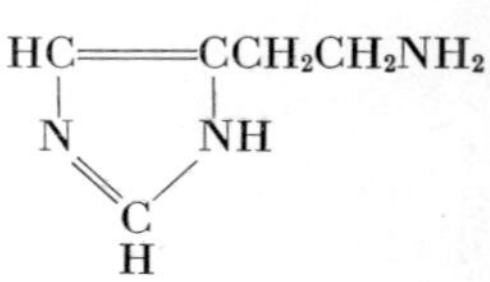

Histamine probably is derived from histidine by decarboxylation and is present in all tissues of the body. It is extremely toxic when administered parenterally, that is by means other than absorption through the intestines, and hence it must be present in the tissues in a combined form with protein. No other chemical has such a wide variety of actions. Nearly every tissue responds to it in some way. Excessive amounts of free histamine are believed to be the cause of many allergies. Since 1941 many synthetic organic compounds have been found to relieve allergic symptoms such as those caused by hay fever, poison ivy and poison oak, and the common cold. They are known as *antihistaminics* (pp. 399, 457, 463).

The five-membered ring containing one oxygen and one nitrogen atom in adjacent positions is known as the **isoxazole** ring, and that in which they occupy the alternate position is called the **oxazole** ring. The sulfur-nitrogen analogs are the **isothiazoles** and the **thiazoles.**

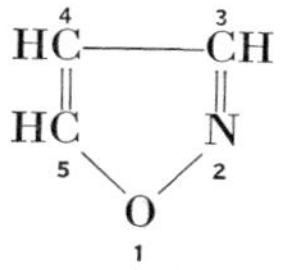

Isoxazole 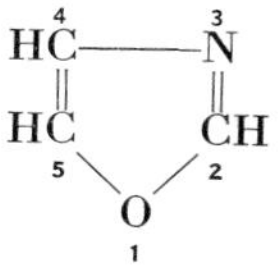 Oxazole 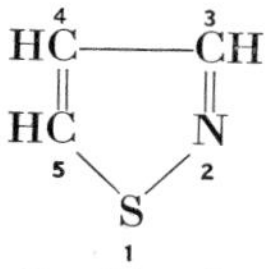 Isothiazole 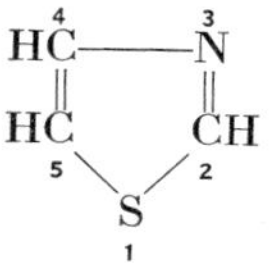 Thiazole

2-Mercaptobenzothiazole (*Captax*) is the most important rubber accelerator. It is formed by heating thiocarbanilide (p. 366) with carbon disulfide and sulfur.

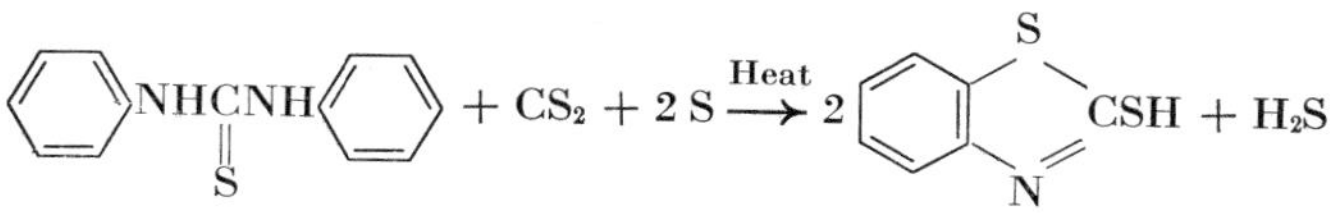

Thiocarbanilide 2-Mercaptobenzothiazole
(Captax)

The natural **penicillins,** the first antibiotics to be used in medicine, contain the thiazole ring system. Almost 273,000 pounds valued at over 140 million dollars was produced in the United States in 1948. The most important of these is penicillin G.

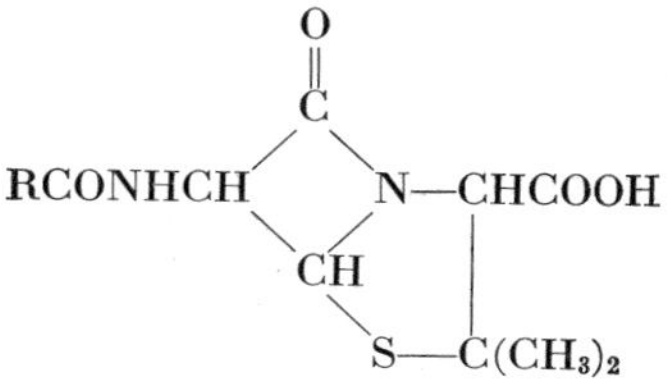

Natural Penicillins

PENICILLIN	R
G or II	$C_6H_5CH_2-$
X or III	$p\text{-}HOC_6H_4CH_2-$
F or I	$CH_3CH_2CH{=}CHCH_2-$
Dihydro F	$CH_3(CH_2)_4-$
Flavicidin	$CH_3CH{=}CH(CH_2)_2-$
K or IV	$CH_3(CH_2)_6-$

The cyclic acetals and carbonates formed from 1,2-glycols (p. 519) contain a five-membered ring with two hetero oxygen atoms.

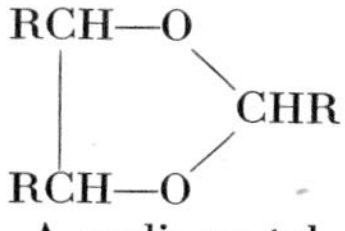

A cyclic acetal 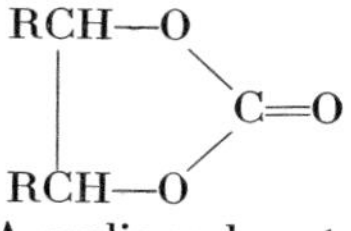 A cyclic carbonate

Six-membered Rings

Three six-membered ring systems containing two nitrogen atoms are known, namely the 1,2-diazines or pyridazines, the 1,3-diazines or pyrimidines, and the 1,4-diazines or pyrazines.

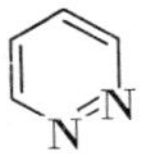

1,2-Diazine
or pyridazine

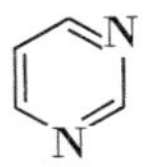

1,3-Diazine
or pyrimidine

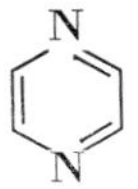

1,4-Diazine
or pyrazine

Compounds containing the **pyrimidine** ring are present in all living cells. Hydrolysis of nucleic acids obtained from nucleoproteins (p. 225) yields the pyrimidines **cytosine, uracil,** and **thymine,** along with purines, pentoses, and phosphoric acid.

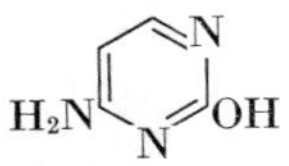

2-Hydroxy-6-amino-
pyrimidine (cytosine)

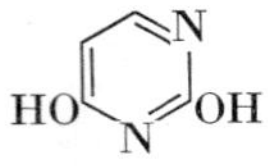

2,6-Dihydroxy-
pyrimidine (uracil)

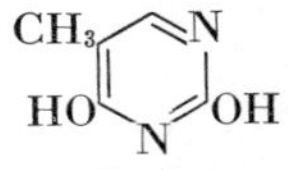

2,6-Dihydroxy-5-
methylpyrimidine (thymine)

The **barbiturates** form an important group of pyrimidine derivatives. They are cyclic diimides prepared by condensing urea or thiourea with di-substituted malonic esters, and form stable sodium salts.

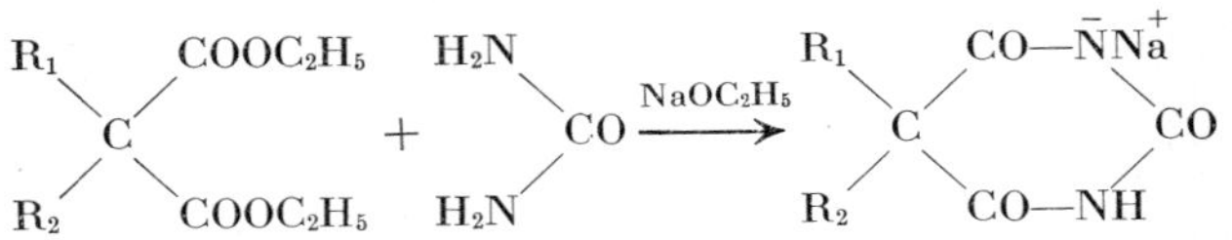

Although these compounds as a class are called **barbiturates** by the medical profession, the free compounds as well as their sodium salts are used medicinally. The ending commonly used for the free compound is *al*, and *sodium* is added as a separate word to indicate the sodium salt, for example *barbital* and *barbital sodium*.

The barbiturates have a depressant action on the central nervous system and are valuable sedatives and soporifics. **Barbital** (R_1 and $R_2 = C_2H_5$) was synthesized by Emil Fischer at the request of von Mering, who thought that it should be a good anesthetic because it was a urea derivative that contained two ethyl groups. von Mering studied its physiological action and called it *Veronal* because he considered Verona to be the most restful city in the world. Veronal was introduced into medicine as a hypnotic in 1903 and still is one of the best. Barbital is its nonproprietary name. **Phenobarbital** ($R_1 =$ ethyl, $R_2 =$ phenyl) was introduced several years later under the trade name *Luminal*. It has a specific action in preventing epileptic seizures. **Amytal** ($R_1 =$ ethyl, $R_2 =$ isoamyl), and **pentobarbital** (**Nembutal**) ($R_1 =$ ethyl, $R_2 =$ 2-pentyl) act more quickly but have a shorter duration of action than either barbital or phenobarbital. **Seconal** ($R_1 =$ allyl, $R_2 =$ 2-pentyl) acts still more quickly and for a relatively short period.

Unfortunately the indiscriminate distribution and use of barbiturates and the danger of overdosage make them a hazard to a large proportion of the population. Almost 280,000 pounds of phenobarbital and over 390,000 pounds of other barbiturates having a value of $3,000,000 were produced in the United States in 1948. This amount is equivalent to ten 0.2 gram doses per capita.

Pentothal Sodium is a thiobarbiturate that is used for general anesthesia by intravenous injection. The use of barbiturates for general anesthesia re-

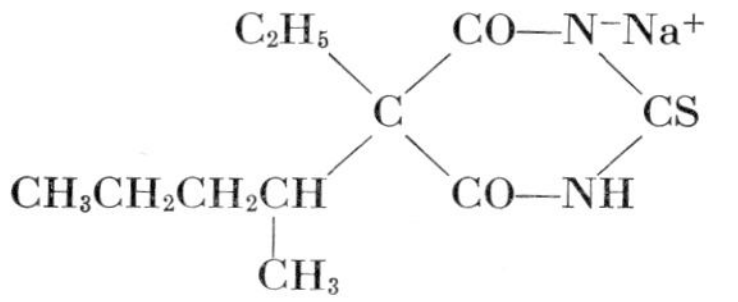

$$CH_3CH_2CH_2CH(CH_3)C(C_2H_5) \begin{cases} CO-N^-Na^+ \\ CO-NH \end{cases} CS$$

Pentothal Sodium

$$CO \begin{cases} CO-NH \\ CO-NH \end{cases} CO$$

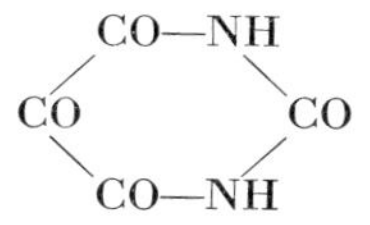

Alloxan

quires careful technique, since the anesthetic dose is 50 to 70 per cent of the lethal dose. However their ease of administration and rapid action, and the rapid recovery of the patient, led to their use for major surgical operations in the front battle lines during World War II, and the experience gained has been carried over to civilian practice.

Alloxan was isolated from the oxidation products of uric acid in 1817 (p. 464). The discovery in 1943 that either oral or parenteral administration to animals brings about destruction of the islets of Langerhans in the pancreas, resulting in diabetes, has brought about renewed interest in the compound.

Thiamine (*vitamin B_1, aneurin*) contains a pyrimidine nucleus joined through a methylene group to a thiazole nucleus. Its absence from the diet causes the deficiency diseases known as beriberi in man and polyneuritis in birds.

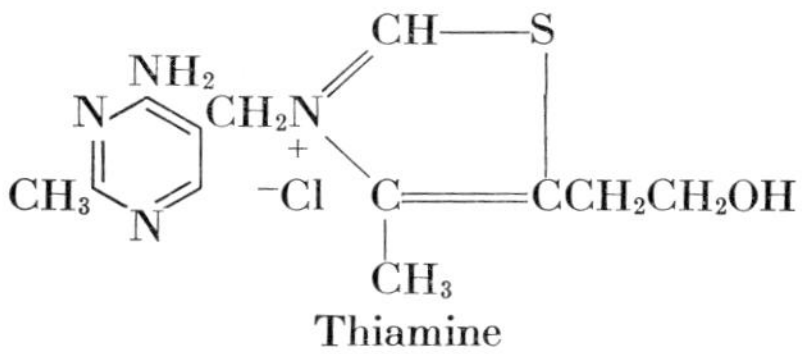

Thiamine
(vitamin B_1, aneurin)

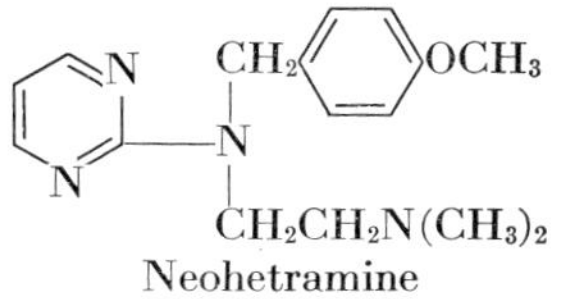

Neohetramine
(Thonzylamine)

Neohetramine (*Thonzylamine*) was among the first of the antihistaminics (p. 461) that the U. S. Federal Drug Administration permitted to be sold without a physician's prescription.

COMPOUNDS WITH CONDENSED HETERO RINGS

The **purines** are the most important class of compounds containing two condensed heterocyclic rings. They contain both a pyrimidine ring and an imidazole ring.

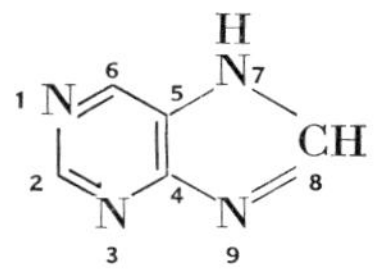

Purine

Amino and hydroxy derivatives of purine accompany pyrimidines as the hydrolysis products of nucleic acids (p. 462). **Adenine** is 6-aminopurine, **hypoxanthine** is 6-hydroxypurine, **guanine** (from guano) is 2-amino-6-hydroxypurine, and **xanthine** is 2,6-dihydroxypurine.

Uric acid is 2,6,8-trihydroxypurine. It is present in blood and urine and can cause the formation of urinary calculi, from which it first was isolated by Scheele in 1776. Crystals of the monosodium salt deposited in the joints cause the painful condition known as gout. Although uric acid is eliminated only in small amounts by mammals, it is the chief product of nitrogen metabolism by caterpillars, birds, and reptiles. Guano, which contains about 25 per cent uric acid, is one of the best sources.

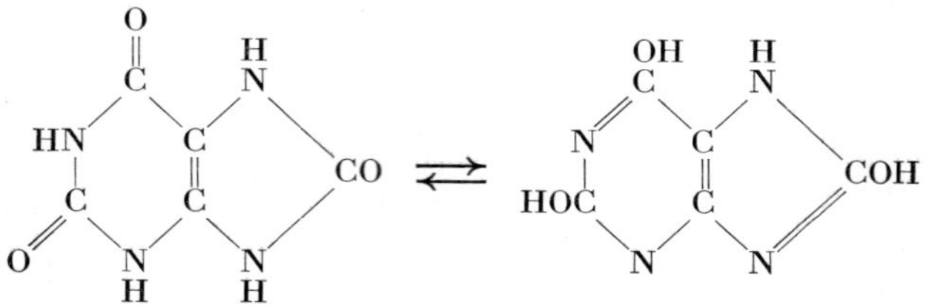

Uric acid

The compounds responsible for the stimulating action of coffee, tea, and cocoa are methyl derivatives of xanthine. **Theophylline** is present in tea (*Thea sinensis*), **theobromine** in cocoa (*Theobroma cacao*), and **caffeine** in tea, coffee (*Coffea arabica*), cola nuts (*Cola acuminata*), maté (*Ilex paraguayensis*), and many other plants. Numerous legends are told concerning the origin

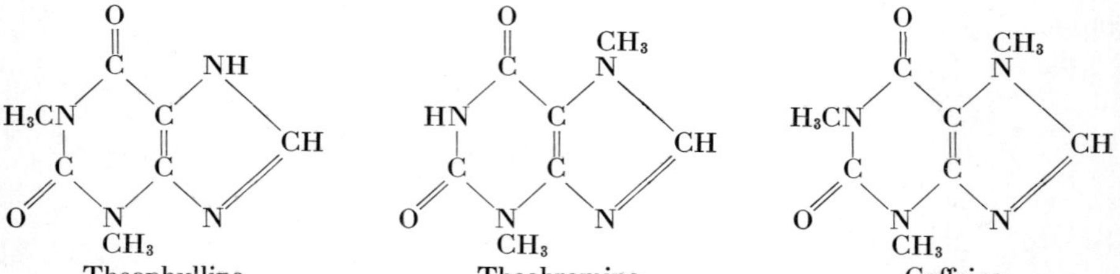

Theophylline · Theobromine · Caffeine

of the use of coffee and tea as beverages. It is of interest that wherever plants having a high caffeine content are indigenous to an area, the natives use extracts of the plant as a beverage. All of these compounds stimulate the central nervous system, caffeine being most active and theobromine least. The effective dose of caffeine is 150 to 250 mg., corresponding to 1 to 2 cups of coffee or tea. About 80 per cent is broken down in the body to urea, and the remainder excreted unchanged or partially demethylated. The fatal dose of caffeine has been estimated as 10 grams, but no deaths from it have been reported. In recent years the use of caffeine-containing beverages has increased enormously, largely because of their stimulating effect. Production of natural and synthetic caffeine in the United States in 1948 was 1,400,000 pounds valued at over $7,000,000. This amount is equivalent to over 2 billion 150-mg. doses or about thirty per capita.

Riboflavin (vitamin B₂) contains a pyrimidine ring fused to a benzo-pyrazine ring. It is yellow and has a yellow-green fluorescence. The polyhy-

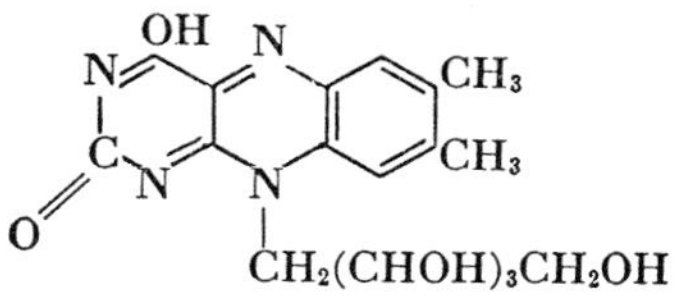

Riboflavin (vitamin B₂)   Biotin

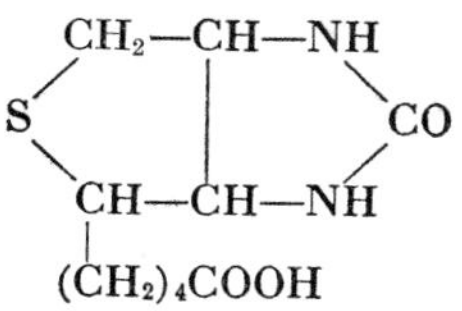

droxy side chain has the ribose configuration. The various *yellow enzymes* or *flavoproteins* consist of riboflavin combined with phosphoric acid and proteins. They play a part in aerobic biological oxidation. Production of riboflavin in the United States in 1948 amounted to 113,000 pounds valued at over 7 million dollars.

Biotin, another member of the vitamin B complex that may be involved in the metabolism of pyruvic acid, contains an imidazole ring fused to a thiophene ring.

ALKALOIDS

The term *alkaloid* means *like an alkali*, and alkaloids usually are defined as basic nitrogenous plant products having a marked physiological action when administered to animals. Some compounds, however, are included under the term which do not conform to this definition. For example piperine, the alkaloid of pepper, is not basic and has practically no physiological activity. On the other hand some compounds such as caffeine are so innocuous that though they definitely are alkaloids, they usually are not considered with the alkaloids and in fact have been omitted from a recent standard reference work on alkaloids. Further some compounds either are so closely related in structure to the alkaloids or have such similar physiological action that it is natural to think of them along with the alkaloids even though they do not come within the usual definition. Thus epinephrine and ephedrine are closely related but only ephedrine is a plant product; opium and hashish (marijuana) are both habit-forming drugs having similar action, yet the active principle of the latter is not basic and does not contain nitrogen.

Coniine is present in all parts of the poison hemlock (*Conium masculatium;* Gr. *konas* to whirl around). It is α-*n*-propylpiperidine, and the simplest of the alkaloids. It has been synthesized from α-picoline.

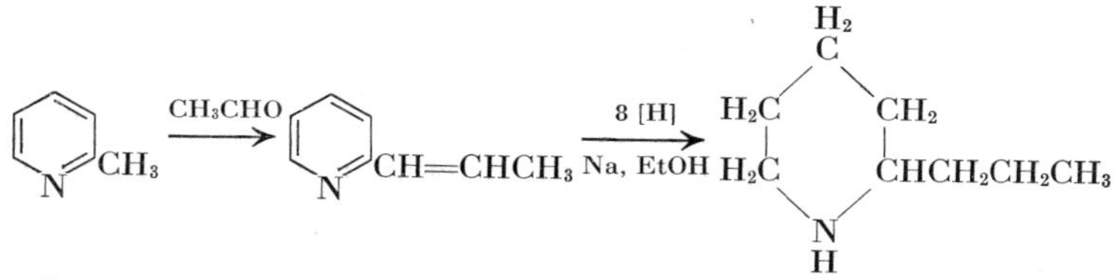

α-Picoline   Coniine

At least ten alkaloids are present in tobacco (*Nicotiana tabacum*). About three fourths of the total alkaloids is **nicotine.** An interesting synthesis starts with 3-cyanopyridine and the Grignard reagent of γ-bromopropyl ethyl ether.

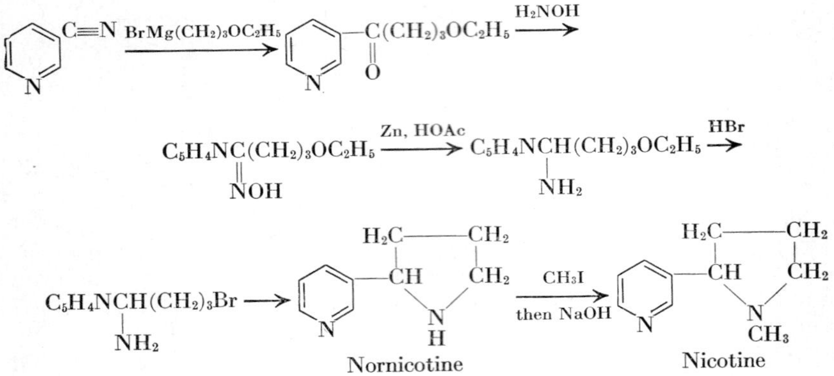

Nicotine is highly toxic to animals, but in small amounts it causes an initial and transient stimulation followed by depression. It is used extensively as a contact insecticide.

Piperine is the alkaloid of black pepper (*Piper nigrum*). The piperine content varies from 5 to 9 per cent. Hydrolysis yields piperidine and piperic acid, indicating an amide linkage. Piperic acid, $C_{12}H_{10}O_4$, contains two double bonds, and oxidation gives piperonal.

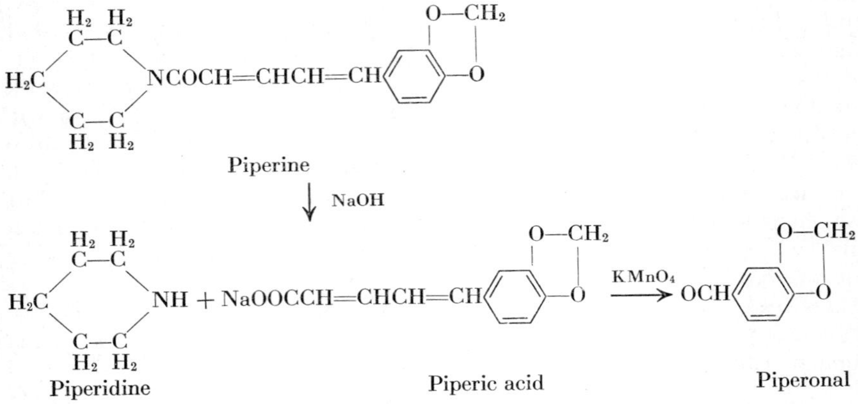

A number of alkaloids have a **tropane ring system,** in which two methylene groups bridge the 2,6 positions of a reduced pyridine ring. **1-Hyoscyamine** is the chief alkaloid of many plants of the family *Solanaceae,* especially henbane (*Hyoscyamus niger*), belladonna (*Atropa belladona*), and the deadly nightshade (*Datura stramonium*). It is racemized readily to **atropine,** which probably does not occur naturally in more than traces. **Cocaine** is the chief alkaloid in the leaves of the Peruvian bush, *Erythroxylum coca.*

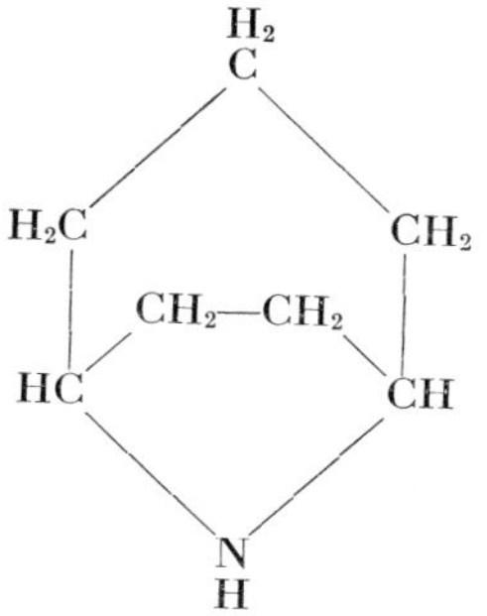

Tropane

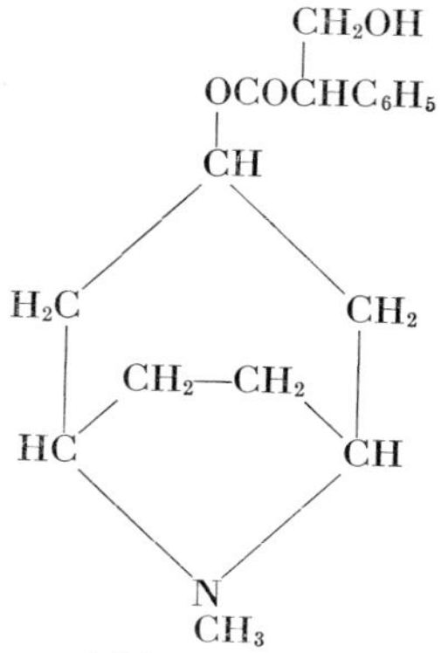

1-Hyoscyamine and atropine

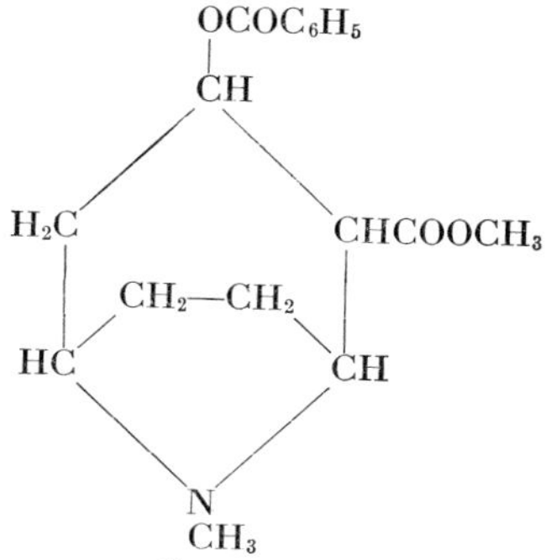

Cocaine

All of the alkaloids of this group are characterized by their mydriatic action. Atropine causes dilation of the pupil of the eye at a dilution of 1 in 130,000 parts of water. Cocaine is noted particularly for its stimulating action on the central nervous system, permitting great physical endurance, and for its local anesthetic action. Before the dangers of addiction were understood, it was self-administered widely in Europe and was a component of many patent medicines. The development of the local anesthetics of the procaine type (p. 418) resulted from the observation that the toxic effects of cocaine are associated with the carbomethoxy group, whereas the anesthetic action is due to the portion that is the benzoic ester of an amino alcohol.

At least twenty-four different alkaloids are present in **opium** (Gr. *opion* poppy juice), the dried latex of the species of poppy (*Papaver somniferum*) that is indigenous to Asia Minor. These alkaloids fall chiefly into two groups, the benzylisoquinoline group and the phenanthrene group. In the former are **papaverine, narcotine,** and **laudanine,** and in the latter **morphine, codeine,** and **thebaine.**

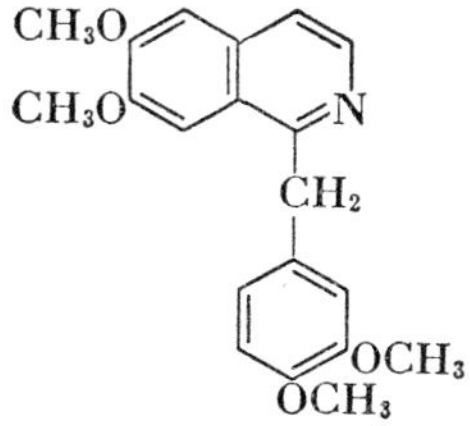

Papaverine

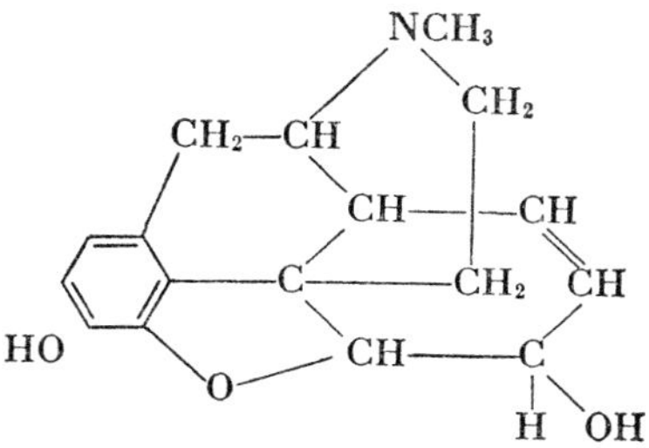

Morphine

One of the hydroxyl groups of morphine is phenolic and can be methylated readily, the resulting methyl ether being identical with natural **codeine.** **Thebaine** is the dimethyl derivative. Acetylation of morphine gives the diacetate, **heroine,** which does not occur in opium.

The effects of opium were known before recorded history, and it has been and remains one of the most valuable drugs at the disposal of the physician.

Morphine, which constitutes about 10 per cent of opium, was isolated by Sertuerner in 1805, and the isolation of other pure components soon followed. Since then the individual alkaloids have been used medicinally. The benzylisoquinoline alkaloids have very little action on the central nervous system but relax smooth muscle. Papaverine is the most important member of the group and is a valuable antispasmodic. Morphine exerts a simultaneous depressing and stimulating action on the central nervous system, producing drowsiness and sleep, yet causing excitation of smooth muscle with resulting nausea and vomiting. The most important use for morphine is for the relief of pain.

At one time it was thought that the phenanthrene portion of the molecule might be the source of the analgesic properties of morphine. Much experimental work was done preparing and testing phenanthrene derivatives, in the hope that one might be found which would have the desirable properties of morphine and yet not lead to addiction. These efforts were unsuccessful, but in 1939 it was discovered accidentally that a relatively simple synthetic compound, which has been named **Demerol,** when injected into rats caused them to hold their tails in a position such as that assumed when morphine is injected. This observation led to the discovery that Demerol has a marked analgesic action although less than that of morphine.

Demerol   Amidone

This discovery turned attention to the fact that morphine also contains a phenylpiperidine structure. Accordingly many derivatives of phenylpiperidine were synthesized and tested, and some of them were found to have marked analgesic activity. About 1941 a compound, which has been named **Amidone,** was found to be even more effective than morphine as an analgesic. Although certain structural features are present in Amidone that may be said to be present in morphine, the relationship is rather remote. Unfortunately continued use of either Demerol or Amidone also leads to addiction.

Another important group of alkaloids is that derived from **cinchona bark.** The name commonly is thought to be derived from that of Countess Anna del Chinchon, wife of the Spanish Viceroy to Peru, who was cured of malaria by treatment with it in 1638. It has been suggested also that the name was derived from the Inca word *kinia* meaning *bark*.

The bark probably reached Europe about 1632, and its use was widespread by 1640. The genus *Cinchona* was established by Linnaeus in 1742, and the tree known as *Cinchona officinalis*, which is native to the high eastern slopes of the Andes, was described by him in 1753. The alkaloids **quinine** and **cinchonine** were not isolated until 1820 by Pelletier and Caventou. By about 1860 the near extinction of the native trees caused such a rise in price of the drug that attempts were made to cultivate cinchona elsewhere. It was grown successfully in India, Ceylon, and Java. Today more than 90 per cent of the quinine produced comes from plantations in Java. The total alkaloid content of the bark of the cultivated trees is 6 per cent, of which 70 per cent is quinine. The last phase of a total synthesis of quinine was completed successfully in 1944.

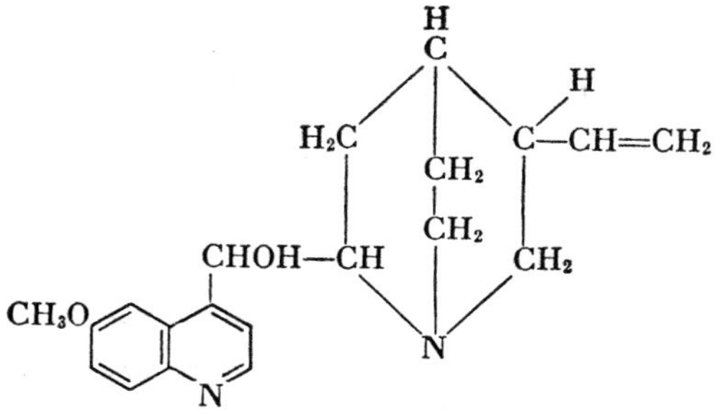

Quinine

Over twenty other alkaloids have been isolated from various species of *Cinchona* and *Cuprea*. **Epiquinine, quinidine,** and **epiquinidine** are stereoisomers of quinine. **Cinchonine, cinchonidine,** and **cinchonicine** are stereoisomeric with each other, and differ from quinine and its isomers in lacking a methoxyl group.

The value of quinine lies in its specific action in the treatment of malaria. It is estimated that throughout the world there are several hundred million cases of malaria per year, resulting in 3 million deaths and partial or total debilitation for the remainder. Although annual production of quinine has reached 600 tons, it is only a fraction of what would be needed to treat all cases even if the cost were not prohibitive for most of the victims. Starting from the observation of Ehrlich (p. 593) in 1891 that methylene blue has antimalarial action, chemists at the I. G. Farbenindustrie of Germany began an extensive program of synthesis and testing which resulted in the introduction of **Plasmochin** (pamaquine) in 1926. It had the desirable property not possessed by quinine of being able to kill the sexual form of the parasite, thus preventing the spread of malaria by mosquitoes. Its toxic effects precluded its general use, however, and **Atabrine** (quinacrine) was introduced in 1930.

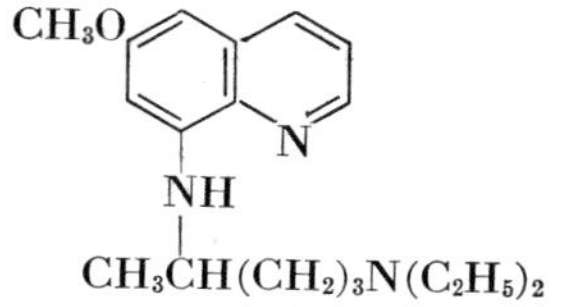

Plasmochin (pamaquine)

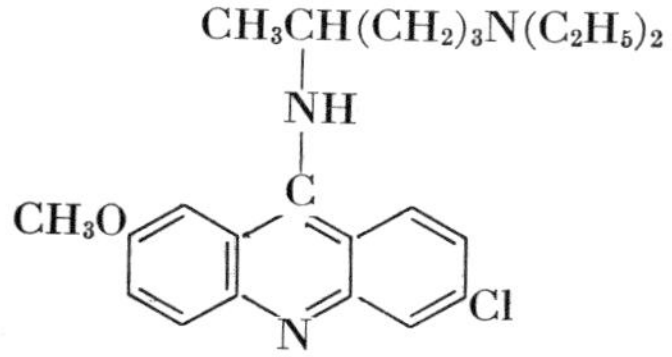

Atabrine (quinacrine)

Atabrine, like quinine, acts on the schizont stage of the parasite and reduces the formation of the gametocytes whose asexual reproduction causes the destruction of red blood corpuscles and leads to the symptomatic chills and fever. Atabrine was not used extensively, however, until World War II cut off supplies of quinine from Java. Having become familiar with Atabrine, physicians now prefer it to quinine.

Between 1920 and 1930, during the development of Plasmochin and Atabrine, over 12,000 compounds were prepared and tested. With the advent of tropical warfare in World War II, an intensive search for better anti-malarials was undertaken in the United States, Canada, and England. In this program over 14,000 compounds were screened. The formulas are given for several that show considerable promise. **Chloroquine** has proved to be more satisfactory than Atabrine in extensive clinical trials with human patients. **Paludrine** is of special interest in that it has marked antimalarial activity but does not contain a nitrogen heterocycle.

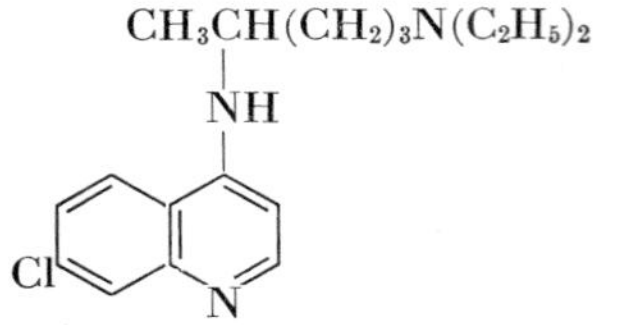

$$CH_3CH(CH_2)_3N(C_2H_5)_2$$

SN 7618
(chloroquine or Aralen)

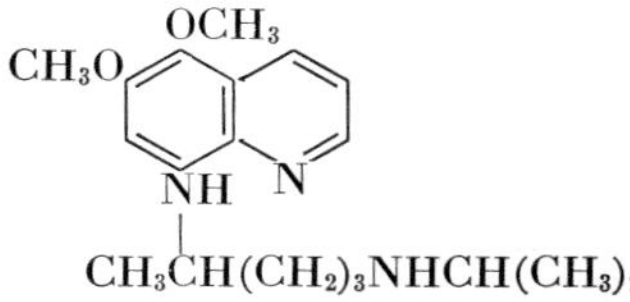

$$CH_3CH(CH_2)_3NHCH(CH_3)_2$$

SN 9972

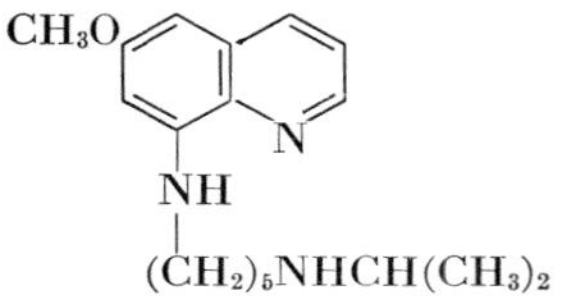

SN 13276
(pentaquine)

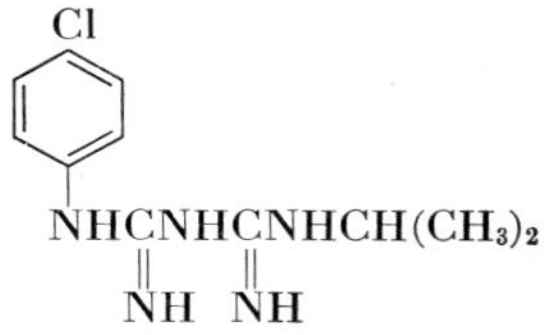

$$(CH_2)_5NHCH(CH_3)_2$$

Paludrine

$$NHCNHCNHCH(CH_3)_2$$
$$NH \quad NH$$

REVIEW QUESTIONS

1. Define the term *heterocyclic compound*. What are the more common hetero atoms?
2. Compare the physical and chemical properties of thiophene and benzene? How did thiophene happen to be discovered? How is it synthesized?
3. What is the best method for the preparation of pyrrole? Compare its physical properties with those of pyridine.
4. The reactions of pyrrole usually are stated to resemble those of phenol. Give specific examples to illustrate this point.
5. What is the *porphin nucleus* and why is it important?
6. Write structural formulas for proline, indole, tryptophan, and skatole, and indicate a source for each.
7. What compound is used as a starting point for the synthesis of furan and its more common derivatives? How is this compound prepared?
8. Give reactions for the action on furfural of aqueous permanganate; hydrogen and a platinum catalyst; strong aqueous sodium hydroxide; dilute aqueous potassium cyanide; acetone and sodium hydroxide; ammonia; acetic anhydride in the presence of sodium acetate.
9. Give equations for the conversion of furoic acid into 1-chloro-2-butanol.
10. What is the source of pyridine? Why is it more stable to substitution reactions than benzene? What are some of its common laboratory uses?
11. Give a reaction for the conversion of pyridine into piperidine. Give a reaction for the synthesis of piperidine that can be considered to be a proof of structure. What are the chemical properties of piperidine?
12. What are the picolines?

13. How can β-picolinic acid be made? What is another name for it and why is it important?
14. Give reactions illustrating what is believed to take place in the Skraup synthesis of quinoline.
15. What is the structural formula for isoquinoline; for phenanthridine?
16. What are the pyrimidines and purines? What is the fundamental ring structure of each?
17. What are the sources and structures of uric acid; theophylline; theobromine; caffeine?
18. Define the term *alkaloid*. What is the constitution of coniine; piperine; cocaine; morphine; quinine?

Chapter 31

COLOR. DYES AND DYEING

Color always has played an important role in the life of man even though its significance is almost wholly esthetic. Throughout man's history dyes and pigments, both natural and synthetic, have been an important article of commerce. Since absorption of light in regions of the spectrum other than the visible also is of interest to chemists, it is desirable to discuss the subject of color from this more general viewpoint.

COLOR

Color Sensation

The human eye is sensitive only to electromagnetic vibrations having a wavelength between 400 mμ and 750 mμ. This region of the electromagnetic spectrum is known as the *visible*. The region of shorter wavelengths in the range 400 mμ to 100 mμ is known as the *ultraviolet*, and that of longer wavelengths in the range 750 mμ to 100,000 mμ is called the *infrared*.

The mixture of all wavelengths in the visible having the relative intensities produced by a body at a white heat is known as *white light*. If the light striking the retina of the eye does not contain all of the wavelengths of the visible spectrum, or if the intensity of some of them is reduced considerably, the sensation of color results.

Light may be colored because only a limited region of the spectrum is emitted by a light source, as for example the yellow light of the sodium flame. Or light may be colored because of the separation or removal of certain wavelengths of the visible light. Because light of different wavelengths is refracted (velocity reduced) to different degrees on passing through a transparent medium, it is possible to separate the different wavelengths of white light by the use of a prism and produce a colored spectrum. Another way in which portions of the spectrum may be removed is by interference. When light is reflected from the two surfaces of a thin film, the thickness of the film may be such that a light wave reflected from the far surface travels a sufficiently longer path to be thrown out of phase with a light wave reflected from the near surface. Cancellation of this wavelength results, and if white light is being reflected, the reflected light is colored. Colored bird feathers and colors of soap bubbles are examples of this phenomenon. Finally certain wavelengths of white light may be removed by absorption, which is by far the most common cause of color. The color may be observed as the light transmitted through a solution of the substance in a transparent medium, or as the light reflected from an opaque substance.

The visual color is complementary to the color absorbed; that is it is the color sensation produced by all of the wavelengths minus the wavelengths absorbed. Table 20 gives the observed colors when relatively narrow bands

TABLE 20
RELATION BETWEEN ABSORPTION AND VISUAL COLOR

WAVELENGTHS ABSORBED (mμ)	COLOR ABSORBED	VISUAL COLOR
400–435	violet	yellow-green
435–480	blue	yellow
480–490	green-blue	orange
490–500	blue-green	red
500–560	green	purple
560–580	yellow-green	violet
580–595	yellow	blue
595–605	orange	green-blue
605–750	red	blue-green

of the visible spectrum are absorbed. If the absorption bands are broader or if more than one absorption band is present, the visible color is altered.

Color and Chemical Structure: Qualitative Aspects

As early as 1868 Graebe and Liebermann discussed the importance of unsaturation in producing color, and noted that reduction of a colored compound always led to a colorless product. In 1876 Witt pointed out that two types of groups usually are present in colored compounds, neither of which produces color if present alone. Thus of the six *para*-disubstituted benzenes, dinitro, diamino, dihydroxy, amino hydroxy, nitro amino, and nitro hydroxy, only the last two are colored. Witt noted also that the salt-forming properties of the amino and hydroxyl groups are necessary, since acetylation of the amino group or methylation of the hydroxyl group destroys the color, but methylation of an amino group does not. Moreover the salts of the phenols are more strongly colored than the free phenol.

Anthraquinone and its derivatives behave similarly. Thus anthraquinone and dihydroxyanthracene are colorless whereas hydroxy and amino anthraquinone are colored. Acylation of the hydroxyl or amino group destroys the color, and conversion of the phenolic hydroxyl to the salt deepens the color.

The unsaturated groups necessary to produce color were called **chromophores** by Witt (Gr. *chroma* color, *phoros* from *pherein* to bear). He assigned the nitro group, the carbonyl group, and the azo group to this class. The compound containing the chromophore, for example nitrobenzene, was called the **chromogen.** Later C=C, C=N, C=S, and N=O were added to the list of chromophores. In 1888 Armstrong [1] added the very important chromophoric quinonoid structure, $=\!\!\left\langle\underset{}{\bigcirc}\right\rangle\!\!=$, pointing out that the structures of most highly colored substances containing an aromatic ring could be written in such a way that they contained a quinonoid structure.

The salt forming groups that Witt considered necessary to produce color were called **auxochromes** (L. *auxilium* aid). To this class he assigned the

---

[1] Henry Edward Armstrong (1848–1937), professor of chemistry at Central Technical College, South Kensington, England. He is remembered not only for his contributions to the theory of color and the structure of benzene, but also for his sharp criticisms of contemporary thinking in the field of chemistry.

phenolic hydroxyl and the amino and alkylated amino groups. Numerous other empirical observations have been made. For example auxochrome groups do not affect the color when in the *meta* position to the chromophore; increasing the size of the alkyl groups in the alkylated amino auxochrome deepens the color.

At the time that Witt discussed the effect of salt-forming groups on color, he mentioned also the necessity for their presence if the colored compound was to act as a dye, that is to have the ability to fix itself to a fiber. This dual property of auxochromes has led to some confusion, since both properties are not always exhibited simultaneously.

The inconsistencies and inadequacy of the chromophore-auxochrome theory long have been recognized, and in recent years it has been reinterpreted in terms of current theory. The nature of fixation of a dye to the fiber and especially to mordants now is better understood, and the function of hydroxyl and amino groups in this respect has been separated from their function as auxochromes. Current views now class the nitro group as an auxochrome and the aromatic nucleus as a chromophore. It has been realized also that unvarying effects cannot be assigned to specific portions of an organic molecule.

DYES AND DYEING

Historical

Natural coloring matters have been used by man since the beginnings of civilization. The first synthetic dye was picric acid, made by Woulfe in 1771 by the action of nitric acid on natural indigo. Not until 1855 was a technical method introduced to prepare it from coal tar. The first dye prepared from coal tar was *aurin* or *rosolic acid* reported by Runge [2] in 1834. He noted that with the usual mordants it produced red colors and lakes which rivaled those produced from cochineal and madder. Since little was known about the components of coal tar at that time and Kekulé's theory of the structure of benzene was not proposed until 1865, Runge's observations were not extended.

As early as 1843, Hofmann had observed that aniline, as prepared at that time, gave red colors under certain conditions. In 1856 Perkin [3] oxidized

---

[2] Ferdinand Runge (1794–1867), professor of chemistry at the University of Breslau. He was the first to isolate aniline, quinoline, pyrrole, and phenol from coal tar in 1834.

[3] William Henry Perkin (1838–1907) entered the Royal College of Chemistry in London in 1853 to study chemistry under Hofmann. He discovered anthraquinone while trying to nitrate anthracene, but did no further work with this compound until 1869, when he devised a commercial synthesis of alizarin from it (p. 487).

In his report on the work of the Royal College of Chemistry in 1849, Hofmann had remarked that the synthesis of quinine would be very desirable. Seven years later Perkin, now 18 years old and research assistant to Hofmann, was impressed by this remark. At that time the chief lead to the structure of a compound was the difference between its molecular formula and that of a known compound. Perkin thought that quinine might result by the oxidation of allyltoluidine.

$$2\ C_{10}H_{13}N + 3\ [O] \longrightarrow C_{20}H_{24}N_2O_2 + H_2O$$

Allyl-   Quinine
toluidine

During the Easter vacation of 1856, he made allyltoluidine in his home laboratory and oxidized the sulfate with potassium dichromate. He obtained only a dirty reddish-brown pre-

aniline sulfate with potassium dichromate and obtained a purple dye called *mauve*, which became the first synthetic coal tar dye to be manufactured commercially. In 1859 a process was patented in France for the oxidation of aniline with stannic chloride to give a magenta colored dye resembling the color of fuchsia flowers and named *fuchsin*. After Hofmann showed that fuchsin is a derivative of triphenylmethane, this class of dyes was investigated extensively and came into widespread use.

Meanwhile the azo dyes were discovered by Griess in 1862, the theory of aromatic structure became established, alizarin was synthesized by Graebe and Liebermann in 1868, and indigo was synthesized by Baeyer in 1879. Sulfur colors from coal tar derivatives were produced in 1893, anthraquinone vat dyes in 1901, acridine dyes in 1910, acetoacetarylides in 1923, and phthalocyanins in 1934.

The synthetic coal tar dye industry developed first in England under Perkin, Nicholson, and others, but gradually passed into German hands. By 1913, just before World War I, Germany produced three fourths of the world production of dyes and 90 per cent of the dyes used in England and the United States. France and Switzerland also had flourishing dye industries, but they were connected with the German cartel. Among the reasons for German predominance were (*1*) favorable American patent laws which permit a foreign country to patent processes and products without requiring manufacture in the United States, (*2*) vigorous research programs by German manufacturers with close collaboration with university laboratories, (*3*) low tariff restrictions, and (*4*) cartel control of prices with price-cutting and dumping to prevent competition. Along with control of the dye industry went control of the manufacture of synthetic medicinals and all other organic chemicals.

During World War I Germany lost control of the organic chemical market because the United States and England had to make their own dyes and pharmaceuticals, and these countries realized that the dye plants with their facilities for nitration and for the manufacture of chlorine and phosgene were potential munitions factories. The Chemical Foundation took over German patents in this country and licensed them to firms in the United States, and after the war adequate tariff laws were passed to ensure the continuance and growth of the organic chemical industry. In 1924 the Interessen Gemeinschaft fuer Farbenindustrie, commonly called the I.G., was formed to combine most of the German chemical industries, in an attempt to regain world trade. As a

---

cipitate, but this behavior interested him, and he decided to try the reaction on a simpler base. On treating aniline sulfate with dichromate, he obtained a black precipitate from which he extracted a purple compound that had the property of a dye and was fast to light. After submitting samples to dyers and receiving favorable comments, he resigned his post at the Royal College and with the aid of his father and brother began manufacture in 1857. The dye was known as *aniline purple* or *mauve*. Material dyed with it became so popular that it gave its name to the *mauve decade*. It is of interest that the total synthesis of quinine was not accomplished until 1944.

Perkin became a successful industrialist but never gave up scientific research. In 1867 he published his first paper on what now is known as the Perkin reaction (p. 404), and in 1868 announced the synthesis of coumarin (p. 420), the first natural perfume to be synthesized from a coal tar component. In 1874 at the age of 36, Perkin retired from business to devote full time to scientific research, especially to the study of the effect of the magnetic field on optical rotation.

counterpart Imperial Chemical Industries was formed in England in 1926. Although no similar organization exists in the United States, the general industrial development and aggressive research programs have permitted its organic chemical industry to flourish. By 1940 each of several large companies exceeded in size either the I.G. or the I.C.I. The largest chemical firm in the United States was the eighth largest U. S. industrial corporation in 1948 with assets of over 1.5 billion dollars. Yet it sold only 7 per cent of the total chemicals and allied products manufactured by more than 7000 other companies. At least ten of these companies have assets greater than 100 million dollars.

Dyeing

Not all colored substances are dyes. A true dye may be defined as a colored substance, fast to light and washing, that will attach itself to a material, usually a textile fiber, from solution. ·

The mechanism of dyeing must differ with the nature of the material, that is whether it is protein, cellulose, or some synthetic substance. The dyeing of wool and silk at one time was held to be chemical, the acidic or basic group in a dye combining with basic or acidic groups in the protein. It now is thought that the acidic and basic groups in the dye aid in the initial adsorption of the dye on the surface of the fiber, but that this process is followed by solution or dispersion of the dye in the fiber.

Direct or Substantive Dyes. Dyes may be classified either according to the method of application or according to their chemical structure. Although the latter classification is of most interest to the chemist, the former involves chemical aspects also. The **direct** or **substantive dyes** are those that are applicable by immersing the fiber or cloth in a hot solution of the dye in water. Those dyes suitable for dyeing *animal fibers* are divided into **acid dyes** and **basic dyes.** Acid dyes are sodium salts of sulfonic acids and are dyed from a bath acidified with sulfuric or acetic acid. **Basic dyes** are the hydrochlorides or zinc chloride complexes of dyes having basic groups. They are dyed from a neutral bath, usually on a fiber that has been treated with tannic acid. Basic dyes frequently also contain sodium sulfonate groups to make them more soluble in water.

In cellulose there are no strongly acidic or basic groups, and the colored compounds of lower molecular weight that dye protein fibers are not fixed by cotton or viscose rayon. However if the dye has a molecular weight sufficiently high to give colloidal solutions, it is adsorbed more strongly and is a direct dye for cotton and viscose rayon. These dyes also are called **salt colors** because adsorption on the fiber usually is assisted by the addition of a salt such as sodium sulfate.

Mordant or Adjective Dyes, and Chrome Dyes. A mordant is any substance which can be fixed to the fiber (L. *mordere* to bite) and which later can be dyed. Thus albumin was used as a mordant for printing cotton cloth to produce calico. The protein was coagulated on the cotton fiber by heat, and then dyed with an acid dye. Tannic acid was used as a mordant for basic dyes. The terms mordant and chrome dye, however, are reserved for those dyes that can form insoluble complexes with metallic oxides. Usually the oxide first is precipitated in the fiber and then dyed. For example cotton is soaked in a solution of aluminum acetate or formate and steamed. The aluminum salt hydrolyzes, and the volatile organic acid vaporizes. Reaction of the aluminum hydroxide with an alkaline solution of alizarin (p. 487), for example, produces a colored, high molecular weight, insoluble chelate complex (p. 520) which is adsorbed strongly by the fiber.

$$3\ O{=}\!\!=\!\!{=}O\ +\ Al(OH)_3\ \longrightarrow\ \left[O{=}\!\!=\!\!{=}O \cdots Al/3 \right]_3\ +\ 3\ H_2O$$

Sometimes a cloth is dyed with a direct dye and then treated with a chromium salt to produce on the fiber a complex that is faster or has a more desirable shade. This process is known as *after chroming*. Dyes also can be *prechromed* and used as direct dyes, or the chroming may be done during the dyeing of the cloth, a process called *meta chroming*.

Ingrain Dyes. Ingrain dyes are water-insoluble azo dyes that are formed on the fiber. They usually are used on cotton. The **ice colors** or **azoic dyes** are applied by impregnating the cloth with a compound capable of coupling with a diazonium salt and then immersing in an ice-cold solution of a diazotized amine. In **developed dyeing** the cloth is dyed with a direct dye containing a free amino group. The dye then is diazotized on the fiber and developed by coupling with an amine or phenol. The new dye on the fiber is faster to washing because of its higher molecular weight. It usually has a deeper color.

Sulfur Dyes. Sulfur dyes contain sulfur and are direct dyes for cotton. They are applied from a solution of sodium sulfide in which they are soluble. Sodium sulfate usually is added as with other direct dyes for cotton. Some sulfur dyes also have the chemical properties of vat dyes and can be applied like vat dyes.

Vat Dyes. Vat dyes are water-insoluble but can be rendered water-soluble by reduction in alkaline solution. Cotton is steeped in this solution and then exposed to air or a chemical oxidizing agent which oxidizes the dye to the insoluble form. The reduction formerly was carried out by fermentation in large vats which gave rise to the name *vat dye*.

Dyes for Cellulose Acetate. Direct dyes are not suitable for cellulose acetate because the acetylated hydroxyl groups make the fiber still less adsorbing than cellulose. Vat and ingrain dyeing cannot be used because the alkaline and acid solutions bring about partial hydrolysis of the ester groups and deluster the fiber. Colored dyes that are soluble in organic solvents, however, are soluble in cellulose acetate. Hence acetate rayon is dyed from colloidal dispersions of water-insoluble dyes that dissolve in cellulose acetate. Acetate dyes are not very fast to washing. A peculiar weakness is that they are subject to fading even in the dark. This fading is due to oxides of nitrogen and of sulfur in the atmosphere and is called *gas fading*.

CHEMICAL CLASSES OF DYES

Nitro Compounds

This class of dyes no longer is of great importance. **Naphthol Yellow S** still is used to some extent. It is made by sulfonating naphthol and nitrating the trisulfonic acid.

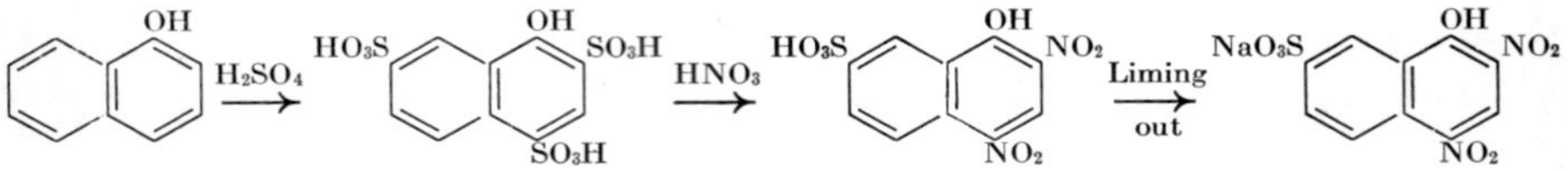

The free acid, known as **flavianic acid,** is an important precipitant for the isolation of the amino acid arginine.

Azo Dyes

This class constitutes the largest single group of dyes, making up over half of the total number of synthetic colors of known structure. It accounted for about 45 per cent of the total production by weight or by value in 1948. Over 87 million pounds were produced at an average unit price of 88 cents per pound. Most azo dyes are sulfonic acids and are used as acid dyes. Those of high molecular weight containing two, three, and four azo groups (disazo, trisazo, and tetrakisazo dyes) are substantive for cotton.

Azo dyes are prepared by coupling a diazotized aromatic amine, the primary component, with a phenol or an aromatic amine, the secondary component (p. 378). In the benzene series coupling takes place *para* to the hydroxyl or amino group, or *ortho* if the *para* position is occupied. If all *ortho* and *para* positions are occupied, no coupling takes place. Occasionally a group such as the carboxyl group in the *para* position may be displaced. Phenols when coupled in strongly alkaline solution undergo some *ortho* substitution. With diamines and dihydroxy compounds only the *meta* isomers couple.

In the naphthalene series, α-naphthol and α-naphthylamine couple in the 4 position. If the 4 position is occupied or if a sulfonate group is in the 3 or 5 position, coupling takes place in the 2 position. β-Naphthol and β-naphthylamine couple only in the 1 position. If both an amino group and a hydroxyl group are present, the amino group directs in weakly acid solution, and the hydroxyl group directs in alkaline solution.

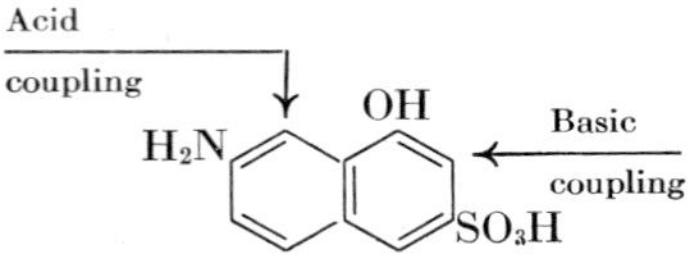

Monazo Dyes.

(*a*) BASIC.

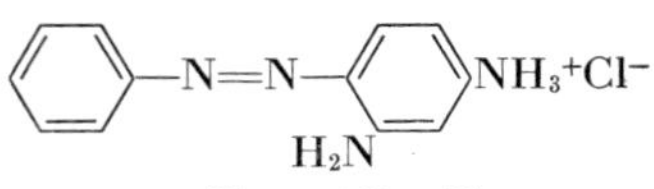

Chrysoidine Y

(*b*) ACID.

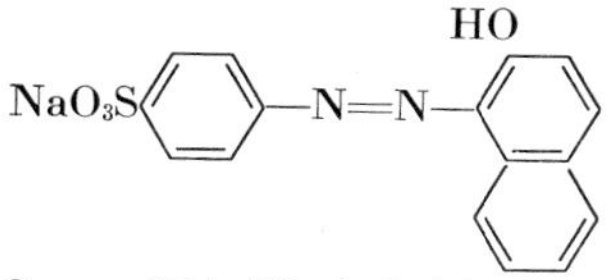

Orange II (β-Naphthol Orange)

(*c*) INGRAIN.

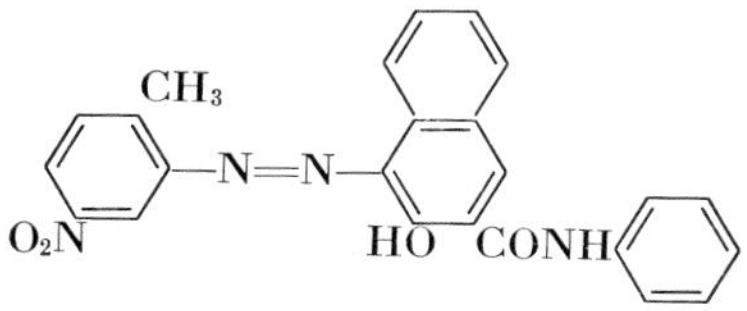

Fast Scarlet G

(*d*) MORDANT.

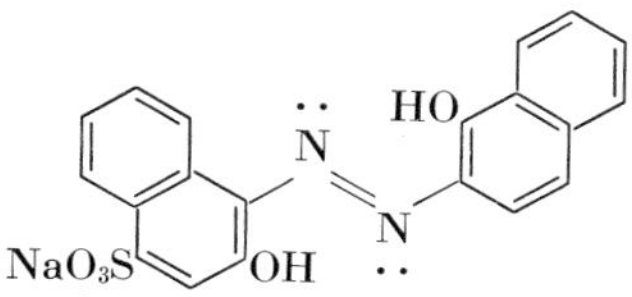

Chrome Blue Black R

The fiber may be treated with chroming solution before, after, or during the dyeing (p. 477). The chroming deepens the color and produces on the fiber a molecule of much higher molecular weight and hence of greater fastness.

Disazo Dyes.

(*a*) BASIC. **Bismarck Brown R** is made by the action of nitrous acid on 2,4-diaminotoluene (*m*-toluylenediamine). The original Bismarck Brown from *m*-phenylenediamine was discovered by Martius in 1863.

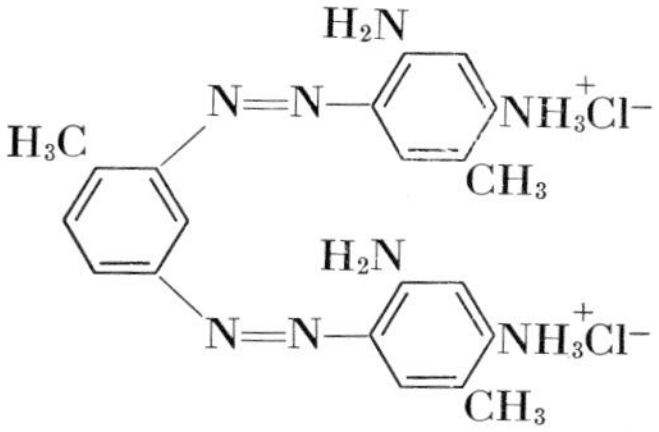

Bismarck Brown R

(*b*) ACID. The discovery that the disazo acid dyes derived from benzidine are direct dyes for cotton gave enormous impetus to the synthetic dye industry. **Congo Red,** derived from benzidine and naphthionic acid, was the first dye of this class, but it is sensitive to acids. The direct cotton dye which established the Badische Anilin und Soda Fabrik in Germany was **Benzopurpurin 4B** made from *o*-tolidine (p. 427) and naphthionic acid (p. 434).

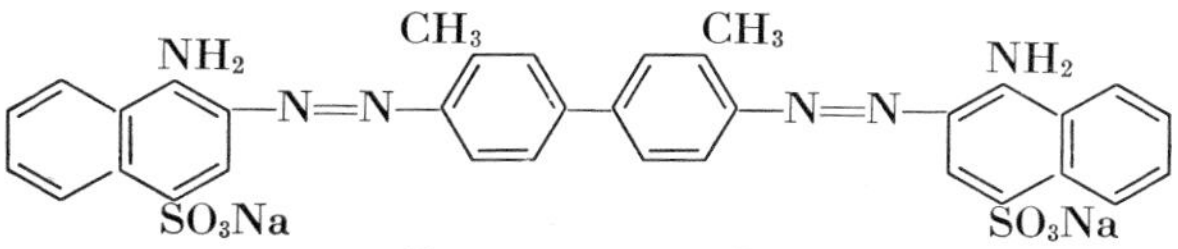

Benzopurpurin 4B

Many other important dyes are derived from benzidine. Thus **Direct Blue 2B** is made by coupling diazotized benzidine with H-acid (p. 435).

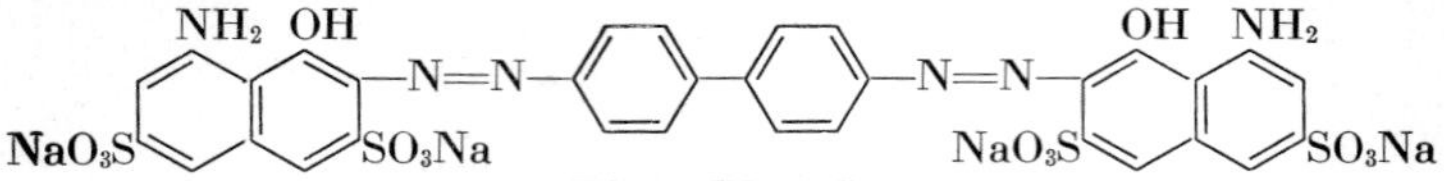

Direct Blue 2B

(*c*) DEVELOPED COLORS. **Developed Black BH** is made by coupling diazotized benzidine first with one mole of γ-acid (p. 435) and then with one mole of H-acid in alkaline solution.

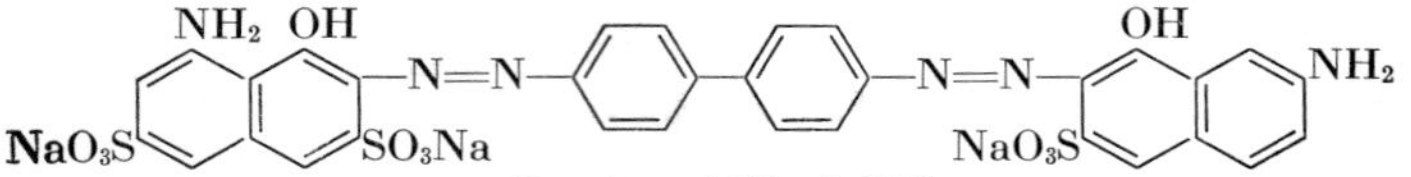

Developed Black BH

It dyes cotton a bright blue. When diazotized on the fiber and coupled with β-naphthol, it gives a navy blue; if coupled with *m*-phenylenediamine, a black color is produced.

Trisazo Dyes. The most widely used black azo dye is **Direct Black EW.** It is made by coupling diazotized benzidine with one mole of *H*-acid in acid solution, then coupling diazotized aniline with the *H*-acid portion in alkaline solution. Finally the second diazonium group of the benzidine portion is coupled with *m*-phenylenediamine.

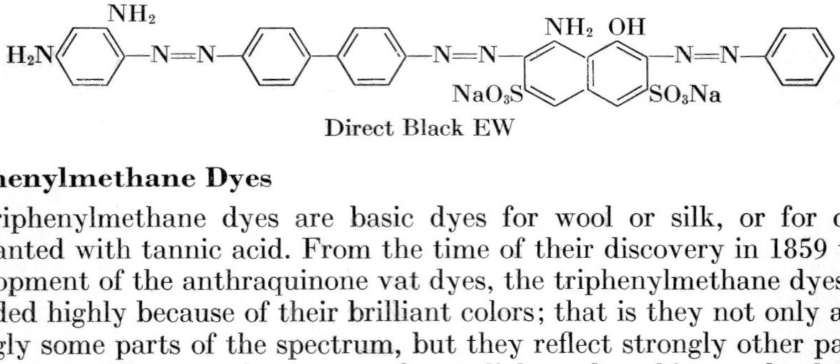

Direct Black EW

Triphenylmethane Dyes

Triphenylmethane dyes are basic dyes for wool or silk, or for cotton mordanted with tannic acid. From the time of their discovery in 1859 to the development of the anthraquinone vat dyes, the triphenylmethane dyes were regarded highly because of their brilliant colors; that is they not only absorb strongly some parts of the spectrum, but they reflect strongly other parts of the spectrum. However they are not fast to light and washing, and only a few still are manufactured.

Malachite Green Series. Dyes of this group are derivatives of bis-(*p*-aminophenyl)phenylmethane. **Malachite Green** is made by condensing benzaldehyde with dimethylaniline to give bis(*p*-dimethylaminophenyl)-phenylmethane, which is known as the *leuco base* (Gr. *leukos* white). Oxidation converts it to the carbinol which also is colorless and is known as the *color base* or the *carbinol base*. Strong acids convert the color base into the colored dye.

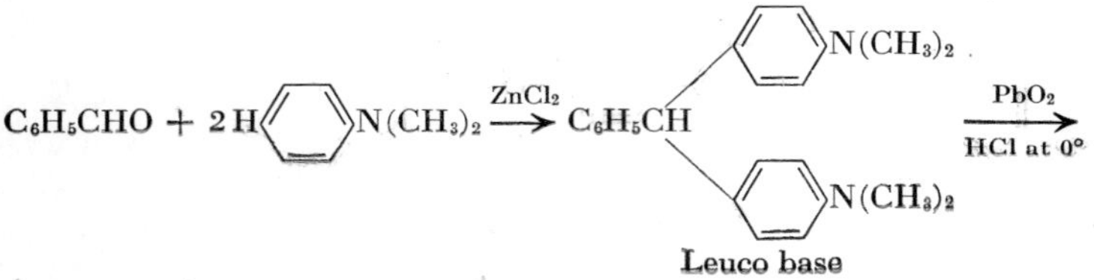

Leuco base

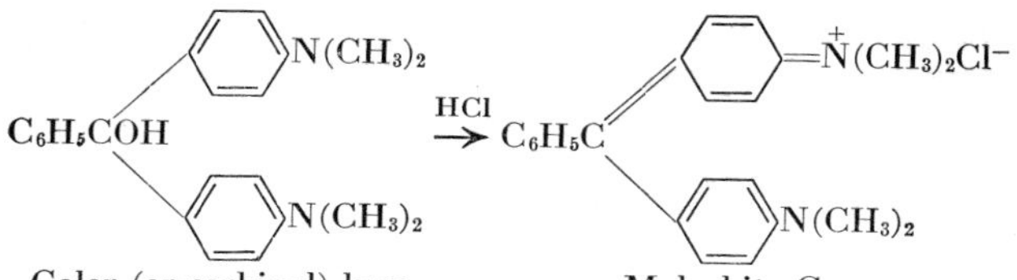

Color (or carbinol) base   Malachite Green

Rosaniline Series. The rosanilines are derivatives of tris(*p*-amino-phenyl)methane.

(*a*) PARAROSANILINE. **Pararosaniline,** patented by Verguin in France in 1859, was the first triphenylmethane dye. Like mauve, it was prepared by the oxidation of aniline, but with stannic chloride, nitrobenzene, or arsenic oxide, instead of dichromate. The dye was manufactured by the Society for Chemical Industry in Basle (Ciba) until the plant was forced to shut down because the aniline imported from France no longer gave satisfactory yields. Hofmann found that the formation of the dye depended on the presence of toluidine in the aniline, and the results of his investigations established the structure of rosaniline. The methyl group of the *p*-toluidine supplies the methine or methylidyne (CH) carbon atom of the leuco base.

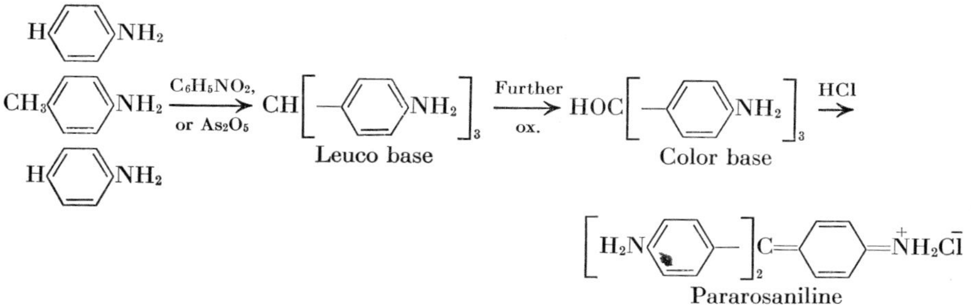

The commercial *fuchsins*, *rosanilines*, and *magentas* usually are mixtures of pararosaniline with its methyl homologs.

The decolorization of fuchsin by sulfur dioxide appears to involve the formation of the leucosulfonic acid and also the addition of sulfur dioxide to two amino groups. Subsequent reaction with an aldehyde gives an addition product which loses sulfurous acid to form a new colored compound.

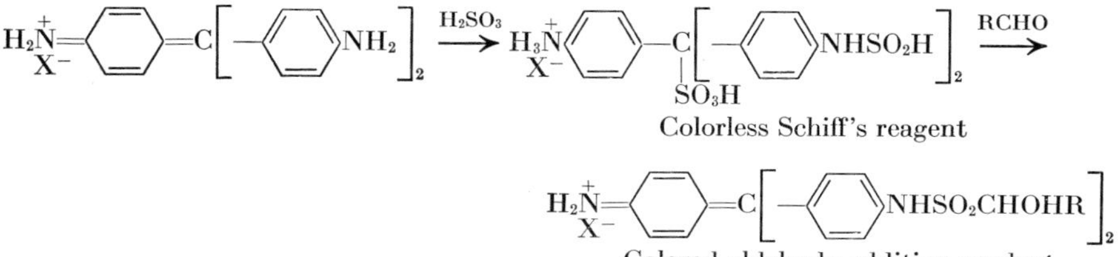

Colorless Schiff's reagent

Colored aldehyde addition product

(*b*) METHYL VIOLET AND CRYSTAL VIOLET. These dyes are the only members of the triphenylmethane group that are of real importance today. Production of **Methyl Violet** in the United States amounted to over 1.6 million pounds in 1948. It is the dye commonly used in purple inks, indelible pencils, and typewriter ribbons. Methyl Violet is made by oxidizing dimethyl-aniline with cupric chloride. It is believed that one methyl group of a molecule of dimethylaniline is oxidized to formaldehyde, which then undergoes condensation and further oxidation.

$$C_6H_5N(CH_3)_2 + [O] \xrightarrow[NaCl]{CuSO_4} C_6H_5NHCH_3 + HCHO$$

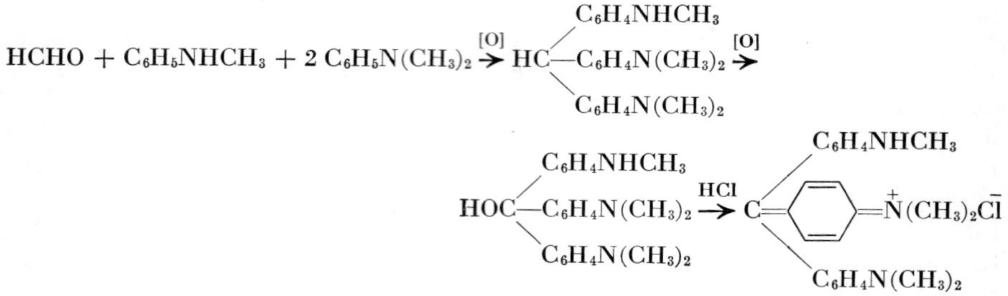

$$HCHO + C_6H_5NHCH_3 + 2\ C_6H_5N(CH_3)_2 \xrightarrow{[O]} HC \begin{matrix} C_6H_4NHCH_3 \\ | \\ C_6H_4N(CH_3)_2 \\ | \\ C_6H_4N(CH_3)_2 \end{matrix} \xrightarrow{[O]}$$

$$HOC \begin{matrix} C_6H_4NHCH_3 \\ | \\ C_6H_4N(CH_3)_2 \\ | \\ C_6H_4N(CH_3)_2 \end{matrix} \xrightarrow{HCl} C \begin{matrix} C_6H_4NHCH_3 \\ | \\ \\ | \\ C_6H_4N(CH_3)_2 \end{matrix} = \langle \rangle = \overset{+}{N}(CH_3)_2 \overset{-}{Cl}$$

Methyl Violet

Crystal Violet is the completely methylated compound obtained by condensing Michler's ketone (p. 407) with dimethylaniline.

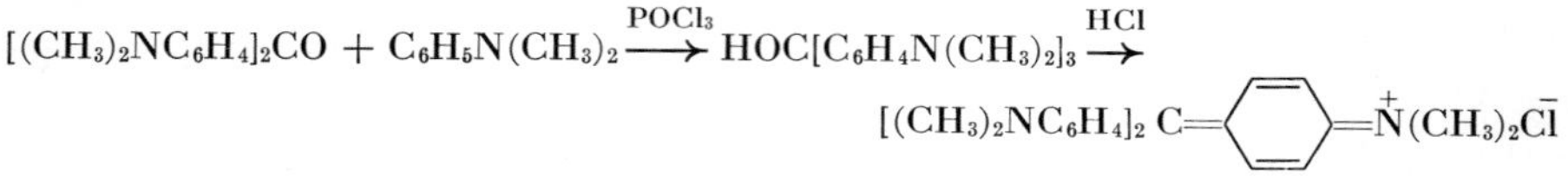

$$[(CH_3)_2NC_6H_4]_2CO + C_6H_5N(CH_3)_2 \xrightarrow{POCl_3} HOC[C_6H_4N(CH_3)_2]_3 \xrightarrow{HCl}$$

$$[(CH_3)_2NC_6H_4]_2 C = \langle \rangle = \overset{+}{N}(CH_3)_2 \overset{-}{Cl}$$

Crystal Violet

Gentian Violet which is used as an antiseptic is a mixture of Methyl Violet and Crystal Violet.

Phthaleins. Although not used as a dye, **phenolphthalein** is the most important member of this group of which it is typical. It is prepared by condensing phthalic anhydride and phenol in the presence of an anhydrous acid catalyst.

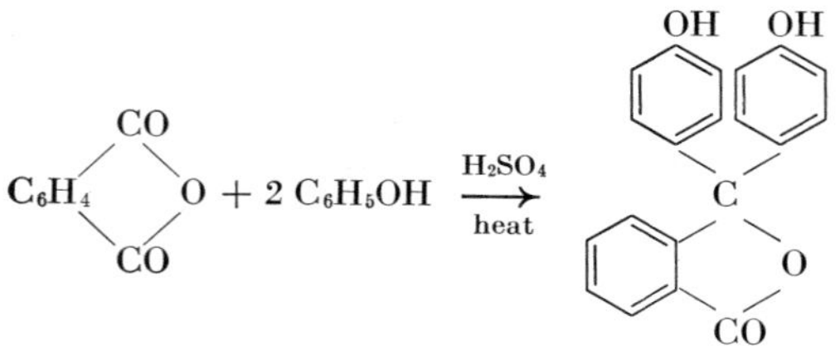

$$C_6H_4 \begin{matrix} CO \\ \\ CO \end{matrix} O + 2\ C_6H_5OH \xrightarrow[heat]{H_2SO_4}$$

Phenolphthalein
(colorless)

Although some phenolphthalein is used as an acid-base indicator (p. 492), its chief commercial importance is as a medicinal. It is the usual active ingredient of the candy-type laxatives. **Tetraiodophenolphthalein** is made by the direct iodination of phenolphthalein in alkaline solution. It is used in the

X-ray examination of the gallbladder, because it accumulates there, and the heavy iodine atoms are opaque to X-rays.

The **sulfonphthaleins** result from the condensation of phenols with sulfobenzoic anhydride.

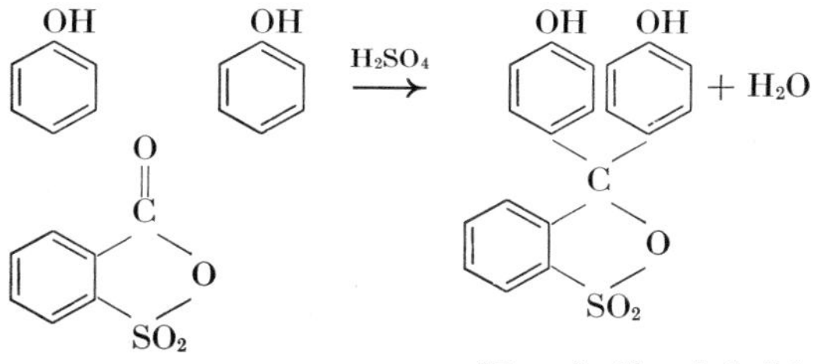

Phenolsulfonphthalein

Like phenolphthalein and its derivatives, the sulfonphthaleins are used as indicators.

Xanthenes. The xanthenes are related to the phthaleins and are made in the same way. They are derived, however, from *m*-dihydroxy compounds or *m*-hydroxy amines, which permit the formation of the xanthene (1,5-dibenzopyran) ring system. A typical example is **fluorescein** or **Uramine.**

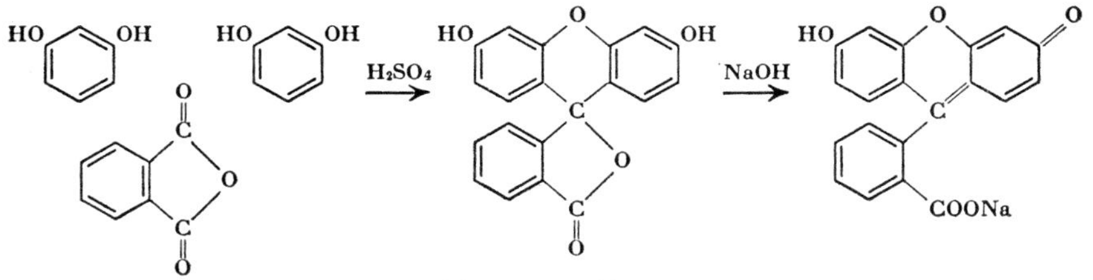

Fluorescein (Uramine)

Aqueous solutions of the sodium salt of fluorescein even at very low concentration have an intense yellow-green fluorescence when exposed to sunlight. There is distinct visual evidence of its presence at one part in 40 million parts of water. It has been used to trace the course of underground waters and to detect the source of contamination of water supplies. Production in normal times is negligible but over a million pounds was manufactured in the United States in 1943. It was supplied in packets to airmen during World War II for use as a sea marker, and many rescued men owe their lives to this dye. Other dyes that fluoresce brilliantly also found wartime use. For example planes were landed at night on aircraft carriers by signal men whose dyed flags and clothing were made to glow by illumination with ultraviolet light. Fluorescent dyes are finding many peacetime uses. An interesting application is the *optical bleach.* Colorless dyes that fluoresce in the blue are mixed with soap. The fabric is dyed in the washing process and assumes an added brightness when exposed to sunlight.

Tetrabromofluorescein, prepared by direct bromination, is known as **eosin,** and the sodium salt is the usual dye in red ink. **Mercurochrome,** an

antiseptic dye (p. 588), is the sodium salt of hydroxymercuridibromoflu-
orescein. **Erythrosin,** a red dye used as a food color and photographic sensitizer is tetraiodofluorescein.

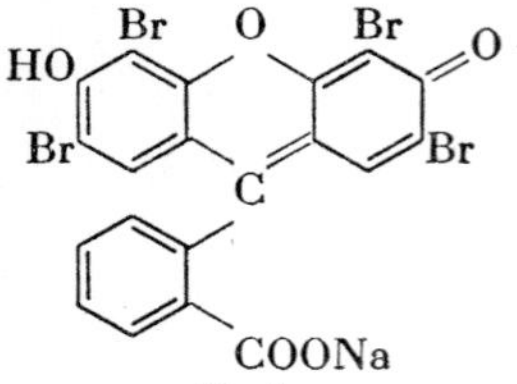

Eosin 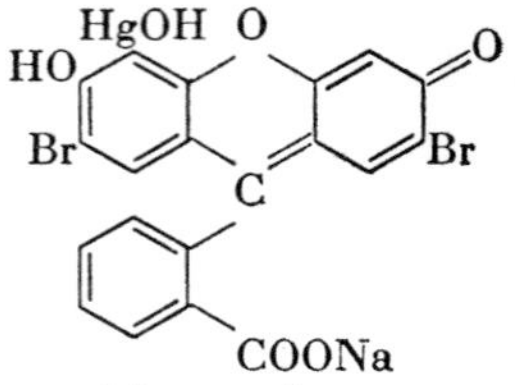   Mercurochrome

Indigoid Dyes

Indigos. The oldest known recorded use of an organic dye is that of
indigo. Egyptian mummy cloths estimated to be over four thousand years
old were dyed with it. It is present in many plants as a glucoside, *indican,*
but has been obtained in the western world from woad (*Isatis tinctoria*), and
from plants of the *Indigofera* species.

The earliest source of indigo in Europe was the woad plant, which was
known to the ancient Indo-Germanic tribes. It is believed that the art of cultivation and methods of application had spread to them from India. The growing of woad continued to modern times, although towards the end it was used
only for the fermentative reduction of indigo (p. 486). Woad was last cultivated in France in 1887, in Germany in 1910, and in England in 1931. Indigo
from the *Indigofera* species, which grows only in tropical countries, was known
to the Greeks and Romans, but was not known in Europe between the fifth
and twelfth centuries. After the twelfth century it became an important
article of commerce. Production reached a maximum of about five million
pounds in 1890, valued at about $3 per pound. In India alone, 250,000 acres
were planted to indigo.

The first synthesis of indigo from a product not derived from it was reported by Baeyer in 1880. He tried to make it commercially by another process in 1882, but it was not until 1897, eighteen years after the first synthesis of
indigo in the laboratory, that the Badische Anilin und Soda Fabrik placed
synthetic indigo on the market at a price below that of the natural product.
For the development of its process, this firm used the profits from the manufacture of synthetic alizarin (p. 487).

Two processes for the commercial synthesis of indigo have been important,
the basic reactions of both having been discovered by Heumann in 1890. One
involves cyclization of *N*-phenylglycine to indoxyl and the other of *N*-phenyl-
glycine-*o*-carboxylic acid to indoxylic acid by fusion with sodium hydroxide.
Either product on air oxidation yields indigo. The second process which starts
with naphthalene was the one decided upon by Badische.

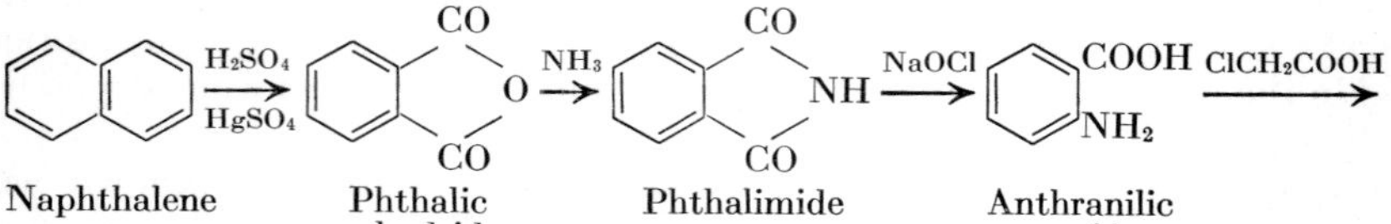

Naphthalene   Phthalic   Phthalimide   Anthranilic
                  anhydride   acid

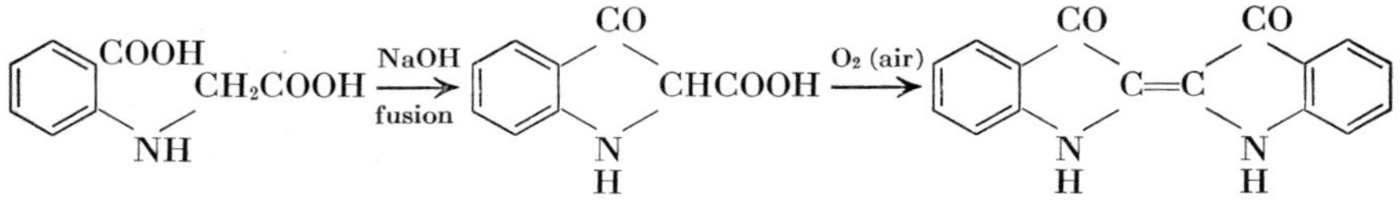

N-Phenylglycine-o-   Indoxylic acid   Indigo
carboxylic acid

It required cheap phthalic anhydride to make anthranilic acid, cheap chlorine to make chloroacetic acid and hypochlorite, and cheap caustic soda for the condensation. The first requirement was met after Sapper accidentally broke a thermometer and discovered the mercury-catalyzed oxidation of naphthalene by sulfuric acid. The need for cheap chlorine and sodium hydroxide led to the development of the electrolytic method of production.

Shortly after the Badische process went into operation, a modification of Heumann's other process, previously discarded by Badische, was developed at the Hoechst dye works. This process, which starts with aniline and chloroacetic acid, was found to be practical if sodium amide was substituted for sodium hydroxide in the cyclization step. It soon became the standard method of synthesis.

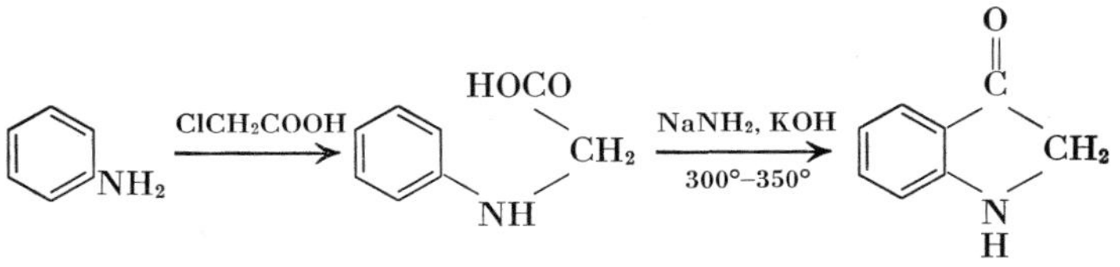

N-Phenylglycine   Indoxyl

Recent developments have been the synthesis of *N*-phenylglycine from aniline, formaldehyde, bisulfite, and sodium cyanide, or from aniline, formaldehyde, and hydrogen cyanide.

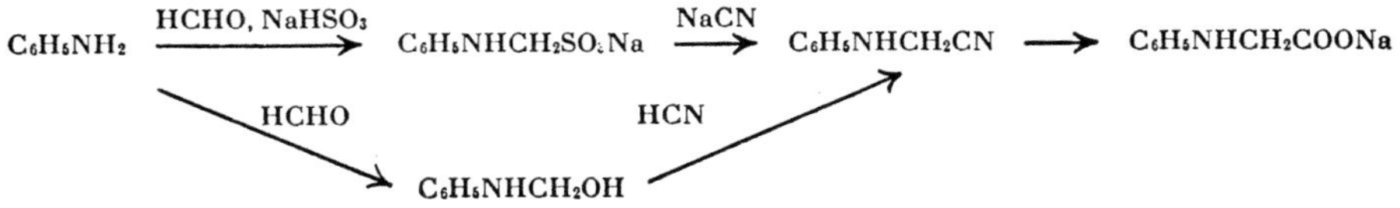

An interesting German process disclosed at the end of World War II starts with aniline and ethylene oxide. Ring closure results from dehydrogenation rather than dehydration.

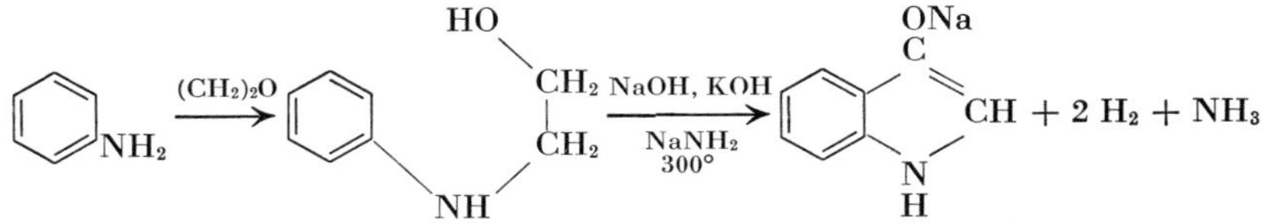

N-Phenylethanolamine   Sodium indoxyl

Indigo is a deep blue water-insoluble substance having a bronze reflex. Its application to textiles depends on its easy reduction to a bright yellow dihydroxy compound known as *indigo white*. The latter is soluble in alkali because of the acidic nature of the hydroxyl groups. The cloth is dyed in the hot indigo white solution and then exposed to air, which rapidly oxidizes the indigo white and deposits the insoluble indigo within the fiber.

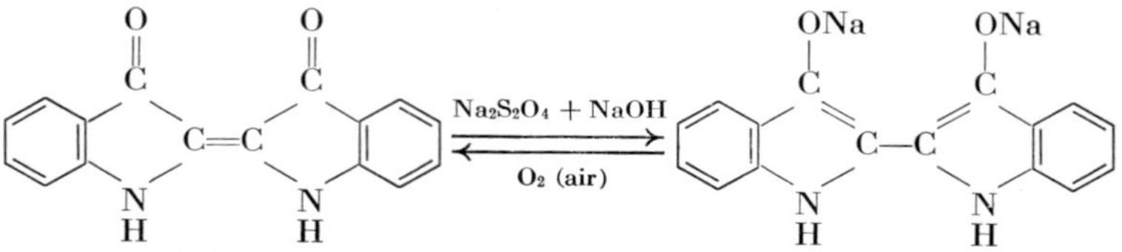

Indigo
(water-insoluble)

Indigo white
(water-soluble)

Formerly indigo was reduced by a fermentation process. The necessary bacteria to start the process were supplied by the natural fermentation of woad. Sugars, lime and indigo paste were added as needed to keep the bath at the desired strength of indigo white. Since the process was carried out in large open vats, it was called *vat dyeing*. The woad vat and other fermentation processes have been discontinued in industrialized countries, the commonly used reducing agent being alkaline sodium hydrosulfite solution. However the term *vat dye* still is retained for dyes applied in a reduced form. They usually are supplied as aqueous pastes containing 10 to 20 per cent of the insoluble dye, in order to permit easy dispersion in water for the reduction process. Indigo is fairly fast to light and washing. Its cheapness makes it still the most widely used blue dye. Production in the United States in 1948 amounted to 4.5 million pounds on a 100 per cent basis. The selling price was $1.00 per pound.

Ordinary indigo is the *trans* form. The *cis* form was unknown until 1939. It is of interest that the indigo white is adsorbed on the fiber as the *cis* form, and the product first formed on air oxidation is *cis* indigo, which goes over to the *trans* form in the solid state on the fiber.

Tyrian Purple is another natural dye used by the ancients. It is believed to have been used in Crete as early as 1600 B.C. It was derived from several species of mollusk of the family *Murex*. The term *royal purple* and the phrase *born to the purple* testify to its limited use, 9000 mollusks being required to yield one gram of dye. Modern investigations have shown that the chief constituent of the dye is 6,6'-dibromoindigo. 5,5',7,7'-Tetrabromoindigo (**Bromindigo Blue 2BD**) sold for $5.00 per pound on a 100 per cent basis, and 200,000 pounds was made in the United States in 1945.

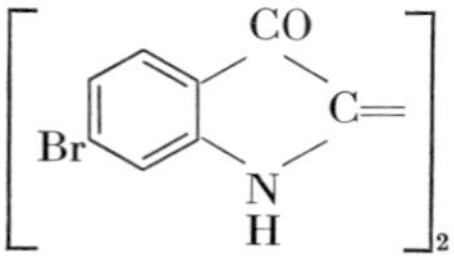

Tyrian Purple

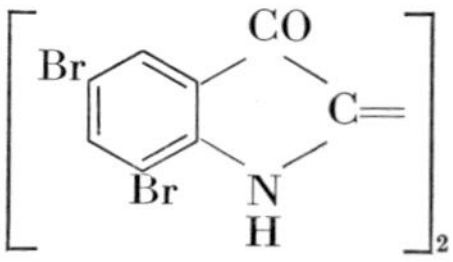

Bromindigo Blue 2BD

Anthraquinone Dyes

Mordant Dyes. The best known member of this class is **alizarin,** another natural dye known to the ancient Egyptians and Persians. It occurs in the root of the madder (*Rubia tinctorum:* Fr. *garance,* Ger. *krapp,* Ar. *alizari*). Cultivation in Europe resulted in a production of 70,000 tons of madder in 1868. Although alizarin had been isolated in 1826, all early attempts to determine its structure failed, chiefly because chemists assumed that it was a naphthalene derivative. In 1868 Graebe and Liebermann applied Baeyer's newly discovered reduction method, namely distillation with zinc dust, and obtained anthracene. From the similarity in behavior of alizarin to 5,6-dihydroxynaphthoquinone (naphthazarin), they guessed that alizarin was 1,2-dihydroxyanthraquinone. In the following year they synthesized alizarin by fusing 1,2-dibromoanthraquinone with alkali. This process was not technically useful, but in the same year patents were issued in England to Caro, Graebe, and Liebermann, and almost simultaneously to Perkin, for the production of alizarin from sodium β-anthraquinonesulfonate.

Alizarin

In contrast to the story of indigo, the process immediately was technically successful and soon drove the natural product from the market. Needless to say a considerable disturbance to the agricultural economy of Western Europe resulted. The cost of alizarin (100 per cent) dropped from $15 per pound in 1870 to $0.55 per pound in 1914.

Alizarin is *polygenetic,* yielding different colors with different mordants. Thus a magnesium mordant gives a violet color, calcium a purple-red, barium a blue, aluminum a rose-red, chromium a brown-violet, and ferrous iron a black-violet. Alizarin was used chiefly to produce the color known as *Turkey Red* on cotton mordanted with aluminum hydroxide (p. 477) in the presence of sulfated castor or olive oil. Although the dye now is obsolete, sulfated oils still are known as Turkey Red oil (p. 158).

Vat Dyes. The anthraquinones, like indigo, give on reduction dihydro derivatives that are soluble in alkali and are oxidized back to the insoluble anthraquinone on exposure to air or by chemical oxidizing agents (p. 440). The simple quinones are not fixed to animal or vegetable fibers, but the more complex compounds are.

(*a*) HYDROAZINES. This group is the oldest of the anthraquinone vat dyes. **Indanthrene Blue R,** the first anthraquinone vat dye, was discovered accidentally by Bohn in 1901. He was trying to make diphthaloylindigo by the alkaline fusion of the glycine derived from β-aminoanthraquinone. A blue vat dye was obtained which proved to be a dehydrogenation product of β-aminoanthraquinone. He found that the dye could be made by the action of alkali on β-aminoanthraquinone in the presence of an oxidizing agent.

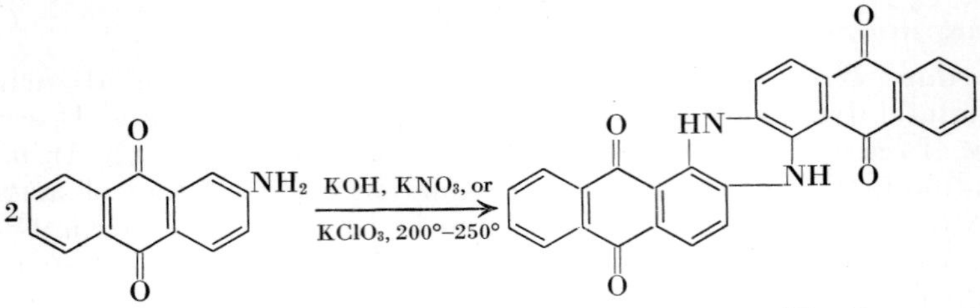

Indanthrene Blue R
(Anthraquinone Vat Blue RS)

Indanthrene Blue is one of the most stable organic compounds known. It can be heated in air at 470°, with strong hydrochloric acid at 400°, and with potassium hydroxide at 300° without decomposition. When applied to cloth, it is extremely fast to washing and light, a property shared by all anthraquinone vat colors. Indanthrene Blue and its di- and trichloro derivatives, **Anthraquinone Vat Blues 9CD** and **BCS**, are manufactured currently on a large scale.

(b) COMPLEX CARBOCYCLIC COMPOUNDS. Anthraquinone is not colored and not fixed to fibers, but complex anthraquinones are. It is not necessary that the two carbonyl groups be present in a single ring provided that they are connected through aromatic rings by a conjugated system which involves either a pyrene or perylene ring (pp. 441, 442). Such complex ring systems can be made either by dehydration or by dehydrogenation reactions.

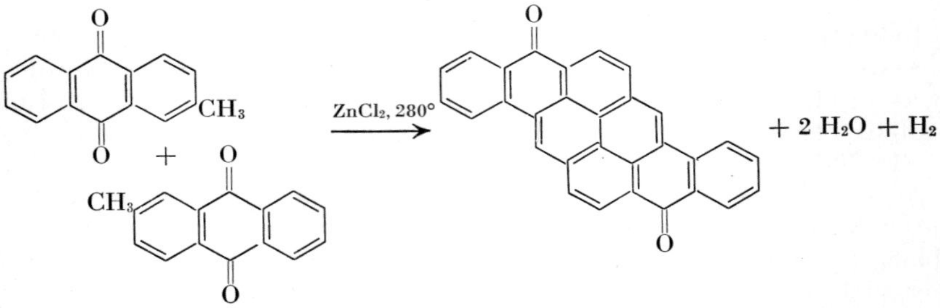

Anthraquinone Vat Golden Orange G

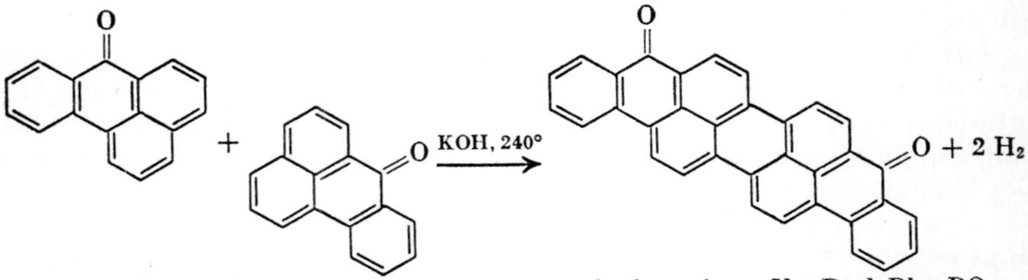

Benzanthrone   Anthraquinone Vat Dark Blue BO

The finest cotton dye, *Jade Green*, a British discovery first produced in 1920, is a dimethoxy derivative of Dark Blue BO.

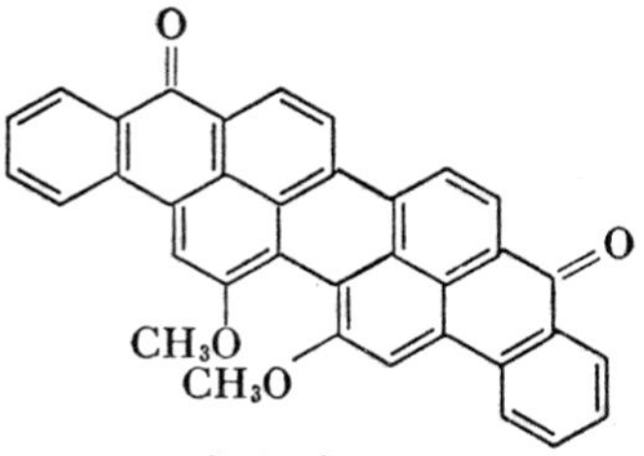

Jade Green

Almost a quarter of a million pounds (100 per cent basis) valued at $20 per pound was produced in the United States in 1948.

Anthraquinone vat dyes are applied from a hydrosulfite bath (p. 440) which must be considerably more strongly alkaline than that for dyeing indigo. Hence in the past they have been used only on cotton and viscose rayon. More recently processes have been developed for applying them to wool at a lower temperature than is used for cotton. The greater difficulty of manufacture has made the anthraquinone vats more expensive than most other dyes. Thus the average price per pound for various classes of dyes (100 per cent basis) in 1948 was sulfur, $0.29; azo, $0.88; indigoid, $1.80; anthraquinone vat, $10.90. Nevertheless, the superior fastness of anthraquinone vats to light and washing, the brilliance of their colors, and their high tinctorial power have resulted in a rapid expansion in their use in recent years. The value of their annual sales in the United States in 1948 was about $33,000,000 compared to $71,-000,000 for azo dyes and $10,000,000 for indigoid dyes.

Sulfur or Sulfide Dyes

This important class of dyes ordinarily includes those dyes made by heating organic materials with sulfur and sodium sulfide, and does not include other sulfur-containing dyes such as the thiazines, thioindigos, and the thiazoles. The first sulfur dyes were yellows and browns produced by heating sawdust, bran, or manure with sulfur. In 1893 Vidal introduced the use of derivatives of benzene and naphthalene to produce black dyes, and later blues, reds, yellows, and oranges were developed. Sulfur dyes are used only for cotton and viscose rayon, since they are applied from a sodium sulfide solution.

Little is known about the chemical structures of the sulfur dyes except that they are high molecular weight compounds, probably related to the thiazines. A structure has been assigned to **Hydron Blue R** made from carbazole, *p*-nitrosophenol, and sulfur.

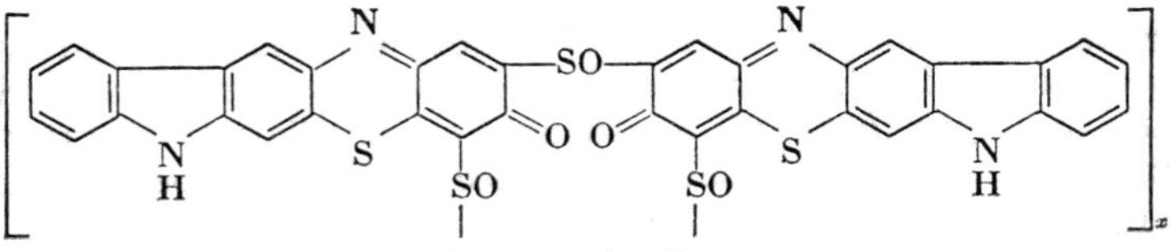

Hydron Blue R

Sulfur Black is made from 2,4-dinitrophenol. It is the cheapest dye, and the volume of production is several times that of any other single dye. Production in the United States in 1948 was over 13 million pounds valued at $0.20 per pound. **Sulfur Blue** is made from carbazole and *p*-nitrosophenol. Its manufacture is the chief use for carbazole. Blues also are made from the indophenols and from diphenylamine derivatives such as *p*-dimethylamino-*p'*-hydroxy-diphenylamine. **Sulfur Green** is made by adding copper salts to melts for blue dyes. **Sulfur Yellow, Orange,** and **Brown** are made from compounds having reactive groups in the *meta* position such as *m*-toluylenediamine.

Flavones and Flavylium Salts

These compounds are benzopyrans. They rarely are used as dyes but are distributed widely as the coloring matter of flowers.

Flavones. 2-Benzo-4-ketopyran, which is known as *chromone*, is colorless. So is 2-phenylchromone, which is called *flavone*. The presence of one or more hydroxyl groups, however, leads to colored compounds (L. *flavus* yellow).

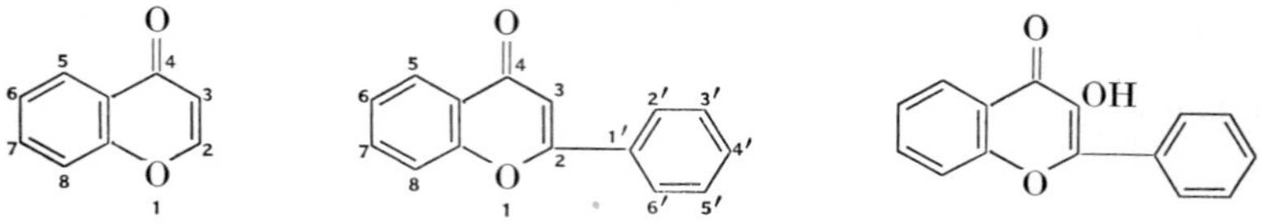

Chromone
(colorless)

Flavone
(colorless)

Flavonol
(yellow)

Quercitrin is a glucoside (at position 3) present in many plants, but obtained best from the bark of the black oak, *Quercus tinctoria*. Hydrolysis gives **quercitin** which has been used since the earliest times as a mordant dye.

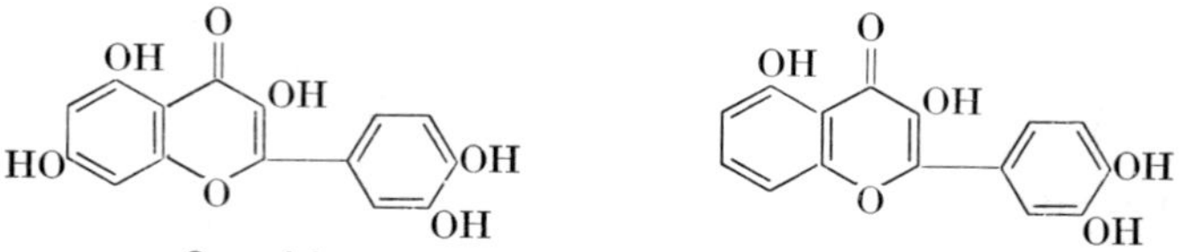

Quercitin

Morin

Rutin, the 3-rhamnoglycoside of quercitin, has been produced from the buckwheat plant, and is used in the treatment of capillary bleeding. It is present in many other plants and is the yellow coloring matter on the stems and leaves of the tomato plant. **Morin** is a sensitive reagent for aluminum.

Flavylium Salts. Reaction of an *o*-hydroxy aromatic aldehyde with an aldehyde or ketone in the presence of acid yields a benzopyran derivative known as a *benzopyrylium salt*. A probable intermediate in the reaction is cyclic hemiacetal, which is a pseudo base since it appears to be in equilibrium with the oxonium hydroxide.

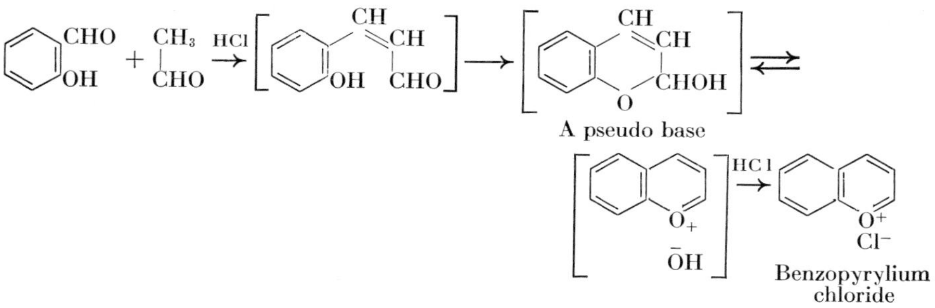

A pseudo base

Benzopyrylium chloride

Most of the red and blue pigments of flowers are derivatives of 2-phenyl-benzopyrylium salts, which are known as *flavylium salts*. They occur in the plants as glucosides known as **anthocyanins,** the aglycone being called an **anthocyanidin.** The anthocyanidins derived from natural anthocyanins belong to three groups. All have hydroxyl groups in the 3, 5, and 7 positions. **Pelargonidin chloride** (scarlet pelargonium, orange dahlia) contains an additional hydroxyl group in the 4 position; **cyanidin chloride** (red rose, blue cornflower, red dahlia, black cherry, plum) has two hydroxyl groups in the 3' and 4' positions; **delphinidin chloride** (delphinium, violet pansy, purple grape) contains three hydroxyl groups in the 3', 4', and 5' positions.

The anthocyanidins have been synthesized by the general method for the synthesis of benzopyrylium salts using the properly substituted aldehydes and ketones as intermediates.

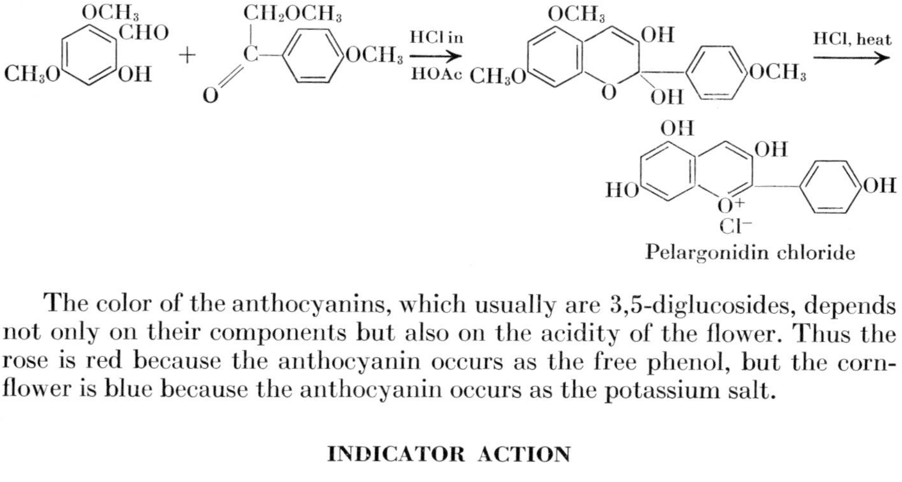

Pelargonidin chloride

The color of the anthocyanins, which usually are 3,5-diglucosides, depends not only on their components but also on the acidity of the flower. Thus the rose is red because the anthocyanin occurs as the free phenol, but the cornflower is blue because the anthocyanin occurs as the potassium salt.

INDICATOR ACTION

Many compounds have different colors at different hydrogen ion concentrations. These color changes occur because the compounds themselves are acids or bases which enter into proton transfer reactions, and the acid form has a different color than the base form. The hydrogen ion concentration at which the color change takes place depends on the strength of the compound as an acid or a base.

Methyl Orange in solutions that are more basic than pH 4.4 exists almost entirely as the yellow negative ion. In solutions more acidic than pH 3.1 it combines almost completely with a proton and forms the red dipolar ion.

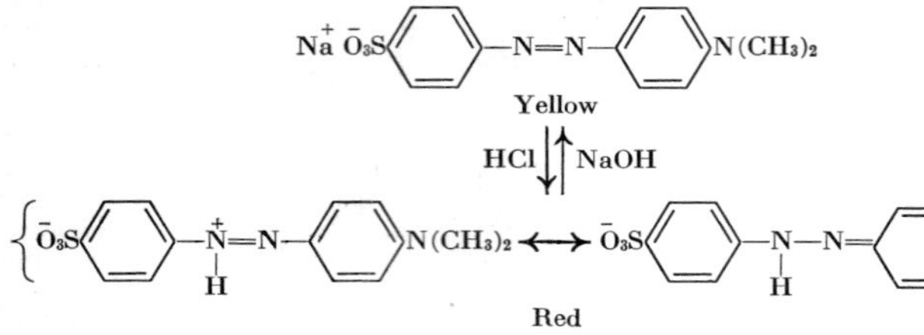

Yellow

HCl ⇅ NaOH

Red

The interaction of the unsaturation electrons over a considerable distance is easier in the dipolar ion than in the negative ion, and hence the dipolar ion absorbs at longer wavelength. This type of resonance hybridization is less important in the negative ion ($\lambda_{max.} = 460$ mμ) because the quinonoid structure would require a separation of charge in the ion.

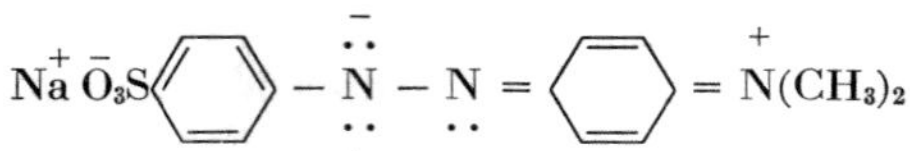

Phenolphthalein is colorless in solutions having a pH less than 8.3, where it exists almost entirely as the phenolic lactone. At pH greater than 10 it is in the form of a salt which is red. In very strongly alkaline solutions it is converted slowly to the carbinol which again is colorless.

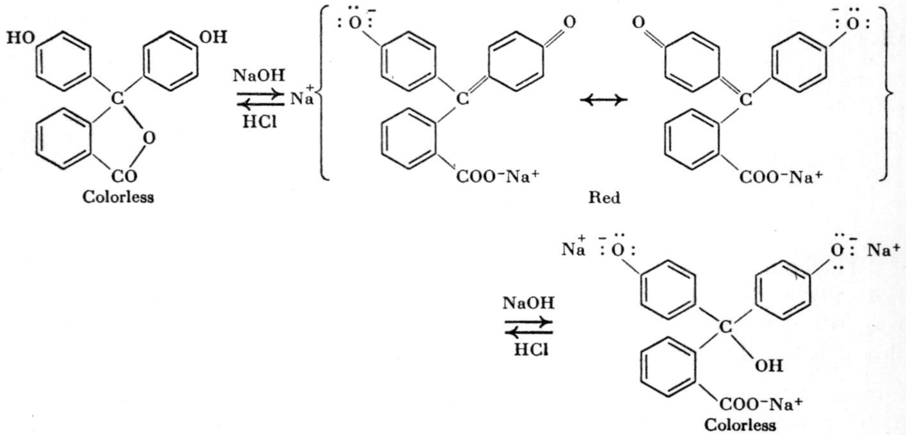

Colorless   Red

Colorless

The reason that Methyl Orange changes color on the acid side whereas phenolphthalein changes on the alkaline side is that the salt from Methyl Orange and an acid is a much stronger acid than phenolphthalein, just as an amine hydrochloride is a stronger acid than phenol. The conversion of the red ion of phenolphthalein to the colorless carbinol is characteristic of all triphenylmethane dyes, and merely is the reverse of the formation of the dye from the carbinol base (p. 481).

REVIEW QUESTIONS

1. (*a*) How do direct azo dyes for cotton differ in structure from direct azo dyes for wool and silk? (*b*) Discuss the application of mordant dyes, ice-colors, developed dyes, and vat dyes. Why are vat dyes suitable only for cotton? (*c*) What, in principle, is the difference between the dyeing of acetate rayon and other textiles?
2. Define the term *chromophore group* and give three common examples.
3. Describe and illustrate by a formula the type of chemical reaction that takes place between a metallic hydroxide mordant and a dye.
4. Give equations illustrating the preparation from coal tar crudes of each of the following dyes: Orange II; Congo Red; Malachite Green; Fluorescein; Indigo; Indanthrene Blue. To what chemical class does each belong and how is each applied?
5. (*a*) Explain the color change of Methyl Orange with change of pH. (*b*) Phenolphthalein is colorless in acid solution, red in weakly alkaline solutions, but decolorizes again in strongly alkaline solutions; explain.
6. What are the anthocyanins? What is the general structure of the anthocyanidins?

Chapter 32

DIENES, RUBBER, AND SYNTHETIC RUBBERS

DIENES

The chemical properties of dienes differ according to the relative positions of the double bonds. If the double bonds are isolated, that is separated by two or more single bonds, each double bond reacts independently, and the reactions are no different from those when only a single double bond is present. If both double bonds are attached to a single carbon atom, they are known as *cumulative* or *twin double* bonds and readily undergo rearrangement. Hydrocarbons having a pair of twin double bonds are known as *allenes* after the name of the first member of the series, $CH_2{=}C{=}CH_2$. If two double bonds are separated by a single bond, they are said to be *conjugated* and exhibit a still different type of chemical behavior.

Allenes

Allene or **propadiene** is the simplest hydrocarbon containing two double bonds and can be made by a series of reactions from glycerol.

$$
\begin{array}{ccccccc}
CH_2OH & & CH_2Br & & CH_2 & & CH_2 \\
| & \xrightarrow{HBr} & | & \xrightarrow{\text{Alc. KOH}} & \| & \xrightarrow[\text{alcohol}]{\text{Zn in}} & \| \\
CHOH & & CHBr & & C\,Br & & C \\
| & & | & & | & & \| \\
CH_2OH & & CH_2Br & & CH_2Br & & CH_2 \\
& & & & & & \text{Allene}
\end{array}
$$

Its most characteristic behavior is reaction with sodium to give sodium methylacetylide.

$$
CH_2{=}C{=}CH_2 \xrightarrow[\text{ether}]{\text{Na in}} CH_3C{\equiv}CNa
$$

The greater stability of the acetylenic linkage over the allene structure is indicated by the fact that dihalides having the halogen atoms on adjacent carbon atoms yield chiefly acetylenes on reaction with alcoholic alkali (p. 109). For example the gas obtained by the reaction of propylene bromide with hot alcoholic potassium hydroxide solution is about 95 per cent methylacetylene and 5 per cent allene.

Conjugated Dienes

The most important conjugated diene is **1,3-butadiene.** Because of its technical use in the manufacture of synthetic rubbers, the methods of preparation are deferred to page 500. A characteristic chemical behavior of conjugated dienes is 1,4 addition. Thus if one mole of bromine is added to 1,3-butadiene, the chief product is 1,4-dibromo-2-butene.

$$CH_2{=}CH{-}CH{=}CH_2 + Br_2 \longrightarrow \underset{\underset{\text{80 per cent}}{Br}}{CH_2{-}CH{=}CH{-}CH_2} + \underset{\underset{\text{20 per cent}}{Br \quad Br}}{CH_2{=}CH{-}CH{-}CH_2}$$

This behavior is in accord with the stepwise mechanism postulated for halogen addition (p. 100).

$$CH_2{=}CH{-}CH_2{=}CH_2 \underset{Br^-}{\overset{Br_2}{\rightleftarrows}} \left\{ \underset{+}{CH_2{=}CH{-}CH{-}CH_2Br} \longleftrightarrow \underset{+}{CH_2{-}CH{=}CH{-}CH_2Br} \right\} \overset{Br_2}{\rightarrow}$$

$$BrCH_2{-}CH{=}CH{-}CH_2Br + \overset{-}{Br}$$

Conjugated dienes also add 1,4 to the double bond of maleic anhydride (p. 546), a reaction that can be used for their quantitative estimation.

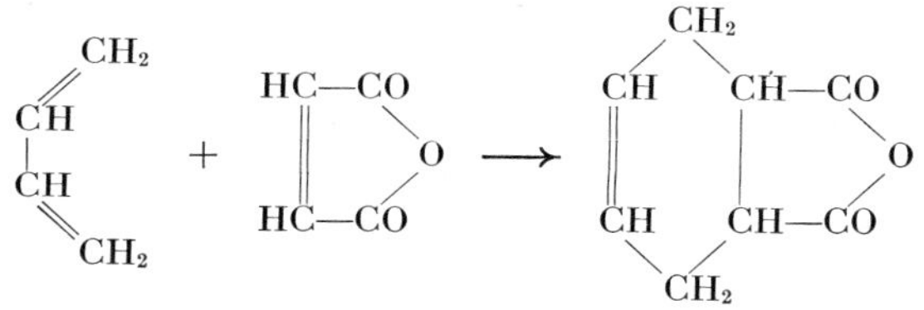

The most important reaction of conjugated dienes is their polymerization by 1,4 addition to rubber-like products under the influence of catalysts of the free-radical type (p. 502).

$$x\ CH_2{=}CH{-}CH{=}CH_2 \xrightarrow[\text{catalyst}]{\text{Free-radical}} ({-}CH_2{-}CH{=}CH{-}CH_2{-})_x$$

RUBBER

Sources

Rubber was introduced to Europe shortly after the discovery of America. Early Spanish explorers found that South and Central American natives used the substance to waterproof household utensils and to make balls for their games. The name *rubber* was given to it by Joseph Priestley, who used it to rub out pencil marks.

Rubber is distributed extensively in the plant kingdom. It usually occurs as a colloidal solution in a white fluid known as *latex*. If the milky fluid from goldenrod or dandelion is rubbed between the fingers, a small ball of rubber soon is formed. Many such sources have been investigated, but the principal commercial production is from the rubber tree, *Hevea braziliensis*, which accounted for 98 per cent of the world production of 1.4 million tons in 1940. The tree is a native of the Amazon valley, but commercial production has been almost entirely from plantations in the Far East.

Latex is not the sap of the rubber tree. It occurs in microscopic tubules distributed throughout the plant and is obtained from those in the cortex layer between the bark and the cambium layer. A sloping V-shaped incision is made one third of the way around the trunk starting 3 feet above the ground, and the latex is drained into a cup attached to the trunk at the end of the incision. Since there is no flow in the tubules, a thin slice must be removed every other day to expose a fresh surface, the cut being lowered about 1 inch per month. From 15 to 30 cc. of latex containing 35 per cent rubber is obtained per tapping. A single worker can tap 350 to 400 trees per day.

The latex is diluted to 15 per cent rubber and coagulated by the addition of salt and acetic acid. The precipitate is rolled into sheets, washed, and smoked to preserve it against mold. This product is dark brown. In the preparation of the light colored crepe rubber, bisulfite is added before precipitation to prevent oxidation, and the product is washed more thoroughly to remove the serum and prevent spoilage.

Increasing quantities of rubber are shipped as latex, although the total amounted to less than 50,000 tons in 1940. For shipment the latex is stabilized by the addition of ammonia and concentrated to 60 to 75 per cent solids in one of three ways: (*1*) by centrifuging, (*2*) by *creaming* in which the addition of a small amount of a hydrated colloid such as Irish moss or gum tragacanth causes a more concentrated layer to separate, or (*3*) by evaporation.

Small amounts of rubber are produced from the guayule shrub, *Parthenium argentatum*, a native of northern Mexico and southwestern United States. The rubber occurs as particles throughout the plant and is separated by grinding the whole plant, allowing it to ret in water, and skimming off the rubber particles which float to the top. In recent years extensive breeding experiments have been undertaken and attempts made to grow it economically in the United States. Guayule has a much higher resin content (18 to 25 per cent) than plantation rubber (1 to 4 per cent), but for certain purposes a higher resin content than that present in plantation rubber is desirable. Hence guayule always has been in demand for blending purposes. It can be deresinated if conditions bring it into direct competition with natural rubber.

Constitution

Crude plantation rubber contains 2 to 4 per cent protein and 1 to 4 per cent resins, the latter being the substances soluble in acetone. The remainder is the *rubber hydrocarbon*, which has the empirical formula C_5H_8 as established by Faraday in 1826. Many attempts have been made to determine its molecular weight. One recent investigation indicates that 80 per cent of the molecules have molecular weights in the range 60,000 to 190,000, and hence contain 1000 to 3000 C_5H_8 units. Other investigations lead to average values of 250,000 to 350,000, or 3700 to 5100 C_5H_8 units.

Destructive distillation of rubber yields among other products a hydrocarbon called **isoprene,** which has the molecular formula C_5H_8 and is 2-methyl-1,3-butadiene, $CH_2{=}C(CH_3)CH{=}CH_2$. The fact that isoprene reverts gradually to a rubber-like product led to the view that rubber is a polymerization product of isoprene. Rubber is unsaturated, adding one mole of hydrogen catalytically, one mole of bromine, or one mole of hydrogen chloride for each five carbon atoms. Hence one double bond is present for each isoprene unit. Harries [1] in 1904 prepared the ozonide of rubber and isolated from the hydrolysis products levulinic aldehyde and levulinic acid. A more recent

---

[1] Carl Dietrich Harries (1866–1923), professor at the University of Kiel. He is known for his extensive work on the ozonation of unsaturated organic compounds.

painstaking quantitative investigation of the products of ozonolysis accounted for 95 per cent of the carbon content of the rubber molecule, and 90 per cent of the products isolated can be considered as derived from levulinic aldehyde. These results leave little doubt that the rubber hydrocarbon is a linear polymer of isoprene having the structure first postulated by Pickles in 1910. The nature of the end groups has not been determined.

$$\left[\substack{-CH_2C=CHCH_2(CH_2C=CHCH_2)_x \\ CH_3 \qquad\qquad CH_3} \substack{CH_2C=CHCH_2- \\ CH_3} \right] \xrightarrow{\text{Ozonolysis}} (x+2) \substack{O=CHCH_2CH_2C=O \\ CH_3}$$

Rubber hydrocarbon Levulinic aldehyde

Vulcanization

Because there is little if any cross-linkage of the chains of the molecules, rubber is thermoplastic and becomes soft and sticky on heating. When cooled to low temperatures it becomes hard and brittle. These properties were undesirable even in the early use of rubber, which was chiefly for the waterproofing of textiles. In 1834 Charles Goodyear began experiments attempting to overcome this disadvantage. Mixtures with sulfur had been experimented with previously, and in 1839, while attempting to improve these mixtures, Goodyear [2] accidentally dropped one of his preparations on a hot stove, thus discovering the process which he called **vulcanization.** Development of the process led to the production of a material with much greater toughness and elasticity than natural rubber, and one which withstood relatively high temperatures without softening and which retained its elasticity and flexibility at low temperatures.

Vulcanization is a chemical reaction of the rubber hydrocarbon with sulfur in which sulfur adds to the double bonds. Addition takes place in such a way that the chains of rubber molecules are tied together giving a large cross-linked molecule.

$$\substack{[-CH_2C(CH_3)=CHCH_2-]_x \\ \\ [-CH_2C(CH_3)=CHCH_2-]_x} + 2S \longrightarrow \substack{\left[-CH_2C(CH_3)CHCH_2-\right]_x \\ S \\ \left[-CH_2C(CH_3)CHCH_2-\right]_x \\ S-}$$

As little as 0.5 per cent of sulfur or 1 per cent of that necessary to saturate the double bonds will effect a cure. Commercial rubber is either low in sulfur (1 to 3 per cent) for soft rubber, or high in sulfur (23 to 35 per cent) for hard rubber or ebonite. Rubbers containing intermediate amounts are intractable and of no value. Since the amount of sulfur necessary to saturate the double bonds is 32 per cent, hard rubber has the maximum amount of cross-linking.

Vulcanizing agents other than sulfur or sulfur-containing compounds are known. When thin sheets of rubber are exposed to light sufficient cross-linking takes place to produce the same effect as vulcanization. Rubber vulcanized

[2] Charles Goodyear (1800–1860) was a New England inventor. His first patent was granted in 1844 and was followed in subsequent years by over sixty more. Many honors were bestowed on Goodyear, but he was kept in poverty because of litigations arising from infringements of his patents.

with certain aromatic nitro compounds is used as an insulating coating for copper wire. It has the advantage that it does not cause discoloration of the copper.

Accelerators and Other Additives

Many types of compounds, both inorganic and organic, will increase the rate of vulcanization, and permit vulcanization to be carried out rapidly at a lower temperature with less sulfur. These compounds are known as **accelerators.** Some of the more important accelerators in current use are zinc butyl xanthate (ZBX, p. 250), 2-mercaptobenzothiazole (*Captax,* p. 241), diphenylguanidine (*D.P.G.,* p. 371), tetramethylthiuramdisulfide (*Tuads,* p. 251), and the piperidine salt of 1-piperidinedithiocarboxylic acid (*Pip-pip*), $C_5H_{10}N\overset{-}{C}SS\overset{+}{H}_2NC_5H_{10}$ (pp. 455, 251). More recently compounds prepared by the oxidative condensation of 2-mercaptobenzothiazole and aliphatic amines have been developed which are especially useful for milled rubber goods and synthetic rubbers.

$$\underset{\substack{\text{2-Mercapto-}\\\text{benzothiazole}}}{\overset{S}{\underset{N}{\bigcirc\!\!\diagdown}}}\text{CSH} + \underset{\substack{\text{Cyclo-}\\\text{hexylamine}}}{H_2NC_6H_{11}} \overset{\text{NaOCl}}{\longrightarrow} \overset{S}{\underset{N}{\bigcirc\!\!\diagdown}}\text{CSNHC}_6H_{11} + \text{NaCl} + H_2O$$

Most organic accelerators work best in the presence of **accelerator activators,** the most commonly used being zinc oxide.

One of the outstanding developments in the rubber industry has been the use of **antioxidants** (p. 582) to prolong the life of rubber articles. The ageing of rubber is due to the reaction of the double bonds with oxygen, with subsequent scission of the double bond and reduction in the molecular weight. This reaction is autocatalytic and can be prevented by the addition of secondary aromatic amines such as phenyl-α-naphthylamine. The aldehyde-aromatic amine condensation products, such as the mixture of condensation products from acetaldehyde or *n*-butyraldehyde and aniline (p. 365), not only are antioxidants but also have an accelerating action.

Reinforcing agents increase the stiffness, tensile strength, and resistance to abrasion. *Carbon black* is used most for this purpose, production in the United States reaching 500,000 tons in 1945. Recently a superfine silica powder has been introduced called *carbon white,* which is said to be more effective in increasing tear and abrasion resistance, and which does not interfere with translucence or added color. **Fillers** such as barium sulfate, calcium carbonate, and diatomaceous earth decrease the strength and are used to reduce cost of articles where strength is not important. **Softeners** such as fatty acids or pine oil also may be added.

Manufacturing Operations

Rubber is compounded by incorporating the various ingredients on mixing rolls, an operation known as *milling.* The rubber is squeezed through two large metal rolls rotating slowly in opposite directions at different speeds. The rubber mass is so handled that it encircles one of the rolls and is passed continuously between them. The rubber thus is subjected to a shearing action, which causes it to become warm. Air oxidation takes place, the chain length of the rubber molecules is reduced, and the mass becomes sticky and plastic. The rubber is said to be *broken down* or *masticated* by this operation. In this condition the various solids and liquids that are to be added to the rubber can be worked in on the rolls. The thoroughly mixed compounded rubber is cut from the roll and rolled into sheets. The sheets are used to line a mold which then is subjected to heat and pressure to form the finished product.

Latex can be compounded with the various finely powdered ingredients of the rubber mix by simple mixing. Articles are shaped by gelation on a mold and then vulcanized. The mix also can be deposited by electrodeposition. Thread can be spun from latex into a coagulating bath. The use of latex is increasing, because expensive heavy machinery and high power consumption are not required in the manufacturing operations. Moreover the products are stronger because the rubber is not broken down in a milling operation.

SYNTHETIC RUBBERS

Historical

Isoprene was obtained first by the distillation of rubber by Gregory in 1835. In 1879 Bourchardt reported the polymerization of isoprene to an elastic product which again gave isoprene on distillation. Continuously since then attempts have been made to develop a commercial process for the synthesis of rubber. For years some of the most able English and German chemists, both industrial and academic, vied with each other in their efforts to solve the problem. In 1910 Harries discovered the catalytic effect of sodium on the polymerization of isoprene and found that homologs of isoprene such as butadiene and 2,3-dimethylbutadiene also polymerized to rubber-like products. Although the synthetic rubber industry usually is thought to be a recent development, and in some ways rightly so, it is of interest that Matthews and Perkin, Jr., had worked out a process based on sodium polymerization in 1910, and the Badische Company exhibited a pair of automobile tires made of synthetic rubber at the Eighth International Congress of Pure and Applied Chemistry held in New York in 1912.

There are two principal reasons for the slow technical development of synthetic rubber. First it was practically impossible to compete with a product whose price ranged from $0.03 to $3.00 per pound, and second the synthetic product was not so satisfactory as the natural product for most uses. Hence in the past, synthetic rubbers have been used only when a nation has been excluded from world markets either by war or by a controlled economy. By the end of World War I Germany was producing 165 tons per month of *methyl rubber* from dimethylbutadiene starting with acetone, but the product was not good for general purposes. Research was continued after the war and better products known as *Buna* rubbers (contraction of *butadiene* and *natrium*) were developed. Under the controlled economies of Germany and Russia, they were manufactured on a large scale. The German Minister of Economy boasted in 1936 that the cost was only 60 to 80 per cent higher than the market price of natural rubber, and the Russians claimed that their product was cheaper in terms of man-hours of labor. The first synthetic product to compete with natural rubber in a free economy was *neoprene*, a purely American development. It did not result from direct attempts to produce a synthetic rubber but from Nieuwland's purely academic investigations of acetylene.[3] This product was competitive solely because of its superior properties for certain purposes, the introductory price in 1932 being $1.00 per pound, when rubber was selling for $0.15 per pound.

With the loss of the East Indies and the Malay Peninsula as a source of rubber during World War II, American chemists and chemical engineers were faced with the problem of creating a synthetic rubber industry within two years to replace the total output of 9 million acres of plantations employing over 2 million people and resulting from 60 years of development. Fortunately far-sighted industries had built experimental pilot plants before the war, and the remarkable feat was accomplished. By 1945 total synthetic rubber production was at the rate of 700,000 tons per year. The synthetic industry now is firmly established and although natural rubber has regained most of its original market, it never again will dominate the market and probably eventually will become of minor importance.

Manufacture

Actually there is no synthetic true rubber. Even the product made by the polymerization of isoprene has properties different from those of natural rubber. The latter has an entirely *cis* configuration at the double bonds (p. 255), whereas the synthetic product probably is the equilibrium mixture of both *cis* and *trans* configurations. An attempt has been made to introduce the term *elastomers* for all substances having rubber-like properties, but the term *synthetic rubbers* is used most frequently. Although a synthetic true rubber is unknown, many different synthetic products are made, each of which has its own desirable characteristics that frequently are superior to those of rubber.

Butadiene Syntheses. The synthetic rubbers produced in largest amounts are based on butadiene, and a number of technical processes for its manufacture have been developed.

1. FROM ALCOHOL. This process was developed in Russia by Ostromislensky and Lebedev and in an improved form was used to produce much of the synthetic rubber made in the United States during World War II. The Russian process passed alcohol vapor over a silica catalyst at a high temperature, which caused simultaneous dehydrogenation, condensation and dehydration, but the yields were unsatisfactory.

$$2\ C_2H_5OH \xrightarrow[\text{heat}]{SiO_2} CH_2{=}CH{-}CH{=}CH_2 + 2\ H_2O + H_2$$

The American improvement consisted in dehydrogenating alcohol first to acetaldehyde (p. 161) and then causing another mole of alcohol to react using a silica catalyst containing 2 per cent of tantalum or zirconium oxide.

$$C_2H_5OH + CH_3CHO \xrightarrow{SiO_2-TaO_2\ (375°)} CH_2{=}CH{-}CH{=}CH_2 + 2\ H_2O$$

[3] Julius Arthur Nieuwland (1879–1936), American professor of chemistry at the University of Notre Dame. Besides being well known for his investigations of the chemistry of acetylene, he was a distinguished botanist.

An alcohol-aldehyde ratio of 2.5 to 1 was used and the unreacted material recycled. The yield of butadiene was 64 per cent. At least 25 co-products are formed. The C_4 fraction is 98 per cent butadiene.

2. FROM PETROLEUM. In the thermal cracking of naphtha or light oil at 700°–760° about 0.5 to 0.8 per cent is converted to butadiene. Better yields are obtained by dehydrogenating butane or butene.

$$CH_3CH_2CH_2CH_3 \xrightarrow[600°]{MgO-Fe_2O_3-CuO-K_2O} CH_3CH=CHCH_2 \xrightarrow[650°]{MgO-Fe_2O_3-CuO-K_2O} CH_2=CHCH=CH_2$$

The conversion reaches 30 per cent per pass. The chief problem is the purification of the product. Selective solubility in furfural or in ammoniacal cuprous acetate solutions, and azeotropic distillation with ammonia have been used.

During the war it was necessary to produce alcohol from grain, and at a cost of $0.60 per gallon for alcohol, production of butadiene from petroleum was much cheaper. However at the time that the first plants were built, technical knowledge for the alcohol process was farther advanced than for the petroleum process. Moreover the butane fractions were required for the synthesis of high octane gasoline (p. 51). It is estimated that under normal conditions alcohol can be made for $0.10 per gallon from ethylene, or cheaper as a co-product of the Fischer-Tropsch synthesis (p. 56). At this price it would be at least competitive with butane and butene as raw material.

3. FROM ACETYLENE. Germany, deficient in both petroleum and carbohydrates, based her syntheses on acetylene (p. 112). The process most used consisted of a series of conventional reactions (pp. 110, 168).

$$HC\equiv CH \xrightarrow[HgSO_4]{H_2O, H_2SO_4,} CH_3CHO \xrightarrow{Dil. NaOH} CH_3CHOHCH_2CHO \xrightarrow{H_2, Ni}$$

Aldol

$$CH_3CHOHCH_2CH_2OH \xrightarrow[heat]{NaH_2PO_4,} CH_2=CHCH=CH_2$$

1,3-Butanediol

By the end of the war the Reppe process was being used. A mixture of acetylene, steam, and 30 per cent formaldehyde was passed at 110° and 45 pounds pressure over silica coated with cuprous acetylide. The acetylene added to the formaldehyde to give 1,4-dihydroxy-2-butyne. A sufficient excess of acetylene was used to convert all of the formaldehyde to the diol. The aqueous solution of diol was hydrogenated to 1,4-butanediol, which was dehydrated first to tetrahydrofuran and then to butadiene.

$$HC\equiv CH + 2\ HCHO \xrightarrow[110°, 45\ lbs.]{Cu_2C_2\ on\ SiO_2,} HOCH_2C\equiv CCH_2OH \xrightarrow{H_2, Ni}$$

1,4-Dihydroxy-2-butyne

$$HO(CH_2)_4OH \xrightarrow[270°]{H_3PO_4} \begin{matrix} CH_2—CH_2 \\ | \quad\quad | \\ CH_2 \quad CH_2 \\ \diagdown\ /\ \\ O \end{matrix} \xrightarrow{H_2SO_4} CH_2=CH—CH=CH_2$$

1,4-Butanediol Tetrahydrofuran

The chief danger of the process is the handling of exothermic acetylene under pressure. Contrary to previous views it is not sensitive to impurities, but all contact with copper or copper alloys must be avoided. Pipe lines must be kept short and all free space reduced to a minimum. No pipes should be larger than 35 mm. diameter, all larger pipes being filled with small pipes. Under these conditions local explosions may take place but no detonation occurs. The nonexplosive pressure that can be attained increases with the amount of diluent, such as steam or nitrogen, that is present.

Buna S or GRS, GRS-10, and Cold Rubber. The useful butadiene rubbers are copolymers with other compounds. That made in the largest quantity is a copolymer of three parts of butadiene and one part of styrene (p. 425). Sodium polymerization, which requires three months for completion, no longer is used, all polymerizations being carried out in aqueous emulsions. The butadiene and styrene are emulsified with soap, and a peroxide catalyst (hydrogen peroxide, ammonium or potassium persulfate, or sodium perborate) is added, together with a modifier such as dodecylmercaptan. A latex of the polymer is formed which is precipitated by the addition of salt and acetic acid.

Since 1,3-dienes react largely in the 1,4 positions, the principal repeating unit in the butadiene-styrene copolymer may be represented by the structure

$$\left[-CH_2CH=CHCH_2CH_2CH=CHCH_2CH_2CH=CHCH_2CH_2CH- \atop \underset{C_6H_5}{|} \right]_x$$

However some 1,2 addition also takes place giving rise to some units having a structure such as

$$\left[-CH_2CH=CHCH_2CH_2CHCH_2CH=CHCH_2CH_2CH- \atop {\underset{CH_2}{\overset{CH}{\underset{||}{|}}} \qquad \qquad \underset{C_6H_5}{|}} \right]$$

Because of the unsaturated side chain, this unit can cause branching and cross-linking of chains.

When soap is used as an emulsifier, the product lacks *building tack*, the ability of layers of unvulcanized rubber mix to cohere and retain cohesion after vulcanization. This property is extremely important in the manufacture of rubber articles. A great improvement in this respect results if the sodium salt of disproportionated abietic acid (p. 566) is used as an emulsifying agent instead of soap. The resulting product is called **GRS 10.** More recently it has been found that peroxide-catalyzed polymerizations proceed much faster in the presence of oxidation-reduction systems. Using cumene hydroperoxide (p. 573) as the catalyst, fructose as a reducing agent, and ferric pyrophosphate as an activator, it is possible to bring about the production of GRS at a practical rate at 5° compared with the previously used 50°. The product, known as *cold rubber*, has improved tensile strength, elongation, and processibility.

Buna N or GRN. This product is a copolymer of butadiene and acrylonitrile, $CH_2=CHCN$ (p. 537). It is hard to mill and its light resistance is poor, but it has good resistance to oil.

Butyl Rubber or GRI. The polymerization of isobutylene (p. 43) gives a viscous to rubber-like product that is completely saturated and hence cannot be vulcanized. If it is copolymerized at −100° with a small amount of a diene such as butadiene or isoprene, one double bond remains for each molecule of the diene used. By using 1 to 2 per cent of the diene, sufficient double bonds are present to give on vulcanization a rubber-like product that is practically saturated and hence has good resistance to chemicals and oxidation. Moreover it is very impermeable to gases, and was used during World War II for automobile inner tubes. Its other physical properties are only fairly satisfactory.

Neoprene or GRM. During his investigations of the chemistry of acetylene Nieuwland discovered the formation of a dimer, **vinylacetylene,** by the action of cuprous salts. Carothers[4] found that the dimer adds hydrogen chloride to yield 2-chloro-1,3-butadiene, known as **chloroprene.**

$$2 \text{ HC}\equiv\text{CH} \xrightarrow[\text{NH}_4\text{Cl}]{\text{Cu}_2\text{Cl}_2} \underset{\text{Vinylacetylene}}{\text{H}_2\text{C}=\text{CH}-\text{C}\equiv\text{CH}} \xrightarrow{\text{HCl}} \underset{\underset{\text{Cl}}{|}}{\text{H}_2\text{C}=\text{CH}-\text{C}=\text{CH}_2}$$

2-Chloro-1,3-butadiene
(chloroprene)

Polymerization of chloroprene takes place rapidly, being complete in 10 days even in the absence of a catalyst. This product is known as **neoprene.** Without vulcanization it resembles soft vulcanized rubber, being nonplastic and unworkable on the mill. If polymerization is allowed to proceed only partially, an elastic product is obtained which can be stabilized by the addition of phenyl-β-naphthylamine as an antioxidant. This material can be worked on rolls for the addition of other substances. The properties are enhanced by the addition of metallic oxides, but carbon black does not greatly increase its strength. The plastic mix is molded into the desired article, and the polymerization completed by heating. Neoprene latex can be made by allowing chloroprene emulsions to polymerize.

Neoprene is a good general purpose rubber, but its high cost of manufacture has limited its use to those applications that require its unique properties, such as resistance to oils, chemicals, air, light, heat, and flame. The decontrolled price in 1948 was $0.32 per pound, a considerable reduction from its introductory price of $1.00, but still higher than the free market price of $0.16 for natural rubber and the controlled price of $0.18 for GRS rubber. A number of different neoprenes are on the market which presumably are modified by copolymerization.

Thiokols. Thiokols are made by condensing a polychloro compound with sodium polysulfide. **Thiokol A** is made from ethylene chloride.

$$(x+1) \text{ ClCH}_2\text{CH}_2\text{Cl} + x \text{ Na}_2\text{S}_4 \longrightarrow \underset{\underset{\text{S}^- \quad \text{S}^-}{|\quad\;\;|}}{\text{Cl}(\text{CH}_2\text{CH}_2-\text{S}_+-\text{S}_+-)_x\text{CH}_2\text{CH}_2\text{Cl}} + 2x \text{ NaCl}$$

Thiokol A

---

[4] Wallace Hume Carothers (1896–1937), American-trained chemist and director of a laboratory for fundamental research in organic chemistry at the du Pont Experimental Station. In addition to his work on neoprene he conducted an investigation of the reactions of polyfunctional molecules which led to the discovery of Nylon (p. 544).

Thiokol B and **Thiokol D** start with β-chloroethyl ether.

$$\text{ClCH}_2\text{CH}_2\text{OCH}_2\text{CH}_2\text{Cl} \xrightarrow{\text{Na}_2\text{S}_4} \text{Cl(CH}_2\text{CH}_2\text{OCH}_2\text{CH}_2\text{—S}_+\text{—S}_+\text{—)}_x\text{CH}_2\text{CH}_2\text{OCH}_2\text{CH}_2\text{Cl} \xrightarrow{\text{NaOH}}$$

β-Chloroethyl ether

$$\overset{\displaystyle |}{\underset{\displaystyle \text{S}^-}{}} \quad \overset{\displaystyle |}{\underset{\displaystyle \text{S}^-}{}}$$

Thiokol B

$$\text{Cl(CH}_2\text{CH}_2\text{OCH}_2\text{CH}_2\text{—S—S—)}_x\text{CH}_2\text{CH}_2\text{OCH}_2\text{CH}_2\text{Cl}$$

Thiokol D

The thiokols show the best resistance of any synthetic rubbers to oils, but their physical properties are poor. They were used to line underground concrete storage tanks for liquid fuels during the war, but find their principal peacetime use as gasket material.

REVIEW QUESTIONS

1. How do the reactions of conjugated dienes differ from those of nonconjugated dienes?
2. What is the principal source of natural rubber? How is it obtained and prepared for market?
3. Give the arguments for the accepted structure of the rubber hydrocarbon. How does it differ from the hydrocarbon of gutta-percha and balata?
4. Discuss the chemistry of vulcanization. What is meant by the term accelerator; antioxidant; reinforcing agent; milling?
5. What procedures are used for the production of butadiene?
6. What are the chief differences in constitution between GRS, neoprene, butyl rubber, and Buna N?

Chapter 33

CHLORINATED AND FLUORINATED ALIPHATIC HYDROCARBONS

CHLORINATED HYDROCARBONS

Over 1.6 million tons of chlorine was produced in the United States in 1948, and 80 per cent was used for the preparation of chlorinated organic compounds. The total production of noncyclic halogenated hydrocarbons alone amounted to 888,000 tons in 1948 and was valued at over $177,000,000. Both substitution and addition reactions are used in their preparation.

The **chlorination of methane** at one time was investigated extensively for the production of methyl chloride to be used as a source of methyl alcohol, but these investigations were discontinued with the advent of the synthesis of methyl alcohol from carbon monoxide and hydrogen (p. 66). More recently, chlorination has been applied to the synthesis of methyl chloride, methylene chloride, chloroform, and carbon tetrachloride. The reaction is strongly exothermic, and the chief problem is to bring the gases to the reacting temperature (250°–400°) without the deposition of carbon. In one procedure the mixture of chlorine and methane is blown through a molten bath kept at the desired temperature, and in another the gases are preheated separately, and the chlorine added through jets to a high-velocity stream of methane. The velocity of the gases exceeds that of the rate of propagation of the flame, and no explosion results. In still another process the gases react between room temperature and 100°, the reaction being catalyzed by light from mercury vapor arc lamps.

Methylene chloride, CH_2Cl_2, b.p. 40°, is a noninflammable solvent that frequently can be used for extractions in place of ether. **Chloroform,** b.p. 61°, also is a useful solvent. It formerly was made by the reaction of ethanol or acetone with calcium hypochlorite, and later by the reduction of carbon tetrachloride with iron. **Carbon tetrachloride,** b.p. 77°, is used in fire extinguishers, although it has the disadvantage that it is partially oxidized to phosgene, which may reach dangerous concentrations in closed spaces. It rapidly is being displaced for this purpose by liquid carbon dioxide. The most important use is in degreasing compounds and noninflammable dry cleaning solvents although its toxicity is a hazard. It is used as a solvent in the rubber industry, because it is less toxic than benzene. Large quantities are used to prepare dichlorodifluoromethane (p. 513). Besides its preparation from methane, carbon tetrachloride is made by the reaction of chlorine with carbon disulfide (p. 250).

$$CS_2 + 3\ Cl_2 \longrightarrow CCl_4 + S_2Cl_2$$

$$2\ S_2Cl_2 + CS_2 \longrightarrow CCl_4 + 6\ S$$

The sulfur is reconverted into carbon disulfide. Some carbon tetrachloride also is obtained by chlorinolysis of compounds containing several carbon atoms.

505

$$\text{CH}_3\text{CHClCH}_2\text{Cl} + 6 \text{ Cl}_2 \xrightarrow{250°-425°} \text{Cl}_2\text{C}{=}\text{CCl}_2 + \text{CCl}_4 + 6 \text{ HCl}$$

Propylene chloride   Tetrachloro-
                              ethylene

Ethylene chloride, 1,2-dichloroethane, b.p. 84°, may be made by passing ethylene and chlorine over anhydrous calcium chloride, copper, or iron at 80°–100°. Chlorine addition can be brought about in the liquid phase at 40° using ethylene chloride or some other chlorinated hydrocarbon as a solvent. Some induced substitution, that is substitution that takes place in the presence but not in the absence of olefin, accompanies addition. The amount of substitution is reduced considerably if small amounts of ferric chloride are present. Ethylene chloride also is a co-product of the action of hypochlorous acid on ethylene (p. 54). It is used as a solvent, in dry-cleaning fluids, and for the preparation of vinyl chloride (p. 507).

Numerous polyhalogenated compounds are produced from acetylene. The addition of chlorine to acetylene with the formation of **1,1,2,2-tetrachloro-ethane** takes place explosively, and antimony pentachloride has been used as the chlorinating agent. Acetylene and chlorine are introduced alternately into the liquid. Some penta- and hexachloroethane also are formed.

$$\text{HC}{\equiv}\text{CH} + 2 \text{ SbCl}_5 \longrightarrow \text{HCCl}_2\text{CHCl}_2 + 2 \text{ SbCl}_3$$

1,1,2,2-Tetrachloroethane
(acetylene tetrachloride)

$$2 \text{ SbCl}_3 + 2 \text{ Cl}_2 \longrightarrow 2 \text{ SbCl}_5$$

Tetrachloroethane can be prepared also by mixing solutions of acetylene and chlorine in tetrachloroethane at 70°–95° using ferric chloride as a catalyst. To prevent explosions the tetrachloroethane is circulated downwards, acetylene mixed with it, and the chlorine bubbled in at a point below, where it reacts with a dilute solution of the acetylene in tetrachloroethane. Tetrachloroethane, b.p. 146°, is an excellent solvent, but it is highly toxic and corrodes metals in the presence of moisture. Most of it is used for the production of **trichloroethylene** by the action of an aqueous slurry of lime.

$$\text{CHCl}_2\text{CHCl}_2 \xrightarrow{\text{Ca(OH)}_2} \text{CHCl}{=}\text{CCl}_2$$

Trichloroethylene

This product boils at 87° and is one of the most important of the chlorinated solvents. It is stable and noncorrosive and is about as toxic as carbon tetra-chloride. It is used chiefly for degreasing metal parts. The cold metal part is passed through the hot vapors which condense on the metal and wash away the oil and dirt.

Reaction of tetrachloroethane with iron or reduction of trichloroethylene with iron and water gives a mixture of the *cis-* and *trans-***dichloroethylenes** (*cis*, b.p. 48°, *trans*, b.p. 60°).

$$\text{CHCl}_2\text{CHCl}_2$$
$$\xrightarrow{\text{Fe}}$$
$$\text{CHCl}{=}\text{CHCl}$$
$$\xrightarrow{\text{Fe, H}_2\text{O}}$$
$$\text{CHCl}{=}\text{CCl}_2$$

Dichloro-
ethylenes

Addition of chlorine to trichloroethylene gives **pentachloroethane,** b.p. 162°, which can be converted to **tetrachloroethylene** (perchloroethylene),[1] b.p. 118°, by the action of lime. Further addition of chlorine yields **hexachloroethane.**

$$CHCl{=}CCl_2 \xrightarrow{Cl_2} CHCl_2CCl_3 \xrightarrow{Ca(OH)_2} CCl_2{=}CCl_2 \xrightarrow{Cl_2} CCl_3CCl_3$$

Penta-   Tetra-   Hexachloroethane   chloroethylene   chloroethane

Both hexachloroethane and tetrachloroethylene are obtained by the thermal decomposition of carbon tetrachloride.

$$2\ CCl_4 \xrightarrow{600°} Cl_2 + CCl_3CCl_3 \xrightarrow{800°-900°} Cl_2 + CCl_2{=}CCl_2$$

Tetrachloroethylene also is one of the products of chlorinolysis of propylene chloride (p. 506). Tetrachloroethylene is an important solvent for the dry-cleaning industry. Hexachloroethane is used in the production of naval smoke screens. A mixture with zinc powder, when ignited, reacts vigorously to give zinc chloride vapor, which causes moisture to condense from the air and form a heavy smoke.

The relative importance of some of these halogen compounds is indicated by the following rounded figures for production in the United States in 1948 in millions of pounds: ethyl chloride, 275; ethylene chloride, 234; carbon tetrachloride, 215; methylene chloride, 18; chloroform, 13. The prices ranged from $0.05 per pound for carbon tetrachloride to $0.15 per pound for chloroform. Figures for 1948 for methyl chloride, tetrachloroethane, trichloroethylene, and tetrachloroethylene were not reported by the U. S. Tariff Commission.

Vinyl chloride (chloroethylene) can be produced by the dehydrohalogenation of ethylene chloride. The usual laboratory reagent for this type of reaction is methyl alcoholic sodium hydroxide, but the reaction can be brought about thermally at relatively low temperatures in the presence of 0.5 to 1 per cent of chlorine.

$$CH_2ClCH_2Cl \xrightarrow[\text{(Cl}_2)]{310°} CH_2{=}CHCl + HCl$$

Vinyl chloride

Vinyl chloride is made also by the catalytic addition of hydrogen chloride to acetylene.

$$HC{\equiv}CH + HCl \xrightarrow[+ \text{ Hg}_2Cl_2]{\text{Act. carbon}} CH_2{=}CHCl$$

Vinyl chloride polymerizes readily in the presence of peroxides to a hard brittle resin in which the units are linked regularly in a head to tail fashion.

$$x\ CH_2{=}CHCl \longrightarrow [{-}CH_2CHCl{\mid}CH_2CHCl{\mid}CH_2CHCl{-}]_x$$

---

[1] The prefix *per* (L. *per* through) is used to indicate not only a high state of oxidation, but also the maximum amount of substitution or addition.

It can be plasticized by the addition of cresyl phosphate (p. 391) or butyl phthalate (p. 415) to give tough, long-wearing, leather- or rubber-like materials. Many other commercial plastics are copolymers with vinyl chloride (cf. p. 516).

The halogen atom in vinyl chloride is about as unreactive as that in chlorobenzene (p. 329). This reduced reactivity is characteristic of halogen on a doubly-bonded carbon atom, and is ascribed to the interaction of the unshared electrons of the halogen atom with the electrons of the double bond, which leads to greater bond strength and decreased bond length and reactivity.

$$\left\{ CH_2{=}CH\ddot{\underset{..}{C}l} : \;\longleftrightarrow\; \bar{C}H_2CH{=}\overset{+}{\underset{..}{C}}l : \right\}$$

The decrease in the C—Cl bond distance is observable, the interatomic distance for ethyl chloride being 1.77 Å and for vinyl chloride 1.69 Å.

Vinylidene chloride, 1,1-dichloroethylene, may be made by the action of lime on 1,1,2-trichloroethane. The latter compound results from the controlled chlorination of ethylene or the addition of chlorine to vinyl chloride.

$$CH_2{=}CH_2 \;\xrightarrow{\;2\ Cl_2\;}\; CH_2ClCHCl_2 \;\xrightarrow[90°]{Ca(OH)_2}\; CH_2{=}CCl_2$$
$$CH_2{=}CHCl \;\xrightarrow{\;Cl_2\;}\;$$

Vinylidene
chloride

Vinylidene chloride can be prepared also by the reaction of acetylene with chlorine at 135° in the presence of ferric chloride, a reaction that may involve substitution and addition of hydrogen halide.

$$HC{\equiv}CH + Cl_2 \xrightarrow[135°]{FeCl_3} CH_2{=}CCl_2$$

Vinylidene chloride polymerizes to a material that is characterized by chemical inertness, high tensile strength, and resistance to abrasion. The commercial products, known as Sarans, usually are copolymers with a small amount of vinyl chloride or acrylonitrile to improve their working properties. Emulsions of vinylidene chloride polymers have the unusual property of forming tough coherent sheets when spread on a smooth surface and allowed to dry.

Both vinyl chloride and vinylidene chloride and their polymers have been known for over a hundred years. Their rapid development since 1927 has resulted from a reduction in the cost of raw materials, and from the accumulation of knowledge concerning the nature of polymerization reactions that has permitted the production of materials having useful properties.

Allyl chloride, $CH_2{=}CHCH_2Cl$, is made by the chlorination of propylene at a high temperature.

$$CH_2{=}CHCH_3 + Cl_2 \xrightarrow{500°-600°} CH_2{=}CHCH_2Cl + HCl$$

Although secondary base olefins (those yielding secondary alkyl derivatives on the addition of unsymmetrical addenda) add halogen readily in the liquid phase, they do not do so in the vapor phase, and at sufficiently high temperatures rapid substitution takes place without addition. Thus propylene gives 85–90 per cent of allyl chloride. The principal use for allyl chloride is as a starting point for the preparation of allyl alcohol (p. 517) and glycerol (p. 524).

Substitution of a second chlorine atom into allyl chloride by high temperature chlorination produces a mixture of 10 per cent 3,3-dichloropropene and 90 per cent 1,3-dichloropropene.

$$CH_2\!=\!CHCH_2Cl \xrightarrow[(500°-600°)]{Cl_2} CH_2\!=\!CHCHCl_2 \text{ and } ClCH\!=\!CHCH_2Cl$$
$$\phantom{CH_2\!=\!CHCH_2Cl \xrightarrow{Cl_2}} \text{10 per cent} \qquad\qquad \text{90 per cent}$$

The mixed **dichloropropenes** are valuable as a soil fumigant for the destruction of nematodes.

With tertiary base olefins (those that can give tertiary alkyl derivatives) the ratio of substitution to addition is not affected by temperature, and substitution is extremely rapid in the liquid phase or at higher temperatures in the vapor phase in contact with porous materials. By taking proper precautions to minimize side reactions, it is possible to obtain up to 87 per cent **methallyl chloride** from isobutylene. Some isocrotyl chloride also is formed.

$$(CH_3)_2C\!=\!CH_2 + Cl_2 \xrightarrow[\substack{\text{contact time} \\ \text{1 sec.}}]{300°,} CH_2\!=\!CCH_2Cl \text{ and } (CH_3)_2C\!=\!CHCl + HCl$$
$$\phantom{(CH_3)_2C\!=\!CH_2 + Cl_2 \xrightarrow{300°}} \overset{|}{CH_3}$$

| Methallyl | Isocrotyl |
| chloride | chloride |

This reaction was discovered by Kondakov in 1891, but has been operated commercially only in recent years. Methallyl chloride may be used as a raw material for the preparation of methyl methacrylate (p. 537).

When halogen is united to a carbon atom which in turn is doubly bound to another atom, as for example in the allyl halides, the halogen is much more reactive than that in a simple primary alkyl halide (cf. p. 330). The system C=C—C is known as the **allylic system.** In addition to conferring high reactivity on halogen atoms attached to the carbon atom remote from the double bond, the allylic system is very prone to rearrangement. Thus heating either pure 1-bromo-2-butene or 3-bromo-1-butene gives an equilibrium mixture.

$$CH_3CH\!=\!CHCH_2Br \overset{Heat}{\rightleftarrows} CH_3\underset{\underset{Br}{|}}{CH}CH\!=\!CH_2$$

Moreover when either of the corresponding alcohols reacts with hydrogen bromide, the equilibrium mixture of the bromides is obtained. Similarly the reaction of either bromide with magnesium gives an equilibrium mixture of both Grignard reagents. This behavior is known as the **allylic rearrangement.**

Both the high reactivity and the rearrangement of allyl halides appear to result from resonance of the carbonium ion.

$$\left\{ CH_2\!=\!CHCH_2{}^+ \longleftrightarrow \overset{+}{C}H_2CH\!=\!CH_2 \right\}$$

The resonance stabilizes the carbonium ion, and makes it easier for halogen to leave the molecule as a halide ion. When the carbonium ion combines with a negative ion, the latter may fix itself to either end of the allylic system. With the symmetrically constituted ions, only one product results, but if the intermediate is unsymmetrical, two isomers are formed and the composition depends on their relative thermodynamic stability.

FLUORINATED HYDROCARBONS

The extensive contributions to the chemistry of fluorine compounds in recent years tend to obscure the fact that the fundamental chemistry of these compounds has been known for a long time. The pioneering work of Moissan [2] was completed about 1900 and that of Swarts [3] by about 1925. The discovery of commercial uses for organic fluorine compounds, however, has led to the entrance of a large number of workers into the field, particularly chemists connected with industrial research laboratories. The commercial production of liquid hydrogen fluoride and fluorine, the development of methods for handling them safely, and the ready availability of commercially manufactured chlorinated organic compounds have led to a rapid extension of the work of the early investigators.

Chemical and Physical Properties

Fluorine compounds are characterized by extremes and opposites. Some are the most reactive of organic compounds and others are the most inert. Some are extremely toxic and others are as nontoxic as nitrogen or water. The introduction of fluorine may raise or lower the boiling point, and the progressive introduction of fluorine not only reduces the solubility in water but also in other organic solvents. Thus completely fluorinated hydrocarbons, known as *fluorocarbons*, are soluble in ether and in chlorofluorocarbons but are insoluble in most other solvents.

Compounds containing a single fluorine atom attached to a carbon atom differ markedly in their properties from those having two or more fluorine atoms attached to the same carbon atom. Whereas the alkyl fluorides hydrolyze readily to the alcohol and, with the exception of methyl fluoride, are very unstable and lose hydrogen fluoride spontaneously at ordinary temperatures, the *gem*-difluorides [4] are extremely inert to all chemical reactions. Fluorocarbons are surpassed in stability only by the inert gases. They are decomposed only at a red heat, when carbon and carbon tetrafluoride are formed. They react with sodium or potassium at 300°–400° and with sodium in liquid ammonia. Above 400° they react with silica to form silicon tetrafluoride. It is the reactions with sodium and silica that must be used for analytical purposes.

[2] Ferdinand Frederic Henri Moissan (1852–1907), professor of chemistry at the University of Paris. He was the first to isolate fluorine in 1886, and in 1892 he prepared calcium carbide by heating lime and carbon in the electric arc furnace. He investigated many other reactions at high temperatures and was awarded the Nobel Prize in Chemistry in 1906.

[3] Frederic-Jean Edmond Swarts (1866–1940), professor at the University of Ghent. He developed methods for the synthesis of many organic fluorine compounds, particularly the reaction of antimony fluoride and mercurous fluoride on chloro derivatives, and studied extensively the thermochemistry and refractometry of fluorine compounds. He also prepared many organic chlorine compounds for purposes of comparison.

[4] The prefix *gem*- (L. *geminus* twin) refers to two like atoms or groups attached to the same carbon atom.

Two fluorine atoms also reduce the reactivity of other halogen atoms attached to the same carbon atom. Thus the reactivity of the chlorine atoms in CCl_2F_2 is less than that in CH_2Cl_2 or CCl_4. Whereas monofluorides are toxic compounds, *gem*-difluorides usually are nontoxic. Even CCl_2F_2 lacks the toxicity and anesthetic action of CH_2Cl_2 or CCl_4. Exceptions to this rule are some extremely toxic polyfluorocyclopropanes.

The unexpected chemical behavior of organic fluorine compounds extends also to their physical properties. The progressive replacement of hydrogen by chlorine causes a continual increase in the boiling point, but progressive replacement by fluorine causes an initial rise, which then is followed by a decrease. Thus the boiling points of methane, methyl fluoride, methylene fluoride, fluoroform, and carbon tetrafluoride are respectively $-161°$, $-78°$, $-52°$, $-83°$, and $-128°$. Similarly the boiling points of chloro-, chlorofluoro-, chlorodifluoro-, and chlorotrifluoromethane are $-24°$, $-9°$, $-41°$, and $-81°$. When the nuclear hydrogen atoms of aromatic compounds are replaced by fluorine, little change in boiling point takes place. Thus benzene, fluorobenzene, *o*-, *m*-, and *p*-difluorobenzene, trifluorobenzene, and hexafluorobenzene all boil within the range $80°$–$91°$.

A striking difference between mono- and polyfluoro compounds is observed in the interatomic distances. Although there is no detectable difference in the C—Cl bond distances in the chlorinated methanes, the C—F distance in methyl fluoride is 1.42 Å, whereas that in *gem*-difluoro compounds is 1.36 Å. Moreover the bond distances to other atoms attached to the same carbon atom are detectably decreased. Thus the C—Cl distance of 1.76 Å in carbon tetrachloride is decreased to 1.70 Å in dichlorodifluoromethane, and the C—C distance of 1.54 Å in ethane is decreased to 1.48 Å in 1,1,1-trifluoroethane.

Preparation

1. **Direct Fluorination.** The amount of energy liberated when fluorine reacts with a hydrocarbon to give a fluoro derivative and hydrogen fluoride is 103 kcal. per mole, and when fluorine adds to a double bond, 107 kcal. per mole. The corresponding values for chlorine substitution and addition are 23 and 33 kcal. per mole. Since the energy necessary to dissociate a carbon-carbon bond is about 85 kcal. per mole, it is not surprising that the uncontrolled reaction of fluorine with organic molecules is violent and that the only product identifiable in quantity is carbon tetrafluoride.

In recent years several methods have been devised for moderating this reaction. In one procedure the reactants are diluted with nitrogen and passed over a large heat-conducting surface such as metal gauze or turnings. One of the most satisfactory reactor packings is silver-plated copper turnings. By this procedure heptane gives a 62 per cent yield of **perfluoroheptane,** C_7F_{16}, and benzene gives a 58 per cent yield of **perfluorocyclohexane,** C_6F_{12}.

A second method of fluorination consists of using a less reactive fluorinating agent than fluorine itself. Certain metallic fluorides such as CoF_3, AgF_2, CeF_4, and MnF_3 are suitable for this purpose. Cobaltic fluoride is used most often. The heat of reaction is only about half that when fluorine is used, the other half being evolved during the formation of the cobaltic fluoride. The reaction is carried out as a cycle. The cobaltic fluoride is prepared by passing fluorine over cobaltous fluoride at $250°$, the excess fluorine is flushed out with nitrogen, and the hydrocarbon vapor passed over the cobaltic fluoride. The operations then are repeated.

Neither of the above processes can be used to prepare high molecular weight fluorocarbons, which are of interest as lubricating oils. These products are prepared by using fluorocarbons boiling in the range 150°–200° as a diluent for the reaction between lubricating oil and cobalt trifluoride. Unfortunately these products have a poor viscosity index (p. 54). Processes also have been developed for carrying out fluorinations directly in the electrolytic cell used to generate the fluorine.

In direct fluorinations rearrangement, degradation, and polymerization take place as well as substitution. For example fluorination of heptane with cobaltic fluoride gives a 69 per cent yield of perfluoroheptane, but the completely fluorinated derivatives of ethylcyclopentane (8 per cent), dimethylcyclopentane (3 per cent), hexane (1 per cent), and polymeric fluorocarbons (1 per cent) also have been isolated. Similarly fluorination of methane yields some hexafluoroethane and octafluoropropane. Such products are to be expected if the reaction takes place by a free radical mechanism.

2. *Addition of Hydrogen Fluoride to Olefins.* Hydrogen fluoride adds to carbon-carbon double bonds, the mode of addition following the Markovnikov rule. The position of equilibrium is unfavorable at ordinary temperature for the simple olefins, but if a halogen atom already is present on a doubly-linked carbon atom, a stable product results.

$$CH_3CCl{=}CH_2 + HF \longrightarrow CH_3CClFCH_3$$

Acetylenes also yield stable products.

$$CH{\equiv}CH \xrightarrow{HF} CH_2{=}CHF \xrightarrow{HF} CH_3CHF_2$$

$$CH_3C{\equiv}CH \xrightarrow{HF} CH_3CF{=}CH_2 \xrightarrow{HF} CH_3CF_2CH_3$$

3. *Replacement of Halogen.* Exchange reactions take place between many organic halides and inorganic fluorides. This behavior is known as the *Swarts reaction* and has been the most fruitful method for the preparation of organic fluoro compounds. Usually chlorine is exchanged for fluorine. Fluorides of silver, mercury, antimony, arsenic, and cobalt, and hydrogen fluoride have been used. Simple alkyl halides are converted to fluorides best with mercurous fluoride.

$$2\ CH_3Br + Hg_2F_2 \longrightarrow 2\ CH_3F + Hg_2Br_2$$

Hydrogen fluoride will replace chlorine if all of the chlorine is on a single carbon atom.

$$CH_3CCl_3 + 3\ HF \longrightarrow CH_3CF_3 + 3\ HCl$$

$$CH_3CCl_2CH_3 + 2\ HF \longrightarrow CH_3CF_2CH_3 + 2\ HCl$$

Antimony trifluoride containing some pentavalent antimony halide is used on polychloro compounds.

$$3 \text{ CCl}_4 + \text{SbF}_3 \longrightarrow 3 \text{ CCl}_3\text{F} + \text{SbCl}_3$$

$$3 \text{ CCl}_3\text{F} + \text{SbF}_3 \longrightarrow 3 \text{ CCl}_2\text{F}_2 + \text{SbCl}_3$$

$$\text{CHCl}_3 \xrightarrow{\text{SbF}_3} \text{CHCl}_2\text{F} \xrightarrow{\text{SbF}_3} \text{CHClF}_2$$

$$\text{CH}_2\text{Cl}_2 \xrightarrow{\text{SbF}_3} \text{CH}_2\text{ClF} \xrightarrow{\text{SbF}_3} \text{CH}_2\text{F}_2$$

The small amount of pentavalent antimony halide added to the trifluoride undoubtedly is the active agent and is regenerated by exchange with the antimony trifluoride.

$$\text{CH}_2\text{Cl}_2 + \text{SbF}_5 \longrightarrow \text{CH}_2\text{ClF} + \text{SbF}_4\text{Cl}$$

$$\text{SbF}_4\text{Cl} + \text{SbF}_3 \longrightarrow \text{SbF}_5 + \text{SbF}_2\text{Cl}$$

The antimony trifluoride is regenerated, usually continuously, by reaction with hydrogen fluoride.

$$\text{SbF}_2\text{Cl} + \text{HF} \longrightarrow \text{SbF}_3 + \text{HCl}$$

The replacement reactions stop when two fluorine atoms have been introduced at a single carbon atom, because their presence decreases the reactivity of the remaining chlorine atoms. If the halogen is activated by a double bond (allyl halides), three atoms can be replaced.

$$\text{CCl}_2{=}\text{CHClCCl}_3 + \text{SbF}_3 \longrightarrow \text{CCl}_2{=}\text{CHClCF}_3 + \text{SbCl}_3$$

The unreactive vinyl type halogen atoms are not replaced, nor is antimony fluoride able to react with a primary halide such as methyl chloride.

Commercially Important Products

Interest in fluorine compounds in recent years arises from a few technical applications. The most important compound is **dichlorodifluoromethane** (Freon-12), which is used as a refrigerant for household refrigerators and air-conditioning equipment, and as a solvent-propellant for aerosol-type insecticidal preparations. It is entirely noncorrosive, nontoxic, and noninflammable. Its cheap production depends on the reconversion of antimony trichloride to antimony trifluoride by reaction with anhydrous hydrogen fluoride, on the relatively high boiling point of hydrogen fluoride, on the decrease in boiling point of 40°–50° for each replacement of chlorine by fluorine, and on the fact that the reaction will not proceed beyond the desired stage. The reactions are

$$\text{CCl}_4 \xrightarrow{\text{SbF}_3} \text{CCl}_3\text{F} \xrightarrow{\text{SbF}_3} \text{CCl}_2\text{F}_2 + 2 \text{ SbF}_2\text{Cl}$$

$$2 \text{ SbF}_2\text{Cl} + 2 \text{ HF} \longrightarrow 2 \text{ SbF}_3 + 2 \text{ HCl}$$

The boiling points of the reactants and products in decreasing order are carbon tetrachloride, 76°; trichlorofluoromethane (Freon-11), 25°; hydrogen fluoride 20°; dichlorodifluoromethane, −29°; and hydrogen chloride, −85°. Hence hydrogen fluoride and carbon tetrachloride can be added continuously to a reactor, and hydrogen chloride and dichlorodifluoromethane removed through a column and condenser, the hydrogen chloride being absorbed in water.

Chlorodifluoromethane (Freon-22), b.p. 41°, can be made by a similar process from chloroform. **1,2-Dichloro-1,1,2,2-tetrafluoroethane** (Freon-114), b.p. 3.8°, is made from hexachloroethane and antimony fluorochloride, SbF_3Cl_2. The reaction always takes place to produce a symmetrical product, and stops when four chlorine atoms have been replaced.

$$CCl_3CCl_3 \xrightarrow{SbF_3Cl_2} CCl_3CCl_2F \longrightarrow CCl_2FCCl_2F \longrightarrow CCl_2FCClF_2 \longrightarrow CClF_2CClF_2$$

Tetrafluoroethylene is made by pyrolysis of chlorodifluoromethane.

$$2\ CHClF_2 \xrightarrow[1\ sec.]{700°\ for} F_2C{=}CF_2 + 2\ HCl$$

It can be polymerized at 700 p.s.i. in the presence of peroxide catalysts to give a product known as *Teflon* which is characterized by extreme chemical inertness. It withstands the attack of all reagents except molten alkali metals. Aqueous alkalies, concentrated acids, oxidizing agents, and organic solvents have no effect on it. It can be used in the temperature range −70° to 250°. It softens above 250°, changes to a rubbery state at 325°, and depolymerizes at 600°–800° without charring. Although it thus is thermoplastic, it is much more difficult to work than most plastics. A property useful in the laboratory is the ability of small pieces to prevent bumping in boiling operations.

Chlorotrifluoroethylene can be made by the action of zinc dust in methanol on 1,1,2-trichloro-1,2,2-trifluoroethane, a product of the action of antimony fluorochloride on hexachloroethane (p. 514).

$$CCl_2FCClF_2 \xrightarrow[CH_3OH]{Zn,} CClF{=}CF_2$$

Polymerization gives the product called *Kel-F* which like Teflon is chemically inert but softens at 230°. Thus Kel-F cannot be used at as high a temperature as Teflon but can be molded or extruded more readily.

In the development during World War II of the separation of uranium isotopes by the gaseous diffusion of uranium hexafluorides, the need arose for nonvolatile liquids that could be used for seals and lubricants for pumps and for a volatile liquid which would not be attacked by the highly reactive uranium hexafluoride. The volatile liquid used was **perfluoro-1,3-dimethyl-cyclohexane,** b.p. 100°. It was prepared by chlorinating *m*-xylene to *m*-bis-(trichloromethyl)benzene, converting to the hexafluoro compound, and then fluorinating to the perfluoro derivative.

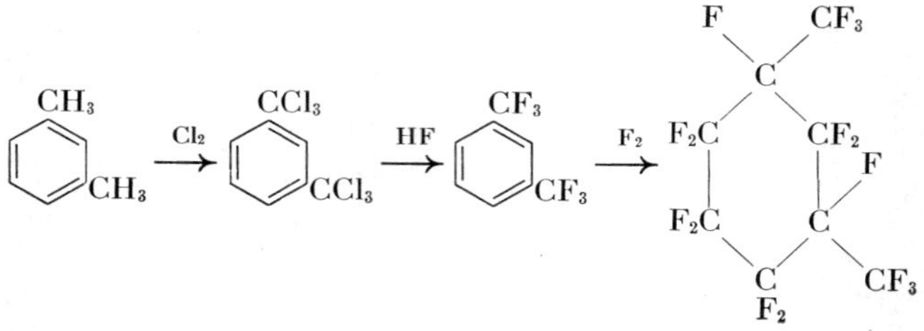

The nonvolatile fluorocarbons were prepared by direct fluorination of non-volatile hydrocarbons (p. 512).

REVIEW QUESTIONS

1. Give in chart form the reactions by which chlorinated hydrocarbons are produced commercially from (*a*) methane; (*b*) ethylene; (*c*) propylene; (*d*) acetylene.
2. What is meant by the term allylic rearrangement?
3. Discuss the effect of the presence of more than one fluorine atom on a single carbon atom on the physical and chemical properties of a compound.
4. Give reactions for the preparation of (*a*) Freon-12 from carbon disulfide; (*b*) benzotrifluoride from toluene; (*c*) 1,2-dichloro-2-fluoropropane from allyl chloride; (*d*) chlorotrifluoroethylene from hexachloroethane.

Chapter 34

UNSATURATED ALCOHOLS, POLYHYDRIC ALCOHOLS, AND THEIR DERIVATIVES. AMINO ALCOHOLS AND POLYAMINES

UNSATURATED ALCOHOLS

The first member of this series, **vinyl alcohol,** is unknown in the monomeric state because the keto form is more stable.

$$[CH_2=CHOH] \longrightarrow CH_3CHO$$
$$\text{Vinyl} \qquad \text{Acetalde-}$$
$$\text{alcohol} \qquad \text{hyde}$$

Vinyl acetate can be made by the catalyzed addition of acetic acid to acetylene either in the liquid or the vapor phase, or by reaction of ethylene chloride and sodium acetate.

$$HC\equiv CH + HOCOCH_3 \xrightarrow[\substack{\text{or Zn (OAc)}_2 \text{ at} \\ 210°-250°}]{\text{HgSO}_4 \text{ at } 75°-80°} H_2C=CHOCOCH_3$$
$$\text{Vinyl acetate}$$

$$ClCH_2CH_2Cl + 2\ NaOCOCH_3 \longrightarrow H_2C=CHOCOCH_3 + NaCl + CH_3COOH$$

It boils at 72° and can be polymerized readily using peroxide catalysts to give a tough, thermoplastic resin, soluble in aromatic hydrocarbons.

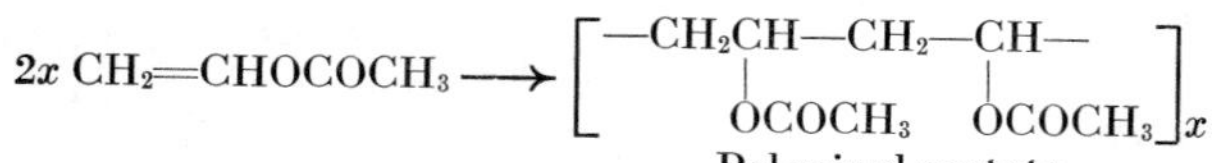

$$2x\ CH_2=CHOCOCH_3 \longrightarrow \begin{bmatrix} -CH_2CH-CH_2-CH- \\ \quad | \qquad\qquad | \\ \quad OCOCH_3 \quad OCOCH_3 \end{bmatrix}_x$$
$$\text{Polyvinyl acetate}$$

Copolymerization of vinyl acetate and vinyl chloride in various proportions and to varying degrees of polymerization gives products known as *Vinylite* resins, which have a wide range of properties. They are very inert to chemical agents and weathering, and can be used to produce rigid sheets, flexible sheeting and films, textile fibers (Vinyon), molded and extruded articles, and surface coatings that are long-wearing and scuff and stain resistant.

Saponification of polyvinyl acetate gives **polyvinyl alcohol.** Its physical

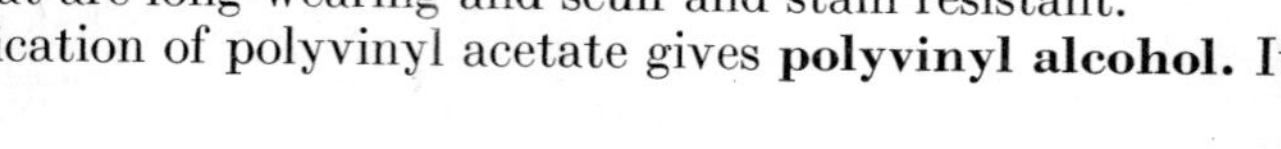

$$\begin{bmatrix} -CH_2CH-CH_2-CH- \\ \quad | \qquad\qquad | \\ \quad OCOCH_3 \quad OCOCH_3 \end{bmatrix}_x \xrightarrow{\text{NaOH}} \begin{bmatrix} -CH_2CHCH_2CH- \\ \quad | \qquad\quad | \\ \quad OH \quad OH \end{bmatrix}_x$$
$$\text{Polyvinyl alcohol}$$

properties are similar to those of starch, and it finds use where a coating soluble in water but insoluble in organic solvents is desired.

Although polyvinyl alcohol is chiefly a linear polymer with a head to tail

516

arrangement, about 0.4 per cent of the oxygen is present as carbonyl groups. Moreover a small amount of tail to tail addition during polymerization results in a few of the hydroxyl groups occupying 1,2 instead of 1,3 positions.

Because most of the hydroxyl groups of polyvinyl alcohol occupy 1,3 positions, it reacts readily with aldehydes to give cyclic acetals having six-membered rings.

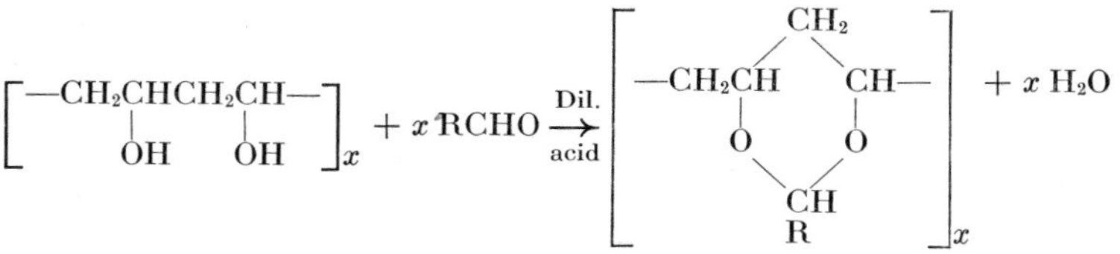

$$\left[\begin{array}{c} -CH_2CHCH_2CH- \\ | \qquad | \\ OH \quad OH \end{array}\right]_x + x\,RCHO \xrightarrow[\text{acid}]{\text{Dil.}} \left[\begin{array}{c} CH_2 \\ / \quad \backslash \\ -CH_2CH \quad CH- \\ | \qquad | \\ O \qquad O \\ \backslash \quad / \\ CH \\ | \\ R \end{array}\right]_x + x\,H_2O$$

The condensation product with *n*-butyraldehyde is known as **polyvinyl butyral** and is used as the filling to make a very strong safety glass.

1-Methylvinyl acetate, $CH_2{=}COCOCH_3$, is made by passing ketene into
$$| \atop CH_3$$
acetone containing a trace of sulfuric acid.

$$CH_3COCH_3 \underset{}{\overset{[H^+]}{\rightleftarrows}} \left[CH_2{=}\underset{\underset{CH_3}{|}}{C}{-}OH\right] \xrightarrow{CH_2{=}C{=}O} CH_2{=}\underset{\underset{CH_3}{|}}{C}{-}OCOCH_3$$

Alcohols will add to acetylene in the presence of potassium hydroxide at elevated temperatures to give *vinyl alkyl ethers*. These vinyl ethers polymerize and have found some commercial uses. **Polyvinyl methyl ether** may be ob-

$$HC{\equiv}CH + HOR \xrightarrow[150°-180°]{KOH} H_2C{=}CHOR$$

tained as a sticky thick liquid or as a soft solid. It is soluble in organic solvents and in cold water but is precipitated from aqueous solutions by heating to 35°. It is used as an adhesive coagulant in aqueous media. Since the monomeric alkyl vinyl ethers hydrolyze to vinyl alcohol and the alkanol, they can serve as intermediates for the synthesis of acetaldehyde from acetylene.

$$H_2C{=}CHOR + H_2O \xrightarrow{HCl} ROH + [H_2C{=}CHOH] \longrightarrow CH_3CHO$$

Allyl alcohol may be prepared by the reductive dehydration of glycerol by heating with formic or oxalic acid.

$$\underset{\alpha\text{-Glyceryl formate}}{HOCH_2CHOHCH_2OCHO} \xrightarrow{\text{Heat}} \underset{\text{Allyl alcohol}}{HOCH_2CH{=}CH_2} + CO_2 + H_2O$$

It now is made on a large scale commercially by the hydrolysis of allyl chloride (p. 508) at pH 8 to 11.

$$CH_2\!\!=\!\!CHCH_2Cl \xrightarrow[\text{NaOH}]{\text{Na}_2\text{CO}_3,} CH_2\!\!=\!\!CHCH_2OH$$

Allyl chloride   Allyl alcohol

Although simple allyl compounds do not polymerize readily, some of their esters such as allyl phthalate do and the polymers have found use, particularly as laminating resins. Other more complex esters give hard transparent resins. Since 1948 allyl alcohol has been used as an intermediate in the production of synthetic glycerol (p. 525).

Crotyl alcohol is made by the Meerwein-Ponndorf reduction (p. 164) of crotonic aldehyde, and **methallyl alcohol** by the hydrolysis of methallyl chloride (p. 509).

$$CH_3CH\!\!=\!\!CHCHO + (CH_3)_2CHOH \xrightarrow{\text{Al}(OC_3H_7)_3} CH_3CH\!\!=\!\!CHCH_2OH + CH_3COCH_3$$

Crotonic aldehyde   Crotyl alcohol

$$CH_2\!\!=\!\!C(CH_3)CH_2Cl \xrightarrow{\text{NaOH}} CH_2\!\!=\!\!C(CH_3)CH_2OH$$

Methallyl chloride   Methallyl alcohol

POLYHYDRIC ALCOHOLS

Aldehyde Hydrates

Compounds having two hydroxyl groups on the same carbon atom usually are unstable and lose water to form the carbonyl derivative. Methanediol, the hydrate of formaldehyde, appears to exist in aqueous solution only. The presence of electron-attracting groups, however, increases the stability of the hydrate. Thus dichloroacetaldehyde forms a hygroscopic monohydrate melting at 55°. **Chloral** (trichloroacetaldehyde) is a water-insoluble liquid prepared by the reaction of ethyl alcohol with chlorine.

$$C_2H_5OH + 4\,Cl_2 \longrightarrow Cl_3CCHO + 5\,HCl$$

Chloral

On shaking chloral with water, heat is evolved and the crystalline hydrate separates. In order to produce anhydrous chloral again, it is mixed with concentrated sulfuric acid. Whereas chloral gives a color with Schiff's reagent, **chloral hydrate** does not. Hence the water has reacted with the aldehyde.

$$Cl_3CCHO + H_2O \longrightarrow Cl_3CCH(OH)_2$$

Chloral hydrate

Chloral hydrate is a quickly acting soporific commonly known as *knock-out drops*.

1,2-Glycols

Preparation. Several general methods of preparation of 1,2-glycols commonly are used.

1. OXIDATION OF OLEFINS (p. 40).

$$RCH\!\!=\!\!CHR + H_2O + [O] \longrightarrow RCHOHCHOHR$$

Suitable oxidizing agents are dilute aqueous permanganate, hydrogen peroxide in acetic acid, and hydrogen peroxide in the presence of osmium tetroxide.

2. HYDROLYSIS OF CHLOROHYDRINS. The olefin chlorohydrins, prepared by the addition of hypochlorous acid to an olefin, hydrolyze much more easily than simple primary or secondary alkyl halides.

$$\text{RCHOHCHClR} + H_2O + Na_2CO_3 \longrightarrow \text{RCHOHCHOHR} + NaCl + NaHCO_3$$

3. HYDROLYSIS OF 1,2-EPOXIDES (ETHYLENE OXIDES, p. 521).

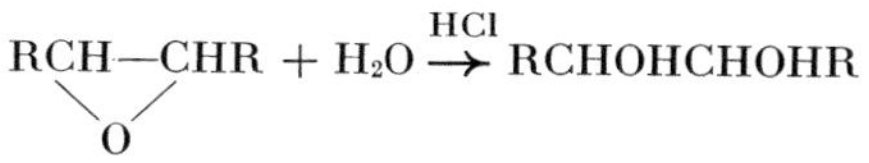

$$\text{RCH—CHR} + H_2O \xrightarrow{\text{HCl}} \text{RCHOHCHOHR}$$
$$\diagdown \text{O} \diagup$$

4. PINACOL REDUCTION OF KETONES (p. 176).

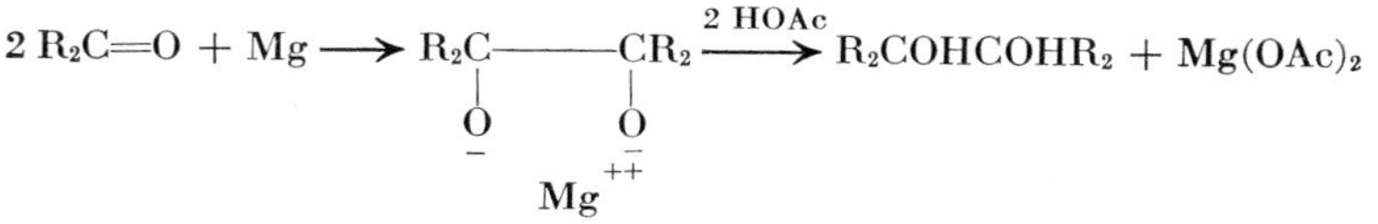

$$2\,R_2C{=}O + Mg \longrightarrow R_2C\text{———}CR_2 \xrightarrow{2\,\text{HOAc}} R_2COHCOHR_2 + Mg(OAc)_2$$

Reactions. 1,2-Glycols exhibit several characteristic reactions not given by simple alcohols.

1. FORMATION OF CYCLIC COMPOUNDS. Because of the 1,2 position of the hydroxyl groups, reactions leading to the formation of 5-membered rings are common. Thus reaction with aldehydes or ketones yields **cyclic acetals.**

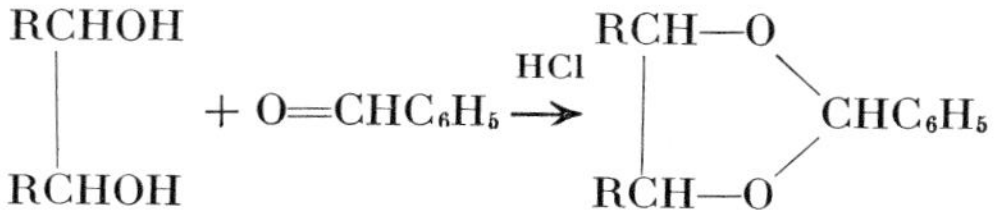

$$\begin{array}{c}\text{RCHOH}\\|\\\text{RCHOH}\end{array} + O{=}\text{CHC}_6H_5 \xrightarrow{\text{HCl}} \begin{array}{c}\text{RCH—O}\\|\qquad\qquad \diagdown\text{CHC}_6H_5\\\text{RCH—O}\diagup\end{array}$$

Benzylidene
derivative

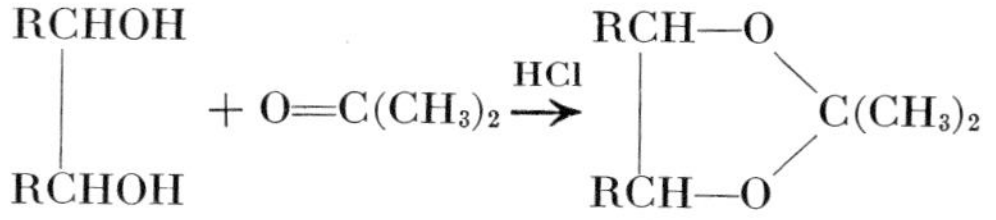

$$\begin{array}{c}\text{RCHOH}\\|\\\text{RCHOH}\end{array} + O{=}\text{C(CH}_3)_2 \xrightarrow{\text{HCl}} \begin{array}{c}\text{RCH—O}\\|\qquad\qquad \diagdown\text{C(CH}_3)_2\\\text{RCH—O}\diagup\end{array}$$

Isopropylidene
derivative

Phosgene gives **cyclic carbonates.**

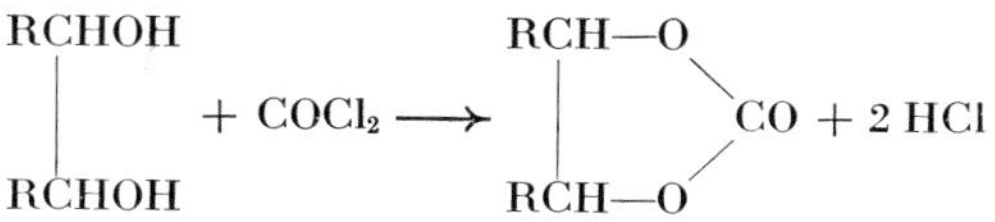

$$\begin{array}{c}\text{RCHOH}\\|\\\text{RCHOH}\end{array} + \text{COCl}_2 \longrightarrow \begin{array}{c}\text{RCH—O}\\|\qquad\qquad \diagdown\text{CO} + 2\,\text{HCl}\\\text{RCH—O}\diagup\end{array}$$

Cyclic carbonate

1,2-Glycols increase the conductivity of boric acid solutions, because after formation of the borate, the unshared pair of electrons of the fourth hydroxyl group fills the empty orbital of the boron atom, permitting ionization of a proton.

$$\begin{matrix} \text{RCHOH} \\ | \\ \text{RCHOH} \end{matrix} + \text{B(OH)}_3 + \begin{matrix} \text{HOCHR} \\ | \\ \text{HOCHR} \end{matrix} \longrightarrow 3\ \text{H}_2\text{O} + \left[\begin{matrix} \text{RCH—O} & \quad & \text{O—CHR} \\ | & \diagdown \text{B} \diagup & | \\ \text{RCH—O} & \diagup \ :\text{O—CHR} \end{matrix} \right] \longrightarrow$$

$$\underset{\text{H}}{}$$

$$\left[\begin{matrix} \text{RCH—O} & \quad & \text{O—CHR} \\ | & \diagdown \text{B} \diagup & | \\ \text{RCH—O} & \diagup \quad \text{O—CHR} \end{matrix} \right]^{-} \text{H}^{+}$$

Cyclic compounds in which the ring is closed by coordination with an unshared pair of electrons are known as **chelate compounds** (Gr. *chele* claw), the ring closure being thought of as a pincer-like action. The process is called **chelation.**

2. PINACOL-PINACOLONE REARRANGEMENT (p. 176).

$$\text{RCHOHCH}_2\text{OH} \xrightarrow{\text{HCl}} \text{RCH}_2\text{CHO} + \text{H}_2\text{O}$$

$$\text{RCHOHCHOHR} \longrightarrow \text{RCH}_2\text{COR}$$

$$\text{R}_2\text{COHCOHR}_2 \longrightarrow \text{R}_3\text{CCOR}$$

The easy preparation of isobutyraldehyde by hydrolysis of methallyl chloride, and of methyl isopropyl ketone by hydrolysis of 2,3-dichloro-2-methylbutane is the result of a pinacol-pinacolone rearrangement.

$$\text{CH}_2{=}\text{C(CH}_3)\text{CH}_2\text{Cl} \xrightarrow[\text{heat}]{\text{H}_2\text{O—H}_2\text{SO}_4} [(\text{CH}_3)_2\text{COHCH}_2\text{Cl}] \longrightarrow [(\text{CH}_3)_2\text{COHCH}_2\text{OH}] \longrightarrow$$
$$(\text{CH}_3)_2\text{CHCHO}$$

$$(\text{CH}_3)_2\text{CClCHClCH}_3 \xrightarrow[\text{heat}]{\text{H}_2\text{O—H}_2\text{SO}_4} [(\text{CH}_3)_2\text{COHCHOHCH}_3] \longrightarrow (\text{CH}_3)_2\text{CHCOCH}_3$$

3. OXIDATIVE SCISSION. The bond between the two hydroxylated carbon atoms can be split readily by oxidation. If reagents such as permanganate or acid dichromate are used, two moles of acid are formed (p. 121). By choosing the proper reagents, the oxidation stops at the aldehyde stage. Lead tetraacetate is the preferred reagent for this purpose in anhydrous solvents (*Criegee reaction*), and periodic acid is the preferred reagent in aqueous solutions (*Malaprade reaction*).

$$\text{RCHOHCHOHR} + \text{Pb(OCOCH}_3)_4 \longrightarrow 2\ \text{RCHO} + \text{Pb(OCOCH}_3)_2 + 2\ \text{HOCOCH}_3$$

$$\text{RCHOHCHOHR} + \text{HIO}_4 \longrightarrow 2\ \text{RCHO} + \text{HIO}_3 + \text{H}_2\text{O}$$

Since both lead tetraacetate and periodic acid can be estimated readily by iodimetric methods, the reactions can be used for the quantitative determination of 1,2-glycols.

Important 1,2-Glycols. After deciding that the structural formula for glycerol is 1,2,3-propanetriol, Wurtz reasoned that an analogous 1,2-ethanediol should be possible. In 1859 he reported its synthesis by the saponification of the acetate which he prepared by the action of silver acetate on ethylene iodide. Because the product resembled glycerol in its properties, it was called *glycol*.

In recent years **ethylene glycol** has become technically important and it was one of the first organic chemicals to be produced commercially from petroleum. Its development was not planned, but resulted from a research program. One of the first industrial fellowships to be established at Mellon Institute was that by the Prest-O-Lite company for the development of a cheaper process for the manufacture of acetylene. A process was developed for the thermal cracking of natural gas or petroleum to acetylene, but large amounts of ethylene also were obtained. Attempts to utilize the ethylene led to the production of ethylene glycol. When glycol first became available in quantity in 1922 there were no important uses for it. Its 1948 production of 370 million pounds placed it sixth in quantity among synthetic organic chemicals.

At present three processes of manufacture are used. In the oldest process ethylene is passed into a solution of hypochlorous acid at 0° (cf. p. 42). Distillation gives a constant-boiling mixture of ethylene chlorohydrin and water. Some ethylene chloride is obtained as a co-product. Hydrolysis of the ethylene chlorohydrin solution with sodium bicarbonate gives the glycol (b.p. 197°) which is freed of water by distillation.

In the second process ethylene is oxidized by air to ethylene oxide, which is hydrolyzed to glycol by heating with water in a pressure system.

$$CH_2{=}CH_2 + O_2 \text{ (air)} \xrightarrow[250°]{\text{Ag cat.,}} \underset{\substack{\text{O} \\ \text{Ethylene} \\ \text{oxide}}}{CH_2{-}CH_2} \xrightarrow[\text{heat}]{H_2O} \underset{\substack{\text{Ethylene} \\ \text{glycol}}}{HOCH_2CH_2OH}$$

In the third process formaldehyde, carbon monoxide, and water are combined catalytically at high pressure to glycollic acid which is converted to the methyl ester and reduced to glycol.

$$HCHO + CO + H_2O \longrightarrow \underset{\text{Glycollic acid}}{HOCH_2COOH} \longrightarrow HOCH_2COOCH_3 \longrightarrow HOCH_2CH_2OH$$

The chief use for ethylene glycol is as a nonvolatile antifreeze for automobile radiators, and as a coolant for airplane motors. Like glycerol it is hygroscopic and can replace glycerol for many technical uses. Ethylene glycol should not be used in foods or cosmetics, however, because it is relatively toxic. A large part is oxidized to oxalic acid by the body, and calcium oxalate (p. 539) deposits in the renal tubules causing anuria.

Much ethylene glycol is used for the manufacture of other chemicals. The **dinitrate** is an explosive and is used to lower the freezing point of nitroglycerin (p. 525). When the glycol is distilled with 4 per cent aqueous sulfuric acid it gives **1,4-dioxane.**

$$2 \text{ HOCH}_2\text{CH}_2\text{OH} \xrightarrow[\text{heat}]{\text{Dil. H}_2\text{SO}_4,} \begin{array}{c} \text{O} \\ \text{H}_2\text{C} \diagup \quad \diagdown \text{CH}_2 \\ | \qquad | \\ \text{H}_2\text{C} \diagdown \quad \diagup \text{CH}_2 \\ \text{O} \end{array} + 2 \text{ H}_2\text{O}$$

1,4-Dioxane

Dioxane is a valuable solvent and paint remover, but should be used with good ventilation because it is fairly toxic.

When ethylene oxide reacts with an alcohol, or a phenol, a monoalkyl or monoaryl ether of ethylene glycol is formed.

$$(\text{CH}_2)_2\text{O} + \text{ROH} \longrightarrow \text{HOCH}_2\text{CH}_2\text{OR}$$

$$(\text{CH}_2)_2\text{O} + \text{ArOH} \longrightarrow \text{HOCH}_2\text{CH}_2\text{OAr}$$

The **monoethyl ether** was called *Cellosolve*, because it is a solvent for cellulose nitrate and is used in the formulation of lacquers. Other glycol ethers and their acetates also are useful for this purpose.

Ethylene glycol reacts with successive molecules of ethylene oxide to give **diethylene glycol, triethylene glycol,** higher condensation products, and finally high molecular weight **polyethylene glycols.**

$$\text{HOCH}_2\text{CH}_2\text{OH} \xrightarrow{(\text{CH}_2)_2\text{O}} \text{HOCH}_2\text{CH}_2\text{OCH}_2\text{CH}_2\text{OH} \xrightarrow{(\text{CH}_2)_2\text{O}}$$

Diethylene glycol

$$\text{HOCH}_2\text{CH}_2\text{OCH}_2\text{CH}_2\text{OCH}_2\text{CH}_2\text{OH} \xrightarrow{(\text{CH}_2)_2\text{O}} \text{HO}(\text{CH}_2\text{CH}_2\text{O})_x\text{CH}_2\text{CH}_2\text{OH}$$

Triethylene glycol   Polyethylene glycols

The polyethylene glycols vary in properties from sticky viscous liquids to wax-like solids (*Carbowaxes*) and all are soluble in water.

Reaction of monoalkyl ethers of ethylene glycol with ethylene oxide gives the **monoalkyl ethers of diethylene glycols** which are known as *Carbitols* and are used in lacquer formulation. When monoaryl ethers of ethylene glycol react with an excess of ethylene oxide, the **monoaryl ethers** of **polyethylene glycols** are formed.

$$\text{ArOCH}_2\text{CH}_2\text{OH} + x\,(\text{CH}_2)_2\text{O} \longrightarrow \text{ArO}(\text{CH}_2\text{CH}_2\text{O})x\text{CH}_2\text{CH}_2\text{OH}$$

Products of this type are good detergents and being nonionic can be combined with either anionic or cationic surface active compounds.

Before the discovery of the direct oxidation of ethylene to ethylene oxide, the latter was made by the action of concentrated alkali on the chlorohydrin.

$$\text{HOCH}_2\text{CH}_2\text{Cl} + \text{NaOH} \longrightarrow \begin{array}{c} \text{CH}_2\text{---CH}_2 \\ \diagdown \; \diagup \\ \text{O} \end{array} + \text{NaCl} + \text{H}_2\text{O}$$

This reaction is general for 1,2-halohydrins. Ethylene oxides frequently are called **epoxides** or **epoxy derivatives.** Thus ethylene oxide may be called *epoxyethane.*

The three-membered ring is more reactive than higher-membered rings, and ethylene oxides react with all compounds containing active hydrogen to give open chain products. The reactions with alcohols give β-hydroxy ethers (p. 522); with mercaptans, β-hydroxy sulfides; with amines, β-hydroxy amines; and with carboxylic acids, β-hydroxy esters. Grignard reagents react to give alcohols. The ring of monosubstituted ethylene oxides usually opens to give a secondary hydroxyl group.

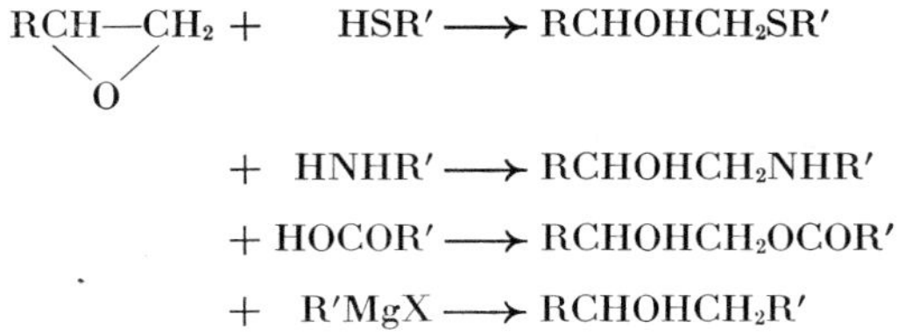

$$RCH{-}CH_2 + \quad HSR' \longrightarrow RCHOHCH_2SR'$$
$$\underset{O}{\diagdown\diagup}$$

$$+ \quad HNHR' \longrightarrow RCHOHCH_2NHR'$$

$$+ \quad HOCOR' \longrightarrow RCHOHCH_2OCOR'$$

$$+ \quad R'MgX \longrightarrow RCHOHCH_2R'$$

The reaction of Grignard reagents with ethylene oxide is very useful in organic synthesis, since it permits building up a carbon chain, two atoms at a time.

$$RMgX + (CH_2)_2O \longrightarrow RCH_2CH_2OMgX \overset{HX}{\rightarrow} RCH_2CH_2OH + MgX_2$$

Propylene glycol is made by a series of reactions analogous to that for the preparation of ethylene glycol.

$$CH_3CH{=}CH_2 \overset{HOCl}{\longrightarrow} CH_3CHOHCH_2Cl \overset{H_2O-Na_2CO_3}{\longrightarrow} CH_3CHOHCH_2OH$$
$$\text{1,2-Propanediol}$$
$$\text{(propylene glycol)}$$

Propylene glycol has properties similar to those of ethylene glycol. Unlike ethylene glycol, however, it is nontoxic and can be used to replace glycerol in food products and cosmetics. It is toxic to lower forms of life and aerosols of it have been used in hospitals and schools to reduce the incidence of air-borne infections. Mixed with ethylene glycol it is used as radiator antifreeze.

The reaction of propylene chlorohydrin with alkali gives **propylene oxide** or **epoxypropane.** It has properties analogous to those of ethylene oxide.

2,3-Butanediol (β-butylene glycol) is the principal product of the fermentation of starch by *Aerobacillus polymyxa.* Ethyl alcohol, acetone, acetic acid, diacetyl, aldehydes, and higher alcohols also are formed during the fermentation.

1,3-Glycols

Trimethylene glycol is formed merely by boiling trimethylene bromide with water. The 1,3-dibromide results almost exclusively by the addition of hydrogen bromide to allyl bromide in the absence of antioxidants.

$$CH_2{=}CHCH_2Br + HBr \longrightarrow Br(CH_2)_3Br$$

Trimethylene glycol also is formed in the reductive fermentation of glycerol by bacteria and frequently is available as a by-product of soap manufacture. Its principal use is for the synthesis of trimethylene halides and halohydrins used in laboratory syntheses. **Trimethylene chloride** is used for the preparation of cyclopropane (p. 561).

Aldol condensation of *n*-butyraldehyde, followed by reduction, gives **2-ethyl-1,3-hexanediol.**

$$n\text{-}C_3H_7CHO + CH_2CHO \xrightarrow{\text{Dil. NaOH}} C_3H_7CHOHCHCHO \xrightarrow{\text{H}_2\text{—Ni}} C_3H_7CHOHCHCH_2OH$$

$$\underset{C_2H_5}{} \quad \underset{C_2H_5}{} \quad \underset{C_2H_5}{}$$

2-Ethyl-1,3-hexanediol

It is an effective insect repellent, marketed as "6–12."

α,ω-Glycols

Glycols in general may be made by the hydrolysis of the corresponding dihalide. Frequently the reaction of the dihalide with sodium acetate in acetic acid solution to produce the diacetate proceeds better, and the ester can be hydrolyzed to the glycol.

$$Br(CH_2)_xBr + 2\ NaOCOCH_3 \longrightarrow CH_3COO(CH_2)_xOCOCH_3 \xrightarrow{\text{NaOH}} HO(CH_2)_xOH$$

If the proper dicarboxylic acids are available, the glycol can be prepared by the reduction of the diester.

$$CH_3OOC(CH_2)_xCOOCH_3 \xrightarrow[\text{Na—ROH}]{\text{H}_2\text{—Ni, or}} HOCH_2(CH_2)_xCH_2OH$$

Tetramethylene glycol can be made from acetylene (p. 501) or from tetrahydrofuran (p. 453). Tetramethylene halohydrins are useful intermediates in laboratory syntheses and tetramethylene chloride is used technically for the synthesis of hexamethylene diamine (p. 554). Since these halogen derivatives can be obtained directly from tetrahydrofuran by reaction with halogen acids (p. 453), tetramethylene glycol itself has little use.

Tri- to Hexahydric Alcohols

The only trihydric alcohol of importance is **glycerol.** It was isolated first by Scheele in 1779 as a saponification product of fats (p. 153). He called it *oelsuess* because of its sweet taste. It was named *glycerin* (Gr. *glykeros* sweet) by Chevreul (p. 568), and its structural formula was assigned to it by Wurtz in 1855. Until 1948 it was obtained almost exclusively as a co-product of the manufacture of soap, and its price varied greatly. In 1939 it sold for $0.12, in 1946 for as high as $0.75, and in 1949 for $0.24 per pound.

A small amount of glycerol is formed during alcoholic fermentation, and the amount can be increased by the addition of sodium sulfite or by keeping the fermenting liquors slightly alkaline. Isolation is difficult, however, and the process cannot compete under normal conditions with glycerol from fats.

Many synthetic processes for glycerol manufacture have been developed, but it was not until 1948 that a plant was built utilizing a process announced in 1938. In this process propylene is chlorinated to allyl chloride and the latter hydrolyzed to allyl alcohol (p. 517). The allyl alcohol is converted with hypochlorous acid to glycerol α-chlorohydrin, a product that can be hydrolyzed easily to glycerol.

$$CH_2=CHCH_2OH \xrightarrow{HOCl} ClCH_2CHOHCH_2OH \xrightarrow[NaOH]{Na_2CO_3,} HOCH_2CHOHCH_2OH$$

A contract was made for the entire output of the first plant for the synthesis of glycerol at the reputed price of $0.19 per pound when natural glycerol was selling for $0.33 per pound.

Production of glycerol from fats reached over 200 million pounds in 1947. About half was used for four purposes: (*1*) for the manufacture of alkyd type resins (p. 415); (*2*) as a humectant for tobacco; (*3*) for the manufacture of nitroglycerin; and (*4*) as a softening agent for viscose films (p. 305). The remaining half was used in cosmetics, pharmaceutical preparations, printing inks, textile processing, food products, and in the manufacture of emulsifying agents (p. 159) and other chemicals.

When glycerol is heated in the presence of an acid catalyst such as potassium bisulfate, it loses two molecules of water to form **acrolein.**

$$HOCH_2CHOHCH_2OH \xrightarrow[KHSO_4]{Heat} [HOCH_2CH=CHOH] \longrightarrow [HOCH_2CH_2CHO] \longrightarrow CH_2=CHCHO$$
$$\text{Acrolein}$$

Acrolein is a sharply lachrymatory substance and is responsible for the disagreeable nature of the fumes from overheated fats.

Glyceryl nitrate, commonly called *nitroglycerin*, is an important explosive made by the reaction of glycerol with nitric acid in the presence of sulfuric acid.

$$\begin{matrix} CH_2OH \\ | \\ CHOH \\ | \\ CH_2OH \end{matrix} + 3\ HNO_3 \xrightarrow{(H_2SO_4)} \begin{matrix} CH_2ONO_2 \\ | \\ CHONO_2 \\ | \\ CH_2ONO_2 \end{matrix} + 3\ H_2O$$
$$\text{Glyceryl}$$
$$\text{nitrate}$$
$$\text{(nitroglycerin)}$$

It is an oil which freezes at 13°. Formerly it was the chief explosive ingredient of **dynamite,** being mixed in amounts up to 40 per cent with a combustible mixture such as powdered wood pulp and sodium nitrate in the ratio of about 1 to 3. At present dynamites contain up to 45 per cent ammonium nitrate mixed with sodium nitrate and wood pulp, and some nitroglycerin is added merely as a sensitizer for the ammonium nitrate. **Gelatin dynamite** is a mixture of wood pulp, sodium nitrate, and nitroglycerin gelatinized with 2 to 6 per cent of cellulose nitrate. It is plastic and can be loaded solidly into bore holes. It has a high water-resistance, a requirement for work in wet places. Dynamite has many useful applications such as in mining, road building, and agriculture. Over 600 million pounds was used in the United States in 1947. Double-base military smokeless powders such as *Ballistite* and *Cordite* consist of about 60 per cent cellulose nitrate gelatinized with 40 per cent nitroglycerin.

1,2-Dithioglycerol (2,3-dimercapto-1-propanol), known as **BAL** (British Anti-Lewisite), was developed during World War II as an antidote for arsenical war gases such as Lewisite (p. 592). The toxicity of the trivalent arsenic compounds is believed to be due to the inhibition of enzyme action by the combination of arsenic with thiol groups in enzymes. 1,2-Alkanethiols form a more stable cyclic reaction product with the arsenic and prevent combination of the arsenic with the enzyme. BAL has found general use as an antidote for poisoning by heavy metals.

Pentaerythritol is the most important tetrahydric alcohol. It is prepared by the reaction of an aqueous solution of acetaldehyde with an excess of paraformaldehyde in the presence of lime. The reaction consists of an aldol condensation followed by a crossed Cannizzaro reaction (p. 403).

$$3 \text{ HCHO} + \text{CH}_3\text{CHO} \xrightarrow{\text{Ca(OH)}_2} (\text{HOCH}_2)_3\text{CCHO} \xrightarrow{\text{HCHO—Ca(OH)}_2} \underset{\substack{\text{Pentaery-}\\\text{thritol}}}{(\text{HOCH}_2)_4\text{C}} + \underset{\substack{\text{Calcium}\\\text{formate}}}{\tfrac{1}{2} \text{ Ca(OCHO)}_2}$$

The highly symmetrical structure accounts for the high melting point of 262°. Over 20 million pounds was produced in 1948, most of which was used for the up-grading of drying oils. By esterification with unsaturated fat acids an ester is produced that has a higher molecular weight than the glycerides of natural fats. Hence a lower degree of polymerization is needed to produce films having the necessary toughness and hardness. Thus soybean oil is not a very good drying oil (p. 156). If the soybean oil is hydrolyzed and the fat acids are reesterified with pentaerythritol, the product "dries" more rapidly. A second use for pentaerythritol is for the preparation of the nitrate known as **PETN.** Mixed with 30 per cent TNT it is used as a high explosive charge for bombs, torpedoes, and mines, and for demolition purposes. Some is used in peacetime in blasting caps and pulverulent dynamite.

The sugar alcohols are straight-chain tetra-, penta-, and hexahydric alcohols (p. 307).

AMINO ALCOHOLS AND POLYAMINES

Like the aldehyde hydrates, the **1-hydroxy-1-amino compounds** (aldehyde ammonias) and **1,1-diamino compounds** usually are unstable, undergoing dehydration or deamination, and polymerization (p. 171).

1-Hydroxy-2-amino compounds can be prepared by the general methods, but those compounds most readily available are prepared by the reaction of ethylene oxides with ammonia or primary or secondary amines, or by the reduction of nitro alcohols. Reaction of ethylene oxide with ammonia gives 2-aminoethanol or 2-hydroxyethylamine, commonly called **ethanolamine.** A second molecule of ethylene oxide gives bis(2-hydroxyethyl)amine or **diethanolamine,** and a third yields tris(2-hydroxyethyl)amine or **triethanolamine.**

$$\underset{\substack{\diagdown\,\diagup\\O}}{\text{CH}_2\text{—CH}_2} \xrightarrow{\text{NH}_3} \underset{\text{Ethanolamine}}{\text{HOCH}_2\text{CH}_2\text{NH}_2} \xrightarrow{(\text{CH}_2)_2\text{O}} \underset{\text{Diethanolamine}}{(\text{HOCH}_2\text{CH}_2)_2\text{NH}} \xrightarrow{(\text{CH}_2)_2\text{O}} \underset{\text{Triethanolamine}}{(\text{HOCH}_2\text{CH}_2)_3\text{N}}$$

Salts of the ethanolamines with fat acids are soluble in both water and hydrocarbons and are good emulsifying agents. Thus kerosene or paraffin oil containing a small amount of triethanolamine oleate can be mixed with water to give stable emulsions useful as agricultural sprays, or as lubricating coolants during high speed metal-cutting operations.

Ethanolamine and its trimethylammonium salts, the cholines (p. 195), constitute a portion of an important class of biological substances known as the *phospholipids.* Thus the **cephalins** (or kephalins) are mixed esters of glycerol and ethanolamine (cholamine) with fat acids and phosphoric acid. The **lecithins** contain the trimethylammonium group instead of the ammonium group. **Sphingomyelin** contains the unsaturated dihydroxy amine *sphingosine* instead of glycerol.

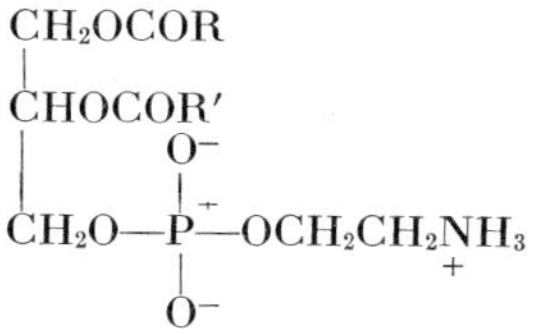

$$CH_2OCOR$$
$$CHOCOR'$$
$$\qquad O^-$$
$$CH_2O-\overset{|}{\underset{|}{P}}-OCH_2CH_2\overset{+}{N}H_3$$
$$\qquad O^-$$

Cephalins

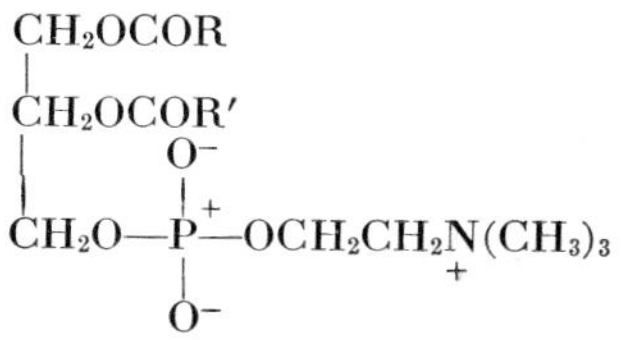

$$CH_2OCOR$$
$$CH_2OCOR'$$
$$\qquad O^-$$
$$CH_2O-\overset{|}{\underset{|}{P}}-OCH_2CH_2\overset{+}{N}(CH_3)_3$$
$$\qquad O^-$$

Lecithins

$$CH_3(CH_2)_{12}CH=CHCHOH$$
$$CHNHCOR$$
$$\qquad O^-$$
$$CH_2O-\overset{|}{\underset{|}{P}}-OCH_2CH_2\overset{+}{N}(CH_3)_3$$
$$\qquad O^-$$

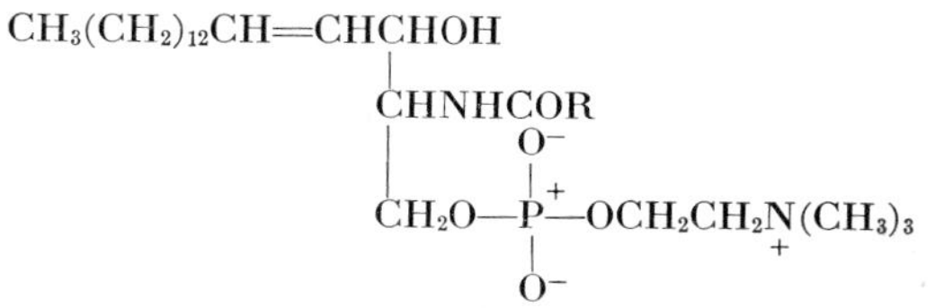

Sphingomyelin

The phospholipids are components of all animal and vegetable cells and are abundant in the brain, spinal cord, eggs, and soybeans. They possibly function as emulsifying agents for fats and are important in the metabolism of fats. *Soybean lecithin* is used in large quantities for the stabilization of emulsified food fats such as oleomargarin and mayonnaise.

Reaction of methyldiethanolamine hydrochloride with thionyl chloride or phosphorus trichloride gives **methylbis(2-chloroethyl)amine hydrochloride.**

$$(HOCH_2CH_2)_2NHCH_3^+\ ^-Cl + 2\ SOCl_2 \longrightarrow (ClCH_2CH_2)_2NHCH_3^+\ ^-Cl + 2\ HCl + SO_2$$

The free base is the nitrogen analog of mustard gas (p. 221) and belongs to the class of compounds known as **nitrogen mustards.** Many nitrogen mustards were prepared and investigated as toxic agents during World War II. They have a local vesicant action similar to that of mustard gas and in addition penetrate the skin and exert a generalized systemic action on living cells similar to the action of X-rays. Exposure to very low concentrations may cause opacity of the cornea.

In the reaction of propylene oxide with ammonia the point of attack is the 1 position giving rise to **1-amino-2-propanol.**

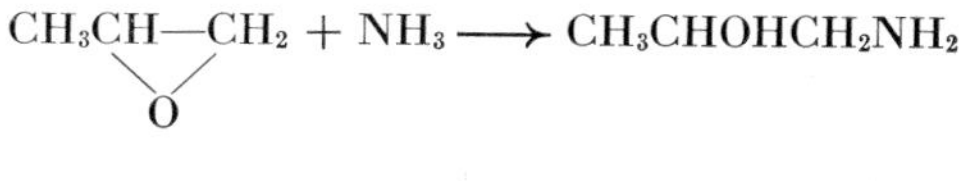

$$CH_3CH{-}CH_2 + NH_3 \longrightarrow CH_3CHOHCH_2NH_2$$
$$\underset{O}{\diagdown\diagup}$$

2-Amino-1-hydroxy compounds are available by reduction of the corresponding nitro alcohols obtained by the condensation of aldehydes with aliphatic nitro compounds (p. 205).

$$(CH_3)_2CCH_2OH \xrightarrow{H_2-Ni} (CH_3)_2CCH_2OH$$
$$\underset{NO_2}{|} \qquad\qquad \underset{NH_2}{|}$$

Diamino compounds can be prepared by the usual methods for preparing amines. Thus they are formed by the reaction of ammonia with primary or secondary dihalides, by the reduction of dinitriles, or by the Hofmann degradation of diamides.

Ethylenediamine is obtained by the reaction of ethylene chloride with ammonia.

$$ClCH_2CH_2Cl + 4\ NH_3 \longrightarrow H_2NCH_2CH_2NH_2 + 2\ NH_4Cl$$

Further reaction with ethylene chloride and ammonia gives the co-products **diethylenetriamine**, $H_2NCH_2CH_2NHCH_2CH_2NH_2$, **triethylenetetramine**, $H_2N(CH_2CH_2NH)_2CH_2CH_2NH_2$, and **tetraethylenepentamine**, $H_2N(CH_2CH_2NH)_3CH_2CH_2NH_2$. All of these compounds are manufactured on a large scale commercially and are used in the synthesis of pharmaceuticals, textile finishing agents, emulsifying agents and fungicides. **Ethylenediammonium tartrate** crystals are piezo-electric and thin plates cut from them are used instead of quartz plates for the control of high frequency electric currents in telephony, radio, radar, and television. Ethylenediamine is used also in the preparation of basic ion exchange resins by copolymerizing it with formaldehyde and *m*-phenylenediamine (p. 390) or urea (p. 242).

Tetramethylenediamine, known as *putrescine*, and **pentamethylenediamine,** known as *cadaverine*, occur among the bacterial decomposition products of proteins. They arise from the decarboxylation of ornithine and lysine, respectively.

$$\underset{\text{Ornithine}}{H_2N(CH_2)_3CHNH_2COOH} \xrightarrow{\text{Bacteria}} \underset{\text{Putrescine}}{H_2N(CH_2)_4NH_2} + CO_2$$

$$\underset{\text{Lysine}}{H_2N(CH_2)_4CHNH_2COOH} \xrightarrow{\text{Bacteria}} \underset{\text{Cadaverine}}{H_2N(CH_2)_5NH_2} + CO_2$$

Spermine, $H_2N(CH_2)_3NH(CH_2)_4NH(CH_2)_3NH_2$, is widely distributed in the organs of mammals and has been isolated also from yeast.

Hexamethylenediamine is an intermediate for the synthesis of *Nylon* (p. 544) and is made commercially by the catalytic reduction of tetramethylene cyanide (adiponitrile, p. 544) in the presence of ammonia to prevent the formation of imino derivatives.

$$\underset{\text{Adiponitrile}}{NC(CH_2)_4CN} + 4\ H_2 \xrightarrow{Ni\ (NH_3)} \underset{\substack{\text{Hexamethylene-}\\\text{diamine}}}{H_2N(CH_2)_6NH_2}$$

REVIEW QUESTIONS

1. Give two reactions by which ethylene glycol is prepared commercially starting with ethylene.

2. Give reactions for the conversion of ethylene chlorohydrin into 2-chloroethyl ether and dioxane; of ethylene oxide into 2-ethoxyethyl alcohol (Cellosolve), ethanolamine, diethanolamine, triethanolamine, and *n*-hexyl alcohol.

3. Give balanced equations for the reaction of 1,2-glycols with lead tetraacetate (Criegee reagent), periodic acid (Malaprade reagent), and strong acids (pinacol rearrangement).

4. What are chelate compounds? How does the formation of a chelate compound explain the fact that boric acid becomes a stronger acid in the presence of 1,2-glycols?

5. What is the best source of trimethylene glycol; tetramethylene glycol? Give two general methods for the synthesis of α,ω-glycols.

6. What is the formula and source of each of the following compounds: glycerol; pentaerythritol; mannitol; sorbitol?

7. Discuss the preparation and properties of vinyl alcohol and vinyl acetate; polyvinyl alcohol and polyvinyl acetate.

8. Give reactions for the conversion of glycerol into allyl alcohol; allyl chloride into glycerol. How is allyl chloride made commercially?

9. α-Methylallyl alcohol (methallyl alcohol) on distillation with dilute sulfuric acid is converted into isobutyraldehyde. Explain.

Chapter 35

HALOGENATED, HYDROXY, AMINO, AND UNSATURATED ACIDS

It is convenient to group the halogenated, hydroxy, amino, and unsaturated acids together, because they frequently are interconvertible, and their reactions often yield the same type of product.

HALOGENATED ACIDS

Preparation

α-**Chloro** and **bromo acids** are prepared by the Hell-Volhard-Zelinsky reaction, which involves a direct halogenation in the presence of a small amount of phosphorus trihalide (p. 137).

$$RCH_2COOH \xrightarrow[(PX_3)]{X_2} RCHXCOOH + HX$$

The rate of halogenation of acids, unlike the halogenation of aldehydes and ketones, is dependent on the concentration of the halogen, is not subject to general acid catalysis, and is increased greatly by the presence of a small amount of acyl halide. Hence it is believed that the halogenation takes place through the acyl halide. Because of the equilibrium between the acid and the acyl halide, a small amount of the latter suffices to permit the reaction to take place at a practical rate.

$$RCH_2COX + X_2 \longrightarrow RCHXCOX + HX$$

$$RCHXCOX + RCH_2COOH \rightleftarrows RCHXCOOH + RCH_2COX$$

Monoiodo acids result from the reaction of the chloro acid with sodium iodide (p. 81). **Fluoroacetic acid** has been prepared by the hydrolysis of its methyl ester. The latter was obtained by the reaction of the iodo ester with mercurous fluoride (p. 512). Fluoroacetic acid is made commercially by the direct combination of carbon monoxide, formaldehyde and hydrogen fluoride.

$$CO + HCHO + HF \xrightarrow[750 \text{ at.}]{160°,} FCH_2COOH$$

Trifluoroacetic acid results in 50 per cent yield from the vigorous oxidation of benzotrifluoride.

$$C_6H_5CF_3 \xrightarrow[\text{boil 2 weeks}]{Na_2Cr_2O_7-H_2SO_4,} HOOCCF_3 + 5 CO_2 + 2 H_2O$$

This method demonstrates the remarkable stability of the trifluoromethyl group. The reaction takes place more readily if an amino group is present in the ring, but the best method of preparation is by the oxidation of 2,3-dichloro-perfluoro-2-butene.

$$F_3CCCl{=}CClCF_3 \xrightarrow[\text{(aq. KMnO}_4)]{2\,[O],\,2\,H_2O} 2\ F_3CCOOH + 2\ HCl$$

β-Chloro or **bromo acids** are made by the addition of halogen acids to α,β-unsaturated acids or by the reaction of β-hydroxy acids with halogen acids.

Hydrogen halide always adds to the β carbon atom of an α,β-unsaturated acid regardless of the prediction of the Markovnikov rule, because of 1,4 addition.

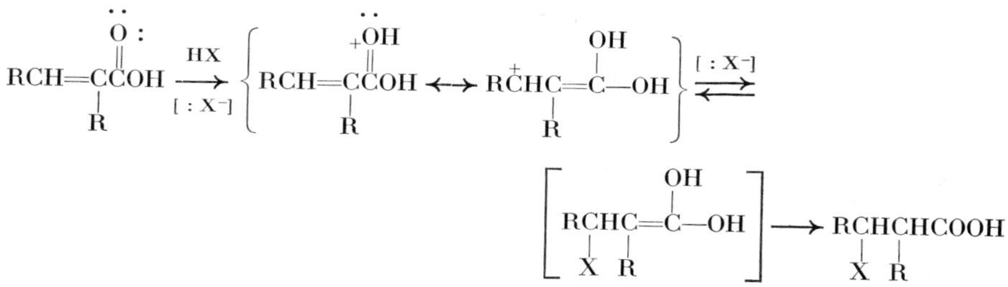

γ-Halogen acids result from the reaction of γ-hydroxy acids with halogen acid. **ω-Halogen acids** are obtained from α, ω-dihalides by reaction with one mole of sodium cyanide and hydrolysis of the nitrile.

$$Br(CH_2)_xBr + NaCN \longrightarrow Br(CH_2)_xCN \xrightarrow{HBr-H_2O} Br(CH_2)_xCOOH + NH_4Br$$

Properties and Reactions

Increasing substitution by halogen on the α carbon atom increases the acidity of carboxylic acids. The dissociation constants for acetic, chloro-, dichloro-, and trichloroacetic acids are respectively 1.7×10^{-5}, 1.4×10^{-3}, 5×10^{-2}, and 1.3×10^{-1}. Thus trichloroacetic acid is almost as strong as sulfuric acid. Trifluoroacetic acid is considerably stronger than trichloroacetic acid. Only halogen in the α position has an appreciable effect on the acidity of the carboxyl group.

Chloroacetic acid is toxic to microorganisms at very low concentrations and is an excellent sterilizing agent. Its use as a food preservative is prohibited in the United States. Fluoroacetic acid is much more toxic to mammals than chloroacetic acid, and its sodium salt, known as *1080*, is used as a poison for rodents and other wild animal pests. In contrast sodium di- and trifluoro-acetates are reported to be harmless (cf. p. 511).

Trichloroacetic acid decomposes into chloroform and carbon dioxide (cf. haloform reaction, p. 174).

$$Cl_3CCOOH \longrightarrow Cl_3CH + CO_2$$

This reaction takes place slowly even on boiling aqueous solutions and proceeds rapidly in alkaline solutions. Trifluoroacetic acid on the other hand is very stable.

The halogen in halogenated saturated acids behaves like that in alkyl halides and can be replaced by other functional groups by means of the usual reagents. The α-, β-, γ-, and δ-halogenated acids show characteristic differences in their reactions with aqueous or alcoholic alkali. The α-halogenated acids hydrolyze most readily to the α-hydroxy acids, boiling with water or dilute alkali being sufficient. β-Halogenated acids under the same conditions lose halogen acid to give the α,β-unsaturated acid, frequently mixed with the β,γ-unsaturated acid. Boiling with aqueous carbonate solution may lead to decarboxylation as well as loss of halogen acid.

$$\underset{\underset{CH_3}{|}}{CH_3CHBrCHCOONa} + Na_2CO_3 + H_2O \xrightarrow{\text{Heat}} CH_3CH=CHCH_3 + 2\,NaHCO_3 + NaBr$$

γ- and δ-Halogenated acids on boiling with water or aqueous carbonate solution give five- or six-membered cyclic esters known as *lactones*.

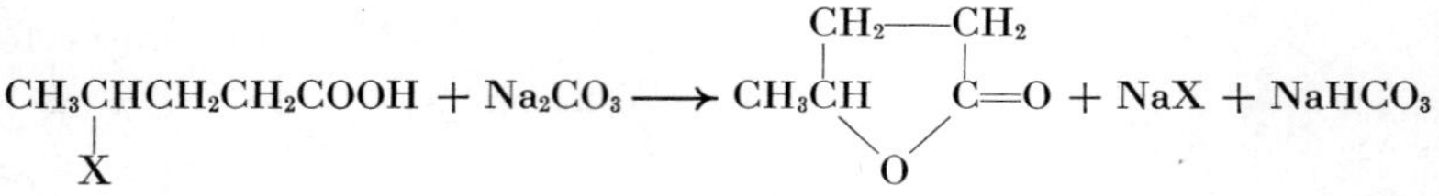

$$\underset{\underset{X}{|}}{CH_3CHCH_2CH_2COOH} + Na_2CO_3 \longrightarrow CH_3CH \quad C=O + NaX + NaHCO_3$$

γ-Valerolactone

$$\underset{\underset{X}{|}}{CH_2CH_2CH_2CH_2COOH} + Na_2CO_3 \longrightarrow \quad + NaX + NaHCO_3$$

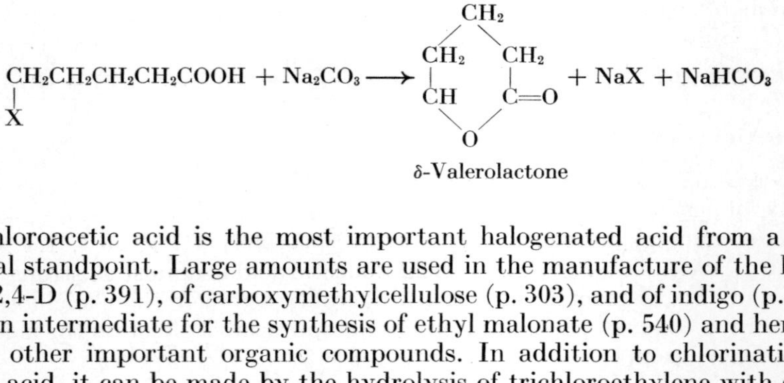

δ-Valerolactone

Chloroacetic acid is the most important halogenated acid from a commercial standpoint. Large amounts are used in the manufacture of the herbicide, 2,4-D (p. 391), of carboxymethylcellulose (p. 303), and of indigo (p. 484). It is an intermediate for the synthesis of ethyl malonate (p. 540) and hence of many other important organic compounds. In addition to chlorination of acetic acid, it can be made by the hydrolysis of trichloroethylene with dilute acids.

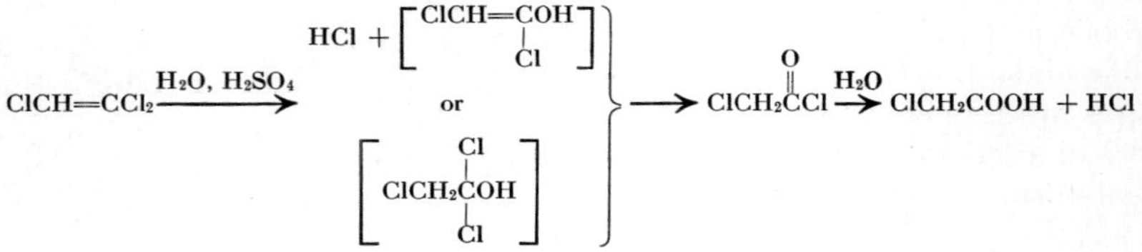

$$ClCH=CCl_2 \xrightarrow{H_2O,\ H_2SO_4} \begin{array}{c} HCl + \left[\underset{\underset{Cl}{|}}{ClCH=COH}\right] \\ \text{or} \\ \left[\underset{\underset{Cl}{|}}{ClCH_2COH}\right] \end{array} \longrightarrow ClCH_2\overset{O}{\overset{||}{C}}Cl \xrightarrow{H_2O} ClCH_2COOH + HCl$$

HYDROXY ACIDS

Preparation

α-**Hydroxy acids** may be prepared by the hydrolysis of α-halogen acids, or by the hydrolysis of the cyanohydrins of aldehydes or ketones.

$$\text{RCHO} \xrightarrow{\text{HCN}} \text{RCH} \overset{\text{OH}}{\underset{\text{CN}}{\diagup\diagdown}} \xrightarrow{\text{H}_2\text{O—HCl}} \text{RCHOHCOOH} + \text{NH}_4\text{Cl}$$

β-**Hydroxy acids** may be made by the catalytic reduction of β-keto esters followed by hydrolysis. The β-hydroxy esters are obtained also by the **Re-formatsky reaction.** This reaction is brought about by the addition of zinc to a mixture of a β-halogen ester, usually the β-bromo ester, with an aldehyde or ketone in ether or aromatic hydrocarbon solution.

$$\text{RCHO} + \text{BrCH}_2\text{COOC}_2\text{H}_5 + \text{Zn} \longrightarrow \underset{\text{OZnBr}}{\text{RCHCH}_2\text{COOC}_2\text{H}_5} \xrightarrow{\text{HCl}} \text{RCHOHCH}_2\text{COOC}_2\text{H}_5$$

Chloro esters react if a zinc-copper couple is used in place of zinc. Because of the ease of dehydration of β-hydroxy acids, the product may be accompanied by varying amounts of α,β- and β,γ-unsaturated ester.

The Reformatsky reaction is closely related to the Grignard reaction. The initial product undoubtedly is the organozinc compound, $\text{XZnCH}_2\text{COOC}_2\text{H}_5$, which then adds to the carbonyl group. The organomagnesium compounds are more reactive and lead to self condensation with the ester group and with the reactive halogen. For the same reason the organozinc compound must be prepared in the presence of the aldehyde or ketone, with which it reacts more rapidly than with the ester group or halogen.

Compounds containing the hydroxyl group further removed from the carboxyl group than the β position are prepared by hydrolysis of the halogenated acid or by reduction of the keto acid.

Reactions

α-Hydroxy acids undergo bimolecular esterification with the formation of a six-membered ring. Such cyclic esters are known as *lactides*.

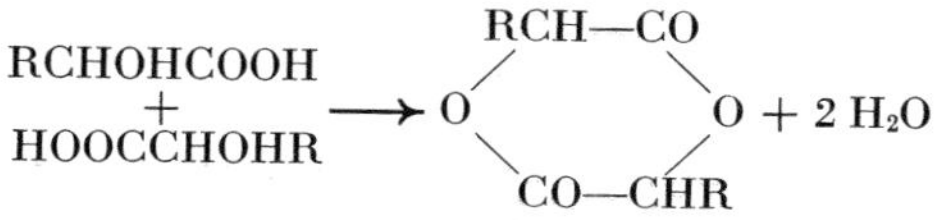

$$\begin{matrix}\text{RCHOHCOOH} \\ + \\ \text{HOOCCHOHR}\end{matrix} \longrightarrow \text{O} \overset{\text{RCH—CO}}{\underset{\text{CO—CHR}}{\diagup\diagdown}} \text{O} + 2\,\text{H}_2\text{O}$$

A lactide

This reaction takes place so readily that it is possible to keep α-hydroxy acids in their monomolecular state only in the form of their sodium salts.

When α-hydroxy acids are boiled with dilute sulfuric acid, carbon monoxide and water are lost with the formation of an aldehyde.

$$RCHOHCOOH \xrightarrow[\text{heat}]{H_2SO_4-H_2O} RCHO + CO + H_2O$$

This reaction is valuable for the synthesis of higher aldehydes from acids through the α-bromo acid. Since one carbon atom is lost in the process, the series of reactions may be used for the stepwise degradation of a carbon chain.

β-Hydroxy acids lose water easily to give α,β-unsaturated acids, frequently mixed with β,γ-unsaturated acids. γ- and δ-Hydroxy acids are stable only in the form of their salts. The free acids spontaneously cyclize to lactones.

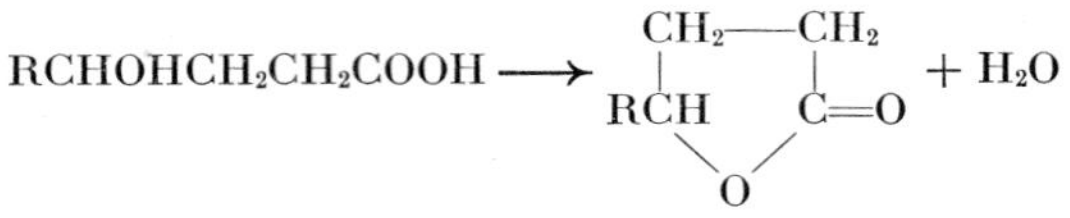

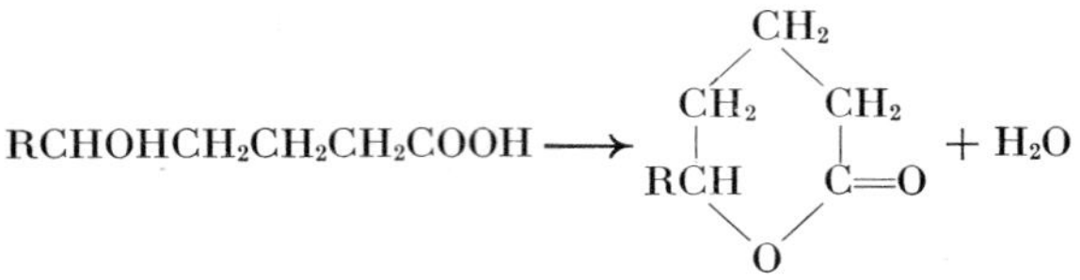

$$RCHOHCH_2CH_2COOH \longrightarrow \begin{array}{c} CH_2{-\!-}CH_2 \\ | \qquad | \\ RCH \quad\; C{=}O \\ \diagdown \;\; \diagup \\ O \end{array} + H_2O$$

$$RCHOHCH_2CH_2CH_2COOH \longrightarrow \begin{array}{c} CH_2 \\ \diagup \;\; \diagdown \\ CH_2 \quad CH_2 \\ | \qquad\;\; | \\ RCH \quad\; C{=}O \\ \diagdown \;\; \diagup \\ O \end{array} + H_2O$$

Lactic acid, $CH_3CHOHCOOH$, the acid formed when milk turns sour because of the action of *Lactobacillus* on the lactose, was isolated from sour milk by Scheele in 1780. It is manufactured by the fermentation of lactose from whey, of molasses, or of starch hydrolysates, in the presence of an excess of calcium carbonate. It can be synthesized by the hydrolysis of acetaldehyde cyanohydrin. About 5 million pounds was manufactured in the United States in 1948 and over half of this was edible grade. Esters of lactic acid are valuable high-boiling solvents for the formulation of lacquers, and can be used for the manufacture of acrylic esters (p. 537).

Lactic acid contains an asymmetric carbon atom, and the lactic acid formed on muscular contraction is dextrorotatory. It is known as **sarco-lactic acid** (Gr. *sarx* flesh). Fermentation lactic acid may be dextro- or levorotatory or inactive depending on the organisms involved. The lactide of lactic acid has a higher rotation of opposite sign from that of the acid. Hence the rotation of an active lactic acid on standing first will decrease to zero and then increase again in the opposite sense as more lactide is formed, until the equilibrium mixture of lactide, water, and lactic acid is reached.

AMINO ACIDS

Preparation

The synthesis of the natural α-amino acids is discussed on page 232. Acids having an amino group in other positions can be prepared from the corresponding halogenated acid, or by reduction of the oxime of the keto acid. β-Amino acids can be made by the addition of ammonia to α,β-unsaturated acids.

$$RCH{=}CHCOOH + NH_3 \longrightarrow \underset{\underset{NH_2}{|}}{RCHCH_2COOH}$$

Reactions

Amino acids in general exist as dipolar ions and are less likely to undergo the types of reactions noted for the hydroxy acids. Nevertheless comparable reactions take place under more drastic conditions. Thus α-amino acids, when heated in glycerol solution to 170°, lose water and form cyclic amides known as *2,5-diketopiperazines*.

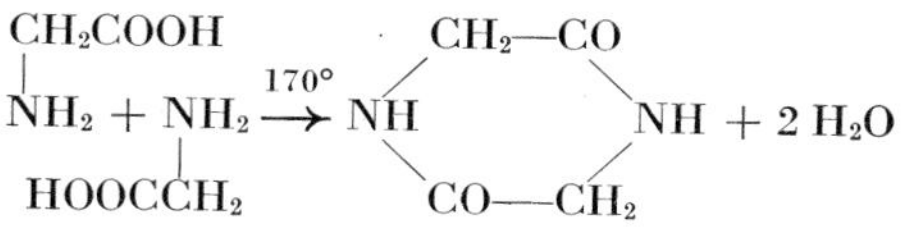

$$
\begin{array}{c}
\text{CH}_2\text{COOH} \\
| \\
\text{NH}_2 + \text{NH}_2 \\
| \\
\text{HOOCCH}_2
\end{array}
\xrightarrow{170°}
\begin{array}{c}
\text{CH}_2\text{—CO} \\
\diagup \qquad \diagdown \\
\text{NH} \qquad\quad \text{NH} + 2\text{ H}_2\text{O} \\
\diagdown \qquad \diagup \\
\text{CO—CH}_2
\end{array}
$$
2,5-Diketopiperazine

When the salts of β-amino acids are heated to decomposition, α,β-unsaturated acids are formed.

$$
\begin{array}{c}
\text{RCHCH}_2\text{COOH} \\
| \\
\text{NH}_3{}^+\text{—PO}_4\text{H}_2
\end{array}
\xrightarrow{\text{Heat}}
\text{RCH}{=}\text{CHCOOH} + (\text{NH}_4)\text{H}_2\text{PO}_4
$$

γ- and δ-Amino acids on heating yield cyclic amides, which are known as *lactams*.

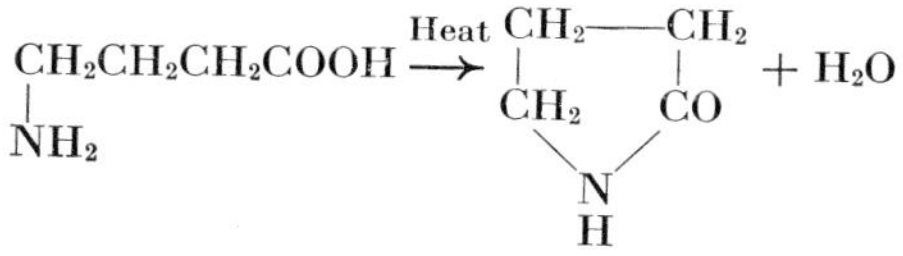

$$
\begin{array}{c}
\text{CH}_2\text{CH}_2\text{CH}_2\text{COOH} \\
| \\
\text{NH}_2
\end{array}
\xrightarrow{\text{Heat}}
\begin{array}{c}
\text{CH}_2\text{——CH}_2 \\
| \qquad\quad | \\
\text{CH}_2 \qquad \text{CO} \\
\diagdown \quad \diagup \\
\text{N} \\
| \\
\text{H}
\end{array}
+ \text{H}_2\text{O}
$$
γ-Butyrolactam

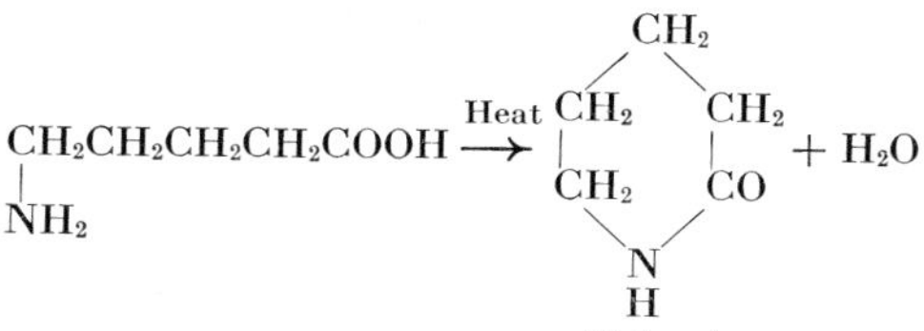

$$
\begin{array}{c}
\text{CH}_2\text{CH}_2\text{CH}_2\text{CH}_2\text{COOH} \\
| \\
\text{NH}_2
\end{array}
\xrightarrow{\text{Heat}}
\begin{array}{c}
\text{CH}_2 \\
\diagup \quad\; \diagdown \\
\text{CH}_2 \qquad \text{CH}_2 \\
| \qquad\qquad | \\
\text{CH}_2 \qquad \text{CO} \\
\diagdown \qquad \diagup \\
\text{N} \\
| \\
\text{H}
\end{array}
+ \text{H}_2\text{O}
$$
δ-Valerolactam

The internal quaternary ammonium salts of amino acids are known as *betaines* after betaine itself, which is the simplest representative. **Betaine** is present in juice of beets (*Beta vulgaris*), and the residue from the manufacture of beet sugar is an abundant source. Betaine can be made by the reaction of trimethylamine with chloroacetic acid.

$$
2\,(\text{CH}_3)_3\text{N} + \text{ClCH}_2\text{COOH} \longrightarrow (\text{CH}_3)_3\overset{+}{\text{N}}\text{CH}_2\text{CO}\bar{\text{O}} + (\text{CH}_3)_3\text{NHCl}
$$
Betaine

β-**Alanine** is of special interest since it comprises a portion of the **pantothenic acid** molecule, $\text{HOCH}_2\text{C}(\text{CH}_3)_2\text{CHOHCONHCH}_2\text{CH}_2\text{COOH}$, one of the B vitamins.

UNSATURATED ACIDS

Preparation

Usually only α,β-unsaturated acids are readily available. The methods for the preparation of these compounds are numerous. They can be formed by the oxidation of α,β-unsaturated aldehydes, which are available through the aldol condensation of an aldehyde with acetaldehyde (p. 167). They result also from the dehydrohalogenation of β-halogen acids (p. 532), the dehydration of β-hydroxy acids (p. 534), and the deamination of β-amino acids (p. 535). A very practical method is the reaction of an aldehyde and malonic acid (p. 542).

$$\text{RCHO} + \text{H}_2\text{C(COOH)}_2 \xrightarrow{\text{Pyridine}} \text{H}_2\text{O} + \text{RCH}=\text{C(COOH)}_2 \xrightarrow{\text{Heat}} \text{RCH}=\text{CHCOOH} + \text{CO}_2$$

The β-aryl-substituted α,β-unsaturated acids may be obtained by the Perkin reaction (p. 404).

If the proper unsaturated halide is available, unsaturated acids having the double bond in more remote positions can be synthesized through the cyanide (p. 121) or by the use of ethyl malonate (p. 545). In other cases more complicated syntheses must be used.

Reactions

α,β- and β,γ-Unsaturated acids yield equilibrium mixtures of both types when heated with alkali. The position of equilibrium depends on the structure of the acid. Thus vinylacetic acid isomerizes completely to crotonic acid, γ-methylvinylacetic acid gives 75 per cent of the conjugated acid, β,γ-dimethylvinylacetic acid gives 25 per cent of the conjugated acid, and γ,γ-dimethylvinylacetic acid gives 5 per cent of the conjugated acid.

$$\text{CH}_2=\text{CHCH}_2\text{COOH} \rightleftharpoons \text{CH}_3\text{CH}=\text{CHCOOH}$$
0 per cent   100 per cent

$$\text{CH}_3\text{CH}=\text{CHCH}_2\text{COOH} \rightleftharpoons \text{CH}_3\text{CH}_2\text{CH}=\text{CHCOOH}$$
25 per cent   75 per cent

$$\text{CH}_3\text{CH}=\text{C(CH}_3)\text{CH}_2\text{COOH} \rightleftharpoons \text{CH}_3\text{CH}_2\text{C(CH}_3)=\text{CHCOOH}$$
75 per cent   25 per cent

$$(\text{CH}_3)_2\text{C}=\text{CHCH}_2\text{COOH} \rightleftharpoons (\text{CH}_3)_2\text{CH}-\text{CH}=\text{CHCOOH}$$
95 per cent   5 per cent

As with other α,β-unsaturated carbonyl compounds, numerous reagents add to the double bond of α,β-unsaturated acids. Thus halogen acid, hydrogen cyanide, hydrogen sulfide, and ammonia give β-halogen, β-cyano, β-mercapto, and β-amino acids. Mercaptans and amines give the corresponding sulfides and substituted amino derivatives, whereas alcohols and phenols give β-alkoxy and β-phenoxy acids. Sodium bisulfite gives the sodium β-sulfonate. Esters and nitriles of the α,β-unsaturated acids behave towards these reagents like the free acids. Frequently the reactions take place with greater ease, especially when base-catalyzed.

Individual Unsaturated Acids

Acrylonitrile, methyl acrylate, and methyl methacrylate are the most important α,β-unsaturated compounds from a technical viewpoint. **Acrylonitrile** may be made from either ethylene or acetylene as a starting point.

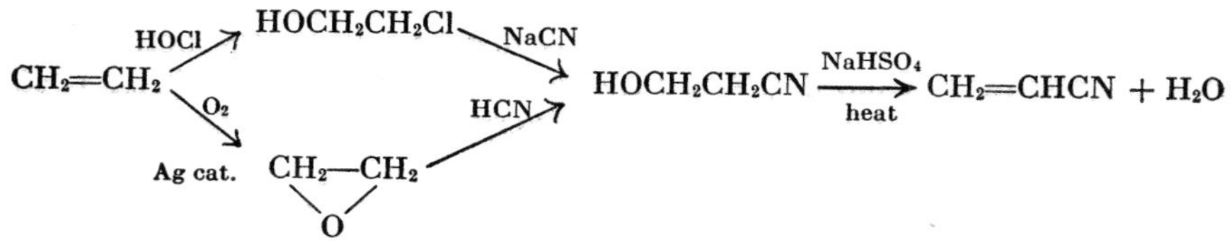

$$CH_2{=}CH_2 \xrightarrow[\text{O}_2]{\text{HOCl}} \begin{array}{c} HOCH_2CH_2Cl \\ CH_2{-}CH_2 \\ \diagdown O \diagup \end{array} \xrightarrow[\text{HCN}]{\text{NaCN}} HOCH_2CH_2CN \xrightarrow[\text{heat}]{\text{NaHSO}_4} CH_2{=}CHCN + H_2O$$

Ag cat.

$$HC{\equiv}CH + HCN \xrightarrow[60°-110°]{\text{CuCl, NH}_4\text{Cl, HCl}} H_2C{=}CHCN$$

Acrylonitrile long has been used as a co-monomer in the synthesis of synthetic rubbers (p. 502) and plastics (p. 508). When polymerized alone, it gives a solid resin which because of its infusibility and insolubility in organic solvents was believed to be a cross-linked polymer. Actually it is a linear polymer, and the discovery that it could be dissolved in N, N-dimethylformamide and that the solution could be spun into threads led to the introduction in 1948 of a new synthetic fiber known as *Orlon*. This fiber is especially resistant to deterioration by weathering and sunlight and should find extensive use for fabrics for outdoor use. *Acrilan* and Dynel are related products.

The esters of acrylic acid and α-methylacrylic acid polymerize in the presence of peroxide catalysts to give the *acrylic* or *acryloid resins*. **Methyl acrylate** is made by the dehydration of methyl lactate (p. 534) or by the methanolysis of acrylonitrile.

$$CH_3CHOHCOOCH_3 \longrightarrow CH_2{=}CHCOOCH_3 + H_2O$$

$$CH_2{=}CHCN + CH_3OH \xrightarrow{\text{H}_2\text{SO}_4} \underset{\text{Methyl acrylate}}{CH_2{=}CHCOOCH_3}$$

It can be prepared also by the reaction of acetylene, carbon monoxide, and methanol in the presence of nickel carbonyl at high temperature and pressure.

$$HC{\equiv}CH + CO + CH_3OH \xrightarrow[\text{heat and pressure}]{\text{Ni(CO)}_4,} H_2C{=}CHCOOCH_3$$

Methyl α-methylacrylate, commonly called **methyl methacrylate,** is made from acetone, although other processes are possible.

$$(CH_3)_2CO \xrightarrow{\text{HCN}} (CH_3)_2COHCN \xrightarrow[\text{heat}]{\text{KHSO}_4} \underset{CH_3}{CH_2{=}CCN} \xrightarrow[\text{H}_2\text{SO}_4]{\text{CH}_3\text{OH,}} \underset{\substack{CH_3 \\ \text{Methyl} \\ \text{methacrylate}}}{CH_2{=}CCOOCH_3}$$

Polymerization of methyl methacrylate using peroxide catalysts gives a strong thermoplastic solid that is highly transparent and has a high refractive index. It is sold under the names *Lucite, Crystallite, Plexiglas,* or *Perspex* and is used in place of glass and for molding transparent objects. Numerous other esters also are manufactured commercially for the production of polymers and copolymers for a variety of uses. The monomeric esters are stabilized by the addition of 0.005 to 0.25 per cent of hydroquinone.

Crotonic acid is made by the oxidation of crotonic aldehyde (p. 169). Its esters do not polymerize as easily as those of acrylic acid or of α-methylacrylic acid. **Angelic acid** (from *Angelica archangelica*) and **tiglic acid** (from *Croton tiglium*) are the *cis* and *trans* forms respectively of α-methylcrotonic acid.

Angelic acid   Tiglic acid

10-Undecenoic acid, commonly known as **undecylenic acid,** is one of the products of the destructive distillation of castor oil, the other principal product being heptaldehyde.

$$CH_3(CH_2)_5CHOHCH_2CH=CH(CH_2)_7COOH \xrightarrow{\text{Heat}} CH_3(CH_2)_5CHO + CH_2=CH(CH_2)_8COOH$$

Ricinoleic acid   Heptaldehyde   Undecylenic acid

Several long-chain unsaturated acids such as oleic, isooleic, petroselenic, linoleic, linolenic, eleostearic, and erucic acid can be obtained by the saponification of natural fats (p. 151).

REVIEW QUESTIONS

1. What is the Hell-Volhard-Zelinsky reaction? Why is the phosphorus trichloride necessary?
2. What reactions lead to β-halogen acids?
3. Compare the behavior of α-, β-, γ-, and δ-halogen acids on heating in the presence of one mole of aqueous potassium hydroxide.
4. Discuss the action of alkali on α,β-unsaturated acids.
5. Give two general procedures for the synthesis of α-hydroxy acids.
6. Give two general procedures for the synthesis of β-hydroxy acids. What name is associated with one of the methods?
7. Compare the dehydration of α-, β-, γ-, and δ-hydroxy acids. What is the action of sulfuric acid on α-hydroxy acids?
8. How do the reactions of α-, β-, γ-, and δ-amino acids differ from each other?
9. What can be said concerning the structure of each of the following compounds: (*a*) a hydroxy acid on standing gave a neutral compound having a molecular weight greater than that of the original compound; (*b*) a bromo acid on heating with alkali gave an unsaturated acid; (*c*) an amino acid on heating lost water but no other change in the molecular weight occurred?
10. Give reactions for the preparation of (*a*) α-aminobutyric acid from butyric acid; (*b*) leucine from isovaleraldehyde; (*c*) γ-chlorovaleric acid from γ-ketovaleric acid; (*d*) 5-bromopentanoic acid from tetrahydrofuran; (*e*) β-methyl-β-bromobutyric acid from acetone; (*f*) undecanal from lauric acid; (*g*) 9-aminononanoic acid from oleic acid; (*h*) β-alanine from ethylene bromide; (*i*) 3,4-dimethoxycinnamic acid from vanillin; (*j*) β-mercaptobutyric acid from acetaldehyde.

Chapter 36

POLYCARBOXYLIC ACIDS

Of the polycarboxylic acids, the dicarboxylic acids are encountered most frequently, and some are of considerable importance. Thus the ethyl ester of malonic acid is a valuable intermediate for organic syntheses. Adipic acid and the unsaturated maleic acid are technically important intermediates. Some of the hydroxy polycarboxylic acids, such as malic, tartaric, and citric acids, occur in fruit juices.

Nomenclature

The unsubstituted polycarboxylic acids have common names which are in general use and serve as family names for the substituted acids. The names of the normal dibasic acids having 2 to 10 carbon atoms are oxalic, malonic, succinic, glutaric, adipic, pimelic, suberic, azelaic, and sebacic acids.

Dicarboxylic Acids

Preparation. Several general methods of preparation are available.

1. OXIDATION OF α,ω-GLYCOLS.

$$(CH_2)_x(CH_2OH)_2 \xrightarrow[\text{or } H_2Cr_2O_7]{HNO_3, \ KMnO_4} (CH_2)_x(COOH)_2$$

2. HYDROLYSIS OF DINITRILES.

$$(CH_2)_x(CN)_2 \xrightarrow{H_2O-HCl} (CH_2)_x(COOH)_2 + 2\ NH_4Cl$$

3. ELECTROLYSIS OF THE ACID ESTERS OF LOWER DICARBOXYLIC ACIDS (cf. p. 131).

$$2\ CH_3OOC(CH_2)_xCOONa \xrightarrow{Electrolysis} CH_3OOC(CH_2)_x(CH_2)_xCOOCH_3 +$$
$$2\ CO_2(+ \text{ NaOH and } H_2 \text{ at cathode})$$

Frequently special methods are used for the preparation of individual dicarboxylic acids. **Oxalic acid** was known at an early date. The presence of its potassium acid salt in the sorrels (various species of *Rumex* and *Oxalis;* Gr. *oxys* sharp or acid) was observed at the beginning of the seventeenth century. It is present in many other plants such as spinach, rhubarb, sweet potatoes, cabbage, grapes, and tomatoes. When these fruits and vegetables are eaten, microscopic star-shaped crystals of the insoluble calcium oxalate may appear in the urine.

Nitric acid oxidation of any α,β-oxygenated or aminated substance such as the carbohydrates or the amino acids will produce oxalic acid. It can be obtained in good yield by the nitric acid oxidation of sucrose in the presence of vanadium pentoxide. Commercially it is manufactured by heating sodium formate and liberating the free acid from the sodium salt with sulfuric acid.

$$2\ HCOONa \xrightarrow{Heat} H_2 + NaOOCCOONa \xrightarrow{H_2SO_4} HOOCCOOH$$

Malonic acid is so named because it first was obtained in 1858 as an oxidation product of malic acid (p. 547). It ordinarily is prepared by a series of reactions from sodium chloroacetate. The intermediate cyanoacetate may be hydrolyzed to the acid or alcoholyzed to the ester.

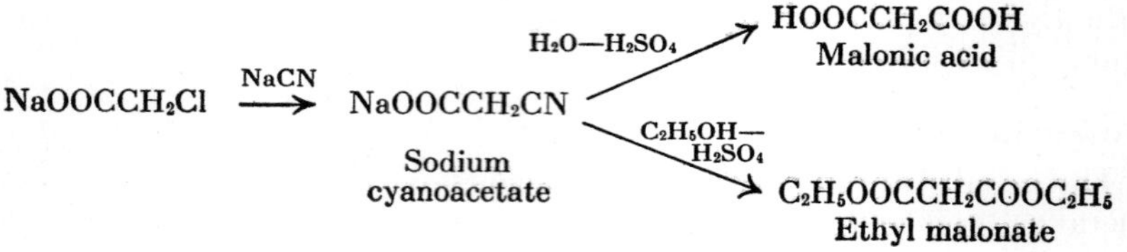

$$NaOOCCH_2Cl \xrightarrow{NaCN} NaOOCCH_2CN$$

Sodium
cyanoacetate

$$\xrightarrow{H_2O-H_2SO_4} \begin{array}{l} HOOCCH_2COOH \\ \text{Malonic acid} \end{array}$$

$$\xrightarrow[H_2SO_4]{C_2H_5OH-} \begin{array}{l} C_2H_5OOCCH_2COOC_2H_5 \\ \text{Ethyl malonate} \end{array}$$

The preparation of substituted malonic acids is described under the reactions of the ester (p. 545).

Succinic acid was known in the sixteenth century as a distillation product of amber, a fossil resin (*L. succinum* amber). It can be obtained by the hydrolysis of ethylene cyanide, but is manufactured now by the catalytic reduction of maleic acid or the electrolytic reduction of fumaric acid (p. 546).

$$HOOCCH{=}CHCOOH + 2[H] \xrightarrow[\substack{electrolytic \\ reduction}]{Cat.\ or} HOOCCH_2CH_2COOH$$

Maleic or fumaric
acid

Succinic acid

Derivatives of succinic acid can be made by the hydrolysis of β-cyano esters formed by the addition of hydrogen cyanide to α,β-unsaturated acids (p. 536).

$$RCH{=}CHCOOH \xrightarrow{HCN} \underset{\underset{CN}{|}}{RCHCH_2COOH} \xrightarrow{H_2O-HCl} \underset{\underset{COOH}{|}}{RCHCH_2COOH}$$

Numerous other synthetic methods also are available.

Glutaric acid was prepared first from the readily obtainable glutamic acid (p. 232) by converting the latter into α-hydroxyglutaric acid and reducing with hydrogen iodide. It is not a commercial product but is made in the laboratory by the hydrolysis of trimethylene cyanide or by the nitric acid oxidation of cyclopentanone (p. 543).

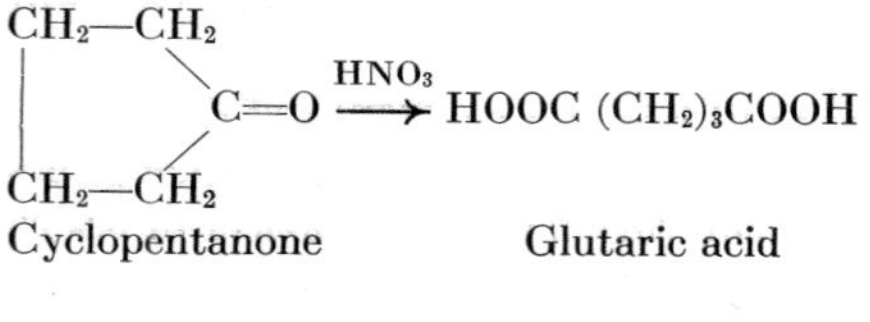

$$\begin{array}{c} CH_2{-}CH_2 \\ | \qquad\quad \diagdown \\ \qquad\qquad C{=}O \xrightarrow{HNO_3} HOOC\ (CH_2)_3COOH \\ | \qquad\quad \diagup \\ CH_2{-}CH_2 \end{array}$$

Cyclopentanone   Glutaric acid

Adipic acid (L. *adeps* fat) is one of the compounds formed when many unsaturated fats or fat acids are oxidized. It is the chief product from the oxidation of cyclohexanol (p. 559) or cyclohexanone with nitric acid.

$$\begin{array}{ccc}
\text{CH}_2\text{—CH}_2 \quad \text{H} & \text{CH}_2\text{—CH}_2 & \\
\text{CH}_2 \quad\quad \text{C} & \text{CH}_2 \quad\quad \text{C==O} & \longrightarrow \text{HOOC(CH}_2)_4\text{COOH} \\
\text{CH}_2\text{—CH}_2 \quad \text{OH} & \text{CH}_2\text{—CH}_2 & \\
\text{Cyclohexanol} & \text{Cyclohexanone} & \text{Adipic acid}
\end{array}$$

$$\xrightarrow{\text{HNO}_3}$$

Adipic acid is manufactured on a large scale as an intermediate for the production of Nylon (p. 544). It formerly was made from cyclohexanol (p. 559) but now is produced by the catalytic air oxidation of cyclohexane (p. 559) in the liquid phase.

$$\begin{array}{c}
\text{CH}_2\text{—CH}_2 \\
\text{CH}_2 \quad\quad \text{CH}_2 \xrightarrow[\text{95°, 150 p.s.i.}]{\text{O}_2,\ \text{Co salts}} \text{HOOC(CH}_2)_4\text{COOH} + \text{H}_2\text{O} \\
\text{CH}_2\text{—CH}_2 \\
\text{Cyclohexane}
\end{array}$$

Cyclohexanol and cyclohexanone are intermediates in the reaction. Adipic acid can be obtained also by the hydrolysis of adiponitrile (p. 544).

Pimelic acid (Gr. *pimele* fat) also is an oxidation product of unsaturated fats. It is not available commercially, but it can be synthesized by the hydrolysis of pentamethylene cyanide or by several other procedures.

$$\text{CN(CH}_2)_5\text{CN} \xrightarrow{\text{H}_2\text{O—HCl}} \text{HOOC(CH}_2)_5\text{COOH}$$

$$\begin{array}{cc}
\text{Penta-} & \text{Pimelic acid} \\
\text{methylene} & \\
\text{cyanide} &
\end{array}$$

Suberic acid (L. *suber* cork oak), $\text{HOOC(CH}_2)_6\text{COOH}$, is obtained in small amounts by the oxidation of cork with nitric acid. It usually is prepared by the nitric acid oxidation of castor oil, although the yield still is low.

Azelaic acid is the chief product of the oxidation of unsaturated fat acids with nitric acid (F. *azote* nitrogen and Gr. *elaion* olive oil).

$$\text{CH}_3\text{(CH}_2)_7\text{CH==CH(CH}_2)_7\text{COOH} \xrightarrow{\text{Ox.}} \text{CH}_3\text{(CH}_2)_7\text{COOH} + \text{HOOC(CH}_2)_7\text{COOH}$$

$$\begin{array}{ccc}
\text{Oleic acid} & \text{Nonylic acid} & \text{Azelaic acid}
\end{array}$$

Oxidation of the ozonide of oleic acid with dichromic acid gives better yields.

Sebacic acid (L. *sebum* tallow) is a waxy solid. The sodium salt is one of the products of the destructive distillation of the sodium soap from castor oil with excess alkali. The other chief product is 2-octanol (**capryl alcohol**).

$$\text{CH}_3\text{(CH}_2)_5\text{CHOHCH}_2\text{CH==CH(CH}_2)_7\text{COONa} + \text{NaOH} + \text{H}_2\text{O} \xrightarrow{\text{Heat}}$$

Sodium ricinoleate

$$\text{CH}_3\text{(CH}_2)_5\text{CHOHCH}_3 + \text{NaOOC(CH}_2)_8\text{COONa} + \text{H}_2$$

$$\begin{array}{cc}
\text{2-Octanol} & \text{Sodium sebacate}
\end{array}$$

Brassylic acid can be obtained easily by the oxidation of erucic acid (p. 151) or the geometrical isomer (p. 254), brassidic acid.

$$CH_3(CH_2)_7CH\!\!=\!\!CH(CH_2)_{11}COOH \xrightarrow{HNO_3} CH_3(CH_2)_7COOH + HOOC(CH_2)_{11}COOH$$

Erucic or brassidic acid   Nonylic acid   Brassylic acid

The C_{19}, C_{20}, and C_{21} dibasic acids have been reported as saponification products of Japan wax (from *Rhus succedaneum*).

Reactions. The dicarboxylic acids, like all polyfunctional compounds, have certain characteristic behaviors depending on the relative positions of the functional groups. Being an electron-attracting group, the presence of one carboxyl close to another increases the ease of ionization of the first hydrogen ion. This effect rapidly decreases as the carboxyl groups become more separated. Thus oxalic acid is somewhat stronger than phosphoric acid, the first dissociation constants being 3.8×10^{-2} and 1.1×10^{-2} respectively. For malonic acid $K_A = 1.6 \times 10^{-3}$, but when two or more methylene groups intervene, the two carboxyl groups have little effect on each other. Thus succinic acid, $K_A = 6.4 \times 10^{-5}$, is only slightly stronger than acetic acid, $K_A = 1.8 \times 10^{-5}$.

The dicarboxylic acids differ in their *behavior on heating with or without dehydrating agents*. When **oxalic acid** is heated slowly to 150° it sublimes unchanged, but rapid heating to a higher temperature decomposes it into carbon dioxide and formic acid, and the latter decomposes further into carbon monoxide and water.

$$HOOCCOOH \xrightarrow{Heat} CO_2 + HCOOH \longrightarrow CO + H_2O$$

These reactions are brought about better by warming with concentrated sulfuric acid.

Malonic acid and substituted malonic acids, when heated above the melting point, lose carbon dioxide to give the monocarboxylic acid.

$$HOOCCH_2COOH \xrightarrow{Heat} CO_2 + CH_3COOH$$

$$RCH(COOH)_2 \xrightarrow{Heat} CO_2 + RCH_2COOH$$

$$R_2C(COOH)_2 \xrightarrow{Heat} CO_2 + R_2CHCOOH$$

Unsubstituted malonic acid with its active methylene group condenses with aldehydes to give α,β-unsaturated malonic acids, which lose carbon dioxide on heating to give α,β-unsaturated acids.

$$RCHO + H_2C(COOH)_2 \xrightarrow{Pyridine} H_2O + RCH\!\!=\!\!C(COOH)_2 \xrightarrow{Heat} RCH\!\!=\!\!CHCOOH + CO_2$$

Bases stronger than pyridine may give an $\alpha,\beta:\beta,\gamma$-mixture (p. 536).

Succinic and **glutaric** acids and their substitution products lose water on heating to give the stable five- and six-membered cyclic anhydrides.

$$\begin{array}{ccc}
\text{CH}_2\text{COOH} & & \text{CH}_2\text{—CO} \\
| & \xrightarrow{\text{Heat}} & | \qquad\qquad \searrow \\
\text{CH}_2\text{COOH} & & \text{CH}_2\text{—CO}
\end{array} \text{O} + \text{H}_2\text{O}$$

Succinic
anhydride

$$\begin{array}{ccc}
\text{CH}_2\text{COOH} & & \text{CH}_2\text{—CO} \\
\diagup & \xrightarrow{\text{Heat}} & \diagup \qquad\qquad \searrow \\
\text{CH}_2 & & \text{CH}_2 \qquad\qquad \text{O} + \text{H}_2\text{O} \\
\diagdown & & \diagdown \qquad\qquad \diagup \\
\text{CH}_2\text{COOH} & & \text{CH}_2\text{—CO}
\end{array}$$

Glutaric
anhydride

These reactions take place at much lower temperatures in the presence of de-hydrating agents. Thus simple refluxing of succinic acid with acetyl chloride and allowing to cool gives good yields of succinic anhydride.

Adipic acids and acids having the carboxyl groups more widely separated do not give cyclic anhydrides. On heating with dehydrating agents they give linear polymeric anhydrides.

$$(x + 1)\ \text{HOOC(CH}_2)_4\text{COOH} + x\ (\text{CH}_3\text{CO})_2\text{O} \xrightarrow{\text{Heat}}$$

$$\text{HOOC(CH}_2)_4[\text{COOCO(CH}_2)_4]_x\text{COOH} + 2\,x\ \text{CH}_3\text{COOH}$$
Polyadipic anhydride

When adipic acids are heated, especially in the presence of a small amount of barium hydroxide, five-membered cyclic ketones are formed.

$$\begin{array}{ccc}
\text{CH}_2\text{CH}_2\text{COOH} & & \text{CH}_2\text{—CH}_2 \\
| & \xrightarrow{\text{Ba(OH)}_2,\ \text{heat}} & | \qquad\qquad \searrow \\
\text{CH}_2\text{CH}_2\text{COOH} & & \text{CH}_2\text{—CH}_2
\end{array} \text{CO} + \text{H}_2\text{O} + \text{CO}_2$$

Cyclopentanone

Pimelic acids on similar treatment yield six-membered cyclic ketones.

$$\begin{array}{ccc}
\text{CH}_2\text{CH}_2\text{COOH} & & \text{CH}_2\text{—CH}_2 \\
\diagup & \xrightarrow{\text{Ba(OH)}_2,\ \text{heat}} & \diagup \qquad\qquad \searrow \\
\text{CH}_2 & & \text{CH}_2 \qquad\qquad \text{CO} + \text{H}_2\text{O} + \text{CO}_2 \\
\diagdown & & \diagdown \qquad\qquad \diagup \\
\text{CH}_2\text{CH}_2\text{COOH} & & \text{CH}_2\text{—CH}_2
\end{array}$$

The generalization that succinic and glutaric acids give cyclic anhydrides, whereas adipic and pimelic acids yield cyclic ketones, is known as **Blanc's rule.** It has been of considerable value in determining whether oxygenated or unsaturated rings in compounds of unknown constitution are five- or six-membered. Thus a five-membered ring on oxidation will give a glutaric acid which will cyclize to an anhydride, whereas a six-membered ring on oxidation will give an adipic acid which will cyclize to a ketone. The rule is not infallible, however, since at least one example is known in which a nonterminal six-membered ring in a polycyclic compound gives on oxidation an adipic acid that forms a seven-membered cyclic anhydride.

Adipic acid is the most important of the dicarboxylic acids commercially. It is an intermediate for the synthesis of *Nylon 66*, which is a polyamide formed by heating the hexamethylenediamine (p. 528) salt of adipic acid. The number 66 indicates that this particular Nylon has two six-carbon constituents.

$$(x + 1)^-OOC(CH_2)_4COO^-H_3\overset{+}{N}(CH_2)_6NH_3^+ \xrightarrow[200°-300°]{Heat}$$
Nylon salt

$$^-OOC(CH_2)_4CO[NH(CH_2)_6NHCO(CH_2)_4CO]_xNH(CH_2)_6NH_3^+ + x\ H_2O$$
Nylon 66

The molecular weight of Nylon 66 is about 10,000 and the melting point around 260°. It is insoluble in water and most organic solvents with the exception of formic acid and phenols. It can be extruded from a melt into monofilaments used for brush bristles, or spun from a solution in formic acid or phenol. The filaments are cold-drawn to four times their original length to orient the molecules along the axis of the fiber. The resulting fibers are elastic and lustrous and either dry or wet have a higher tensile strength than silk. Disadvantages are the low melting point and the difficulty in dyeing the fibers. Similar polyamides can be made from any dibasic acid and any diamine and the generic term *Nylon* has been coined for all of them.

Hexamethylenediamine is made by the reduction of **adiponitrile** (p. 528), which before 1948 was made from adipic acid by passing the vapors with an excess of ammonia over a catalyst such as boron phosphate at 350°.

$$(CH_2)_4(COONH_4)_2 \longrightarrow 2\ H_2O + (CH_2)_4(CONH_2)_2 \longrightarrow 2\ H_2O + (CH_2)_4(CN)_2$$
Ammonium adipate   Adipamide   Adiponitrile

With the growing scarcity of benzene, a process has been developed for preparing adiponitrile from furfural by way of tetrahydrofuran and tetramethylene chloride (Fig. 42, p. 453).

$$(CH_2)_4Cl_2 + 2\ NaCN \longrightarrow (CH_2)_4(CN)_2 + 2\ NaCl$$

Tetramethylene chloride can be made also from acetylene by way of tetrahydrofuran (p. 501), or from 1,3-butadiene (p. 494).

$$CH_2{=}CHCH{=}CH_2 \xrightarrow{Cl_2} ClCH_2CH{=}CHCH_2Cl \xrightarrow{H_2-Ni} (CH_2)_4Cl_2$$

These reactions illustrate the diverse raw materials that frequently are available to the manufacturer of organic chemicals.

Reactions of Malonic Esters

The reactions of the esters of malonic acid are sufficiently important to require special attention. Usually the ethyl ester is used, and the term *malonic ester* ordinarily means ethyl malonate. The methylene group joined to the two carbethoxy groups is unusually reactive. Bromination takes place with extreme ease, although ethyl malonate does not give a color with ferric chloride and other tests indicate the absence of a detectable amount of an enol form.

The most important reaction of malonic esters is *carbon alkylation*. Reaction of ethyl malonate with sodium ethoxide in absolute alcohol gives a sodium salt which reacts with an alkyl halide to give an alkyl-substituted malonic ester. A second alkyl group may be introduced if desired. Since the esters can be saponified and decarboxylated, the reaction leads to the preparation of substituted acetic acids.

$$CH_2(COOC_2H_5)_2 \xrightarrow{NaOC_2H_5} Na^+\bar{C}H(COOC_2H_5)_2 \xrightarrow{RX} NaX + RCH(COOC_2H_5)_2 \xrightarrow[HCl]{NaOH, then}$$

Ethyl sodiomalonate   Ethyl alkylmalonate

$$RCH(COOH)_2 \xrightarrow{Heat} RCH_2COOH + CO_2$$

An alkylmalonic   An alkylacetic
acid   acid

$$RCH(COOC_2H_5)_2 \xrightarrow{NaOC_2H_5} Na^+\bar{R}C(COOC_2H_5)_2 \xrightarrow{R'X}$$

$$\begin{array}{c} R \\ \diagdown \\ \diagup \quad C(COOC_2H_5)_2 \\ R' \end{array} \xrightarrow[HCl]{NaOH, then} \begin{array}{c} R \\ \diagdown \\ \diagup \quad C(COOH)_2 \\ R' \end{array} \xrightarrow{Heat} \begin{array}{c} R \\ \diagdown \\ \diagup \quad CHCOOH + CO_2 \\ R' \end{array}$$

Ethyl   A dialkylmalonic   A dialkylacetic
dialkylmalonate   acid   acid

Reaction of the sodium salt with iodine causes coupling of two malonic ester units and provides a method for the synthesis of α,β-disubstituted succinic acids.

$$2 I_2 + 2 Na^+\bar{R}C(COOC_2H_5)_2 \longrightarrow 2 NaI + \begin{array}{c} R—C(COOC_2H_5)_2 \\ | \\ R—C(COOC_2H_5)_2 \end{array} \xrightarrow[HCl]{NaOH, then}$$

$$\begin{array}{c} RC(COOH)_2 \\ | \\ R\bar{C}(COOH)_2 \end{array} \xrightarrow{Heat} \begin{array}{c} RCHCOOH \\ | \\ RCHCOOH \end{array} + 2 CO_2$$

Ethyl malonate can be used also for the synthesis of alicyclic compounds (p. 559).

The halogen compounds must undergo displacement reactions at least as readily as alkyl halides or reaction with ethyl sodiomalonate will not take place. Thus aryl halides will not react. Aryl substituted malonic esters usually are made by a Claisen ester condensation (p. 551). For example ethyl phenylmalonate can be made by the reaction of ethyl phenylacetate with ethyl carbonate.

$$C_6H_5CH_2COOC_2H_5 + C_2H_5OCOOC_2H_5 \xrightarrow{NaOC_2H_5} \begin{array}{c} C_6H_5CHCOOC_2H_5 + C_2H_5OH \\ | \\ COOC_2H_5 \end{array}$$

Unsaturated Dicarboxylic Acids

A few unsaturated dicarboxylic acids are of special interest. **Maleic** and **fumaric acids** (*cis*- and *trans*-ethylenedicarboxylic acids) are the classical examples of geometrical isomerism (p. 254). Maleic acid readily yields an anhydride on heating, indicating that the carboxyl groups are on the same side of the double bond. Fumaric acid on the other hand does not yield an anhydride easily. When heated to a sufficiently high temperature (250°–300°), isomerization takes place and maleic anhydride is formed.

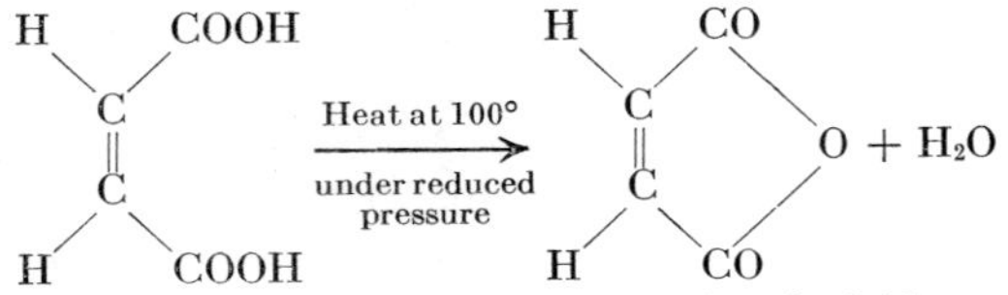

$$\underset{\text{Maleic acid}}{\overset{\displaystyle H\diagup\overset{\textstyle C}{\text{---}}\diagdown COOH}{\underset{\displaystyle H\diagup\underset{\textstyle C}{\text{---}}\diagdown COOH}{}}} \xrightarrow[\substack{\text{under reduced}\\\text{pressure}}]{\text{Heat at }100°} \underset{\text{Maleic anhydride}}{\overset{\displaystyle H\diagup\overset{\textstyle C}{\text{---}}\diagdown CO}{\underset{\displaystyle H\diagup\underset{\textstyle C}{\text{---}}\diagdown CO}{}}}O + H_2O$$

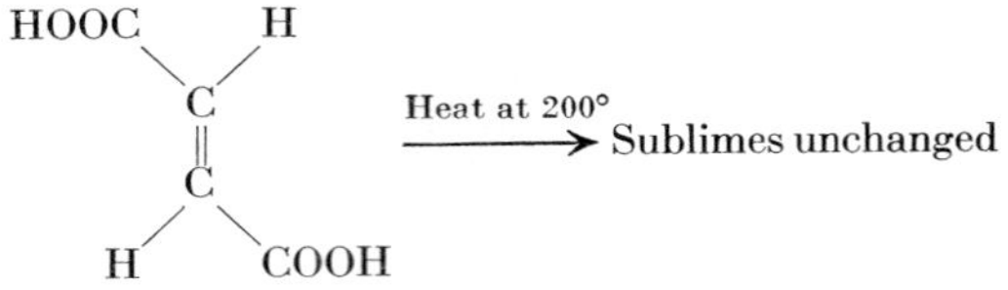

$$\underset{\text{Fumaric acid}}{\overset{\displaystyle HOOC\diagup\overset{\textstyle C}{\text{---}}\diagdown H}{\underset{\displaystyle H\diagup\underset{\textstyle C}{\text{---}}\diagdown COOH}{}}} \xrightarrow{\text{Heat at }200°} \text{Sublimes unchanged}$$

Maleic acid is obtained in the form of its anhydride by the catalytic air oxidation of benzene.

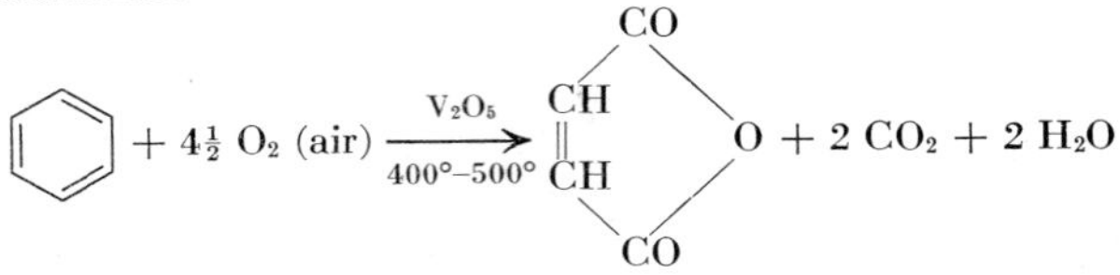

$$\bigcirc + 4\tfrac{1}{2}\,O_2\,\text{(air)} \xrightarrow[400°\text{--}500°]{V_2O_5} \overset{CO}{\underset{CO}{\overset{CH}{\underset{CH}{\|}}}}O + 2\,CO_2 + 2\,H_2O$$

Unsaturated compounds such as crotonic aldehyde can be used in this process when benzene is in short supply.

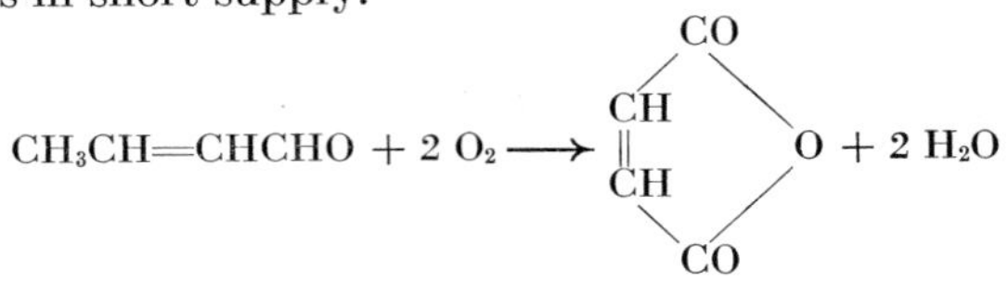

$$CH_3CH{=}CHCHO + 2\,O_2 \longrightarrow \overset{CO}{\underset{CO}{\overset{CH}{\underset{CH}{\|}}}}O + 2\,H_2O$$

Maleic anhydride is formed to the extent of 5 to 8 per cent in the production of phthalic anhydride (p. 415) and is separated as a co-product. **Fumaric acid** can be made by the isomerization of maleic acid or by a fermentation process from starch or other carbohydrates using molds of the genus *Rhizopus*.

The most characteristic reaction of maleic anhydride is its 1,4 addition to conjugated dienes (p. 495).

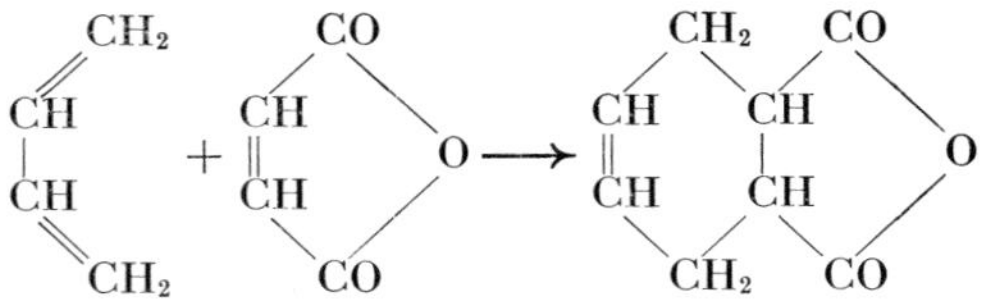

4,5-Cyclohexenedi-carboxylic anhydride

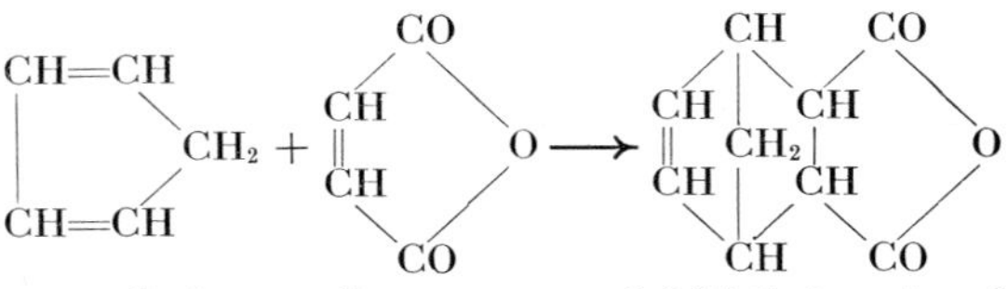

Cyclopentadiene   3,6-Methylene-4-cyclo-hexene-1,2-dicarboxylic anhydride

Other compounds containing a double or triple bond conjugated with a carbonyl group or a nitrile group, such as acrolein, crotonic aldehyde, acrylic acid, crotononitrile, acetylenedicarboxylic esters, and quinones, also add to a system of conjugated carbon-carbon multiple bonds. The first group of compounds are called *dienophiles*, the second are the *dienes*, and the product of the reaction of a dienophile with a diene is called the *adduct*. These reactions commonly are known as **Diels-Alder diene syntheses.**

Commercial production of maleic anhydride began in the United States in 1933 and in 1948 amounted to 12 million pounds. About 85 per cent of it is used in the manufacture of synthetic resins, mostly of the alkyd type (p. 416).

Hydroxy Dicarboxylic Acids

Tartronic acid is hydroxymalonic acid, HOOCCHOHCOOH. It is made by the hydrolysis of bromomalonic acid or by the reduction of mesoxalic acid, HOOCCOCOOH.

Malic acid is hydroxysuccinic acid, HOOCCH₂CHOHCOOH. It is present in many fruit juices and was isolated by Scheele in 1785 from unripe apples (L. *malum* apple). Calcium acid 1-malate separates during the concentration of maple sap and is known as *sugar sand*. Inactive malic acid is manufactured by the hydration of maleic or fumaric acid (p. 545).

Tartaric acid is dihydroxysuccinic acid, HOOCCHOHCHOHCOOH, and is one of the most widely distributed plant acids. Its potassium acid salt is present in grape juice and is the chief constituent of the lees of wine. The crude product is called *argol*. The pure product is called *cream of tartar*. It is used as the acid component in baking powder. Neutralization with sodium hydroxide yields sodium potassium tartrate, which is known as *Rochelle salts* (after Rochelle, France) and is used as a purgative. Tartar was known to the ancients, but tartaric acid was isolated first by Scheele in 1769.

Fehling's solution (p. 173) is prepared from copper sulfate, sodium hydroxide, and Rochelle salts. The tartrate ion forms a chelate complex (p. 520) which decreases the cupric ion concentration below that necessary for the precipitation of cupric hydroxide. The complex salt is formed by a series of steps analogous to those for the formation of the cupric complex of biuret (p. 244).

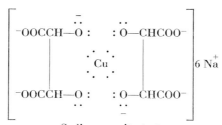

Sodium cupritartrate

Hydroxy Tricarboxylic Acids

Citric acid, HOOCCH₂COHCH₂COOH, is 2-hydroxy-1,2,3-propanetri-

COOH

carboxylic acid. It is the chief acid constituent of citrus fruits, amounting to 6 to 7 per cent of lemon juice. It is present also in currants, gooseberries and many other fruits, as well as in the roots and leaves of many plants. It was obtained in a crystalline form from unripe lemons by Scheele in 1784. Commercial manufacture is from cull lemons, or by the fermentation of molasses or starch with *Aspergillus niger* at pH 3.5. Production in the United States in 1942 was over 23 million pounds, most of which was used by the soft drink industry.

Benedict's solution (p. 173) is prepared from copper sulfate, sodium carbonate, and sodium citrate. The structure of the complex is similar to that of the tartrate complex except that a carboxyl group has entered into complex formation instead of a hydroxyl group.

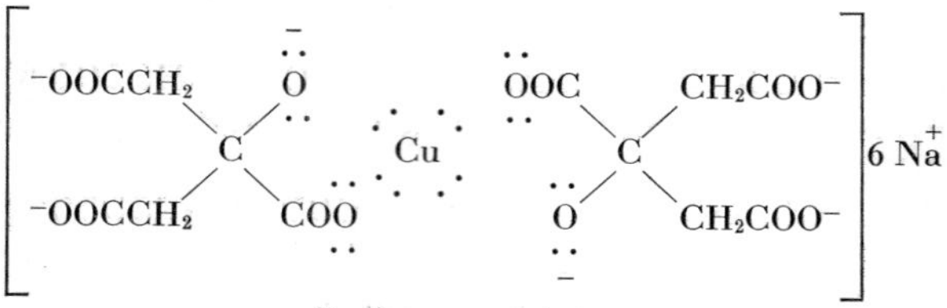

$$
\left[\begin{array}{c}
{}^-OOCCH_2 \quad\quad O \quad\quad\quad OOC \quad\quad CH_2COO^- \\
\diagdown\quad\quad\quad\quad\quad\quad\quad\quad\quad\quad\quad\quad\diagup \\
C \quad\quad\quad Cu \quad\quad\quad C \\
\diagup\quad\quad\quad\quad\quad\quad\quad\quad\quad\quad\quad\quad\diagdown \\
{}^-OOCCH_2 \quad\quad COO \quad\quad\quad O \quad\quad CH_2COO^-
\end{array} \right] 6\,\overset{+}{Na}
$$

Sodium cupricitrate

REVIEW QUESTIONS

1. Give reactions for three general methods for the preparation of α,ω-dicarboxylic acids.
2. Give the name and the best method of preparation for the normal α,ω-dicarboxylic acids containing from two to ten carbon atoms.
3. How can chemical reactions be used to determine the number of carbon atoms separating the carboxyl groups in a dicarboxylic acid? What is Blanc's rule?
4. Give equations for the reaction of ethyl sodiomalonate (from ethyl malonate and sodium ethoxide) with alkyl halides; with iodine; with urea.
5. Give reactions for the synthesis from malonic acid or ethyl malonate of (*a*) 2-hexenoic acid; (*b*) 2,4-dimethylbutanoic acid; (*c*) α,α'-diethylsuccinic acid.
6. Give reactions for the preparation of (*a*) 1,10-dihydroxydecane from adipic acid; (*b*) glutaric acid from phenol; (*c*) succinic acid from acetaldehyde; (*d*) α,ω-tridecanedicarboxylic acid from erucic acid; (*e*) hexahydrophthalic acid from 1,3-butadiene.

Chapter 37

KETO ACIDS

Keto acids are used frequently in organic syntheses. They also have played a leading role in the interpretation of the phenomenon known as tautomerism.

α-Keto Acids

The simplest compound containing both a carbonyl group and a carboxyl group is **glyoxylic acid,** OCHCOOH. It can be made by logical reactions such as the ozonolysis of maleic or fumaric acid, or the hydrolysis of dichloroacetic acid. It can be prepared also by the electrolytic reduction of oxalic acid. Like chloral, it forms a stable hydrate having the structure $(HO)_2CHCOOH$.

Pyruvic acid (α-ketopropionic acid), the first true α-keto acid, is made by the pyrolysis of tartaric acid and hence frequently is called *pyrotartaric acid.*

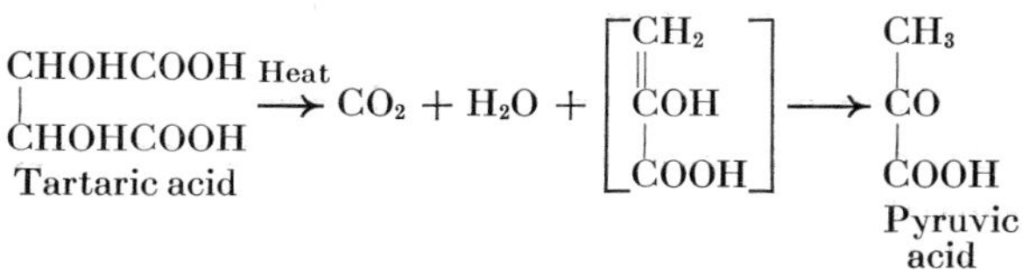

$$\underset{\text{Tartaric acid}}{\overset{\displaystyle |}{\underset{\displaystyle |}{\text{CHOHCOOH}}}{\text{CHOHCOOH}}} \xrightarrow{\text{Heat}} CO_2 + H_2O + \begin{bmatrix} CH_2 \\ \| \\ COH \\ | \\ COOH \end{bmatrix} \longrightarrow \underset{\substack{\text{Pyruvic} \\ \text{acid}}}{\overset{CH_3}{\underset{COOH}{\overset{|}{\underset{|}{CO}}}}}$$

It plays an important part in the fermentation and metabolism of carbohydrates.

A general method of preparation of α-keto acids is the hydrolysis of acyl cyanides prepared from acyl chlorides.

$$RCOCl + CuCN \longrightarrow RCOCN \xrightarrow{\text{Hydrolysis}} RCOCOOH$$

α-Keto acids are oxidized easily to carbon dioxide and the monocarboxylic acid having one less carbon atom. Thus pyruvic acid reduces Tollen's reagent and is oxidized to carbon dioxide and acetic acid. α-Keto acids are stable to dilute acids and alkalies. When heated to a relatively high temperature (above 170°) or at a lower temperature in the presence of concentrated sulfuric acid, carbon monoxide is lost and the carboxylic acid results.

$$CH_3COCOOH \xrightarrow{170°} CH_3COOH + CO$$

Likewise α-keto esters on heating lose carbon monoxide to give the ester of the carboxylic acid having one less carbon atom.

$$RCOCOOC_2H_5 \xrightarrow{\text{Heat}} RCOOC_2H_5 + CO$$

When the C-2 carbonyl group of ethyl pyruvate is labeled with radioactive C^{14} and decomposed at 130°, the carbon monoxide evolved is not radioactive. Hence the carbonyl group lost is that from the carboethoxy group.

β-Keto Acids

β-Keto acids can be obtained by the saponification of their esters with cold dilute sodium hydroxide solutions. The free acids decompose on heating to carbon dioxide and a ketone.

$$RCOCH_2COOH \xrightarrow{\text{Heat}} RCOCH_3 + CO_2$$

This easy loss of carbon dioxide resembles the behavior of malonic acid (p. 542) and is characteristic of any acid having strongly electron-attracting groups on the α carbon atom.

In the combustion of fat acids by the animal organism, two carbon atoms are removed at a time, the intermediates being the β-hydroxy and β-keto acids. In the next to the last stage acetoacetic acid is converted to acetic acid. This step requires the simultaneous combustion of carbohydrates which in turn requires the hormone insulin. The diabetic lacking insulin excretes carbohydrates as glucose, and acetoacetic acid accumulates in his blood stream. Decarboxylation of the acetoacetic acid gives rise to acetone.

$$CH_3COCH_2COOH \longrightarrow CH_3COCH_3 + CO_2$$

Both acetoacetic acid and acetone can be detected in the blood and in the urine of uncontrolled diabetics. The toxic effects of the acetoacetic acid (sometimes called *diacetic acid*) and acetone lead to coma and death.

Preparation of β-Keto Esters. The esters of β-keto acids are stable, and since they are prepared easily and contain an active methylene group, they form an important class of organic compounds. In 1863 Geuther, who thought that acetic acid contained two hydrogen atoms replaceable by metals, attempted to prepare a sodium salt of ethyl acetate by reaction with metallic sodium. He observed the evolution of hydrogen, and the formation of sodium ethoxide and a crystalline compound $C_6H_9O_3Na$. The latter compound on acidification gave a liquid which though neutral to litmus reacted with bases to form salts. It was shown later that a small amount of alcohol is necessary for the reaction to take place and that the actual catalyst is sodium ethoxide, which brings about condensation with the liberation of ethyl alcohol. The condensation product reacts with the sodium ethoxide to give Geuther's sodium salt. Hence a molar proportion of sodium ethoxide or metallic sodium is needed to complete the reaction.

$$C_2H_5OH + Na \longrightarrow C_2H_5ONa + \tfrac{1}{2} H_2$$

$$\overset{O}{\overset{\|}{CH_3C}}OC_2H_5 + \overset{O}{\overset{\|}{CH_3C}}OC_2H_5 \xrightarrow{NaOC_2H_5} C_2H_5OH + CH_3COCH_2COOC_2H_5 \xrightarrow{NaOC_2H_5}$$

$$C_2H_5OH + [CH_3CO\bar{C}HCOOC_2H_5]Na^+ \xrightarrow{HOAc} CH_3COCH_2COOC_2H_5 + NaOAc$$
Ethyl acetoacetate

Later Claisen [1] and others showed that esters can be condensed by means of sodium ethoxide with a wide variety of compounds having hydrogen α to a

---

[1] Ludwig Claisen (1851–1930), professor at the University of Kiel. He is noted chiefly for his work on the condensation of aromatic aldehydes with ketones, on the ester condensations which bear his name, and on tautomeric compounds.

carbonyl group. The reaction usually is called the *Claisen ester condensation* and should not be confused with the Claisen reaction (p. 404).

The best yields are obtained in the condensation of like molecules of esters having two α hydrogen atoms or in mixed condensations in which one of the esters lacks α hydrogen atoms.

$$RCH_2COOC_2H_5 + RCH_2COOC_2H_5 \xrightarrow{NaOC_2H_5} RCH_2COCHCOOC_2H_5 + C_2H_5OH$$
$$\underset{R}{|}$$

$$\overset{O}{\overset{||}{HC}}OC_2H_5 + CH_3COOC_2H_5 \xrightarrow{NaOC_2H_5} \overset{O}{\overset{||}{HC}}CH_2COOC_2H_5 + C_2H_5OH$$

Ethyl
formate

Ethyl formylacetate
(formylacetic ester)

$$C_2H_5OCOCOOC_2H_5 + CH_3COOC_2H_5 \xrightarrow{NaOC_2H_5} C_2H_5OCOCOCH_2COOC_2H_5 + C_2H_5OH$$

Ethyl oxalate

Ethyl oxalacetate
(oxalacetic ester)

$$C_6H_5COOC_2H_5 + CH_3COOC_2H_5 \xrightarrow{NaOC_2H_5} C_6H_5COCH_2COOC_2H_5 + C_2H_5OH$$

Ethyl
benzoate

Ethyl benzoylacetate
(benzoylacetic ester)

If the ester being acylated contains only one α hydrogen atom, the ethoxide ion is not a sufficiently strong base to catalyze the reaction. However a stronger base such as the triphenylmethide ion will effect the condensation.

$$C_6H_5COOC_2H_5 + (CH_3)_2CHCOOC_2H_5 \xrightarrow{Na^{+-}C(C_6H_5)_3} C_6H_5COC(CH_3)_2COOC_2H_5 + C_2H_5OH$$

Ethyl
benzoyldimethylacetate

The Claisen ester condensation of ethyl acetate may be represented by the following series of equilibria.

$$CH_3COOC_2H_5 \underset{C_2H_5OH}{\overset{[^-OC_2H_5]}{\rightleftarrows}} [^-CH_2COOC_2H_5] \underset{[^-OC_2H_5]}{\overset{CH_3COOC_2H_5}{\rightleftarrows}} CH_3COCH_2COOC_2H_5 \underset{C_2H_5OH}{\overset{[^-OC_2H_5]}{\rightleftarrows}} [CH_3CO\bar{C}HCOOC_2H_5]$$

The position of equilibrium for the first stage is determined by the acidity of the ester and the basicity of the catalyst. Any catalyst sufficiently basic to bring about this step will form a salt with the product of the second step, since the β-keto esters are much more acidic than the esters. Hence the reaction will go to completion.

Reactions of β-Keto Esters. Geuther reported the reaction of his sodium salt of ethyl acetoacetate with ethyl iodide and isolated an ethyl derivative of ethyl acetoacetate in 1863. He showed in 1868 that reaction with sodium ethoxide in alcohol gave ethyl butyrate, but it was not until 1877 that the work of Wislicenus [2] led to an understanding of the reactions involved. The sub-

---

[2] Johannes Adolf Wislicenus (1835–1902). His father was a Lutheran minister who was forced to leave Germany because of his liberal views and brought his family to America in 1853. Young Wislicenus obtained a position at Harvard University, but with the family returned to Germany in 1855. He completed his studies at Halle and later became professor of chemistry at Wuerzburg and at Leipzig. Among his many chemical interests were the condensation of aldehydes with ammonia, the synthesis of α-hydroxy acids from cyanohydrins, the chemistry of the lactic acids, ester condensations, the alkylation of acetoacetic esters, and stereochemistry.

sequent investigations of Wislicenus, Claisen, and others showed the great value of these reactions for the synthesis of organic compounds and soon led to the discovery of the related reactions of malonic esters (p. 544).

An appreciable amount of the enol form of β-keto esters exists in equilibrium with the keto form.

$$CH_3COCH_2COOC_2H_5 \rightleftarrows CH_3C{=}CHCOOC_2H_5$$
$$\underset{OH}{|}$$

Hence β-keto esters decolorize bromine readily and give a red color with ferric chloride. Like ethyl malonate (p. 545), they undergo carbon alkylation.

$$RCOCH_2COOC_2H_5 \xrightarrow{NaOC_2H_5} [RCO\bar{C}HCOOC_2H_5]Na^+ \xrightarrow{R'X} RCOCHR'COOC_2H_5 \xrightarrow{NaOC_2H_5}$$

$$[RCO\bar{C}R'COOC_2H_5]Na^+ \xrightarrow{R''X} RCOCR'COOC_2H_5$$
$$\underset{R''}{|}$$

The anion of the sodium salt of β-keto esters is a resonance hybrid.

$$\left\{ \underset{O}{\overset{\|}{RC}}{-}\bar{C}HCOOC_2H_5 \longleftrightarrow RC{=}\underset{O^-}{\overset{|}{CHCOOC_2H_5}} \right\}$$

Thus ethyl chloroformate gives *O*-alkylation instead of *C*-alkylation. Acetyl chloride gives both *O*- and *C*-acylation.

Hydrolysis and decarboxylation of the carbon-alkylated esters give good yields of the substituted ketones.

$$RCOCHR'COOC_2H_5 \xrightarrow[\text{then HCl}]{\text{Dil. NaOH,}} RCOCHR'COOH \xrightarrow{\text{Heat}} RCOCHR' + CO_2$$

$$RCOCR'COOC_2H_5 \xrightarrow[\text{then HCl}]{\text{Dil. NaOH,}} RCOCR'COOH \xrightarrow{\text{Heat}} RCOCHR' + CO_2$$
$$\underset{R''}{|} \qquad\qquad\qquad \underset{R''}{|} \qquad\qquad \underset{R''}{|}$$

Hydrolysis and decarboxylation can be brought about simultaneously by boiling the keto ester with dilute acid, but the yields and purity of the product usually are inferior. The alkaline hydrolysis is carried out at room temperature with dilute alkali to avoid carbon-carbon scission.

β-Keto esters undergo carbon-carbon scission with concentrated alkali.

$$RCOCR'COOC_2H_5 + 2\ NaOH \longrightarrow RCOONa + R'R''CHCOONa + C_2H_5OH$$
$$\underset{R''}{|}$$

Although these reactions give satisfactory yields, substituted acetic acids usually are prepared from ethyl malonate. However the carbon-carbon scission reaction sometimes is used for the preparation of higher β-keto esters from acylated acetoacetic esters.

$$CH_3COCH_2COOEt \xrightarrow[\text{then RCOCl}]{NaOC_2H_5,} CH_3COCHCOOC_2H_5 \xrightarrow{NH_3}$$
$$| \atop COR$$

$$RCOCH_2COOC_2H_5 + CH_3CONH_2 (+ RCONH_2 + CH_3COCH_2C_2H_5)$$

Since either acyl group may be eliminated, a mixture of the new ester with acetoacetic ester is obtained.

Tautomerism. Ethyl acetoacetate is the classical example of tautomerism, which usually is defined as the ability of a substance to possess or to react as if it possesses more than one structure. This definition is satisfactory except for the implication that the substance concerned is a single compound, the view held by Laar who coined the term tautomerism (Gr. *tauto* the same) in 1885. Actually tautomerism is the dynamic equilibrium existing between two readily interconvertible isomers. The first recognized case of tautomerism is the acid-catalyzed equilibrium between the two isomeric diisobutylenes postulated by Butlerov[3] in 1877.

$$(CH_3)_3CCH{=}CCH_3 \rightleftarrows (CH_3)_3CH_2C{=}CH_2$$
$$\qquad | \qquad\qquad\qquad\qquad |$$
$$\quad CH_3 \qquad\qquad\qquad\qquad CH_3$$

In 1887 Wislicenus reported the isolation of two isomeric ethyl formylphenyl-acetates, $C_6H_5CHCOOC_2H_5$, a liquid which gave a color with ferric chloride

$$| \atop CHO$$

and a solid which did not. The solid slowly changed to the liquid on standing. In 1893 Claisen reported two forms of acetyldibenzoylmethane. One melted at 85°–90°, was soluble in dilute carbonate solution, gave in alcoholic solution a red color with ferric chloride, and reacted at once with cupric acetate to give an insoluble blue copper salt. Crystallization from alcohol of the product melting at 85°–90° gave a compound melting at 109°–112°, which at first was completely insoluble in dilute alkali but which slowly dissolved. Alcoholic solutions gave no color immediately on adding ferric chloride, and no blue precipitate on adding cupric acetate, but both reactions slowly took place on standing. In an article published in 1896 Claisen postulated that the lower melting form had an enol structure and that the higher melting form was completely ketonic.

$$CH_3C{=}C(COC_6H_5)_2 \qquad\qquad CH_3COCH(COC_6H_5)_2$$
$$| \qquad\qquad\qquad\qquad\qquad \text{Ketonic form of}$$
$$OH \qquad\qquad\qquad\qquad\qquad \text{acetyldibenzoylmethane}$$
Enolic form of
acetyldibenzoylmethane

---

[3] Alexander Mikhailovich Butlerov (1828–1886), eminent Russian chemist and professor at the Universities of Kazan and St. Petersburg. He was the first to prepare polymeric formaldehyde, hexamethylenetetramine, and the carbohydrate mixture formed by the action of dilute calcium hydroxide on formaldehyde. He was a strong advocate of the structural concept of organic chemistry and was the first to use the expression "the chemical structure of organic compounds." Butlerov prepared the first tertiary alcohol by the reaction of methylzinc on acetyl chloride. His studies of the reactions of *t*-butyl alcohol led him to the preparation of the isomeric butanes and butenes and to the discovery of the tautomerism of the diisobutylenes.

In the same year Hantzsch isolated two forms of phenylnitromethane. The solid form had acidic properties and changed spontaneously to the nonacidic liquid form.

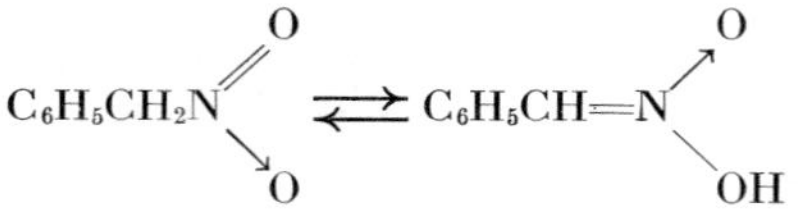

$$C_6H_5CH_2N{\overset{O}{\underset{O}{\diagup\diagdown}}} \rightleftarrows C_6H_5CH{=}N{\overset{O}{\underset{OH}{\diagup\diagup}}}$$

It was not until 1911 that Knorr succeeded in isolating two forms of ethyl acetoacetate. The ketonic form separated when solutions in alcohol, ether, or petroleum ether were cooled to $-78°$. It did not give a color immediately with ferric chloride, and did not decolorize bromine. When dry hydrogen chloride was passed into a solution of the sodium salt of ethyl acetoacetate at $-78°$, a glassy solid was obtained which reacted instantaneously with both ferric chloride and bromine. On permitting either isomer to reach room temperature, the equilibrium mixture was obtained.

$$CH_3COCH_2COOC_2H_5 \rightleftarrows CH_3COH{=}CHCOOC_2H_5$$

This interconversion is catalyzed by traces of acids or bases. By using specially treated quartz apparatus, K. H. Meyer in 1920 succeeded in separating the two forms by distillation. Since alcohols boil higher than ketones, it is surprising that the enol form of ethyl acetoacetate boils lower than the keto form. An explanation is that the enol form contains an internal proton bond which prevents intermolecular proton-bonding.

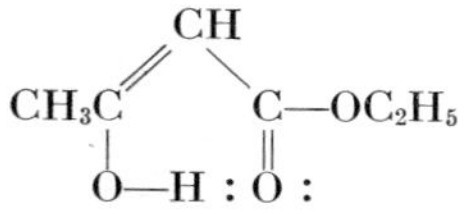

$$CH_3C{\overset{CH}{\underset{O-H\,:\,O\,:}{\diagup\diagdown}}}C{-}OC_2H_5$$

Knorr determined the refractive index of the keto form to be $n_D^{10} = 1.4225$ and of the enol form $n_D^{10} = 1.4480$. From the refractive index of the equilibrium mixture, $n_D^{10} = 1.4232$, the enol content was estimated to be 3 per cent. Meyer found that the keto form does not isomerize too rapidly to prevent the estimation of the enol content by reaction with bromine if the procedure is carried out quickly. He mixed a solution of the ester with an excess of a solution of bromine at $0°$ and removed the excess bromine by the addition of a solution of β-naphthol within a period of only fifteen seconds.

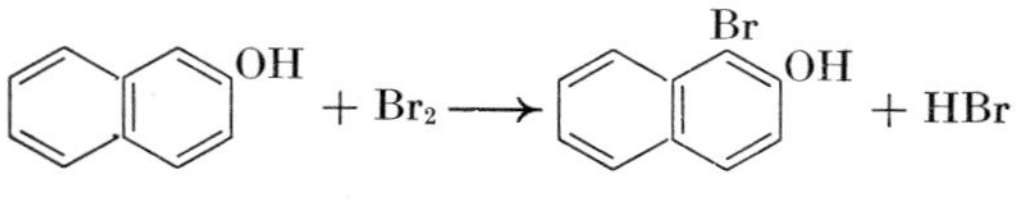

$$CH_3C{=}CHCOOC_2H_5 + Br_2 \longrightarrow \left[CH_3\overset{Br}{\underset{OH}{C}}CHBrCOOC_2H_5 \right] \longrightarrow CH_3COCHBrCOOC_2H_5 + HBr$$

Since α-bromo ketones are reduced by hydrogen iodide, they can be estimated by acidifying, adding sodium iodide, and titrating the iodine with standard thiosulfate solution.

$$CH_3COCHBrCOOC_2H_5 + 2\ HI \longrightarrow CH_3COCH_2COOC_2H_5 + I_2 + HBr$$

By this procedure the amount of enol form in the pure ester was estimated to be 8 per cent.

The amount of enol form in solutions varies widely with the solvent. In water it is 0.4 per cent, in acetic acid 6 per cent, in nitrobenzene 10 per cent, in ethyl alcohol 12 per cent, in benzene 16 per cent, in ether 27 per cent, and in hexane 46 per cent. The poor correlation of the extent of enolization with properties of the solvent such as basicity or dielectric constant indicates that several factors probably are acting simultaneously.

The difference between simple aldehydes and ketones, β-keto esters, and phenols is purely one of degree. In the aldehydes and ketones, the position of equilibrium is far on the keto side; in β-keto esters appreciable quantities of both the keto and enol forms are present at equilibrium; and in phenols the position of equilibrium is far on the enol side. It also is realized now that the anions of the metallic salts are resonance hybrids and that whether the product of a reaction is a derivative of the enol or keto form depends on the effective point of attack of the reagent.

Other Keto Acids

The only γ-keto acid of importance is **levulinic acid** which is formed by the hydrolysis of hexoses with strong acids (p. 287).

$$C_6H_{12}O_6 \xrightarrow{\text{Conc. HCl}} HCOOH + CH_3COCH_2CH_2COOH + H_2O$$
$$\text{Levulinic acid}$$

Levulinic acid and substituted levulinic acids can be synthesized from β-keto esters.

$$CH_3COCH_2COOC_2H_5 + ClCH_2COOC_2H_5 \xrightarrow{\text{NaOC}_2\text{H}_5} CH_3COCHCOOC_2H_5 \xrightarrow{\text{Hydrolysis}}$$
$$\underset{\displaystyle CH_2COOC_2H_5}{|}$$

$$CH_3COCHCOOH \xrightarrow{\text{Heat}} CH_3COCH_2CH_2COOH + CO_2$$
$$\underset{\displaystyle CH_2COOH}{|}$$

Another synthesis of γ-keto acids involves the reaction of cyclic anhydrides with Grignard reagents.

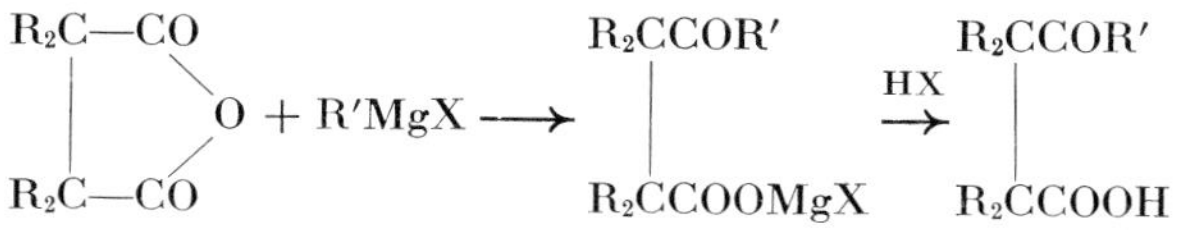

$$
\begin{array}{ccc}
\begin{matrix} R_2C{-}CO \\ | \qquad\quad \diagdown \\ \qquad\quad O + R'MgX \\ | \qquad\quad \diagup \\ R_2C{-}CO \end{matrix}
\longrightarrow
\begin{matrix} R_2CCOR' \\ | \\ R_2CCOOMgX \end{matrix}
\xrightarrow{\text{HX}}
\begin{matrix} R_2CCOR' \\ | \\ R_2CCOOH \end{matrix}
\end{array}
$$

Licanic acid, $CH_3(CH_2)_3CH{=}CHCH{=}CHCH{=}CH(CH_2)_2CO(CH_2)_4{-}COOH$, makes up 70 to 80 per cent of the fat acids from *oiticica oil*, the seed fat of *Licania rigida* (p. 152).

When γ- and δ-keto acids are heated, they slowly lose water with the formation of unsaturated lactones.

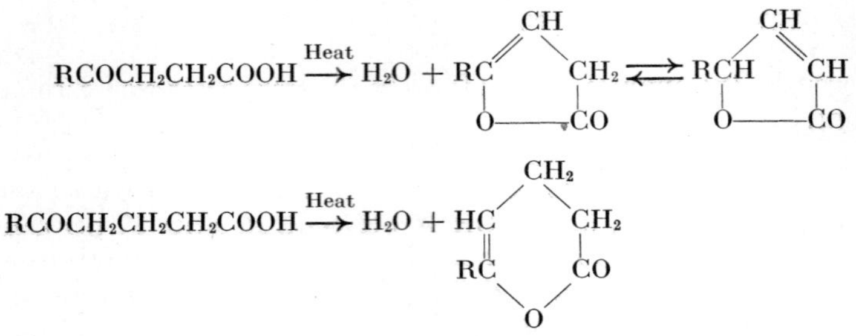

$$RCOCH_2CH_2COOH \xrightarrow{\text{Heat}} H_2O + RC \overset{CH}{\underset{O \quad CO}{\diagup\diagdown}} CH_2 \rightleftarrows RCH \overset{CH}{\underset{O \quad CO}{\diagup\diagdown}} CH$$

$$RCOCH_2CH_2CH_2COOH \xrightarrow{\text{Heat}} H_2O + HC \overset{CH_2}{\underset{RC \quad CO}{\diagup\diagdown}} CH_2$$

REVIEW QUESTIONS

1. How is pyruvic acid prepared? What happens in the thermal decomposition of α-keto acids and esters?
2. How are β-keto acids prepared and what is their most characteristic reaction? What other type of compound behaves in a similar fashion?
3. What is the Claisen ester condensation?
4. Discuss the mechanism of the Claisen ester condensation.
5. Give two ways for preparing ethyl phenylmalonate, each making use of Claisen ester condensations.
6. Ethyl acetoacetate forms an oxime, a phenylhydrazone, an O-methyl ether, a sodium salt, readily decolorizes bromine, and gives a color with ferric chloride. Explain. Define the term *tautomerism*.
7. Give two procedures for the separation of the keto and enol forms of ethyl acetoacetate. Why does the enol form have the lower boiling point? How may the per cent of enol form in an equilibrium mixture be estimated?
8. Discuss the behavior of β-keto esters to cold dilute alkali, hot dilute acid, and hot concentrated alkali.
9. Why does methyl acetoacetate fail to give the iodoform test?
10. Give reactions for the preparation of (*a*) methyl *n*-butyl ketone from ethyl acetoacetate; (*b*) α-methylbutyric acid from ethyl acetoacetate; (*c*) α-keto-γ-phenylbutyric acid from cinnamic acid; (*d*) 2-amino-4-hydroxypyrimidine from ethyl acetate.

Chapter 38

ALICYCLIC COMPOUNDS. TERPENES AND STEROIDS

ALICYCLIC COMPOUNDS

Alicyclic compounds are cyclic compounds having aliphatic properties. In a strict sense the term should apply to both carbocyclic and heterocyclic compounds, but in practice it usually is limited to carbocyclic compounds. The saturated alicyclic hydrocarbons frequently are called *cycloparaffins* or *cyclanes* although petroleum technologists usually call them *naphthenes* because cyclopentane (pentamethylene) and cyclohexane (hexamethylene) and their homologs have been isolated from the naphtha fraction of petroleum. Those compounds obtainable by the hydrogenation of aromatic rings frequently are called *hydroaromatic* compounds.

General Theory Regarding Cyclic Compounds

Previous to 1879 only five- and six-membered ring compounds were known. They could be accounted for without too much difficulty, since the internal angles of a regular pentagon are 108 degrees and of a regular hexagon 120 degrees. The synthesis of a four-membered ring compound by Markovnikov in 1879 and of three-membered ring compounds by Freund in 1882 and Perkin Jr.[1] in 1883, and the chemical properties of these compounds led Baeyer in 1885 to propose his **strain theory.** Baeyer postulated that the ease of formation of a ring depends on the amount which the bond must deviate from its normal tetrahedral angle of 109°28' in order to form the bond. The amount of deviation was designated as the *strain* in the ring. The greater the amount of strain, the easier it should be to open the ring, that is the more reactive the compound should be. Thus in the formation of the highly reactive double bond, which in older theory consisted of two identical single bonds, each bond must be bent through one-half of the tetrahedral angle or 54° 44'; for a cyclopropane ring, $\frac{1}{2}$ (109° 28' − 60°) = 24° 44'; for cyclobutane, $\frac{1}{2}$ (109° 28' − 90°) = 9° 44'; for cyclopentane, $\frac{1}{2}$ (109° 28' − 108°) = 0° 44'; and for cyclohexane, $\frac{1}{2}$ (109° 28' − 120°) = −5° 44'. Since rings having more than seven atoms were unknown, Baeyer assumed that all of the atoms must be in a plane, which would require increasing negative strain for larger rings. This assumption was questioned at once by Werner, and other discrepancies were obvious. For example although olefins are highly reactive, they are obtained easily in excellent yield. Moreover although in certain reactions cyclopentanes are formed in better yields than cyclohexanes, all evidence indicated that once formed the two ring systems are of equal stability.

The reality of planar alicyclic rings above C_5 was questioned from time to time, but it was not until the period 1921–1926 that sufficient evidence ac-

---

[1] William Henry Perkin, Jr., (1860–1929), student of Wislicenus and Baeyer, and professor of chemistry at the University of Oxford. He is noted for his synthetic and degradative work in the field of natural products, particularly the terpenes and alkaloids.

cumulated to cause this feature of Baeyer's theory to be abandoned. The most convincing of this evidence was the synthesis of rings containing from seven to over thirty carbon atoms, all of which appeared to be as stable as cyclopentane or cyclohexane. Currently it is assumed that the ease of formation of cyclic compounds, that is the tendency for intramolecular reaction, depends on the proximity of the atoms being joined in the reaction. This tendency is high for the formation of a double bond, where the two atoms are adjacent to each other.

If the atoms were forced to remain in an extended chain, the chance for intramolecular reaction would decrease as more and more carbon atoms separated the reacting groups. However rotation about the single bonds permits the assumption of a spiral structure as indicated in Fig. 43. If in this figure the

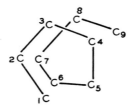

Fig. 43. Spiral arrangement of a carbon chain.

distance between C-1 and C-2 is 1.54 Å, then C-1 to C-3 = 2.51 Å, C-1 to C-4 = 2.52 Å, and C-1 to C-5 = 1.67 Å. Hence the double bond and the five-membered ring can be formed readily, but it is more difficult to form three- and four-membered rings. Because of the flexibility of the molecule, C-1 and C-6 can approach each other to any desired distance. Therefore once the bond is formed the ring is entirely strainless. The same situation exists for longer chains, but above five carbon atoms other atoms in the chain begin to get in the way of the reacting groups, and a greater amount of maneuvering of the chain is necessary to bring the reacting groups into the proper space relationship for reaction to take place. As a result intermolecular reaction to give polymeric products becomes predominant, and the yields of cyclic compounds are very low. In confirmation of this theory, large ring compounds can be obtained in excellent yields if the reaction is carried out at extremely high dilution where the chances of intramolecular reaction is again greater than the chance of intermolecular reaction.

The question of the relative stability of cyclopentane and cyclohexane has acquired renewed interest in recent years. Precise work on the heats of combustion of cyclopentane, cyclohexane, and cycloheptane indicates that cyclohexane is more stable by about 1 kcal. per mole than either cyclopentane or cycloheptane. In other words cyclohexane is less strained than cyclopentane or cycloheptane even though all of these compounds should have tetrahedral valence angles. An explanation can be given from a consideration of the fact that the configuration of the ethane molecule in which the methyl groups are rotated 60 degrees with respect to each other and the hydrogen atoms are staggered is more stable by about 3 kcal. per mole than the configuration in which the hydrogen atoms are opposite each other (p. 24). In the *trans* form of cyclohexane (Fig. 44, p. 562), the hydrogen atoms are completely staggered and hence cyclohexane is the most stable of the cycloparaffins. In the larger rings some of the hydrogen atoms can be staggered but not all. In cyclopentane none of the hydrogen atoms are staggered if the carbon atoms are all in a plane, and it is believed that the carbon atoms actually are forced into a nonplanar configuration to permit some staggering of the hydrogen atoms.

Preparation of Alicyclic Compounds

1. *From Dihalides.*

$$(CH_2)_nX_2 + Zn \longrightarrow (CH_2)_n + ZnX_2$$

2. *From Dicarboxylic Acids* (p. 128).

$$(CH_2)_n(COOH)_2 \xrightarrow[\text{Th salt}]{\text{Heat, Ca or}} (CH_2)_nCO + CO_2 + H_2O$$

3. *From Polymethylene Halides and Ethyl Malonate.*

$$X(CH_2)_nX + CH_2(COOC_2H_5) \xrightarrow{NaOC_2H_5} X(CH_2)_nCH(COOC_2H_5)_2 \xrightarrow{NaOC_2H_5}$$

$$(CH_2)_nC(COOC_2H_5)_2 \xrightarrow[\text{HCl and heat}]{\text{NaOH, then}} (CH_2)_nCHCOOH$$

4. *From Polymethylenebismalonic Esters.*

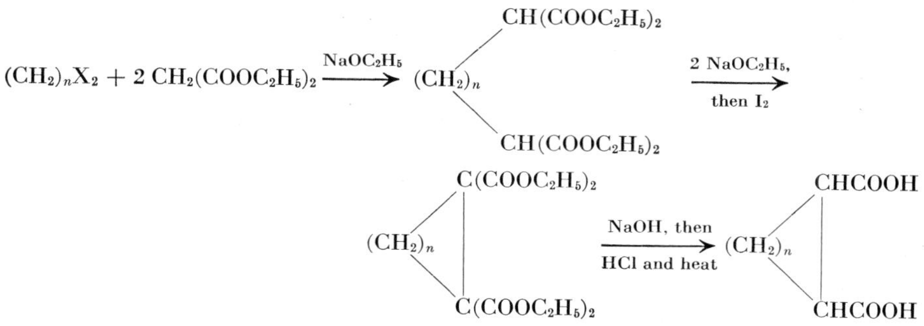

$$(CH_2)_nX_2 + 2\ CH_2(COOC_2H_5)_2 \xrightarrow{NaOC_2H_5}$$

$$(CH_2)_n \begin{matrix} CH(COOC_2H_5)_2 \\ \\ CH(COOC_2H_5)_2 \end{matrix} \xrightarrow[\text{then } I_2]{2\ NaOC_2H_5,}$$

$$(CH_2)_n \begin{matrix} C(COOC_2H_5)_2 \\ \\ C(COOC_2H_5)_2 \end{matrix} \xrightarrow[\text{HCl and heat}]{\text{NaOH, then}} (CH_2)_n \begin{matrix} CHCOOH \\ \\ CHCOOH \end{matrix}$$

5. *By Reduction of Aromatic Compounds* (p. 311).

$$C_6H_6 + 3\ H_2 \xrightarrow[200°]{Ni,} C_6H_{12}$$

Cyclohexane
(hexahydrobenzene,
hexamethylene)

Similarly phenol gives **cyclohexanol** (*hexalin*), and aniline gives **cyclohexylamine**. Naphthalene gives 1,2,3,4-tetrahydronaphthalene (tetralin, p. 429) and the decahydronaphthalenes (decalins, p. 430).

Reactions of Alicyclic Compounds

In general the reactions of alicyclic compounds are identical with those of aliphatic compounds except that the three- and four-membered rings are less stable. Thus cyclopropane and most of its derivatives react with the same reagents as olefins to give open-chain compounds.

$$(CH_2)_3 + H_2SO_4 \longrightarrow CH_3CH_2CH_2OSO_3H$$

$$(CH_2)_3 + HBr \longrightarrow CH_3CH_2CH_2Br$$

$$(CH_2)_3 + Br_2 \longrightarrow BrCH_2CH_2CH_2Br$$

$$(CH_2)_3 + H_2 \xrightarrow[80°]{Pt} CH_3CH_2CH_3$$

The rates of reactions of cyclopropanes may differ greatly from those of olefins. For example cyclopropane reacts more rapidly than propylene with sulfuric acid but more slowly with bromine. Catalytic reduction of cyclopropane requires a somewhat higher temperature than reduction of propylene. Unlike propylene, cyclopropane does not react with alkaline permanganate solution. Moreover in reactions with unsymmetrical reagents such as sulfuric acid or hydrogen bromide, cyclopropane yields *n*-propyl derivatives and not *i*-propyl derivatives.

Cyclobutane does not react with sulfuric acid, hydrobromic acid, or bromine. However it can be reduced catalytically at 120°, whereas cyclopentane and higher cyclanes are not reduced at temperatures up to 200°.

The hydroaromatic compounds show none of the properties of the aromatic compounds. Thus cyclohexane does not undergo direct nitration, sulfonation, or the Friedel-Crafts reaction. Cyclohexanol is not soluble in alkali and reacts like a secondary alcohol.

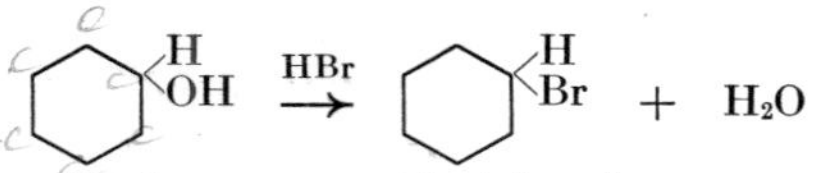

Cyclo-
hexanol

Cyclohexyl
bromide

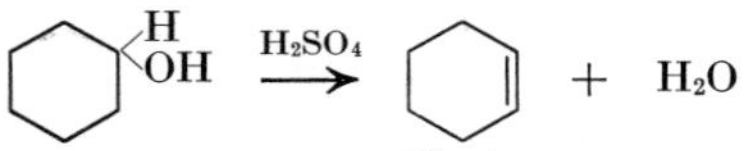

Cyclo-
hexene

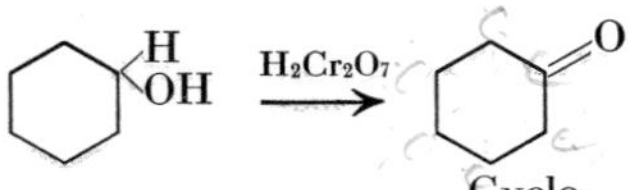

Cyclo-
hexanone

Cyclohexyl bromide reacts with silver hydroxide to give cyclohexanol, with alcoholic potassium hydroxide to give cyclohexene, and with sodium cyanide to give cyclohexyl cyanide. Cyclohexene decolorizes permanganate to give first the diol and then adipic acid, and decolorizes bromine to form cyclohexene bromide (1,2-dibromocyclohexane). Cyclohexylamine is as basic as aliphatic amines ($K_B = 4.4 \times 10^{-4}$), and no diazonium salt can be obtained by reaction with nitrous acid. The unsaturated and oxygenated rings are opened readily by oxidation. Thus cyclohexene and cyclohexanone give good yields of adipic acid (p. 541).

Individual Alicyclic Compounds

Cyclopropane can be obtained in 80 per cent yields by the reaction of zinc dust with trimethylene chloride. It is a gas, b.p. $-34°$, used frequently instead of ether as a general anesthetic.

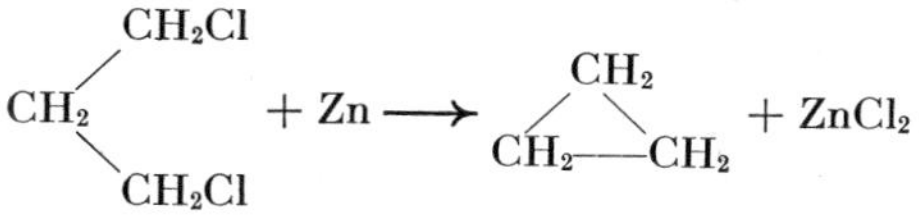

$$
\begin{array}{c}
CH_2Cl \\
CH_2 \\
CH_2Cl
\end{array}
+ Zn \longrightarrow
\begin{array}{c}
CH_2 \\
CH_2—CH_2
\end{array}
+ ZnCl_2
$$

Cyclopropane

Cyclopentadiene, b.p. $41°$, is a component of coal gas. It polymerizes spontaneously to dicyclopentadiene, m.p. $33°$, which depolymerizes at its boiling point $(170°)$ to the monomer.

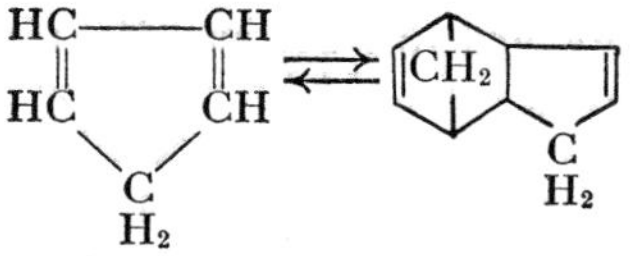

$$
\begin{array}{c}
HC——CH \\
HC \quad\quad CH \\
C \\
H_2
\end{array}
\rightleftharpoons
\begin{array}{c}
CH_2 \\
C \\
H_2
\end{array}
$$

Cyclo-   Dicyclo-
pentadiene   pentadiene

The **naphthenic acids** are carboxylic acids present in small amount in petroleum. Most of those isolated in a pure state are carboxyl derivatives of alkylated cyclopentanes. **Chaulmoogric** and **hydnocarpic acids,** the characteristic fat acids of chaulmoogra oil, long used in the treatment of leprosy, contain a terminal cyclopentene ring.

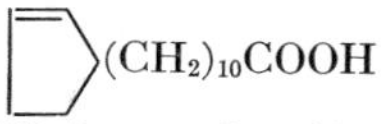

$\square\rangle(CH_2)_{10}COOH$ $\square\rangle(CH_2)_{12}COOH$

Hydnocarpic acid 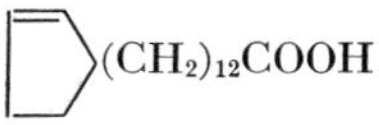   Chaulmoogric acid

Cyclohexane, methylcyclohexane, cyclohexanol, cyclohexanone, cyclohexylamine, tetralin, and **decalin** are commercial products. The last compound exists in two isomeric forms which differ in the space relationship of the 9 and 10 hydrogen atoms. These two forms were postulated as possible

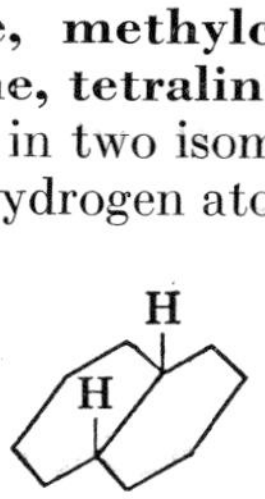

cis-Decalin

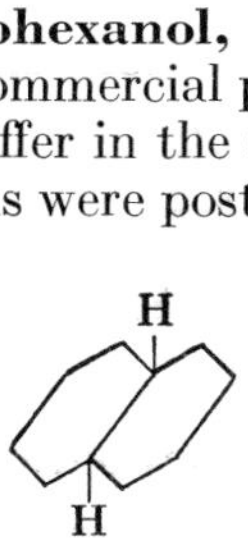

trans-Decalin

by Mohr in 1918 but were not isolated until 1927. Since these two isomers could not exist if the carbon atoms of the rings were planar because of the amount of strain that would be involved, the isolation of the two forms was a proof that carbocyclic rings need not be planar (p. 557).

As early as 1890 Sachse had pointed out that if the carbon atoms of cyclohexane are permitted to assume nonplanar positions, two isomers of cyclohexane should exist. In one form, called the *cis* or *boat* form, two carbon atoms lie on one side of the plane of the other four. In the *trans* or *chair* form, the carbon atoms lie in two parallel planes, three alternate carbon atoms in each plane (Fig. 44). Thus far none of the numerous claims concerning the isolation

cis Form　　　　　　　*trans* Form

Fig. 44. Stereochemical configurations of cyclohexane.

of such isomers has been substantiated. An examination of models indicates that such isomers probably are not sufficiently stable for independent existence, since very little energy should be required for their interconversion.

Cyclooctatetraene has been of considerable interest. It was prepared first by Willstaetter [2] by a rational synthesis from the alkaloid pseudopelletierine, a tropane derivative (p. 467). More recently it has been prepared in quantity by the polymerization of acetylene.

$$4 \; HC\equiv CH \xrightarrow[\substack{\text{tetrahydrofuran} \\ 65° \text{ and } 250 \text{ p.s.i.}}]{Ni(CN)_2 \text{ in}}$$

$$
\begin{array}{c}
CH\!=\!CH \\
CH \qquad\qquad CH \\
\| \qquad\qquad\quad \| \\
CH \qquad\qquad CH \\
CH\!=\!CH
\end{array}
$$

Cyclooctatetraene

Cyclooctatetraene rearranges to styrene, and the commercial synthesis of styrene from acetylene is thus a possibility.

$$
\begin{array}{c}
CH\!=\!CH \\
CH \qquad\qquad CH \\
\| \qquad\qquad\quad \| \\
CH \qquad\qquad CH \\
CH\!=\!CH
\end{array}
\longrightarrow
\begin{array}{c}
H \\
C \\
HC \qquad\quad C\!-\!CH\!=\!CH_2 \\
\\
HC \qquad\quad CH \\
C \\
H
\end{array}
$$

Originally cyclooctatetraene was prepared to determine whether its chemical properties would resemble those of benzene (cyclohexatriene). They do not, since the compound readily adds four moles of halogen or four moles of

---

[2] Richard Willstaetter (1872–1942), successor to Baeyer at the University of Munich. He was one of the outstanding investigators of the constitution of natural products such as alkaloids, anthocyanins, carotenes, and chlorophyll. He was awarded the Nobel Prize in Chemistry in 1915.

halogen acid, and is oxidized by cold permanganate. The nonaromatic character of cyclooctatetraene no longer is surprising, since resonance of the type characteristic of benzene would require that the carbon atoms be planar. The amount of energy required to produce coplanarity would reduce the resonance energy considerably. Hydrocarbons which might show aromatic properties are cyclodecapentaene, cyclododecahexaene, cyclotetradecaheptaene, and possibly cyclohexadecaoctaene, since in these compounds the carbon atoms could assume the planar configuration without undue strain except for some crowding of the internal hydrogen atoms.

Cyclodecapentaene

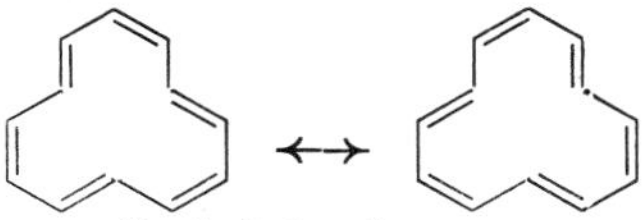

Cyclododecahexaene

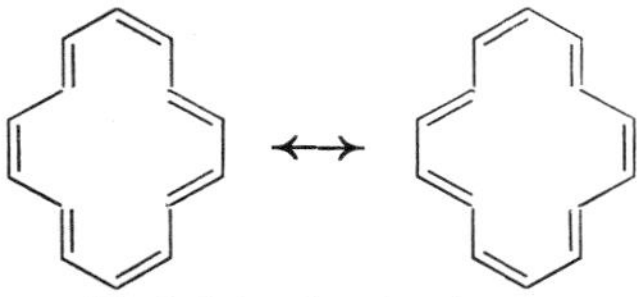

Cyclotetradecaheptaene

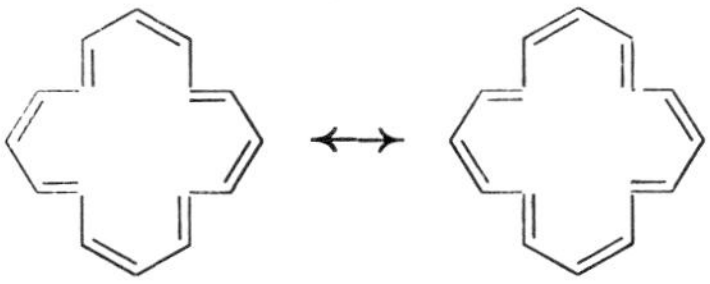

Cyclohexadecaoctaene

The reason for Baeyer's postulation that large rings are planar was that large ring compounds were unknown. It was shown in 1926, however, that muscone from the secretion of the musk deer and civetone from the secretion of the civet cat are fifteen- and seventeen-membered ring compounds respectively.

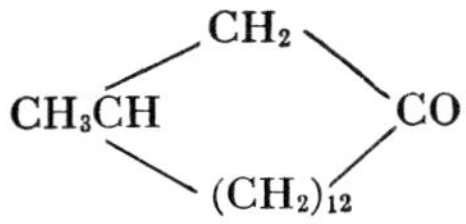

Muscone

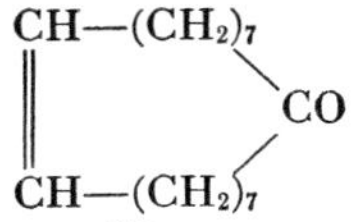

Civetone

In the following year the plant musks from angelica root and ambrette seed were found to be lactones containing sixteen- and seventeen-membered rings.

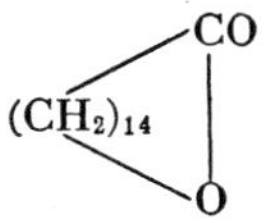

Penta-
decanolide

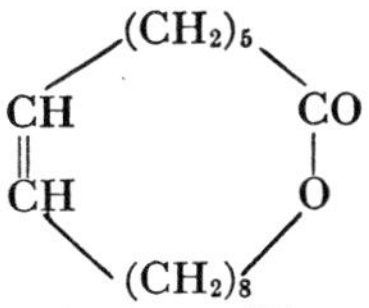

Ambrettolide

During subsequent years several types of compounds containing nine to thirty-four atoms in a ring were synthesized. It is of interest that all cyclic ketones, lactones, carbonates, imines, and formals having fourteen to seventeen atoms in a ring have a musk odor. **Cyclopentadecanone,** known as **Exaltone,** is manufactured commercially for use in perfumery in place of the natural musks. It is used in the laboratory as a solvent for molecular weight determinations, since it has a high cryoscopic constant and melts lower than camphor (Table 2, p. 17).

TERPENES

The odorous components of plants are volatile with steam and usually are separated from the plant material by steam distillation. They are known as the **volatile** or **essential oils.** They consist of hydrocarbons, alcohols, ethers, aldehydes, and ketones. Some of these substances such as anethole, eugenol, safrole, and cinnamaldehyde belong to the aromatic series (pp. 392 and 405). In the exudations of conifers and in the oils from the citrus fruits and from eucalyptus trees, alicyclic hydrocarbons of the composition $C_{10}H_{16}$ are especially abundant, and it is to these compounds that the term *terpene* (Gr. *terebinthos* turpentine tree) was applied in the restricted sense. However closely related open chain hydrocarbons having ten carbon atoms also were included under this term. The oxygenated terpenes were known as *camphors*. It soon became evident, however, that compounds containing 15, 20, 30, and 40 carbon atoms also are closely related to the terpenes. The one common characteristic of all of these compounds was recognized by Wallach,[3] namely that their carbon skeletons are evenly divisible into iso-C_5 units (frequently referred to as isoprene or isopentane units). The term *terpene* in its broadest sense now includes all such compounds, whether hydrocarbons or not. Terpene in the limited sense still refers to compounds containing two iso-C_5 units. Hence the broad class of terpenes is divided into hemiterpenes, C_5; terpenes, C_{10}; sesquiterpenes, C_{15}; diterpenes, C_{20}; triterpenes, C_{30}; tetraterpenes, C_{40}; and polyterpenes, C_{5x}.

Although some of the terpenes are open-chain compounds, most of them are alicyclic. Only a few of the more important representatives are discussed.

Citronellal is the chief component of oil of citronella, the essential oil of an East Indian grass (*Andropogon nardus*). **Citronellol,** the corresponding alcohol, occurs in rose oil.

$$(CH_3)_2C{=}CHCH_2CH_2CHCH_2CHO \qquad (CH_3)_2C{=}CHCH_2CH_2CHCH_2CH_2OH$$

| | |
CH₃ — Citronellal   CH₃ — Citronellol

Limonene is the main terpene constituent of lemon, orange, and many other oils. It contains an asymmetric carbon atom, and both $(+)$ and $(-)$ forms occur naturally. The racemic mixture is known as **dipentene.** In order to simplify the writing of structural formulas of cyclic terpenes, the convention is adopted that carbon and hydrogen atoms are not indicated but only the bonds between the carbon atoms. Hence in these formulas, a carbon atom is present at each intersection of two or more lines and at the end of each line. Other elements and double bonds are indicated, and each carbon atom is at-

[3] Otto Wallach (1847–1931), successor to Victor Meyer as professor of chemistry at Goettingen. He entered the field of terpenes in 1879 by being required to teach pharmacy at the University of Bonn. Wallach, unlike E. Fischer and Baeyer, was primarily an analyst and it was largely through his efforts that the confusion existing in the field of the terpenes was resolved. He announced his famous isoprene rule in 1887. He was awarded the Nobel Prize in Chemistry in 1910.

tached to a sufficient number of hydrogen atoms to satisfy the remaining valences. The dotted line in the skeleton formula indicates the division into isoprene units.

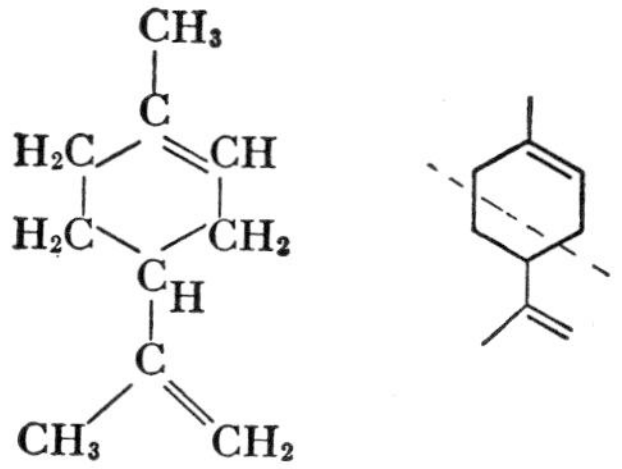

Limonene

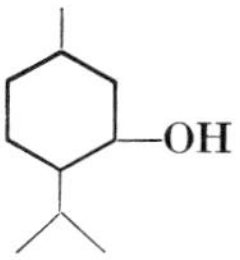

Menthol

l-**Menthol** is produced chiefly from Japanese peppermint oil. The racemic compound is synthesized by hydrogenating thymol (p. 391).

α-Pinene, the principal component of oil of turpentine from pine trees, is a dicyclic hydrocarbon. It is used chiefly as a paint thinner and for the synthesis of camphor.

α-**Pinene**

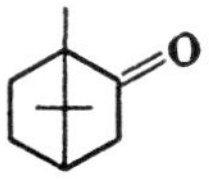

Camphor

Camphor is a dicyclic ketone, the *d* form of which occurs in the wood of the camphor tree, *Cinnamonum camphora*. The tree is native to the Chinese coast from Cochin-China to Shanghai, and to the coastal islands from Hainan to Southern Japan. Camphor formerly was produced chiefly in China, but with the acquisition of Formosa by Japan, its production became a monopoly of the Japanese government. Exorbitant prices forced its production in the more highly industrialized countries by synthesis from pinene.

Camphor has been known and valued for medicinal purposes since the earliest times, although modern medicine has found it to have no therapeutic value. Camphor is not reported in the Greek and Roman literature and probably was introduced into western Europe by the Arabs under the name *kafar*. Its chief industrial importance is as a plasticizer for cellulose nitrate in the manufacture of celluloid and photographic film base (p. 300).

Farnesol, $C_{15}H_{26}O$, is the best known example of the sesquiterpenes. It is present in many essential oils such as those from ambrette seeds, citronella, palmarosa, rose, and neroli.

$$(CH_3)_2C{=}CHCH_2 | CH_2C{=}CHCH_2 | CH_2C{=}CHCH_2OH$$
$$\qquad\qquad\qquad CH_3 \qquad\qquad CH_3$$

Farnesol

Phytol, an acyclic diterpene, $C_{20}H_{39}OH$, constitutes about one third of the chlorophyll molecule (p. 450), from which it is obtained by saponification. The same alcohol has been isolated from the chlorophyll of over 200 species of plants. It has been synthesized starting with pseudoionone.

$$(CH_3)_2CHCH_2CH_2 \mid (CH_2CHCH_2CH_2)_2 \mid CHC{=}CHCH_2OH$$
$$CH_3 \qquad\qquad CH_3$$

Phytol

Vitamin A, a monocyclic diterpene, is the fat-soluble vitamin which is necessary for the growth of rats, which plays a part in the resistance of the animal organism to infection, and which is required for the production of visual purple, a pigment necessary for sight. Its structure has been determined by degradation reactions, and several undisputed syntheses starting with β-ionone have been reported since 1946.

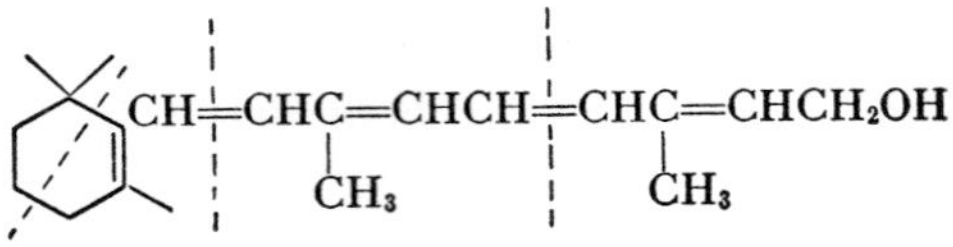

Vitamin A

The pure alcohol melts at 64° and has a biological potency of 4.3×10^6 U.S.P. units per gram or 3.3×10^6 International units per gram. The chief source is the fish liver oils which vary greatly in potency. Thus cod liver oil contains 3000 to 5000 units per gram, halibut liver oil 10,000 to 15,000, and soupfin shark liver oil 15,000 to 500,000 (average 350,000) units per gram. Commercial synthesis of vitamin A was begun in 1950.

The most important diterpene commercially is **abietic acid,** $C_{20}H_{30}O_2$, the chief constituent of rosin or colophony, the resin obtained from various species of pine (L. *abies* fir). Abietic acid is not an original component of the tree secretions but arises from the polymerization and rearrangement of the primary acids during the distillation of the turpentine.

Abietic acid was one of the first resin acids to be investigated. The chief features of its carbon skeleton have been known since 1910 when retene, the product obtained by Vesterberg in 1903 by dehydrogenation with sulfur, was shown to be 1-methyl-7-isopropylphenanthrene (p. 441). Abietic acid is a tricyclic diterpene containing two conjugated double bonds and one carboxyl group.

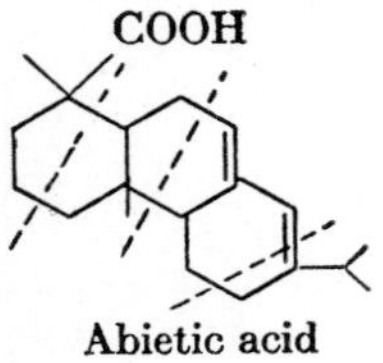

Abietic acid 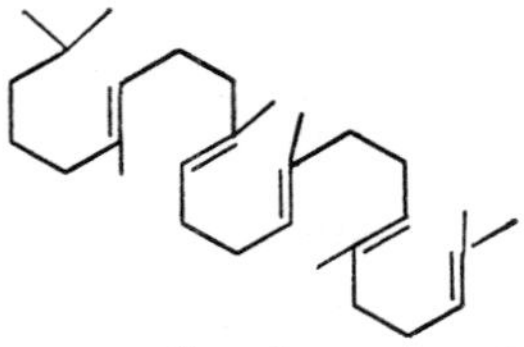   Squalene 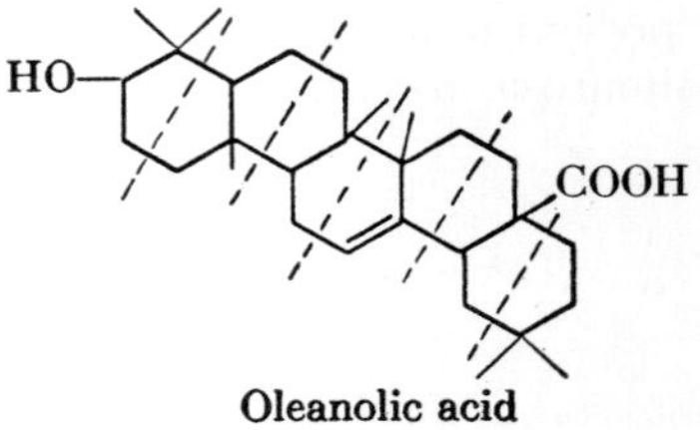   Oleanolic acid

Squalene, $C_{30}H_{50}$, is an acyclic triterpene which makes up 90 per cent of the liver oil of certain species of sharks of the family *Squalidae.* The pentacyclic triterpenes are present in many natural resins. Some of the **saponins,** which are responsible for the foam-producing properties of the so-called soap plants, are glycosides of pentacyclic triterpenes. **Oleanolic acid,** $C_{30}H_{48}O_3$, is a representative member of this class. It occurs as the aglycone of a saponin in guaiac bark, sugar beet, and calendula flowers, and free in olive leaves, clove buds, mistletoe, and grape skins.

Most members of the large group of compounds known as *carotenoids* may be classed as tetraterpenes. They constitute the yellow to red fat-soluble pigments of plants. Usually several pigments occur together. Because of the small amounts present and the close similarities in structure, isolation and purification by the usual crystallization procedures have been difficult. Rapid progress in the chemistry of the carotenoids began with the use of adsorption procedures, which depend on differences in adsorbability on solid adsorbents such as calcium carbonate, alumina, or magnesia. Because the procedure was used originally on colored substances which separated as colored bands in the column of adsorbent, the process became known as **chromatographic adsorption.** By this procedure it has been possible to separate mixtures of isomeric compounds which differ only slightly in their chemical structure or configuration.

Lycopene, $C_{40}H_{56}$, is the red pigment in the ripe fruit of the tomato (*Lycopersicum esculentum*) and of the watermelon (*Cucumis citrullus*).

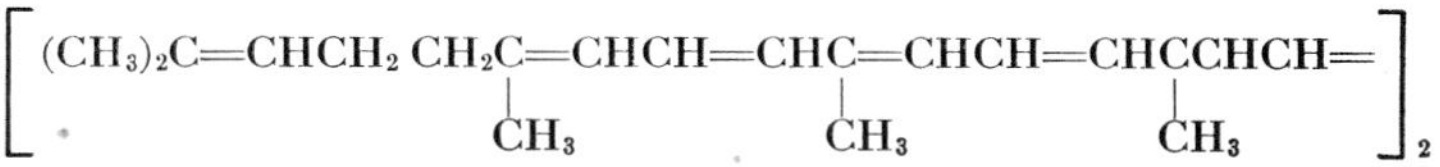

(CH3)2C=CHCH2 CH2C=CHCH=CHC=CHCH=CHCCHCH=
CH3
CH3
CH3
2

Lycopene

β-Carotene is the chief pigment of the carrot (*Daucus carota*). It can be converted by the animal organism into vitamin A and hence has vitamin A activity.

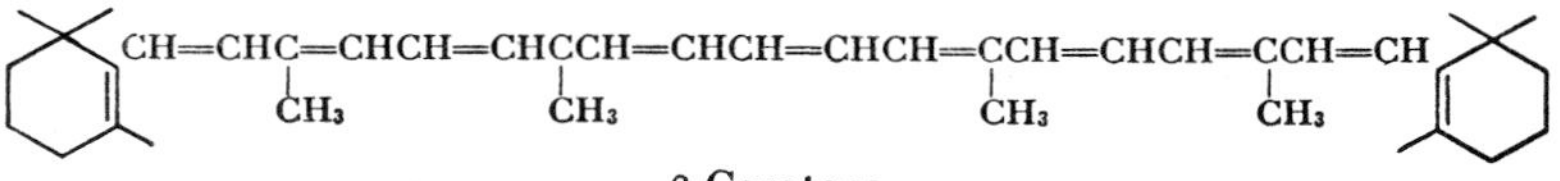

CH=CHC=CHCH=CHCCH=CHCH=CHCH=CCH=CHCH=CCH=CH
CH3
CH3
CH3
CH3

β-Carotene

Lutein (*leaf xanthophyll*), $C_{40}H_{56}O_2$, is a yellow pigment present in leaves, yellow flowers, and egg yolk.

CH=CHC=CHCH=CHCCH=CHCH=CHCH=CCH=CHCH=CCH=CH
CH3
CH3
CH3
CH3
HO
OH

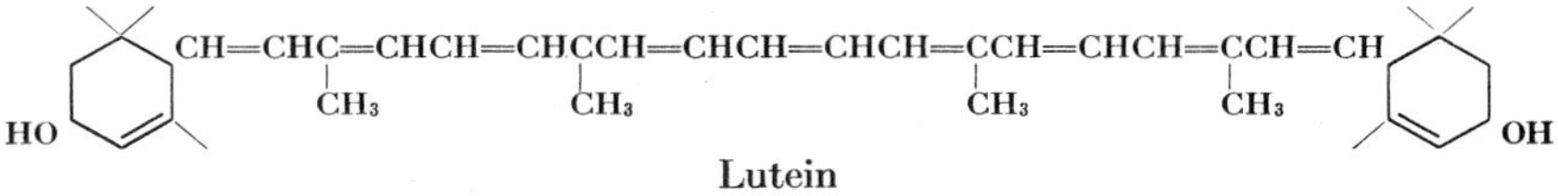

Lutein

Rubber hydrocarbon, $(C_5H_8)_x$, is a polyterpene (p. 497).

STEROIDS

Steroids may be defined as those compounds which contain a ring system like that present in cholesterol. They are characterized by the fact that they yield methylcyclopentenophenanthrene (Diels hydrocarbon) on dehydrogenation with selenium.

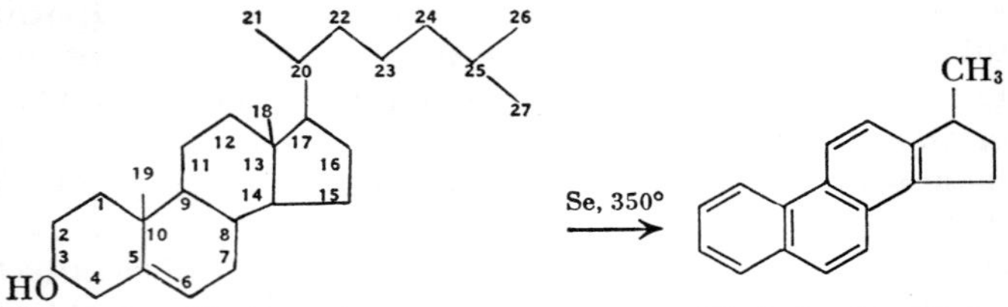

Cholesterol

Se, 350°

Methylcyclopenteno-
phenanthrene
(Diels hydrocarbon)

To this group belong the sterols, the bile acids, the cardiac aglycones, the sex hormones, the adrenal steroids, the toad poisons, and the steroid sapogenins. In view of the complexity of the chemistry and the large number of compounds in the group, the formulas of only a few representatives of the various subgroups are given.

Cholesterol, $C_{27}H_{46}O$, is present in the blood of animals and hence in all parts of the body. It is concentrated in the spinal cord, the brain, skin secretions, and gallstones. It was isolated first from gallstones by Conradi in 1775 and was named cholesterine (Gr. *choli* bile, *stereos* solid) in 1816 by Chevreul,[4] who showed that unlike the fats it was not saponifiable. Berthelot (p. 68) recognized that it was an alcohol in 1859, but the correct molecular formula, $C_{27}H_{46}O$, was not proposed until 1888 by Reinitzer. The currently accepted structure was not arrived at until 1932 after over eighty years of active chemical investigation.

Ergosterol, $C_{28}H_{44}O$, was isolated first from ergot, but is obtained more readily from yeast. Irradiation by ultraviolet light transforms it into a number of products, one of which is **calciferol** or **vitamin D₂.**

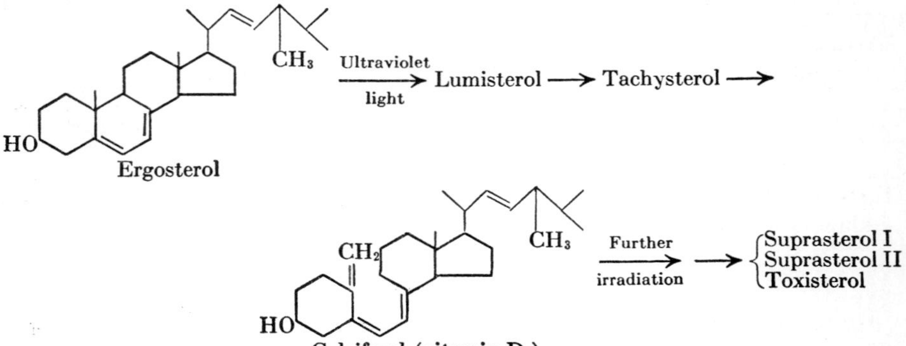

Ergosterol

Ultraviolet
light
⟶ Lumisterol ⟶ Tachysterol ⟶

Calciferol (vitamin D₂)

Further
irradiation
⟶ { Suprasterol I
Suprasterol II
Toxisterol

---

[4] Michael Eugene Chevreul (1786–1889), professor of chemistry at Paris. He was among the first to study the chemistry of complex natural products and is noted principally for his work on fats begun in 1811. He was the first to show the nature of saponification and isolated valeric, caproic, capric, palmitic, stearic, and oleic acids, and in 1818 discovered cetyl alcohol in the unsaponifiable fraction of spermaceti. He isolated the glycoside quercitrin (p. 490) in 1810 and creatine (p. 249) in 1834. He was an active investigator until his death at the age of 102 years and 7 months.

The nature of the side chain does not appear to be important and several compounds have vitamin D activity. Thus irradiation of 7-dehydrocholesterol gives vitamin D_3. The vitamins D control the amount and ratio of calcium and phosphorus in the blood. In the absence of vitamin D these elements fall below normal, the bones soften and bend, and the joints swell. This condition is known as rickets.

The **bile acids** are obtained by the alkaline hydrolysis of bile salts which are present in the bile of various animals. In the bile salts, the bile acids are combined by an amide linkage between their carboxyl group and the amino group of glycine, H_2NCH_2COOH, or taurine, $H_2NCH_2CH_2SO_3H$. Thus **glycocholic acid** on hydrolysis gives cholic acid and glycine, whereas **taurocholic acid** gives cholic acid and taurine. The function of the bile salts is to act as emulsifying agents for fats and hence to promote the hydrolysis and absorption of fats from the intestinal tract. The four bile acids occurring in human and ox bile are **cholic acid, desoxycholic acid, chenodesoxycholic acid,** and **lithocholic acid.** The first two are the more abundant.

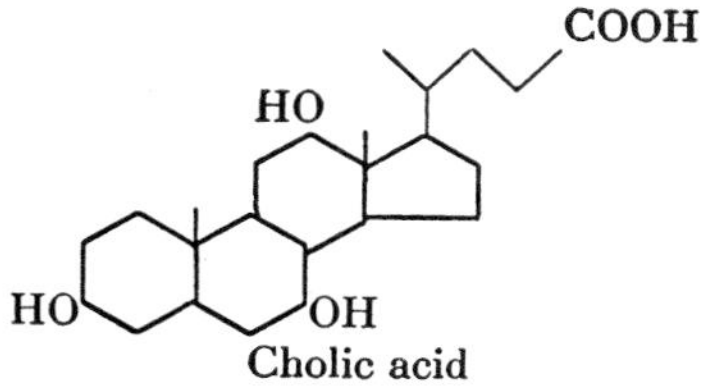

Cholic acid 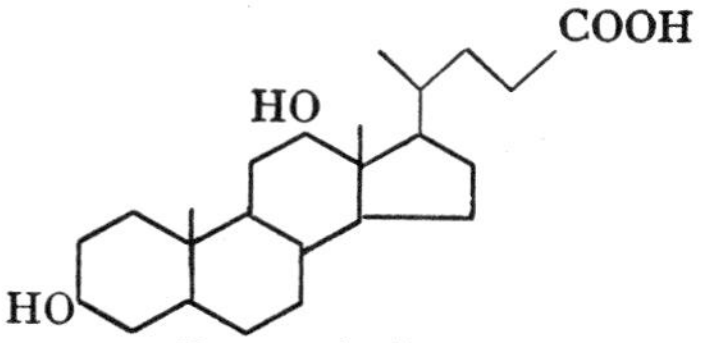 Desoxycholic acid

The **sex hormones** are substances responsible for the sex characteristics and the sexual processes of the animal organism. They are formed in the testes and ovaries, which are stimulated by other hormones, the gonadotropic hormones secreted by the anterior lobe of the pituitary gland. **Testosterone** is secreted by the testes and controls the development of the genital tract, accessory male organs, and secondary male characteristics such as the comb and wattles of a rooster. **Estradiol** is produced in the ovaries, probably in the

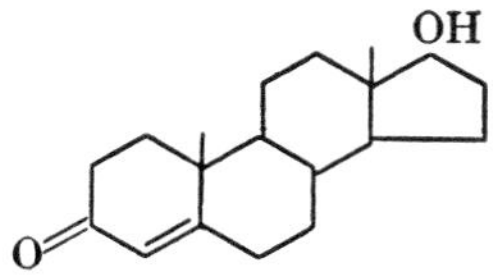

Testosterone 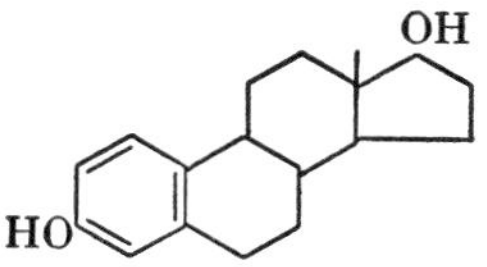 Estradiol

ripening follicles. It controls the development of female characteristics and initiates the first phase in the menstrual cycle, namely the proliferation of cells in the uterus. The estrogenic effect is not very specific and a synthetic compound, **diethylstilbestrol,** is used more commonly than natural estradiol to alleviate trouble arising from a deficiency of the hormone. **Progesterone** is secreted by the corpus luteum (yellow body) formed after the expulsion of the ovum. This hormone prepares the bed of the uterus for the implantation of the fertilized ovum. It is used clinically to prevent abortion.

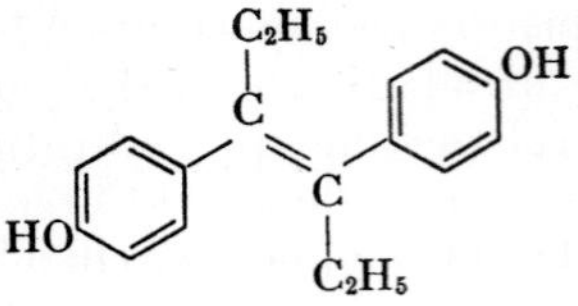

Diethylstilbestrol

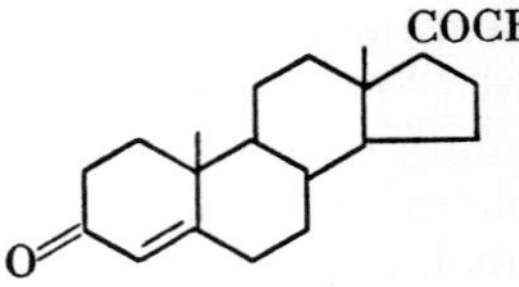

Progesterone

The adrenals are two small glands, one above each kidney, that have two important functions, namely the secretion of epinephrine (Adrenalin, p. 400) and the secretion of cortin. Both secretions are essential to life, but the secretion of cortin is the more important, since it is secreted only by the adrenals whereas epinephrine is secreted by other organs as well. A deficit of cortin leads to a bronzing of the skin, muscular weakness, and an increase in blood urea (Addison's disease). An excess in children produces precocious sex development.

Cortin activity resides in the steroidal fraction present in the adrenal cortex. Twenty-eight different compounds of the androstane and pregnane series have been isolated from this fraction and their structure identified. Six of these have cortin activity. The structures of **corticosterone, desoxycorticosterone**, and **cortisone** are indicated.

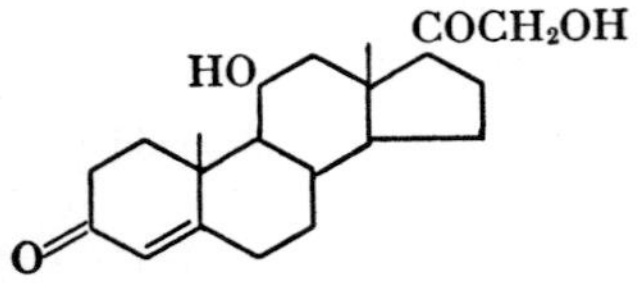

Corticosterone

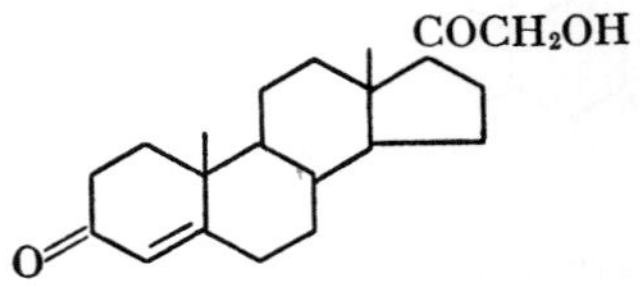

Desoxycorticosterone

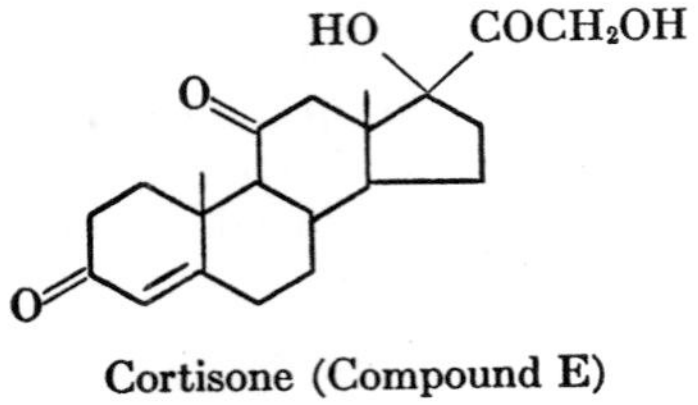

Cortisone (Compound E)

It is of interest that desoxycorticosterone was synthesized from stigmasterol before it was isolated from the adrenal cortex. Since 1948 considerable interest has centered on the component called Compound E or cortisone, because of its beneficial effects in the treatment of some forms of arthritis. Previously both desoxycorticosterone and Compound E were used with spectacular success in the treatment of surgical shock, burn shock, and other prostrating conditions.

REVIEW QUESTIONS

1. What are alicyclic compounds? What other names are applied to the parent hydrocarbons?
2. Discuss the synthesis of alicyclic hydrocarbons, ketones, and dibasic acids by ring closure.

3. Compare the ease of formation and stability of carbocyclic rings. What was Baeyers' strain theory and how has it been modified?

4. What are the most readily available alicyclic compounds and how are they prepared? Compare their chemical properties with those of the corresponding aromatic compounds.

5. What are the terpenes and camphors?

6. Write structural formulas for and indicate the source of limonene, menthol, pinene, and camphor.

7. What are the more important classes of steroids, and what structural feature is characteristic of each class?

Chapter 39

ORGANIC PEROXIDES. AUTOXIDATION
AND ANTIOXIDANTS

The use of organic peroxides as catalysts and their formation by autoxidation have become increasingly important in recent years. This chapter summarizes the synthesis of the various classes of peroxides by conventional methods, the formation of peroxides by autoxidation, and the mechanism of antoxidation and its inhibition by antioxidants.

ORGANIC PEROXIDES

Organic peroxides may be considered as derivatives of hydrogen peroxide, HO—OH, in which the hydrogen atoms are replaced by organic groups. The more common types are tabulated below.

R—O—OH   Alkyl hydroperoxide

R—O—O—R   Alkyl peroxide

$$\underset{RC}{\overset{O}{\parallel}}\text{—O—OH}$$ Acyl hydroperoxide (peracid)

$$\underset{RC}{\overset{O}{\parallel}}\text{—O—O—}\underset{CR}{\overset{O}{\parallel}}$$ Acyl peroxide

$$\underset{RC}{\overset{O}{\parallel}}\text{—O—O—R}$$ Acyl alkyl peroxide (perester)

Other peroxides analogous in structure to aldehyde hydrates, hemiacetals, and cyclic acetals also are known.

RCH—O—OH   Hydroxyalkyl hydroperoxide
|
OH

RCH—O—O—CHR   Hydroxyalkyl peroxide
| |
OH   OH

RCH—O—O—R   Hydroxyalkyl alkyl peroxide
|
OH

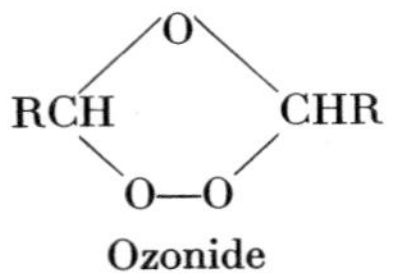

Ozonide 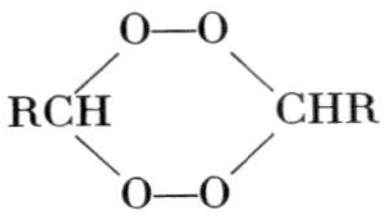   Alkylidene peroxide

The constitution of many of the peroxides obtained by autoxidation is uncertain or entirely unknown. The purification and determination of the constitution of organic peroxides has been particularly difficult because of the ease with which they decompose, often with explosive violence.

Alkyl Hydroperoxides and Alkyl Peroxides

Alkyl hydroperoxides are made by the monoalkylation of hydrogen peroxide. Further alkylation yields the **alkyl peroxides.** For methyl, ethyl, and *n*-propyl derivatives, the reaction is brought about by the use of the alkyl sulfate and aqueous alkali.

$$H_2O_2 + R_2SO_4 + NaOH \longrightarrow R{-}O{-}OH + NaRSO_4 + H_2O$$

$$R{-}O{-}OH + R_2SO_4 + NaOH \longrightarrow R{-}O{-}O{-}R + NaRSO_4 + H_2O$$

t-Butyl hydroperoxide and *t*-butyl peroxide result from the action of *t*-butyl hydrogen sulfate on 30 per cent hydrogen peroxide.

$$H_2O_2 + (CH_3)_3COSO_3H \longrightarrow (CH_3)_3C{-}O{-}OH + H_2SO_4$$

$$(CH_3)_3C{-}O{-}OH + (CH_3)_3COSO_3H \longrightarrow (CH_3)_3C{-}O{-}OC(CH_3)_3 + H_2SO_4$$

Tertiary alkyl hydroperoxides can be formed also by the reaction of hydrocarbons containing a tertiary hydrogen with molecular oxygen in either the gaseous or liquid phase. Thus *t*-butyl hydroperoxide results from the reaction of isobutane and oxygen at 155° using hydrogen bromide as a catalyst. Explosion is prevented by coating the surfaces of the reactor with boric acid.

$$(CH_3)_3CH + O_2 \xrightarrow[155°]{HBr} (CH_3)_3C{-}O{-}OH$$

The reaction of liquid alkylcyclopentanes or alkylcyclohexanes with oxygen at 135° also gives hydroperoxides. The reaction is catalyzed by ultraviolet light or by the addition of peroxides.

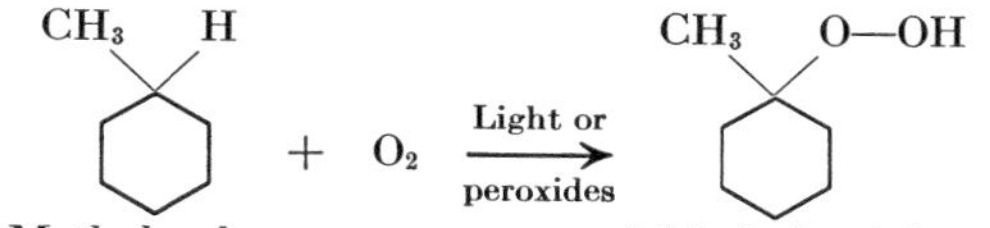

Methylcyclohexane + O₂ (Light or peroxides) → 1-Methylcyclohexyl hydroperoxide

Isopropylbenzene (cumene) gives cumene hydroperoxide.

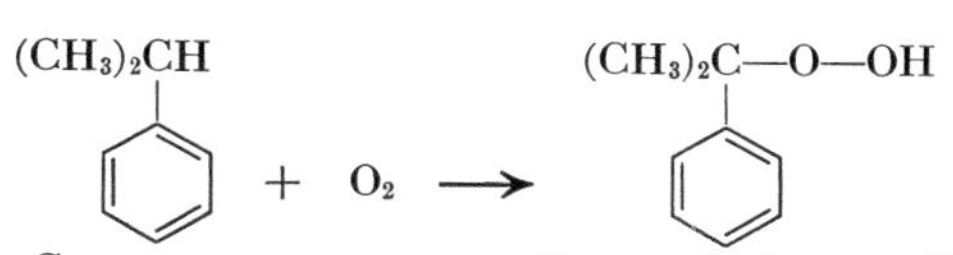

Cumene + O₂ → Cumene hydroperoxide

These oxidations take place by a free-radical chain mechanism. Thus the function of the hydrogen bromide in the preparation of *t*-butyl hydroperoxide is to produce bromine atoms.

$$HBr + O_2 \longrightarrow [HO—O \cdot] + [Br \cdot]$$

The bromine atoms then bring about the following chain reaction.

$$(CH_3)_3CH + [Br \cdot] \longrightarrow [(CH_3)_3C \cdot] + HBr$$

$$[(CH_3)_3C \cdot] + O_2 \longrightarrow [(CH_3)_3C—O—O \cdot]$$

$$[(CH_3)_3C—O—O \cdot] + HBr \longrightarrow (CH_3)_3C—O—OH + [Br \cdot]$$

The lower molecular weight alkyl hydroperoxides and alkyl peroxides are liquids that can be distilled at atmospheric or reduced pressure. Methyl and ethyl hydroperoxides and dimethyl peroxide explode violently on heating or when subjected to shock. Ethyl peroxide is relatively harmless although it decomposes with a mild explosion when superheated, and catches fire at around 250°. The tertiary alkyl hydroperoxides and peroxides are much more stable. Thus, *t*-butyl hydroperoxide is stable up to 75° and decomposes smoothly at 95°–100° to give chiefly *t*-butyl alcohol and oxygen.

$$2 \ (CH_3)_3C—O—OH \xrightarrow{95°-100°} 2 \ (CH_3)_3COH + O_2$$

When *t*-butyl peroxide decomposes, the principal products are acetone and ethane.

$$(CH_3)_3C—O—O—C(CH_3)_3 \xrightarrow{140°-160°} 2 \ (CH_3)_2CO + CH_3CH_3$$

The vapor phase decomposition of *t*-butyl peroxide is a homogeneous, first-order reaction. The first stage undoubtedly is the formation of *t*-butoxide radicals which lose a methyl radical to form acetone. Combination of two methyl radicals yields ethane.

$$(CH_3)_3C—O—O—C(CH_3)_3 \longrightarrow 2 \ [(CH_3)_3CO \cdot]$$

$$2 \ [(CH_3)_3CO \cdot] \longrightarrow 2 \ (CH_3)_2CO + 2 \ [CH_3 \cdot]$$

$$2 \ [CH_3 \cdot] \longrightarrow CH_3CH_3$$

The alkyl hydroperoxides are more acidic than alcohols and form salts with aqueous solutions of strong alkalies. Both the alkyl hydroperoxides and peroxides are less readily reduced than hydrogen peroxide. Methyl and ethyl hydroperoxide liberate iodine from hydrogen iodide, but the reaction is not quantitative. *t*-Butyl hydroperoxide reacts quantitatively. The alkyl peroxides liberate very little iodine. *t*-Butyl peroxide does not react even with concentrated hydrogen iodide. Ethyl peroxide does not react with metallic sodium, but *t*-butyl peroxide gives sodium *t*-butoxide.

$$(CH_3)_3C—O—O—C(CH_3)_3 + 2 \ Na \longrightarrow 2 \ NaOC(CH_3)_3$$

All of the alkyl peroxides are reduced by zinc and acetic acid to the alcohols.

$$R—O—O—R + Zn + 2 \ CH_3COOH \longrightarrow 2 \ ROH + Zn(OCOCH_3)_2$$

t-Butyl hydroperoxide, like hydrogen peroxide (p. 518), converts olefins into glycols in the presence of osmium tetroxide, vanadium pentoxide, or chromium trioxide.

$$RCH{=}CHR + (CH_3)_3COOH + H_2O \xrightarrow{OsO_4} RCHOHCHOHR + (CH_3)_3COH$$

Acyl Hydroperoxides (Peracids) and Acyl Peroxides

Solutions of **acyl hydroperoxides** can be obtained by allowing aliphatic acids to react with 90 per cent hydrogen peroxide solutions in the presence of sulfuric acid.

$$CH_3COOH + H_2O_2 \xrightarrow{H_2SO_4} \overset{\overset{O}{\|}}{CH_3C}{-}O{-}OH + H_2O$$

Peracetic acid

The sodium salts result when acid anhydrides react with an excess of aqueous alkaline solutions of hydrogen peroxide.

$$(CH_3CO)_2O + Na_2O_2 \longrightarrow \overset{\overset{O}{\|}}{CH_3C}{-}O{-}ONa + CH_3COONa$$

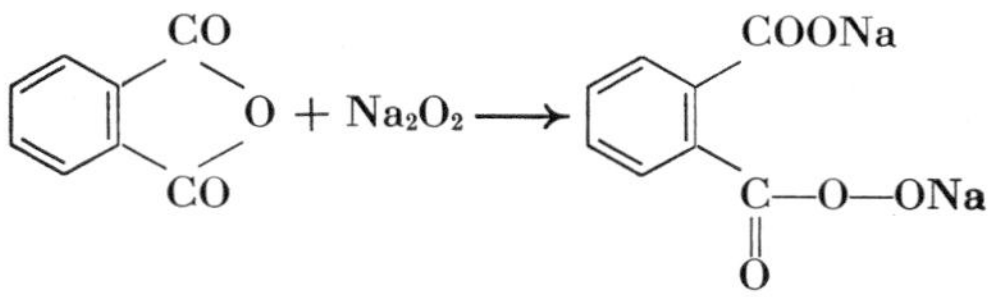

Sodium
monoperphthalate

Acidification and extraction with an organic solvent gives a solution of the peracid. Peracids can be prepared also from acyl peroxides.

Thermal decomposition of the peracids resembles that of *t*-butyl hydroperoxide in that oxygen is one of the products.

$$2\ \overset{\overset{O}{\|}}{RC}{-}O{-}OH \xrightarrow{Heat} 2\ RCOOH + O_2$$

The peracids are useful reagents for the nonconjugated carbon-carbon double bond (p. 414).

Acyl peroxides are obtained by the reaction of an excess of acid anhydride or acyl chloride with alkaline solutions of hydrogen peroxide.

$$2(CH_3CO)_2O + Na_2O_2 \longrightarrow \overset{\overset{O}{\|}}{CH_3C}{-}O{-}O{-}\overset{\overset{O}{\|}}{C}CH_3 + 2\ NaOCOCH_3$$

Acetyl peroxide

$$2\ C_6H_5COCl + Na_2O_2 \longrightarrow \overset{\overset{O}{\|}}{C_6H_5C}{-}O{-}O{-}\overset{\overset{O}{\|}}{C}C_6H_5 + 2\ NaCl$$

Benzoyl peroxide

Violent explosions of acetyl peroxide have been reported and extreme care should be taken when it is prepared or used. Benzoyl peroxide is considerably more stable.

The acyl hydroperoxides and peroxides liberate iodine quantitatively, and hence they can be estimated iodimetrically. The acyl peroxides react with sodium alkoxides to give the sodium salt of the peracid and the alkyl ester.

$$C_6H_5\overset{O}{\overset{\|}{C}}-O-O-\overset{O}{\overset{\|}{C}}C_6H_5 \xrightarrow{NaOCH_3} C_6H_5\overset{O}{\overset{\|}{C}}-O-ONa + CH_3OCOC_6H_5$$

This reaction is the one most frequently used in the laboratory for the preparation of perbenzoic acid, which is liberated from the sodium salt by acidification and extracted with chloroform.

Ozonides

The simplest formula for ozone would be that in which the oxygen atoms form a three-membered ring, each of the oxygen atoms being divalent. If this formula were correct, the infrared absorption spectrum should resemble that of cyclopropane, but instead the spectrum resembles that of nitrosyl chloride in which the atoms occupy the corners of an open triangle. The bond angle is calculated to be 125 degrees. Electron diffraction measurements indicate an angle of 127 degrees $\pm$ 3 degrees. Hence the molecule must be a resonance hybrid of the structures that contain two oxygen atoms linked by a double bond and the third by a coordinate covalence.

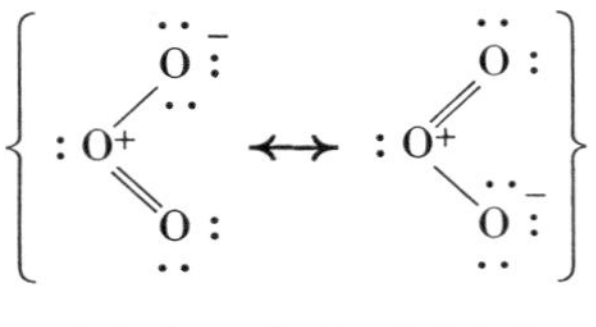

When ozone adds to a double bond, the initial product probably contains a four-membered ring which rearranges to a five-membered ring with scission of the carbon-carbon bond. The initial product is called the *molozonide*, and the rearranged product the *ozonide*.

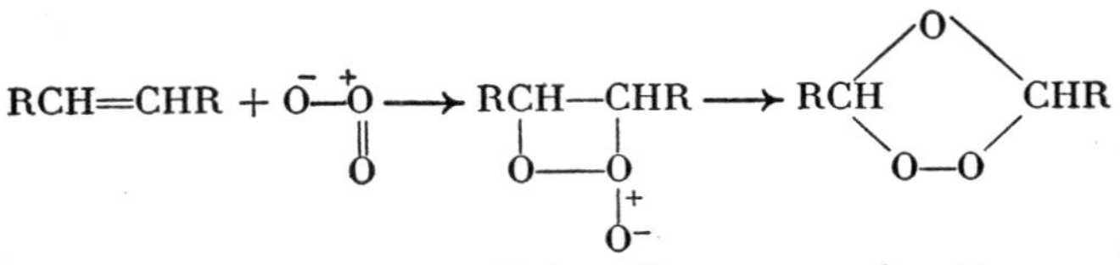

Molozonide   Ozonide

Probably the best proof of this structure for the ozonide is the synthesis of butylene ozonide by the action of phosphorus pentoxide on hydroxyethyl peroxide.

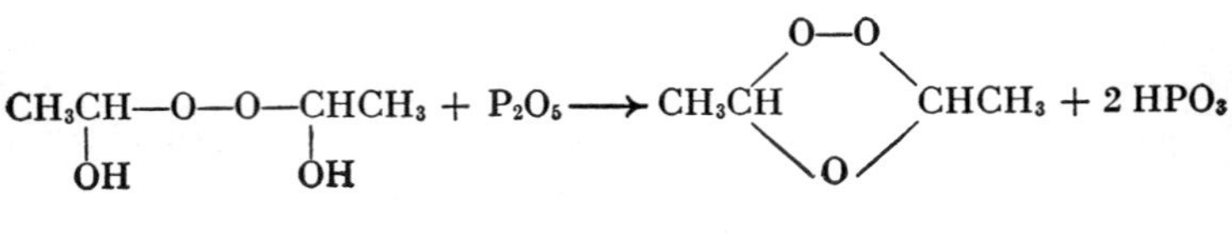

Hydrolysis of the ozonide presumably gives the hydroxyalkyl peroxide as the initial product.

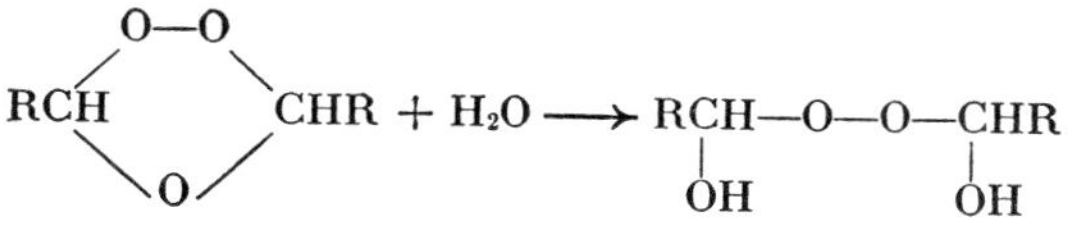

$$RCH \underset{O}{\overset{O-O}{\diagdown}} CHR + H_2O \longrightarrow RCH-O-O-CHR$$
$$\qquad\qquad\qquad\qquad\qquad \underset{OH}{|} \qquad \underset{OH}{|}$$

The hydroxy peroxide decomposes into one mole of acid and one mole of carbonyl compound, or two moles of carbonyl compound and one of hydrogen peroxide (p. 40).

Besides the monomeric ozonides, polymeric ozonides also are formed which probably have the structure $(-O-OCHR-OCHR-)_x$. Hydrolysis yields the same products as the monomeric ozonides. Excessive ozonation leads to the formation of products called *oxozonides* which have a higher oxygen content.

AUTOXIDATION

Autoxidation may be defined as the spontaneous reaction of a compound with molecular oxygen at room temperature. The limiting conditions imposed by the terms *spontaneous* and *room temperature* are artificial, since most autoxidations are accelerated by light or by traces of catalysts, or decelerated by antioxidants (substances that inhibit autoxidation), and many oxidations by oxygen at elevated temperatures are no different than those occurring at room temperature.

The reaction of organic compounds with molecular oxygen of the air is more common than generally is recognized. The initial products are peroxides, which can be detected easily in liquids by shaking with a globule of clean mercury. In the presence of peroxides the surface of the mercury is tarnished. If a considerable amount of peroxide is present, the mixture becomes black because of the formation of mercurous oxide. If this test is applied to various solvents that have been exposed to air over a period of time, many of them will be found to contain peroxides. For example among a group of technical solvents taken from the laboratory shelf, cyclohexane, methylcyclohexane, benzene, toluene, chloroform, ethyl ether, isopropyl ether, and dioxane gave a positive test for peroxides. Significantly, carbon tetrachloride and the alcohols gave negative tests (cf. p. 583).

Hydrocarbons

Autoxidation in general probably does not differ from the reaction for the preparation of *t*-alkyl hydroperoxides at elevated temperatures (p. 573) and may be represented by the following equation.

$$RH + O_2 \longrightarrow R-O-OH$$

The rate of the reaction varies with the nature of R. A tertiary hydrogen is oxidized more easily than primary or secondary hydrogen (p. 573). Nevertheless the controlled oxidations of saturated hydrocarbons such as methane, the propanes and butanes, and higher hydrocarbons (p. 56) undoubtedly also proceed by way of the peroxide.

The presence of a double bond greatly increases the reactivity of hydrogen on adjacent carbon atoms. Thus cyclohexene reacts with oxygen in the presence of ultraviolet light to give 2-cyclohexenyl hydroperoxide.

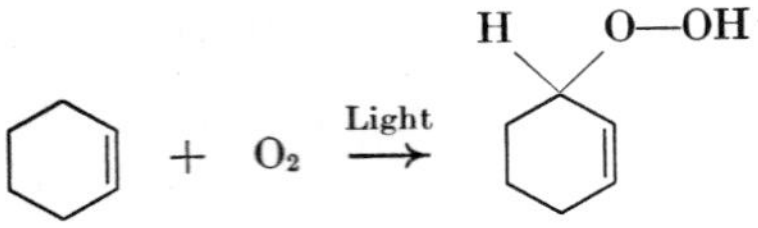

In this reaction the double bond is not attacked. Similarly tetralin reacts in the position α to the aromatic ring.

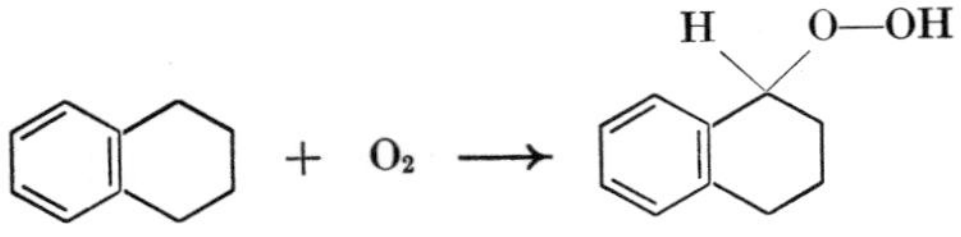

Oxidation takes place fairly rapidly at 75° in the absence of added catalysts, but in the presence of catalysts it is detectable at room temperature. In most of these oxidations further reaction occurs to give more stable oxidation products. Thus α-tetralone can be prepared conveniently by passing air into tetralin at its boiling point, the initially formed hydroperoxide undergoing decomposition.

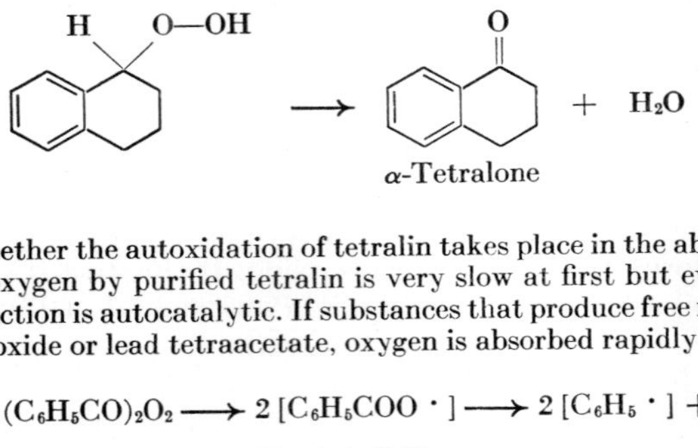

α-Tetralone

It is doubtful whether the autoxidation of tetralin takes place in the absence of catalysts. The absorption of oxygen by purified tetralin is very slow at first but eventually becomes rapid; that is the reaction is autocatalytic. If substances that produce free radicals are added, such as benzoyl peroxide or lead tetraacetate, oxygen is absorbed rapidly at once.

$$(C_6H_5CO)_2O_2 \longrightarrow 2\,[C_6H_5COO \cdot] \longrightarrow 2\,[C_6H_5 \cdot] + CO_2$$

$$RH + [C_6H_5 \cdot] \longrightarrow [R \cdot] + C_6H_6$$

$$[R \cdot] + O_2 \longrightarrow [R-O-O \cdot] \quad \Big\}\ \text{Chain reaction}$$
$$[R-O-O \cdot] + RH \longrightarrow [R \cdot] + ROOH$$

Hence it seems likely that even the initial slow reaction in the absence of added catalysts is caused by the presence of free radicals in low concentration and that the decomposition of the hydroperoxide that is formed provides more free radicals which cause an acceleration of the reaction.

The increased ease of oxidation of olefins and of tetralin over saturated hydrocarbons is believed to result from the stabilization of the intermediate free radical by resonance.

$$RCH{=}CHCH_2R \longrightarrow \Big\{\ RCH{=}CHCHR \longleftrightarrow RCHCH{=}CHR\ \Big\}$$

Direct evidence in favor of this postulation is the isolation of two products from the autoxidation of 1,2-dimethylcyclohexene.

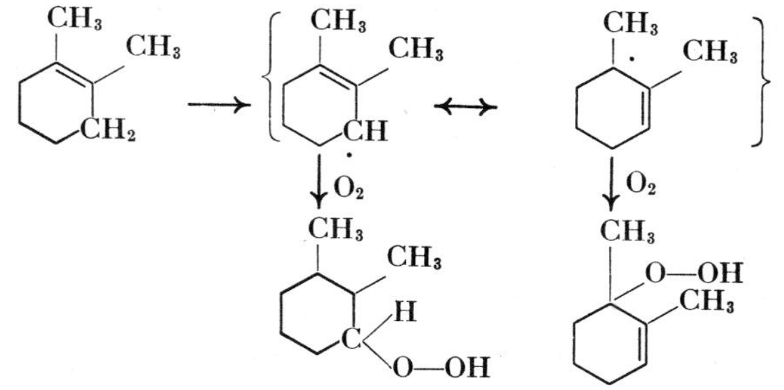

Autoxidation of conjugated polyenes takes place by 1,4 addition to give polymeric peroxides.

$$x \; RCH{=}CHCH{=}CHR + x \; O_2 \longrightarrow (-CH-CH{=}CHCH-O-O-)_x$$
$$\underset{R}{|} \qquad\qquad\qquad \underset{R}{|}$$

This type of reaction takes place even though methylene groups are α to the conjugated system as in methyl sorbate, $CH_3CH{=}CHCH{=}CHCOOCH_3$, methyl eleostearate, $CH_3(CH_2)_3CH{=}CHCH{=}CHCH{=}CH(CH_2)_7COOCH_3$, and 1,3-cyclohexadiene.

The drying oils containing linoleic and linolenic acid also are noted for their ease of oxidation by air. The structure $-CH{=}CHCH_2CH{=}CH-$, having a methylene group α to two double bonds, is especially susceptible to autoxidation, the initial product being a hydroperoxide.

$$RCH{=}CHCH_2CH{=}CHR + O_2 \longrightarrow RCH{=}CHCHCH{=}CHR$$
$$\underset{O-OH}{|}$$

Here the intermediate free radical is stabilized even more strongly by resonance than in the case of olefins with a single bond, because the resonance involves five carbon atoms.

$$\{RCH{=}CHCHCH{=}CHR \longleftrightarrow RCH{=}CHCH{=}CHCHR \longleftrightarrow RCHCH{=}CHCH{=}CHR\}$$

If the R groups are different as with linoleic acid, three different hydroperoxides can be formed. Moreover, the hydroperoxides derived from the second and third of the above structures contain two conjugated double bonds which can form polymeric peroxides. The intermediate free radicals also can undergo carbon-carbon condensation. It is these polymerization reactions that lead to the solidification or drying of the oil.

Ethers

The easy autoxidation of ethers is manifested strikingly by the frequency with which violent explosions have been reported when residues from the distillation of ether have become heated above the boiling point of the ether or rubbed with a sharp glass rod. One instance has been reported in which a partially filled can of isopropyl ether detonated on being jarred. Explosions have been reported also during the distillation of dioxane and of ethyl acetal. Hence compounds of this type should be tested for peroxides before use. The peroxides may be removed by washing with a variety of reducing agents. Perhaps the most convenient procedure is to shake the liquid with a powdered zinc-copper couple. The purified solvents can be stabilized by the addition of 0.001 per cent of hydroquinone or diphenylamine. They should be stored in filled dark bottles to exclude air and light.

Numerous proposals have been made concerning the nature of the peroxides formed from ethyl ether. It seems likely that the initial product is the hydroperoxide.

$$CH_3CH_2OCH_2CH_3 + O_2 \longrightarrow CH_3\underset{\underset{O-OH}{|}}{C}HOCH_2CH_3$$

All investigators have noted the presence of hydrogen peroxide as an autoxidation product, and ethyl vinyl ether has been postulated as another of the oxidation products. These substances conceivably could arise from the hydroperoxide.

$$CH_3\underset{\underset{O-OH}{|}}{C}HOCH_2CH_3 \longrightarrow CH_2{=}CHOCH_2CH_3 + H_2O_2$$

Hydroxyethyl peroxide also has been reported as an oxidation product of ether. Presumably it arises by a series of reactions.

$$CH_3\underset{\underset{O-OH}{|}}{C}HOCH_2CH_3 + H_2O \longrightarrow CH_3\underset{\underset{O-OH}{|}}{C}HOH + C_2H_5OH$$

$$CH_3\underset{\underset{O-OH}{|}}{C}HOH \rightleftarrows CH_3CHO + H_2O_2$$

$$CH_3\underset{\underset{OH}{|}}{C}H-O-OH + OCHCH_3 \longrightarrow CH_3\underset{\underset{OH}{|}}{C}H-O-O-\underset{\underset{OH}{|}}{C}HCH_3$$

However neither hydrogen peroxide, the hydroperoxides, nor the hydroxyalkyl peroxides are as violently explosive as the peroxidic residues from oxidized ether. Only the dimolecular alkylidene peroxides are as explosive, and it has been postulated that such compounds may be formed from the hydroperoxides.

$$CH_3\underset{\underset{O-OH}{|}}{C}HOC_2H_5 + H_2O \longrightarrow CH_3\underset{\underset{O-OH}{|}}{C}HOH + C_2H_5OH$$

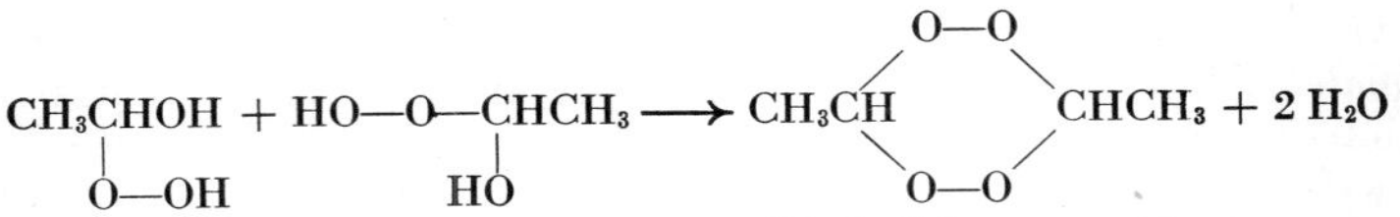

$$CH_3\underset{\underset{O-OH}{|}}{C}HOH + HO-O-\underset{\underset{HO}{|}}{C}HCH_3 \longrightarrow CH_3CH\underset{\underset{O-O}{\diagdown\diagup}}{\overset{O-O}{\diagup\diagdown}}CHCH_3 + 2\,H_2O$$

Diethylidene peroxide

Both dimeric and trimeric acetone peroxides, along with several other substances, have been isolated from the autoxidation products of isopropyl ether.

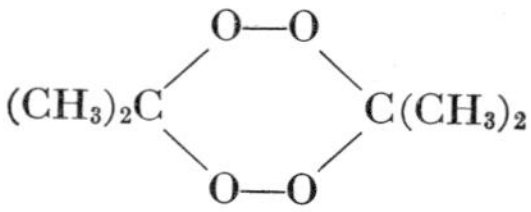

$$(CH_3)_2C \underset{O-O}{\overset{O-O}{<>}} C(CH_3)_2$$

Diisopropylidene
peroxide

$$(CH_3)_2C \overset{O-C(CH_3)_2}{\underset{O-C(CH_3)_2}{<>}} C(CH_3)_2$$

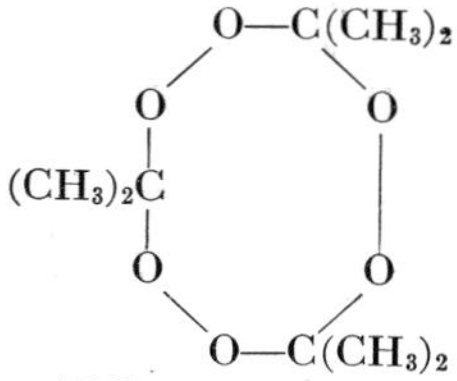

Triisopropylidene
peroxide

The latter product had been made previously by the action of hydrogen per-oxide on acetone. The dimeric product, although present in smaller amount, is more explosive and more sensitive to shock than the trimeric form.

Aldehydes

The ease of oxidation of aldehydes by air has been recognized for a long time. Liebig and Woehler showed in 1832 that the conversion of benzaldehyde to benzoic acid by air is accelerated by light, and since then the autoxidation of benzaldehyde and other aldehydes has been studied by many workers. Perbenzoic acid can be isolated from the oxidation mixture and has been postulated to be the first stable product of the reaction. It reacts with more benzaldehyde to give benzoic acid.

$$C_6H_5\overset{O}{\overset{\|}{C}}H + O_2 \longrightarrow C_6H_5\overset{O}{\overset{\|}{C}}{-}O{-}OH$$

$$C_6H_5\overset{O}{\overset{\|}{C}}{-}O{-}OH + C_6H_5CHO \longrightarrow 2\ C_6H_5COOH$$

It is believed that the formation of the perbenzoic acid results from a chain reaction which is initiated by light or by adventitious free radicals.

$$C_6H_5CHO + [\cdot R] \longrightarrow [C_6H_5\underset{\cdot}{CO}] + RH$$

The activation by light is a more complicated process but may be represented by the over-all reaction

$$C_6H_5CHO + O_2 \overset{Light}{\longrightarrow} [C_6H_5\underset{\cdot}{CO}] + [HO{-}O\cdot]$$

These initiating processes are followed by the chain reactions

$$[C_6H_5\underset{\cdot}{CO}] + O_2 \longrightarrow \left[C_6H_5\overset{O}{\overset{\|}{C}}{-}O{-}O\cdot \right]$$

$$\left[C_6H_5\overset{O}{\overset{\|}{C}}{-}O{-}O\cdot \right] + C_6H_5CHO \longrightarrow C_6H_5\overset{O}{\overset{\|}{C}}{-}O{-}OH + [C_6H_5\underset{\cdot}{CO}]$$

The conversion of the perbenzoic acid into benzoic acid also may be a chain process.

$$C_6H_5\overset{\overset{\textstyle O}{\|}}{C}-O-OH + [C_6H_5\overset{\bullet}{CO}] \longrightarrow \left[C_6H_5\overset{\overset{\textstyle O}{\|}}{C}-O\cdot\right] + C_6H_5\overset{\overset{\textstyle O}{\|}}{C}-OH$$

$$\left[C_6H_5\overset{\overset{\textstyle O}{\|}}{C}-O\cdot\right] + C_6H_5CHO \longrightarrow C_6H_5\overset{\overset{\textstyle O}{\|}}{C}-OH + [C_6H_5\overset{\bullet}{CO}]$$

In addition to being accelerated by light, the autoxidation of benzaldehyde is catalyzed by traces of salts of metals of variable valence such as those of iron, nickel, manganese, chromium, and copper. Moreover the reaction is autocatalytic; that is the reaction is catalyzed by some product of the reaction. The autocatalysis may be explained by the decomposition of the perbenzoic acid, which leads to twice the number of free radicals that are required to produce it.

$$C_6H_5\overset{\overset{\textstyle O}{\|}}{C}-O-OH \longrightarrow \left[C_6H_5\overset{\overset{\textstyle O}{\|}}{C}-O\cdot\right] + [\cdot OH]$$

The metallic ions probably initiate autoxidation by increasing the concentration of free radicals. Ferrous ion, for example, may transfer an electron to the oxygen molecule to give the anion of the hydroperoxide free radical, thus in effect activating the oxygen molecule.

$$Fe^{++} + O_2 \longrightarrow Fe^{+++} + \cdot O{-}O\overset{-}{\vdots}$$

$$C_6H_5CHO + \cdot O{-}O\overset{-}{\vdots} \longrightarrow C_6H_5\overset{\bullet}{CO} + HO{-}O\overset{-}{\vdots}$$

Ferric ion may produce benzoyl radicals from benzaldehyde and be reduced to ferrous ion.

$$Fe^{+++} + C_6H_5CHO \longrightarrow Fe^{++} + H^+ + C_6H_5\overset{\bullet}{CO}$$

ANTIOXIDANTS

Many substances when present in small amount inhibit autoxidation and are known as **antioxidants.** These substances have the common property of being easily oxidized. Thus sulfites, iodides, benzyl alcohol, hydroquinone, or diphenylamine will decrease autoxidations to a negligible rate in concentrations as low as 0.001 per cent.

Peroxides are important because of their ability to catalyze polymerization and other reactions catalyzed by free-radicals, but antioxidants are important because of their ability to inhibit unwanted oxidation or unwanted reactions catalyzed by free radicals. Thus the tocopherols (p. 460) are used to prevent foods from becoming rancid, diphenylamine is used to stabilize cellulose nitrate, phenyl-α-naphthylamine to prolong the life of rubber articles, α-naphthol or di-*s*-butyl-*p*-phenylenediamine to prevent gum formation in cracked gasolines, and hydroquinone to prevent the spontaneous polymerization of readily polymerized monomers.

Just as the positive catalysis of autoxidation can be explained by an increase in the concentration of free radicals necessary for the propagation of a chain reaction, the action of antioxidants can be ascribed to a decrease in the concentration of free radicals. Thus a transfer of a hydrogen atom to a free radical would give a stable molecule.

$$C_6H_5\overset{\bullet}{CO} + RH \longrightarrow C_6H_5CHO + R\cdot$$

Since this process also generates a free radical, only those substances act as inhibitors which give rise to short-lived free radicals, that is free radicals which are converted rapidly into stable molecules thus breaking the chain. Primary and secondary alcohols inhibit autoxidation because the initial free radical formed from them can transfer a second hydrogen atom and give an aldehyde or ketone.

$$[C_6H_5\overset{\cdot}{C}O] + RCH_2OH \longrightarrow C_6H_5CHO + [R\overset{\cdot}{C}HOH]$$

$$[R\overset{\cdot}{C}HOH] + [C_6H_5\overset{\cdot}{C}O] \longrightarrow C_6H_5CHO + RCHO$$

Alternatively the process may involve initial removal of a hydrogen atom from the hydroxyl group.

$$[C_6H_5\overset{\cdot}{C}O] + RCH_2OH \longrightarrow C_6H_5CHO + [RCH_2O \cdot]$$

$$[RCH_2O \cdot] + [C_6H_5\overset{\cdot}{C}O] \longrightarrow C_6H_5CHO + RCHO$$

Perbenzoate radicals likewise can be destroyed by conversion into the more stable perbenzoic acid. Tertiary alcohols are ineffective because the tertiary carbon atom does not carry a hydrogen atom, and neither the first step of the first process nor the second step of the second process can take place. Substances like hydroquinone and diphenylamine are more effective than alcohols because they are much more easily oxidized to quinone or an indophenol than are alcohols to aldehydes or ketones. Ease of oxidation alone, however, is not sufficient to cause inhibition of autoxidation. Thus the aldehyde formed as a product of the inhibition by a primary alcohol is more readily oxidized under the proper conditions than the alcohol. However aldehydes are not antioxidants because the radical formed cannot be stabilized without the formation of a new radical. If such were not the case, aldehydes would not undergo rapid autoxidation, since they would act as their own antioxidants. Conversely alcohols do not undergo rapid autoxidation because they do act as their own antioxidants. It has been reported, however, that the photochemical air oxidation of isopropyl alcohol can give up to 0.4 mole of peroxide per liter. Iodides and sulfites act as antioxidants because of their ready oxidation to iodine and dithionate ion.

$$[C_6H_5\overset{\cdot}{C}O] + HI \longrightarrow C_6H_5CHO + [I \cdot]$$

$$2[I \cdot] \longrightarrow I_2$$

$$[C_6H_5\overset{\cdot}{C}O] + [HSO_3^-] \longrightarrow C_6H_5CHO + [\cdot SO_3^-]$$

$$2[\cdot SO_3^-] \longrightarrow [S_2O_6^=]$$

REVIEW QUESTIONS

1. What are organic peroxides? Give the names and structures for the more important types of organic peroxides.
2. Give equations for the preparation of (*a*) ethyl peroxide; (*b*) *t*-butyl hydroperoxide; (*c*) benzoyl peroxide; (*d*) monoperphthalic acid; (*e*) formyl peroxide.
3. Discuss the autoxidation of (*a*) benzaldehyde; (*b*) olefins.
4. What are antioxidants, how do they act, and what use is made of them?
5. What is the current view concerning the structure of (*a*) ozone; (*b*) ozonides?
6. Give reactions illustrating the preparation of α-tetralone (*a*) from benzene and (*b*) from naphthalene.
7. How can the presence of peroxides in ether be detected? Why should they be removed before the ether is used?

Chapter 40

ORGANOMETALLIC COMPOUNDS. SILICON COMPOUNDS

ORGANOMETALLIC COMPOUNDS

Organometallic compounds are defined as those compounds in which carbon is linked to a metal. The bonds with different metals may have a wide range of polarity from largely covalent to the ion-pair type. Typical organometallic compounds are the Grignard reagents (p. 85) and the metallic acetylides (p. 111). Metallic derivatives in which the anion is a resonance hybrid as is postulated for ethyl sodiomalonate (p. 545) or ethyl sodioacetoacetate (p. 552) usually are not classed with the organometallic compounds.

A few **organolithium** compounds can be made in good yields directly from alkyl or aryl halides using ether, benzene, or cyclohexane as a solvent.

$$n\text{-}C_4H_9Cl + 2\ Li \longrightarrow n\text{-}C_4H_9Li + LiCl$$
n-Butyllithium

$$C_6H_5Br + 2\ Li \longrightarrow C_6H_5Li + LiBr$$
Phenyllithium

$$p\text{-}(CH_3)_2NC_6H_4Br + 2\ Li \longrightarrow p\text{-}(CH_3)_2NC_6H_4Li + LiBr$$
p-Dimethylamino-
phenyllithium

There is some indication that metallic sodium reacts similarly with alkyl halides, but the process is complicated by further reaction with the solvent, by the formation of disodium derivatives, and by coupling. Triphenylmethylsodium is formed directly from triphenylmethyl chloride in ether.

$$(C_6H_5)_3CCl + Na\text{-}Hg \xrightarrow{\text{Ether}} (C_6H_5)_3CNa + Hg + NaCl$$

Since 1 to 3 per cent amalgam must be used, it is not convenient to prepare large quantities. The solution may be used to remove oxygen from inert gases, and as a strongly basic catalyst.

A general method is available for the preparation of alkyl derivatives of any of the alkali metals. It consists of heating the metal with an alkylmercury (p. 587) in a sealed tube.

$$(C_2H_5)_2Hg + 2\ Na \longrightarrow 2\ C_2H_5Na + Hg$$
Ethylmercury   Ethylsodium

If a hydrogen atom of an organic compound is sufficiently acidic, it will react with the alkali metal directly.

$$RC{\equiv}CH + Na(\text{molten}) \longrightarrow RC{\equiv}CNa + \tfrac{1}{2} H_2$$

$$(C_6H_5)_2CH_2 + K \xrightarrow{230°} (C_6H_5)_2CHK + \tfrac{1}{2} H_2$$

Cyclopentadiene, indene, and fluorene are sufficiently acidic to react with sodium amide.

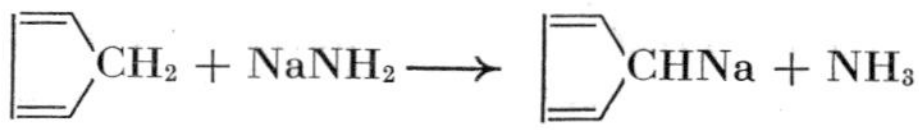

$$\square\!\!\!\!\diagdown CH_2 + NaNH_2 \longrightarrow \square\!\!\!\!\diagdown CHNa + NH_3$$

If another compound is more acidic than that from which an organometallic compound is derived, an ordinary acid-base exchange reaction similar to the reaction with sodium amide will take place. For example benzene reacts with ethylsodium to give ethane and phenylsodium.

$$C_6H_6 + C_2H_5Na \longrightarrow C_6H_5Na + C_2H_6$$

From reactions such as this, hydrocarbons may be listed in the following order of increasing acidity.

$$C_2H_6 < C_6H_6 < C_6H_5CH_3 < (C_6H_5)_2CH_2 < (C_6H_5)_3CH$$

This exchange reaction has practical value, since it can be used to synthesize organometallic compounds that may be difficult to synthesize by other methods. For example α-picolyllithium is made easily from α-picoline and phenyllithium.

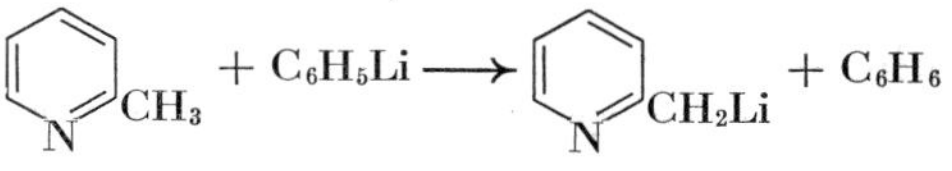

$$\text{[pyridine]}CH_3 + C_6H_5Li \longrightarrow \text{[pyridine]}CH_2Li + C_6H_6$$

The reactivities of the organometallic compounds also vary in these exchange reactions, because the more ionic the carbon-metal bond, the stronger in effect is the substance as a base. Thus RMgX does not react with dibenzofuran, RLi gives a lithium derivative, and RNa gives a disodium derivative.

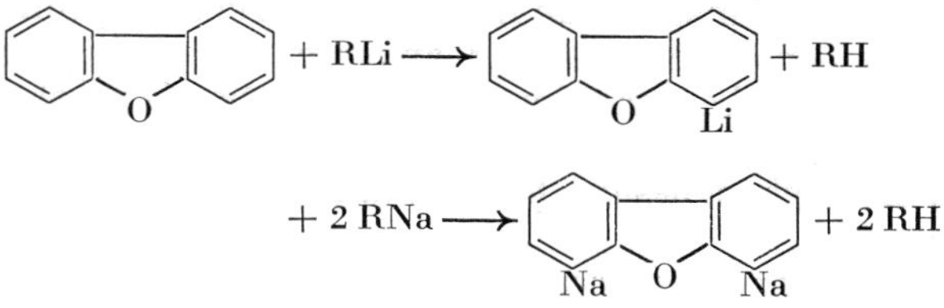

$$\text{[dibenzofuran]} + RLi \longrightarrow \text{[dibenzofuran-Li]} + RH$$

$$+ 2 RNa \longrightarrow \text{[dibenzofuran-Na, Na]} + 2 RH$$

The term *metalation* has been coined for this type of reaction, but it merely is a typical acid-base exchange reaction.

Alkyl- and aryllithiums are sufficiently covalent to be soluble in ether, benzene, and hexane. The other alkali metals form colorless nonvolatile derivatives that are insoluble in most organic solvents. With increasing charge on the nucleus the bond to carbon becomes more and more ionic. Thus the molar conductivities in ethylzinc solution of ethyllithium, -sodium, -potassium, and -rubidium are 0.13, 4.01, 6.49, and 9.39. Not only is the basicity of these organometallic compounds in this order, but also their reactivity in the usual Grignard type reactions, the lithium compounds being least reactive.

The preparation and reactions of the **alkyl-** and **arylmagnesium halides**

(**Grignard reagents**) are discussed in Chapter 6 and subsequently. The rates of reactions of different Grignard reagents with different types of compounds vary greatly. Thus the time in hours required for complete disappearance of RMgBr in the presence of an excess of benzonitrile under standardized conditions is as follows: R=mesityl, 0.01; *p*-tolyl, 0.10; phenyl, 0.31; ethyl, 0.85; benzyl, 1.60; *n*-butyl, 4.57; *s*-butyl, 11.65; *t*-butyl, 25.5; phenylethynyl ($C_6H_5C\equiv C$), 77.0. By allowing one mole of a Grignard reagent to react with a mixture of one mole of each of two compounds, and determining the amounts of the products formed, it is possible to determine which compound is the more reactive. By a series of such competitive reactions with phenylmagnesium bromide, the following order of reactivity was obtained.

$$C_6H_5CHO > C_6H_5COCH_3 > C_6H_5NCO > C_6H_5COF > C_6H_5COC_6H_5 > C_6H_5COCl >$$
$$C_6H_5COBr > C_6H_5COOC_2H_5 > C_6H_5CN$$

Although such results are helpful in estimating the relative rate of reaction of a Grignard reagent, they should not be relied on completely, since different series of reactions do not yield wholly concordant results.

Alkylmagnesiums may be made by heating the alkylmercury with magnesium in a sealed tube.

$$R_2Hg + Mg \longrightarrow R_2Mg + Hg$$

They are solids soluble in ether.

In ether solution the alkylmagnesium halides are in equilibrium with alkylmagnesium and magnesium halide.

$$2\ RMgX \rightleftharpoons R_2Mg + MgX_2$$

Although the ether complexes of the components of the equilibrium are soluble in ether, the dioxane complex of magnesium halide is not. Hence addition of dioxane precipitates the magnesium halide and shifts the equilibrium giving a solution of alkylmagnesium. Varying amounts of alkylmagnesium halide may be precipitated at the same time, but the solution is substantially free of halogen. The reactions of solutions of alkylmagnesiums are essentially the same as those of alkylmagnesium halides, although there appear to be some minor differences.

The simpler primary and secondary **alkylzincs** and **alkylzinc halides** can be prepared directly from the alkyl halide and a zinc-copper couple.

$$C_2H_5I + Zn(Cu) \longrightarrow C_2H_5ZnI$$

$$2\ C_2H_5ZnI \longrightarrow (C_2H_5)_2Zn + ZnI_2$$

This reaction was discovered by Frankland [1] in 1849 while he was attempting to prepare free ethyl radicals. Higher alkyl halides give largely disproportionation products, and tertiary alkyl halides give olefins and hydrogen. Alkyl-

---

[1] Edward Frankland (1825–1899), successor to Hofmann at the Royal School of Mines (previously the Royal College of Chemistry) at London. He was the originator of the theory of valence as applied to what now are known as covalent compounds, and along with Kolbe and Kekulé was largely responsible for its development.

zincs can be prepared also from the Grignard reagent and zinc halide, or from the alkylmercury and zinc.

$$ZnX_2 \xrightarrow{RMgX} RZnX \xrightarrow{RMgX} R_2Zn$$

$$R_2Hg + Zn \longrightarrow R_2Zn + Hg$$

The alkylzincs react with the same types of compounds as do Grignard reagents, and although methyl- and ethylzinc are spontaneously inflammable in air, they were used for syntheses before the discovery of Barbier and Grignard. The alkylzinc halides undergo addition to carbonyl groups less readily than Grignard reagents, and may be used to prepare ketones from acyl chlorides without appreciable formation of tertiary alcohol.

$$RCOCl + RZnCl \longrightarrow RCOR' + ZnCl_2$$

In order to carry out a comparable reaction with a Grignard reagent a low temperature ($-80°$) must be used.

Among the organometallic compounds, those of **mercury** are next in importance to those of magnesium. They are not so useful in organic syntheses but have considerable use as antiseptics and medicinals. Most of them are highly toxic and special care should be used in handling the volatile alkylmercury compounds.

Aryl- or alkylmercury compounds can be prepared from the halides and sodium amalgam, or from the Grignard reagent and mercuric halide.

$$2\ RX + Na_2Hg \longrightarrow R_2Hg + 2\ NaX$$

$$HgX_2 \xrightarrow{RMgX} RHgX \xrightarrow{RMgX} R_2Hg$$

Ethylmercuric chloride, which is an important fungicide used to prevent sap stain in lumber and to disinfect seeds, is made from mercuric chloride and tetraethyllead.

$$2\ HgCl_2 + Pb(C_2H_5)_4 \longrightarrow 4\ C_2H_5HgCl + PbCl_4$$

Aromatic mercury compounds can be made by the replacement of groups other than halogen. Sulfinic acid and boric acid groups can be replaced by heating with mercuric chloride.

$$C_6H_5SOOH + HgCl_2 \longrightarrow C_6H_5HgCl + SO_2 + HCl$$

$$C_6H_5B(OH)_2 + HgCl_2 \longrightarrow C_6H_5HgCl + HBO_2 + HCl$$

The preparation of mercury compounds by substitution of hydrogen or addition to a double bond is called *direct mercuration*. Olefins, for example, add mercuric acetate.

$$RCH{=}CHR + Hg(OAc)_2 \longrightarrow \underset{\underset{OAc}{|}}{RCH}{-}\underset{\underset{HgOAc}{|}}{CHR}$$

Since crystallizable solids frequently are obtained from liquid unsaturated compounds, the reaction is used for the isolation and purification of unsaturated compounds such as the unsaturated fat acids. The unsaturated compound is regenerated by heating with hydrochloric acid.

$$\underset{\substack{| \quad |\\ \text{OAc} \ \text{HgOAc}}}{\text{RCH—CHR}} + 2\,\text{HCl} \longrightarrow \text{RCH}{=}\text{CHR} + \text{HgCl}_2 + 2\,\text{HOAc}$$

Acetylenes react with mercuric cyanide to give cyanomercuric derivatives.

$$\text{RC}{\equiv}\text{CH} + \text{Hg(CN)}_2 \longrightarrow \text{RC}{\equiv}\text{CHgCN} + \text{HCN}$$

Readily substituted aromatic compounds react with mercuric acetate in alcohol solution.

$$\text{C}_6\text{H}_5\text{OH} + \text{Hg(OAc)}_2 \longrightarrow o\text{- and } p\text{-HOC}_6\text{H}_4\text{HgOAc} + \text{HOAc}$$

The reaction is very mild compared to the usual substitution reactions. Hence compounds like furan which are sensitive to acids and do not give good yields of substitution products on bromination, nitration, or sulfonation because of ring scission and polymerization, can be mercurated readily.

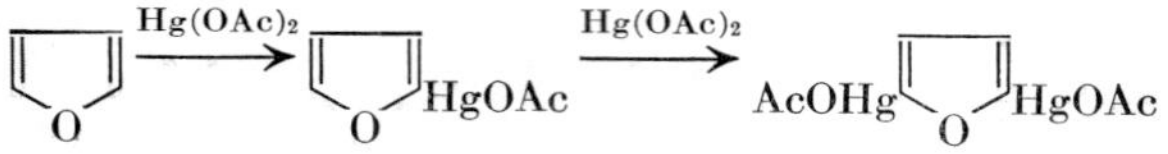

The lower alkylmercury compounds are volatile liquids soluble in organic solvents indicating that they are covalent compounds. They are the least reactive of any of the organometallic compounds of the first two groups of the periodic table.

Alkylmercury compounds are not hydrolyzed by water but are split by halogen acids or halogens.

$$\text{R}_2\text{Hg} \xrightarrow{\text{HX}} \text{RH} + \text{RHgX} \xrightarrow{\text{HX}} \text{RH} + \text{HgX}_2$$

$$\text{R}_2\text{Hg} \xrightarrow{\text{X}_2} \text{RX} + \text{RHgX} \xrightarrow{\text{X}_2} \text{RX} + \text{HgX}_2$$

$$\text{R}_2\text{Hg} \xrightarrow{\text{(SCN)}_2} \text{RSCN} + \text{RHgSCN} \xrightarrow{\text{(SCN)}_2} \text{RSCN} + \text{Hg(SCN)}_2$$

The last two reactions may be used for the preparation of halogen or thiocyanogen compounds. Thus o- and p-acetoxymercuriphenol, made by direct mercuration of phenol, react with sodium chloride to give the chloromercuric compounds, which can be separated readily by crystallization. Reaction of either purified compound with one mole of halogen or thiocyanogen gives the halogenated phenol or the hydroxyphenyl thiocyanate. Similarly bromo- and iodofuran can be made from chloromercurifuran.

Several aromatic mercury compounds are used as antiseptics. One of the most widely used is **Mercurochrome** (p. 483) although it has poor penetrating power and really is a poor antiseptic. Because of the deep red stain, a potency which it does not possess is attributed to it by the user. Its effectiveness against most organisms is about one-hundredth that of an equal concentration of mercuric chloride. **Metaphen** and **Merthiolate** on the other hand are about ten times more effective than mercuric chloride. None of the mercurials, however, is very effective in killing spores. This deficiency is not surprising since their high molecular weights and insolubility in fats would tend to prevent penetration of cellular tissue.

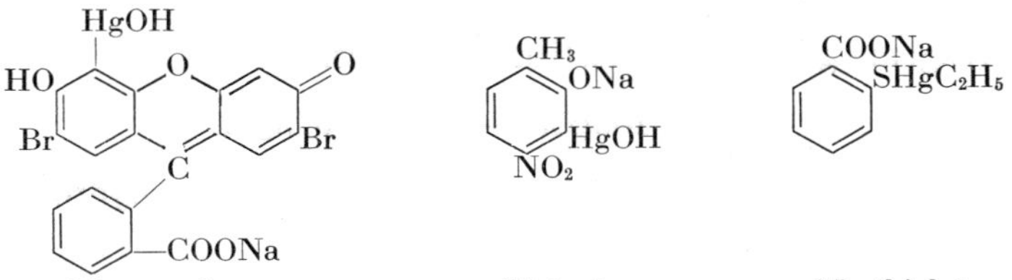

Mercurochrome   Metaphen   Merthiolate

Both Metaphen and Merthiolate are colorless. Hence it was necessary to add a dye to their solutions before the public would accept them.

The alkylmercury compounds are valuable for the synthesis of other organometallic compounds since the mercury can be exchanged for any metal above it in the electromotive series.

$$R_2Hg + 2\,M' \longrightarrow 2\,RM + Hg$$

$$R_2Hg + M'' \longrightarrow R_2M + Hg$$

$$3\,R_2Hg + 2\,M''' \longrightarrow 2\,R_3M + 3\,Hg$$

Alkylmercury compounds react also with the halides of nonmetals.

$$3\,R_2Hg + 2\,BX_3 \longrightarrow 2\,BR_3 + 3\,HgX_2$$

$$2\,R_2Hg + SiX_4 \longrightarrow SiR_4 + 2\,HgX_2$$

When lead chloride reacts with the Grignard reagent, the product may be the **di-, tri-** or **tetraalkyl-** or **aryllead,** depending on the nature of the hydrocarbon group.

$$2\,PbCl_2 + 4\,RMgX \longrightarrow PbR_4 + Pb + 4\,MgX_2$$

$$3\,PbCl_2 + 6\,RMgX \longrightarrow 2\,PbR_3 + Pb + 6\,MgX_2$$

$$PbCl_2 + 4\,RMgX \longrightarrow PbR_4 + Pb + 4\,MgX_2$$

If a di- or trisubstituted lead is formed, chlorine will add to give the tetravalent chloro derivative which then will react with more Grignard reagent to give the tetrasubstituted lead. **Tetraethyllead,** the most important lead compound (p. 53), is made from ethyl chloride and sodium-lead alloy.

$$4\,C_2H_5Cl + Na_4Pb \longrightarrow (C_2H_5)_4Pb + 4\,NaCl$$

The tetraalkylleads behave much like the alkylmercury compounds. Thus they are stable to hydrolysis but can be cleaved by halogen acid or halogen.

Arsenic is a borderline element between the metals and the nonmetals. However the organic derivatives of arsenic differ considerably from those of nitrogen and phosphorus, and it is convenient to consider the organic arsenic compounds here along with those of antimony and bismuth.

The alkyldichloroarsines, dialkylchloroarsines, and trialkylarsines may be prepared by the reaction of arsenic trichloride with an alkylmercury.

$$AsCl_3 \xrightarrow{R_2Hg} RAsCl_2 \xrightarrow{R_2Hg} R_2AsCl \xrightarrow{R_2Hg} R_3As$$

Grignard reagents give the trisubstituted arsines.

$$AsCl_3 + 3 \ RMgCl \longrightarrow R_3As + 3 \ MgCl_2$$

Reduction of the chloroarsines with amalgamated zinc and hydrochloric acid gives the alkylarsines.

$$RAsCl_2 + 2 \ Zn(Hg) + 2 \ HCl \longrightarrow RAsH_2 + 2 \ ZnCl_2$$

$$R_2AsCl + Zn(Hg) + HCl \longrightarrow R_2AsH + ZnCl_2$$

The arsines are insoluble in water and do not form salts with acids. They react with alkyl iodides to give quaternary salts.

$$R_3As + RI \longrightarrow R_4As^+I^-$$

The more volatile arsines fume in air because of rapid oxidation, and sometimes are spontaneously inflammable. The initial oxidation products differ with the type of arsine oxidized.

$$CH_3AsH_2 + O_2 \longrightarrow CH_3AsO + H_2O$$
Methylarsine   Methylarsenoxide (arsenosomethane)

$$2 \ (CH_3)_2AsH + O_2 \longrightarrow (CH_3)_2AsOAs(CH_3)_2 + H_2O$$
Dimethylarsenoxide (cacodyl oxide)

$$2 \ (CH_3)_3As + O_2 \longrightarrow 2 \ (CH_3)_3AsO + H_2O$$
Trimethylarsine oxide

Methylarsenoxide and dimethylarsenoxide are different types of compounds from trimethylarsine oxide in that in the former the oxygen atoms are linked by nonpolar bonds, whereas in the latter the oxygen atom is linked by a semipolar bond. The difference is indicated by calling the one type *arsenoxides* and the other *arsine oxides*. The AsO group which formally is analogous to the nitroso group is called the *arsenoso* group, and methylarsenoxide can be called arsenosomethane.

Because of the nauseating odor of the volatile arsenic compounds, Berzelius called them *kakodyls* (Gr. *kakodes* stinking), the English transliteration being cacodyl. The first of these substances was *Cadet's liquid*, which is chiefly dimethylarsenoxide and was prepared by Cadet in 1760 by heating a mixture of arsenic trioxide and potassium acetate.

$$As_2O_3 + 4 \ KOCOCH_3 \longrightarrow (CH_3)_2AsOAs(CH_3)_2 + 2 \ K_2CO_3 + 2 \ CO_2$$

Bunsen [2] during the years 1837–1843 showed that this liquid could be considered as the oxide of the radical C_2H_6As and that the same radical, which was called *cacodyl*, was present in the products obtained by numerous chemical reactions. Thus cacodyl oxide reacts with hydrochloric acid to give cacodyl chloride, which can be converted to cacodyl cyanide, cacodyl sulfide, and cacodyl disulfide. This work substantiated the earlier work of Gay-Lussac on cyanogen (1815) and of Liebig and Woehler on benzoyl (1832), and helped to establish the fact that a group of atoms can be carried intact through a series of chemical transformations.

In the air oxidation of the primary and secondary arsines, water is formed, and the oxidation may proceed further to give alkyl derivatives of arsenic acid.

$$CH_3AsO + H_2O + [O] \longrightarrow CH_3AsO(OH)_2$$
$$\text{Methanarsonic acid}$$

$$(CH_3)_2AsOAs(CH_3)_2 + H_2O + [O] \longrightarrow (CH_3)_2AsOOH$$
$$\text{Dimethylarsinic acid}$$

The sodium alkanarsonates can be made also by the alkylation of sodium arsenite.

$$Na_3AsO_3 + (CH_3)_2SO_4 \text{ (or } CH_3Cl) \longrightarrow CH_3AsO(ONa)_2 + NaCH_3SO_4 \text{ (or NaCl)}$$

Reduction with sulfurous acid gives the arsenoxide.

$$CH_3AsO(ONa)_2 + H_2SO_3 \longrightarrow CH_3AsO + Na_2SO_4 + H_2O$$

Sodium hydroxide converts the arsenoxide to the disodium alkylarsinate, which can be alkylated to the sodium dialkylarsinate.

$$CH_3AsO + 2\ NaOH \longrightarrow H_2O + CH_3AsO_2Na_2 \xrightarrow{(CH_3)_2SO_4} (CH_3)_2AsOONa$$

Reduction of the sodium dialkylarsinate gives the cacodyl oxide. The oxide gives a salt with sodium hydroxide that can be alkylated to the arsine oxide.

$$2\ (CH_3)_2AsOONa \xrightarrow{2\ H_2SO_3} 2\ NaHSO_4 + H_2O + (CH_3)_2AsOAs(CH_3)_2 \xrightarrow{2\ NaOH}$$
$$H_2O + 2\ (CH_3)_2AsONa \xrightarrow{(CH_3)_2SO_4} (CH_3)_3AsO$$

These reduction products can be reduced to the arsines, or converted to the chloroarsines with hydrochloric acid.

$$CH_3AsO(OH)_2 + 3\ Zn\ (Hg) + 6\ HCl \longrightarrow CH_3AsH_2 + 3\ H_2O + 3\ ZnCl_2$$

$$CH_3AsO + 2\ HCl \longrightarrow CH_3AsCl_2$$

---

[2] Robert Wilhelm Bunsen (1811–1899), professor of chemistry at the University of Heidelberg. He is known popularly for the burner, gas valve, and clamp that bear his name. Except for his early work on cacodyl compounds, most of his contributions dealt with inorganic and physical chemistry. He is noted particularly for his work on spectral analysis which was done in collaboration with the physicist Kirchoff, and for his explanation of the action of geysers. Among his students were Baeyer, Beilstein, Carius, Curtius, Erlenmeyer, Graebe, Ladenburg, V. Meyer, and Thorpe.

All the arsenic compounds are highly toxic. **Methyl-** and **ethyldichloroarsine** were tried as military gases in World War I but were not so effective as mustard gas. **2-Chlorovinyldichloroarsine** (*primary Lewisite*) is a vesicant that is considerably more toxic than mustard gas but was not prepared on a large scale until the end of World War I. Since no war gas was used extensively in World War II, the effectiveness of Lewisite in combat has not been tested. It is prepared by the reaction of arsenic trichloride and acetylene in the presence of aluminum chloride.

$$HC \equiv CH + AsCl_3 \xrightarrow{AlCl_3} ClCH \equiv CHAsCl_2, \ (ClCH \equiv CH)_2AsCl, \ and \ (ClCH \equiv CH)_3As$$

Primary   Secondary   Tertiary
Lewisite   Lewisite   Lewisite

The secondary and tertiary Lewisite which are formed as co-products are less effective and may be converted to the primary Lewisite by reaction with more arsenic trichloride. The development during World War II of BAL as an antidote for arsenic poisoning (p. 525) has decreased the potential effectiveness of Lewisite as a war gas.

Of the *aryl arsenic compounds*, the **arsonic acids** are the most important. They can be made from diazonium salts (p. 479) by the Bart reaction.

$$ArN_2Cl + Na_2HAsO_3 \longrightarrow ArAsO_3HNa + NaCl + N_2$$

Aromatic phenols and amines can be arsonated directly using syrupy arsenic acid.

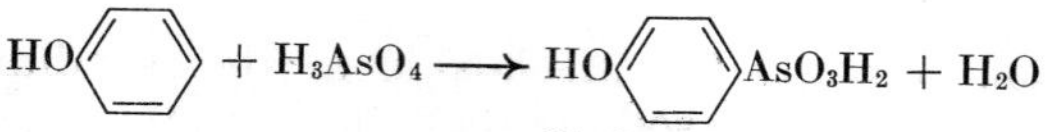

$$HO\langle\ \rangle + H_3AsO_4 \longrightarrow HO\langle\ \rangle AsO_3H_2 + H_2O$$

p-Hydroxyphenyl-
arsonic acid

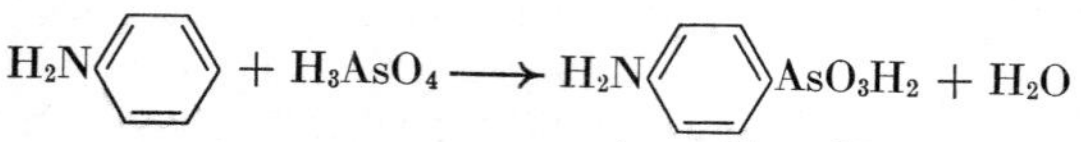

$$H_2N\langle\ \rangle + H_3AsO_4 \longrightarrow H_2N\langle\ \rangle AsO_3H_2 + H_2O$$

Arsanilic acid

Arsenobenzene, the arsenic analog of azobenzene, can be made from phenylarsine and phenylarsenoxide, or by the reduction of phenylarsonic acid.

$$C_6H_5AsH_2 + OAsC_6H_5 \longrightarrow C_6H_5As \equiv AsC_6H_5 + H_2O$$

$$2\ C_6H_5AsO_3H_2 + 8\ [H] \longrightarrow C_6H_5As \equiv AsC_6H_5 + 6\ H_2O$$

Arsenobenzene is less stable than azobenzene. On heating, it decomposes into triphenylarsine and arsenic, and reaction with chlorine, oxygen, or sulfur breaks the arsenic-arsenic bond.

$$3\ C_6H_5As \equiv AsC_6H_5 \xrightarrow{Heat} 2\ (C_6H_5)_3As + 4\ As$$

$$C_6H_5As \equiv AsC_6H_5 + Cl_2 \longrightarrow 2\ C_6H_5AsCl_2$$

$$+ O_2 \longrightarrow 2\ C_6H_5AsO$$

The sodium salt of **arsanilic acid** (*p*-aminophenylarsonic acid) was introduced into medicine in 1905 by Thomas, who found it to be more effective than inorganic arsenic compounds for the treatment of sleeping sickness and other diseases caused by trypanosomes. It was called **atoxyl** because it once was thought to be nontoxic, although it now is known to be especially dangerous because of its effect on the optic nerve. A derivative of atoxyl, **tryparsamide,** *p*-$H_2NCOCH_2NHC_6H_4AsO_3HNa$, is highly trypanocidal and much safer to use. Moreover tryparsamide is particularly valuable in the treatment of late syphilis involving the central nervous system, although it is of no use for early syphilis since it is not highly treponemicidal.

Modern chemotherapy began with the work of Ehrlich.[3] Beginning with the knowledge that certain dyes stain some tissues and not others, he developed azo dyes which were effective in combating trypanosomes in mice. With the publication of the work of Thomas on atoxyl and the discovery in the same year that a member of the Protozoa, *Treponema pallidum*, was the cause of syphilis, Ehrlich prepared and tested arsenic analogs of azo compounds. One of these, called **Salvarsan** or **arsphenamine,** was the most widely used agent for the treatment of syphilis up to the advent of penicillin. Salvarsan also has been called 606 because it was the 606th product in the series of compounds being investigated. It is marketed as the dihydrochloride and must be

$$HO\langle\ \rangle AsO_3H_2 \xrightarrow{HNO_3} HO\langle\ \rangle \underset{NO_2}{AsO_3H_2} \xrightarrow[\text{(Na}_2\text{S}_2\text{O}_4)]{\text{Reduction}}$$

$$HO\langle\ \rangle\underset{NH_2}{AsO} \xrightarrow[\text{Oxidation}]{\text{Further reduction}} \underset{NH_2}{HO\langle\ \rangle As}=\underset{NH_2}{As\langle\ \rangle OH}$$

m-Amino-*p*-
hydroxyphenylarsenoxide
(arsenoxide or Mapharsen)

Arsphenamine (606 or
Salvarsan)

converted to the sodium salt just before administration. It must be protected from air to avoid oxidation to the more toxic arsenoxide. The latter, however, is believed to be the active agent in the blood, since it will kill the protozoa *in vitro* whereas arsphenamine will not. Ehrlich had considered the use of the arsenoxide but rejected it because of its high toxicity. He overlooked, however, the high therapeutic index, that is the ratio of the minimum lethal dose to the therapeutic dose. In recent years the arsenoxide has been re-evaluated and was adopted officially as an antisyphilitic agent by the U. S. Army in 1941. It bears the common name arsenoxide, or Mapharsen, coined from letters in its chemical name.

SILICON COMPOUNDS

The part played by silicon in organic chemistry may be considered from two points of view. First since silicon is just below carbon in the periodic table,

---

[3] Paul Ehrlich (1854–1915), physiologist and professor of experimental therapy at the University of Frankfurt. He was the first to attempt to synthesize chemical compounds that are more toxic for a pathogenic organism than for the host, a field of investigation to which he gave the name *chemotherapy*.

it would be expected to resemble carbon in its chemical properties and give rise to a group of silicon analogs of carbon compounds. However since the valence electrons are farther away from the nucleus and are held less strongly than in carbon, silicon is more electron-donating or metallic in its properties. Hence silicon does not give rise to all of the many types of compounds derived from carbon, and the silicon analogs of carbon compounds that are known exhibit markedly different properties. The second aspect of the place of silicon in organic chemistry lies in the preparation and properties of compounds in which silicon is linked to carbon. Both of these aspects are considered here, sometimes independently and sometimes simultaneously.

When crude magnesium silicide, prepared by heating silica with magnesium, reacts with mineral acids, a mixture of **silicon hydrides** is obtained consisting of 40 per cent silane (silicane), SiH_4; 30 per cent disilane, Si_2H_6; 15 per cent trisilane, Si_3H_8; and 10 per cent tetrasilane, Si_4H_{10}. The remaining 5 per cent is a mixture of higher silanes, the highest identified being Si_6H_{14}. **Silane** boils at $-112°$ and decomposes at $400°$ to silicon and hydrogen. The higher silanes decompose to mixtures of lower silanes and silicon at progressively lower temperatures. The silanes are stable to aqueous acids but are hydrolyzed by boiling with bases.

$$SiH_4 + H_2O + 2\,NaOH \longrightarrow Na_2SiO_3 + 4\,H_2$$

Silicon tetrachloride, $SiCl_4$, was discovered by Berzelius in 1823. It is prepared by the reaction of chlorine with silicon, some Si_2Cl_6 and Si_3Cl_8 being formed at the same time.

$$Si + 2\,Cl_2 \longrightarrow SiCl_4 \text{ (and } Si_2Cl_6 \text{ and } Si_3Cl_8)$$

The boiling point is $58°$, or $19°$ lower than carbon tetrachloride. It is hydrolyzed readily by water, although it may be distilled from sodium with which it does not react below $200°$.

$$SiCl_4 + 3\,H_2O \longrightarrow H_2SiO_3 + 4\,HCl$$

Reaction with alcohols gives the orthosilicates.

$$SiCl_4 + 4\,ROH \longrightarrow (RO)_4Si + 4\,HCl$$

Reduction with lithium aluminum hydride gives almost quantitative yields of silane.

$$SiCl_4 + LiAlH_4 \longrightarrow SiH_4 + LiAlCl_4$$

Trichlorosilane (*silicochloroform*) results along with silicon tetrachloride from the action of dry hydrogen chloride on silicon.

$$Si + 3\,HCl \longrightarrow SiHCl_3 + H_2 \text{ (and } SiCl_4)$$

It boils at $32°$, or $29°$ below chloroform. It fumes in moist air because of its ready hydrolysis.

$$SiHCl_3 + 3\,H_2O \longrightarrow H_2SiO_3 + 3\,HCl + H_2$$

The first compound containing a carbon-silicon bond was prepared by Friedel and Crafts in 1863 by the reaction of methylzinc and silicon tetrachloride.

$$SiCl_4 + 2 Zn(CH_3)_2 \xrightarrow{200°} Si(CH_3)_4 + 2 ZnCl_2$$

It boils at 27°. Although it is fairly stable to most reagents, it reacts with methyl alcohol at 250° to give the monomethoxy derivative.

$$Si(CH_3)_4 + CH_3OH \longrightarrow (CH_3)_3SiOCH_3 + CH_4$$

The first arylsilicon compound was prepared by Ladenburg in 1873 by the reaction of silicon tetrachloride and phenylmercury at 300°.

$$SiCl_4 + Hg(C_6H_5)_2 \longrightarrow C_6H_5SiCl_3 + C_6H_5HgCl$$

Kipping began his study of silicon compounds in 1889 with the object of synthesizing a tetrasubstituted silicon compound and determining whether it could be resolved into optically active isomers. During the next forty-five years he continued the study of silicon compounds and most of our basic knowledge of these substances resulted from his work. He found in 1904 that the Grignard reagents react with the halogenated silicon compounds, and this reaction has been the most fruitful in the synthesis of organosilicon compounds. Silicon tetrachloride reacts with Grignard reagents to give a mixture of the compounds having from one to four chlorine atoms replaced by hydrocarbon groups.

$$SiCl_4 \xrightarrow{RMgX} RSiCl_3 \xrightarrow{RMgX} R_2SiCl_2 \xrightarrow{RMgX} R_3SiCl \xrightarrow{RMgX} R_4Si$$

By regulating conditions it is possible to obtain good yields of the desired products.

Trialkylchlorosilanes, R_3SiCl, are silicon analogs of tertiary alkyl chlorides; yet it is not possible to eliminate hydrogen chloride to form an unsaturated compound with a carbon-silicon double bond. Hydrolysis in the presence of ammonia gives the silanol.

$$R_3SiCl + H_2O + NH_3 \longrightarrow R_3SiOH + NH_4Cl$$

These silanols lose water easily and form the oxides.

$$2 R_3SiOH \longrightarrow R_3SiOSiR_3 + H_2O$$

Often this reaction takes place spontaneously, but the more stable compounds such as triphenylsilanol require the presence of alkali. The silanols do not esterify with acids, but acyl chlorides give the chloro derivatives as occurs with tertiary alcohols.

$$R_3SiOH + CH_3COCl \longrightarrow R_3SiCl + CH_3COOH$$

It is impossible to obtain unsaturated compounds by the loss of water.

Hydrolysis of dialkyldichlorosilanes, R_2SiCl_2, gives diols which are insoluble in water but soluble in aqueous alkali.

$$R_2SiCl_2 + 2\ H_2O \longrightarrow 2\ HCl + R_2Si(OH)_2 \overset{\text{NaOH}}{\longrightarrow} R_2Si(ONa)_2 + 2\ H_2O$$

The diols lose water readily to give compounds which are called **silicones,** a name that was given to them before their structure was known, in the belief that they corresponded to ketones. No silicon analog of a ketone is known, however. Apparently silicon is not able to form a double bond with an oxygen atom any more than with a carbon atom. From the dehydration products of diphenylsilanediol, Kipping was able to isolate a number of individual products, some of which were linear polymers and others cyclic polymers.

$$\underset{\overset{|}{C_6H_5}}{\overset{\overset{C_6H_5}{|}}{HOSi}}{-O-}\underset{\overset{|}{C_6H_5}}{\overset{\overset{C_6H_5}{|}}{SiOH}}$$

$$HO[Si(C_6H_5)_2{-}O]_2Si(C_6H_5)_2OH$$

$$HO[Si(C_6H_5)_2{-}O]_3Si(C_6H_5)_2OH$$

In 1928 he reported the formation of much more complex polymers of high molecular weight. Polymers of this type sometimes are called *siloxanes* although the term silicone is used more frequently.

The products of hydrolysis of alkyltrichlorosilanes, $RSiCl_3$, were believed at first to be analogous to the carboxylic acids and were assigned the formula $RSiOOH$, but Kipping found them to be complex compounds of high molecular weight. These compounds also now are grouped with the silicones.

In a summary of his work in 1937, Kipping pointed out that the number of types of silicon compounds was small compared to carbon, and because of the limited number of reactions which they undergo, he concluded that "the prospect of any immediate and important advance in this section of organic chemistry does not seem to be very hopeful." At that very time, however, industrial chemists were trying to make use of Kipping's polymeric compounds because of their insolubility, nonreactivity, and stability to heat. A Russian publication in 1939 indicated that polymers from diphenylsilanediol and from benzylsilanetriol were suitable as dielectrics and insulating materials at elevated temperatures. American publications followed in 1941. Commercial production in the United States of the silicones in the form of oils, greases, resins, and elastomers was announced in 1944. In general the silicones are made by hydrolyzing the alkyl- or aryldichloro- or trichlorosilanes or mixtures of the two. Hydrolysis of the pure dichlorosilanes can give only linear polymers which are oils or greases.

$$x\ R_2SiCl_2 + (x+1)H_2O \longrightarrow HO\left[-\underset{\overset{|}{R}}{\overset{\overset{R}{|}}{Si}}{-O-}\right]_{x-1}\underset{\overset{|}{R}}{\overset{\overset{R}{|}}{Si}}\ OH + 2x\ HCl$$

The trichlorosilanes permit cross-linking of the chains after hydrolysis and give three-dimensional solid resins.

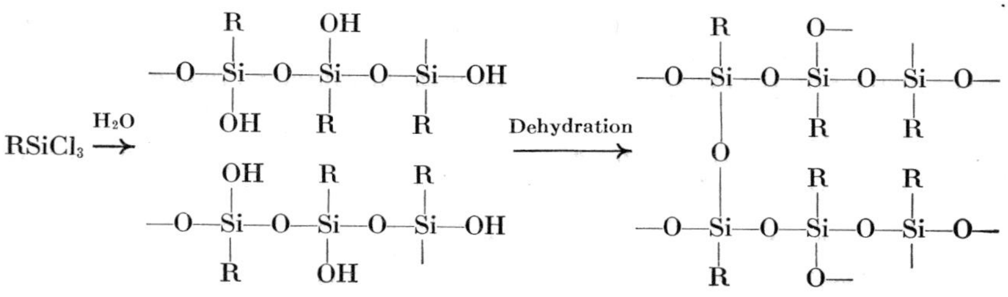

By using mixtures of the dichloro- and trichlorosilanes and varying the nature of the R group, it is possible to obtain products with widely varying properties.

All of the silicones have to a marked extent the properties of not being wet by water and of resistance to a relatively high temperature. Films and coatings are used to waterproof materials and machines, and the resins are used to fill the voids and act as a binder for glass fiber insulation of magnet wire, thus permitting motors to operate at a higher temperature than if the usual organic resins were used. The oils have the unique property of remaining fluid at low temperatures. The explanation appears to be that as cooling takes place, the molecules of the linear polymers become coiled and less entangled than at higher temperatures. Hence the reduction in thermal agitation, which causes an increase in viscosity on cooling, is offset by the molecules becoming more spherical in shape. Silicone rubber in contrast to other rubbers does not become set under compression at high temperatures and retains its flexibility at low temperatures.

The organochlorosilanes at first were manufactured by the Grignard reaction, but less expensive methods now have been developed. The alkyl derivatives can be made by passing the alkyl chlorides over heated silicon and metallic copper. The predominant reaction yields dialkyldichlorosilanes, although other products such as the alkyltrichlorosilanes, the trialkylchlorosilanes, silicon tetrachloride, and hydrocarbons also are formed.

$$2 \text{ RCl} + \text{Si(Cu)} \xrightarrow{300°} \text{R}_2\text{SiCl}_2$$

$$4 \text{ RCl} + 2 \text{ Si(Cu)} \longrightarrow \text{RSiCl}_3 + \text{R}_3\text{SiCl}$$

In the reaction with methyl chloride, it appears that methylcopper is an intermediate product. The best yields of phenylchlorosilanes are obtained by reaction of chlorobenzene with a silver-silicon alloy at 400°.

REVIEW QUESTIONS

1. What are organometallic compounds?
2. How are the alkylzincs prepared and what are their properties?
3. How are Grignard reagents prepared and what advantage do they have over alkylzincs? What is the function of the solvent? What side reactions may take place during the preparation of the reagent?
4. Give two examples of the indirect preparation of Grignard reagents.
5. Give equations for the reaction of Grignard reagents with oxygen, carbon dioxide, carbon disulfide, sulfur dioxide, water, alcohols, primary and secondary amines; with

halides of zinc, mercury, aluminum, and tin; with formaldehyde, other aldehydes, ketones, esters, acyl chlorides, ethylene oxide, benzonitrile, and phenyl isocyanate.

6. How are alkylmercuric halides and dialkylmercury compounds prepared?
7. What is meant by direct mercuration? Give a specific example.
8. How may alkylmercury compounds be used to prepare other alkylmetals?
9. Give equations for the preparation of ethylsodium; butyllithium; sodium acetylide.
10. Compare the physical properties and chemical reactivity of alkyl alkali metals with alkylmercury compounds.
11. What are the structural formulas for primary Lewisite, cacodyl, arsanilic acid, Salvarsan, Mapharsen, and tryparsamide, and of what interest are they? What organic compound has been found to be a specific for arsenic and other heavy-metal poisoning?
12. Give reactions for the preparation of (a) 2-iodofuran from furan; (b) Merthiolate from anthranilic acid; (c) ethylpotassium from ethyl bromide; (d) n-propyl benzyl ketone from butyryl chloride; (e) p,p'-dichlorobiphenyl from p-bromochlorobenzene; (f) 2-pyridylacetic acid from α-picoline.
13. What is the best method for the preparation of silane? How does the number of known hydrides of silicon compare with the number of hydrides of carbon?
14. Compare the chemical properties of carbon tetrachloride with those of silicon tetrachloride; of 1,1-alkanediols with those of 1,1-silanediols.
15. What are the silicones? Why is this term a misnomer? What are some of the advantages of silicones in certain technical applications over other high molecular weight polymers?

Appendix A

THE PRONUNCIATION OF ORGANIC CHEMICAL WORDS

This guide to pronunciation is based on a report of the Nomenclature, Spelling, and Pronunciation Committee of the American Chemical Society published in the News Edition of Industrial and Engineering Chemistry, Volume 12, page 202, 1934. It is not an attempt to standardize pronunciation but is a summary of current usage based on replies to a questionnaire sent to a representative group of chemists in the United States. The inclusion of more than one pronunciation indicates that usage is divided.

Several departures from the customary rules for English pronunciation may be noted. The ending -ine is pronounced -ēn or -ĭn rather than -īn and the ending -ime is pronounced -ēm instead of -īm. The ending -ol is pronounced -ōl except in the word alcohol. The endings -oin, -oine, -aine, -eine, -iene, and -ool should be pronounced as two syllables. Although the use of a dieresis would be helpful, the current tendency in the United States is to omit it.

The symbols used in the respelling for pronunciation have the following values: āle, senăte, ăm, ăccount, ärm; ēve, ĕvent, ĕnd, recĕnt, makēr; īce, ĭll; ōld, ŏbey, ôrb, ŏdd, cŏnnect; ūse, ūnite, ûrn, ŭp, circŭs; fōōd; oil; chair; go; thin.

abietic	ăb′ĭ-ĕt′ĭk	
acetal	ăs′ĕt-ăl	
acetaldehyde	ăs′ĕt-ăl′dĕ-hīd	
acetaldoxime	ăs′ĕt-ăl-dŏk′sēm	
acetamide	ăs′ĕt-ăm′ĭd	ăs′ĕt-ăm′ĭd
		ă-sĕt′ă-mīd
acetanilide	ăs′ĕt-ăn′ĭ-līd	ăs′ĕt-ăn′ĭ-lĭd
acetic	ă-sē′tĭk	
acetoacetate	ăs′ĕ-tō-ăs′ĕ-tāt	ă-sē′tō-ăs′ĕ-tāt
acetoacetic	ăs′ĕ-tō-ă-sē′tĭk	ă-sē′tō-ă-sē′tĭk
acetone	ăs′ĕ-tōn	
acetonitrile	ăs′ĕ-tō-nī′trĭl	ăs′ĕ-tō-nī′trĭl
acetonyl	ă-sĕt′ō-nĭl	ăs′ĕ-tō-nĭl
acetophenone	ăs′ĕ-tō-fĕ-nōn′	ă-sē′tō-fĕ-nōn′
acetoxime	ăs′ĕt-ŏk′sēm	
acetyl	ăs′ĕ-tĭl	
acetylene	ă-sĕt′ĭ-lēn	
aci-	ăs′ĭ-	ā′sē
acrolein	ă-krō′lĕ-ĭn	
acyclic	ă-sī′klĭk	ā-sī′klĭk
acyl	ăs′ĭl	
aglycon	ā-glī′kŏn	
aldehyde	ăl′dĕ-hīd	
aldehydic	ăl′dĕ-hĭd′ĭk	
alicyclic	ăl′ĭ-sī′klĭk	
alizarin	ă-lĭz′ă-rĭn	
alkaline	ăl′kă-lĭn	ăl′kă-līn

alkyl	ăl′kĭl	
allylamine	ăl′ĭl-ă-mēn′	
amide	ăm′īd	ăm′ĭd
amine	ă-mēn′	
amino	ă-mē′nŏ	
ammine	ăm′ēn	
ammino	ăm′ĭ-nō	ă-mē′nō
amyl	ăm′ĭl	
anethole	ăn-ēth′ōl	
anhydride	ăn-hī′drīd	
aniline	ăn′ĭ-lēn	ăn′ĭ-lĭn
anisic	ă-nĭs′ĭk	
anisole	ăn′ĭs-ōl	
anthranilic	ăn′thră-nĭl′ĭk	
aqueous	ā′kwĕ-ŭs	
arabitol	ă-răb′ĭ-tōl	
arabonic	ăr′ă-bŏn′ĭk	
arachidic	ăr′ă-kĭd′ĭk	
arsine	är-sēn′	
arsonic	är-sŏn′ĭk	
aryl	är′ĭl	
asymmetric	ā′sĭ-mĕt′rĭk	ăs′ĭ-mĕt′rĭk
atropine	ăt′rŏ-pēn	
azelaic	ăz′ĕ-lā′ĭk	
azide	ăz′īd	āz′īd
azo	ă′zŏ	ā′zŏ
barbiturate	bär′bĭ-tūr′āte	bär-bĭ′chŭr-āte
behenic	bĕ-hĕn′ĭk	
benzamide	bĕn-zăm′īd	bĕn-zăm′ĭd
benzanilide	bĕn-zăn′ĭ-līd	bĕn-zăn′ĭ-lĭd
benzene	bĕn′zēn	
benzil	bĕn-zĭl′	
benzilic	bĕn-zĭl′ĭk	
benzohydrol	bĕn′zŏ-hī′drōl	bĕn′zŏ-hī-drōl′
benzoin	bĕn′zŏ-ĭn	
benzophenone	bĕn′zŏ-fĕ-nōn′	
benzoyl	bĕn′zŏ-ĭl	
benzyl	bĕn′zĭl	
betaine	bē′tă-ēn	bā′tă-ēn
biuret	bī′û-rĕt′	bī′û-rĕt
borneol	bôr′nĕ-ōl	
bromine	brō′mēn	
butadiene	bū′tă-dī′ēn	
butane	bū′tān	
butyl	bū′tĭl	
butyronitrile	bū′tĭ-rŏ-nī′trīl	bū′tĭ-rŏ-nī′trĭl
cacodyl	kăk′ŏ-dĭl	
caffeine	kăf′ĕ-ēn	kăf′ĕ-ĭn
		kăf′ēn
caproate	kăp′rŏ-āt	
caprylate	kăp′rĭ-lāt	
carbamate	kär′bă-māt	kär-băm′āt
carbamide	kär-băm′ĭd	kär-băm′ĭd
carbanilide	kär-băn′ĭ-līd	kär-băn′ĭ-lĭd
carboethoxy	kär′bŏ-ĕth-ŏk′sē	
carbinol	kär′bĭ-nōl	
carbonyl	kär′bŏ-nĭl	
catechol	kăt′ĕ-chōl	kăt′ĕ-kōl
cetyl	sē′tĭl	sĕt′ĭl
chalcone	kăl′kōn	chăl′kōn

chelate	kēl′āt	
chloral	klō′răl	
cholesterol	kŏ-lĕs′tĕr-ōl	
cholic	kō′lĭk	
choline	kō′lēn	
cineole	sĭn′ē-ōl	
cinnamal	sĭn′ă-măl	
cinnamate	sĭn′ă-māt	sĭ-năm′āt
cinnamic	sĭ-năm′ĭk	
cis	sĭs	
citrate	sĭt′rāt	
cocaine	kō-kān′	kō′kā-ēn
codeine	kō′dĕ-ēn	
coniine	kō′nĭ-ēn	
coumarin	kōō′mă-rĭn	kū′mă-rĭn
creatine	krē′ă-tēn	krē′ă-tĭn
cresol	krē′sōl	
cresyl	krĕs′ĭl	krē′sĭl
crotonic	krŏ-tŏn′ĭk	
cyanamide	sī′ăn-ăm′īd	sī′ăn-ăm′ĭd
		sī-ăn′ă-mīd
cyanogen	sī-ăn′ŏ-jĕn	
cyclic	sī′klĭk	
cyclohexane	sī′klŏ-hĕk′sān	
cysteine	sĭs′tĕ-ēn	
decyl	dĕs′ĭl	
decylene	dĕs′ĭ-lēn	
dehydro	dē-hīd′rŏ	
desoxy	dĕs-ŏk′sĭ	
dextro	dĕks′trŏ	
diazo	dī-ăz′ŏ	dī-āz′ŏ
diethylamine	dī-ĕth′ĭl-ă-mēn′	
diphenylethane	dī-fĕn′ĭl-ĕth′ān	
elaidic	ĕl′ă-ĭd′ĭk	
enol	ē′nōl	
enolic	ē-nō′lĭk	ē-nŏl′ĭk
enzyme	ĕn′zīm	
ephedrine	ĕf′ĕ-drēn	ē-fĕd′rĭn
ergosterol	ēr-gŏs′tĕr-ōl	
erythrose	ĕr′ĭ-thrōs	ē-rĭth′rōs
ester	ĕs′tĕr	
ethane	ĕth′ān	
ether	ē′thĕr	
ethoxide	ĕth-ŏk′sīd	
ethyl	ĕth′ĭl	
ethylidene	ĕth-ĭl′ĭ-dēn	ĕth′ĭl-ĭ-dēn
fluorene	flōō′ŏ-rēn	
fluorescein	flōō′ŏ-rĕs′ē-ĭn	flōō-ôr′ĕ-sēn
formamide	fôrm-ăm′īd	fôrm-ăm′ĭd
fructose	frŭk′tōs	
fulminic	fŭl-mĭn′ĭk	
fumaric	fů-măr′ĭk	
furan	fū′răn	fūr-ān′
furfural	fûr′fŭr-ăl	
furoin	fū′rŏ-ĭn	
gallic	găl′ĭk	
geraniol	jĕ-rā′nē-ōl	
globin	glōb′ĭn	
globulin	glŏb′ū-lĭn	
gluconic	glōō-kŏn′ĭk	

glucosamine	glōō′kōs-ă-mēn′	
glucose	glōō′kōs	
glucoside	glōō′kŏ-sīd	
glutamic	glōō-tăm′ĭk	
glutaric	glōō-tăr′ĭk	glōō-tär′ĭk
glycaric	glī-kăr′ĭc	
glyceric	glĭ-sĕr′ĭk	
glycerol	glĭ′sĕr-ōl	
glycine	glī′sēn	
glycolic	glī-kŏ′lĭk	glī-kŏl′ĭk
glycose	glī′cōs	
glyoxal	glī-ŏk′săl	glī′ŏk-săl′
glyoxyl	glī-ŏk′sĭl	
guaiacol	gwī′ă-kōl	
guanidine	gwä′nĭ-dēn	
guanine	gwä′nēn	
gulose	gū′lōs	
hematin	hĕm′ă-tĭn	hē′mă-tĭn
hemoglobin	hē′mŏ-glō′bĭn	hĕm′ŏ-glō′bĭn
heroine	hĕr′ŏ-ēn	hĕr′ŏ-ĭn
hydantoin	hī-dăn′tŏ-ĭn	
hydrazide	hī′dră-zīd	hī′dră-zĭd
hydrazine	hī′dră-zēn	
hydrazo	hī-drăz′ŏ	hī-drāz′ŏ
hydrazoic	hī-dră-zō′ĭk	
hydroquinone	hī′drŏ-kwĭ-nōn′	
hydroxy	hī′drŏk′sĭ	
hydroxylamine	hī-drŏk′sĭl-ă-mēn′	
idose	ī′dōs	
imide	ĭm′īd	ĭm′ĭd
imido	ĭ-mē′dŏ	ĭm′ĭ-dŏ
imino	ĭ-mē′nŏ	ĭm′ĭ-nŏ
indoxyl	ĭn-dŏk′sĭl	
inositol	ĭn-ō′sĭ-tōl	
iodoso	ī′ŏ-dō′sŏ	
ionone	ī′ŏ-nōn′	
isatin	ī′să-tĭn	
iso	ī′sŏ	
isomer	ī′sŏ-mēr	
itaconic	ĭt′ă-kŏn′ĭk	
ketone	kē′tōn	
ketonic	kĕ-tŏn′ĭk	
leucine	lōō′sēn	lū′sēn
levo	lēv′ŏ	
linalool	lĭn-ăl′ŏ-ōl	lĭn′ă-lŏ-ōl′
linoleic	lĭn′ŏ-lē′ĭk	
linolenic	lĭn′ŏ-lĕn′ĭk	lĭn′ŏ-lē′nĭk
lutidine	lōō′tĭ-dēn	lū′tĭ-dēn
maleic	mă-lē′ĭk	mā-lē′ĭk
malic	măl′ik	māl′ĭk
malonic	mă-lŏn′ĭk	mă-lō′nĭk
malonate	măl′ŏ-nāt	
mandelic	măn-dĕl′ĭk	
mannonic	mă-nŏn′ĭk	
mannose	mă′nōs	
menthol	mĕn′thōl	
mercaptal	mēr-kăp′tăl	
mercaptan	mēr-kăp′tăn	
mesaconic	mĕs′ă-kŏn′ĭk	
mesityl	mĕs′ĭ-tĭl	

mesitylene	mĕ-sĭt′ĭl-ēn	
meso	mēs′ŏ	
mesoxalic	mĕs′ŏk-săl′ĭk	mĕz′ŏk-săl′ĭk
meta	mĕt′ă	
methane	mĕth′ān	
methanol	mĕth′ă-nōl	
methyl	mĕth′ĭl	
methylal	mĕth′ĭl-ăl	mĕth′ĭl-ăl′
methylamine	mĕth′ĭl-ă-mēn′	
mono	mŏn′ŏ	mō′nŏ
morphine	môr′fēn	
naphthalene	năf′thă-lēn	
naphthenic	năf-thē′nĭk	năf-thĕn′ĭk
naphthol	năf′thōl	
nitrile	nī′trīl	nī′trĭl
nitro	nī′trŏ	
nitrosamine	nī′trŏ-să-mēn′	
nitroso	nī-trŏ′sŏ	
nonane	nō′nān	
nucleic	nû-klē′ĭk	
nucleotide	nū′klĕ-ŏ-tīd	
oleic	ŏ-lē′ĭk	
orcinol	ôr′sĭ-nōl	
ortho	ôr′thŏ	
osazone	ō′să-zōn	ō′să-zōn′
oxalic	ŏk-săl′ĭk	
oxime	ŏk′sēm	
oxindole	ŏk-sĭn′dōl	ŏk′sĭn-dōl′
ozone	ō′zōn	
pelargonic	pĕl′är-gŏn′ĭk	
peptide	pĕp′tīd	
phenazine	fĕn′ă-zēn	
phenetidine	fĕn-ĕt′ĭ-dēn	
phenol	fē′nōl	
phenolic	fĕ-nō′lĭk	fĕ-nŏl′ĭk
phenolphthalein	fē′nōl-thăl′ĕ-ĭn	fē′nōl-thăl′ēn
phenyl	fĕn′ĭl	
phthalein	thăl′ĕ-ĭn	thăl′ēn
phthalic	thăl′ĭk	
phthalide	thăl′ĭd	
phthalimide	thăl-ĭm′īd	thăl-ĭm′ĭd
phytol	fī′tōl	
phytosterol	fī-tŏs′tēr-ōl	
picric	pĭk′rĭk	
pimelic	pĭ-mĕl′ĭk	
pinacolone	pĭn-ăk′ŏ-lōn	
pinene	pīn′ēn	
piperidine	pĭ-pĕr′ĭ-dēn	pĭp′ĕr-ĭ-dēn
polymer	pŏl′ĭ-mēr	
polymerize	pŏl′ĭ-mēr-īz	pŏ-lĭm′ēr-īz
porphyrin	pôr′fĭ-rĭn	
propane	prō′pān	
propionamide	prō′pi-ŏn-ăm′īd	prō′pĭ-ŏn-ăm′ĭd
propionic	prō′pĭ-ŏn′ĭk	
propionyl	prō′pĭ-ŏ-nĭl	
propyl	prō′pĭl	
propylidene	prō-pĭl′ĭ-dēn	prō′pĭl-ĭ-dēn
protein	prō′tĕ-ĭn	
pyridine	pĭr′ĭ-dēn	
pyrogallol	pī′rŏ-găl′ōl	

pyrrole	pĭr′ōl	pĭ-rōl′
pyrrolidine	pĭ-rō′lĭ-dēn	pĭ-rŏl′ĭ-dēn
pyruvic	pĭ-rōō′vĭk	
quinine	kwĭn′ēn	kwĭ′nĭn
quinone	kwĭn-ōn′	
quinonoid	kwĭn′ŏ-noid	kwĭ-nōn′oid
racemic	rā-sēm′ĭk	
racemize	răs′ĕ-mīz	
ribose	rī′bōs	
rosaniline	rōz-ăn′ĭ-lēn	rōz-ăn′ĭ-lĭn
saccharic	să-kăr′ĭk	
saccharide	săk′ă-rīd	
salicylate	săl′ĭ-sĭl-āt	să-lĭs′ĭ-lāt
saligenin	să-lĭj′ĕ-nĭn	
sebacic	sĕ-băs′ĭk	
semicarbazide	sĕm′ĭ-kär′bă-zīd	sĕm′ĭ-kär′bă-zĭd
serine	sĕr′ēn	
skatole	skā′tōl	
stearic	stĕ-ăr′ĭk	
stearin	stĕ′ă-rĭn	
steroid	stĕr′oid	
stibine	stĭb′ēn	
styrene	stī′rēn	
sulfinic	sŭl-fĭn′ĭk	
sulfonal	sŭl′fō-năl	
sulfone	sŭl-fōn′	sŭl′fōn
sulfonic	sŭl-fŏn′ĭk	
tartaric	tär-tăr′ĭk	tär-tär′ĭk
taurocholic	tô′rō-kō′lĭk	
tautomer	tôt′ŏ-mēr	
tautomerism	tô-tŏm′ēr-ĭz′m	
terephthalic	tĕr′ĕf-thăl′ĭk	tĕr′ĕ-thăl′ĭk
thebaine	thē′bă-ēn	
thiazole	thī′ă-zōl	
thiol	thī′ōl	
toluene	tŏl′ū-ēn	
trans	trănz	
urea	û-rē′å	
ureide	ū′rĕ-īd	ū′rĕ-ĭd
valeric	vă-lĕr′ĭk	
valine	văl′ēn	vā′lēn
vanillin	văn′ĭ-lĭn	
veratrole	vĕr′ă-trōl	
vinyl	vī′nĭl	
vitamin	vī′tă-mĭn	

Appendix B

GREEK ALPHABET

α	alpha		ν	nu
β	beta		ξ	xi
γ	gamma		o	omicron
δ	delta		π	pi
ϵ	epsilon		ρ	rho
ζ	zeta		σ	sigma
η	eta		τ	tau
θ	theta		υ	upsilon
ι	iota		ϕ	phi
κ	kappa		χ	chi
λ	lambda		ψ	psi
μ	mu		ω	omega

INDEX

Å, abbreviation for Ångstrom unit, 85
Abietic acid, 566
  retene from, 441
Absolute alcohol, 69
Absolute configuration, 273
Absolute ether, 118
Absorption and visual color, 472
α carbon atom, 125
Accelerators, 498
Acenaphthene, 324, 437
Acetal, 166
Acetaldehyde, 179
  acetic acid from, 134
  from alcoholic fermentation, 67
Acetaldehyde cyanohydrin, 534
Acetaldol, 168
Acetaldoxime, 171
Acetals, 166
  cyclic, 462, 519
  hydrolysis, 283
Acetamide, 197
Acetanilide, 363, 371
Acetate rayon, 305
Acetic acid, 124, 133
  from acetaldehyde, 134
  anhydride from, 139
  from ethyl alcohol, 133
  by fermentation, 133
  ketene from, 139
  from pyroligneous liquor, 133
  salts of, 135
  synthetic, 134
Acetic anhydride, 138, 180
Acetoacetic acid, 550
Acetoacetic ester, see Ethyl acetoacetate, 551
Acetobacter, 133
Acetoin, see Methylacetylcarbinol, 156
Acetonaphthalenes, 431
Acetone, 180
  conversion to ketene, 140
Acetone cyanohydrin, 537
Acetonitrile, 198
Acetophenone, 407
2-Acetothiophene, see 2-Thienyl methyl ketone, 445
Aceto-*p*-toluidide, 364
Acetoxime, 171
Acetoxymercuriphenols, 588
Acetyl chloride, 136
Acetyldibenzoylmethane, tautomerism, 553

Acetylene, 112
  acidity, 111
  addition of hydrogen fluoride, 512
  reaction with acetic acid, 139
  uses, 113
Acetylene dichlorides, see 1,2-Dichloroethylenes, 506
Acetylenes, see Alkynes
Acetylene tetrachloride, 506
Acetylides, 111
Acetylmethylcarbinol, 156
Acetyl peroxide, 575
Acetylsalicylic acid, 419
2-Acetylthiophene, 445, 446
Acetyl value, 154
Acid anhydrides, see Anhydrides, 138–165
Acid-base reactions, 191
Acid dissociation constants, see Acidity
Acid dyes, 476
Acid halides, see Acyl halides, 135–138
  inorganic, reaction with alcohols, 74
Acidity, alcohols, 127
  aliphatic carboxylic acids, 127
  aromatic carboxylic acids, 412
  carbonic acid, 127
  dicarboxylic acids, 542
  halogen acids, 531
  hydrocarbons, relative, 585
  phenols, 381
  water, 127
Acids and bases, general concepts, 191
Acids, see type, e.g. Carboxylic acids
Aci form, 203
Acridine, 459
Acrolein, 525
Acrylic acid, 537
Acrylic resins, 537
Acryloid resins, 537
Acrylonitrile, 537
Activated catalysts, 75
Activated complex, see Transition state, 91
Activating group, aromatic substitution, 333
Activation of benzene nucleus, cause, 339
Activation energy, 24
Active amyl alcohol, 67
Active components, 263
Active forms, 263
Active hydrogen, see Reactive hydrogen, 87
Active methylene group, acetoacetic esters, 552
  alkylation, 545, 552

Active methylene group
  β-keto esters, 552
  malonic esters, 544
Acylation, aliphatic amines, 188
  aromatic amines, 363
Acyl chlorides, preparation, 135
Acyl halides, mechanism of reactions, 137
  nomenclature, 136
  physical properties, 136
  preparation, 135, 413
  reactions, 136
  reactivity, 137
Acyl hydroperoxides, 575
Acyl-oxygen scission of esters, 143
Acyl peroxides, 575
Addition, alcohols to aldehydes and ketones,
  166
  ammonia to aldehydes and ketones, 171
  1,4 to conjugated dienes, 494
  Grignard reagents to aldehydes and ke-
    tones, 164
  Grignard reagents to carbon dioxide, 89,
    104
  halogen to alkenes, 38, 100
  halogen to alkynes, 110
  halogen acid to alkenes, 42, 101, 103
  halogen acid to alkynes, 110
  hydrogen to aldehydes and ketones, 163
  hydrogen to alkenes, 39
  hydrogen to alkynes, 110
  hydrogen cyanide to aldehydes and ke-
    tones, 164
  hypohalous acid to alkenes, 42
  ozone to alkenes, 39
  sodium bisulfite to aldehydes and ketones,
    165
  sodium bisulfite to α, β-unsaturated
    carbonyl compounds, 218
  sulfuric acid to alkenes, 41
  water to alkynes, 110
Addition complexes of ethers, 117
Addition reactions, 38
Adducts, 547
Adenine, 464
Adipamide, 544
Adipic acid, preparation, 541
  reactions, 543, 544
Adipic anhydride, 543
Adiponitrile, 544
Adjective dyes, 476
Adrenal hormones, 400, 570
Adrenalin, 400
Aerosols, 222
After-chroming, 477
Agar, 306
Alanine, 227
β-Alanine in pantothenic acid, 535
Albuminoids, 225
Albumins, 225
Alcohol, *see* Ethyl alcohol, 66–70

Alcoholates, *see* Alkoxides, 72, and Coordination complexes, 71
Alcoholic fermentation, 66–68
Alcohols, aliphatic, nomenclature, 58
  physical properties, 60
  preparation, 65–71
    from acids, 129
    from aldehydes and ketones, 164
    from esters, 147, 148
    from Grignard reagents, 147, 164
  reactions, 71–78
    addition to aldehydes and ketones, 166
    dehydration, 75, 100, 107
    dehydrogenation, 77, 161
    esterification, 140, 144
    ether formation, 115
    with Grignard reagents, 87
    with halogen acids, 74, 98
    oxidation to acids, 121
      to aldehydes and ketones, 77, 161
  structure, 58
Alcohols, aromatic, 398
Alcoholysis, acyl halides, 136
  anhydrides, 139
  cyanides, 199
  esters, 145
Aldals, 170
Aldehyde-ammonias, 171
Aldehyde hydrates, 518
Aldehyde resins, 169
Aldehydes, aliphatic, nomenclature, 162
  physical properties, 163
  preparation, 161, 162
    from nitroalkanes, 205
  reactions, 163–175
    autoxidation, 581
    condensation with nitroalkanes, 205
  uses, 176–180
Aldehydes, aromatic, 401
Aldimines, 183
Aldol condensation, 168
Aldols, 168
Aldonic acids, 278
Aldoses, constitution and configuration, 278
  special reactions, 280
Aldoximes, 171
  dehydration to cyanides, 199
Alicyclic compounds, general theory, 557
  preparation, 559
  reactions, 559
Alizarin, 440, 487
Alkali cellulose, 302
Alkaloids, 465
Alkanes, nomenclature, 25–30
  number of isomers, 30
  physical properties, 30–32
  preparation, 106, 107, 131
  reactions, aromatization, 52
    autoxidation, 577
    chlorination, 84, 505

Alkanes
  combustion, 33
  dehydrogenation, 52
  fluorination, 511
  halogenation, 84, 505
  isomerization, 34, 52
  nitration, 202
  oxidation by air, controlled, 56, 577
  oxidation to carboxylic acids, 135
  pyrolysis, 33, 49
  sulfonation, 219
  structure, 21
Alkenes, nomenclature, 37, 38
  physical properties, 38
  preparation, 75, 107, 108
    from alkynes, 110
    from quaternary ammonium hydroxides, 194
    from sulfonium hydroxides, 215
  purification through dihalides, 108
  reactions, addition of halogen, 38
    of halogen acid, 42
    of hydrogen, 39, 107
    of hydrogen fluoride, 512
    of hypohalous acid, 42
    of ozone, 39, 576
    of sulfuric acid, 41
  autoxidation, 578
  mechanism of addition of halogen, 100
    of halogen acid, 101, 103
  mechanism of formation
    from alkyl halides, 99
    from alcohols, 100
    by pyrolysis of alkanes, 92
  oxidation to acids, 121
    to glycols, 40
  polymerization, 43
  test for double bond, 39, 41, 205
  structure, 36
Alkoxides, formation, 72
  hydrolysis, 73
Alkoxycarbonyl group, 144
Alkyd resins, 416
Alkylacetic acids, 545
N-Alkylanilines, 363
Alkyl arsenites, 78
Alkylation, active methylene compounds, 545, 552
  aliphatic amines, 191
  alkenes, 51
  aromatic amines, 363
  β-keto esters, 552
  malonic esters, 545
  phenols, 382
  thiophene, 446
Alkyl borates, 78, 79
Alkylcadmiums, reaction with acyl halides, 137
Alkyl carbamates, 238, 244, 246
Alkyl cyanides, *see* Cyanides, alkyl

Alkyl groups, 26–28
Alkyl halides, physical properties, 81
  preparation from alcohols, 74, 75
    from alkanes, 84, 505
    from alkenes, 42
    from silver salts of carboxylic acids, 132
  reactions, 82, 83
    with ammonia, 185
    dehydrohalogenation, mechanism, 99
    displacement reactions, mechanism, 95
    hydrolysis, mechanism, 96
    with mercaptans, 212
    with metallic salts to carboxylic acids, 131
    reduction to alkanes, 106
    with sodium sulfide, 213
    with sodium sulfite, 218
Alkyl hydrogen sulfates, 41, 76
Alkyl hydroperoxides, 573
Alkyl isocyanates, *see* Isocyanates
Alkyl isocyanides, *see* Isocyanides
Alkylmagnesium halides, *see* Grignard reagents
Alkylmalonic esters, 545
Alkyl nitrates, 75, 78
Alkyl nitrites, 75, 78
Alkyl-oxygen scission of esters, 144
Alkyl peroxides, 573
Alkyl phosphates, 78
Alkyl phosphites, 74, 78
Alkylpyridines, 456
Alkyl silicates, 78, 79
Alkyl sulfates, 75, 78
Alkyl sulfites, 74, 78
N-Alkylthioureas, 252
S-Alkylthioureas, 252
  sulfonyl chlorides from, 220
N-Alkylureas, 244
O-Alkylureas, 247
Alkynes, 108–113
Allenes, 494
Alloxan, 463
Allyl alcohol, 517
Allyl chloride, 508
Allylic rearrangement, 509
Allylic system, 509
Allyl isothiocyanate, 251
Allyl phthalate polymers, 518
Aloes, cathartic principle, 440
α carbon atom, 125
Alternation in melting points, of alkanes, 31
  of carboxylic acids, 126
Aluminum acetate, 135
Aluminum t-butoxide, 73
Aluminum ethoxide, 73
Aluminum halides, reaction with Grignard reagents, 88
Aluminum i-propoxide, 73
Amber, succinic acid from, 540
Ambrettolide, 563

Amides, 195–198
　dehydration to cyanides, 198
　N-substituted, 189
　of sulfonic acids, 220, 357
Amidone, 468
Amination of pyridines, 456
Amine oxides, 190
Amines, aliphatic, nomenclature, 183
　physical properties, 187
　preparation, 184–187
　　from cyanides, 199
　　from isocyanates, 246
　　from isocyanides, 200, 201
　　from nitroalkanes, 204
　　from Schiff bases, 403
　reactions, 187–193
Amines, aralkyl, 398
Amines, aromatic, physical properties, 361
　physiological action, 361
　preparation, 362
　reactions, 362–369
Amines, Hinsberg reaction, 357
Amino acids, 534
　configuration of natural, 275
　essential, 231
　isoelectric point, 227
　from malonic esters, 232
　metabolism, 231
　from proteins, 227
　syntheses, 232
　test for, 235
Amino alcohols, 526
Aminoanthraquinones, 439
p-Aminoazobenzene, 379
o-Aminobenzaldehyde, 458
p-Aminobenzaldehyde, 401
Aminobenzenesulfonic acids, 369
p-Aminobenzoic acid, 417
2-Aminoethanol, 526
Amino groups, estimation, 236
2-Amino-6-hydroxypurine, 464
2-Amino-2-methyl-1-propanol, 528
Aminonaphthalenesulfonic acids, 434, 435
Aminonaphthols, 435
Aminonaphtholsulfonic acids, 435
Aminophenols, 392, 394
p-Aminophenylarsonic acid, 593
1-Amino-2-propanol, 527
6-Aminopurine, 464
Aminopyridines, 456
p-Aminosalicylic acid, 419
2-Aminothiophene, 446
Ammonium carbamate, 240
Ammonium cyanate, conversion to urea, 240
Ammonolysis, acid anhydrides, 139
　acyl halides, 136
　alkyl halides, 184
　aryl halides, 362
　esters, 146
Amphetamine, 400

Amygdalin, 405
i-Amyl acetate, 148
(+)Amyl alcohol, *see* Active amyl alcohol, 67
i-Amyl alcohol, 67
s-Amyl alcohol, 71
t-Amyl alcohol, 71
Amyl alcohols, from amyl chlorides, 85
　from amylenes, 71
　in fusel oil, 67
Amyl amines, 85
Amyl chlorides, 84
Amylenes, 37
　conversion to amyl alcohols, 71
i-Amyl ether, 119
Amyl mercaptans, 85
i-Amyl nitrite, 79
Amylopectin, 295
Amylose, 295
Amyl sulfides, 85
i-Amyl valerate, 148
Amytal, 462
Analgesic action of salicylates, 419
Analysis of organic compounds, accuracy, 18
　for the elements, 12–15
Analyzer, 260
Anesthesin, 418
Anesthetics, general, 118, 463, 561
　local, 418, 467
Anethole, 392, 405
Aneurin, 463
Angelic acid, 538
Ångstrom unit, 85
Anhydrides, 138–140
　cyclic, from dicarboxylic acids, 542
Aniline, from chlorobenzene, 370
　from nitrobenzene, 369
　oxidation, 366
Aniline acetate test for furfural, 454
Anils, 365, 403
Animal fats and oils, 152
Anionoid reagents, 98
Anisaldehyde, 405
Anise oil, 392
Anisic aldehyde, 405
Anisole, 382
Anomeric carbon atom, 283
Anomers, 283
Anthocyanidins, 491
Anthocyanins, 491
Anthracene, 437
　isolation, 324
Anthracene oil, 323, 324, 437
Anthranilic acid, 417
Anthraquinone, 438
Anthraquinone dyes, 487
Anthraquinonesulfonic acids, 438
Anthraquinone Vat Blues, 488
Anthraquinone Vat Dark Blue BO, 488
Anthraquinone Vat Golden Orange G, 488

anti- prefix, 408
Antibiotics, 401, 461
Antihemorrhagic factors, 436
Antihistaminics, 461
Antiknock agents, *see* Knock inhibitors, 53
Antimalarials, 469
Antioxidants, 582
   as gum inhibitors for gasoline, 51, 582
   for rubber, 498
Antipyretics, 371, 398, 419
Antispasmodics, 468
Arabinose, 279
L-Arabitol, 307
Arachidic acid, 124, 152
Arago, biography, 259
Aralen, 469
Aralkylamines, 398
Aralkyl halides, preparation, 328
   reactions, 320
Arginine, 228
Argol, 547
Armstrong, biography, 473
Arochlors, 426
Aromatic compounds, 310 ff., *see also individual type, e.g.,* Nitro compounds *and* Condensed nuclear hydrocarbons
Aromatization, alicyclic compounds, 318
   alkanes, 52, 318
Aroyl chlorides, 413
Arsanilic acid, 593
Arsenic compounds, 590
Arsenobenzene, 592
Arsenoso group, 590
Arsenosomethane, 590
Arsenoxides, 590
Arsine oxides, 590
Arsinic acids, 591
Arsonic acids, 591, 592
Arsphenamine, 593
Artificial leather, 301
Arylalkanes, 422
Arylalkenes, 424
Arylation of aromatic amines, 363
Aryl cyanides from diazonium salts, 378
   from sulfonic acids, 255
Aryl ethers of polyethylene glycols, 522
Aryl groups, 322
Aryl halides, preparation, 327
   from diazonium salts, 377
   reactions, 329
Ascorbic acid, 290
Aspartic acid, 228
Aspergillus oryzae, fermentation, 67
Aspirin, 419
Association, alcohols, 60
   carboxylic acids, 125
   proton bonding, 64
A-stage resin, 388
Asymmetric carbon atom, 263
Atabrine, 469

Atoxyl, 593
Atropine, 466
Aubepine, 405
Autoxidation, 577
Auxins, 437
Auxochromes, 473
Azelaic acid, 541
Azeotrope, *see* Constant-boiling mixture, 69
Azobenzene, 347
Azo compounds, aromatic, 347, 378, 478
Azo dyes, 478
Azoic dyes, 477
Azoxybenzene, 347

Bacillus acetobutylicus, see *Clostridium,* 70
Baeyer, biography, 451
Baeyer strain theory, 557
Baeyer test for unsaturation, 41
Bakelite, 388
BAL, 525
Balancing oxidation-reduction equations, 122
Ballistite, 300, 525
Barbier, biography, 86
Barbital, 462
Barbiturates, 462
Barrel process for vinegar, 133
Bartholinus, biography, 257
Bart's reaction, 592
Bases and acids, general concepts, 191
Basic dissociation constants, *see* Basicity
Basic dyes, 476
Basicity, 71, 191
   acetamide, 241
   acetoxime, 172
   aliphatic amines, 187, 191
   alkyl cyanides, 199
   amides, 196
   amine oxides, 191
   aromatic amines, 362
   hydroxylamine, 172
   piperidine, 455
   pyridine, 455
   urea, 241
Beckmann, biography, 409
Beckmann rearrangement, 409
Beeswax, 150
Beet sugar, 292
Behenic acid, 124
Belladonna, 466
Benadryl, 399
Benedict's solution, constitution, 548
   oxidation of aldehydes, 173
Benzal-, *see also* Benzylidene-
Benzalacetone, 404
Benzalacetophenone, 407
Benzalaniline, 403
Benzal chloride, hydrolysis to benzaldehyde, 405
   preparation, 328

Benzaldehyde, 405
  autoxidation, 581
Benzaldoximes, stereochemistry, 408
Benzanilide, 409
2,3-Benzanthracene, 441
Benzanthrone, 488
Benzedrine, 400
Benzene, 310–318
  fluorination, 511
  homologs, 316
  removal of thiophene, 446
Benzenediazonium chloride, 376
m-Benzenedisulfonic acid, 353
Benzene hexachloride, 326
Benzenesulfinic acid, 358
Benzenesulfonamides, 357
Benzenesulfonic acid, 353
Benzenesulfonyl chloride, 356
1,3,5-Benzenetrisulfonic acid, 353
Benzhydrol, 398
Benzhydryl ether, 398
Benzidam, 369
Benzidine, 427
Benzidine Blue, 427
Benzidine rearrangement, 427
Benzil, 408
Benzilic acid, 408
Benzilic acid rearrangement, 408
Benzoate radicals, 578, 581, 582
Benzoic acid, 413
Benzoic anhydride, 456
Benzoin, 404
Benzoin condensation, 404
Benzol, 311, 323
Benzonitrile, 355
1,2-Benzophenanthrene, 441
Benzophenone, 407
Benzophenone oxime, 409
Benzopurpurin 4B, 479
Benzopyrans, 460
Benzopyrroles, 451
Benzopyrylium salts, 490
Benzoquinones, 395
Benzotrichloride, benzoic acid from, 411
Benzoylacetic ester, 551
Benzoylation, *see* Schotten-Baumann reaction, 413
o-Benzoylbenzoic acid, 438
Benzoyl chloride, 402, 413
Benzoyl peroxide, 414, 575
  free benzoate radicals from, 578
Benzoyl radicals, 581, 582
Benzyl acetate, 398
Benzyl alcohol, 398
Benzylamine, 399
Benzyl benzoate, 398
Benzyl bromide, 330
Benzyl chloride, 328
Benzyl chloroformate, 234

Benzyl group, removal by catalytic reduction, 234, 399
Benzyl halides, theory of reactivity, 349
Benzylidenacetone, 404
Benzylidenacetophenone, 407
Benzylidenaniline, 403
Benzylidene chloride, hydrolysis, 405
  preparation, 328
Benzylisoquinolines, 467
S-Benzylthiourea, 253
S-Benzylthiuronium salts, 253
Bergius process, 56
Bergman, biography, 3
Bergmann, biography, 234
Berthelot, biography, 68
Berzelius, biography, 3
Betaine, 535
BHC, 326
Bile acids, 569
Bile pigments, 582
Bile salts, 569
Bimolecular mechanism, displacement reactions, 96
Biot, biography, 260
Biotin, 465
Biphenyl, 426
2,3'-Biphenyldicarboxylic acid, 440
Bischler-Napieralski reaction, 459
1,1-Bis-p-chlorophenyl-2,2,2-trichloroethane, 423
Bis(2-hydroxyethyl)amine, 526
Bismarck Browns, 479
1,1-Bis-p-methoxyphenyl-2,2,2-trichloroethane, 423
Bisulfite addition compounds, 165
Bitter almond oil, 350, 405
Biuret, 244
Biuret reaction, 235, 244
Black pepper, 466
Blanc's rule, 543
Blood pigments, 449
Boiling points, 9
  of alkanes, alkyl halides, and alcohols, 82
  of n-alkyl derivatives of water, ammonia, and hydrogen sulfide, 210
  and dipole moments, 63
  effect of branching, 31
  effect of proton bonding, 60, 63
  and van der Waals forces, 31, 62
Bond angles, 23
  benzene, 330
Bond distances, *see* Interatomic distances
Bond moments, 64
Bond strengths, 92
Bond types, 5
Bone oil, 447
Boric acid, conductivity change with glycols, 519
Boron trifluoride, polymerization catalyst, 43

Branching of chain, effect on boiling and melting points, 31
Brassidic acid, 542
Brassylic acid, 542
British Anti-Lewisite, 525
Bromination, 85, 94, *see also* Halogenation
  acyl halides, 137, 530
  aldehydes, 174
  aromatic compounds, 327
  carboxylic acids, 137, 530
  ketones, 174
  nitroalkanes, 203
Bromindigo Blue 2BD, 486
p-Bromoacetanilide, 368
ω-Bromoacetophenone, 408
Bromo acids, 530
Bromobenzene, 329
Bromobutenes, 509
Bromocyanogen, *see* Cyanogen bromide, 247
Bromoform, 174
2-Bromofuran, 588
Bromonium ion, *see* Halonium ion, 101
Bromophenols, 383
Bromopyridines, 456
Bronsted, biography, 192
Bronsted theory of acids and bases, 192
Bucherer reaction, 433
Buna *N*, 502
Buna rubbers, 499
Buna *S*, 502
Bunsen, biography, 591
Butacite, *see* Polyvinylbutyral, 517
1,3-Butadiene, preparation, 52, 500
  reactions, 494
    addition of maleic anhydride, 546
  synthetic rubbers, 499, 502
1,4-Butanediol, 501
2,3-Butanediol, 523
Butanes, equilibrium composition of isomeric, 52
  structure, 22
Butanols, *see* Butyl alcohols
Butenes, butyl alcohols from, 70
2-Butenes, configuration, 254
Butesin, 418
Butlerov, biography, 553
t-Butoxide radicals, 574
Butter, 152
  flavor, 156
n-Butyl acetate, 148
i-Butyl alcohol, abnormal behavior, 75
  from fusel oil, 67
n-Butyl alcohol, from acetaldehyde, 179
  by fermentation, 70
  from Fischer-Tropsch synthesis, 56
s-Butyl alcohol, 70
t-Butyl alcohol, 71
n-Butylamines, 194
n-Butyl-p-aminobenzoate, 418

Butyl bromides, *see* Alkyl halides
n-Butyl n-butyrate, 148
t-Butyl chloride, dipole moment, 97
β-Butylene glycol, 523
Butylenes, conversion to butyl alcohols, 70
n-Butyl ether, 119
i-Butyl halides, reactivity, 96
t-Butyl hydroperoxide, 573
n-Butyllithium, 584
n-Butyl mercaptan, 221
n-Butyl nitrite, 79
t-Butyl peroxide, 573
t-Butyl peroxide radicals, 574
t-Butylphenol, 389
n-Butyl phthalate, 415
i-Butyl propionate, 148
t-Butyl radicals, 574
Butyl rubber, 502
t-Butylthiophenes, 446
i-Butyraldehyde, 520
n-Butyraldehyde, 180
n-Butyric acid, 124, 135, 152
γ-Butyrolactam, 535

Cacodyl oxide, 590
Cacodyls, 590
Cadaverine, 528
Cadet's liquid, 590
Cadmium alkyls, reaction with acyl halides, 137
Caffeine, 464
Calciferol, 568
Calcium carbide, 112
  conversion to cyanamide, 248
Calcium cyanamide, 248
Calcium propionate, 135
C-alkylation, *see* Carbon alkylation
Camphor, 565
Camphor oil, 392
Cane sugar, 292
Cannizzaro, biography, 4
  and molecular weights, 4, 15
Cannizzaro reaction, aliphatic aldehydes, 178
  aromatic aldehydes, 403
  crossed, 403
Capric acid, 124, 152
Caproic acid, 124, 152
Capryl alcohol, 541
Caprylic acid, 124, 152
Captax, 461
Carbamates, 240, 244
Carbamic acid, 238, 240
Carbamide, 239
Carbamidine, *see* Guanidine, 248
Carbanions, 91, 424
Carbazole, 451
  isolation, 324
Carbethoxy group, *see* Carboalkoxy group, 144

Carbides, 111
Carbinol base, 481
Carbinols, 58
Carbitols, 522
Carboalkoxy group, 144
Carbobenzoxy chloride, 234
Carbobenzoxy group, 234
Carbobenzyloxy chloride, 234
Carbobenzyloxy group, 234
Carbocyclic compounds, 444
Carbohydrates, *see also individual compound*
    e.g. Glucose
  acetates, 286
  action of strong acids, 287
  aldonic acids, 278
  aldoses, 277
  anomers, 283
  benzoates, 287
  carbonates, 287
  classification, 277
  configuration, 278
  definition, 277
  desoxy sugars, 280
  disaccharides, 290
  ester formation, 286
  families, D and L, 279
  glycaric acids, 281
  glyconic acids, 278
  glycoside formation, 283
  glycuronic acids, 306
  gums, 300
  Haworth formulas, 288
  heteropolysaccharides, 306
  hexoses, 278
  homopolysaccharides, 295
  immunopolysaccharides, 307
  ketoses, 288
  mesyl derivatives, 287
  methylation, 284
  methylpentoses, 280
  monosaccharides, 277
  mucilages, 307
  mutarotation, 285
  nitrates, 287
  nomenclature, 277
  nonreducing disaccharides, 292
  oligosaccharides, 290
  osazone formation, 282
  osazones, solubility, 292
  oxidation by Fehling's solution, 280
    to glycaric acids, 281
    by periodic acid, 284
  pectins, 305
  pentoses, 279
  phosphates, 287
  polysaccharides, 295
  reducing disaccharides, 290
  ring structures, 283, 288
  saccharic acids, 281
  sugar alcohols, 307

  sulfonates, 287
  sweetness, 289
  tosyl derivatives, 287
Carbolic acid, 381
Carbolic oil, 323
Carbomethoxy group, 144
Carbon, analysis for, 12, 13
Carbon alkylation of β-keto esters, 552
  of malonic esters, 545
Carbonates, 237, 239
  cyclic, 462, 519
Carbonation of Grignard reagents, 89, 120
Carbon black, 46
Carbon dioxide, reaction with Grignard re-
  agents, 89
Carbon disulfide, 249
Carbonic acid derivatives, 237–253
Carbonium ions, 91, 424
Carbonium-ion intermediates, acid-cat-
  alyzed polymerizations, 103
  addition reactions, 102
  dehydration of alcohols, 100
  hydrolysis of alkyl halides, 97
  reactions of alcohols with halogen acids,
    99
  removal of halogen acids from alkyl hal-
    ides, 99
Carbonization of coal, 322
Carbon monoxide, from natural gas, 46
  synthesis of acids, 134
    of aldehydes, 181
    of ethylene glycol, 521
    of glycollic acid, 521
    of hydrocarbons, 56
    of ketones, 181
    of methyl alcohol, 66
    of sodium formate, 132
Carbon oxysulfide, 249
Carbon tetrachloride, 505
  as derivative of orthocarbonic acid,
    237
Carbonyl chloride, 237
Carbonyl group, polarization of, 104
Carbowaxes, 522
Carboxylic acids, aliphatic, nomenclature,
  124
  physical properties, 125
  preparation, 120–122
    from cyanides, 199
    from β-keto esters, 552
    from malonic esters, 545
    from nitroalkanes, 204
  reactions, 126–129, 135
    of salts, 131, 132
Carboxylic acids, aromatic, 411, 412
Carboxymethylcellulose, 303
Carbylamine test, 189
Carcinogenic hydrocarbons, 442
Carius method, 14
Carnauba wax, 150

Carotenes, 567
Carotenoids, 567
Carothers, biography, 503
Carvacrol, 392
Cascara, cathartic principle, 440
Casein, 226, 229
Cassia oil, 405
Castor oil, 152
  dehydration, 154
  destructive distillation, 538
  sulfation, 158
Catalytic hydrogenation, *see* Hydrogenation
Catalytic reduction, *see* Hydrogenation
Catalysts, 91
Catechol, 392
Cationoid reagents, 97
Cellobiose, 291
Cellophane, 305
Cellosolve, 522
Celluloid, 300
Cellulose, 297
  acetates, 302
  acetatebutyrates, 302
  acetatepropionates, 302
  esters, 299
  ethers, 302
  nitrates, 299
  oxidized, 303
  xanthate, 304
α-Cellulose, 299
Cellulose acetate dyeing, 477
Center of symmetry, 263
Cephalins, 527
Cerotic acid, 124
Cetane, 54
Cetane number, 54
Cetyl palmitate, 150
Cetylsulfonic acid, 219
Cetyltrimethylammonium chloride, 195
Chain reaction, 94, 578, 581
Chalcones, 407
Chaulmoogra oil, 561
Chaulmoogric acid, 561
Chelate compounds, alizarin, 477
  aluminum, 477
  biuret, 244
  boron, 520
  citric acid, 548
  copper, 235, 244, 547, 548
  1,2-glycols, 520
  8-hydroxyquinoline, 458
  iron, 450, 459
  magnesium, 450, 458
  mordant dyeing, 477
  o-phenanthroline, 459
  porphyrins, 450
  proteins, 235
  tartaric acid, 547
Chelation, 520
Chemical Foundation, 475

Chemisorption, 93
Chemotherapy, 593
Chemstrand, 537
Chenodesoxycholic acid, 569
Chevreul, biography, 568
Chichibabin, biography, 456
Chichibabin reaction, 456
Chloral, 518
Chloral hydrate, 518
Chloramine-B, 358
Chloramine-T, 358
Chloramphenicol, 401
Chlorex, 119
  in refining lubricating oils, 54
Chlorinated hydrocarbons, aliphatic, 505–509
  aromatic, 326–330
Chlorination, 85, *see also* Halogenation
  aldehydes and ketones, 174
  alkanes, 85, 505
  alkenes, 508, 509
  aromatic compounds, 327
  carboxylic acids, 137, 530
  thiophene, 445
Chloroacetic acid, 531, 532
ω-Chloroacetophenone, 408
Chloro acids, 530
1-Chloro-4-aminobutane, pyrolysis, 449
m-Chloroaniline, 367
2-Chloroanthraquinone, 439
Chlorobenzene, 327
2-Chloro-1,3-butadiene, 503
Chlorocarbonates, 237, 239
Chlorocarbonic acid, 237
Chlorocyanogen, *see* Cyanogen chloride, 247
Chlorodifluoromethane, 513, 514
Chloroethylene, 507
β-Chloroethyl ether, 119
  in refining of lubricating oils, 54
β-Chloroethyl sulfide, 221
Chlorofluoromethane, 512, 513
2-Chloro-2-fluoropropane, 512
Chloroform, 174, 505
Chloroformates, 237, 239
Chloroformic acid, 237
Chlorohydrins, 42, 519
2-Chloromercurifuran, 588
Chloromercuriphenols, 588
2-Chloromercurithiophene, 445
Chloromethylation, 329
  naphthalene, 437
  thiophene, 445
2-Chloromethylthiophene, 445
Chloromycetin, 401
Chloronaphthalenes, 430, 433
4-Chlorophthalic anhydride, 439
Chlorophylls, 450
Chloropicrin, 205, 391
Chloroprene, 503
Chloropyridines, 456

Chloroquine, 469
N-Chlorosulfonamides, 357
Chlorosulfonation of aromatic compounds, 356
Chlorosulfonic acid, 356
2-Chlorothiophene, 455
Chlorotrifluoroethylene, 514
N-Chloro-*p*-toluenesulfonamide sodium salt, 358
2-Chlorovinyldichlorarsine, 592
Cholesterol, 568
Cholic acid, 569
Choline chloride, 195
Chromatographic adsorption, 567
Chrome Blue Black R, 479
Chrome dyes, 476
Chromium trioxide, as oxidizing agent, 161
Chromogens, 473
Chromone, 490
Chromophores, 473
Chromoproteins, 225
Chrysene, 441
Chrysoidine Y, 478
Cinchomeronic acid, 459
Cinchona bark, 468
Cinchonicine, 469
Cinchonidine, 469
Cinchonine, 469
Cinnamaldehyde, 404, 405
Cinnamic acid, 420
    decarboxylation to styrene, 425
Cinnamic aldehyde, 404, 405
Cinnamon oil, 405
cis isomers, 255
Citric acid, 547
Citronellal, 564
Citronella oil, 564
Citronellol, 564
Civetone, 563
Claisen, biography, 551
Claisen ester condensation, 551
Claisen reaction, 404
Clarke-Othmer process, 134
Clemmensen reduction of ketones, 175
Cleve's acid, 434
Clostridium acetobutylicum, 70
Clove oil, 392
Coal gas, 323
Coal products, 322
Coal tar, 323
Coal tar dyes, historical, 474
Coca bush, 466
Cocaine, 466
Cocarboxylase, 463
Cocoa, 464
Coconut oil, 152
Codeine, 467
Coffee, 464
    aroma, 454

Coke, from coal, 322
    from petroleum, 55
Cola nuts, 464
Cold rubber, 502
Collagen, 225
Collodion cotton, 300
Colophony, 566
Color, absorption of light, 472
    cause, 472
    and chemical structure, 473
    of flowers, 491
    sensation, 472
Color base, 481
Columbian spirits, *see* Methyl alcohol, 65, 66
Common names, 25
Composition, 254
Compound E, 570
Condensed nuclear hydrocarbons, 428
Condensed rings, 428
Configuration, 254
    absolute, 273
    amino acids, 275
    monosaccharides, 278
    relative, 273
    various compounds, 274
Congo Red, 479
Coniine, 465
Conjugated dienes, 494
    addition of maleic anhydride, 546
    autoxidation, 579
Constant-boiling mixtures, 69
Constitution, 254
Coordinate covalence, 189
Coordination complexes, alcohols and metallic salts, 71, *see also* Chelate compounds
Cordite, 300, 525
Cori ester, 287
Corn oil, 152, 295
Corn starch, 295
Corn steep water, 295, 308
Corn syrup, 297
Coronene, 442
Corticosterone, 570
Cortin, 570
Cortisone, 570
Cotton, 298
Cottonseed oil, 152
Coumarin, 420
Couper, biography, 9
Coupling reaction of diazonium salts, 378
    with naphthols and naphthylamines, 478
Covalence, 6
Covalent bond, 7
Cracking, 33
    basic equipment, 49
    catalytic, 50
    Dubbs' process, 50
    Fluid Catalyst process, 50
    hydrocarbons to acetylene, 112

Cracking
  petroleum, 49, 50
  thermal, 49
  Thermofor process, 50
Crafts, biography, 315
Cream of tartar, 547
Creatine, 249
Creatinine, 249
Creosote oil, 323, 391
Crepe rubber, 496
Cresols, 324, 391
Cresylic acid, 380
  in refining lubricating oils, 54
Cresyl phosphate, 391
Criegee reaction, 520
Critical complex, *see* Transition state, 91
Crossed Cannizzaro reaction, 403
Crotonaldehyde, 169
Crotonic acid, 538
Crotonic aldehyde, 169
Crotyl alcohol, 518
Cryoscopic molecular weight determination, 16
Crystallite, 538
Crystallization, 11
Crystal Violet, 482
Cumar resin, 324
Cumene, 319
Cumene hydroperoxide, 573
Cumulative double bonds, 244, 494
Cuprammonium solution, 298
Cuprous acetylide, 111
Cuprous carbide, 111
Cyamelide, 243
Cyanamide, 247
  secondary amines from, 186
Cyanates, 245
Cyanic acid, 243
Cyanides, alkyl, nomenclature, 198
  physical properties, 199
  preparation, 198, 199
  reactions, 199
Cyanides, aryl, from diazonium salts, 378
  from sulfonic acids, 355
  reaction with Grignard reagents, 586
Cyanidin chloride, 491
Cyanoacetic acid, 540
Cyanogen bromide, 247
Cyanogen chloride, 247
Cyanogenetic glycosides, 405
Cyanogen iodide, 247
Cyanohydrins, 164
Cyanurates, 245
Cyanuric acid, 243
Cyanuric chloride, 247
Cyclanes, 557
Cyclic acetals, 519
Cyclic anhydrides from dicarboxylic acids, 542
Cyclic carbonates, 519

Cyclobutane, reactions, 560
Cyclodecapentaene, 563
Cyclododecahexaene, 563
Cycloheptane, 558
Cyclohexadecaoctaene, 563
Cyclohexane, 559
  oxidation to adipic acid, 541
Cyclohexanes, stereoisomerism, 562
Cyclohexanol, 551
  oxidation to adipic acid, 541
  reactions, 560
Cyclohexanone, 560
  oxidation to adipic acid, 541
Cyclohexene, 560
4,5-Cyclohexenedicarboxylic anhydride, 546
Cyclohexylamine, 559, 560
Cyclohexyl bromide, 560
Cyclonite, 177
Cyclooctatetraene, 562
Cycloparaffins, 557
Cyclopentadecanone, 563
Cyclopentadiene, 561
  addition of maleic anhydride, 546
Cyclopentane, 558
Cyclopentanone, 543
  oxidation to glutaric acid, 540
Cyclopropane, 561
  reactions, 560
Cyclotetradecaheptaene, 563
p-Cymene, 319
Cysteine, 228
Cystine, 228
Cytosine, 462

2,4-D, 391
δ, symbol in mechanism, 102
Dacron, 416
Dandelion rubber, 495
Dative bond, definition, 189
DDT, 423
Deactivating groups in aromatic substitution, 333
Deactivation of benzene nucleus, cause, 339
Dead oil, 323
Deadly nightshade, 466
Debye unit, 63
Decahydronaphthalenes, 430, 561
Decalins, 430, 561
Decanes, 26
Decarboxylation, aromatic acids, 394, 413
  gallic acid, 393
  β-keto acids, 550
  malonic acids, 542
  phthalic acid, 416
  pyridinecarboxylic acids, 458
  pyrrolecarboxylic acids, 449
  2,4,6-trinitrobenzoic acid, 351
Defecation of cane juice, 293
Degras, 150

Dehydration, alcohols, 75, 100, 107
　aldols, 168
　aldoximes, 199
　amides, 197, 198
7-Dehydrocholesterol, 569
Dehydrogenation, alcohols, 77, 161
　alicyclic hydrocarbons, 318
　alkanes, 52
　with sulfur, 441
Delphinidin chloride, 491
δ, symbol in mechanism, 102
Demerol, 468
Denatured alcohol, 69
Density, alkanes, 32
Depolymerization, 170, 561
Depsides, 419
Desoxycholic acid, 569
Desoxycorticosterone, 570
6-Desoxy-L-galactose, 280
6-Desoxy-L-mannose, 280
Desoxy sugars, 280
Destructive distillation, coal, 322
　wood, 65
Destructive hydrogenation of carbonaceous
　material, 55
Detergents, alkylated aromatic sulfonic
　acids, 355, 432
　Aerosols, 222
　nonionic, 522
　soaps, 157
　sulfated higher alcohols, 159
　synthetic, 158
Deuterium, as tracer element, 337
Deuterium exchange, aromatic nucleus, 337
Developed Black BH, 480
Developed dyeing, 477
Developers, photographic, 395
Dewaxing lubricating oils, 54
Dextrins, 297
Dextrorotation, 260
Dextrose, 277
D family, 274
　sugars, 279
Diacetic acid, 550
Diacetone alcohol, 168
　dehydration to mesityl oxide, 169
Diacetyl, 156
Diacetyl peroxide, *see* Acetyl peroxide, 575
Dialkylacetic acids, 545
N,N-Dialkyl anilines, 363
1,1-Diamino compounds, 526
Di-*i*-amyl ether, *see* *i*-Amyl ether, 119
Diastase, 67
Diastereoisomers, 264
Diazines, 462
Diazoaminobenzene, 379
Diazo compounds, aromatic, 375–379
Diazonium salts, 375–379
Diazotization, 376
Dibenzalacetone, 404

Dibenzanthracenes, 442
1,2:7,8-Dibenzophenanthrene, 442
2,4-Dibenzopyrrole, 451
Dibenzoyl peroxide, *see* Benzoyl peroxide,
　414, 575
Dibenzylamine, 399
Dibenzylidenacetone, 404
3,5-Dibromopyridine, 456
2,6-Dibromoquinone chloroimide, 397
Dibutyl ether, *see* Butyl ether, 119
Di-*t*-butyl peroxide, *see* *t*-Butyl peroxide,
　573
Dibutyl phthalate, *see* Butyl phthalate, 415
Dicarboxylic acids, preparation, 539
　reactions, 542
Dichloramine T, 358
Dichloroacetaldehyde, 518
Dichloroacetic acid, 531
Dichlorobenzenes, 327
Dichlorodifluoromethane, 513
1,2-Dichloroethane, 506
1,1-Dichloroethylene, 508
1,2-Dichloroethylenes, 506
　configuration, 256
Di-β-chloroethyl ether, *see* β-Chloroethyl
　ether, 119
Dichlorofluoromethane, 513
Dichloromethane, *see* Methylene chloride,
　505
1,5-Dichloronaphthalene, 432
2,4-Dichlorophenoxyacetic acid, *see* 2,4-D,
　391
Dichloropropenes, 509
2,6-Dichloroquinone chloroimide, 397
2,4-Dichlorostyrene, 425
1,2-Dichloro-1,1,2,2-tetrafluoroethane, 514
N,N-Dichloro-*p*-toluenesulfonamide, 358
Dichroism, 259
Dicoumarin, 420
Dicoumarol, 420
Dicyanamide, 248
Dicyclopentadiene, 561
Dielectric constant, 8, 63
Diels-Alder diene syntheses, 547
Diels hydrocarbon, 568
Dienes, conjugated, addition of maleic
　anhydride, 546
Dienophiles, 547
Diesel engines, 53
Diesel oil, 53
Diethanolamine, 526
Diethyl, *see also* Ethyl
Diethylene glycol, 522
Diethylenetriamine, 528
Diethyl ether, *see* Ethyl ether, 118
Diethylidene peroxide, 580
Diethyl peroxide, *see* Ethyl peroxide, 574
Diethyl phthalate, *see* Ethyl phthalate, 415
Diethylstilbestrol, 569
Diethyl sulfate, *see* Ethyl sulfate, 78

1,1-Difluoroethane, 512
Difluoromethane, 513
2,2-Difluoropropane, 512
Difurfurylidenacetone, 452
Digallic acid, 419
Digestion, fats and oils, 155
    proteins, 231
    starch, 296
9,10-Dihydroanthracene, 438
Dihydroanthraquinone, 440
2,5-Dihydropyrrole, 449
9,10-Dihydroxyanthracene, 440
1,2-Dihydroxyanthraquinone, 440, 487
Dihydroxybenzenes, 393
1,4-Dihydroxy-2-butyne, 501
5,6-Dihydroxynaphthoquinone, 487
2,6-Dihydroxypurine, 464
Diisobutylene, 43
    synthesis of 3,5,5-trimethylhexanol, 181
Diisopropylidene peroxide, 581
2,5-Diketopiperazines, 534
2,3-Dimercapto-1-propanol, 525
Dimethylamine, 193
p-Dimethylaminoazobenzene, 378
p,p'-Dimethylaminobenzophenone, see
    Michler's ketone, 407
N,N-Dimethylaniline, 365, 371
Dimethylarsenoxide, 590
Dimethylarsinic acid, 591
Dimethylbenzenes, see Xylenes, 316
2,3-Dimethyl-1,3-butadiene, 499
1,2-Dimethylcyclopentane, toluene from,
    318
Dimethyl ether, see Methyl ether, 118
2,3-Dimethyl-1,4-naphthoquinone, 436
Dimethyl phthalate, see Methyl phthalate,
    415
Dimethyl sulfate, see Methyl sulfate, 78, 79
Dinaphthocoronene, 442
m-Dinitrobenzene, 331
    reduction to m-nitroaniline, 346
3,5-Dinitrobenzoic acid, 414
3,5-Dinitrobenzoyl chloride, 414
2,2'-Dinitrobiphenyl-6,6'-dicarboxylic acid,
    427
Dinitronaphthalenes, 431
2,4-Dinitrophenol, 391
2,4-Dinitrophenylhydrazine, 362
2,4-Dinitrophenyl sulfide, 348
2,5-Dinitrothiophene, 446
2,4-Dinitrotoluene, 332
1,4-Dioxane, 521
Dipentene, 564
Diphenic acid, 441
Diphenyl, see Biphenyl, 426
Diphenylamine, 363, 371
Diphenylbenzenes, 426
Diphenylcarbinol, 398
1,1-Diphenylethane, 423
Diphenyl ether, see Phenyl ether, 387

1,1-Diphenylethylene, 425
Diphenylguanidine, 371
Diphenylmethane, 422
Diphenyl oxide, see Phenyl ether, 387
Diphenyl sulfone, see Phenyl sulfone, 353,
    358
Diphenylthiourea, 366
Dipolar ions, 230, 369, 535
Dipole, definition, 7, 63
Dipole association, 63
Dipole-dipole attraction, 63
Dipole moment, 63
    alkanes, 63
    alkenes, 102
    benzene derivatives, 341
    bonds, 64
    1-butene, 102
    t-butyl chloride, 97
    C—N bond, 200
    cyanide group, 200
    p-dinitrobenzene, 339
    direction, 339
    hydroquinone, 340
    isocyanide group, 200
    methyl chloride, 97
    methyl ethyl ether, 210
    methyl sulfide, 210
    p-nitrochlorobenzene, 340
    p-nitrotoluene, 340
    p-phenylenediamine, 340
    phenylethylene, 343
    saturated hydrocarbons, 63
    single bonds, 64
    trimethylamine, 210
Dippel's oil, 447
Di-i-propyl ether, see i-Propyl ether, 119
Direct Black EW, 480
Direct Blue 2B, 480
Direct dyes, 476
Directive influence of substituents in ben-
    zene, 333
    in naphthalene, 430–432
    theory, 335–344
Disaccharides, 290
    nonreducing, 292
    reducing, 290
Disazo dyes, 479
Disilane, 594
Dispersion, rotatory, 260
Displacement reactions, alkyl halides, 82
    mechanism, 95
Disproportionation in preparation of Gri-
    gnard reagents, 87
    in reduction of sulfones, 217
Dissociation constants, of acids, see Acidity
    of bases, see Basicity
Distillation, 9
    fractional, 10

Distillation
  steam, 11
  vacuum, 11
Disulfides, 213, 214
  by oxidation of mercaptans, 211
  reduction to mercaptans, 210
  sulfonyl chlorides from, 220
Disulfones, 218
Diterpenes, 564, 566
Dithiocarbamates, 250
Dithiocarbonates, 250
Dithiocarboxylic acids, 214
1,2-Dithioglycerol, 525
Divinylbenzene, 425
DMP, 415
Docosanes, 26
Dodecanes, 26
Dodecanesulfonic acid, 219
Double bond, 36
  estimation with perbenzoic acid, 414
  tests for, 39, 41, 205
Double refraction, 257
Dow process for phenol, 387
Drying oils, 152, 156
  autoxidation, 579
  up-grading, 156, 526
Dubbs process, 50
Dulcite, *see* Dulcitol, 307
Dulcitol, 307
Dumas, biography, 3
  and substitution, 85
Dumas molecular weight determination, 16
Dumas nitrogen determination, 13
Durene, 316
Dyeing, 476
Dyes, *see also individual name, e.g.* Direct
    Black EW
  anthraquinone, 487
  azo, 478
  flavones and flavylium salts, 490
  historical, 474
  indigoid, 484
  nitro, 478
  production and prices, 489
  sulfur or sulfide, 489
  triphenylmethane, 480
Dynamite, 525
Dynamite cotton, 300
Dynel, 537

Ebonite, 497
Ebullioscopic molecular weight determina-
    tion, 16
Edeleanu process, 53
Edestin, 226
Egg yolk pigments, 567
Ehrlich, biography, 593
Eicosanes, 26
Elaidic acid, geometrical isomerism, 254, 256
Elaidinization of oils, 155

Elastins, 225, 226
Electrical dipole, permanent, 63
  transient, 62
Electric moment, *see* Dipole moment, 63
Electrodotic reagents, 98
Electrolysis of salts, 131
Electromeric effect in aromatic substitution,
    343
Electron-affinity, 5, 98
Electronegative groups, 5, 97
Electronic theory of structure, 5
Electron-pair bond, 7
Electrophilic reagents, 97
Electrophoresis, 226
Electropositive groups, 98
Electrovalence, 6
Eleostearic acid, 151
Elon, 395
Emodin, 440
Empirical formulas, 15
Emulsifying agents, 158, 526
Emulsin, 290
Enanthaldehyde, *see n*-Heptaldehyde, 180
Enanthic acid, 124
Enantiomorphs, 259
Energy barrier, 24
Energy hump, 24
Enol form, aldehydes and ketones, 168
  estimation, 554
Enolization, aldehydes and ketones, 168
Enolization and racemization, 271
Enols, *see* Tautomerism
Enteric coating for pills, 418
Enzymes, 66
Eosin, 483
Ephedrine, 400
Epinephrine, 400
Epiquinidine, 469
Epiquinine, 469
Epoxides, 522
Epoxy derivatives, 522
Epoxyethane, 522
Epoxypropane, 523
Equations, oxidation-reduction, balancing,
    122
Equilibrium constant, effect of temperature,
    142
  esterification, 141
Ergosterol, 568
Erlenmeyer, biography, 428
Error, absolute and relative, 18
Erucic acid, 151, 542
Erythrosin, 484
Essential amino acids, 231
Essential oils, 564
Ester condensations, *see* Claisen ester con-
    densations, 551
Esterification, 141–144
  aromatic acids, 412
  neopentyl alcohol, 144

Esterification law of Victor Meyer, 412
Esters, 140–148
  from cyanides, 199
  of inorganic acids, 78
  from quaternary ammonium salts, 194
  of sulfonic acids, 221, 356
Estradiol, 569
Estrogenic hormones, 569
Ethane, barrier to free rotation, 24
  structure, 21, 24
1,2-Ethanediol, 520
Ethanol, *see* Ethyl alcohol, 66–70
Ethanolamine, 526
Ethavan, 406
Ethene, *see* Ethylene
Ether, *see* Ethyl ether, 119, 579
Ethers, 114–119
  from alkyl halides, 108
  autoxidation, 579
  from esters of sulfonic acids, 356
  peroxides in, 579
Ethionic acid, 42
Ethonium ion, 102
Ethoxyl determination, 118
Ethyl acetate, 148
  from acetaldehyde, 179
Ethyl acetoacetate, 551
  tautomerism, 554
Ethyl alcohol, 66–70
Ethylamine, first synthesis, 246
Ethyl *p*-aminobenzoate, 418
Ethylbenzene, 318
  styrene from, 425
Ethyl benzoate, 399
Ethyl benzoylacetate, 551
Ethyl borate, 79
Ethyl bromide, *see* Alkyl halides
Ethyl carbonate, 239
Ethyl cellulose, 302
Ethyl chloride, 84
Ethyl chlorocarbonate, *see* Ethyl chloro-
    formate, 239
Ethyl chloroformate, 239
Ethyldichloroarsine, 592
Ethylene, conversion to acetone and pro-
    pionaldehyde, 181
  ethyl alcohol from, 68
  structure, 36
Ethylene bromide, use in Ethyl Fluid, 53
Ethylene chloride, 506
  use in Ethyl Fluid, 53
Ethylene chlorohydrin, 521
Ethylene cyanohydrin, 537
Ethylenediamine, 528
Ethylenediammonium tartrate, 528
Ethylene dibromide, *see* Ethylene bromide,
  53
Ethylene dichloride, *see* Ethylene chloride,
  506

Ethylene glycol, 521
  monoethyl ether, 522
  nitrate, 521
Ethylene oxide, 521
Ethyl ether, 119
  autoxidation, 579
Ethyl Fluid, components, 53
Ethyl formate, 148
Ethyl formylacetate, 551
2-Ethyl-1,3-hexanediol, 524
Ethyl hydrogen sulfate, 68, 116
Ethyl hydroperoxide, 574
Ethylidene acetate, 139
Ethyl iodide, *see* Alkyl halides
Ethyl malonate, reactions, 544
  synthesis, 540
Ethylmercuric chloride, 587
Ethyl nitrate, 79
Ethyl nitrite, 79
Ethyl oxalacetate, 551
Ethyl perchlorate, 79
Ethyl peroxide, 574
Ethyl phenylacetate, 399
Ethyl phenylmalonate, 545
Ethyl phosphate, 79
Ethyl phthalate, 415
Ethyl pyrophosphate, 79
Ethyl silicate, 79
Ethyl sodiomalonate, 545
Ethylsodium, 584
Ethyl sulfate, 78
Ethylsulfuric acid, *see* Ethyl hydrogen sul-
    fate, 68, 116
Eugenol, 392
Exaltone, 563
Exhaustive methylation, 455
Explosives, ballistite, 300, 525
  cellulose nitrate, 299
  cordite, 300, 525
  cyclonite, 177
  dynamite, 525
  ethylene glycol nitrate, 521
  flashless, 249
  gelatin dynamite, 525
  glyceryl nitrate, 525
  glycol dinitrate, 521
  guncotton, 300
  hexogen, 177
  nitrocellulose, 299
  nitroglycerin, 525
  nitroguanidine, 249
  nitrostarch, 297
  pentaerythritol nitrate, 526
  PETN, 526
  RDX, 177
  smokeless, 300
  starch nitrate, 297
  tetryl, 373
  TNT, 351

Explosives
  trimethylenetrinitramine, 177
  trinitrotoluene, 351
Extraction, 11
Extraordinary ray, 258
Extreme pressure lubricants, 54

Families of stereoisomers, 274
  of sugars, 279
Faraday, biography, 68
Farnesol, 565
Fast Scarlet G, 479
Fat acids, 124, 151
  separation, 155
Fat metabolism, 745
Fats and oils, 151–160, *see also* Oils
Fatty acids, 124
Fehling's solution, constitution, 547
  oxidation of aldehydes, 173
  oxidation of carbohydrates, 280
Fermate, 251
Fermentation, acetic acid, 133
  acetone, 70
  alcoholic, 66–68
  butyl alcohol, 70
  butyric acid, 135
  fumaric acid, 546
  lactic acid, 534
  propionic acid, 135
Fibers, natural, 229, 298
  synthetic, *see individual fiber, e.g.,* Nylon
Fiber V, 416
Fibroin, 229
Fibrous proteins, 229
Fire damp, 32
Fischer, E., biography, 233
Fischer-Tropsch synthesis, 56
Fish oil, 152
Fittig, biography, 329
Flavianic acid, 478
Flavones, 490
Flavonol, 490
Flavoproteins, 465
Flavor of fruits, 148
Flavylium salts, 490
Flax, 298
Flower pigments, 491
Fluid Catalyst process, 50
Fluorene, 441
  in coal tar, 324
Fluorescein, 483
Fluorescent dyes, 483
Fluorinated hydrocarbons, aliphatic, 510
Fluorination, 511
Fluoroacetic acid, 530
Fluorocarbons, 510, 511
Fluoro compounds, 510
Folic acids, 234
Formal charge, 130

Formaldehyde, 176
  test for, 178
Formaldehyde hydrate, 518
Formaldehyde-urea resins, 243
Formalin, 177
Formamide, 197
Formic acid, 124, 132
Formylacetic ester, 551
Fractionating columns, 10
Frankland, biography, 586
Free groups, 424
Free-radical catalysis of geometrical isom-
    erization, 256
Free-radical mechanisms, 91
Free radicals, 91, 424, 574–583, *see also in-
    dividual radical, e.g.,* Methyl radical
Free rotation, barrier to, in single bonds, 24
  restriction by double bonds, 254
Free triphenylmethyl radicals, 424
Freons, 513, 514
Friedel, biography, 315
Friedel-Crafts reaction, 315
  ketones by, 406
  mechanism, 338
  naphthalene, 431
  thiophene, 445, 446
Friedlaender's synthesis of quinolines, 458
Fructose, 288
  fermentation, 68
Fruit flavors and odors, 148
Fuchsin, 481
Fucose, 280
Fuel oil, 53
Fulminic acid, 246
Fumaric acid, 545
  reduction to succinic acid, 540
Functional groups, 43
Functional isomers, 254
Furan, 451, 453
Furanosides, 294
Furfural, 451, 454
  from pentoses, 287
  refining lubricating oils, 54
Furfuryl alcohol, 452
Furfurylidenacetone, 452
α-Furfuryl mercaptan, 454
Furil, 453
Furilic acid, 453
Furoic acid, 453
Furoin, 453
Furylacrylic acid, 452
Fused rings, 428
Fusel oil, 67

G-acid, 434
γ-acid, 435
Galactaric acid, 281
Galactitol, 307
Galactose, 278
D-Galacturonic acid, 305

Gallic acid, 419
  decarboxylation, 393
Gallotannin, 419
m-Galloylgallic acid, 419
Gamma acid, 435
Gammexane, 326
Gardenia odor, 398
Garlic oil, 222
Gas from petroleum, 48
Gas black, *see* Carbon black, 46
Gases, poison, *see* Poison gases
Gas-fading of dyes, 477
Gas oil, 53
Gasoline, 48
  by alkylation, 51
  octane number, 49
  by polymerization, 51
  straight run, 48
Gasoline engine, 48
Gas turbines, 53, 54
Gattermann, biography, 402
Gattermann hydrogen cyanide synthesis, 402
  reaction of diazonium salts, 377
Gelatin, 226
Gelatin dynamite, 525
Gem-, prefix, 510
General anesthetics, 118, 463, 561
Geneva system of nomenclature, 28, *see also* Nomenclature
Gentian Violet, 482
Geometrical isomerism, 254–257
3-Geranylcatechol, 393
Globulins, 225
D-Glucitol, 307
Gluconic acid, 278, 281
Glucosazone, *see* Glucose phenylosazone, 282
Glucose, from cellulose, 299
  configuration, 278
  constitution, 278
  fermentation, 67, 68
  α and β forms, 285
  glycoside formation, 283
  methylation, 284
  mutarotation, 285
  osazone formation, 282
  oxidation by Fehling's solution, 280
  pentaacetates, 286
  phosphates, 287
  ring structure, 283, 285
  from starch, 297
Glucose phenylosazone, 282
Glucose phosphates, 287
α- and β-Glucosidase, 290
Glucosides, *see* Glycosides, 283
Glucuronic acids, *see* Glycuronic acids, 306
Glutamic acid, 228, 232
Glutaric acid, preparation, 540
  reactions, 542

Glutaric anhydride, 543
Glutathion, 235
Glutelins, 225
Glycaric acids, 281
  conversion to pyrrole, 447
(+)Glyceraldehyde, configuration, 273
(−)Glyceric acid, configuration, 274
Glycerides, 151
Glycerin, 153, 524
Glycerol, 153, 524
Glyceryl nitrate, 525
Glycine, 227
  photographer's, 395
Glycocholic acid, 569
Glycocoll, *see* Glycine, 227
Glycogen, 297
Glycol, 521
  dinitrate, 521
Glycollic acid, 521
1,2-Glycols, 176, 518
1,3-Glycols, 523
α,ω-Glycols, 524
Glyconic acids, 278
Glycoproteins, 225
Glycoses, 277
Glycosides, 283
  cyanogenetic, 405
Glycuronic acids, 306
Glyoxalic acid, *see* Glyoxylic acid, 549
Glyoxylic acid, 549
Glyptal resins, 415
Gmelin, biography, 4
Goldenrod rubber, 495
Gomberg, biography, 423
Goodyear, biography, 497
Graebe, biography, 428
Grain alcohol, 67
Gramicidin-S, 235
Grape odor and flavor, 417
Gray acetate of lime, 133
Greases, lubricating, 55, 159
Green oil, 323, 437
GRI, 502
Griess, biography, 375
Grignard, biography, 86
Grignard reagents, 85–89, 586
  abnormal reactions, 350, 448
  acetylenic, 112
  coupling reaction, 86, 88
  mechanism of abnormal reactions, 350
  mechanism of addition to carbon-oxygen double bond, 104
  preparation, 86
  reactions, acetylene, 112
    acyl halides, 137
    aldehydes and ketones, 164
    alkylsulfonates, 221
    carbon dioxide, 89, 120
    carbon disulfide, 215
    carboxylic esters, 147

Grignard reagents, reactions,
  halogen, 87
  inorganic halides, 88
  isocyanates, 364
  ketones, 164
  oxygen, 88
  pyrrole, 447
  reactive hydrogen, 87
  silicon tetrachloride, 595
  sulfur dioxide, 216
 relative reactivity, 586
 role of ether as solvent, 117
 side reactions in preparation, 86
Grignard syntheses, acetylenic compounds,
    112
  alcohols, 88, 147, 164
  amides, 364
  arsines, 590
  carboxylic acids, 89, 120
  dithiocarboxylic acids, 215
  hydrocarbons, 87, 221
  ketones, 137
  organometallic compounds, 88, 585–590
  pyrrole derivatives, 448
  silicon compounds, 595
  sulfinic acids, 216
GRM, 503
GRN, 502
GRS and GRS-10, 502
Guaiacol, 392
Guaiac resin, 392
Guanidine, 248
Guanine, 464
Guano, 464
Guar flour, 307
Guayule rubber, 496
Gum arabic, 307
  benzoin, 310, 413
  catechu, 392
  tragacanth, 307
Gum inhibitors, 51
Gums, 307
Guncotton, 300

H-acid, 435
Hair, 229
Half second cotton, 301
Haloform reaction, 174
Halogen, addition to alkenes, 38
  addition to aromatic compounds, 326
  detection in organic compounds, 12
  determination, 14
  mechanism of addition to double bond,
    100
  reaction with alkanes, 84, 85
    with alkenes, 38, 508, 509
    with alkynes, 110
    with aromatic compounds, 326, 327
    with Grignard reagents, 87

Halogen acids, addition to alkenes, 42
  to alkynes, 110
  mechanism of addition to double bond,
    101
    of reaction with alcohols, 98
    of removal from alkyl halides, 98
α-Halogen acids, 137, 530
Halogenated acids, 530
Halogenated hydrocarbons, aliphatic, 505–
    514
  aromatic, 326–330
Halogenation, 84, 85
  acids and acyl halides, 137
  aldehydes and ketones, 174
  aliphatic, mechanism, 94
  alkenes, 508, 509
  aromatic, mechanism, 338
  aromatic aldehydes to acyl halides, 402
  aromatic amines, 367
  benzene, 314
  naphthalene, 430
  phenols, 393
Halogen compounds, aliphatic, 505–514
  aromatic, 326–330
    effect of *m*-directing groups in reac-
      tivity, 348
Halonium ion, intermediate in addition re-
    actions, 101
Hard rubber, 497
Harries, biography, 496
Haworth formulas for sugars, 288
Hawthorn odor, 405
Häuy, biography, 260
Heat of combustion of alkanes, 33
Heavy hydrogen as tracer element, 337
Heavy oil, 323, 324
Heavy oxygen as tracer element, 144, 146
Heliotropin, 406
Hell-Volhard-Zelinsky reaction, 137, 530
Heme, 450
Hemiacetals, 166
Hemicelluloses, 298
Hemihedral facets, 261
Hemin, 450
Hemiterpene, 564
Hemlock, 465
Hemocyanins, 225, 226
Hemoglobins, 225, 226
Hemp fiber, 298
Henbane, 466
Heneicosanes, 26
Heneicosanoic acid, 124
Hennel, biography, 68
Hentriacontanes, 26
n-Heptaldehyde, 180, 538
n-Heptane, as standard fuel, 49
  sources, 32
Heroine, 467
Herschel, biography, 262
Heterocyclic compounds, 444

Heterogeneous reactions, 93
Heterolytic fission, 98
Heteropolysaccharides, 306
Hexachloroethane, 507
Hexadecane, 26, 54
Hexadecanesulfonic acid, 219
Hexahydrobenzene, 559
Hexalin, 559
Hexamethylene, 559
Hexamethylenediamine, 528
  from adiponitrile, 544
Hexamethylenetetramine, 177
Hexaphenylethane, 423
Hexogen, 177
n-Hexylresorcinol, 393
Hinsberg reaction, 357
Hippuric acid, 413
Hirschfelder models, 23
Histamine, 460
Histidine, 228, 460
Histones, 225
van't Hoff, biography, 262
Hofmann, biography, 185
Hofmann decomposition of quaternary am-
      monium hydroxides, 194, 455
  exhaustive methylation procedure, 194,
      455
  rearrangement of amides, 185, 197
Hofmeister, biography, 233
Homologous series, 21
Homologs, 21
Homolytic fission, 98
Homopolysaccharides, 295
Honey, 278, 288
Hormones, adrenal, 400, 569
  sex, 569
Huygens, biography, 257
Hydnocarpic acid, 561
Hydrazines, from diazonium salts, 378
  reaction with aldehydes and ketones, 172
Hydrazobenzene, 347
Hydrazones, 172
o-Hydrazotoluene, 427
Hydroaromatic compounds, 557
Hydroazines, 487
Hydrobenzamide, 403
Hydrocarbons, mechanism of pyrolysis, 92
  see also Alicyclic hydrocarbons, Alkanes,
      Alkenes, Alkynes, and Aromatic hy-
      drocarbons
Hydroforming, 317
Hydrofurfuramide, 452
Hydrogen, detection in organic compounds,
      12
  determination, 13
  from natural gas, 46
  reactivity in compounds, 73, 585
Hydrogenation, catalytic, of acids, 129
  of aldehydes and ketones, 163
  of alkenes, 39

of alkynes, 110
of aromatic hydrocarbons, 559
of coal, 56
of cyanides, 200
of esters, 147
of fat oils, 154
of isocyanides, 200
of nitro compounds, 204, 345
of petroleum, 55
mechanism, 93
Hydrogen bonding, see Proton bonding
Hydrogen bromide, abnormal addition to
      double bond, 103
Hydrogen cyanide, addition to aldehydes
      and ketones, 164
Hydrogen exchange, benzene, 337
Hydrogen peroxide, oxidation with, 190,
      212, 518
Hydrolysis, acetals, 283
  acid anhydrides, 139
  acyl halides, 136
  alkyl halides, mechanism, 96
  amides, 197
  aromatic amines, 433
  aryl halides, 381
  cyanides, 199
  dihalides, 405
  esters, 79, 145, 412
  fats and oils, 155
  isocyanides, 201
  nitroalkanes, 204, 205
  ozonides, 162
  steric hindrance, 145, 412
Hydron Blue R, 489
Hydroperoxides, 573
Hydroquinone, 393
Hydroxy acids, 533
Hydroxy amino compounds, 526
p-Hydroxyazobenzene, 378
o-Hydroxybenzaldehyde, 402, 420
Hydroxybenzoic acids, 418
Hydroxybenzyl alcohols, 385
Hydroxy dicarboxylic acids, 547
2-Hydroxyethylamine, 526
Hydroxylamine, from nitroalkanes, 204
  reaction with aldehydes and ketones, 171
Hydroxyl group, 58
  Zerevitinov determination, 87
5-Hydroxymethyl furfural, 287
p-Hydroxyphenylarsonic acid, 592
p-Hydroxyphenylglycine, 395
Hydroxyproline, 227
6-Hydroxypurine, 464
8-Hydroxyquinoline, 458
Hydroxytricarboxylic acids, 547
l-Hyoscyamine, 466
Hyperconjugation, 344
Hypohalous acid, addition to alkenes, 42
Hypoxanthine, 464

Ice colors, 477
I.C.I., Imperial Chemical Industries, 476
I.G., Interessen Gemeinschaft fuer Farbenindustrie, 475
Imidazoles, 460
Imides, 195, 241
  cyclic, 416
Immunopolysaccharides, 307
Imperial Chemical Industries, 476
Indanthrene Blue R, 487
Indene, 441
Indican, 484
Indicator action, 491
Indigo, 484
Indigoid dyes, 484
Indigo white, 486
Indispensable amino acids, 231
Indoaniline, 367
Indole, 451
Indophenin reaction, 444
Indophenol, 385
Indoxylic acid, 485
Inductive effect, 97
  alkyl groups, 97
  aromatic substitution, 342
Industrial alcohol, 67
Infrared spectrum, 472
Ingrain dyes, 477
Ink, blue-black, 419
  red, 483
Inorganic acid halides, reaction with alcohols, 74
Inorganic halides, reaction with Grignard reagents, 88
Inositols, 308
Insect repellents, 524
Insulin in metabolism, 550
Interatomic distance and resonance, 130, 313, 342
Interatomic distances, C—C in alkanes, 313
  C—C in benzene, 313
  C=C in alkenes, 313
  C≡C in alkynes, 313
  C—Cl in *t*-butyl chloride, 342
  C—Cl in chlorobenzene, 342
  C—Cl in vinyl chloride, 508
  C—F in fluorine compounds, 511
  C—O in carboxylate ion, 130
  C—O in carboxyl group, 131
  C—O in ethers, 130
  C=O in aldehydes and ketones, 130
  C=O in carboxyl group, 131
  hydrogen to other elements, 64
Interessen Gemeinschaft fuer Farbenindustrie, 475
International Union of Chemistry, system of nomenclature, 28, *see also* Nomenclature
Inulin, 297
Inversion of sucrose, 293

Invertase, *see* Sucrase, 68
Invert soaps, 195
Invert sugar, 293
Iodination, aromatic compounds, 328
Iodine, adsorption complex with starch, 295
  catalyst for dehydration, 169
  color of solutions, 169
Iodine number, 154
  of fats and oils, 152
Iodo acids, 530
p-Iodoaniline, 368
Iodobenzene, 328
Iodocyanogen, *see* Cyanogen iodide, 247
Iodoform, 174
2-Iodofuran, 588
Iodogorgoic acid, 228
Ion-dipole attraction, 63
Ion-exchange resins, 390
Ionic bonds, 6
Ionic catalysis of geometrical isomerization, 256
Ionic mechanisms, 91
Ionization constants, of acids, *see* Acidity
  of bases, *see* Basicity
Ionization potential, 98
Ions, hydration, 8
Iso-, prefix, 26, *see also* compound, *e.g. i*-Propyl alcohol
Isocrotyl chloride, 509
Isocyanates, alkyl, 245
  from isocyanides, 200
  aryl, 364
Isocyanic acid, 243
Isocyanides, 200, 201, 366
  structure, 189
Isoelectric point, 230
Isoeugenol, 406
Isomerism, 22
  geometrical, 254–257
  optical, 261
  structural, 22
  types, 254
Isomerization, 34
  alkanes, 34, 52
  of oils, 154
Isomers, 22
  types, 254
Isonicotinic acid, 457
Isonitriles, *see* Isocyanides
"Isooctane," *see* 2,2,4-Trimethyl pentane, 49, 51
Isophorone, 169
Isophthalic acid, 414, 416
Isoprene, from rubber, 496
Isoprene rule, 564
Isoquinoline, 458
(+)Isoserine, configuration, 274
Isothiazole, 461
Isothiocyanates, 201, 251
Isothioureas, 252

Isothiuronium salts, *see* Thiuronium salts, 253
Isoxazole, 461
I.U.C. system of nomenclature for alkanes, 28

Jade Green, 488
Japan wax, 542
Jasmine odor, 398
Jet engines, 53
Jute, 298

Kekulé, biography, 4
Kel-F, 514
Kephalins, 527
Keratins, 225
Kerosene, 53
Ketene, 139, 180
Ketimines, 183
α-Keto acids, 549
β-Keto acids, 550
γ-Keto acids, 555
Keto-enol tautomerism, *see* Tautomerism
β-Keto esters, preparation, 550
  reactions, 551
Ketones, nomenclature, 162
  physical properties, 163
  preparation, 161, 162
    from acyl halides, 137
    aromatic, 406
    from carboxylic acids, 128
    from β-keto esters, 552
    from nitroalkanes, 205
  reactions, 163–175
  uses, 180, 181
Ketoses, 288
Ketoximes, 171
  stereochemistry, 408
Kjeldahl method for nitrogen, 14
Knocking characteristics of fuels, 49
Knocking in gasoline engines, 48
Knock inhibitors, 53
Knock-out drops, 518
Koch's acid, 435
Koerner, biography, 320
Koerner's absolute method of orientation, 320
Kolbe, biography, 3
Kolbe hydrocarbon synthesis, 131
  synthesis of dicarboxylic acid esters, 539
    of phenolcarboxylic acids, 418
Kopp, biography, 32
Kraft process for wood pulp, 298
Krystallin, 369
Kyanol, 369

Lacquers, 301
Lactalbumin, 225, 226
Lactams, 535
Lactic acid, 534

(−)Lactic acid, configuration, 274
Lactides, 533
γ- and δ-Lactones, from halogenated acids, 532
  from hydroxyacids, 534
  from keto acids, 555
Lactose, 292
Ladenburg rearrangement, 591
Lamp black, *see* Carbon black, 46
Lanolin, 150
Lanum, 150
Lapworth, biography, 165
Lard, 152
Lard oil, 152
Latex, 495, 499
Laudanine, 467
Lauric acid, 124, 151
Laurylsulfonic acid, 219
Lavoisier, biography, 3
L. casei factor, 235
Lead acetate, 135
Lead compounds, 589
Lead susceptibility, 53
Lead tetraacetate, oxidizing agent, 520
Lead tetraethyl, *see* Tetraethyllead, 589
Leaf pigments, carotenoids, 567
  chlorophylls, 450
Le Bel, biography, 262
Lecithins, 527
Lederer-Manasse reaction, 385
Lees of wine, 547
Lemon grass oil, 564
Lemon juice, 547
Lemon oil, 564
Lepidine, 458
Leucine, 227
Leuco base, 480
Levorotation, 260
Levulinic acid, 555
  from carbohydrates, 287
Levulinic aldehyde, 497
Levulose, 288
Lewis, biography, 192
Lewisite, 592
Lewis theory of acids and bases, 192
L family, 275
  of sugars, 279
Licanic acid, 151
Liebermann, biography, 385
Liebermann's nitroso reaction, 385
Liebig, biography, 3
Light, catalysis of halogenation, 94
  modes of propagation, 257
Light oil, 323
Lignin, 298
Lignoceric acid, 124, 152
Ligroins, 55
Liming-out process, 353
Limit dextrin, 296
Limonene, 564

Lindane, 326
Linoleic acid, 151
Linolenic acid, 151
Linoleum, 157
Linolic acid, 151
Linseed oil, 152
  isomerization, 154
  in paint, 156
Liquefied petroleum gas, 48
Lithium aluminum hydride, reduction of
    acids, 129
  reduction of aldehydes and ketones, 164
  reduction of esters, 147
Lithium compounds, 584
Lithocholic acid, 569
Local anesthetics, 418, 467
Loschmidt, biography, 310
Lowitz, biography, 2
Lowry, biography, 192
LP gas, *see* Liquefied petroleum gas, 48
Lubricating oils, 54
Lubrication, 54
Lucas test, 75
Lucite, 538
Luminal, 462
Lumisterol, 568
Lutein, 567
Lycopene, 567
Lysine, 228
L-Lyxitol, 307

Macroanalysis, 15
Madder, 487
Magenta, 481
Magnesium compounds, 585
Magnesium methoxide, 73
Malachite Green, 480
Malaprade reaction, 520
Maleic acid, 545
  reduction to succinic acid, 540
Maleic anhydride, 546
Malic acid, 547
(−)Malic acid, configuration, 274
Malonic acid, preparation, 540
  reactions, 542
Malonic ester, preparation, 540
  reactions, 544
Malt, 67
Maltase, hydrolysis of maltose, 67, 290
Maltose, 290
Malus, biography, 259
Mandelic acid, 420
Mandelonitrile, 420
Mannaric acid, 282
Mannite, *see* Mannitol, 307
D-Mannitol, 307, 308
Mannose, 278
Mannose phenylhydrazone, 283
Mapharsen, 593
Maple sugar, 293

Marfanil, 373
Margaric acid, 124
Markovnikov, biography, 41
Markovnikov rule, 41, 102
Marsh gas, 32
Masking of odors, 406
Maté, 464
Mauve, 475
Mechanism of organic reactions, 90–105
  abnormal addition of hydrogen bromide,
      103
  abnormal Grignard reactions, 350
  acetal formation, 166
  addition, Grignard reagents, 104
    halogen, 100
    halogen acid, 101
    hydrogen bromide, 95, 103
    hydrogen cyanide to carbonyl groups,
      165
  aldol condensation, 168
  aromatic halogenation, 338
  aromatic nitration, 337
  aromatic substitution, 335
  aromatic sulfonation, 338
  autoxidation, 578, 581
  benzoin condensation, 404
  bimolecular mechanisms, 96
  catalytic reduction, 93
  Claisen ester condensation, 551
  condensation of phenols and aldehydes,
      386
  decomposition of peroxides, 574
  dehydration of alcohols, 100
  displacement of aromatic halogen, 349
  displacement reaction, 95
  esterification, carboxylic acids, 142, 211
    tertiary alcohols, 144
  ether formation, 116
  free-radical mechanisms, 91, 92, 574–583
  Friedel-Crafts reaction, 338
  halogenation, alkanes, 94
    alkenes, 508, 509
    aromatic compounds, 338
  hemiacetal formation, 166
  hydrolysis, alkyl halides, 96
    esters, 146
  iodine catalysis of dehydration, 169
  ionic mechanisms, 91, 95
  isomerization, geometrical isomers, 256
  nitration of aromatic compounds, 337
  oxidation, isobutane, 574
    sulfides by hydrogen peroxide, 212
    tertiary amines by hydrogen peroxide,
      190
  pinacol-pinacolone rearrangement, 176
  polymerization, addition, 94, 103
    aldehydes, 170
    alkenes, acid catalyzed, 103
    alkenes, free-radical catalyzed, 94
  pyrolysis, 92

Mechanism of organic reactions
 reactions of acyl halides, 137
 reactions of alcohols with halogen acids, 98
 removal of halogen acid, 99
 S$_N$1 and S$_N$2 reactions, 98
 substitution in aromatic nucleus, by electron-donating reagents, 344
  by electron-seeking reagents, 335
 substitution in pyridine, 456
 sulfonation of aromatic compounds, 339
 unimolecular mechanisms, 97
 Walden inversion, 95, 271
Meerwein-Ponndorf reduction of aldehydes and ketones, 164
MEK, see Methyl ethyl ketone, 181
Melamine, 248
Melamine resins, 248
Melibiose, 292
Melting points, alternation for alkanes, 31
 alternation for carboxylic acids, 126
Menthol, 565
Mercaptans, nomenclature, 210
 physical properties, 210
 preparation, 209, 217
 reactions, 211, 212
2-Mercaptobenzothiazole, 461
Mercerized cotton, 299
Mercuration, 587
 of thiophene, 445
Mercuric halides, reaction with Grignard reagents, 88
Mercurochrome, 483, 588
Mercury compounds, 587
Mercury fulminate, 246
Merthiolate, 588
Mesitylene from acetone, 170, 319
Mesityl oxide, 204
meso forms, 267
meso-inositol, 308
Mesomeric effect in aromatic substitution, 343
Mesyl derivatives of sugars, 287
Metabolism, amino acids, 231
 fat acids, 550
 fats, 155
 nitrogen, 224
 proteins, 231
 starch, 296
Meta chroming, 477
Metadiazine, see 1,3-Diazine, 462
Metalation, 585
Metaldehyde, 179
Metallic halides, reaction with Grignard reagent, 88
Metalloorganic compounds, see Organometallic compounds
Metals, reaction with alcohols, 72
Metanilic acid, 369

Metaphen, 588
Methacrylonitrile, 537
Methallyl alcohol, 518
Methallyl chloride, 509
Methanarsonic acid, 591
Methane, chlorination, 505
 fluorination, 511
 sources, 32
 structure, 21, 23
Methanediol, 518
Methanesulfonic acid, 219
Methanesulfonyl chloride, 222
Methanesulfonyl derivatives of sugars, 287
Methanol, *see* Methyl alcohol, 65, 66
Methine group, 481
Methionine, 228, 232
Methoxycarbonyl group, 144
Methoxychlor, 423
Methoxyl determination, 118
N-Methylacetanilide, 363
"Methyl acetone," 65
Methylacetylcarbinol, 156
Methyl acrylate, 537
α-Methylacrylonitrile, 537
Methylal, 166
Methyl alcohol, 65, 66
 structural formula, 58
2-Methylallyl alcohol, 518
2-Methylallyl chloride, 509
Methylamine, 193
 first synthesis, 246
p-(Methylamino)phenol, 395
N-Methylaniline, 364
Methyl anthranilate, 417
Methylarsenoxide, 590
Methylarsine, 590
Methylation of carbohydrates, 284
 of phenols, 382
2-Methylbenzothiazole, 461
Methylbis(2-chloroethyl)amine, 527
Methyl bromide, 84
Methyl *i*-butyl ketone, 181
Methylcellulose, 303
Methyl chloride, 84
 dipole moment, 97
 from methane, 505
Methylcholanthrene, 442
Methyl cyanide, 198
Methylcyclohexane, toluene from, 317, 318
1-Methylcyclohexyl hydroperoxide, 573
Methylcyclopentane, 318
Methylcyclopentenophenanthrene, 568
Methyldichloroarsine, 592
Methylene chloride, 505
3,6-Methylene-4,5-cyclohexenedicarboxylic anhydride, 546
Methyl ether, 118
Methyl ethyl ketone, 181
Methyl fluoride, 512
N-Methylformamide, 197, 537

Methyl glycosides, 283
Methyl hydroperoxide, 574
Methylidyne group, 481
Methyl iodide, *see* Alkyl halides
Methyl methacrylate, 537
Methylnaphthalenes, 432
  in coal tar, 324
Methyl naphthyl ketones, 431
Methylolurea, 242
Methyl Orange, indicator action, 491
Methylpentoses, 280
α-Methylphenylhydrazine as reagent for
      fructose, 289
Methyl phthalate, 415
1-Methyl-4-*i*-propylbenzene, 316
Methyl propyl ether, 119
Methyl *i*-propyl ketone, 520
1-Methyl-7-*i*-propylphenanthrene, 441
Methylpyridines, 456
Methylquinolines, 458
Methyl radicals, 574
Methyl rubber, 499
Methyl salicylate, 419
Methyl sulfate, 78, 79
Methyl 2-thienyl ketone, 445
Methyl thiocyanate, 251
N-Methylurea, 246
O-Methylurea, 247
1-Methylvinyl acetate, 517
Methyl vinyl ether, 517
Methyl Violet, 481
Metol, 395
Metopryl, 119
Meyer, V., biography, 16
Michler's ketone, 407
Microanalysis, 15
Microcrystalline wax, 55
Middle oil, 323
Milk sugar, 292
Millimicron, 85
Mineral oils, 55
Mirror images, 263
Miticide, benzyl benzoate, 398
Mitscherlich, biography, 310
Mixed ethers, 114
m*μ*, abbreviation for millimicron, 85
Moissan, biography, 510
Molding powders, 389
Molecular formula, 15
Molecular rearrangements, alcohols, 76
  alkanes, 34
  alkenes, 76
  allylic, 509
  Beckmann, 409
  benzidine, 427
  benzilic acid, 408
  Hofmann, 197
  pinacol-pinacolone, 176
Molecular rotation, 261
Molecular weight determination, 16–18

Molozonides, 576
Monazo dyes, 478
Monoglycerides, emulsifying agents, 159
Monoperphthalic acid, 575
Monosaccharides, 277, 278
  α and β forms, 285
Monosodium glutamate, 232
Monothiocarbonic acid, 238
Mordant dyes, 476
Mordanting, 135
Mordants, 476
Morin, 490
Morphine, 467
Mother of vinegar, 133
Mucic acid, 281
Mucilages, 307
Mucins, 225
Mucoids, 225
Muscone, 563
Musk ambrette, 350
Muskene, 350
Musk ketone, 350
Musks, natural, 563
  synthetic, 350
Musk tibetine, 350
Musk xylene, 350
Mustard gas, 221
Mustard oils, 251
Mutarotation, 285
Mydriatics, 400, 467
Myristic acid, 124, 152

Naphtha, coal tar, 323
  petroleum, 55
Naphthacene, 441
Naphthalene, 428
  isolation, 323
  reactions, 429
Naphthalenedisulfonic acids, 432
Naphthalenesulfonic acids, 431
Naphthalene tetrachloride, 430
Naphthalic acid, 437
Naphthalic anhydride, 437
Naphthalimide, 437
Naphthazarin, 487
Naphthenes, 557
Naphthenic acids, 561
Naphthionic acid, 434
Naphthoic acids, 436
α- and β-Naphthol, 432
Naphtholdisulfonic acids, 434
α- and β-Naphthol Orange, 435, 479
Naphtholsulfonic acids, 434
Naphthol Yellow S, 478
Naphthoquinones, 435
α-Naphthylacetic acid, 437
α-Naphthylamine, oxidation, 429
Naphthylamines, 433
Naphthylaminesulfonic acids, 434, 435
Narcotine, 467

Natural gas, 45, 46
  acetylene from, 112
  carbon black from, 46
  gasoline from, 56
  hydrogen from, 46
  methyl alcohol from, 66
  oxygenated compounds from, 56
Neat's foot oil, 152
Nef reaction, 205
Nekals, 432
Nembutal, 462
Neo-, prefix, 26
Neohetramine, 463
Neohexane, 51
Neopentane, structure, 25
Neopentyl alcohol, esterification, 144
Neopentyl halides, reactivity, 96
Neoprene, 503
Neosynephrine, 400
Neutralization equivalent, 127
Neville-Winther acid, 434
Niacin, 457
Niamide, 457
Nicol, biography, 258
Nicol prism, 258
Nicotinamide, 457
Nicotine, 466
  oxidation, 457
Nicotinic acid, 457
Nieuwland, biography, 500
Nightshade, 466
Ninhydrin reaction, 235
Nitration, alkanes, 202
  aromatic amines, 368
  aromatic compounds, 331
  benzene, 314
  mechanism for aromatic compounds, 337
  naphthalene, 430
  phenols, 384
  thiophene, 445
Nitricidium ion in aromatic nitrations, 338
Nitriles, *see* Cyanides
Nitrites, test for, 385
Nitroacetanilides, 368
Nitroalkanes, 201–205
Nitroanilines, 368, 370
  basicity, 364
α-Nitroanthraquinone, 439
Nitrobenzene, 350
  reduction products, 348
Nitrobenzenesulfonic acids, 354
Nitrobenzid, 350
Nitrocellulose, 299
Nitrochlorobenzenes, 332
Nitro compounds, aliphatic, 201–205
  aromatic, 331
    displacement reactions, 345
    physical properties, 344
    physiological action, 345
    reduction products, 345–348

Nitro dyes, 478
Nitroethane, 202
Nitro form, 203
Nitrogen cycle, 224
Nitrogen determination, 12, 13
Nitrogen metabolism, 224
Nitrogen mustards, 527
Nitrogen rings, opening by exhaustive
  methylation, 455
Nitroglycerin, 525
Nitro group, aromatic, effect on reactivity
  of other substituents, 348
  resonance structure, 203, 339
Nitroguanidine, 249
Nitrolic acids, 204
Nitromethane, 202
Nitromethylnaphthalenes, 432
α-Nitronaphthalene, oxidation, 429
Nitronaphthalenes, 430
Nitronaphthalenesulfonic acids, 434
Nitronium ion in aromatic nitrations, 337
Nitroparaffins, *see* Nitroalkanes, 201–205
p-Nitrophenacyl bromide, 408
p-Nitrophenacyl esters, 408
Nitrophenols, acidity, 381
  physical properties, 384
  preparation, 384
3-Nitrophthalic acid, 429
Nitropropanes, 202
3-Nitropyridine, 456
3-Nitropyrrole, 448
Nitrosation, nitroalkanes, 204
  phenols, 385
  secondary amines, 190, 364
  tertiary aromatic amines, 365
Nitrosoamines, 190, 364, 365
Nitrosobenzene, by oxidation of *N*-phenyl-
  hydroxylamine, 347
p-Nitrosodimethylaniline, 365
Nitroso dyes, 478
N-Nitroso-*N*-methylaniline, 364
p-Nitrosophenol, 385
Nitrostarch, 297
2-Nitrothiophene, 445
Nitrotoluenes, 332
Nitrourea, 247
Nitrous acid, reactions, aliphatic amines,
  190
  amides, 197
  aromatic amines, 364, 365
  nitroalkanes, 204
  phenols, 385
  urea, 241
No-bond resonance, 344
Nomenclature, acid anhydrides, 138
  acyl halides, 136
  alcohols, 58
  aldehydes, 162
  alkanes, 25
  alkenes, 37

Nomenclature
alkyl groups, 27
alkynes, 109
amides, 196
amines, 183
aromatic compounds, 321
carbohydrates, 277
carboxylic acids, 124
disulfides, 213
esters, 144
ethers, 114
Geneva system, 28
I.U.C. system, 28
ketones, 162
mercaptans, 210
sulfides, 212
sulfones, 218
sulfonic acids, 219, 352
sulfoxides, 216
Nonadecanoic acid, 124
Nonreducing disaccharides, 292
"Nonylaldehyde," *see* 3,5,5-Trimethyl-
hexanal, 181
Nonylic acid, from oleic acid, 541
Novocain, 418
Nucleophilic reagents, 98
Nucleoproteins, 225
Nylon 66, 544
Nylon salt, 544

O^{18}, as tracer element, 144, 146
O-alkylation, *see* Oxygen alkylation
Octaacetylsucrose, *see* Sucrose octaacetate,
293
Octane number, 49
2-Octanol, 541
Odor of fruits, 148
Odors, masking of, 406
Oe-, *see* E-
Oil cloth, 157
Oil of, *see also source, e.g.* Orange oil
Oil of bitter almonds, artificial, 350
Oil of mirbane, 350
Oils, 151, *see also individual oil, e.g.,* Olive oil
acetyl value, 154
animal, 152
digestion, 155
drying, 152, 156
essential, 564
fish, 152
hydrogenation, 154
hydrolysis, 155
iodine number, 152–154
isomerization, 154
lubricating, 54
nondrying, 152
rancidity, 154
reactions, 153
saponification, 153
saponification number, 152, 153

semidrying, 152
sulfated, 158
thiocyanogen value, 154
uses, 155–160
vegetable, 152
volatile, 564
Oiticica oil, 152
Oleanolic acid, 567
Olefiant gas, 38
Olefins, *see* Alkenes
Oleic acid, 151
geometrical isomerism, 254, 256
Oleomargarin, 156
Oligosaccharides, 290
Olive oil, 152
Opium, 467
Oppenauer oxidation, 164
Optical activity, 259
Optical antipodes, 263
Optical bleaches, 483
Optical isomerism, 261
Optical isomers, 254
number, 264
Optical rotation, 260
Orange I, 435
Orange II, 435, 479
Orange oil, 564
Orcinol, 393
Ordinary ray, 258
Organic chemistry, definition, 4
fundamental principles, 9
historical, 1
Organic compounds, classification, 19
isolation and purification, 9
number, 5, 8, 18
Organometallic compounds, 86, 584, *see
also individual metal, e.g.,* Sodium
compounds
Orientation of aromatic compounds, 320
Orlon, 537
Orthanilic acid, 369
Orthocarbonates, 237
Orthocarbonic acid, 237
Orthodiazine, *see* 1,2-Diazine, 462
Orthothiocarbonic acid, 238
Osazone formation, 282
Osazones of disaccharides, solubility, 292
Osones, 82
Ovalbumin, 225, 226
Oxalacetic ester, 551
Oxalic acid, reactions, 542
synthesis, 539
Oxazole, 461
Oxidation, *see also* Autoxidation *and indi-
vidual oxidizing agent, e.g.* Lead
tetraacetate
alcohols, 77, 121, 133, 161
aldehydes, 172
alkanes, 33, 56, 577
alkenes, 39, 40, 121

Oxidation
  aniline, 366
  anthracene, 438
  anthraquinone vats, 487
  aromatic amines, 366
  aromatic side chains, 316, 401, 411
  benzene to maleic anhydride, 546
  benzene to phenol, 388
  carbohydrates, 280, 281, 284
  crotonic aldehyde to maleic anhydride, 546
  disulfides, 214
  1,2-glycols, 520
  Grignard reagents, 88
  indigo white, 486
  isoquinoline, 459
  ketones, 172
  leuco bases, 480
  mercaptans, 211
  naphthalene, 415
  α-naphthylamine, 429
  nicotine, 457
  1-nitronaphthalene, 429
  phenanthrene, 441
  phenols, 383, 395
  picolines, 457
  quinoline, 458
  saturated hydrocarbons, 33, 56, 577
  sulfides, 212
  tertiary amines, 190
  o-xylene, 415
Oxidation number, 122
Oxidation-reduction equations, balancing, 122
Oxides, *see* Alkoxides, Amine oxides, Sulfoxides, Epoxides, *and* Ethers
Oxidized cellulose, 303
Oximes, 171
  Beckmann rearrangement, 409
  dehydration to cyanides, 199
  reduction to primary amines, 186
  stereochemistry, 408
Oxonium ions, intermediates, in ether formation, 116
  in reactions of alcohols and acids, 98, 100
Oxonium salts, alcohols, 71
  ethers, 117
Oxo process, 181
Oxozonides, 577
Oxyacetylene flame, 113
Oxygen, autoxidation by, 577–582
  catalyst for polymerization, 94
  as free biradical, 94
  inhibition of chain reactions, 94
  reaction with Grignard reagents, 88
Oxygen alkylation, β-keto esters, 552
  urea, 247
Ozonation, alkenes, 39

Ozone, addition to alkenes, 39
  structure, 576
Ozonides, 39, 162, 576
Ozonization, *see* Ozonation, 39
Ozonolysis, 39

Paint, 156
Paint thinners, 55, 156, 565
Palmitic acid, 124, 151
Palmitoleic acid, 151
Palm oil, 152
Palm sugar, 293
Paludrine, 470
Pamaquine, 469
Pantothenic acid, 535
P.A.P., 394
Papaverine, 467
Paradiazine, *see* 1,4-Diazine, 462
Paradichlor, *see* Dichlorobenzenes, 327
Paraffin hydrocarbons, *see* Alkanes
Paraffin oils, 55
Paraffin wax, 55
Paraformaldehyde, 177
Paraldehyde, 179
Pararosaniline, 481
Parchment paper, 299
Paris green, 135
Pasteur, biography, 67
Peanut oil, 152
Pectic acids, 305
Pectins, 305
Pelargonic acid, 124
Pelargonidin chloride, 491
Penicillins, 461
Pentaacetylglucose, 286
Pentacene, 442
Pentachloroethane, 507
Pentachlorofluoroethane, 514
Pentachlorophenol, 391
Pentacosanoic acid, 124
Pentadecanoic acid, 124
Pentadecanolide, 563
Pentadigalloylglucose, 419
Pentaerythritol, 526
  nitrate, 526
Pentamethylenediamine, 455, 528
Pentanes, equilibrium composition of isomeric, 52
  structure, 25
Pentanols, *see* Amyl alcohols
Pentaquine, 470
Pentasol, 85
Pentenes, *see* Amylenes, 37, 71
Pentobarbital, 462
Pentoses, color reactions, 288
  furfural from, 287
Pentothal sodium, 463
Pepper, 466
Pepsin, 231
Peptides, 233

Per-, prefix, 507
Peracetic acid, 575
Peracids, 575, 581
Perbenzoic acid, 414, 576, 581
Perchloroethylene, 507
Perfluorocyclohexane, 511
Perfluoro-1,3-dimethylcyclohexane, 514
Perfluoroheptane, 511
Perfumes, *see individual odor, e.g.* Jasmine
    odor
Periodic acid as oxidizing agent, 284, 520
Periodic table, *inside back cover*
Perkin, biography, 474
Perkin, Jr., biography, 557
Perkin synthesis, 404
Peroxide-catalyzed addition of hydrogen
    bromide, mechanism, 103
Peroxides, 572–583
    detection, 118, 577
Perspective formulas, 265
Perspex, 538
Perylene, 442
PETN, 526
Petrolatum, 55
Petroleum, 45–56
Petroleum ether, 54
Petroleum jelly, 55
Petroselenic acid, 151
Phenacyl bromide, 408
Phenacyl chloride, 408
Phenacyl esters, 408
Phenanthraquinone, 441
Phenanthrene, 440
    isolation, 324
Phenanthridine, 459
o-Phenanthroline, 459
Phene, 322
Phenetole, 382
Phenobarbital, 462
Phenol, from coal tar, 324
    commercial syntheses, 386
Phenol coefficient, 386
Phenol ethers from diazonium salts, 377
    from phenols, 382
Phenol-formaldehyde resins, 388
Phenolic resins, 388
Phenolphthalein, 482
    indicator action, 492
Phenols, 380–392
    physical properties, 381
    physiological action, 386, 393
    preparation, 380
    reactions, 381
    test for, 397
Phenolsulfonic acids, 381
Phenolsulfonphthalein, 483
Phenoquinone, 381
Phenyl, 322
Phenyl acetate, 382
Phenylalanine, 227

Phenylarsenoxide, 592
Phenylarsine, 592
Phenylarsonic acid, 592
N-Phenylcarbamyl chloride, 364
Phenyl cyanide, 355
Phenylenediamines, 370
Phenylene group, 322
N-Phenylethanolamine, 485
Phenyl ether, 387
β-Phenylethyl alcohol, 399
β-Phenylethylamine, 399
Phenylethylene, 424
    substitution reactions, 343
Phenylglucosazone, *see* Glucose phenylosa-
    zone, 282
N-Phenylglycine, 485
N-Phenylglycine-*o*-carboxylic acid, 485
Phenylhydrazine, reaction with aldehydes
    and ketones, 172
N-Phenylhydroxylamine, by reduction of
    nitrobenzene, 346
Phenyl isocyanate, 252, 364
Phenyl isothiocyanate, 366
Phenyllithium, 584
Phenylmalonic ester, 545
Phenyl methyl ether, *see* Anisole, 382
Phenyl mustard oil, 366
Phenylnitromethane, tautomerism, 554
Phenylphenols, 387
Phenyl phosphate, 391
Phenyl radicals, 578
Phenyl salicylate, 418
Phenylsilicon trichloride, 595
N-Phenylsulfamic acid, 369
Phenyl sulfone, 353, 358
Phenyl tolyl ketoximes, 409
Phloroglucinol, 394
    reaction with furfural, 454
Phorone, 169
Phosgene, 237, 239
Phosphagen, 249
Phosphatides, *see* Phospholipids, 527
Phospholipids, 527
Phosphoproteins, 225
Phosphorus, determination in organic com-
    pounds, 14
Phosphorus trihalides, reaction with acids,
    121
    with alcohols, 74
    with Grignard reagents, 88
Photographic developers, 395
    film base, 301
    image development, 395
Phthaleins, 482
Phthalic acid, 414
Phthalic anhydride, 414
Phthalimide, 416
Physcion, 440
Physical properties, covalent and electro-
    valent compounds, 4, 7

Physiological action, *see* Toxicity
Phytic acid, 308
Phytin, 308
Phytol, 566
Picene, 442
Picolines, 456
Picolinic acids, 457
α-Picolyllithium, 585
Picramide, 364
Picric acid, 384, 391
Picryl chloride, *see* 2,4,6-Trinitrochloro-benzene, 362
Pigments, *see* Plant pigments
Pimelic acid, preparation, 541
    reactions, 543
Pinacol, 176
Pinacolone, 176
Pinacol-pinacolone rearrangement, 176
Pinacol reduction, 176
Pineapple, volatile oils, 148
α-Pinene, 565
Pine splint test for pyrrole, 447
Piperic acid, 466
Piperidine, 455
Piperine, 466
Piperonal, 406
Pitch, coal tar, 323
    petroleum, 55
Pivalic aldehyde, 178
Plane of symmetry, 263
Plane-polarized light, 258
Plantation rubber, 495
Plant fibers, 298
    gums, 307
    mucilages, 307
    pigments, anthocyanins, 491
        anthraquinone, 440
        carotenoid, 567
        chlorophylls, 450
Plasmochin, 469
Plastics, melamine, 248
    phenol-formaldehyde, 388
    polyethylene, 43
    polymethyl methacrylate, 537
    polystyrene, 425
    polytetrafluoroethylene, 514
    polyvinyl, 507, 516
    urea-formaldehyde, 243
Plexiglas, 538
Poison gases, chloroarsines, 592
    Lewisite, 592
    mustard gas, 221
    nitrogen mustards, 527
    phosgene, 239
Poison ivy, 393
Poison oak, 393
Polarimeter, 260
Polarimeter tube, 260
Polariscope, 260
Polarizability of molecules, 62

Polarization, of light, 257
    of molecules, 62
Polarized light, 257
Polarizer, 260
Polar molecules, 63
Polar number, 122
Polaroid, 259
Polyacrylates, 537
Polyacrylonitrile, 537
Polyamines, 526
Polycarboxylic acids, 539
Polyenes, autoxidation, 579
Polyesters, 415, 416
Polyethylene, 43
Polyethylene glycol, 522
Polygenetic dyes, 487
Polyhydric alcohols, 518
Polyhydric phenols, 392
Polyisobutylene, 43
    to improve viscosity index, 54
Polymerization, acid catalyzed, 103
    aldehydes, 169, 170
    alkenes, 43
    cracked gases to liquid fuels, 51
    free-radical catalyzed, 94
    methyl methacrylate, 537
    pyrroles, 447
    styrene, 425
    tetrafluoroethylene, 514
    vinyl compounds, 507, 516
Polymethyl methacrylate, 537
Polynuclear hydrocarbons, *see* Biphenyl, 426, *and* Condensed nuclear hydro-carbons, 428
Polyoxymethylene, 177
Polypeptides, 233
Polysaccharides, 295–307
Polystyrene, 425
Polytetrafluoroethylene, 514
Polythene, *see* Polyethylene, 43
Polyuronides, 306
Polyvinyl acetate, 516
Polyvinyl alcohol, 516
Polyvinyl butyral, 517
Polyvinyl chloride, 507
Polyvinyl methyl ether, 517
Ponndorf reduction, *see* Meerwein-Ponn-dorf reduction, 164
Porphins, 449
Porphyrins, 449
Position isomers, 254
Prechromed dyes, 477
Pressor activity of β-phenylethylamines, 400
Primary alcohols, 59
    amines, 183, 185
        from nitroalkanes, 204
    carbon atoms, 59
Primary component in coupling reactions, 378
Procaine, 418

Progesterone, 569
Projection formulas, 265
Prolamines, 225
Proline, 227, 449
Prontosil, 372
"Proof" of alcohol, 70
Propadiene, 494
Propadrine, 400
Propane, pyrolysis, 92
   structure, 22, 23
1,2-Propanediol, 523
Propanols, *see* Propyl alcohols
Propionaldehyde by oxo process, 181
Propionic acid, 124, 135
i-Propyl alcohol, synthesis, 70
n-Propyl alcohol, 67
i-Propylbenzene, 316
Propyl bromides, 42
Propylene, chlorination, 508
Propylene chlorohydrin, 42, 523
Propylene glycol, 523
Propylene oxide, 523
i-Propyl ether, 119
α-*n*-Propylpiperidine, 465
Prosthetic groups, 224
Protamines, 225
Protective coatings, lacquer, 301
   paint, 156
   synthetic enamel, 415
   varnish, 157
Proteins, 224–226
Proton-bonding, 63
   alcohols, 60
   amines, 187
   carboxylic acids, 125
   ethyl acetoacetate, 554
   nitrophenols, 384
Protonoid reagents, 193
Protopectins, 305
Protoporphyrin, 450
Prototropy, 98
Pseudo acids, 203
Pseudoasymmetric carbon atoms, 267
Pseudo base, 491
Pteroylglutamic acid, 235
Purines, 463
Purity, criteria, 11
Putrescine, 528
Pyranosides, 291, 292
Pyrans, 459
Pyrazines, 462
Pyrazole, 460
Pyrene, 441
Pyribenzamine, 457
Pyridazines, 462
Pyridine, 454
   isolation, 324
Pyridinecarboxylic acids, 457
2,3-Pyridinedicarboxylic acid, 458
3,4-Pyridinedicarboxylic acid, 459

Pyridines, 454
3-Pyridinesulfonic acid, 456
Pyridoxal, 457
Pyridoxin, 457
Pyrimidines, 462
Pyrogallic acid, 393
Pyrogallol, 393
Pyroligneous acid, 65, 133
Pyrolysis, 53
   carboxylic acids, 162, *see also* Decar-
      boxylation
   hydrocarbons, 30
   mechanism, 92
Pyromucic acid, 453
Pyrotartaric acid, 549
Pyroxylins, 300
Pyrrole, 446
Pyrrolecarboxylic acids, 448, 449
Pyrrolidine, 449
Pyrroline, 449
2-Pyrryl ketones, 448
Pyruvic acid, 549
Pyrylium salts, 459

Quartz, optical activity, 259, 262
Quaternary ammonium compounds, 194
Quercitin, 490
Quercitrin, 490
Quick process for vinegar, 133
Quinacrine, 469
Quinaldine, 458
Quinhydrone, 396
Quinidine, 469
Quinine, 468
Quinoline, 458
Quinolinic acid, 458
Quinone, 396
Quinone chloroimide, 367
Quinone chloroimides, 397
Quinonediimines, 396
Quinonemonoxime, 385
Quinones, 395, 435
Quinonimines, 396

Racemic acid, 261
Racemic forms, 267
Racemization, 270
R-acid, 434
Radicals, *see* Free radicals
Raffinose, 294
Rancidity of fats and oils, 154
Rape seed oil, 152
Raschig process for phenol, 387
Rast camphor method, 18
Rayon, 303
RDX, 177
Reactive hydrogen, Zerevitinov determina-
      tion, 87
Reactive methylene groups, 544, 552

Reactivity, alcohols with halogen acids, 74
  alcohols with inorganic acid halides, 74
  alkenes, 41, 42
  alkyl halides, 83, 92, 96
  allyl halides, 509
  aryl halides, 329
  benzyl halides, 330
  carboxylic acids, 140, 412
  change in relative order, 98
  dehydration of alcohols, 76
  Grignard reagents, 586
  hydrogen, 73, 585
  organometallic compounds, 585
  vinyl halides, 508
Rearrangements, *see* Molecular rearrangements
Red ink, 483
Red oil, 158
Reducing disaccharides, 290
Reduction, acids, 129
  aldehydes, 163
  alkenes, 39
  alkynes, 110
  aromatic nitro compounds, **345**
  aromatic ring, 559
  catalytic, mechanism, 93
  cyanides, 199
  disulfides, 210, 214
  esters, 147
  isocyanides, 200
  ketones, 163
  naphthalene, 430
  nitroalkanes, 204
  oximes, 186
  Schiff bases, 403
Red, white, and blue reaction, 204
Reformatsky reaction, 533
Reforming of gasoline, 51
Reimer-Tiemann reaction, 402
Relative configuration, 273
Remsen, biography, 416
Reppe process for 1,3-butadiene, **501**
Resin acids, 566
Resins, acrylic or acryloid, 537
  alkyd, 416
  glyptal, 415
  ion-exchange, 390
  melamine, 248
  methylmethacrylate, 537
  natural, 566
  phenol-formaldehyde, 388
  urea-formaldehyde, 243
Resole, 388
Resolution of racemic mixtures, 268
Resonance, acidity of aromatic acids, 412
  acidity of carboxylic acids, 129
  acidity of phenols, 382
  allyl carbonium ion, 509
  aniline, 363
  and aromatic substitution, 343

and autoxidation, 579
  benzene, 313
  carboxylate ion, 129
  carboxyl group, 130
  chlorobenzene, 392
  1,3-dienes, 495
  energy, 130
  enolate ion of β-keto esters, 552
  free radicals, 424
  guanidinium ion, 249
  hybrid, 130
  hyperconjugation, 344
  and interatomic distance, 130
  isocyanates, 246
  Methyl Orange, 492
  naphthalene, 429
  nitrobenzene, 344
  nitro group, 203, 339
  no-bond, 344
  phenolate ion, 343
  phenolphthalein, 492
  phenylethylene, 343
  stabilization of free radicals, 424, 579
  thiophene, 446
  triphenylmethyl, 424
  vinyl chloride, 508
Resorcinol, 393
Resorcylaldehyde, 402
Restricted rotation, about double bonds, 254
  in ethane, 24
Retene, 441, 566
Rhamnose, 280
Rhubarb, cathartic principle, 440
Riboflavin, 465
Ribose, 279
Ricinoleic acid, 151
Ring structures, carbohydrates, 283, 285, 288
  perspective formulas, 288
Robison ester, 287
Rochelle salts, 547
Rosaniline dyes, 481
Rose oil, 399, 564
Rosin, 566
  disproportionated, 502
Rotation, optical, 261
Rotatory dispersion, 260
Royal purple, 486
Rubber, natural, 495–499
  synthetic, 499–504
Runge, biography, 474
Rutin, 490

Saccharic acids, 281
Saccharides, 277
Saccharin, 416
Safrole, 392
Salicin, 398

Salicylaldehyde, 402, 420
Salicylic acid, 418
Saligenin, 385, 398
Salol, 418
Salt colors, 476
Salts of carboxylic acids, reactions, 131, 132, 136
   of sulfonic acids, reactions, 354
Salvarsan, 593
Sandmeyer reaction, 377
Saponification of esters, 145
   of fats and oils, 153
   steric effect with aromatic acids, 412
Saponification equivalent, 145
Saponification number, 153
   fats and oils, 152
Saponins, 567
Sarans, 508
Sarcolactic acid, 534
Sassafras oil, 392
Saturated hydrocarbons, *see* Alkanes
Schaeffer's acid, 434
Scheele, biography, 2
Schiff bases, 365, 403
Schiff's reagent, 173
   structure, 481
Schotten-Baumann reaction, 413
Schweitzer's reagent, 298
Scleroproteins, 225
Sebacic acid, 541
Seconal, 462
Secondary alcohols, 59
   alkyl groups, 27
   amines, 183, 186, 403
   carbon atoms, 28, 59
Secondary component in coupling reactions, 378
Selenides, 217
Selenium dehydrogenation, 441
Selenonium salts, 215
Semicarbazide, *see* Semicarbazine, 247
Semicarbazine, 247
   reaction with aldehydes and ketones, 172
Semicarbazones, 172
Semimicroanalyses, 15
Semipolar bonds, 189
   amine oxides, 190
   isocyanides, 189
   nitro group, 201
   sulfur compounds, 208
Senna, cathartic principle, 440
Serine, 227
Serum albumins, 225, 226
Serum globulins, 226
Sesquiterpenes, 564, 565
Sex hormones, 569
Side chain, aromatic, halogenation, 328
   oxidation, 316
Silane, 594
Silanols, 595

Silicane, 594
Silicochloroform, 594
Silicoethane, *see* Disilane, 594
Silicon compounds, 593
Silicones, 596
Silicon hydrides, 594
Silicon tetrachloride, 594
   reaction with Grignard reagents, 88, 595
Silk, 229
Siloxanes, 596
Silver acetylide, 111
Silver carbide, 111
Silver salt, 438
6–12 (six-twelve), 524
606 (six-o-six), 593
666 (six-six-six), 326
Skeletal isomers, 254
Skraup synthesis of quinolines, 458
Skunk secretion, 221
Smokeless powder, 300
Smoke screens, 507
SN-7618, 469
SN-9972, 469
SN-13276, 470
S_N1 and S_N2 reactions, 98
Soap plants, 567
Soaps, 157
   invert, 195
Soda process for wood pulp, 298
Sodioacetoacetic ester, 550
Sodiomalonic ester, 545
Sodium acetate, 135
Sodium acetylide, 111
Sodium alcoholates, *see* Sodium alkoxides
Sodium alkoxides, 72
Sodium benzenesulfonate, 353
Sodium bisulfite, addition to aldehydes and ketones, 165
   addition to double bonds, 218
Sodium carbide, 111
Sodium chloride, electronic structure, 5
   hydration of ions, 8
Sodium compounds, 584
Sodium cupricitrate, 548
Sodium cupritartrate, 547
Sodium ethoxide, 73
Sodium formate, 132
Sodium methoxide, 72
Sodium oxalate, 132
Solubility, 61, 64
   effect of bond type, 7
Solvents, 65
L-Sorbitol, 307, 308
Sorbose, 289
Sorghum, 293
Soybean oil, 152
Spans, 308
Specific rotation, 261
Spermaceti, 150
Spermine, 528

Sphingomyelin, 527
Sphingosine, 527
Spontaneous combustion, 157
Spruce turpentine, *see* p-Cymene, 319
Spun rayon, 305
Squalene, 567
Stannic chloride, reaction with Grignard reagents, 88
Staple fiber, 304
Starch, 295
Starch nitrates, 297
Steam distillation, 11
Stearic acid, 124, 151
Stereoisomerism, 254–276
  geometrical, 254
  optical, 257
  oximes, 408
Stereoisomers, 254
Steric effect, 98
  alkyl groups, 96, 98
  esterification, 145, 412
Steric hindrance, 96
  effect on reactivity of alkyl halides, 96
  esterification, 145, 412
Steroids, 567–570
Sterols, 568
cis- and *trans*-Stilbene, 426
Stilbestrol, *see* Diethylstilbestrol, 569
Storax, 425
Strain theory, 557
Straw oil, 323
Strecker synthesis, 232
Structural isomers, 254
Structure, electronic theory, 5
Stuart models, 23
Styphnic acid, 393
Styrene, 425
  from cyclooctatetraene, 562
Suberic acid, 541
Substantive dyes, 476
Substitution reactions, 85
  aromatic compounds, 332, 335, 344
  halogenation, 84, 327, 508
  mechanism, 335
  nitration, 202, 331
  pyridine, 456
  sulfonation, 219, 352
  thiophene, 446
Succinic acid, preparation, 540
  reactions, 542
Succinic acids, α,β-disubstituted, 545
Succinic anhydride, 543
Sucrase, hydrolysis of sucrose, 68
Sucrose, 292
Sucrose octaacetate, 293
Sugar alcohols, 307
Sugar of lead, 135
Sugar sand, 547
Sugars, *see* Carbohydrates
Suida process, 133

Sulfadiazine, 372
Sulfa drugs, 372
Sulfaguanidine, 373
Sulfanilamide, 372
Sulfanilic acid, 369
Sulfapyridine, 372
Sulfated fats and oils, 158
Sulfathiazole, 373
Sulfhydryl group, 210
Sulfide dyes, 489
Sulfides, 212, 213
Sulfinic acids, 216, 358
Sulfinyl group, 216
Sulfite liquors, fermentation, 68
Sulfite process for wood pulp, 298
Sulfonal, 222
Sulfonamides, 220, 357
Sulfonated fats and oils, 158
Sulfonates, 221, 356
Sulfonation, alkanes, 219
  anthracene, 438
  aromatic amines, 369
  aromatic compounds, 353
  benzene, 315
  mechanism, 338
  naphthalene, 431
  phenols, 383
  thiophene, 445
Sulfones, 217, 358
Sulfonic acid esters, 221, 356
Sulfonic acids, 218, 352
Sulfonium hydroxides, 215
Sulfonium salts, 215
  from sulfides, 213
Sulfonphthaleins, 483
Sulfonyl chlorides, 219, 220, 356
  reduction to mercaptans, 217
Sulfonyl group, 218
Sulfoxides, 216
Sulfur, detection in organic compounds, 12
  determination, 14
Sulfur compounds, aliphatic, 208–223
Sulfur dehydrogenations, 441, 566
Sulfur dioxide, addition of Grignard reagents, 216
  refining kerosene, 53
  refining lubricating oils, 54
Sulfur dyes, 477, 489
Sulfuric acid, addition to alkenes, 41
Superimposability, 263
Suprarenine, *see* Epinephrine, 400
Suprasterols, 568
Surface-active agents, *see* Detergents
Swarts, biography, 510
Swarts' reaction, 512
Sweetness, saccharin, 416
  sugars, 289
sym-, prefix, 37
Symmetry and optical activity, 263
Sympathomimetic amines, 399

syn-, prefix, 408
Synthetic detergents, *see* Detergents
    fibers, 303
    fuels, 55
    musks, 350
    rubbers, 499
    wool, 229

Tachysterol, 568
Tall oil, 298
Tallow, 152
Tannic acid, 419
Tannin, 419
Tar acids, 323, 380
Tar bases, 324
Tartar, 547
Tartaric acid, 547
(−)Tartaric acid, configuration, 274
Tartaric acids, optical isomerism, 261, 266
Tartronic acid, 281, 547
Taurine, 569
Taurocholic acid, 569
Tautomeric effect in aromatic substitution, 343
Tautomerism, 203, 553
    β-keto esters, 554
    nitroalkanes, 203, 554
    phloroglucinol, 394
    thioacids and thioamides, 214
Tea, 464
Teflon, 514
TEL, *see* Tetraethyllead, 589
1080 (ten-eighty), 531
TEPP, *see* Ethyl pyrophosphate, 79
Terephthalic acid, 416
Terpenes, 564
Terphenyl, 426
Tertiary alcohols, 60, 140, 144
    alkyl groups, 28
    amines, 224
    carbon atoms, 28, 59
Terylene, 416
Testosterone, 569
Tetrabromofluorescein, 483
Tetrachloro-1,2-difluoroethane, 514
1,1,2,2-Tetrachloroethane, 506
Tetrachloroethylene, 507
Tetracontanes, 26
Tetradecanes, 26
Tetraethylenepentamine, 528
Tetraethyllead, 589
    as knock inhibitor, 53
Tetraethylpyrophosphate, *see* Ethyl pyrophosphate, 79
Tetraethylthiuram disulfide, 251
Tetrafluoroethylene, 514
Tetrahedral configuration of carbon compounds, 23, 263
Tetrahydrofuran, 453, 454
Tetrahydrofurfuryl alcohol, 452

Tetrahydronaphthalene, 430
Tetrahydropyrrole, 449
Tetraiodophenolphthalein, 482
Tetraiodopyrrole, 448
Tetralin, 430
    autoxidation, 578
α-Tetralone, 578
Tetramethylammonium hydroxide, 194
Tetramethylammonium salts, decomposition, 194
1,2,4,5-Tetramethylbenzene, 316
Tetramethylene chloride, 453
Tetramethylene chlorohydrin, 453
Tetramethylenediamine, 528
Tetramethylene glycol, 524
2,3,4,6-Tetramethylglycose, 285
Tetramethylsilane, 595
Tetramethylthiuram disulfide, 251, 498
Tetranitromethane, 205
Tetraphenylethylene, 426
Tetraphenylmethane, 423
Tetraterpenes, 564, 567
Tetronal, 222
Tetryl, 373
Thebaine, 467
2-Thenylammonium chloride, 445
2-Thenyl chloride, 445
Theobromine, 464
Theophylline, 464
Therapeutic index, 593
Thermal decomposition, *see* Pyrolysis
Thermofor process, 50
Thiamine, 463
Thiazoles, 461
2-Thienyl chloride, 445
2-Thienylmercuric chloride, 445
2-Thienyl methyl ketone, 445
Thioacetals, 222
Thioaldehydes, 214
Thioamides, tautomerism, 214
Thiocarbamates, 252
Thiocarbamic acid, 238
Thiocarbanilide, 366
Thiocarbonic acid derivatives, 249–253
Thiocarboxylic acids, 214
Thiocyanates, 251
    sulfonyl chlorides from, 220
Thiocyanogen, 252
Thiocyanogen value, 154
Thioesters, 214
    from mercaptans, 211
Thioketones, 214
Thiokols, 503
Thiols, *see* Mercaptans
Thionyl chloride, reaction with acids, 135
    with alcohols, 74
Thiophene, 444
Thiophenecarboxylic acid, 445, 446
Thiophenes, 444–446
2-Thiophenesulfonic acid, 445

Thiophenols, 358
Thiourea, 252
Thiourethans, 252
Thiouronium salts, 253
Thiuram disulfides, 251
Thiuronium salts, 253
Thonzylamine, 463
Threonine, 227
Thyme oil, 392
Thymine, 462
Thymol, 391
Thyroglobulin, 226
Thyroxine, 228
Tiglic acid, 538
Tischenko reaction, 179
TNT, 351
Tobacco, 466
Tobacco mosaic virus, 226
Tocopherols, 460
o-Tolidine, 427
Tollen's reagent, oxidation of aldehydes, 173
Tolu balsam, 310
Toluene, 317
o-Toluenesulfonamide, 417
p-Toluenesulfonic acid, 356
o-Toluenesulfonyl chloride, 356, 417
p-Toluenesulfonyl chloride, 356
Toluidines, 370
Toluol, 323
Tolyl groups, 322
Tomato pigment, 567
Tonka bean, 420
Tosylation, 357
Tosyl chloride, 357
Tosyl derivatives of sugars, 287
Tourmaline, 259
Toxicity, aromatic amines, 361
    aromatic nitro compounds, 345
    arsenic compounds, 592
    benzene, 313
    cyanides, 199
    fluorine compounds, 511
    halogen compounds, 505, 506
    isocyanides, 200
    mercaptans, 210
    mercury compounds, 587
    phenol, 386
Toxisterol, 568
Tragacanth gum, 307
Transeterification, 145
    up-grading of drying oils, 156
trans isomers, 255
Transition complex, *see* Transition state, 91
Transition state, 91
Tretolites, 432
Triacontanes, 26
2,4,6-Triaminobenzoic acid, 394
Tribenzylamine, 399
2,4,6-Tribromoaniline, 367
1,2,4-Tribromobenzene, 327

1,3,5-Tribromobenzene, 377
2,4,6-Tribromophenol, 384
Trichloroacetaldehyde, 518
Trichloroacetic acid, 531
2,4,6-Trichloroaniline, 367
1,2,4-Trichlorobenzene, 327
1,1,2-Trichloroethane, 508
Trichloroethylene, 506
Trichlorofluoromethane, 513
Trichlorosilane, 594
1,1,2-Trichloro-1,2,2-trifluoroethane, 514
1,1,2-Trichloro-3,3,3-trifluoropropene, 513
Tricosanes, 26
Tricosanoic acid, 124
Tricresyl phosphate, 391
Tridecanes, 26
Tridecanoic acid, 124
Tridecylic acid, 124
Triethanolamine, 526
Triethylene glycol, 522
Triethyl phosphate, *see* Ethyl phosphate, 79
Trifluoroacetic acid, 530
1,1,1-Trifluoroethane, 512
Triglycerides, *see* Glycerides, 151
1,2,3-Trihydroxybenzene, *see* Pyrogallol, 393
1,3,5-Trihydroxybenzene, *see* Phloroglucinol, 394
2,6,8-Trihydroxypurine, 464
Triisopropylidene peroxide, 581
Triketohydrindene hydrate, 235
Trimethylacetaldehyde, 178
Trimethylamine, 193
Trimethylamine oxide, 191
Trimethylarsine oxide, 590
1,3,5-Trimethylbenzene, 313
Trimethylcetylammonium chloride, 195
Trimethylethylammonium hydroxide, decomposition, 194
Trimethylene chloride, 524
Trimethylene glycol, 522
Trimethylene halohydrins, 524
Trimethylenetrinitramine, 177
3,5,5-Trimethylhexanal, 181
2,2,4-Trimethylpentane, as a standard fuel, 49
    synthesis, 51
2,4,6-Trinitroaniline, 364
1,3,5-Trinitrobenzene, 351
2,4,6-Trinitrobenzoic acid, 351, 394
2,4,6-Trinitrochlorobenzene, 362
2,4,6-Trinitrophenol, 384, 391
2,4,6-Trinitroresorcinol, 393
2,4,6-Trinitrotoluene, 351
Triolein, 153
Trional, 222
1,3,5-Trioxane, 177
Trioxymethylene, *see* 1,3,5-Trioxane, 177
Tripalmitin, 153
Triphenylamine, 363

Triphenylcarbinol, 399
Triphenylchloromethane, 399
Triphenylethylene, 426
Triphenylmethane, 422
Triphenylmethane dyes, 480
Triphenylmethide ion, 424
Triphenylmethonium ion, 424
Triphenylmethyl, 424
Triphenylmethyl chloride, 399
Triphenylmethyl sodium, 584
Triphenyl phosphate, 391
Triphenyls, *see* Terphenyls, 426
Triphenylsilanol, 595
Triple bond, 109
Triptane, as high-octane fuel, 49
Trisaccharides, 294
Trisazo dyes, 480
Tris(2-hydroxyethyl)amine, 526
Tristearin, 153
Triterpenes, 564, 567
Tritylation, 399
Trityl chloride, 399
Trivalent carbon, *see* Free radicals
Trivial names, 25
Tropane, 467
Tryparsamide, 593
Trypsin, 231
Tryptophan, 227, 232
Tschischenko reaction, *see* Tischenko reaction, 179
Tschugaev, biography, 87
Tuads, 251
Tung oil, 152
    in paint, 156
Turkey Red, 487
Turkey Red oil, 158
Turpentine, 565
Tweens, 308
Twin double bonds, 244, 494
Two,four-D (2,4-D), 391
Tyrian Purple, 486
Tyrosine, 227

Ullman reaction, 329, 427
Undecanes, 26
Undecanoic acid, 124
10-Undecenoic acid, 538
Undecylenic acid, 538
Undecylic acid, 124
Unimolecular mechanism, displacement reactions, 97
Unsaturated acids, 536
α,β-Unsaturated acids, from malonic acid, 542
Unsaturated alcohols, 516
Unsaturated fat acids, 154, 155
    autoxidation, 579
Unsaturated hydrocarbons, *see* Alkenes *and* Alkynes
Unsaturation, test, 39, 41, 205

unsym-, prefix, 37
Up-grading of drying oils, 156, 526
Uracil, 462
Uramine, 483
Urea, 239–247
Urea-formaldehyde resins, 243
Ureas, *N*-substituted, 246
    O-substituted, 247
Urease, 241
Ureids, 241
Urethans, 238, 244
    from isocyanates, 246
Uric acid, 464
Urinary calculi, 464
Uronic acids, 306
Urushiol, 393

Vacuum distillation, 11
Valeric acid, 124
δ-Valerolactam, 535
Valerolactones, 532
Valine, 227
van der Waals forces, 31, 62
Vanilla beans, 405
Vanilla flavor, 405
Vanillin, 405
Van Slyke method for amino nitrogen, 236
van't Hoff, biography, 262
Varnish, 157
Vaseline, 55
Vat dyes, 477, 484, 487
Vegetable fats and oils, 152
Veratral, 406
Veratrole, 392
Verdigris, 135
Veronal, 462
Victor Meyer apparatus for molecular weight determination, 16
Victor Meyer esterification law, 412
Vinegar, 133
Vinyl acetate, 516
Vinylacetic acid, 536
Vinylacetylene, 503
Vinyl alcohol, 516
Vinyl alkyl ethers, 517
Vinylbenzene, *see* Styrene, 425
Vinyl chloride, 507
Vinylidene chloride, 508
Vinylite resins, 516
Vinyl methyl ether, 517
Vinyl plastics, 508, 516
Vinyon, 516
Virus, tobacco mosaic, 226
Viscose rayon, 304
Viscosity index of lubricating oils, 54
Visible spectrum, 472
Vistanex, 43
Visual color and absorption, 472
Vitalistic theory, 3

Vitamins, A, 566
   B complex, 308
   B₁, 463
   B₂, 465
   B₆, 458
   C, 290
   D, 568
   E, 460
   K, 436
Volatile oils, 564
Vulcanization, 497

van der Waals forces, 31, 62
Walden, biography, 272
Walden inversion, 95, 271
   in addition reactions, 101
   in displacement reactions, 95
Wallach, biography, 564
Warfarin, 420
War gases, *see* Poison gases
Watergas-catalytic process, 46
Watermelon pigment, 567
Waxes, 150
   hydrocarbons in, 33
Werner, biography, 273
Wetting agents, 222, 432
Whale oil, 152
White light, 472
Williamson, biography, 115
Williamson synthesis, 115
Willow bark, 398
Willstaetter, biography, 562
Wintergreen oil, 419
Wislicenus, biography, 551
Woad, 484
Woehler, biography, 3
   synthesis of urea, 240, 244
Wolff-Kishner reduction, 175
Wood, 298
Wood alcohol, *see* Methyl alcohol, 65, 66

Wood distillation, 65
Wood pulp, 298
Wool, 229
   synthetic, 229
Wool grease, 150
Wort, 67
Wurtz, biography, 106
Wurtz-Fittig reaction, 329
Wurtz reaction, 106

Xanthates, 250
Xanthenes, 483
Xanthic acid, 250
Xanthine, 464
Xanthophyll, 567
Xanthoproteic reaction, 235
Xylenes, 316
Xylenols, 380
   in coal tar, 324
Xylidines, 370
Xylol, *see* Xylenes, 316
Xylose, 279
Xylyl groups, 322

Yellow enzymes, 465
Yellow pigments, 490, 567

ZBX, 250
Zein, 225
Zeisel determination of methoxyl and
      ethoxyl, 118
Zerevitinov determination of reactive hy-
      drogen, 87
Zerlate, 251
Zinc butyl xanthate, 250
Zinc compounds, 586
Zinc dust distillation, 383
Zwitter ions, 230
Zymase, fermentation by, 67